TRUMAN'S SCIENTIFIC GUIDE TO

Pest Management Operations

SIXTH EDITION

GARY W. BENNETT, PH.D.

Professor of Entomology and Director, Center for Urban and Industrial Pest Management,
Purdue University, West Lafayette, Indiana

JOHN M. OWENS, PH.D.

State and Industry Affairs Manager, S.C. Johnson & Son, Inc., Racine, Wisconsin

ROBERT M. CORRIGAN, PH.D.

Urban and Industrial Entomologist and Rodent Pest Management Specialist,
RMC Pest Management Consulting, Richmond, Indiana

**A PURDUE UNIVERSITY/
ADVANSTAR COMMUNICATIONS PROJECT**

Truman's Scientific Guide to Pest Management Operations, sixth edition

Copyright © 2003 Advanstar Communications

Printed in the United States of America

10 9 8 7 6 5 4 3 2

ISBN 0-929870-64-6

Library of Congress Control Number 2003110372

Published by Advanstar Communications, Inc., 7500 Old Oak Blvd., Cleveland, Ohio 44130 U.S.A.

Advanstar Communications is a U.S. Business information company that publishes magazines and journals, produces expositions and conferences, and provides a wide range of marketing services.

For additional information on the Purdue University Pest Management Correspondence Courses, please write to Continuing Education Business Office, Purdue University, Stewart Center, Room 116, 128 Memorial Mall, West Lafayette, Indiana, 47907-2034 U.S.A.

For additional copies of this book, please call 1-800-598-6008 or (218) 723-9180.

Cover and interior design: DCGraphics., Brunswick, Ohio.

Product Manager: Theodore C. Mathews

This book is dedicated to
William Oscar Buettner
and
Professor John June Davis

One, the dynamic first leader of the pest control industry.

One, the pioneering entomologist who put principles into pest control.

Together, they started the pest control industry on the road to service and greatness.

Contents

Pictorial Keys

Introduction

Dr. John V. Osmun, Professor Emeritus
Department of Entomology
Purdue University

Pest management is a business of technology. Thus the purpose of this sixth edition of *Truman's Scientific Guide to Pest Management Operations* is the same as that of previous editions: to provide a sound basis for studying the technical aspects of pest control. The emphasis in this book is on urban and industrial pest problems; frequently, this area is referred to as structural pest control. It is the business of managing insects, other arthropods, and vertebrate pests in homes, business establishments, hospitals, industrial plants, and municipal buildings, as well as in outdoor areas frequented by people.

This book is designed to serve three purposes. First, it is written as a series of lessons for those enrolled in the Purdue correspondence course in pest control technology. Second, it may be used as a ready reference for people actively employed in urban and industrial pest management. Third, it provides a valuable source of information for persons seeking state certification under the EPA/state programs for commercial pesticide applicators. Such objectives have necessitated that the book be a combination of basic scientific information and guidelines for practical solutions to pest management problems.

First, I'd like to address those of you who are engaged in some form of pest management service. Your ability to offer good service is bounded by the horizons of your experience. You can push back your horizons—broaden them—in many ways. On-the-job experience is important, but it is often gained only through mistakes, and it is often limited. A working knowledge of the technical and business aspects of pest control can be achieved best by study. Remember, pest management is a business of technology. Thus it is necessary for you to possess a knowledge of the science undergirding the industry: a recognition of the pests to be controlled, an understanding of their environments and habits, a knowledge of the tools and techniques used in pest management, and the ability to choose

proper and safe methods of pesticide application. All are the foundation of successful pest management.

Further, this is a service-oriented industry. The needs and desires of people must be satisfied; therefore, persons in pest management must possess the ability to explain to others the scientific aspects of their pest problems. This approach can rightfully be considered *public relations through technology*. Combine technical competence and a sense of service with a personal awareness of the need for high ethical standards, and you have the foundation on which sound business practices can be built.

Truman's Scientific Guide to Pest Management Operations is designed to provide a sound technical basis for such competence. The book is written for owners, supervisors, service technicians, and sales personnel. Each chapter covers material considered essential to the proper understanding of pest management. In addition to the chapters in this book, supplementary reading material is suggested at the end of each chapter for those desiring to study in more detail. The preparation and publication of this book are the results of excellent teamwork between industry representatives and the university people interested in improved pest management through education.

Although there are many viable approaches to managing a pest, chemical pesticides continue to play a large and important role in the solution of most pest problems in urban and industrial situations. This places a heavy responsibility on the shoulders of the pest management industry. In recent years, we have witnessed a growing concern by the public regarding the use of pesticides. Some chemicals, including some pesticides, have the potential to harm human health, the environment, or both. Therefore, we must operate under the legal restrictions imposed by the Federal Insecticide, Fungicide, and Rodenticide Act and the attendant laws of our fifty states. The many new restrictions on pesticides and their use impact both management and service technicians. As a result, most permanent personnel in pest management firms either are, or soon will be, certified or registered in the states where they operate.

One should not view this situation with alarm. Laws and regulations do not preclude good judgment. The standards of competence for certified commercial applicators are based on principles—the same principles we have been talking about for years as the undergirding elements of pest management technology. These include such factors as pest recognition, label comprehension, proper use of pesticides, appropriate equipment, application techniques, toxicity, safety, and environmental awareness. The certification system is simply an assurance that we have well-trained and qualified persons into whose hands we can place the various types of pesticides. Only through the implementation of such a system can we expect to retain for future use the pesticides that will be needed for successful pest management operations.

Of special importance is a recognition of the environments in which urban and industrial pest management operate. The pests that concern us are associated with diverse environmental complexes. Although there may be significantly different environments, all of them bear the similarity of an interdependence with the daily activities of humans. Too often we think of the environment as only the great outdoors. True, the latter is part of our environment, especially for those engaged in lawn and ornamental work and for those offering certain public health-related services, such as mosquito management.

The human dwelling, however, is the principal site in which structural pest management is conducted. Others include a variety of food handling establishments, office buildings, hospitals, modes of transportation, nonfood industries, and recreational areas. Each of these indoor environments presents its own problems with respect to pesticide use and other approaches to pest management; again, these situations amplify the importance of technical competence in all pest management activities.

For those of you who expect to use this book as the text to the correspondence course in pest management technology, here is how it works. Like any student taking a course through a university, you must register with Purdue University and pay your fee. This can be done at any time you wish to commence the course. The university will provide a comprehensive series of work sheets and questions that will be mailed to you. After you have completed each lesson and perhaps posed some of your own questions, you will mail the sheets back to Purdue, where the material will be graded and commented on by a member of the urban entomology staff. Upon satisfactory completion of the course, the university will provide the student an inscribed certificate of completion as evidence of satisfactory participation.

Approach this study with your mind open and with a determination to see it to successful conclusion. Its value will be measured by what you do with it as well as what it does for you. You are being provided an opportunity to learn and thus improve your value to yourself and to those you serve. The pest management industry, more than many other businesses, is intimately based on a science. This means that technical terms will be used in this text to provide a common ground for understanding both what you study in these chapters and what you read elsewhere.

It also means that some information will be presented that, on the surface, seems relatively unimportant as part of business practices, but that will ease the path for learning the practical aspects to follow. Work especially hard on Chapters 1, 2, and 3; the effort will pay dividends later. This course is intended for the serious student rather than the casual reader, and for such a person, the scientific approach is understandable and provides the only sound way to appreciate the full scope of pest management activity.

This is a good time to do a few things in addition to the direct requirements of the course. For example, it is an ideal opportunity to make an individual insect reference collection. Look for guidelines in the appendix of this book. This is also an excellent chance to become familiar with pesticides by collecting examples of different formulations and labels.

It is important that those of you enrolling in the course complete all of the lessons; even these, however, are but the beginning of a full understanding of the scope of activities in the industry. A technical background is not only essential for correct management procedures, but also the very essence of sales and public relations.

We asked Dr. Truman, who at one time had this material to learn for himself, what advice he would give a student entering the course. His reply was to the point: "Study carefully, study long, allow yourself time for the information to become a part of your thinking, and put it to work for you every day. The course will return to you in knowledge and better service as much as you put into it in time and effort."

Those of you who read this book as a reference or as a modest introduction to entomology will find helpful keys to identification, clear illustrations, and an assemblage of frequently useful information.

Remember, modern pest management is undergirded by scientific principles and a large measure of good judgment. This book will provide the principles as a foundation for the judgment.

Acknowledgements

This book is entitled Truman's Scientific Guide to Pest Management Operations to honor Dr. Lee C. Truman, an Indiana pest control operator, as the senior author of the original editions of this book. Dr. William L. Butts, of Oneonta, New York, served as the co-author of the first two editions. His work and major contributions to the Scientific Guide are gratefully acknowledged here.

The authors express sincere appreciation to the following persons for their valuable contributions and advice:

Jody Aleong, Purdue University; Dean Brad, Purdue University; Gary Braness, Bayer Environmental Science; Dan Collins, RMC Pest Management; John L. Gedeon, General Pest Control; Tim Gibb, Purdue University; Dennis Glennon, Spectros Instruments; Ed Hosoda, Cardinal Professional Products; Walid Kaakeh, United Arab Emirates University; Ed Ligus, Draeger Safety; Judy Loven, Fish and Wildlife Service; Linda Mason, Purdue Univeresity; Brian McSwigan, Cytex Industries; Mike Merchant, Texas A&M University; Phil Nixon, University of Illinois; Shlomo Navarro, Israel Ministry of Agriculture; Tom Parker, Pest Control Services; David Pinniger, Consulting Entomologist; Catina Ratliff, Purdue University; Kristin Saltzmann, Purdue University; Kurt Saltzmann, Purdue University; Mike Scharf, Purdue University; Eric Snell, B&G Equipment; Dan Suiter, University of Georgia; Chris Voglewede, Dow AgroSciences; Changlu Wang, Purdue University; Fred Whitford, Purdue University; David Williams, USDA-ARS, Gainesville; George Williams, Univar; Ralph Williams, Purdue University.

Original Drawings:
Arwin Provonsha, Purdue University

Photography:
Tom Myers, All-Rite Pest Control;
Univar USA, Mike Corbitt

Chapter Cover Illustrations:
Tom Myers, All-Rite Pest Control

Word Processing:
Peg Hague and Sandra Stephens-Reeves, Purdue University

Continuing Education:
Jenny Towler, Purdue University

Design and Production:
DCGraphics, Brunswick, OH

Product Manager:
Theodore C. Mathews,
Advanstar Communications

State of the Industry

A STEADY FORCE IN AN UNSTABLE ECONOMY

The U.S. economy found itself on shaky ground in 2001, particularly after the terrorist attacks of Sept. 11. The good news for pest management professionals is that despite the teetering economy, the industry remains strong and steady. Pest management is not a discretionary expenditure that can be eliminated to cut costs — even in bad times, people still need relief from pest problems. While pest management firms that service larger commercial, manufacturing and institutional accounts might feel the pinch, those whose clients are primarily small commercial and residential customers have expressed little impact.

Despite the economic uncertainty, many PMPs saw smaller, but still positive growth in 2002, compared with 2001. According to Pest Control magazine's 2002 State of the Industry report, 71 percent of those responding to the Penn survey said they had more business in 2002 and were confident about 2003 as well.

While the industry was sheltered somewhat from the recession, that doesn't mean PMPs could go about business as usual. PMPs faced increased operational costs, particularly in insurance and payroll. The tighter economy also brought about more competition, as clients were more diligent about getting the most for their money. Customer loyalty and smart business practice is essential.

To stay ahead of the curve, PMPs must enhance customer relationships by going the extra mile to keep clients satisfied. To offset any potential loss of business, PMPs have come to understand that they must diversify their businesses by adding services and being proactive in attracting new clients and working with existing clients to keep their business in tough times. While most PMPs still rely heavily on referrals to generate business, more are using aggressive marketing tactics and the Internet to attract clients.

INTERNET OPENS A WHOLE NEW WORLD

The Internet has become a vital tool for both pest management firms and their customers. Computer-savvy homeowners are using the Internet to research pest problems and want a solution at the click of a mouse. Business-smart PMPs know it and use it to their advantage. Manufacturers and some PMPs have dedicated web sites that offer homeowners the information they crave while also promoting their services. Smaller PMPs without web sites are partnering with manufacturers and organizations such as the National Pest Management Association to establish a presence on those sites to help generate business leads.

In addition to using the Internet to reach customers, manufacturers are connecting with PMPs by offering business services online. PMPs can order products, obtain label and MSDS information, conduct training sessions and utilize the myriad of business resources available. PMPs also have responded to the demand for less paperwork by using Internet and wireless capabilities for scheduling and paperless billing.

RELATIONSHIPS IMPORTANT BETWEEN DISTRIBUTORS, MANUFACTURERS AND PMPS

With the constantly changing dynamics of the industry in terms of mergers and acquisitions, PMPs have come to rely heavily on distributors and manufacturers for information and support. Distributors and manufacturers are responding to the challenge to provide the customer service its clients need. According to the State of the Industry report, more than 75 percent of Penn survey respondents agreed that distributors are more helpful now compared to five years ago. Additionally, 97 percent of the respondents in the Readex survey have purchased from a distributor, and 61 percent said suppliers or distributor reps are a major source of information. The wave of consolidation of manufacturers and distributors has not affected the customer relationship, with 77 percent of Penn survey respondents agreeing that manufacturers are providing more support now compared with five years ago. Despite that support, PMPs said they would appreciate additional training and technical support and up-to-date information on product changes and improvements.

THE CHANGING FACE OF PEST MANAGEMENT

The pest management industry continues to adjust to the aftermath of the adoption of the 1996 Food Quality Protection Act, which stripped PMPs of products such as Dursban, Ficam and other chemistries. Manufacturers have responded by developing products that are more environmentally friendly, including baits.

Those new products have fallen in line with an increased emphasis on integrated pest management, which combines the use of biological, cultural, physical and chemical methods to minimize health and environmental risks. While baiting has revolutionized the industry, new chemistries are often less powerful and require more patience on the part of homeowners who are accustomed to immediate results. It is the PMP's responsibility to educate the consumer and assure them that the company and the products are working in their best interests. Stricter reporting requirements also require the technicians to think carefully about the treatments being applied, to take their time and to report accurately.

ANTS TAKE TOP PEST SPOT

Pest management has taken on a more targeted approach, in part due to the disappearance of some chemistries. As a result, ants have become the biggest pest management problem. In the past, baseboard spraying for other pests usually eliminated ants by default. With the new targeted focus, PMPs must specifically focus on the ant, tackling the task depending on the species because of their widely varied behavior and food preferences.

Research from the 2002 State of the Industry report exemplifies the growing problem. According to the Penn survey, 89 percent of companies provide ant control, with 52 percent citing ants as the most difficult pests to control and 33 percent citing ants as the pest that results in the most sales.

While ants are the overall prime pest, termites continue to pester PMPs on a regional basis; however, tremendous strides have been made in developing effective, non-repellent liquid soil treatments as well as termite baiting systems. Sixty-eight percent of State of the Industry respondents reported an increase in 2002 termite treatment revenues compared with 2001, but only 24 percent reported an increase of termite retreats – showing the staying power of the popular non-repellents.

Public health pests also have become a pressing concern for customers, who are seeking protection from illnesses borne by mosquitoes, mites and rodents, such as the West Nile Virus, Lyme disease and hantavirus.

THE PEST MANAGEMENT PROFESSIONAL

With the constantly evolving state of pest management, it's comforting to know that PMPs bring experience, education and stability to the industry. The State of the Industry reports 40 percent have worked in the industry for 10 to 20 years, 28 percent between 21 to 30 years, and 15 percent reported industry experience of more than 30 years. The majority of PMPs were between 41 and 50 years old and another 26 percent were 51-60. Only 22 percent were younger than 40. PMPs also are more educated, with 36 percent reporting some college experience. Large companies have a slightly higher tendency in employing more educated PMPs.

With PMPs getting older, finding good, qualified employees to follow in their footsteps is becoming an issue, with 61 percent of the State of the Industry respondents reporting more difficulty in recruitment. Companies continue to rely on newspaper ads and recommendations to find employees. The Internet is also becoming a popular vehicle for recruitment. Employee retention also must be addressed. Companies most commonly use incentive/bonus programs and uniforms as a drawing tool, while some larger companies also offer 401K savings programs to entice employees.

A statement published in the 1996 edition of this book extolled the importance of having well-trained, educated and caring PMPs as the face of the industry. Times have changed, but the quote, paraphrased from a statement of what is now the National Pest Management Association remains a light of truth: "No one – not the company supervisor, nor the company president; not the president [of NPMA], nor the most distinguished urban entomology professor – is more directly responsible for the success, prosperity and image of the industry than the [pest management professional.]"

CHAPTER 1 | Introduction to Entomology and Principles of Pest Management

The insects you managed today are just a minute fraction of the millions that inhabit the world. Humans do well to hold their own in the face of the constant pressures that insects continue to exert upon them. Not only are the total numbers tremendous, but the number of individual kinds, or species, exceeds 800,000—a number greater than that of all other animals, combined.

Many insects are beneficial, but some are especially competitive with humans. Insects are not only numerous, but also among the most adaptable of all animals. In their many forms, insects are fitted for almost any specific way of life. Their adaptability, combined with their tremendous rate of reproduction, gives insects an unequaled potential for survival.

Insects vary in size from as small as 1/100 of an inch long to as large as 10-inches long. The food of insects includes almost anything that can be eaten by any other animal, as well as many things that cannot even be digested by other animals. Insects live in the darkest of surroundings as well as in bright sunlight, and in areas of ice and snow as well as in exceedingly hot locations. Some are adapted to living only in open areas, while others are able to live in extremely confined spaces.

Most insects do not harm human products or carry diseases harmful to humans; however, many do carry diseases, feed on human food, clothing, housing, and manufactured goods, and annoy or injure humans and other animals through painful bites and stings. All of these factors make certain insects a problem to humans and thus of great importance to the pest management professional.

Knowledge of an insect's anatomy, development, and behavior can be an important tool in the development of pest management programs. Proper pest identification often requires a basic understanding of insect anatomy. Targeted control measures that exploit an insect's unique physiology or a vulnerable stage in its life cycle are facilitated by the basic understanding of insect physiology and development. Removing a pest's necessities of life and reducing a structure's appeal as a pest habitat becomes easier for a pest professional who has learned how pests move, what they eat, and where they live. Such knowledge can be an advantage when planning low-impact management programs. The remainder of this book will introduce you to these topics and many more that relate to urban pest management.

Knowing and Using the Right Words

Any field of study involves the use of a specialized vocabulary. The technical words used in the study of insects and their relatives are no more difficult than those used in any other field. It is necessary to understand such terms so that two people talking about an insect or group of insects will be certain they are talking about the same thing. Almost everyone is familiar with the words *carburetor, chrysanthemum, polyethylene, pyrethrum, penicillin, virus,* and *cauliflower.* These are all technical terms and are derived from Latin or Greek words, just as are most of the special terms used in entomology. The specific words used in the study of entomology are no more difficult to remember than these, and once you have become familiar with them, they will also become a part of your regular vocabulary. An understanding of these words is necessary so that you will be able to understand this book as well as the books listed as references at the end of each chapter.

ADULT ANATOMY—EXTERNAL

Knowledge of external anatomy is essential for correct insect identification. Plus, it provides a foundation for understanding insect development processes and how insects interact with their environments. All of this information is needed for developing effective insect management programs.

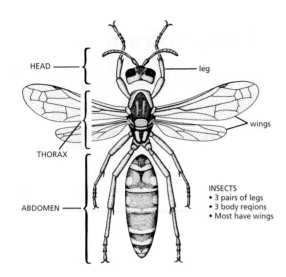

FIGURE 1.1. The three principal regions and parts of an insect's body, as shown on the paper wasp. (Provonsha)

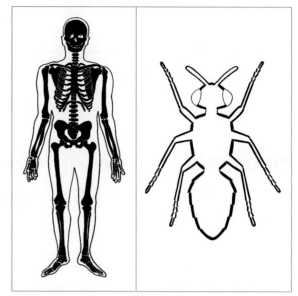

FIGURE 1.2. A human endoskeleton and an insect exoskeleton. (Provonsha)

The insect body is generally an elongated tube with appendages, such as legs, wings, or antennae on either side, so that each side is like the other. This arrangement is termed bilateral symmetry. The body is segmented or jointed, as shown in Figure 1.1, with segments being grouped into three distinct regions: the **head**, **thorax**, and **abdomen**.

In adult insects, the eyes, antennae, and mouthparts are on the head. Legs and wings are attached to the thorax. The appendages on the abdomen, if any are present, are usually on the last segment only. Abdominal appendages are usually sex organs, hairs, or bristlelike extensions known as cerci. Most appendages on the insect body are segmented.

The skeleton of the insect is on the outside rather than on the inside of the body, as with humans and other vertebrates, thus serving not only as an outer covering of the body, but also as the firm portion of the body to which muscles are attached (see Figure 1.2). Such muscle attachment makes it possible for an insect to have overall strength of greater proportion relative to its size.

All of the segments and their associated appendages are covered with the insect's version of a skeleton which, unlike humans and other vertebrates, is on the outside of its body and is called the **exoskeleton**. This exoskeleton serves many physio-

logical and protective functions and defines the shape of the insect's body and its segments. The biological components and physiology of the cuticle exoskeleton will be discussed in more detail later in this chapter, but first we will focus on the distinctive regions of an insect and how they impact on insect biology and identification.

Although more prominent in some species than others, the head, thorax, and abdominal regions are present in all adult insects. How these segments look and the appearance of their appendages are important factors in species identification.

Head

The typical insect head is a hollow capsule (formed from six fused segments) that contains the brain. The primary functions of the head are locating and taking food; recognizing mates, cohorts, and enemies; and sensing danger. The antennae, eyes, and mouthparts are the specialized structures that insects use to accomplish these tasks. Many features of these structures are used in insect identification.

Sense Organs

The antennae are appendages of the head, and they are nearly always made of many segments. The shape, number, and relative size of the segments are characteristics frequently used to identify an insect. Antennae are sense organs having the functions of touch, smell and, in some cases, hearing. They are used for navigation, food location, communications with other members of the same species, mate location, and even grasping in some species. The

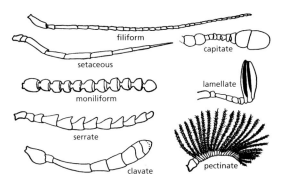

FIGURE 1.3. Some types of antennae found on insects. (From Ross, *A Textbook of Entomology*, by permission of John Wiley and Sons, Inc.)

overall appearance of the antennae as well as the shape, number, and relative size of the segments are characteristics frequently used to identify insects. There are many different kinds of antennae commonly found in urban pest insects (see Figure 1.3), a few of which are listed here:

- filiform—threadlike (cockroach; see Figure 1.12, following page 254)
- setaceous—tapering (dragonfly)
- moniliform—beadlike (termites)
- serrate—sawlike (drugstore beetle)
- clavate—clubbed (ladybird beetle)
- capitate—having a head (some powderpost beetles)
- lamellate—leaflike (June beetle)
- pectinate—comblike (pyrochorid beetle)
- geniculate—elbowed (ants)
- aristate—feathery bristles (flies)

Most adult insects have a pair of relatively large compound eyes located on the head. The surfaces of these eyes are made up of many small lenses, called ommatidia, each of which is the lens to a single portion of the compound eye. Most insects also have simple eyes, called ocelli, located on the upper part of the head between the compound eyes. Some insects have no simple eyes in the adult stage, but among those that do, there may be one, two, or three eyes, depending on the kind of insect. Simple eyes function as supplementary light perception organs; they do not perceive images.

An insect does not get as clear an image of objects as do humans and other vertebrates. The insect's ability to distinguish form is not very well developed. However, it is usually very sensitive to motion. As far as color perception is concerned, insects see farther into the ultraviolet range than do humans, but they do not see as far into the red range of the spectrum.

Characteristics of eyes are sometimes used in

insect identification. The shape, size, color, and separation between the compound eyes are some of the features used when keying-out insects (e.g., flies). As mentioned, the number of simple eyes is also used to distinguish species.

Mouthparts

An insect's mouthparts are made up of extensions of the original head segments and are usually located on the bottom of the head, although on some insects the head is held so the mouthparts extend forward. Variations in insect mouthparts are frequently used in the identification of insects. The mouthparts also tell something about the food habits of the insect and may indicate where to find the insect by looking for a suitable source of food.

The structures that make up the mouthparts of insects vary greatly in shape and function. In many insects, they are formed for biting and chewing solid foods, such as leaves, wood, fabrics, or kernels of grain. In others, they are formed for piercing the skin of animals or the epidermis of plants and sucking up blood or plant sap from beneath the

Mouthparts of Immature Insects

Some immature forms have the same type of mouthparts as their parents, while others do not. In insects that develop without metamorphosis (e.g., silverfish), with gradual metamorphosis (e.g., cockroaches), or with incomplete metamorphosis (e.g., dragonflies), their immature forms have the same type of mouthparts as their parents. In other words, if the adult has piercing-sucking mouthparts, as is the case with some of the lice, the immatures will also have piercing-sucking mouthparts.

Larvae, the growing stage of insects with complete metamorphosis (e.g., butterflies), may or may not have the same kind of mouthparts as their parents. The larvae of beetles, moths, butterflies, and some bees have typical chewing mouthparts, although the various parts may be reduced. Mouthparts of the larvae of ants, wasps, and most bees are much reduced. The larvae of fleas and black flies also have chewing mouthparts, but they are not as well developed as in the just-mentioned insects.

The head of the larval form of flies such as house flies, blow flies, and fruit flies is greatly reduced and withdrawn into the thorax. The food of such larvae has to be in liquid form. Although the immature stages of some flies have no true jaws, there are usually two mouth hooks present, which enable the larvae to lacerate tissue.

surface. In still others, they are shaped so the insect can feed on exposed liquids, such as water and nectar. Knowledge of the different types of mouthparts found among insects, and their relationship to food preferences, is essential to the efficient location and identification of pest insects during inspections.

Based on the form of their food and the method by which they obtain it, the mouthparts of adults may be divided into six principal types or kinds: chewing, rasping-sucking, piercing-sucking, sponging, siphoning, and chewing-lapping.

Chewing type. This is the most primitive and, therefore, the most basic type; it is found on insects that feed on solid food. Examples of such insects are cockroaches, termites, beetles, and chewing lice. Chewing mouthparts are made up of seven well-defined structures. Most of these structures are found in insects with other types of mouthparts, but in these other types, they are usually greatly modified in form (see Figure 1.4, and Figure 1.5, which follows page 254).

Structures found in the chewing mouthparts are :

- upper lip (labrum): This is a simple flap that covers the upper jaws, similar to our upper lip that covers the upper teeth.
- upper jaws (mandibles): There are two upper jaws, each of which is a solid structure with toothlike projections on the inner side. The jaws move from side to side, or transversely, and are used to tear or bite off the food and chew it.
- tongue (hypopharynx): This fleshy organ is found inside the mouth and serves a sensory function.
- lower jaws (maxillae): There are a pair of maxillae, each of which consists of several parts. They serve for picking up and holding food and sometimes for spooning or biting it. Attached to the outside of each is an antenna-like structure called a maxillary palp, which may contain organs of taste, touch, and smell. The lower jaws move from side to side, like the upper jaws.
- lower lip (labium): The lower lip is made up of several parts and bears a labial palpus on either side, which has the same functions as the maxillary palpi.

Piercing-sucking type. In this type, the parts have been modified so the insect can pierce the skin of animals or the epidermis of plants and suck up the blood or plant sap from beneath the surface. Most of the structures found in piercing-sucking mouthparts have the same name as those in chewing mouthparts, although their form and function usually differ.

There are many varieties or subtypes of piercing-sucking mouthparts. Basically there is a proboscis, or snout, which is a slender, tubular beak that encloses four long, slender stylets. These stylets are used to pierce the tissue and suck up the liquid food. Although this is the general arrangement found in the various insects with piercing-sucking mouthparts, there are numerous modifications in mosquitoes, biting flies, fleas, and lice. (Figure 1.7 illustrates the mouthparts of a mosquito.) (See Figure 1.6, following page 254.)

Rasping-sucking type. Insects that possess this type of mouthpart lacerate or rasp the epidermis of plants with three needlelike organs, called stylets, until the sap flows out. They then retract these stylets and suck up the exposed sap. The only insects that have these mouthparts are the thrips. This is a primitive form of piercing-sucking mouthpart.

Sponging type. Some flies, such as house flies, blow flies, and fruit flies, are unable to pierce the skin of animals or the epidermis of plants and, therefore, must feed on exposed liquids. The lower lip, as in other flies, is elongated to form the outer covering of the soft beak, within which are two slender structures that form a salivary duct and a food channel (See Figures 1.8 and 1.9, following page 254). The tip of the lower lip is enlarged into a

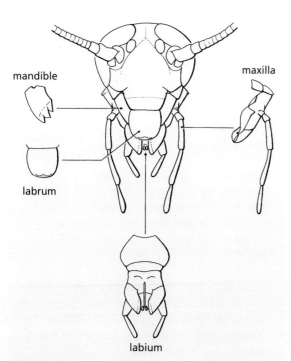

FIGURE 1.4. Typical chewing mouthparts of a cockroach. (Provonsha)

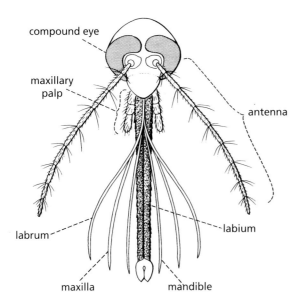

FIGURE 1.7. Piercing-sucking mouthparts (with stylets spread out), as found in a female mosquito. (Provonsha)

sponging organ that has a series of grooves radiating from the center. When the fly dips the end of its beak into liquids, the liquid flows up these grooves until it comes in contact with the food channel. The food is then sucked up through this channel into the esophagus.

Siphoning type. In moths and butterflies, a part of each lower jaw is elongated (see Figure 1.10, following page 254). The parts are interlocked to form a long, slender tube through which exposed liquids, such as nectar and water, are sucked up. This tube, or "tongue," is coiled up like a watchspring when it is not being used.

Chewing-lapping type. In some bees and wasps, the mouthparts are formed both for the chewing of solids and the sucking up of exposed liquids, especially nectar. The upper lip and the upper jaws are the same as in chewing mouthparts. The lower jaws and the lower lip are elongated to form a "tongue" with which the insect can suck or lap up liquids.

In addition to aiding in locating (via food preference) and identifying pest insects, knowing the insect mouthpart types can provide clues about the probable success of different pesticide formulations and application methods available for insect control. For example, an application of a stomach poison to the general environment of an adult flea probably would not be an effective control. Because adult fleas use their piercing-sucking mouthpart to obtain sustenance (blood) from their host animal, the only way to get stomach poisons into fleas is to have the insecticide in the blood of the host animal. Often, considering such seemingly trivial factors

before initiating a management plan can reduce the frequency of callbacks.

Thorax

The middle region of an insect body is known as the thorax. It is made up of three segments to which the legs and wings (if present) are attached. The segments of the thorax are usually quite hard and are frequently fused solidly together to provide a firm base for the many muscles necessary to operate the wings and legs. On either side of the thorax, there are two small, slitlike openings called spiracles (in primitive insects such as cockroaches), which are external openings to the respiratory system. The thorax is connected to the head by a membranous neck region called the cervix, which gives freedom of movement to the head.

Legs

An insect leg is always jointed and consists of six parts: the coxa, trochanter, femur, tibia, tarsus, and pretarsus (see Figure 1.11).

The coxa and trochanter are the two parts that connect the insect leg to the body, with the trochanter positioned between the coxa and the femur. The femur corresponds to the thigh of humans, and the tibia to the lower leg. The tarsus is composed of several joints and corresponds to the foot. The last tarsal segment usually bears a pair of claws and, frequently, pads or lobes between the claws. These claws and pads together form the pretarsus.

Variations in the size and shape of the leg segments can tell a pest management professional many things. The legs may be modified for running, jumping, grasping, digging, or in other ways

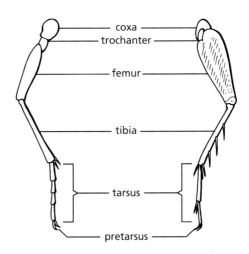

FIGURE 1.11. Two types of leg structure commonly found in insects: the running leg (left) and the jumping leg (right). (Provonsha)

that offer insight into the habits of the insect. Typical running and jumping legs are shown in Figure 1.11. Variations in the leg are also used in identifications.

Pest management professionals must be aware of insect leg features that have control-related implications. Some crawling insects (e.g., cockroaches) have sticky pretarsal pads that enable them to walk on smooth horizontal surfaces and to crawl up smooth vertical surfaces. The pretarsal pads are an important avenue for transferring residual insecticide deposits to pest insects. Insects walking over treated surfaces pick up the insecticide on their tarsal pads; the insecticide is either ingested during grooming or absorbed directly through the pads. Also, the pretarsal pads are a mechanism for spreading disease organisms. Pathogens can be picked up on the tarsal pads and transferred to other areas as the insect walks, or they could be ingested during grooming and subsequently spread in the insect's feces. Therefore knowing something about an insect's legs can provide clues about the amount of damage the insect can produce, and yields insight into possible control measures.

Wings

Functional wings allow insects to forage for food over great distances, permit dispersal across wide geographic ranges, and enable insects to quickly escape danger. Wings are an outgrowth of the body wall on the last two segments of the thorax (See Figure 1.12, following page 254). Most adult insects have two pairs of wings, but some have only one pair, and a few have none. Most insect wings consist of a thin membrane. On some insects, however, the front pair of wings are thickened and leathery or hard. The variation in the number of wings and their size, shape, texture, arrangement of veins, and rest position are also identification characteristics.

Pest management professionals must be aware of the ramifications of the flying ability of an insect pest for management strategies. For example, the sawtoothed grain beetle and the merchant grain beetle are very similar in appearance and damage caused to stored products. Both insects have wings, but only the merchant grain beetle flies. A pest management professional who finds a new infestation of sawtoothed grain beetles should begin looking for an infestation source in materials that have been carried into the account. But, a new infestation of merchant grain beetles could have flown into the account; thus, monitoring and control techniques may differ depending on the flying ability of the pest. A food lure trap for the sawtoothed grain bee-

tle placed near the ceiling of a warehouse is of little use, but a similar trap for the merchant grain beetle could be an effective population-monitoring tool. Therefore, the wings provide important clues in identifying, locating, and controlling pest insects.

Abdomen

The insect abdomen is typically composed of eleven segments, although the last segment is usually so reduced in size, or so modified, that only ten segments are easily visible. In some insects several segments may be fused together, so that there appear to be fewer than ten. There is a small holelike opening on either side of each of the first seven or eight abdominal segments when ten are present. These are the spiracles, which open into the internal respiratory system. Various appendages may appear on the last segment of the abdomen. Of these appendages, the most noticeable on many insects are the cerci, which extend from the last abdominal segment. Genital appendages may be lacking, but when present, the most conspicuous organs are the claspers of the male and ovipositor of the female. These genital organs may be present externally or may be totally enclosed within the abdomen, so that they are not visible. All of the appendages on the last abdominal segment perform sensory functions, primarily in the reproductive process.

Some abdominal features are used in identifying pest insects. The presence or absence of features such as cerci, claspers, and ovipositor are used to identify some insects. Sometimes it is necessary to examine fine details of these structures to distinguish between similar appearing species. For example, distinction between the brown and American cockroaches is based upon the shape of the last segments of the cerci.

The overall shape of the abdomen is also used in identification. Constriction of the first one or two abdominal segments is often an identifying feature of hymenopterous pests. The presence of this constriction is used to separate species with similar appearances (e.g., ants and termites), and the fine details of the constriction are often used to separate one ant species from another. Knowing these subtle differences can have considerable impact on the effectiveness of a management program.

Exoskeleton

As previously mentioned, the shape of an insect's external features is defined by its outer covering, or exoskeleton. This is because, although strong, the exoskeleton has some limitations. One of which is its often restricted ability to change shape and size. To accomplish this, an insect must get rid of its old outer layer and replace it with a new one in a process called molting. Molting involves many hormone interactions and chemical processes, some of which can be exploited by pesticides. Pesticides can also be used to disrupt the protective functions of an insect's cuticle. Both of these provide a unique avenue of control not available for vertebrate pests.

Functions of the Exoskeleton

The insect's exoskeleton provides an anchoring point for muscle attachments and support, and protection and sensing functions. The combination of rigid and flexible materials in the exoskeleton permits very accurate joint movements with minimal amounts of muscle mass and movement. This highly efficient system explains how insects produce such great strength in relation to their size.

The exoskeleton also furnishes insects with a protective covering. This hard cover gives insects a mechanism for protecting themselves from parasites and predators; moreover, it provides protection from abrasive damage caused by hard objects in the insect's environment. In addition, the wax coating found on the outermost layer (epicuticle) provides a barrier to water loss from the insect's body. Disruption of the wax coating can cause a water imbalance in insects which leads to death from desiccation. This is believed to be the mechanism by which some of the inorganic insecticides (e.g., diatomaceous earth) kill insects.

Finally, modifications to structures found in the exoskeleton produce sensory hairs (setae) and gland cells. These specialized structures, as shown in Figure 1.13, are used for communication, food location, and other interactions between the insect and its environment.

Composition of the Exoskeleton

The hard covering on insects known as the exoskeleton consists of a living layer of cells (epidermis) and a non-living layer (cuticle). As shown in Figure 1.13, the cuticle is composed of the endocuticle, exocuticle, and epicuticle.

The cuticle is made primarily of the protein, sclerotin, and the polysaccharide (long-chain sugar molecule), chitin. During sclerotization (i.e., "hardening" of the cuticle), sclerotin molecules bond together to form a protein matrix. Chitin acts as a "packing" material that fills the gaps in the sclerotin matrix. The epicuticle is coated with wax, or sometimes a cement, which produces the waterproof outer layer on the body.

Sclerotin and chitin give the exoskeleton the hard quality that protects the insect from being damaged. The epicuticle is a thin, waxy layer that

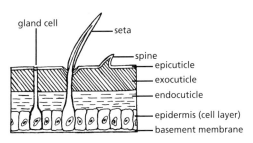

FIGURE 1.13. Lateral view of the body wall section of an insect.

protects the insect body from moisture evaporation. This layer is important to the pest management professional because all insecticides must either pass through the body wall or dry up its outermost layer to be effective.

The body wall completely covers the insect. In some portions, it is hardened to form plates, or sclerites; in others, it is soft and flexible, forming membranous sutures, or joints, between the sclerites. This body wall is always in one piece, with hard and soft portions being merely variations on the same structure. For example, the usual insect abdomen is quite firm because of the segmented rings, or sclerites, that extend around it. It is also flexible and expandable because of the rubber-like sutures that connect these sclerites to each other and join the parts of each sclerite to the other parts.

For insects to grow, they must cast off the old cuticle and form a new one through the process of molting. In Chapter 2, the formation of the exoskeleton through molting will be combined with the information in this chapter on exoskeleton structure and function to serve as the foundation for an examination of the interactions between certain pesticides and the exoskeleton.

ADULT ANATOMY—INTERNAL

Although an insect may be very minute, its body organization and its ability to perform the essential functions of life are as sophisticated as those of people. A brief study of internal anatomy affords a much deeper insight into the life of an insect and provides helpful, fundamental information to pest management professionals for solving pest problems.

Digestive System

An insect's digestive tract is basically a tube that runs the full length of its body, which consists of various parts, as well as glands that enable the insect to digest food. These various parts are modified according to the type of food the insect eats. Insects such as flies and cockroaches usually require much moisture in their diet, and they will usually excrete moist waste material. Others, such as drywood termites and the various grain insects, will excrete a dry pellet. Glands within the digestive tract in the area of the mouth usually secrete saliva. In bloodsucking insects, these glands produce a material that keeps the blood from coagulating while the insect is feeding. In the larvae of bees, wasps, ants, moths, and butterflies, these glands are modified to secrete the silk used in making larval nests and cocoons.

Insects have essentially the same nutritional requirements as people. They, too, require fats, carbohydrates, proteins, vitamins, and minerals. At some stage in the insect's development, it obtains a balanced diet. The German cockroach, for example, obtains its nutrients from a wide variety of foods. Termites, which feed principally on wood or other cellulose-bearing materials, are aided in obtaining essential nutrients by microorganisms in the gut and the presence of fungi in the wood and soil. Mosquitoes, which as adults may feed only on blood, obtain other nutrients in the larval stage. Thus, the required diet is frequently different in the immature stage and the adult stage of the same species. Regardless of any other food requirements, all insects need a regular supply of water. Those that live where a supply of water is readily available will drink it. Many insects, such as grain beetles, which live in relatively dry materials, have developed a system for converting and conserving moisture that is actually present in their food supply.

A knowledge of the food requirements of any given insect is important to the pest management professional. Such knowledge will aid in locating an insect in a given situation. Thus one usually looks for confused flour beetles only in dry cereal products, carpet beetle larvae on woolen or hair products, termites in wood, lice on animals, or German cockroaches generally near the kitchen or a drain where they may obtain food and water.

Circulatory System

The circulatory system of an insect does not consist of a series of blood vessels, as it does in humans. Insect blood is pumped by an open-ended tube located along the upper side and running the entire length of the body. This tube picks up blood from the back portions of the body and pumps it into the head, at which point it simply flows back around the body parts to the rear, where it is picked up and pumped again. Thus, blood flows in an open manner within the body, rather than being restricted within blood vessels.

Insect blood performs several important functions. Food materials are absorbed into the blood from the digestive system and carried to the body

tissues. Blood also picks up waste products, which are carried to the excretory organs to be discharged from the body. The blood may also have dissolved in it a small amount of oxygen, which is carried to the body tissue. This, however, is not a principal function of the blood, as it is in warm-blooded animals. Certain cells in the blood heal wounds and also dispose of bacteria and other organisms that might be harmful. The circulatory system of insects also maintains or changes the pressure inside the body. This pressure can be changed by contractions and expansions of the external skeleton. Localized pressure is used to expand the size of the body after molting and to inflate the wings.

Insecticides entering the body by ingestion or through the cuticle are distributed throughout the insect's body by the circulatory system. Therefore, the circulatory system can play an important role in the transport of insecticides to their sites of action within the insect body.

Excretory System

Excretion is the process of discharging waste products from the body. In insects, waste materials are discharged through the body wall, the digestive tract, and the rectum. Wastes are also removed from the blood by special excretory tubes known as malpighian tubules, which are attached to, and empty into, the hind portion of the digestive tract.

From a pest management perspective, the excretory system can increase or decrease the effectiveness of insecticides. Insecticides that are ingested and broken down by the digestive enzymes usually leave the body through the excretory system. In some instances, such as with cat fleas feeding on an animal treated with a systemic insecticide, the materials can pass through the digestive tract faster than they can be absorbed. Thus, the insecticide is relatively ineffective. However, if the flea's feces is tainted with the insecticide, then the larvae (which feed on adult flea feces) could receive a lethal dose. Similarly, research has demonstrated that some slow-acting toxicants used in cockroach baits are excreted by the affected roaches before they die. Because German cockroaches sometimes consume another cockroach's feces (coprophagy), toxicants can be transferred to cockroaches that have not fed on the bait, thereby increasing the overall effectiveness of a baiting program.

Respiratory System

The respiratory system of an insect is made up of a series of tubes, called tracheae, which extend into the body cavity. These tracheae divide into smaller tubes called tracheoles, which carry oxygen directly to the tissues in the insect body. Tracheae open to the outside of the body through openings known as spiracles, usually located on the sides of the thorax and abdomen. The number of spiracles varies in different groups of insects and varies from larvae to adults. In some water-dwelling larvae, there are no spiracles. In these forms, the spiracles are replaced by fine tracheae that run into gills or directly under the skin, where oxygen is drawn directly from the water in which the larvae live. Many insects can draw air into the tracheae and can expel air by expanding and contracting their body walls. Some insects can also open and close the spiracles to avoid drawing any harmful materials into the tracheae.

The respiratory system is important to the pest management professional. For example, some dusts that are otherwise nontoxic can clog the spiracles and thus deprive the insect of the oxygen it needs to live. Many insecticides, particularly fumigants, actually diffuse into the insect body through the spiracles, permitting internal penetration through the tracheae and tracheoles.

Nervous System

The nervous system of insects is highly developed. As in other animals, it coordinates the activity of the insect in relation to its environment. There is a brain, located in the head, and pairs of nerve centers in each body segment, called ganglia. These nerve centers and the brain are connected by a nerve cord. The ganglia and the nerve cord are located on the bottom side of the insect body. Nerve endings are particularly concentrated in such places as the mouthparts, antennae, and tarsi.

Certain insecticides sprayed or dusted almost anywhere on the body will penetrate the body wall and reach some of these nerve endings. Of particular interest to the pest management professional is the fact that an insecticide applied to surfaces on which insects may walk is taken into the insect through the tarsi of the legs, which will find its way to sensitive and susceptible nerves where poisoning may take place.

The nervous system is the site of action for the majority of the insecticides used against structural pests. For example, carbamates and organophosphates produce their toxic action by inhibiting an important enzyme involved in nerve impulse transmission across synapses. Pyrethrins and pyrethroids block impulse transmission along the nerve fibers. Avermectins block transmission of nerve impulses to muscles. Although the precise mechanisms for which insecticides are used to kill insects vary, blocking vital functions by interfering with normal nerve impulse transmission is a common feature.

Muscular System

The muscular system in the insect body is quite complex. Some insects have more than 2,000 muscles. These muscles are arranged internally so that a very efficient system results. This muscular arrangement can permit unusual strength for the size of the insect, where many insects can lift objects weighing as much as 20 times their own body weight. Because of their powerful leg muscles, fleas can jump as far as five or six inches. Segments of the body are connected by muscle bands that maintain the body form and make possible the many movements noted in insects.

Reproductive System

In most insects there are two sexes, male and female, although there are a few insects in which both male and female sex organs are present in one individual. However, the presence of reproductive organs does not always mean that all members are actively involved in reproduction of the species. For example, social insect populations (e.g., bees, ants, termites) are predominantly nonreproductive females (i.e., workers) that only produce offspring under certain conditions. The variation in reproductive organs makes it possible to differentiate not only between males and females of the same species, but also between one group of insects and another.

The organs important to the pest management professional are the external organs located at the tip of the abdomen. Interestingly, in male German cockroaches treated with juvenoid insect growth regulators (IGRs), deformities observed in the external reproduction structures may interfere with copulation and, therefore, be partly responsible for the population decline typically seen.

INSECT BEHAVIOR

Insects respond to various situations in a largely automatic manner. There is no particular thinking or intelligence involved in their reactions. The nerve pathways involved in insect behavior are largely inherited, and each insect will usually react in the same way as others of the same kind. Many of an insect's reactions are toward or away from a stimulation, such as light, temperature, moisture, chemicals, touch or contact, the force of gravity, or currents of air or water. Many moths fly toward light, while bed bugs avoid it. Some insects locate their food by response to a chemical odor, while certain other chemicals repel insects. Although insects will usually move away when touched or squeezed, the cockroach will force itself into a small opening.

House flies generally move upward to rest at night but do not exhibit this response during the day.

Most insects lay their eggs in a certain way and in certain places, feed in a characteristic place and manner, live in a given type of environment, and move about from place to place in a typical way and by a typical route.

There is good reason why the pest management professional should understand the typical behaviors of each insect species being controlled. Insects are capable of learning or improving their behavior only to a limited degree. Knowing common travel routes and typical breeding, hiding, and feeding places helps the professional conduct a focused inspection. Instead of wasting time looking where the pest probably is not, time is better spent looking where the pest mostly likely is. Once these common areas are located, controlling the pest is also more effective when treatments are targeted where the pest spends the most time. Furthermore, such information will better enable the professional to explain to a customer both the cause of infestation and the reasons for the control measures being prescribed.

PRINCIPLES OF PEST MANAGEMENT

Challenges await the pest management professional in the coming years. The public's attitudes, perceptions, and concerns about pesticides and their effects on health and the environment will result in a continuing trend away from the use of pesticides with higher toxicities and long residual properties. Environmental concerns, such as ozone depletion, will continue to have impacts on pest management. With the public demanding less exposure to all types of toxicants, along with an increase in the resistance of pests to conventional pesticides, a wider range of pest management strategies will have to be implemented. Considering these factors and the potential for litigation associated with pesticide applications and misapplications, it will be necessary to incorporate more nonpesticidal components and low-impact pesticides into pest management programs. The use of biorational and target-specific pesticides will increase as alternatives to conventional toxicants. Nonchemical treatments, proper sanitation, and pestproofing will increase in the status given them by professionals, regulators, and clients. The integration of these techniques and technologies with new chemistries, formulations, biological compounds, and behavior and development-altering active ingredients will make for an exciting future for urban pest managers.

The major pests of the world—insects, rodents, and birds—are giving humans a real battle for supremacy. The competitive nature of life on Earth is a well-known fact, and the extent to which the life requirements of pest species coincide with those of people determines the intensity of the rivalry between them. Health, welfare, comfort, property, and aesthetics are entities on which humans place value and over which we contend with pests. In the struggle, humans must use their knowledge of pest anatomy, classification, growth, development, biology, and behavior to adequately contest pests.

Pest management can be defined as a system integrating preventive and corrective measures to keep pests from causing significant problems. In any type of pest management system, these objectives should be achieved at the lowest possible cost, with minimum risk or hazard to customers and to desirable components of their environment. Such an integrated approach to pest management is now often called **integrated pest management (IPM).**

All species of living organisms have an inherent ability to reproduce. Factors that tend to limit this natural reproductive ability are called control factors. The population of a particular species in a particular place at any given time is the result of the interaction of these two opposing forces.

Urban IPM—Key Elements

Urban integrated pest management is a process that uses regular monitoring to determine if and when a treatment is needed. It employs physical, mechanical, cultural, chemical, biological, and educational programs to keep pest populations low enough to prevent intolerable damage or annoyance. Chemicals should not necessarily be the first choice for solving a pest problem and, when required, target-specific, low-impact chemicals and applications should be employed. Pesticidal treatments are not made according to a predetermined schedule, they are made only when and where monitoring has indicated that the pest will cause unacceptable economic, medical, or aesthetic damage. The IPM program must, as a result, be environmentally, socially, and economically compatible to meet current public expectations. Therefore, key elements of urban IPM include (1) decisions for solving pest problems are made on the basis of determined need, (2) all available management techniques are coordinated into the program, (3) health, aesthetics, satisfaction, comfort, and other subjective factors must be considered when determining the acceptable pest level, and (4) the human factor (IPM programs that directly involve and impact people).

Manipulating the factors that limit the reproductive and survival potential of each pest is the key to effective pest management. This usually involves the use of pesticides, but more and more pest management professionals are turning to sanitation, exclusion, harborage elimination, nonchemical control devices, and least-toxic pesticides as control products. Removing the food, water, and shelter of pests has a significant impact on controlling pest populations. When integrated with appropriate chemical control measures, sanitation provides a longer-lasting level of control.

Each pest management job must be analyzed separately, and five basic steps are involved: (1) **inspection,** (2) **identification,** (3) **recommendation,** (4) **treatment/implementation of pest management,** and (5) **evaluation.**

Inspection is essential to solving pest problems quickly and economically. It includes asking questions of the customer and examining the premises thoroughly to learn as much as possible about the problem. During the inspection, the professional should look for the harborage areas of pests; conditions of moisture, heat, or darkness that favor infestations; food and water that can be used by the pests; probable means of entry of the infestation (such as incoming foods, open sewers, etc.); and evidence of infestation (such as damage, droppings, tracks, and actual specimens or their cast skins). Monitoring is the part of the inspection process that enables the professional to obtain an estimate of the pest population level, which will indicate the severity of the pest problem.

The inspection will also give the professional an idea of the measures that may or may not be used, safety precautions that may be necessary, and when the work can best be done. Site awareness is critical in determining the presence of young, old, pregnant, or otherwise sensitive individuals, pets, pilot lights, exposed food, and other factors critical in IPM progress. Thoroughness during the inspection is of great importance in providing many of these answers. Because inspection is such an important part of a pest management program, some chapters will provide pest-specific inspection techniques.

Once the pest is found, the pest management professional must positively identify it in order to proceed. Positive and accurate **identification** is often needed to make a thorough evaluation of the problem and an appropriate recommendation for control. Once the pest has been identified, it is much easier to inspect for other evidence of infestation, harborage areas, and the means by which the pest gained entry. However, to do this, a knowledge of the biology and habits of the pest is necessary. When pests cannot be located, identification

must be made from damage, tracks, droppings, or cast skins. In any case, identification must be accurate to ensure successful control.

Pest monitoring may also be important in determining the severity of the infestation. Information from monitoring will help in deciding what measures to take against the pest infestation, and will provide justification for specific treatments. The public hires pest management profes-

Inspecting the Premises: Important Considerations

Question the customer for clues. This information helps the pest management professional to determine:

- the kind of pests (perhaps specimens have been saved)
- the number of pests
- the pest location
- any damage that may have occurred
- the length of time pests have been present

It is also important to have the proper tools to make the most efficient and effective inspection possible:

- flashlight (including a spare bulb and batteries)
- magnifying glass or hand lens
- screwdrivers (Phillips tip and standard tip)
- pliers
- adjustable wrench
- flushing agents
- glue boards
- sticky traps
- mechanic's mirror
- collecting vial
- spatula

Flashlights and mirrors are needed to inspect inside cracks and crevices; under appliances; in and around cabinets, closets, and furniture; and in other dimly lit areas. Hand tools are useful to remove switch and electrical outlet plates and duct and vent covers to inspect for pests. Flushing agents are used to flush insects out of hiding places. Glue boards and sticky traps help to locate infestations and to monitor pests before and after treatment. The spatula is used to scrape materials (frass, cast skins, and so forth) from areas occupied by insects. All of these tools are used to determine the extent of the pest problem, so that the pest management professional will know where to begin, the techniques to use, and how to follow up.

sionals to *eliminate* pests from the specific environments in which people have total control—their homes, and in some cases, their workplaces. Most people are unwilling to share their homes and workplaces with "only a few" mice, cockroaches, termites, ants, etc., especially after they have paid for a pest management service. When asked what population level they are willing to tolerate in their environments, most clients respond "zero," or "as close to zero as possible."

Pest thresholds may become somewhat more lax in the commercial sector. In many commercial accounts, it is unrealistic for the client to expect a zero threshold level for all pest problems. Consider the management of pests in facilities such as hospitals, supermarkets, food plants, schools, warehouses, and similar accounts. In these cases, the commercial client, like the residential client, may also desire a zero threshold. However, "low populations" carefully managed over time is more realistic, with the exception of specific, sensitive locations within an account (e.g., the hospital operating room).

Pest Thresholds— What Is an Acceptable Pest Level?

The aesthetic injury level is the point beyond which people will not tolerate a pest's presence. Thresholds are determined by the relationship of the pest to people's health, comfort, shelter, or aesthetics, and they are influenced by:

- *the pest species involved and its appearance*—Spiders are beneficial as predators but may be intolerable in and around dwellings.
- *the individual*—One person may be happy to have a nonpoisonous snake in the garden, while another person may be totally repulsed.
- *the environment*—A small rat infestation may be tolerable in a harbor area, but it certainly will not be tolerated in an upscale neighborhood.
- *the type of business or structure*—A few drain flies in a storage room may be acceptable, but not in a hospital operating room.
- *the specific areas within a structure*—The threshold for oriental cockroaches in the boiler room of a high-rise apartment building will be higher than that in the apartments.
- *the individual pesticide tolerance*—Some individuals may be willing to accept small numbers of pests instead of allowing the application of pesticides into their living environment.

A **recommendation** for eliminating the pest problem should be made only after the inspection has been completed and all the facts surrounding the problem are known. The recommendation should include not only what the professional can do for the customer, but also what the customer should do by way of harborage elimination, building repairs, sanitation, and so forth, to make the control program a more successful and lasting one. At this point, any limitations of the particular job should be explained to the customer.

An important part of a recommendation is the price to be charged for the work. Here again, a thorough understanding of the problem is vital so that the price quoted is economically and ethically sound. The customer deserves professional service for the price, and the pest management professional should receive adequate compensation for the services rendered.

Treatment (implementation of pest management tools and techniques) is the next step in the pest management system. Treatment may include sanitation and harborage removal services, exclusion, the use of traps or other mechanical devices to catch or prevent pests from entering, and any other nonchemical activity used to eliminate pests and prevent their recurrence. Treatment may also involve the use of pesticides. The pesticide chosen must be legal and appropriate for the pest situation involved. Modern-day pesticides offer a wide range of least-toxic environmentally sensitive, biorational synthetic and natural toxicants, attractants, repellants, insect growth regulators (IGRs), biologicals, and other materials that are useful in IPM programs.

The final step in urban pest management is **program evaluation**. Pest population levels must be continually monitored. The customer must also be kept advised on matters of sanitation and how to prevent new pest problems from becoming established, and any recurrence of the pest problem should be attended to before it becomes serious.

In summary, pest management should be considered as a systems approach, principally because of the complex interaction of human and structural factors that distinguish urban and industrial environments. The elements of the system include inspection, determination of pest thresholds, application of pest management procedures, and monitoring pest populations and management programs. Inspection and identification provide the basis on which the strategy can be founded in conjunction with an evaluation of all structural, human, and regulatory factors affecting the program. After determining the acceptable pest level (the threshold), the appropriate management recommendation can be made to the client. Application of pest management procedures (treatments), both nonchemical and chemical, can then commence. Monitoring is the final link in the strategy, and is key to long-term pest management. Constant evaluation is essential in determining pest recurrence or conditions conducive to recurrence, and the modification or reapplication of pest management procedures, as necessary. Thus, the goal of establishing a program that is environmentally, socially, and economically acceptable to the client (and that meets current public expectations) will have been met.

SUPPLEMENTARY READING MATERIAL

Borror, D. J., D. M. DeLong, and C. A. Triplehorn. *An Introduction to the Study of Insects*. 5th ed. New York: Saunders College Publishing, 1981. 827 pp.

Chapman, R. F. *The Insects: Structure and Function*. New York: American Elsevier, 1971. 819 pp.

Comstock, J. H. *An Introduction to Entomology*. 9th ed. Ithaca, New York: Comstock, 1940. 1,064 pp.

Essig, E. O. *College Entomology*. New York: Macmillan, 1942. 900 pp.

Matthews, R. W., and J. R. Matthews. *Insect Behavior*. New York: Wiley, 1978. 507 pp.

Metcalf, R. L., and R. A. Metcalf. *Destructive and Useful Insects*. 5th ed. New York: McGraw-Hill, 1993. 21 chapters.

Pfadt, R. E., ed. *Fundamentals of Applied Entomology*. 4th ed. New York: Macmillan, 1985. 742 pp.

Ross, H. H., C. A. Ross, and J. R. P. Ross. *A Textbook of Entomology*. 4th ed. New York: Wiley, 1982. 550 pp.

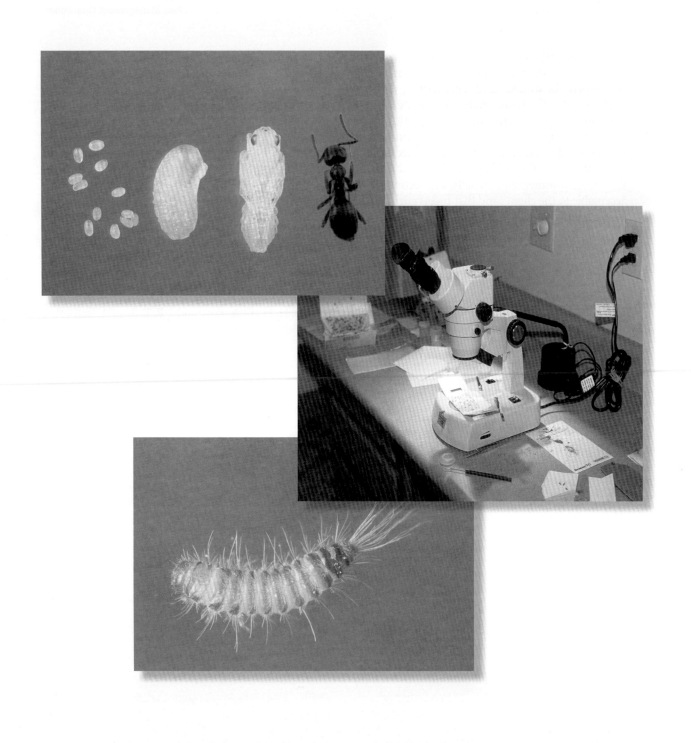

CHAPTER 2 | Insect Development, Classification, and Identification

All insects develop from eggs. The young of most hatch from an egg after it has been laid; however, the young of certain insects are born alive from eggs that have developed inside the body of the female (e.g., the Madagascar hissing cockroach). Insect eggs vary greatly in appearance. Most are rounded or oval, although many other shapes are quite common. The individual egg is covered with a shell that can be quite different in color and surface texture from one kind of insect to another. Eggs are usually laid in a protected location that will provide good conditions for survival of the young when they hatch.

Some insects, such as the cockroach, enclose several of their eggs together in a capsule, or ootheca. Others, such as the grasshopper and the June beetle, lay their eggs in the ground. Plant-feeding insects usually lay their eggs on plants, and parasitic insects frequently lay their eggs on or in the body of the host. Many insects lay their eggs singly, while others lay eggs in characteristic groups or masses. Some just drop their eggs in a suitable location, and others attach them firmly to a solid object.

Once insects hatch, they grow in a series of definite stages. The growth of an insect in each stage is limited by the space available to it within its external skeleton. As the insect develops, it lays down a new skeleton directly beneath the old one. The old body wall splits down the back, and the next stage emerges and expands to a larger size before the skeleton hardens again. This process, known as **molting**, is repeated from four to eight times in the average insect before it reaches adulthood. Some species, however, may have as many as 20 or more molts.

In insects, the molting process involves numerous, complex interactions between hormones, enzymes, cells, and organs. Therefore, a detailed discussion is beyond the scope of this book. Molting begins when the insect's brain receives the "message" that it is time to molt. The origin of this message or stimulus varies from one species to the next. When the brain receives the proper stimulation, a series of chemical events begin that lead to structural changes in the insect's cuticle.

As already indicated, the molting process is complicated, and all of the interactions involved are not completely understood. This is especially true of the hormones involved in initiating and controlling molting.

The primary hormone controlling molting is *ecdysone*. Upon proper stimulation, the prothoracic gland secretes ecdysone into the hemolymph. Ecdysone induces activation or production of the enzymes associated with apolysis, chitin synthesis, and cuticle production (i.e., molting).

Juvenile hormone (JH) is also involved in the molting process. During the between-molt stages of insects, JH levels are relatively high. This maintains the insect in the juvenile stage. When it becomes time to molt, JH levels decrease, and molting begins. Because molting only occurs when JH levels drop off, it is thought (Figures 2.1–2.4) that JH influences or suppresses the action of ecdysone.

Other hormones (e.g., eclosion hormone) are associated with the process of shedding the old cuticle, and the formation and sclerotization of a new cuticle. A reduction in JH levels is also required for activating these hormones.

Insect growth regulators (IGRs) are chemicals currently being used by the pest management industry. These pesticides target specific characteristics in insect growth and development to reduce or eliminate their pest status. Examples of IGRs include juvenile hormone analogs (JHAs), **chitin synthesis inhibitors (CSIs)**, and ecdysone analogs.

Approximately 50% of the dry weight of an insect's exoskeleton is chitin. Clearly, anything that depletes the formation of chitin will have a negative impact on the structural integrity of the exoskeleton. Such is the case with chitin CSIs.

The CSIs currently marketed (e.g., diflubenzuron, hexaflumuron, lufenuron, noviflumeron) inhibit the action of the enzyme, chitin synthetase (they do not specifically inhibit this enzyme), which disrupts chitin desposition during cuticle formation. The precise mechanism by which the enzyme's action is inhibited is unknown. However, the end result is an insufficient concentration of chitin in the newly synthesized culticle, causing morphological problems in molting insects. Disruption of chitin synthesis is usually fatal to the affected insect. Some of the reported effects include:

- Molting is prevented so the insect dies in its old cuticle;

- Molting is initiated, but not completed, or only partially completed;
- Feeding is disrupted because of mouth or digestive tract deformations; and
- Failing to hatch from eggs.

As mentioned earlier in this section, JH levels fluctuate during the different developmental stages of immature insects. High levels of JH inhibit molting, or prolong the immature stages. Because JHAs mimic the action of JH, they have a similar effect on molting to JH. Juvenile hormone is also involved in a great number of other processes in insects. Therefore, it is difficult to attribute specific characteristics observed in JHA-treated insects with any single cause. It is safe to say that some of the cuticular deformities seen in treated insects

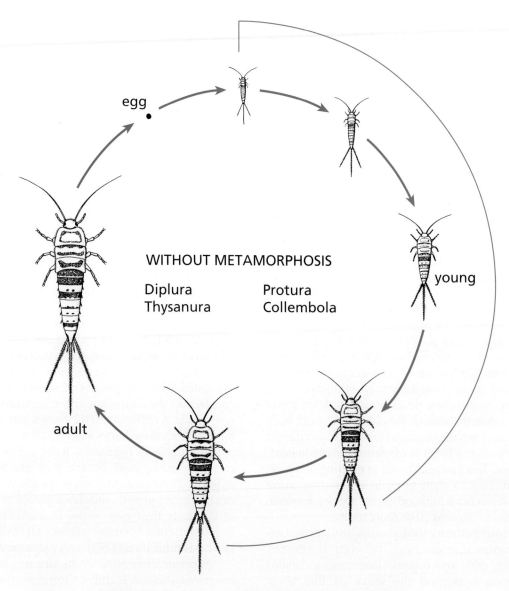

egg

WITHOUT METAMORPHOSIS

Diplura   Protura
Thysanura   Collembola

young

adult

FIGURE 2.1. Development without metamorphosis. (Provonsha)

could be attributed to the JHA's influence on ecdysone's control of molting.

A logical objective in creating highly specific insecticides would be to develop an insecticide that mimics ecdysone. Attempts at making ecdysone analogs have not been too successful. Research in this area is ongoing and may someday yield an effective ecdysone analog.

METAMORPHOSIS

When an insect molts from one stage to the other, it is progressing from one developmental stage, or instar, to another, larger stage. The accompanying changes that take place in the insect's outward appearance differ depending on what type of insect it is. Especially important is the amount of change that occurs when an insect molts from its final larval stage into an adult. The resulting adult can simply be either a larger version of the younger insect with only the added ability to reproduce, or it can be a completely different version with different feeding and harborage preferences, and maybe even different means of locomotion. These resultant changes after metamorphosis of a particular insect can have significant implications for pest control. Knowing the type of the development a pest goes through can be an important tool for its effective management.

Most urban pest insects can be grouped into three categories of metamorphosis: no metamorphosis (ametabolous), gradual and incomplete metamorphosis (hemimetabolous), or complete metamorphosis (holometabolous). Each type will

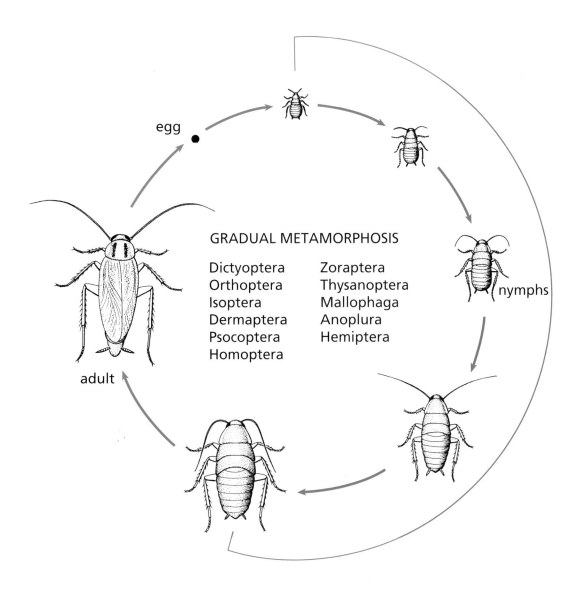

FIGURE 2.2. Development with gradual metamorphosis. (Provonsha)

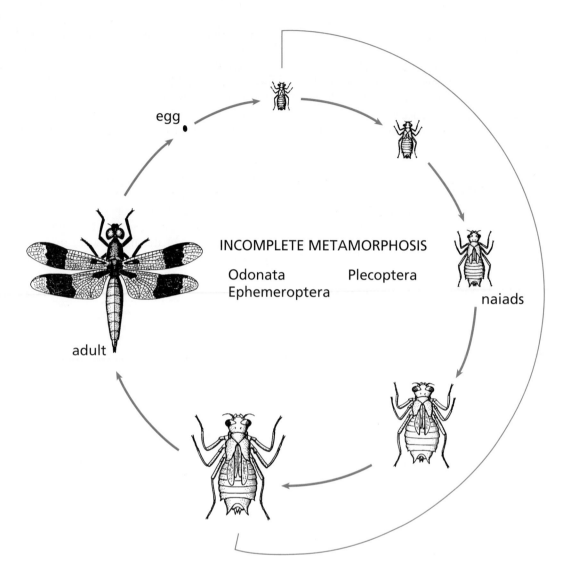

INCOMPLETE METAMORPHOSIS

Odonata   Plecoptera
Ephemeroptera

egg

naiads

adult

FIGURE 2.3. Development with incomplete metamorphosis. (Provonsha)

be discussed, along with examples of insects for each type (refer often to Figures 2.1 to 2.4).

Without Metamorphosis

Some insects, such as silverfish and firebrats, develop without metamorphosis. The adult insect results from a progressive development of the younger stages with each molt resulting in an increase in size and gradual maturation of the reproductive organs (see Figure 2.1). Adult insects are sexually mature, but will continue to molt throughout their lifetime with as many as 45 to 60 molts being observed. Adults of ametabolous insects are like their young in many ways. They share similar food, environmental, and habitat preferences, meaning that all stages of development will be found together in a structure.

Gradual Metamorphosis

Cockroaches, termites, earwigs, crickets, bed bugs,

and lice develop through a gradual metamorphosis. Like insects without metamorphosis, urban hemimetabolous insects share similar habitats, food preferences, and body form, but the development into the adult stage is more distinctive (see Figure 2.2). Reproductive organs and wing pads (when wings are present) do not begin to develop until the later instars of the nymph and neither become functional until the insect reaches the adult stage. Additionally, hemimetabolous insects go through a set number of molts. Though a female of a species may go through one extra nymphal molt, in general, the number is predetermined based on the species, and the adult stage does not molt.

Incomplete Metamorphosis

A subset of the hemimetabolous insects, which includes mayflies, dragonflies, and damselflies, go through incomplete metamorphosis. They have

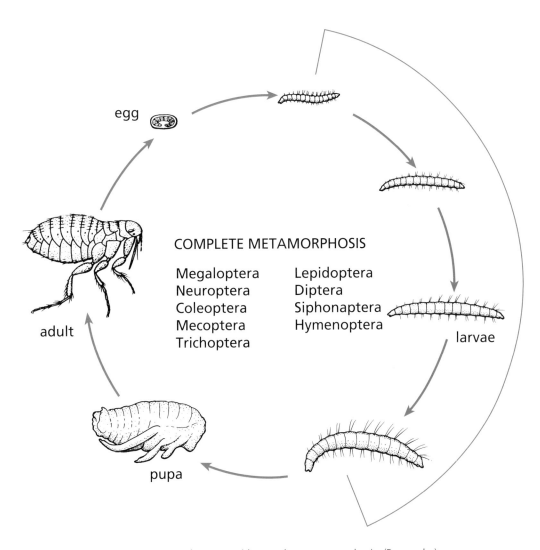

egg

adult

COMPLETE METAMORPHOSIS

Megaloptera	Lepidoptera
Neuroptera	Diptera
Coleoptera	Siphonaptera
Mecoptera	Hymenoptera
Trichoptera	

larvae

pupa

FIGURE 2.4. Development with complete metamorphosis. (Provonsha)

aquatic nymphs called naiads. These do not share the same habitat as their adult stages, and have a more distinctive change after the molt until nymph stage occurs. (see Figure 2.3). Additionally, one group—the Ephermeroptera (mayflies)—even undergoes an additional stage called the subimago stage, where they go through one molt after becoming an adult. These species are generally not considered pests, though they may be found within the urban environment.

Complete Metamorphosis

Fleas, flies, beetles, moths, ants, wasps, and mosquitoes undergo a complete metamorphosis. This means that holometabolous insects have four distinct stages in their life cycle: the **egg**, the **larva** (with multiple instars), the **pupa**, and the **adult** (see Figure 2.4). In these species, the larva that emerges from the egg has an entirely different body form than its parents. It may have different appendages

for movement, different types of eyes (or none at all), and different mouthparts. It may also have distinct environmental and dietary requirements.

The impact of these factors on urban pest management are many. For some species, the larva (see Figure 2.5, following page 254) itself could be the only stage that does economic damage (as with some moths), or it could be a stage that has little or no impact on a homeowner or client (as with fleas, many flies, and mosquitoes). If the larva and adults do not share the same habitats, finding both habitats may be crucial to control, even if the nondamaging state may not be noticed by the client. It would then be up to the pest management professional to know the potential habitats and the means of control needed for all life stages of the pest.

The pupa stage (see Figure 2.6, following page 254) is also an important consideration for holometabolous insects. For some species, it can provide protection from pesticides and environmental conditions and hamper control efforts. For insects with a delayed emergence from the pupal stage, there exists the potential for a new infestation long after the problem appears to be under control.

When the adult insect emerges from the pupal case, it may or may not become a pest. The adult clothes moth does no damage; however, the larva feeds on woolens. Grain beetle adults feed on cereals, as do its larvae. Adult female mosquitoes bite humans, and in some species, carry disease organisms, while its larvae are harmless. However, all adults are in the reproductive stage, and must be attended to since they are responsible for population growth.

The type of metamorphosis a pest insect species undergoes is therefore an important consideration when planning a management strategy. A strategy that works for a pest with no or gradual metamorphosis may not be effective for one that undergoes complete metamorphosis, and depending on the strategy used, the reverse may also be true.

CLASSIFICATION OF INSECTS

Most living things are divided into two big groups, or kingdoms: the plant kingdom and the animal kingdom. (Bacteria, protozoa, mushrooms and molds, and perhaps viruses belong to other kingdoms.) In general, plants are incapable of moving from place to place and use inorganic materials as food; animals are more or less mobile organisms that take in organic materials as food. There are exceptions to these rules, and the number of kingdoms is constantly being disputed.

There are more than a million different kinds of animals in the world, and a systematic study of the animal kingdom necessitates some scheme of arranging them into groups, or classifying them. Classification is based primarily on structural characteristics; those animals with certain structures in common are classified into one group, and those with other structures are placed into other groups. Thus, the animal kingdom is divided into a dozen or so major groups, called phyla (singular *phylum*).

Insects, spiders, mites, ticks, scorpions, centipedes, millipedes, crabs, shrimps, lobsters, sowbugs, and many others belong in the phylum **Arthropoda**, which means "jointed foot or appendage." Arthropods comprise the largest group in the animal kingdom, making up almost 90% of all known animal species. A close look at any of these common animals (refer to Figure 2.7) will reveal the following visible characteristics that distinguish the arthropods from all other animals:

- A segmented (jointed) body, with segments usually grouped into two or three more or less distinct regions

- Paired, segmented appendages, such as legs and antennae
- An external skeleton that is shed and renewed periodically as the arthropod grows
- Bilateral symmetry, that is, the right and left sides of the arthropod are alike

The classification of animals does not stop with phyla; each phylum is further subdivided into groups called classes, classes into orders, orders into families, families into genera (singular genus), and genera into species. The classification of the German cockroach and man can be compared as follows:

Classification	German Cockroach	Man
Kingdom	Animal	Animal
Phylum	Arthropoda	Chordata
Class	Insecta	Mammalia
Order	Dictyoptera	Primata
Family	Blattellidae	Hominidae
Genus	*Blattella*	*Homo*
Species	*germanica*	*sapiens*

When an insect is being identified and someone wants to know what species it is, the answer given usually includes both the genus and the species names (e.g., *Blattella germanica*). This scientific name is always written in italics or underlined. This name may also be followed by a person's name (which may appear in parentheses and may be abbreviated). This individual named or classified the insect.

There are several classes of arthropods that are of interest to pest management professionals. These are described in the following sections and are represented in Figure 2.7.

Crustacea
Crayfish, Lobsters, Sowbugs

Members of this class breathe by means of gills and, therefore, must live either in water or in very damp conditions. All have two pairs of antennae and at least five pairs of legs. The common sowbug, which is frequently found around water-soaked wood or in wet debris around plants, is the principal crustacean that the pest management professional may encounter.

Diplopoda
Millipedes

This class consists of animals whose bodies are made of segments essentially alike, with the excep-

THE ORDERS OF INSECTS

Order	Common Name	Order	Common Name
1. Diplura*	campodeids, japygids, diplurans	15. Mallophaga	chewing lice, bird lice
2. Protura*	telsontails, proturans	16. Anoplura	sucking lice, true lice
3. Thysanura	bristletails, silverfish, firebrats	17. Thysanoptera*	thrips
4. Collembola	springtails	18. Hemiptera	true bugs, bed bugs
5. Ephemeroptera*	mayflies	19. Homoptera	cicadas, aphids, scale insects, leafhoppers
6. Odonata*	dragonflies, damselflies		
7. Orthoptera	grasshoppers, crickets, katydids	20. Neuroptera*	antlions, lacewings
8. Dictyoptera	cockroaches, walkingsticks, mantids	21. Megaloptera*	dobsonflies
		22. Coleoptera	beetles
9. Isoptera	termites	23. Mecoptera*	scorpionflies
10. Plecoptera*	stoneflies	24. Trichoptera*	caddisflies
11. Dermaptera	earwigs	25. Lepidoptera	butterflies, moths
12. Embioptera*	webspinners	26. Diptera	flies, mosquitoes, gnats, midges
13. Psocoptera (Corrodentia)	psocids, booklice		
		27. Siphonaptera	fleas
14. Zoraptera*	zorapterans	28. Hymenoptera	bees, wasps, ants, sawflies

*These orders are of only general interest to the pest management professional because they do not contain insects that usually require control.

tion of the first segment, which is the head. This group can be distinguished by the fact that each of the body segments has two pairs of legs joined to the underside of the body. The antennae are short.

Chilopoda
Centipedes
Members of this class are multisegmented, in much the same manner as millipedes. They can be distin-

guished by the fact that there is only one pair of legs per segment, and these legs are attached close to the underside of the body. The antennae are usually long and many jointed. Some can inflict a painful bite.

Arachnida
Spiders, Mites, Ticks
This class has two body regions, the head and thorax, joined together to form a cephalothorax, and the abdomen. The adults have four pairs of legs and no antennae. Immature ticks have only three pairs of legs.

Insecta (Hexapoda)
Insects
This class has three distinct body regions (head, thorax, abdomen), a pair of antennae, usually one or two pairs of wings, and three pairs of legs.

Many entomologists group the insects into 28 orders. Not all of these orders are important to the pest management professional; however, they are all included in the box above so that it will be easier to understand the relationships between all of the orders, particularly when using other texts as references.

As a matter of interest, Figure 2.8 shows representatives of the various orders not included in the following detailed descriptions. The reference books listed at the end of the chapter can be used to obtain further information on any of these orders.

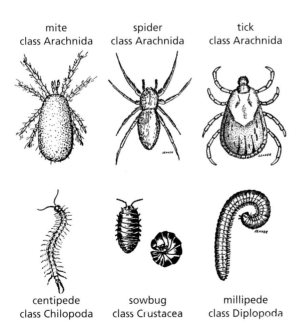

FIGURE 2.7. Representatives of four classes of arthropods. (Lehker)

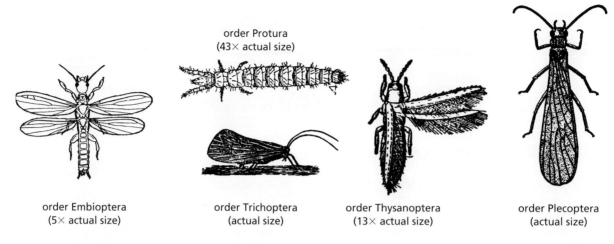

order Protura
(43× actual size)

order Embioptera
(5× actual size)

order Trichoptera
(actual size)

order Thysanoptera
(13× actual size)

order Plecoptera
(actual size)

FIGURE 2.8. Representatives of several orders of insects not usually encountered by the pest management professional.

Pest management professionals should have knowledge of the distinguishing characteristics of the orders of insects they are often called on to control. A knowledge of these characteristics will be valuable in beginning the identification process. It is often necessary to know the exact species of insect involved in a problem; detailed information on the identification of a species will be given in the individual chapter concerning each insect. In the following descriptions, only the 16 orders of particular interest to the pest management professional have been included. The characteristics used are based on adult insects.

Thysanura
Bristletails, Silverfish, Firebrats

These are wingless, flattened, fish-shaped insects, usually not more than 1/2-inch long. They have long antennae and two or three threadlike appendages at the end of the abdomen. They have chewing mouthparts and develop without metamorphosis (see Figure 2.9).

Collembola
Springtails

These are wingless, very small (up to 1/5-inch long) adults that have short antennae and chewing mouthparts. There is usually a springlike projection on the underside of the abdomen, which distinguishes this order from all others. They develop without metamorphosis (see Figure 2.10).

Orthoptera
Grasshoppers, Crickets, Katydids

These medium- to large-sized insects have chewing mouthparts and usually four wings. When present, the front pair of wings is thickened and leathery, and the back pair is membranous and folds beneath the front wings like a fan when at rest. The hind legs are large and adapted for jumping. These insects have a gradual metamorphosis (see Figure 2.11).

Dictyoptera
Cockroaches, Walkingsticks, Mantids

These insects are closely related to crickets and grasshoppers. The major difference is that this group does not have hind legs adapted for jumping, but rather sleek ones for walking and running (see Figure 2.12).

Isoptera
Termites

These small- to medium-sized insects live in social groups and have a highly developed caste system. Workers and soldiers are wingless and dirty-white in color. Swarmers are dark bodied and have four long whitish wings (all of the same length). In all forms, the abdomen is broadly joined to the thorax without a definite visible waist. Termites have chewing mouthparts and a gradual metamorphosis (see Figure 2.13).

Psocoptera
Psocids, Booklice

These tiny, soft-bodied insects have either four wings or none at all. They also have chewing mouthparts and a gradual metamorphosis (see Figure 2.14).

Mallophaga
Chewing Lice, Bird Lice

These small, usually flattened, wingless insects are external parasites on birds and mammals. They are not known to attack man, but people who handle

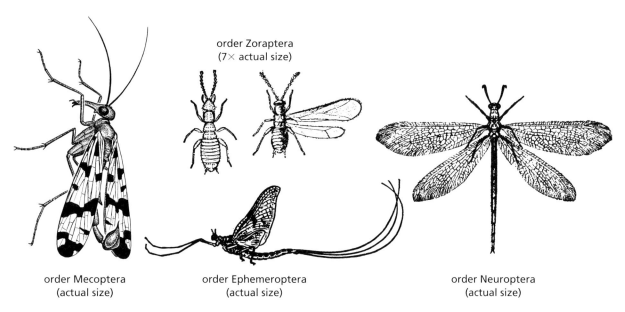

order Zoraptera
(7× actual size)

order Mecoptera
(actual size)

order Ephemeroptera
(actual size)

order Neuroptera
(actual size)

FIGURE 2.8. (continued)

infested animals may get lice on them. They have chewing mouthparts, and their metamorphosis is gradual (see Figure 2.15).

Anoplura
Sucking Lice, True Lice

These small insects are wingless and flat bodied, and the head is distinctly narrower than the thorax. Mouthparts are adapted for piercing the skin and sucking blood. They are external parasites on mammals, and their metamorphosis is gradual (see Figure 2.16).

Hemiptera
True Bugs, Bed Bugs

These bugs usually have four wings, with the front pair thickened and leathery at the base and thin and membranous at the tips. The hind pair of wings is membranous and is folded under the front wings when the insect is at rest. In some forms, such as bed bugs, the wings are lacking. The mouthparts form a noticeable beak for piercing and sucking. Some transmit plant and animal diseases. Metamorphosis is gradual (see Figure 2.17).

Homoptera
Cicadas, Aphids, Scale Insects, Leafhoppers

These small to large insects may or may not have wings. When wings are present, they are of the same thickness throughout their length and are held rooflike over the body when at rest. Mouthparts are adapted for piercing and sucking plants. Metamorphosis is gradual. The scale insects are

highly specialized. Adult females are so different from other insects in body form that they often look like abnormal growths on the host plant (see Figure 2.18).

Dermaptera
Earwigs

These small- to medium-sized insects may or may not have four wings. The front wings are leathery and very short, and when at rest, they meet in a straight line down the back. The hind wings fold under the front wings. Mouthparts are adapted for chewing. The back end of the abdomen has a protruding pair of forceps-like organs that distinguish these insects from nearly all others. Metamorphosis is gradual (see Figure 2.19).

Coleoptera
Beetles

The most distinctive characteristic of beetles is the presence of hard, shell-like front wings that meet, when at rest, in a straight line down the back. The hind wings fold under the front wings. These insects have chewing mouthparts and a complete metamorphosis (see Figure 2.20).

Lepidoptera
Butterflies, Moths

Most Lepidoptera have four wings that are membranous and covered with overlapping scales. The mouthparts are formed into a long, coiled, tongue-like organ adapted for sucking liquids, such as nectar. Metamorphosis is complete (see Figure 2.21).

order Thysanura
(1.5× actual size)

FIGURE 2.9. Firebrat

order Collembola
(9× actual size)

FIGURE 2.10. Springtail

order Orthoptera
(actual size)

FIGURE 2.11. Grasshopper

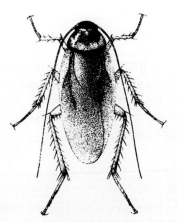

order Dictyoptera
(actual size)

FIGURE 2.12. American Cockroach

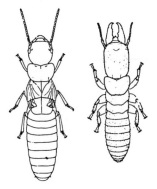

order Isoptera
(3× actual size)

FIGURE 2.13. Termites

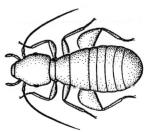

order Psocoptera
(20× actual size)

FIGURE 2.14. Booklouse

order Mallophaga
(10× actual size)

FIGURE 2.15. Chewing Louse

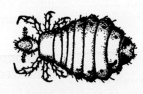

order Anoplura
(8× actual size)

FIGURE 2.16. Sucking Louse

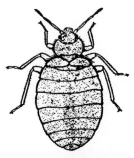

order Hemiptera
(6× actual size)

FIGURE 2.17. Bed Bug

order Homoptera
(6× actual size)

FIGURE 2.18. Aphid

order Dermaptera
(actual size)

FIGURE 2.19. Earwig

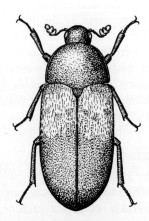

order Coleoptera
(6× actual size)

FIGURE 2.20. Larder Beetle

Diptera
Flies, Mosquitoes, Gnats, Midges

The winged members of this order have only two wings. The second pair of wings is replaced by a pair of knobbed, threadlike organs called halteres (or balancers). Mouthparts are adapted for piercing and sucking or for sponging up liquid food. Metamorphosis is complete (see Figure 2.22).

Siphonaptera
Fleas

These are small, wingless external parasites of warm-blooded animals. The body is compressed laterally (thin from side to side). Adults have piercing-sucking mouthparts. Metamorphosis is complete (see Figure 2.23).

Hymenoptera
Bees, Wasps, Ants, Sawflies

Most members of this order have four wings, but some, such as worker ants, are wingless. The wings are membranous, and the hind pair is usually smaller than the front pair. Mouthparts are adapted for chewing or for chewing and lapping. In most species the abdomen is pinched into a thin pedicel, or waist, where it joins the thorax. Metamorphosis is complete (see Figure 2.24).

IDENTIFICATION

The first question asked when an insect is found is "What is it?" Quite often, a positive identification cannot immediately be made. Most experienced pest management professionals can identify a beetle as a beetle, a fly as a fly, or a moth as a moth, but a more specific determination may be difficult. Occasionally it is even difficult to place an insect in its largest subdivision (order). But in attempting to identify an unknown insect, the first step is to determine the order to which it belongs. **Diagnostic keys** (usually referred to simply as **insect keys**) are devices used to identify insects, and they are the most accurate means of identifying an unknown insect. (See the Key to Common Orders of Insects on pages 26–27.)

Only adult insect identification will be considered in this chapter. Immature insect identification requires specialized knowledge and is beyond the scope of this chapter. Most adults have wings, so you should become as familiar as possible with the adult insects lacking wings: silverfish, springtails, fleas, scale insects, booklice, biting lice, sucking lice, bed bugs, and some ants, termites, earwigs, and cockroaches.

order Lepidoptera
(2× actual size)
FIGURE 2.21. Moth

order Diptera
(4× actual size)
FIGURE 2.22. Fly

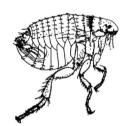
order Siphonaptera
(13× actual size)
FIGURE 2.23. Flea

order Hymenoptera
(actual size)
FIGURE 2.24. Wasp

A KEY TO COMMON ORDERS OF INSECTS
Adapted by W. L. Butts from a key by H. O. Deay and H. W. Smith

1 Winged insects (if all sutures on top of abdomen are not visible, the insect is winged).................................. 14
1¹ Wingless insects 2
2 (1¹) Long antenna-like appendages at end of abdomen .... order Thysanura
2¹ Without long antenna-like appendages at the end of the abdomen... 3
3 (2¹) With springlike appendage (usually forked) underneath abdomen; very small insects ....order Collembola
3¹ Without springlike appendage beneath abdomen 4
4 (3¹) Body strongly flattened from side to side; legs fitted for jumping .... order Siphonaptera
4¹ Body not strongly flattened from side to side... 5
5 (4¹) Mouthparts in the form of a beak, which is usually jointed and
    not capable of being withdrawn into the head.. 6
5¹ Mouthparts not in the form of a definite beak 7
6 (5) Beak arising from underside of head near the front margin;
    body usually somewhat flattened from top to bottom.. order Hemiptera
6¹ Beak arising from behind the middle of the underside of the head, often arising
    from a point so close to the rear margin as to make it appear to be arising from
    between the first pair of legs .... order Homoptera
7 (5¹) Mouthparts withdrawn into head when not in use.
    External parasites of warm-blooded animals .... order Anoplura
7¹ Mouthparts not withdrawn into head when not in use; chewing-type, usually well-developed mandibles..... 8
8 (7¹) Abdomen strongly constricted (pinched in) at base .... order Hymenoptera
8¹ Base of abdomen nearly as wide or as wide as thorax, not strongly constricted 9
9 (8¹) With a pair of forceps-like appendages at end of abdomen .... order Dermaptera
9¹ Without a pair of forceps-like appendages at tip of abdomen 10
10 (9¹) Head, when viewed from above, never wider than the thorax.. 11
10¹ Head, when viewed from above, at least slightly wider than the thorax. Body less than 1/2-inch long........... 12
11 (10) Large insects, usually 1/2-inch or more in length; mouthparts with
    mandibles (jaws) well developed, of chewing type; antennae with more than ten segments 28
11¹ Very small insects, usually less than 1/8-inch long. Mouthparts projected slightly so that they give
    the appearance of a short, off-center cone. Antennae with ten or fewer segments ....order Thysanoptera
12 (10¹) Antennae with five or fewer segments. External parasites of
    warm-blooded animals ....order Mallophaga
12¹ Antennae with more than five segments 13
13 (12¹) Tarsi with three or fewer segments; cerci absent;
    body usually less than 1/12-inch long ....order Psocoptera
13¹ Tarsi with not less than four segments; cerci present (may be quite small);
    body usually more than 1/5-inch long .... order Isoptera

A pictorial key to the orders of adult insects follows this section (see Figure 2.25 on pages 29–37). This key has descriptive characteristics pictured to aid in identification. It should not be difficult to follow. Most of the characteristics can be seen with the unaided eye, but a 10-power hand lens is useful in the identification of insects. Using a key involves nothing more than locating the described structures on the insect and making the proper choice at each descriptive couplet.

A couplet consists of a set of two alternative bits of descriptive information. Select the couplet that agrees with the appearance of the insect and follow the dark line, repeating the procedure at each couplet, until the proper order is located.

For example, take a specimen of any adult cockroach, and with the specimen in front of you, refer to the first couplet. Compare the contrasting statements, "winged" versus "wingless." Since this is a winged insect (although some adult cockroaches, such as the female oriental cockroach, have the wings reduced to small padlike structures), you would follow the line leading from the word "winged" down to the next couplet.

Here again, you have two alternatives that must be compared. Because cockroaches have hardened,

14	(1) With only one pair of wings	order Diptera
14¹	With two pairs of wings	15
15	(14¹) Front wings opaque, thick (at least on the basal half)	16
15¹	Front wings transparent throughout their entire length	21
16	(15) Front wings without veins, shell-like; inner edges meeting in a straight line	17
161	Front wings with veins; inner edges do not meet in a straight line	18
17	(16) Large forceps-like organs at end of abdomen	order Dermaptera
17¹	Without forceps-like organs at end of abdomen	order Coleoptera
18	(16¹) Wings covered with scales. (In some of this group, there may be transparent areas in the wing, but at least parts of the wing surface are definitely scaled.)	order Lepidoptera
18¹	Wings not covered with scales	19
19	(18¹) Mouthparts are not forming a beak	28
19¹	Mouthparts forming a distinct beak, which is usually jointed	20
20	(19¹) Only basal half of wing opaque and thickened, outer end transparent; beak arising from a point close to front margin of head	order Hemiptera
20¹	Entire wing rather opaque and thickened; beak arising from a point behind the middle of the head, usually close to its rear margin	order Homoptera
21	(15¹) Front and hind wing nearly equal in length	22
21¹	Front wing decidedly longer and wider than hind wing	26
22	(21) Wings very narrow, straplike, with few veins; fringed all around the edge with long hairlike setae. Very small insects with mouthparts looking like a small cone, which appears to be off center or twisted	order Thysanoptera
22¹	Wings not narrow and straplike; many veins; not fringed with long hairlike setae	23
23	(22¹) Antennae very short, not as long as head is wide. Wings with dense network of veins, hind wing sometimes slightly wider than front wing at base. No long, many-jointed appendages arising from tip of abdomen	order Odonata
23¹	Antennae many segmented, much longer than the width of the head	24
24	(23¹) Abdomen without cerci	order Neuroptera
24¹	Abdomen with cerci	25
25	(24¹) Tarsi with three segments. Cerci usually many segmented, long; hind wing usually distinctly wider than front wing	order Plecoptera
25¹	Tarsi with at least four segments. Cerci short, never with more than eight segments. Wings of equal length and width	order Isoptera
26	(21¹) Wings with many veins, the many cross veins forming a netlike appearance; antennae very short and threadlike	order Ephemeroptera
26¹	Wings with few veins; antennae not short and threadlike	27
27	(26¹) Tarsi with five joints; a row of small hooks along front edge of hind wing	order Hymenoptera
27¹	Tarsi with two or three joints; no row of small hooks along front edge of hind wing	order Psocoptera
28	(1¹) Hind legs adapted for jumping	order Orthoptera
28¹	Hind legs not adapted for jumping	order Dictyoptera

leathery, and parchmentlike front wings, you should continue down the left-hand side of the key. Compare the next two choices. Because cockroaches have chewing mouthparts, you would proceed to the next two alternatives immediately below the phrase "chewing mouthparts." This insect is without pincerlike cerci at the end of its body, so the line leading from that characteristic should be followed to the next couplet, which reads "front wings with branched veins" versus "front wings hard, without veins; may be lined." You see the front wings have veins, so you move to the next two choices immediately below.

The cockroach is described by the right-hand side of this couplet, since it is a walking insect with an unenlarged hind femur and a five-segment tarsi. Immediately below the drawing showing these characteristics, you will see that you have identified your specimen as belonging to the order Dictyoptera, which includes the cockroaches.

With a little practice you should be able to identify most of the common insects to order by means of this key. Note that certain areas of the key have been highlighted. These highlighted areas single out the orders of insects that you will most likely be requested to control as a pest management specialist.

As a pest management professional studies and gains valuable experience, the many species of pests (insects, spiders, ticks, rodents, birds, etc.) that require control can be identified. Most of these pests can be identified on sight. However, this key can be a valuable tool in gaining experience and knowledge of insect characteristics, can help to identify unknown specimens, and can aid in verifying tentative identifications.

Keep in mind that there are several sources that can be helpful in identifying pest species. The Cooperative Extension Service has agents and specialists throughout the United States and at state universities. State and national pest control associations have technical specialists, and many museums have personnel who can provide help in making identifications. These sources should be used rather than proceeding into a pest management program not knowing for sure what pest is to be controlled.

Appendix A provides information on collect-ing and preserving insects. Making an insect collection is an excellent way to learn more about insects and their identification, biology, and behavior.

SUPPLEMENTARY READING MATERIAL

Borror, D. J., D. M. DeLong, and C. A. Triplehorn. *An Introduction to the Study of Insects.* 5th ed. New York: Saunders College Publishing, 1981. 827 pp.

Comstock, J. H. *An Introduction to Entomology.* 9th ed. Ithaca, New York: Comstock, 1940. 1064 pp.

Essig, E. O. *College Entomology.* New York: Macmillan, 1942. 900 pp.

Metcalf, R. L., and R. A. Metcalf. *Destructive and Useful Insects.* 5th ed. New York: McGraw-Hill, 1993. 21 chapters.

Pfadt, R. E., ed. *Fundamentals of Applied Entomology.* 4th ed. New York: Macmillan, 1985. 742 pp.

Ross, H. H., C. A. Ross, and J. R. P. Ross. *A Textbook of Entomology.* 4th ed. New York: Wiley, 1982. 550 pp.

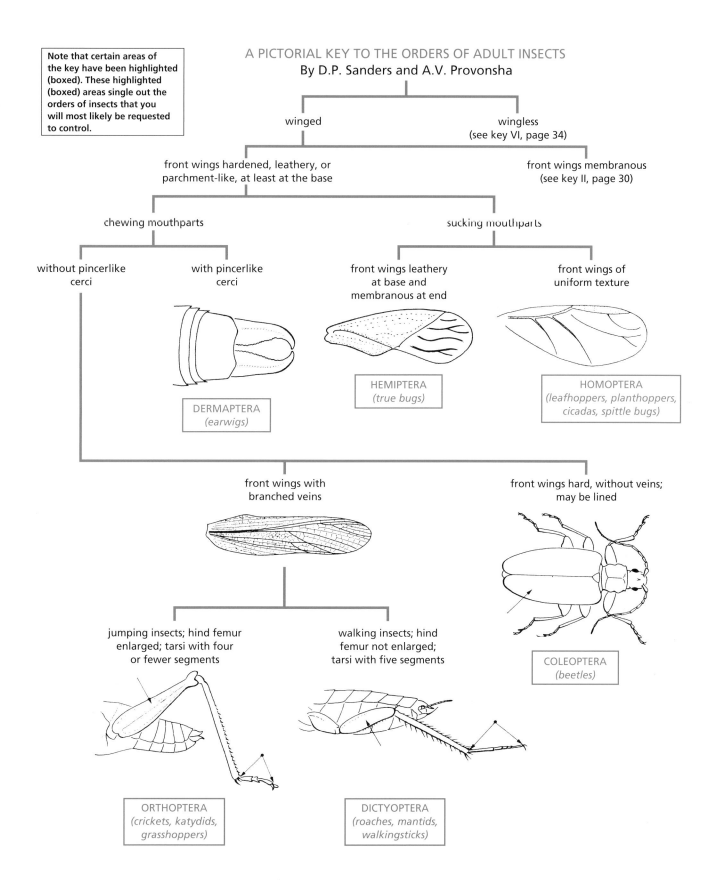

Note that certain areas of the key have been highlighted (boxed). These highlighted (boxed) areas single out the orders of insects that you will most likely be requested to control.

A PICTORIAL KEY TO THE ORDERS OF ADULT INSECTS
By D.P. Sanders and A.V. Provonsha

winged

wingless
(see key VI, page 34)

front wings hardened, leathery, or parchment-like, at least at the base

front wings membranous
(see key II, page 30)

chewing mouthparts

sucking mouthparts

without pincerlike cerci

with pincerlike cerci

front wings leathery at base and membranous at end

front wings of uniform texture

DERMAPTERA
(earwigs)

HEMIPTERA
(true bugs)

HOMOPTERA
(leafhoppers, planthoppers, cicadas, spittle bugs)

front wings with branched veins

front wings hard, without veins; may be lined

jumping insects; hind femur enlarged; tarsi with four or fewer segments

walking insects; hind femur not enlarged; tarsi with five segments

COLEOPTERA
(beetles)

ORTHOPTERA
(crickets, katydids, grasshoppers)

DICTYOPTERA
(roaches, mantids, walkingsticks)

FIGURE 2.25. A pictorial key to the orders of adult insects, used to help identify insects.

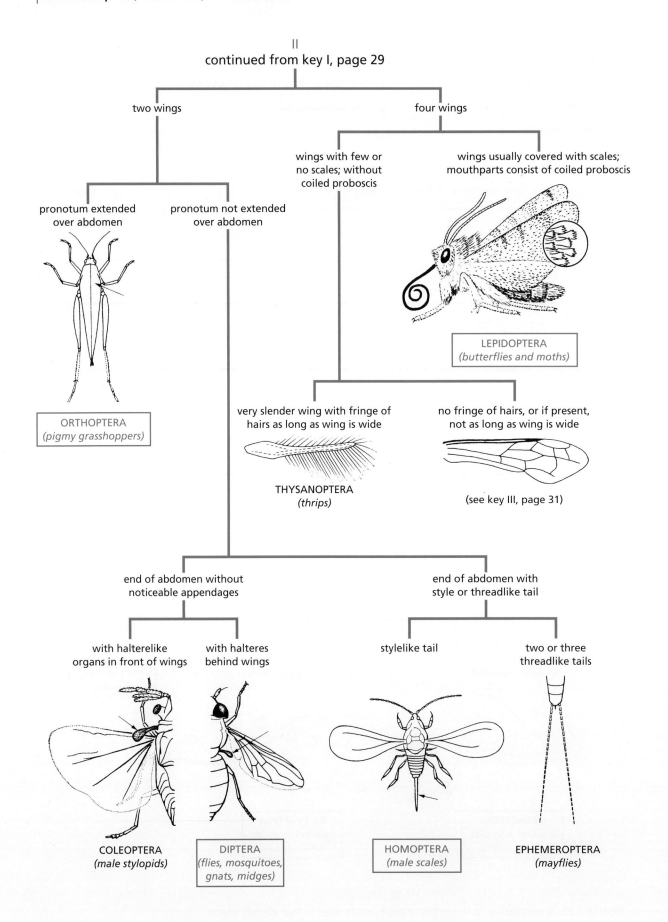

II
continued from key I, page 29

two wings

four wings

wings with few or
no scales; without
coiled proboscis

wings usually covered with scales;
mouthparts consist of coiled proboscis

pronotum extended
over abdomen

pronotum not extended
over abdomen

LEPIDOPTERA
(butterflies and moths)

ORTHOPTERA
(pigmy grasshoppers)

very slender wing with fringe of
hairs as long as wing is wide

no fringe of hairs, or if present,
not as long as wing is wide

THYSANOPTERA
(thrips)

(see key III, page 31)

end of abdomen without
noticeable appendages

end of abdomen with
style or threadlike tail

with halterelike
organs in front of wings

with halteres
behind wings

stylelike tail

two or three
threadlike tails

COLEOPTERA
(male stylopids)

DIPTERA
*(flies, mosquitoes,
gnats, midges)*

HOMOPTERA
(male scales)

EPHEMEROPTERA
(mayflies)

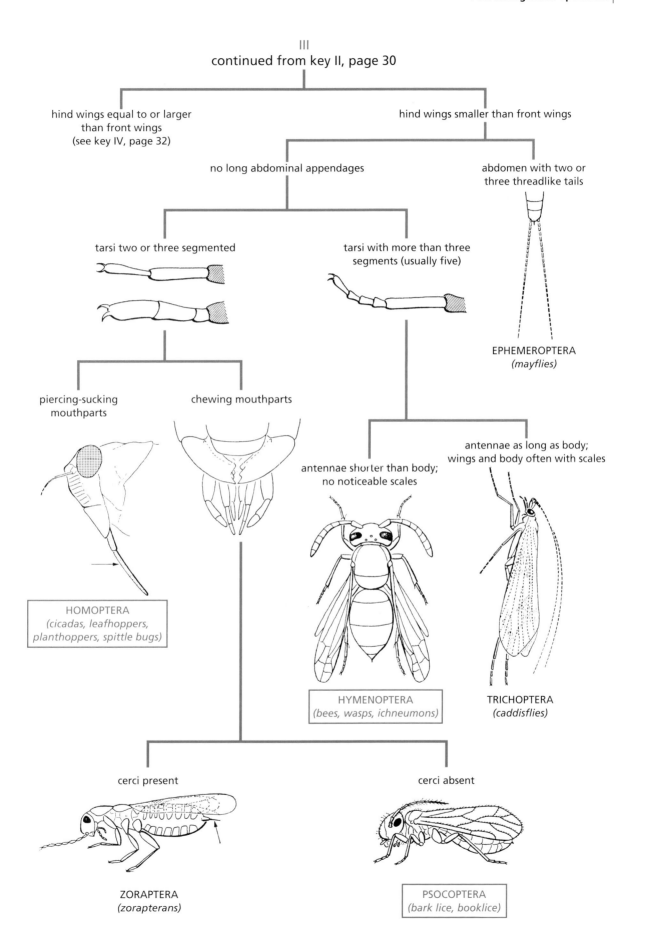

III
continued from key II, page 30

hind wings equal to or larger
than front wings
(see key IV, page 32)

hind wings smaller than front wings

no long abdominal appendages

abdomen with two or
three threadlike tails

tarsi two or three segmented

tarsi with more than three
segments (usually five)

EPHEMEROPTERA
(mayflies)

piercing-sucking
mouthparts

chewing mouthparts

antennae shorter than body;
no noticeable scales

antennae as long as body;
wings and body often with scales

HOMOPTERA
(cicadas, leafhoppers,
planthoppers, spittle bugs)

HYMENOPTERA
(bees, wasps, ichneumons)

TRICHOPTERA
(caddisflies)

cerci present

cerci absent

ZORAPTERA
(zorapterans)

PSOCOPTERA
(bark lice, booklice)

IV
continued from key III, page 31

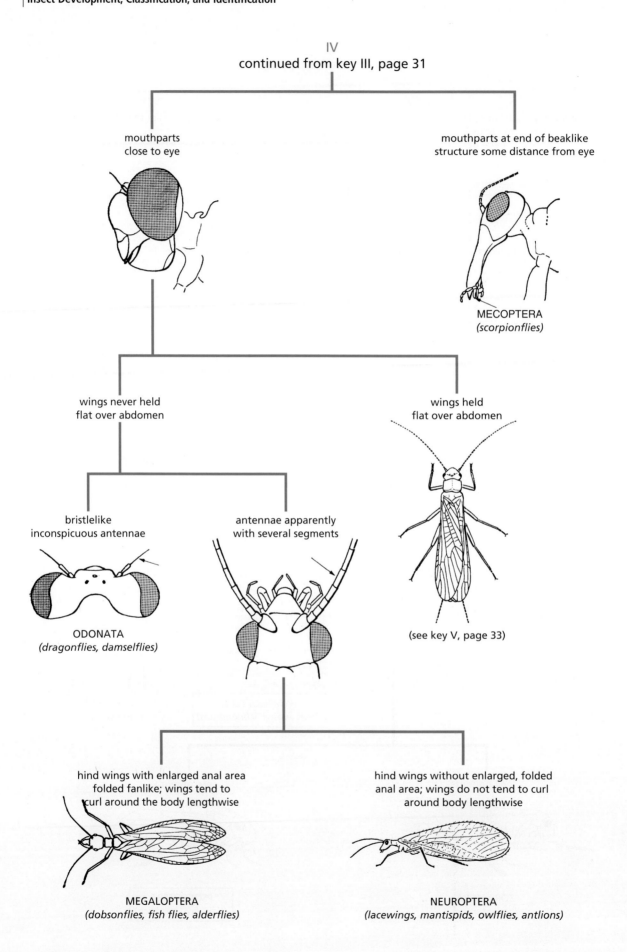

mouthparts
close to eye

mouthparts at end of beaklike
structure some distance from eye

MECOPTERA
(scorpionflies)

wings never held
flat over abdomen

wings held
flat over abdomen

bristlelike
inconspicuous antennae

antennae apparently
with several segments

ODONATA
(dragonflies, damselflies)

(see key V, page 33)

hind wings with enlarged anal area
folded fanlike; wings tend to
curl around the body lengthwise

hind wings without enlarged, folded
anal area; wings do not tend to curl
around body lengthwise

MEGALOPTERA
(dobsonflies, fish flies, alderflies)

NEUROPTERA
(lacewings, mantispids, owlflies, antlions)

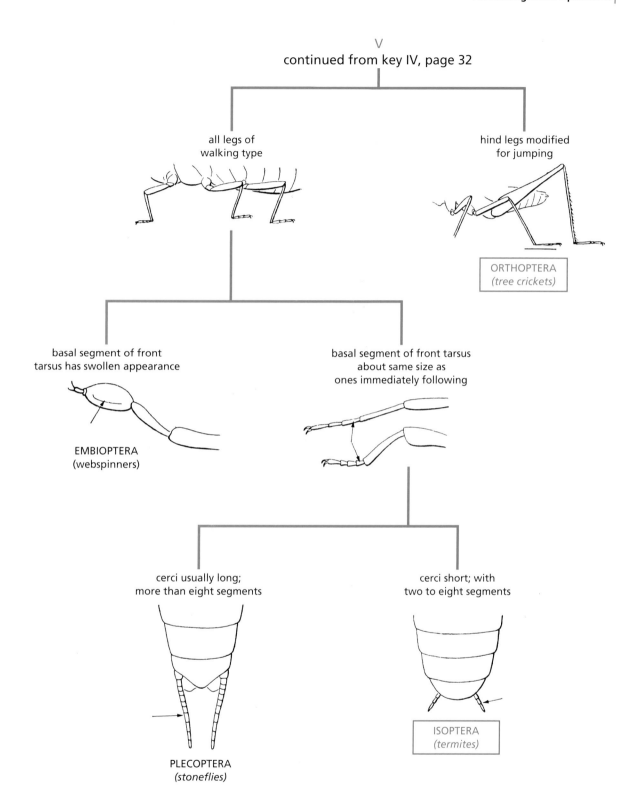

V
continued from key IV, page 32

all legs of
walking type

hind legs modified
for jumping

ORTHOPTERA
(tree crickets)

basal segment of front
tarsus has swollen appearance

basal segment of front tarsus
about same size as
ones immediately following

EMBIOPTERA
(webspinners)

cerci usually long;
more than eight segments

cerci short; with
two to eight segments

ISOPTERA
(termites)

PLECOPTERA
(stoneflies)

VI
continued from key I, page 29

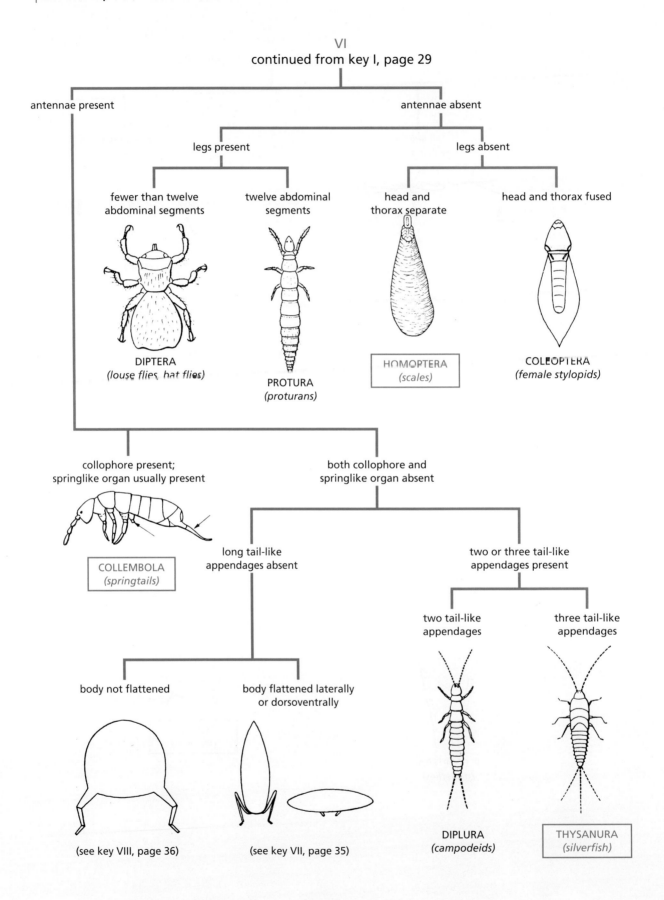

antennae present

antennae absent

legs present

legs absent

fewer than twelve
abdominal segments

twelve abdominal
segments

head and
thorax separate

head and thorax fused

DIPTERA
(louse flies, bat flies)

PROTURA
(proturans)

HOMOPTERA
(scales)

COLEOPTERA
(female stylopids)

collophore present;
springlike organ usually present

both collophore and
springlike organ absent

COLLEMBOLA
(springtails)

long tail-like
appendages absent

two or three tail-like
appendages present

two tail-like
appendages

three tail-like
appendages

body not flattened

body flattened laterally
or dorsoventrally

DIPLURA
(campodeids)

THYSANURA
(silverfish)

(see key VIII, page 36)

(see key VII, page 35)

VII
continued from key VI, page 34

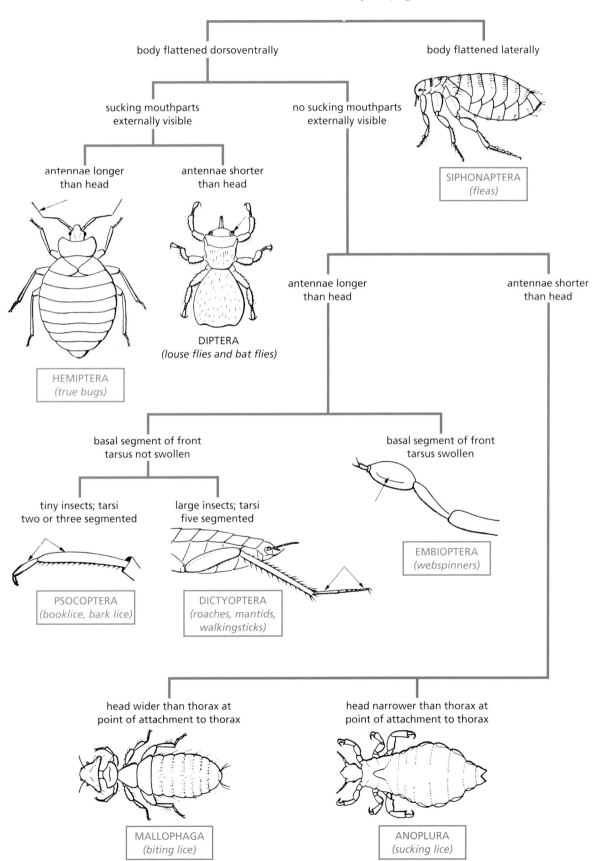

body flattened dorsoventrally

body flattened laterally

sucking mouthparts
externally visible

no sucking mouthparts
externally visible

SIPHONAPTERA
(fleas)

antennae longer
than head

antennae shorter
than head

antennae longer
than head

antennae shorter
than head

DIPTERA
(louse flies and bat flies)

HEMIPTERA
(true bugs)

basal segment of front
tarsus not swollen

basal segment of front
tarsus swollen

tiny insects; tarsi
two or three segmented

large insects; tarsi
five segmented

EMBIOPTERA
(webspinners)

PSOCOPTERA
(booklice, bark lice)

DICTYOPTERA
*(roaches, mantids,
walkingsticks)*

head wider than thorax at
point of attachment to thorax

head narrower than thorax at
point of attachment to thorax

MALLOPHAGA
(biting lice)

ANOPLURA
(sucking lice)

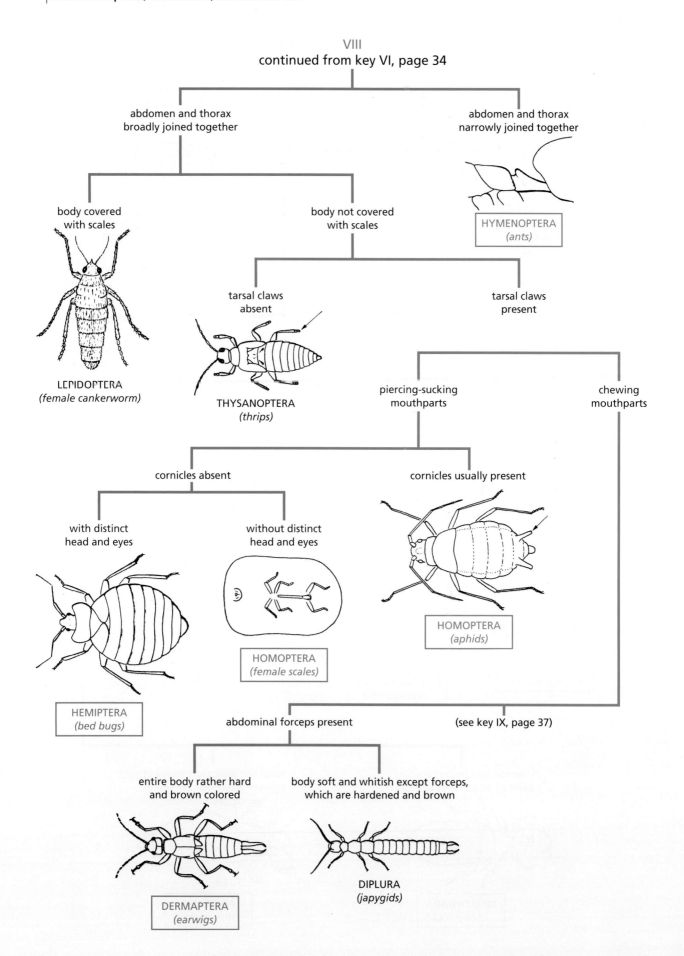

VIII
continued from key VI, page 34

abdomen and thorax
broadly joined together

abdomen and thorax
narrowly joined together

HYMENOPTERA
(ants)

body covered
with scales

body not covered
with scales

LEPIDOPTERA
(female cankerworm)

tarsal claws
absent

tarsal claws
present

THYSANOPTERA
(thrips)

piercing-sucking
mouthparts

chewing
mouthparts

cornicles absent

cornicles usually present

with distinct
head and eyes

without distinct
head and eyes

HOMOPTERA
(aphids)

HOMOPTERA
(female scales)

HEMIPTERA
(bed bugs)

abdominal forceps present

(see key IX, page 37)

entire body rather hard
and brown colored

body soft and whitish except forceps,
which are hardened and brown

DIPLURA
(japygids)

DERMAPTERA
(earwigs)

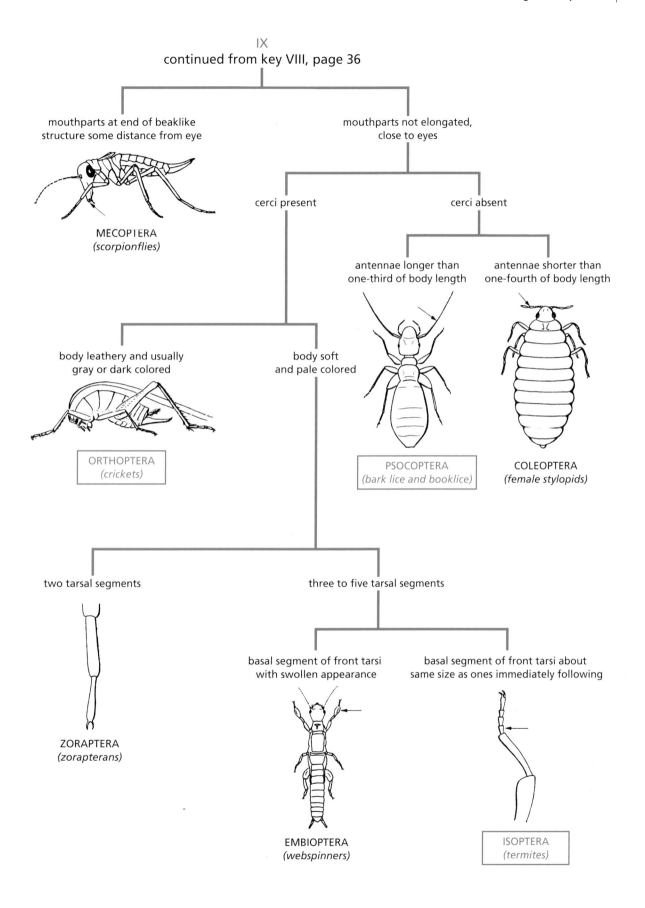

IX
continued from key VIII, page 36

mouthparts at end of beaklike
structure some distance from eye

MECOPTERA
(scorpionflies)

mouthparts not elongated,
close to eyes

cerci present

cerci absent

antennae longer than
one-third of body length

antennae shorter than
one-fourth of body length

body leathery and usually
gray or dark colored

ORTHOPTERA
(crickets)

body soft
and pale colored

PSOCOPTERA
(bark lice and booklice)

COLEOPTERA
(female stylopids)

two tarsal segments

ZORAPTERA
(zorapterans)

three to five tarsal segments

basal segment of front tarsi
with swollen appearance

EMBIOPTERA
(webspinners)

basal segment of front tarsi about
same size as ones immediately following

ISOPTERA
(termites)

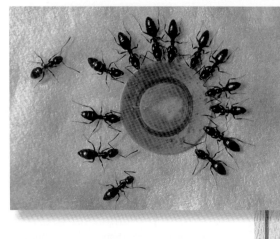

PESTICIDE STORAGE AREA

DANGER

Authorized Personnel Only

CHAPTER 3 | Pesticides

Pesticides are most commonly thought of as chemical substances used to kill, control, or manage pest populations. This definition should be broadened to fit our modern era of rapidly changing pest management technology. First, pesticides are not always chemical substances in the sense of our traditional definition. Some preparations of bacteria (for example, *Bacillus thuringiensis* var. *israelensis*, or Bti) are used to control the larvae of mosquitoes and other biting flies in water. There are even virus preparations registered as pesticides that kill certain insects; most examples come from agricultural or forestry uses. These bacteria and viruses are not synthetic chemical preparations at all, and they are often called **biopesticides.**

Second, the word *pest* is very broad because there are many types of pests (see Table 3.1). An organism may be considered a pest by one person at one place and time, while that same organism may be considered valuable by someone else, either at the same place and time or in another situation. An example of this conflict is the public controversy that can arise over pigeon or other bird management efforts. Many people are disgusted by pigeons, sparrows or European starlings, and the mess they can make. Pest management firms are often contracted to do something about these "pests." However, other citizens may enjoy seeing the birds and take a very different view. They may oppose any control efforts or insist that certain techniques considered cruel and inhumane not be used in their control.

Third, the term *pesticide* is too simple because the *cide* part of the word, which means "to kill," is too narrow in scope. Many types of pesticides do not kill at all but may repel, attract, sterilize, or simply regulate the growth of pests. Such materials control pest populations in an indirect way and often over longer periods of time than traditional pesticides.

Because the manufacture, sale, and use of pesticides is regulated at the federal level in the United States by the U.S. Environmental Protection Agency (EPA) and by other lead agencies at the state level, it is important to understand the accepted legal definition of a pesticide. According to federal and many state laws, a pesticide is "any substance or mixture of substances intended for preventing, destroying, repelling, or mitigating any pests, as well as any substance, or mixture of substances, intended for use as a plant regulator, defoliant, or desiccant." The term *substance* is used to include both chemical and non-chemical formulations used to manage pests (e.g., preparations of bacteria that control insect pests). Further interpretation of this legal definition has brought pest control devices under some government regulation by the U.S. Postal Service and certain state regulatory agencies, if not the U.S. EPA which has generally chosen not to regulate pest control devices (other than for antimicrobial uses). These include devices such as light traps, ultrasonic pest control devices, electromagnetic devices, pheromone traps, and others.

The term *pest* is also broadly defined in legal considerations to mean any insect, rodent, nematode, fungus, or weed. It also means any form of terrestrial or aquatic plant or animal, virus, bacteria, or other microorganism. Excluded are those viruses, bacteria, and microorganisms living on or in humans and other living animals. These exceptions are intended to avoid conflict between pesticide regulations and those that apply to physicians and veterinarians who treat the diseases of humans and other animals. The manufacture and use of human and veterinary medicines is regulated by the U.S. Food and Drug Administration under provisions of the Food, Drug and Cosmetic Act. Pest management professionals may occasionally be asked for opinions or advice, or to make certain

TABLE 3.1. Types of pesticides and pest control agents.

Pesticide or Agent	Effect
Pesticides	
Acaricide	Kills mites and ticks
Algicide	Kills algae
Avicide	Kills selected bird pests (e.g., pigeons, sparrows, or European starlings)
Bactericide	Kills bacteria that cause plant or animal disease
Fungicide	Kills fungi that cause plant diseases, molds, or mildew
Herbicide	Kills weedy plants
Insecticide	Kills insects and related arthropods, like spiders
Miticide	Kills mites
Molluscicide	Kills slugs and snails
Nematicide	Kills soil nematodes that damage plants
Piscicide	Kills fish (prior to restocking)
Rodenticide	Kills rodent pests, such as rats and mice
Termiticide	Kills termites
Other Agents	
Adulticide	Kills adult life stage of pests
Attractant	Attracts insects or vertebrates
Biopesticide	Works like a pesticide but is typically not a synthetic organic chemical but a biological organism, such as a bacterium, a virus, fungus, or a preparation of an insecticidally active compound derived from such organisms
Defoliant	Removes leaves from plants
Desiccant	Causes insect death by dehydration
Disinfectant	Destroys or inactivates harmful microorganisms, like bacteria, molds, and viruses (typically on surfaces)
Growth regulator	Stimulates or retards plant growth
Insect growth regulator (IGR)	Disrupts development and reproduction of insects
Juvenile hormone analog (JHA)	Similar in structure to natural juvenile hormone (JH) and disrupts normal JH function when inside the insect (resulting in death or failure to reproduce)
Juvenoid	An IGR type of insecticide that is not structurally similar to natural juvenile hormone but acts by disrupting its function
Larvicide	Kills insect larvae
Ovicide	Kills insect eggs
Pheromone	A chemical used by insects and vertebrates to communicate with each other (attract, repel, alarm, etc.)
Repellent	Repels insects, mites, ticks, or vertebrate pests
Sanitizer	Provides 99.999% reduction in microbial populations (typically contaminating food utensils or preparation surfaces)
Sterilent	Totally eliminates living microorganisms on medical tools or implements
Synergist	A chemical used with insecticides to enhance, or synergize, the activity of the active ingredient

pest management applications that are rightfully reserved for physicians or veterinarians. The pest management professional must never appear to be acting as a physician or veterinarian and is not licensed to do such work. In turn, many medical professionals may not be well informed about the issues and techniques of safe, practical, and effective urban pest management.

Of those pesticides listed in Table 3.1, the pest management professional is concerned principally with **insecticides** (including repellents, attractants, and synergists), **rodenticides**, **acaricides**, and **avicides**. Those professionals engaged in outdoor pest management activities on lawns, trees, and ornamental plants use herbicides to kill weeds, fungicides to control plant diseases, and plant growth regulators to suppress plant growth. Appendix B lists many of the pesticides more commonly used by pest control professionals and briefly describes the uses and some properties of each.

The Ideal Pesticide

Ideally, any pesticide will act rapidly on pests, yet be completely harmless to people, domestic animals, wildlife, and other aspects of the environment. Its residues would last only as long as was necessary to create the desired effect, usually for very short periods. It would also be inexpensive and readily available in necessary quantities, chemically stable (before application), nonflammable, and otherwise safe to use around homes or industrial sites. It would be easily prepared and applied, noncorrosive, and nonstaining, and it would have no undesirable odor.

Unfortunately, no such pesticide exists. If such a pesticide were available, the work of pest control professionals would be much easier. There would be no need to know how to prepare and store chemicals, or how to use them safely and in a way that is legal and unobjectionable to customers. There are no such ideal materials available, so it is necessary for professionals to know many things about the pesticides, the pests themselves, and the specific situations in which they are working. Great care should be taken whenever pesticides are used. The label on the pesticide container is always a good source of information on the proper and least-risky ways to use that material.

Manufacturers and pest control professionals should never consider or claim that pesticides are safe, but this does not mean that pesticides are unsafe. Proper application of even the most potentially hazardous pesticide—following label directions, common sense, and good judgment under the conditions at hand—will allow safe pesticide use. Pest management and the use of pesticides are matters of great responsibility, warranting careful consideration of possible hazards and potential negative side effects. As a profession, pest management is often a very complicated undertaking. The tools, laws, and other aspects of technology surrounding this activity are constantly changing. The technical nature and important role of pest management in our society demand that pest management professionals be well trained. They have an ongoing responsibility to maintain their competence through appropriate education and training on all aspects of pest management technology. Perhaps most important is the continuing attention to the safest possible, or ideal, use of pesticides in all aspects of the professional's work. Or for some situations, or some clients, effective and safe pest management without use of pesticides may be "ideal."

ROUTES OF ENTRY

Pesticides must contact the pest and enter its body in one of several ways to have a toxic effect. **Stomach poisons** must be swallowed to kill an insect, bird, or rodent. Ant, rodent, and cockroach baits are examples of formulations containing stomach poisons. So, too, are some dusts and liquids that the pests introduce into their mouths as they groom themselves. **Contact pesticides** penetrate the body wall to cause death. Pyrethrins, fipronil, and chlorpyrifos are examples of insecticides that act primarily as contact poisons, although fipronil and chlorpyrifos are sometimes used in insect bait formulations where their primary route of entry is through the stomach. **Fumigants** are gaseous pesticides whose vapors enter the pest's body via inhalation or, in the case of insects, through the spiracles. Sulfuryl fluoride, hydrogen phosphide, and methyl bromide are examples of fumigants used for insect control. Some insecticides, such as dichlorvos (DDVP) and some volatile pyrethroids, while not technically fumigants, typically release vapors that can kill insects in enclosed spaces. This action is generally referred to as vapor toxicity. **Desiccant insecticides** kill by removing or disrupting the protective, waxy outer coating on the insect's cuticle. This causes the loss of body fluids, so that the insect dies of desiccation or dehydration. Silica aerogel and diatomaceous earth are examples of desiccants.

In pest management work, the term *contact insecticide* refers to those chemicals that contact the outside of the insect's body directly while being applied. Direct contact sprays may be ultra-low volume (ULV) or space sprays, pressurized aerosol sprays, smoke or thermal fog applications, or other such applications. The term *residual insecticide* is usually reserved for those chemicals applied in such a way that a crystalline or film-like layer forms on treated surfaces where insects congregate or are expected to walk. Later, when insects come in contact with the residue for a long enough time, a lethal dose of the insecticide will be picked up and penetrate the body, and the insecticidal effect will occur. Some insecticides can kill by both direct contact and residual action. For example, pyrethroid insecticides will kill insects when sprayed directly on them and also when placed on surfaces where insects will pick up a lethal dose at a later time. These same insecticides can work in either way when they are applied as dusts, wettable powders, or microencapsulated formulations. However, the type of formulation can greatly affect the speed of contact action, the length of time that effective residual activity will persist, the variety of surface types on which effective residual action can be achieved, or all of these.

The oral (by mouth) and dermal (by skin) Lethal Dose 50, or LD_{50}, values have been given for many of the pesticides listed in Appendix C. The LD_{50} refers to the amount of the technical pesticide that will kill one half of a group of test animals, usually rats or mice, when either ingested (oral exposure) or applied to the skin (dermal exposure). The figures given are the number of milligrams of toxicant per kilogram of body weight necessary to kill, abbreviated as mg/kg. The higher the number, the lower the toxicity of the pesticide, since a larger amount (dose) of the pesticide had to be administered to kill half of the test population. For pest control technicians (or for a resident or pet in the treated premises), the dermal LD_{50} is an especially important measurement of toxicity, because it helps tell the degree of hazard that could result from skin contact following pesticide mixing or application.

INSECTICIDES

The major groups of insecticide active ingredients used in urban pest management are categorized as:

Synthetic organic compounds — Mode of action

- organophosphates .... disrupt nervous system at synapses
- carbamates .... disrupt nervous system at synapses
- chloronicotines .... disrupt nervous system at synapses
- pyrethroids .... disrupt nervous system along axons
- phenylpyrazoles .... disrupt nervous system along axons
- amidinohydrazones .... inhibit energy production within cells
- fluoroaliphatic sulfonamides .... inhibit energy production within cells
- pyrrols or pyrazole analogs .... inhibit energy production within cells
- insect growth regulators (IGRs)
  – juvenile hormone analogs and juvenoids ...... disrupt molting or other development
  – benzoylphenyl ureas (BPUs) .... inhibit formation of chitin in new cuticle
- fumigant gases .... nonspecific binding within cells

Non synthetic or biologically derived organic compounds

- botanicals (e.g., pyrethrum or pyrethrins) .... disrupt nervous system along axons
- abamectins .... disrupt nervous system along axons

Inorganic compounds

- boric acid and other borates .... inhibit energy production within cells
- silica aerogel and diatomaceous earth .... disrupt outer wax layer of cuticle

Synthetic Organic Compounds

The first synthetic organic insecticides developed were chlorinated hydrocarbon compounds such as DDT, chlordane, aldrin, dieldrin, and lindane. Of these, basically all are now banned for use in the United States and most other countries. The **organophosphates**, also called OPs, were the first insecticides to replace, in some uses, the chlorinated hydrocarbons. Most organophosphates break down quickly in the environment and are not stored for long periods inside the bodies of humans and wildlife. Thus, they generally do not pose the problems of long-term environmental contamination or bioaccumulation sometimes experienced with chlorinated hydrocarbons.

The primary toxic action of organophosphates is to inhibit cholinesterase, an important enzyme in the nervous system of insects and many other animals. Cholinesterase is important in the process where nerve impulses bridge the gap between two nerve cells, so the nervous signal will be transmitted from one nerve cell to the next in a properly controlled manner. The gap between the two nerve cells is called a synapse, and the physical transfer of the nerve impulse across this synapse involves a neurotransmitter chemical. If cholinesterase is inhibited by an OP or a **carbamate** insecticide, the communication of nerve impulses between nerve cells, which rely on acetylcholine as their neurotransmitter substance, is disrupted. If this disruption is strong enough, or sufficiently widespread within the insect's body, it eventually causes muscle and organ failure, leading to death.

The first organophosphates developed in the 1950s were highly toxic to mammals, and some, such as dichlorvos (Vapona® and Vapocide®) and parathion, remain so. However, the insecticidal properties and relatively lower toxicity (to mammals) of diazinon, chlorpyrifos (Dursban®), acephate (Orthene®), and propetamphos (Catalyst®) previously allowed these materials to be used extensively in pest control.

Carbamate insecticides work in much the same way as the organophosphates. The first carbamates were developed in the late 1950s and through the early 1960s. Generally, carbamates such as carbaryl (Sevin®), propoxur (Baygon®), and bendiocarb (Ficam®) have even lower toxicity to mammals than most organophosphates.

Most urban pest management uses of the organophosphate and carbamate insecticides in and around structures have been cancelled in the United States following revised risk assessments that were mandated by the 1996 Food Quality Protection Act (FQPA), which amended the basic pesticide law (FIFRA). Certain other countries have followed the United States lead in canceling or severely restricting the use of these broad-spectrum insecticides, which has caused pesticide manufacturers and pest management professionals to look toward products using different classes of insecticidal active ingredients.

The **chloronicotinyl** compound imidacloprid, which is the active ingredient in Premise®, Advantage® and Pre-Empt®, also disrupts transmission of nerve impulses across synapses that rely on acetylcholine, but by a different mechanism than binding to and inhibiting the cholinesterase enzyme.

Since individual nerve cells in an insect's or other animal's body are generally shaped like elongated fibers, the electrical impulse must also be conducted or propagated along the length of each nerve cell fiber. Biologists who study nervous system function generally call the fiber-shaped length (or lengths) of each nerve cell an "axon," and any substance that disrupts normal movement of nerve impulses along nerve axons is sometimes referred to as an "axonal poison."

The **pyrethroids** are the most commonly and widely used insecticides in urban pest management that act by disrupting the proper functioning of nerve axons. Through research on the mode of action of natural pyrethrum compounds contained within pyrethrum extract (discussed further below, under "botanicals"), chemists and biologists determined that the active compounds in natural pyrethrins act by disrupting nerve impulses along axons. Chemists then synthesized many different pyrethrin-like materials, often called **synthetic pyrethroids**, or just **pyrethroids**, that have a similar mode of action. Development of new pyrethroids, and better understanding of their modes of action, has advanced through what many experts refer to as three or more different "generations." The newer materials, such as those listed in Appendix C, generally have some form of improved action when compared to natural pyrethrins. This can vary between better cockroach flushing action; faster knockdown of flies, mosquitoes, or cockroaches; improved killing power (i.e., synergists not needed); some vapor toxicity; or even very long residual persistence; and effective insecticidal action when applied to surfaces. However, while a particular pyrethroid may have some aspect of superiority to natural pyrethrins, it will often have one or more weaknesses by comparison. For example, pyrethroids that have long residual action against cockroaches typically have rather poor, or slow, flushing and knockdown activity. It is important to know the various characteristics and uses of both natural pyrethrins and the different pyrethroids when selecting among them for specific insect control situations.

The **phenylpyrazole** compound, fipronil, also acts by disrupting transmission of nerve impulses along axons. Fipronil is the active ingredient in products such as Termidor®, Maxforce®, Regent®, and Frontline®.

Each cell within an insect's body must be capable of generating energy in order to survive and function. The primary sites of energy production, or metabolism, within animal cells are the mitochondria. The actual biochemical process by which chemicals from food, and oxygen, are converted into useable energy is complex, but there are a number of classes of insecticidal compounds that act by disrupting these energy metabolism processes within cells of the insect's body. Three of these are synthetically produced; including the **amidinohydrazone** compound, hydramethylnon (e.g., used in Maxforce® and Siege®); the **fluoroaliphatic sulfonamide** compound, sulfluramid (e.g., used in ProControl® and FluorGuard®); and the **pyrrol** or **pyrazole analog** compound, chlorfenapyr (e.g., used in Phantom®). Because these energy or metabolic disruptors are fairly slow-acting insecticides, and they have been found to be nonrepellent to key urban pests like ants, termites and cockroaches, they have been formulated into bait products for urban pest management uses.

Insect Growth Regulators (IGRs) are a group of synthetic organic compounds that can disrupt a number of normal processes in the growth or development of insects. They generally have very little toxicity to mammals and other vertebrates, because IGRs disrupt processes unique to insects and closely related arthropods. Materials like methoprene (Precor®), hydroprene (Gentrol®), and pyriproxyfen (Nylar® and Archer®) mimic the natural juvenile hormones important in controlling normal molting and other developmental processes of immature insects. IGRs that mimic juvenile hormones are often called **juvenile hormone analogs (JHAs)**, or **juvenoids**. They are most successfully used in the control of insects that undergo complete metamorphosis and that cause the most damage in the adult stage. Examples are the IGRs methoprene and pyriproxyfen used against mosquitoes and fleas. These IGRs prevent emergence of the adult flea or mosquito, which is the biting stage. Juvenoid

Pesticide Formulation Terms

When discussing and studying pesticides and their various formulations, it is necessary to first have an understanding of some of the terms associated with formulation technology. Some of the more common terms are as follows:

active ingredient (AI). The chemical or chemicals in a product that are responsible for the pesticidal effect on the pest.

diluent. Any liquid or solid material used to dilute or carry an active ingredient. In liquid formulations, water, refined oils, or some type of solvent can serve as the diluent, but not all diluents are solvents. In dry formulations such as dusts, some inert dust, such as a fine ground clay or talc, is often used as the diluent.

emulsifier. A chemical that aids in suspending one liquid in another. *See also* **surfactant**.

emulsion. A mixture in which one liquid is suspended as microscopic drops in another liquid, such as oil in water. When concentrated pesticide active ingredient is dissolved in oil and both are mixed with emulsifiers, they form emulsifiable concentrates. When emulsifiable concentrates are then mixed in water within a spray tank, they form an emulsion. Emulsions are typically milky in appearance.

formulation. The way in which active and inert ingredients are prepared for sale to the user.

inert ingredient. The inert liquid or solid material added to an active ingredient to prepare a pesticide formulation. For example, in some granular fire ant baits, the coarse corn grit actually serves as a carrier for the active ingredient, which is frequently dissolved in soybean oil (perhaps with some cosolvents) that serves as the feeding attractant. The ants may not ever actually eat the corn grit and would not be especially attracted to it without the soybean oil. By contrast, the food bait matrix in roach, ant, or rodent bait serves both as the carrier for the active ingredient and the feeding attractant, which is a very critical component to an effective bait formulation. An inert ingredient has no, or insignificant, pesticidal activity against the pest.

propellant. The chemicals—usually simple hydrocarbon gases, like propane, butane, and isobutane, or dimethyl ether—used to pressurize aerosol formulations. Propellants often contribute to the solvency of the active ingredient within the liquid intermediate of the aerosol formulation.

soluble ingredient. An ingredient that will dissolve in a liquid, where the liquid is called a solvent. So-called solvent-based spray formulations usually have a petroleum-derived hydrocarbon solvent, such as low-odor kerosene, while aqueous, or water-based, formulations use water as the solvent (and diluent).

spreader. A chemical that increases the area a given volume of liquid will cover on a solid or in another liquid.

sticker. A material added to a pesticide to increase its adherence (especially to the foliage of plants).

surfactant. A chemical that increases the emulsifying, dispersing, spreading, and wetting properties of a pesticide product.

suspension. Finely divided solid particles mixed in a liquid (often due to the addition of a suspending agent) and remaining suspended in the liquid for an extended period of time after shaking.

wetting agent. A chemical that causes a liquid to spread out, wet, or contact surfaces more thoroughly.

IGRs can also cause sterilization of adult insects, such as cockroaches, that receive a sufficient dose while they are immatures. This sterilization occurs because the adult insects fail to develop necessary sexual organs and retain other immature, or juvenile, characteristics. An example of this action is the effect of hydroprene or pyriproxyfen applied in cockroach control programs, or to control certain stored product pests in warehouses. Finally, juvenoid IGRs can sometimes prevent insect egg hatch if eggs are sufficiently exposed prior to hatch. For example, some juvenoid formulations are used to treat pet host fur to block flea eggs produced by adult females from hatching after the eggs fall to the substrate.

Another group of IGRs used in urban pest management are the **benzoylphenyl ureas (BPU)**, commonly called "chitin inhibitors." These materials disrupt normal molting and the development of insects by interfering with the normal function of an enzyme called chitin synthetase. This enzyme is important in the formation of new cuticle after the old cuticle is shed. Affected insects typically die when they are unable to shed their old cuticle successfully during the molting process, or when the new cuticle cannot provide the structural strength and integrity necessary to allow the insect's muscles to act effectively. Affected insects may also die from desiccation, because the defective cuticle may not prevent excessive water loss. The chitin inhibitors hexaflumuron (Sentricon®), noviflumuron and diflubenzuron (Exterra®) have been formulated into baits for subterranean termite control, and lufenuron (Program®) has been marketed through veterinarians for flea control. When lufenuron is added to pet food, sufficient levels will be present in the host blood to cause female fleas feeding on the treated host to lay nonviable eggs. Other chitin inhibitors have been used for cockroach control, primarily outside of the United States.

The **fumigant gases** are a group of chemical gases whose physical properties cause them to be very penetrating of solid articles such as wood (of structures), stored foods (grains, flour, etc.), cloth and clothing, and other items. Aluminum phosphide (Phostoxin®) and magnesium phosphide (Mag Tox®) are available to the pest control industry in various forms but are primarily used as tablets of solid material that release the active gas, hydrogen phosphide or phosphine, when exposed to air. Ecofume® is a fumigant product that combines carbon dioxide and phosphine into one formulation. Other fumigants such as methyl bromide (Meth-o-Gas®) and sulfuryl fluoride (Vikane® or ProFume®) are liquids when held under high pressure in steel tanks, but become gaseous when released into the air. Napthalene and paradichlorobenzene are both solids that give off insecticidal vapors. Typically, the toxic action of fumigants occurs as they bind with important enzymes within the body cells of target insects or other animals, but their specific site and mode of action may be unknown or considered "nonspecific." Other gases, such as carbon dioxide or nitrogen, used to control insect pests are sometimes called "inert gases" since they work primarily by displacing the normal atmosphere in the confined space, so the pests suffocate because the oxygen necessary for animal life is displaced.

Nonsynthetic or Biologically Derived Organic Compounds

Perhaps the first botanical insecticide was discovered many centuries ago when certain varieties of chrysanthemum flowers were found to have insecticidal properties when dried and crushed into a powder. Botanical insecticides are sometimes referred to as the "natural" insecticides because they are derived from plants. Examples of botanical insecticides include pyrethrum, rotenone, ryania, d-limonene, and other related terpenes. Pyrethrum extract is an oily substance extracted from certain varieties of chrysanthemum grown chiefly in Kenya, Rwanda, China, and Tasmania. It has been used in powdered form for pest management for more than a century.

The active ingredients within pyrethrum extract are referred to as **natural pyrethrins** on most pesticide product labels, and they are by far the most widely used botanical insecticide. As discussed above in relation to pyrethroids, the mode of action of the six insecticidally active pyrethrins compounds is to disrupt nerve impulse transmission along nerve cell axons. Natural pyrethrins are generally used in combination with synergists, such as piperonyl butoxide, to add insect-killing power to the rapid-flushing and knockdown action of the pyrethrins. Without the synergist, insects knocked down by the pyrethrins often recover some hours later because they can degrade the pyrethrins inside their bodies before the lethal effect occurs. The synergist typically blocks the enzyme systems that degrade and deactivate the pyrethrin molecules. Under most use conditions, synergized pyrethrins have only contact action and no significant residual properties. Thus, they are frequently used in aerosol or ULV applications, either as directed or space sprays. Pyrethrins have low toxicity to mammals, but they can be quite toxic to most fish, birds, reptiles, and amphibians.

Another class of insecticide compounds derived from living organisms originally found in nature is the macrolactones produced by certain soil fungi, including **abamectin** (Avert® and Affirm®). Abamectin also acts by disrupting normal axonal transmission of nerve impulses.

Inorganics

The **inorganics** are some of our oldest insecticides, and some still have wide use. They are also sometimes called minerals, because they are generally mined from earthen deposits before being refined and formulated for use by professionals. Examples of inorganics include **boric acid** and **other borates**, sodium fluoride, **silica aerogel** (a type of fumed silica), and **diatomaceous earth**. Most inorganics have rather slow killing action. However, materials such as boric acid continue to be widely used because they can offer long residual action in many field situations, are nonrepellent (e.g., to cockroaches), and have no known problems of pest resistance. Boric acid and sodium fluoride kill by slowly interfering with the conversion of energy inside insect cells. Silica aerogel and certain dry clays act by disrupting the waxy layers of the insect's cuticle and causing death by desiccation. Another desiccant is diatomaceous earth, a powder consisting of the dried bodies of diatoms, which are tiny animals that live in oceans.

Other Active Ingredients

Other types of insecticidal active ingredients include the synergists, petroleum distillates, repellents, and attractants.

Synergists are materials that, if used alone, normally would have little toxicity to insects. However, when combined with another active ingredient, they enhance the activity of an insecticide. For example, **piperonyl butoxide** inhibits certain enzymes in insect cells that normally break down pyrethrins or other materials, like bendiocarb, before they can kill the insect. **Synergized pyrethrins** have killing power greater than that of the piperonyl butoxide used alone, or pyrethrins when used alone.

Petroleum distillates include a variety of solvents that are combined with the principal active ingredients in the formulation of an insecticide product. Examples are materials such as deodorized kerosene and the xylenes. All of the petroleum distillates have some insecticidal activity of their own. Thus, the EPA considers them to be active ingredients, and insecticide formulators have found that they can greatly affect an insecticide's activity (e.g., the speed of knockdown, flushing, or other particular activity) by careful selection of the petroleum distillates or other solvents used in the formulation.

There are several insect **repellents** registered by the EPA. The most important and widely used of these is DEET, or diethyltoluimide. DEET is the primary active ingredient in many mosquito repellents applied to the skin, though some products now use other active ingredients such as *p*-Menthane-3,8-diol (Off!®, Repel®), picaridin (Bayrepel® or Autan®), and IR3535 (Avon™). The pyrethroid, permethrin, is also formulated as a mosquito and tick repellent (Permanone®). Most of these personal repellents are sold as consumer products. Materials such as thiuram and methyl anthranilate are registered as animal repellents for use on dogs, cats, and deer (thiuram), or geese (methyl anthranilate, ReJeX-iT® and many other brand names).

The development and availability of insect **attractants** for use in pest management continues to progress. There are a number of insect traps and other survey devices that use insect pheromones (e.g., sex or aggregation pheromones), food attractants, or other chemicals as lures. These materials are sometimes combined with a toxicant to make an effective insecticide bait, and several are now available for controlling cockroaches, ants, and termites. In recent years there have been attempts to use these attractants to control certain stored product pests in warehouses by effectively trapping and removing adult insects, or disrupting mating by attracting males to the artificial lures. However, such approaches have not seen widespread adoption in the urban pest management industry because they either produce slow results or may be inconsistent under changing field conditions. These programs are also feasible for only a very few species of stored product pests and some fruit flies, and generally under specialized conditions.

Rodenticides, Avicides and Others

In addition to insecticides, pest management professionals may also use **rodenticides**, **avicides**, and **herbicides**. More detailed discussion of rodenticides, avicides, and other pesticides used in vertebrate pest management is found in Chapters 15–17 of this book. Refer also to the lists of pesticides in Appendices B and C for additional information.

Herbicides are used by some professionals in conjunction with their insect or vertebrate pest management programs, or when they offer industrial and right-of-way weed control or landscape maintenance services. More detailed discussion of herbicides and weed control practices is beyond the scope of this book. Other pesticide groups used by urban pest management professionals are of relatively minor importance or are so infrequently used that further discussion of them is not included in this text.

PESTICIDE FORMULATIONS

Pesticides are processed and made available to pest management professionals in many different product forms, which are often referred to as **formulations**. The purest form of any pesticide is called **technical grade**. This form is generally not available to pest management professionals. Exceptions are some formulations of boric acid dust and most fumigant gases, which may be nearly 100% pure. Pesticide manufacturers, formulators, or, in some cases, distributors take technical-grade pesticides and blend or process them in various ways to produce the product that the pest management professional buys and uses. This processing can involve the use of solvents, emulsifiers, wetting agents, carriers, suspension agents, bait attractants, or other ingredients. In the case of ready-to-use emulsions and some dusts, dispersants and diluents are also added. This mixture of active and inert (or inactive) ingredients is called a pesticide formulation.

The active ingredients in a pesticide are the chemicals that kill, repel, attract, or otherwise control the target pest. The pesticide products available to pest control professionals are rarely made up of only active ingredients. Usually the pesticide is diluted in a petroleum solvent, or it is formulated into a bait matrix; other chemicals are then added before the product is offered for sale. These formulation ingredients usually make the product more convenient to handle and measure accurately, and easier to apply. Some formulations are ready for

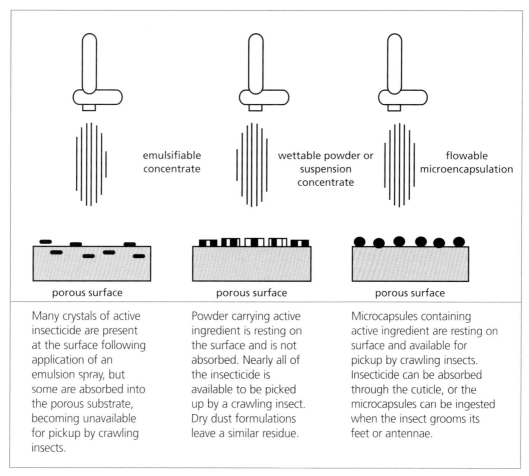

FIGURE 3.1. Residues of emulsifiable concentrates, wettable powders or suspension concentrates, and flowable microencapsulations on a porous surface.

use. Others must be further diluted with water, a petroleum solvent, or air by the user before they are applied. Weights and measurements useful in making dilutions and converting information from one system of measurement to another are found in Appendix D.

There are several different types of pesticide formulations. Not all will be discussed in detail in this chapter, because they may not be commonly used in urban pest management or they may be discussed in detail in another chapter of this book (e.g., fumigants are discussed in Chapter 20). Formulations used in urban pest management are categorized as follows:

I. Liquid formulations
 A. Concentrates
  1. Emulsifiable concentrates (EC or E)
  2. Suspension concentrates (SC)
  3. Flowable microencapsulations (CS, FM, or ME)
 B. Ready-to-use (RTU) sprays (may be oil solutions, water-based emulsions, aerosols, etc.)

C. Fumigants (gases that are liquids when under pressure)
II. Dry formulations
 A. Dusts (D)
 B. Wettable powders (WP or W)
 C. Baits (B)
 D. Granules (G)
 E. Resin strips and other solid carriers
 F. Pellets (P or PS) and Tablets
 G. Fumigants (tablets)

For any given active ingredient, the effective residual life of any particular spray or dust formulation will be about the same when these are applied to a nonporous surface, such as stainless steel or ceramic tile. The persistence of the insecticide residue on a nonporous surface will be largely a function of the inherent volatility of the active ingredient (e.g., chlorpyrifos is more volatile than most residual pyrethroids, like cyfluthrin), though some formulations, like microencapsulations, will greatly reduce loss due to volatilization. However, when the finished product or formulation is applied to a porous surface, such as bare or latex-painted wood, laminated surfaces, concrete or cardboard, the residual performance can be quite different (see Figure 3.1). When dusts, wettable powders, suspension concentrates, or microencapsulated formulations are applied to porous surfaces, most of the insecticidal particles remain on the surface and are available for pickup by a crawling insect. Emulsions (i.e., emulsifiable concentrates) and oil solutions will penetrate into porous surfaces after spraying, carrying part or all of the insecticide below the surface, where it cannot be picked up by the insect. Water-based formulations will usually penetrate porous surfaces less than oil sprays, so they will leave more active ingredient residue on the surface. Some aerosols give good residual performance like dusts when applied to porous surfaces. Other aerosols are actually pressurized emulsions or oil solutions, which will penetrate porous surfaces, leading to less-effective pest control.

Liquid Formulations

Many pesticides are applied in a liquid form as one type of spray or another, with the types of spray applications differing in terms of their particle size. Although there are several different types of liquid formulations (see Table 3.2), four types are most commonly used in pest control: (1) emulsifiable concentrates, (2) suspension concentrates and flowable microencapsulations, (3) ready-to-use sprays (usually solutions or emulsions), and (4) fumigants. Solutions (S) and flowables (F or L) are used mostly in agricultural, horticultural, or right-of-way weed control applications, and will not be further discussed in this book.

Emulsifiable Concentrates (EC or E)

Many pesticide concentrates will not dissolve and mix with water in their pure form. Emulsifiable concentrates are concentrated oil solutions of insecticides with cosolvents and **emulsifiers** added. Emulsifiers are detergent-like materials that make it possible for the millions of insecticide droplets (the active ingredient dissolved in a cosolvent) to form a miscible suspension (or mixture) in water, which is called an emulsion.

An example of a natural emulsion is milk, in which the proteins and butterfats are dispersed in tiny droplets within a water matrix. The ingredients of a typical finished emulsion are, therefore, water, oil solvent (in which the insecticide is dissolved), and an emulsifier to aid the dispersion of solvent and insecticide within the water.

Like milk, most finished emulsions are white in color when mixed. The tiny droplets of the oil-insecticide are not clear in color and are large enough to diffract light as it passes through the emulsion. These relatively large droplets may settle out in the spray tank if left for long periods without shaking (agitation). In recent years, formulation chemists have developed special emulsions, called microemulsions, that have much smaller droplets of suspended solvent and active ingredient. These droplets are small enough that light is not diffracted as it passes through the mixture. The emulsions appear clear and sometimes are called transparent emulsions. True microemulsions do not require as much shaking or agitation in the spray tank.

Some insecticides can be emulsified and remain mixed in water for a considerable period of time, while others will settle out relatively quickly. The pest management professional must be careful that emulsions do not separate in the sprayer while applying sprays such as emulsions and microencapsulates. It is a good practice to give handheld sprayers a brief shaking three or four times per hour of use. Power sprayers require considerable agitation ensuring that the pesticide emulsion is uniformly mixed at all times, and this is accomplished via agitation devices added to power sprayer systems (see Chapter 5).

It is a good practice to drain any emulsion left in a sprayer at the end of the day, rather than letting it stand overnight. This is because the emulsion will likely separate overnight, leaving some "sludge" that might clog some portion of the sprayer. In some cases, pyrethroids, carbamates, and organophosphate insecticides are chemically degraded in water when left for any extended period. Discarded pesticide can either be added to the tank of a large power sprayer (e.g., a termite tank) or, if the product label permits, used to treat along foundation walls outdoors for control of occasional invaders. Do not dispose of leftover spray formulation improperly by pouring it down a drain or onto a small spot of ground. In some cases, leftover spray mixture may have to be stored in another container temporarily until it can be properly disposed of as hazardous waste. Contact your state pesticide regulatory and waste management officials for details on how to do this safely and properly.

Emulsions can be sprayed without harm on many surfaces that would be damaged by oil solutions. It should be remembered that an emulsifiable concentrate itself contains an oil solvent that, even though mixed with water, may damage some surfaces. Because water is a general solvent, the water portion of an emulsion may cause some wallpaper or carpet dyes to run or change color, as well as stain or mark various types of wood and other surfaces.

Other aspects to consider are that emulsions are nonflammable, so they are relatively safe for use near open fires and heat. On the other hand, water

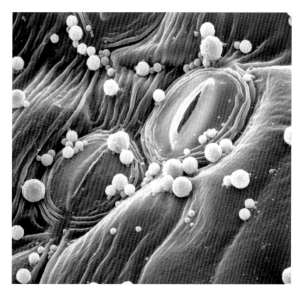

FIGURE 3.2. Scanning electron micrograph of insecticide microcapsules deposited on plant leaf. Capsules are typically about 30 microns in diameter. (Whitmire-Microgen)

emulsions are good conductors of electricity and must not be used close to electrical installations.

Suspension Concentrates (SC) and Flowable Microencapsulations (CS, FM, or ME)

Suspension concentrates are formed when finely ground particles of active ingredient are suspended in a liquid formulation. In many respects, an SC formulation can be considered a wettable powder that has been packaged in a liquid form. The liquid phase of the SC formulation contains dispersant and surfactant ingredients that disperse and maintain the particles in suspension, both while in the concentrate form and after the proper amount of SC is mixed with water in the spray tank. The liquid form of the SC facilitates accurate measurement of the concentrate and eliminates the chance for inhalation exposure during measurement and handling (e.g., as exists when wettable powders or dusts are handled).

Flowable microencapsulations are formed when the insecticide particle is enclosed, or encapsulated, inside tiny spheres of plastic or other polymer material. These capsules are usually 10 to 30 microns (or millionths of a meter) in diameter (see Figure 3.2). For comparison, a human hair is about 100 microns in diameter. Encapsulated particles readily pass through coarse screens and most sprayer nozzles. In addition to the encapsulated insecticide, CS concentrates are similar to suspension concentrates in that they contain dispersants to keep the particles from clumping or caking in the container, so they will remain suspended and "flowable." Microencapsulated formulations also contain surface-active agent, or "surfactant," ingredients to help disperse and maintain the particles in suspension while they are mixed with water in the spray tank. It is important to read and follow the mixing instructions carefully when using these SC and CS formulations, and to use the recommended size of sprayer screen to avoid clogging.

Suspensions and microencapsulated formulations have similar advantages and disadvantages to wettable powders when applied to porous surfaces, but may leave objectionable visible residues. They require agitation in the spray tank after they are mixed. The polymer coating, or shell, of CS formulations generally protects the insecticide particles from the degrading effects of water, thereby extending the residual life of the insecticide so unused spray mixture can be stored for short periods between uses. Thorough mixing is still necessary before the material is reused. Consult the label for detailed instructions and handling precautions.

Another benefit of microencapsulation is that the insecticide particle inside the shell is protected from environmental factors that normally break down other types of spray residues after they are applied, so microencapsulations will often have longer effective residual life than other spray formulations. Residues of microencapsulations are typically somewhat less repellent to crawling insects than are residues of most other types of formulations, which is generally an advantage. Finally, the toxicity of microencapsulated formulations to mammals is usually lower than other formulations of the same active ingredient, making them less potentially hazardous to use around people and pets.

Ready-to-Use (RTU) Sprays

There are several different types of **ready-to-use spray** formulations. Two of the most commonly used are **oil concentrates** and **pressurized aerosol** formulations (see Figure 3.3). Oil concentrates are made by dissolving a high percentage of technical insecticide in a solvent. This concentrate is then diluted with refined oil by the pest management specialist to get the proper concentration for use in the field. Oil-based sprays are rarely used for residual applications indoors. Most oil-based formulations are now used for ultra-low volume (ULV) or other applications of nonresidual insecticides, either indoors (e.g., food warehouses) or outdoors (e.g., for mosquito control).

Oil solutions of an insecticide, in the form of finished sprays, will usually knock down and kill insects by direct or contact spray quicker than other formulations such as water-based emulsion or wet-

TABLE 3.2. Some of the more commonly used pesticide formulations and their characteristics.

Formulation	Characteristics	Advantages/Disadvantages	Product Examples
1. Liquid Formulations			
a. Emulsifiable Concentrates (EC or E)	Diluted with water to form milky or clear liquid for spraying.	**Advantages** • Ease in mixing and application • Little agitation required • Little or no visible residue **Disadvantages** • Easily absorbed through skin • Solvents may cause sprayer software to corrode • Phytotoxic to some plants	Archer; Biflex; Catalyst; DZN; Cynoff EC; Demon EC; Dragnet; Dursban Pro TC; Flee; Gentrol; Nylar; Precor; Saga; Tempo 2
b. Solutions (S)	Soluble in water or oil. Form clear liquid for spraying.	Few products available in urban pest management	Orthene PCO Formula II
c. Flowable microencapsulations (FM or ME) and suspension concentrates (SC)	Active ingredient is in fine particles or encased in tiny plastic capsules, which are suspended in other formulation ingredients and diluted in water for spraying.	**Advantages** • Excellent residual activity • Very low in toxicity • Do not readily break down in water **Disadvantages** • Constant agitation required • Visible residues on some surfaces	Demand CS; Empire 20; Knox-out 2FM; Optem; Sectrol; Suspend SC
d. Ready-to-use (RTU) sprays	Active ingredient is diluted to finished spray concentration and packaged as a pressurized aerosol or in a trigger sprayer.	**Advantages** • No dilution or other preparation required for use in field • Diluted forms are generally less toxic than concentrates (in case of spill or accident) • Specialized applications like crack and crevice and total release are available **Disadvantages** • May be more expensive to purchase than concentrates • Bulky to transport	Whitmire Micro-Gen PT system and other aerosols
e. Fumigants	Active ingredients are sometimes gases that become liquids when packaged under pressure. They become gases when released during application. Some are volatile liquids and become gases when released.	**Advantages** • Toxic to wide range of pests • Penetrate structures, soils, grains, stored goods, etc. • Single treatment will usually kill most pests in treated area **Disadvantages** • Treated area must be enclosed or covered to prevent gas from escaping • Highly toxic to people—special training, protective equipment, and site preparation procedures must be used	Meth-o-Gas and other methyl bromide; Vikane

TABLE 3.2. *Continued*

Formulation	Characteristics	Advantages/Disadvantages	Product Examples
2. Dry Formulations			
a. Dusts (D)	Active ingredient carried on dry particles (inert clay or talc), or dust is 100% active ingredient	**Advantages** • Ready to use, no mixing • Exceptional residual when active ingredient dry **Disadvantages** • Takes experience to apply correctly • Visible residues possible • Difficult to control dispersal of dust particles to nontarget areas	Boric acid; DeltaDust; Diatect; diazinon; Drione; Dursban D; Ficam D; Sevin; Tempo 0.1%D
b. Wettable Powders (WP)	Usually contain 50% or more active ingredient. Powders do not dissolve in water — they remain suspended.	**Advantages** • Better residual on porous surfaces than ECs • Lower phytotoxicity hazard than ECs • Less skin and eye absorption than ECs **Disadvantages** • Inhalation hazard to applicator while pouring and mixing the concentrated powder • Require constant agitation in the spray tank • Residues may be visible	Baygon 70 WP; Cynoff WP; Demand CS; Demand Pestab; Demon WP; Dursban 50 W; Ficam W; Karate; Premise 75; Saga WP; Tempo 20 WP
c. Soluble powders (SP)	Similar in appearance to wettable powders, but when mixed with water, SP's dissolve readily and form a true solution.	**Advantages** • Same as for WPs **Disadvantages** • Inhalation hazard to applicator while pouring and mixing the concentrated powder	Orthene
d. Baits (B)	Active ingredient mixed with food or another attractive substance. May be solid or liquid. Active ingredient is usually less than 5%.	**Advantages** • Ready to use • Long residual activity • Entire area need not be covered, because pest will go to bait **Disadvantages** • Some baits may pose hazards to children, nontarget animals • Dead pests may cause odor problems	Arthitrol; Avert; Avitrol (birds); BanBug; Combat; Contrac (rodents); Drax; FluorGuard; LarvaLur; Subterfuge; MaxForce; Mesurol (slugs); NiBan; ProControl; Sentricon (termites); Siege; Talon
e. Granules (G)	Granular particles are larger than dusts. Active ingredient carried by clay or ground nutshells. Active ingredient either coats the outside of the granules or is absorbed into them. Active ingredient is usually between 1 and 15%.	**Advantages** • Ready to use; no mixing • Low drift hazard • Provide longer residuals than WPs or ECs **Disadvantages** • More costly than WPs or ECs • May need moisture to activate pesticidal action	Abate; diazinon; Dursban
f. Fumigants	Tablets or pellets. Fumigant is slowly released as pellet reacts with moisture in air or substrate.	**Advantages** • Ease in handling • Very little application equipment required **Disadvantages** • Requires relatively long fumigation period • Highly toxic to people — special training, protective equipment, and site preparation procedures must be used	Mag Tox; Phostoxin

FIGURE 3.3. Pressurized aerosol insecticides are an example of ready-to-use (RTU) liquid spray formulation. Some are designed to spray the liquid into the air or onto surfaces, while the aerosol shown is designed for highly controlled crack and crevice insecticide applications. (Myers)

table-powder sprays, or dry dusts. This is because of the action of the oil, which aids penetration of the insecticide through the waxy layers of the insect body wall. In addition, certain oils are fairly good insecticides by themselves. Oil solutions will typically flow into cracks and crevices (where insects often hide) more readily than water-based sprays or dusts. Because oil solutions do not conduct electricity, they can be used around electrical installations with greater safety than can water-based sprays. However, oil sprays may harm the insulation used on older wiring.

There are other cautions to observe with oil solutions. Oil solutions work well in many types of spray equipment, but their solvents may degrade sprayer gaskets and hose linings. These parts should be inspected frequently and replaced as needed, preferably with parts that are solvent-resistant. Similarly, materials such as some dyes in fabrics and wallpaper, some synthetic fibers and paints, linoleum, rubber, and asphalt floor tiles can be badly damaged by oil-based insecticides.

By their nature, solutions in oil will burn; hence, they should not be used near open flames or near excessive heat. They also tend to have more odor than other formulations. Since the oil and various solvents used will usually be toxic to plants, do not use oil solutions directly on green plants unless the solutions are specifically labeled for plant use.

When applied to porous surfaces such as unpainted wood, wallboard, brick, stone or concrete, oil solutions tend to penetrate deeply. This process will carry a large portion of the active ingredient below the surface, where it will not be available to crawling insects. Other types of formulations should be used where such penetration is undesirable.

When cold, oil solutions tend to drop, or precipitate, the active insecticide out of the solution. The appearance of any appreciable amount of sludge in the bottom of a container means that at least a portion of the active material is no longer in the solution. Therefore, the percentage of the dissolved insecticide may be too weak to kill insects. When this happens, it is necessary to warm the solution to room temperature and stir or shake it until the sludge has been redissolved. If it is not possible to warm the solution, the insecticide formulations should be returned to the distributor. Oil solution concentrates and ready-to-use sprays must always be stored in a warm place during cold weather. Care must also be taken to keep them from unusually high temperatures in summer.

An aerosol is not technically a formulation type. Rather, an aerosol is simply defined as very fine particles mixed in air. They may be liquid, dust, or smoke. Pressurized aerosol dispensers are convenient, ready-to-use liquid spray formulations packaged in metal cans. The liquid formulation is usually an oil solution with refined kerosene or some other form of petroleum solvent, but some aerosols are produced from emulsions. A few aerosol products have powder particles or microencapsulated insecticides suspended in the liquid phase. The pressure is created by adding a propellant gas to the can, such as mixtures of hydrocarbon gases including butane, isobutane, and propane. Aerosols using these hydrocarbon gases as propellants should be used with great caution around any source of flame (e.g., pilot lights) or sparks (e.g., electrical motors), as these hydrocarbon gases are flammable. Other aerosol dispensers are pressurized with carbon dioxide, which is not flammable. More information on pressurized aerosols and mechanical aerosol or ULV application devices is presented in Chapter 5.

Fumigants

Fumigants are pesticides that become a gas when released into the atmosphere. Some active ingredients are gases that become liquids when packaged under high pressure; these formulations become gases when released during application. Other active ingredients are volatile liquids when enclosed in an unpressurized container, so they are not formulated under pressure. They become gases during application. Others are solids that release gases when applied under conditions where water vapor is present (e.g., where humidity is high).

Fumigants are used for structural pest control, in food and grain storage facilities, and in regulatory pest control (e.g., in quarantine or preshipment applications) at ports of entry, and at state and national borders.

Dry Formulations

As with the liquid formulations, there are several types of dry formulations (refer to Table 3.2). The types commonly used in urban pest management include (1) dusts, (2) wettable powders, (3) baits, (4) granules, (5) resin strips and other solid carriers, and (6) fumigants (as tablets or pellets—see Chapter 20).

Dusts (D)

Most dusts consist of an insecticide mixed with an inert powder such as clay or talc. Some dusts, such as boric acid, diatomaceous earth and silica aerogel, are used as they are refined, without the addition of another insecticide or inert powder. Dusts are generally available as ready-to-use products.

Dusts are composed of fine particles, about 250 to 350 mesh. (Mesh is a unit that refers to the number of grids through which a particle will pass, per inch.) However, fumed silicas like silica aerogel (Dri-Die® and Drione®) often have an extremely fine particle size smaller than 400 mesh.

Dusts can be used to create a residual deposit of insecticide (or rodenticide, as in the case of a tracking powder) on most surfaces without harming them, but visible dust may create an unsightly appearance indoors. Care and experience in applying dusts will permit their use in most situations because it is not necessary to leave a visible residue to effectively control crawling insects. Due to their small particle size, properly applied dusts will float in the air and, therefore, they can be blown into cracks, crevices, and voids in walls or below cabinets or other furniture (see Figure 3.4). They can be applied around some areas and objects where treatment with liquids is not possible or safe. However, these same properties—small particle size and the ability to remain airborne and disperse—can also lead to unsafe contamination of nontarget surfaces if dusts are not carefully applied. Dusts generally leave an effective residual deposit as long as the deposit remains dry; they may "cake" and become ineffective under moist conditions.

Some dusts act as stomach poisons that kill after being ingested by an insect or rodent as it cleans the dust off its body. Other dusts kill by contact when the active ingredient is absorbed through the insect's cuticle, while silica aerogel and diatomaceous earth cause insects to desiccate.

FIGURE 3.4. Insecticidal dusts can be applied into cracks & crevices or voids where crawling insect pests are harboring, and the residue deposited can be effective for extended periods while presenting virtually no exposure risk to humans or pets. (Myers)

Wettable Powders (WP or W)

Wettable powders are essentially an inert dust carrier impregnated with an insecticide. A wetting agent is added to the dust-insecticide mixture so that the dust particles can be suspended in water. Some wettable powder suspensions must have frequent agitation to prevent the solid particles from settling at the bottom of the spray tank.

While the water from a wettable-powder mixture will penetrate porous materials, the insecticide powder is left on the surface for insect control (see Figure 3.1).

Wettable powders form a visible, white, or off-white residue that will be especially visible on smooth, dark-colored surfaces. This tends to limit the usefulness of wettable powder sprays in some indoor situations, and care in placement of the spray will be critical. Wettable powders can be used indoors in areas where the presence of a powder residue on the treated surface is not objectionable. Such areas include carpeting, concrete walls and floors, or light-colored surfaces. However, there is less chance of injuring plants with wettable powders than with emulsions or oil solutions, so wettable powders are often the most desirable spray formulation for treating lawns or ornamental plants to control pests that crawl on or chew foliage. Wettable powders tend to clog strainers and nozzles of sprayers more rapidly than do oils or emulsions. Nozzles on power spraying equipment will wear out more quickly with wettable powders than with EC formulations. Equipment maintenance needs to be a priority when using wettable powder formulations.

Baits (B)

Several insecticides and most rodenticides are available as granular, paste, gel, or tablet **baits**. Some insecticide baits come ready-to-use within a **bait station** (e.g., certain cockroach, ant, and termite baits), while rodenticides are usually available in loose form for placement in bait stations. The pesticidal active ingredient is impregnated into a bait material that acts as a food substance attractive to the pest. **Gel baits** or **paste baits** are pesticide mixed into a gel medium that contains the feeding attractant. Some products are available in pressurized aerosol cans that allow precise placement of insecticidal foam bait. These gel, paste, or foam baits are very effective tools for cockroach control (see Figure 3.5). Against pharaoh ants and certain other household-infesting ants, properly formulated paste baits may be the most effective means of control. The insecticide bait within ready-to-use plastic bait stations is similar to paste baits, except that it is either a solid or semisolid gel material.

Most rodenticides are combined with grain bait materials to make them attractive as a food source to rodents. Many formulations also include paraffin or plastic materials to allow the bait to be shaped into blocks that are resistant to moisture (after placement). Another important advantage of the bait block form of rodenticides is that it can be secured within a tamper-resistant bait station or inside a manhole access. This limits the chance that the rodents will move the bait out of the secured location to areas where children or pets might come in contact with it. Baits formulated for bird control generally use intact or cracked seeds or grain as the attractant (e.g., Avitrol®).

Baits can be used safely when carefully placed at ground or floor level, or when located where they will not fall into any hazardous situation due to either vibrations or scattering by pest activity. They should be used with great caution, or not at all, in food-processing areas because it is possible for certain baits to contaminate food products even when they have been placed on the floor.

Granules (G)

Some pesticides are formulated as **granules**. The pesticide may be coated on coarse granules, such as sand, or impregnated throughout the carrier granule (i.e., clay), vermiculite, seed hull, or other grain byproduct. Granules are typically applied by spreading them in the outdoor treatment area. It is usually necessary to wet the granules that are applied to release the active ingredient. However, some insecticide baits for cockroach control indoors (or for general crawling insect control out-

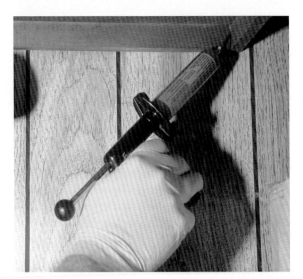

FIGURE 3.5. Gel bait formulation being applied with a syringe-type bait gun, as for cockroach or ant control. (Myers)

doors) are formulated in a granular form that should not be watered.

Resin Strips and Other Solid Carriers

Insecticides such as dichlorvos (or DDVP) can be impregnated into **plastic strips** for use in grain bins or other situations when flies and certain other flying insects become a problem. The active material impregnated into the strip is released slowly as a vapor. These vapors will kill insects in areas where they are confined, but the vapors can be effective only where conditions can maintain a sufficient airborne concentration lethal to insects. These strips should not be used around people who occupy the treated area for a major portion of the day, and especially if infants, invalids, or elderly people will be present. They should not be used in food processing or serving areas, or in areas where workers will be exposed to their vapors for extended periods. Some state health inspectors prohibit the use of resin strips altogether under certain conditions, and the permissible uses of all forms of dichlorvos have been changing significantly in recent years. Pest management professionals should follow the most current regulations pertaining to these products, which can be obtained from the manufacturer, supplier, or state pesticide regulatory agency. As with the cancellations of urban pest management uses of most other organophosphate insecticides in the United States, the continued availability of dichlorvos to pest management professionals is uncertain.

In addition to DDVP strips, certain volatile pyrethroid insecticides and plant-derived terpenes (e.g., lavandin oil) are now being formulated into resin or fabric strips used in closets or other areas where clothes moths or carpet beetles can attack woolens, furs, or other susceptible items. Also, many types of insect pheromones used in pest management programs to monitor pest presence are formulated into rubber strips or plugs, or into small tubes (which are then usually placed on a sticky surface within a cardboard trap, so that insects will be attracted to the sticky surface).

Which Type of Formulation to Choose

To choose the best insecticide (or rodenticide or avicide) formulation for any particular job, the pest management professional must first consider the relevant biological (pest related), structural, environmental, and human factors and then determine how the pesticide is to be applied. He or she must choose the formulation that will be best for each specific situation, which is an analysis often based on professional experience. In choosing, the professional must consider

- *the pesticide label directions and precautions*
- *the surface area* to be treated (metal, wood, tile, carpet, fabric, paint, concrete, soil, etc.)
- *the application equipment* available and best suited to the job
- *the hazard of drift and runoff* (the nearness to sensitive areas and the likelihood of wind or rain)
- *the safety to the applicator, helpers, and other humans and pets* likely to be exposed
- *the habits or growth patterns of the pest* (which will determine bait versus spray or dust, or granular versus foliar spray)
- *the cost of the product and application* (including equipment, labor, etc.)
- *the type of environment* in which the application must be made (outdoors, damp areas, dusty areas, dry rooms, indoor areas frequently cleaned, etc.)
- *any special circumstances, sensitivities, or preferences* of the residents or clients involved (e.g., no odor, no sprays, no visible residues, no visible dead pests, minimal visits by pest control personnel, etc.)
- *any regulatory restrictions* that might apply to the situation at hand (e.g., restricted-use versus general-use labeling; restrictions in food-handling establishments, meat and poultry plants, and healthcare facilities; and local ordinances requiring prenotification and/or posting of signs)

For a space spray, an insecticide in oil solution may be best. For long residual performance in dry and unexposed situations, a dust will probably be best for controlling crawling insects, such as cockroaches, ants, or silverfish. However, it is difficult to control the exact placement of dusts, so their use around such sensitive areas as food contact surfaces in restaurants should be avoided unless exact placement can be guaranteed. Dusts are particularly suited for application into infested void areas in walls. An emulsion would be best for residual applications in visible areas. For surface applications where the appearance of visible residue is not objectionable, wettable-powder, suspension, or microencapsulated formulations will generally provide the longest and most effective residual action among spray formulations. These forms do not leave a visible residue on all surfaces, so if care is taken when they are applied, they can often be used in most areas of a treatment location. Bait formulations are typically unaffected by substrate factors, but they may be a poor choice in some environmental situations (e.g., high-moisture, humid, dusty, or unsanitary conditions).

RESISTANCE

In addition to considering the properties and uses of specific pesticides and their formulations, it is important to understand and consider the phenomenon called resistance. *Resistance* refers to the measurable lessening of the effectiveness of a pesticide as a result of previous exposure of a pest population to that pesticide or related types. This means that within an insect, rodent, or other pest population there is some change wherein the same amount of pesticide applied under comparable conditions does not kill as large a percentage of the population as it did previously (or as large a percentage as against a known susceptible pest population, such as a laboratory strain).

The general public has become familiar with the process of immunity to disease. The immune response is derived from antibodies present within the blood of an individual following the injection of vaccine or a previous experience or exposure to the disease, which was overcome by the body. Immunity is usually the first thought that comes to mind when insect resistance is mentioned. This thought is wrong because this is not the way pesticide-resistant populations arise.

Resistance is due to selection within the population; it is not an internal response or adaptation by one individual that would protect it during later exposure to the pesticide. The pesticide is the agent of selection. To illustrate, suppose a pesticide is applied and kills 98 percent of the individuals it contacts, but there are 2 percent that survive the treatment because they are not as susceptible to it as the others. This lack of susceptibility does not occur as a result of previous exposure to the pesticide. These "select few" are naturally resistant to the pesticide and make up the entire breeding stock (or a majority of it) from which the next generation will arise. It is quite likely that the next generation, having had resistant parents, will include a larger percentage of resistant individuals than was present in the original population (2 percent). When the same pesticide is applied to this new generation, a yet larger percentage of the population will survive. When this process is repeated over a number of generations, it may require only a relatively short period of time before the majority of the members of the population will not be killed by normal pesticidal applications. What has happened is that a pesticide has acted as a selecting agent, killing those members of a population that are susceptible to the chemical and leaving those that are resistant to breed and produce more resistant generations. This process is fundamentally different from the immune response to disease organisms that occurs in humans or other animals during their lifetime. Resistance to pesticides is a *population* response, which takes place over several or many generations. Immunity is an internal response that takes place within *individuals*, thus protecting each one from subsequent exposure to the disease. Further, humans are unable to become immune to inanimate materials like pesticidal chemicals, though they may (or may not) become more tolerant under circumstances of repeated exposure.

Resistance does not develop in all pests, nor in all places where a particular pest is found. It usually appears first in local situations and then becomes common throughout the geographical range of a pest, both by continued development in new local situations or by migration of resistant individuals. In the case of German cockroaches, only localized groups of individuals within certain parts of an infested premise, or populations within a few units of a large multifamily complex, may become resistant.

Resistance develops most frequently and rapidly in insects, and especially in those that have high rates of reproduction, short life cycles, and the ability to move rapidly from one locality to another. House flies and other filth flies are good examples. They are well known to develop insecticide resistance as fast as any group when subjected to consistent and high insecticide pressure. For similar biological reasons, resistance is much more common, and occurs much more rapidly, in German cockroach populations than with the American, smokybrown, or oriental cockroaches.

The most common type of pesticide resistance is known as **physiological resistance**. For example,

the pesticide might be degraded more quickly or may not be able to penetrate to the active site within the insect's body. Researchers have identified several types of physiological resistance in cockroaches, flies, and fleas, but discussion of these specific types of resistance is beyond the scope of this book. Sometimes pests exhibit another type of resistance, called **behavioral resistance**. In such situations, resistant individuals either avoid a chemically treated surface or bait altogether, or they do not remain on a treated surface or feed on a bait long enough to pick up sufficient pesticide to kill them. This is not a learned behavior, but one that occurs as an automatic or instinctive response that has been inherited.

The solution to control problems involving resistance may involve choosing a new pesticide or adopting a scheme of rotation between products with active ingredients of different modes of action. Rather, it may require closer study of the pest's habits and better pesticide application or placement, so that the pesticide will continue to be effective. In most cases where the professional believes the insects are resistant, this cannot be scientifically proven. In many cases, the pesticide applicator has failed to place the insecticide in the right areas, or *all* the right areas, or the rates applied were below label directions.

LAWS AND THE PESTICIDE LABEL

Pest management professionals must carefully study and understand the label on each pesticide product before using it (see Figure 3.6). All pest management companies should require complete familiarity with the pesticide products they use, and strict adherence to all the directions and precautions listed on each label.

The registration and use of pesticides are regulated by the Federal Insecticide, Fungicide, and Rodenticide Act (FIFRA) (see Appendix E). While federal law and regulation is generally predominant, state laws regarding many aspects of pesticide registration, labeling, and use affect the professional pest control operation. Pest control professionals must be aware of, and comply with, all aspects of these federal and state regulations and, in some areas, even local ordinances. In addition, the professional should be aware that most of the enforcement of federal and state laws and regulations pertaining to pest control and pesticide use is conducted by state-level officials. This is important because state-level officials (e.g., from the state Department of Agriculture, Pesticide Regulation, or Environmental Protection Agency [EPA]) represent the federal enforcement officials in their state.

The statement "ALWAYS READ AND FOL-

FIGURE 3.6. Reading, understanding and carefully following all pesticide label directions and precautions should be constantly reinforced in training sessions. (Myers)

LOW ALL LABEL DIRECTIONS" is perhaps the most important overall statement not only in this textbook, but also in the pest control industry. These words can never be stressed too much, or too often. They should always serve as the professional's general guide for all applications of all types of pesticides.

Figures 3.7 and 3.8 show the format and information required by the EPA on general-use and restricted-use pesticides. The labels are keyed as follows:

1. Product name
2. Company name and address
3. Net contents
4. EPA pesticide registration number
5. EPA formulator/manufacturer establishment number
6A. Ingredient statement
6B. Pounds/gallon statement (if liquid)
7A. Child hazard warning, "Keep Out of Reach of Children"
7B. Signal word: DANGER, WARNING, or CAUTION
7C. Skull and crossbones and the word "Poison" in red
7D. Statement of practical treatment
7E. Referral statement
8. Side- or back-panel precautionary statements
8A. Hazards to humans and domestic animals
8B. Environmental hazards
8C. Physical or chemical hazards
9. "Directions for Use" heading
9A. "Restricted-Use Pesticide" block
9B. Statement of pesticide classification
9C. Misuse statement
10A. Reentry statement
10B. "Storage and Disposal" block
10C. Directions for use (continued)

Product Name

Most primary manufacturers of technical pesticides (active ingredients) have a product name, also called a brand name or trade name, for each chemical they sell to a specific industry sector (e.g., Demand® for lambda-cyhalothrin, or Premise® for imidacloprid). In addition, each formulator that may use a chemical (active ingredient) will have a product name for each of its products. Some formulators may use different product names for any particular active ingredient. Companies sometimes also use the same product name, but with slight variations, to designate formulations which can contain different pesticidal active ingredients. Applicators must be careful about choosing a pesticide product by its product name alone.

Ingredient Statement

Each label must list the active ingredients in the product. This list is written so that the user can quickly see each active ingredient and its amount in percentage by weight. The ingredient statement must list the official chemical names and/or the accepted common chemical names (if available) for each active ingredient. Inert ingredients are normally not named, unless an inert ingredient is of toxicological concern to the applicator, and the label must show what percentage of the total weight is inert ingredients.

Type of Pesticide

The type of pesticide is often listed on the front panel of the pesticide label. This short statement usually indicates in general terms the pests to be controlled and the pesticide's formulation. Examples are as follows:

• "Insecticide for the control of cockroaches, ants, silverfish, etc."
• "Insecticide for the control of termites"
• "Herbicide for the control of unwanted trees, brush, and weeds"
• "Rodenticide for the control of rodents in and around urban structures"
• "Spot fumigant for spot treatment of food and feed processing equipment"

Net Contents

The front panel of the label indicates how much formulation is in the container. For dry formula-

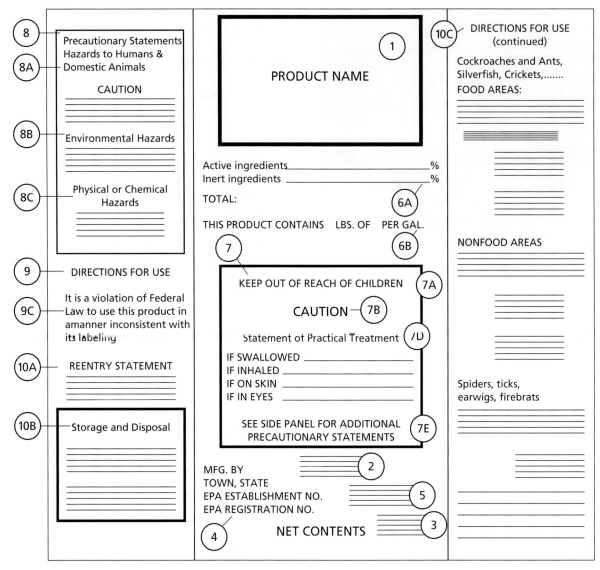

FIGURE 3.7. Generic label for a general-use pesticide.

tions, this can be expressed in metric units, such as grams or kilograms, or in nonmetric units, such as pounds or ounces. For liquids, the contents can be listed in milliliters, liters, gallons, quarts, pints, or ounces (meaning fluid ounces). Liquid formulations may also list the pounds of active ingredient per gallon of product.

Registration and Establishment Number

An EPA Registration Number appears on all pesticide labels. This indicates that the pesticide label has been granted registration by the EPA, but not that the product has been approved or warranted to be safe or effective (though product safety data are always required before registration is granted, and efficacy data must also be generated and are sometimes required). All pesticide manufacturers must

also be registered with the EPA, and their different manufacturing facilities are assigned unique numbers. This EPA Establishment Number appears on either the pesticide label or the container, and it identifies the facility that produced the product.

Signal Words and Symbols

Every label includes a signal word that is a generic measure of the product's acute toxicity to humans and that indicates the product's potential hazard to humans or other non-target animals. Knowing the product's general level of toxicity helps you choose the proper precautionary measures for handling and applying the pesticide.

The signal word must appear in large letters on the front panel of the label. It immediately follows the statement "Keep Out of Reach of Children,"

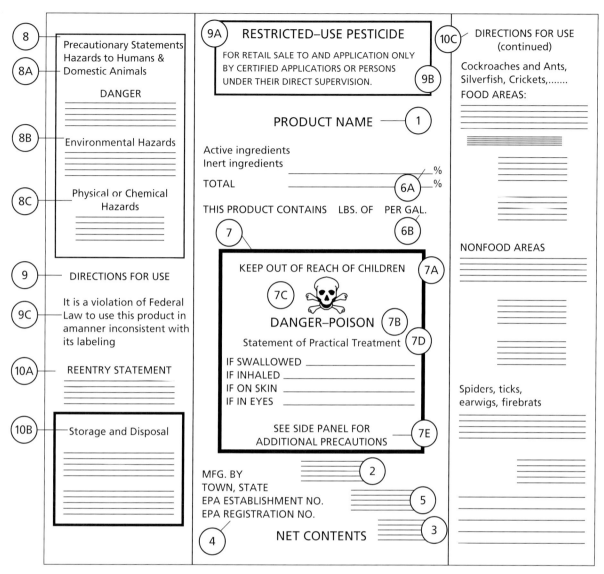

FIGURE 3.8. Generic label for a restricted pesticide.

which must also appear on all pesticide labels.

There are three signal words: DANGER, WARNING, and CAUTION.

The word DANGER signals that the pesticide is highly toxic. Any product that is highly toxic orally, dermally, or through inhalation or that causes severe eye and skin burning will be labeled DANGER. A teaspoonful of the undiluted product, taken by mouth, could kill an average-sized adult.

If the label carries the DANGER signal word, it will also carry the word "Poison" printed in red and the skull-and-crossbones symbol (see Figure 3.8). Many restricted-use pesticides carry these signal words and symbols if the product is especially toxic to humans. Pesticides are sometimes classified as restricted-use pesticides because of their potential to leach through soil and into groundwater if improperly applied or disposed of, or to otherwise

signal a special potential hazard to non-target aspects of the environment.

The word WARNING signals that the product is moderately toxic. Any product that is moderately toxic orally, dermally, or through inhalation or that causes moderate eye and skin irritation will be labeled WARNING. As little as a teaspoonful to a tablespoonful of the undiluted product, taken by mouth, could kill the average-sized adult.

The word CAUTION signals that the product is slightly toxic. Any product that is slightly toxic orally, dermally, or through inhalation or that causes slight eye and skin irritation will be labeled CAUTION. An ounce to more than a pint of the undiluted product, taken by mouth, could kill the average-sized adult. Even the least-toxic pesticides, such as some of the diluted, ready-to-use formulations, must carry the CAUTION signal word on their label.

Precautionary Statements

All pesticide labels contain precautionary statements that instruct the user on what precautions must be taken to reduce the risk to applicators, customers, livestock, and pets. These statements are listed under the heading "Hazards to Humans and Domestic Animals."

Statement of Practical Treatment

These statements are the first-aid treatments recommended in case of poisoning. Typical statements include the following:

- "In case of contact with skin, wash immediately with plenty of soap and water."
- "In case of contact with eyes, flush with water for fifteen minutes and get medical attention."
- "If swallowed, drink large quantities of milk, egg white, or water. Do not induce vomiting."
- "If swallowed, induce vomiting."

All DANGER labels, and some WARNING and CAUTION labels, contain a section for physicians describing the appropriate medical procedures for poisoning emergencies. In some cases, the label provides phone numbers that can be called for advice and information when emergency situations occur. The label may also identify an antidote.

Environmental Hazards

Pesticides may be harmful to the environment. Some products are classified as restricted-use pesticides because of potential environmental hazards alone. Watch for special warning statements on the label concerning hazards to the environment, such as to birds or fish and other aquatic organisms.

Physical or Chemical Hazards

This section of the label notes any special potential hazards, such as fire, explosion, or chemical hazards that the product may pose. Examples are as follows:

- "Flammable: Do not use, pour, spill, or store near heat or open flame. Do not cut or weld container."
- "Corrosive: Store only in a corrosion-resistant tank."

Classification Statement and "Restricted-Use Pesticide" Block

Every pesticide is classified by the EPA as either **general** or **restricted** in terms of its use. Every product classified as restricted use must carry the following statement in a prominent place, usually in a word block or box, at the top of the front panel of the label:

> RESTRICTED-USE PESTICIDE. For retail sale to and use only by certified applicators or persons under their direct supervision and only for those uses covered by the certified applicator's certification.

Restricted-use pesticides can be purchased only by a certified applicator. General-use pesticides are any pesticide products not considered restricted-use, but the words "General Use" do not appear on the product label. If the label does not say "Restricted Use," then the product is considered a "General Use" pesticide. Anyone can purchase general-use pesticides, though some pesticides sold primarily to commercial users, such as pest control professionals, are distributed only through firms that will not sell them to general consumers.

Reentry Statement

Some pesticide labels include a reentry precaution statement, that may even specify an interval which tells how much time must pass before the applicator, the customer, or any other people can reenter a treated area without appropriate protective clothing. It is illegal to ignore reentry intervals. These statements are often found on formulations used in total-release aerosols, foggers, ULV machines, or fumigants.

"Storage and Disposal" Block

All labels include general instructions for the appropriate storage and disposal of the pesticide and its container. State and local laws vary considerably, so specific instructions usually are not included. However, typical statements include the following:

- "Store at temperatures above 32°F (0°C)."
- "Do not reuse container."
- "Triple rinse and offer this container for recycling or reconditioning, or dispose in an approved landfill."
- "Do not reuse bag."

One or more of these statements may appear on a pesticide label. Use them to determine the best storage and disposal procedures for the operation and location. These statements generally appear in a special section of the label titled "Storage and Disposal" or under headings such as "Important," "Note," or "General Instructions."

Directions for Use

The instructions on how to use the pesticide are a very important part of the label. These directions are the best way to find out the proper and safe way to apply the product. Directions for use are specific to each product label. The use directions will provide the following information:

- The pests that the manufacturer claims the product will control. (Note: Professionals may legally apply a pesticide to control a pest not specified on the label if the application is to a site that the labeling approves, and so long as no specific label statement restricts such an application. This presumes knowledge of the safe and effective use of the pesticide, and that the manufacturer will not cover such use under its warranty.)
- The crop, animal, or site the product is intended to protect
- The proper equipment to use
- How much to use
- Mixing directions
- Compatibility with other often-used products
- Phytotoxicity and other possible injury or staining problems
- Where the material should be applied
- When it should be applied

LOOKING INTO THE FUTURE FOR PEST CONTROL INSECTICIDES

This discussion on future directions in pesticide technology focuses on insecticides; consult Chapters 15–17 for discussions pertaining to pesticides, formulations, and technologies for the control of vertebrate pests. The use of many insecticides has come and gone for most urban pest management situations. Use of materials such as DDT, chlordane, lindane, aldrin, dieldrin, and pentachlorophenol is either not permitted or severely restricted in the United States and most other countries. In fact, international treaties have been ratified to effectively ban the worldwide sale and use of many organochlorine pesticides. As mentioned previously, the organophosphate and carbamate insecticides are no longer permitted for most nonagricultural uses in the United States. However, pesticide manufacturers continue to invest in discovery and development of new chemical pesticides that typically have low to very low toxicity to humans and other mammals, as well as better environmental safety. The efficacy of such technologies is expected to continuously improve, thereby providing pest control professionals with new tools for the future.

There are also many so-called biotechnology research companies working on a number of insect and other pest management technologies, and the U.S. EPA, which regulates the registration of pesticides, has adopted formal policies to help encourage and streamline the registration of so-called 'reduced-risk' or environmentally preferable technologies, such as pheromones and baits or other products of the biotechnology industry. The Sentricon® termite baits mentioned earlier were one of the first pesticides registered under the EPA's reduced-risk pesticide registration policy; the agency is seeking to encourage such alternatives to the traditional high-volume soil application of termiticides (which has a higher risk of environmental contamination) (see Figure 3.9). During the product research and development process, biotechnology firms typically use modern techniques of molecular biology, sometimes called genetic engineering, to improve these biological control organisms. These efforts will no doubt result in new options for both pest management professionals and homeowners who purchase products in retail outlets.

FIGURE 3.9. Sentricon® termite baits were one of the first pesticide products registered by the U.S. EPA as a "reduced risk" pesticide. (Myers)

SUPPLEMENTARY READING MATERIAL

Buchel, K. H., ed. *Chemistry of Pesticides.* New York: Wiley, 1983.

Coats, J. R., ed. *Insecticide Modes of Action.* New York: Academic Press, 1982. 470 pp.

Larson, L. L., E. E. Kenaga, and R. W. Morgan. *Commercial and Experimental Organic Insecticides.* College Park, Md.: Entomological Society of America, 1985. 105 pp.

Matsumura, F. *Toxicology of Insecticides.* New York: Plenum Press, 1975. 503 pp.

Moreland, D. 1996. "Formulations: Preparing for the New Millennium." *Pest Control Technology* (special issue, May 1996).

Purdue Pesticide Programs series documents: PPP-24, *Pesticides and the Label* (47 pp.); PPP-31, *Pesticides and Formulation Technology* (24 pp.); PPP-36, *Pesticides and the Law* (27 pp.); Purdue University Cooperative Extension Service, West Lafayette, IN 47907.

Shankland, D. L., R. M. Hollingworth, and T. Smith Jr., eds. *Pesticide and Venom Neurotoxicity*. New York: Plenum Press, 1978. 283 pp.

Tomlin, C., ed. *The Pesticide Manual*. 10th ed. Bath, England: Bath Press, 1994. 1,341 pp.

Ware, G. W. *Fundamentals of Pesticides: A Self-Instruction Guide*. Fresno, Calif.: Thomson Public, 1991. 300 pp.

Ware, G. W. *The Pesticide Book*. Fresno, Calif.: Thomson Public, 1993. 340 pp.

Wilkinson, C. F., ed. *Insecticide Biochemistry and Physiology*. New York: Plenum Press, 1976. 768 pp.

CHAPTER 4 | Safety and the Environment

Pest management professionals are unique among service providers in that they must control or eliminate pests by use of pesticides and nonchemical means in close proximity to people and their homes, workplaces, child-care centers, and hospitals, or in areas holding valuable commodities (e.g., food products, computer facilities, etc.). The use of pesticides tends to be controversial.

A pest management professional has **legal, professional** and **ethical obligations** to follow all pesticide label directions and provide service in a way that avoids any significant risks to all people, pets, property, and other aspects of the environment (plants, wildlife, streams, etc.). Since in a legal, regulatory, and practical sense no pesticides are considered safe, they can only be applied in a safe manner—by qualified applicators taking all necessary precautions to minimize exposure of the applicator and all other non-target organisms to any pesticides applied. The professional is responsible for safety in these areas at the time of and after any pesticide applications. Whenever a long-lasting pesticide is used, such as when soil is treated with a termiticide, this responsibility and legal liability may extend for many months or years.

Public perception and opinion about the risks and dangers of pesticides are often negative. There is considerable concern and negative publicity in the news media, and professionals will encounter many people who ask difficult questions about the safety of pesticides. These people, especially customers, will have to be educated by the applicator. Often, people are generally chemophobic, and so have extreme concern about the use of any pesticides and virtually any other chemicals. Chemophobic people generally cannot be reassured, but there are several points that can be made to reassure other people concerned about pesticides. First, assure people that you understand their concern. Explain that pesticides will be

used in an only-as-necessary manner and applied in such a way that neither their health, their property, nor the environment will be compromised. Explain that use of the particular pesticides chosen is specifically permitted by the products' labels. Mention that this occurs only after many millions of dollars and years of research have been spent to ensure that proper application, according to label directions, will not present significant risks to people, pets, or the environment. It is not sufficient to say that these pesticides are EPA labeled. Moreover, saying that your pesticides are safe because they are EPA approved is misleading. This implies that the EPA warranties their safety, which is not the case. The EPA only grants a label registration; the pest management professional is responsible for safe use. Finally, individuals who cannot be thus reassured should seek the professional advice of their physician for perspective and recommendations as to the relative risks of the careful and conservative application of pest control chemicals versus the health risks posed by various types of household pests (e.g., cockroaches, fleas, or rodents).

Careful study of health and safety records has shown that pesticides are responsible for very few accidental poisonings each year (about 5 to 10 deaths occur each year in the United States, primarily as a result of suicide). This compares favorably to the more than 35,000 deaths from auto accidents, 17,000 from handgun incidents, 3,000 from swimming accidents, and about 20 from organized football. Furthermore, other studies have shown that pesticides present a very low long-term cancer risk, far lower than hundreds of other frequently contacted substances and foods. By way of perspective, the total lifetime cancer death risk for U.S. citizens is about 0.25 (2,500 out of 10,000 people will die of cancer), but the additional cancer risk attributable to all chemicals a person is exposed to in the environment is estimated to be 0.0001 (or 1 additional death per 10,000). Pesticides can be considered safely applied when properly and carefully applied according to label directions and precautions. Professionals should try to assure customers that they have the necessary experience, understanding, judgment, and equipment to make such safe applications. Addressing customer concerns about safety and ensuring that each professional can use the necessary pesticides safely under all types of field situations should be important matters for continuing discussion at training sessions and safety meetings.

At the same time, the pesticide applicator should be concerned about personal short- and long-term safety. All aspects of the so-called pesticide-use cycle, including the safe storage, transportation, application, and disposal of pesticides and their containers, are the responsibility of the pest management professional. Fortunately, the most effective use of pesticides generally involves careful application to only those areas where the pests hide or frequently travel, such as crack and crevice applications for cockroaches or proper placement of rodenticide bait boxes. These procedures lessen the potential for safety problems and contribute to a safe and profitable operation.

There is much more to safety in pest management work than just the responsibilities involved with pesticide use. Pest management professionals often have to drive a vehicle from one location to another, so all aspects of vehicle and driving safety are important to the overall safety and efficiency of the work. In addition, frequently used tools and equipment, such as ladders and electric drills, are potentially hazardous if not properly maintained and used.

Safety consciousness is important in every phase of the pest management operation to avoid personal injury, costly delays or accidents, and legal suits for damages. This requires an ongoing commitment to thinking, planning, and acting in a safe manner. Regardless of the firm's size, regular meetings should be held to discuss such safety topics as general pest management operating procedures, including review of safe pesticide use and handling procedures; the proper use of safety, emergency, and first-aid equipment; proper safety procedures, including practice (e.g., fire extinguisher practice, practice in cleaning up chemical spills, and practice in first-aid techniques, such as CPR); vehicle and equipment maintenance; and management supervision oversight to ensure that clear safety policies and procedures are well understood within the company *and followed*. Stated simply, your company should be training and retraining constantly to reduce the chances of mishaps and the serious losses they can create.

If the professional or company is sued for an accident or some other mishap involving a pesticide safety issue, a key aspect of the legal defense is the ability to demonstrate and document the company's rigorous and ongoing commitment to safety in all aspects of its operation. Therefore, it is important to document the various aspects of the safety program. This should include clear policy guidelines and standard operating procedures (SOPs), meeting notes and attendance records for safety training sessions, and evidence of timely follow-up on safety concerns identified for action. Safety training sessions should emphasize familiarity with the company's written SOPs, labels of pesticides used, and other safety-related topics.

The federal Occupational Safety and Health Act (OSHA) was passed in 1970. It charged all employers with providing a safe workplace, safe tools to work with, and adequate safety training appropriate to the job. In addition to this legislation and all the OSHA regulations that have followed it, there are many other state and federal laws relating to this area of safety. OSHA, under SARA Title 3, and states have enacted employee right-to-know laws that require employers to educate employees on the important aspects of safe chemical use and any possible short- or long-term hazards. Employers must also make sufficient technical information available to employees, such as Material Safety Data Sheets (MSDS), so they can be informed of any potential hazards to themselves and others in the course of their work. Employees must be trained in how to use tools, equipment, and chemicals safely, and they are responsible for carrying out the prescribed safety practices. Safety practices must be observed in the shop, on the job, and with the vehicles used in pest management service work. In recent years these concepts of notification and posting (e.g., of signs) in relation to pesticide applications have even been extended to include residents, neighbors, schoolchildren, and others who might be exposed to pesticides applied in or around homes and other structures. This is especially common for applications to landscapes and at schools. The pest management professional must be aware of these regulations and comply with them.

State regulatory agencies are also requiring increased training of applicators on safety and environmental concerns. Likewise, any certified pesticide applicator is required to be well informed on the following pesticide safety factors:

- Pesticide product toxicity and hazard to humans and pets; common pesticide entry (exposure) routes

- Common types and causes of pesticide accidents
- Precautions necessary to guard against injury to applicators and other individuals in or near treated areas
- Use of protective clothing and equipment
- Symptoms of pesticide poisoning
- First-aid and other procedures to be followed in case of a pesticide accident

ACUTE VERSUS CHRONIC TOXICITY

There are two basic types of toxic action recognized for most pesticides: acute and chronic. **Acute toxicity** is a rapid response, often within minutes or hours, to a single exposure or dose of the chemical. For example, the rodenticide zinc phosphide is an acute poison of relatively high toxicity to mammals (i.e., it has a low acute oral LD_{50} value of 12 mg/kg for rats). The pest management professional must always be extremely careful to avoid exposure to an acutely toxic dose of any chemical.

Repeated exposures over time to doses of some chemicals can result in **chronic toxicity**. This can result in sudden onset of severe symptoms, possibly leading to death. A variety of effects, such as liver or kidney damage, nervous system damage, respiratory damage, reproductive toxicity, dizziness, nausea, or other health problems can also occur. Levels of some pesticides can build up inside the body after repeated exposures, while other materials are rapidly removed from the body by normal functions but may still cause problems due to the repeated exposures. Also, it is assumed that small children, senior citizens, or those suffering from an illness, as well as fetuses, may be more susceptible to some pesticide effects than average adults. Special care should be taken when using pesticides around any of these potentially more susceptible groups. In fact, the increased risk to them may be justification for not using a pesticide, or that the product used is of low toxicity. Extreme care must be taken to ensure appropriate placement of the pesticide. Some states require pest control firms to notify sensitive people prior to any pesticide application near their property or so parents can keep their school-age children away from applications needed in or around schools and day-care centers.

The federal EPA's registration process required for all pesticides considers the potential for both acute and chronic toxicity problems. As a result, most materials are formulated, or the use directions are carefully written, to limit the possibility of any significant toxicity problems. Safe use of these chemicals requires an understanding of the basic toxic properties of each material used, a strict following of all label directions for proper application,

Toxicity and Hazard

Pesticide **toxicity** is the innate capacity of a chemical to be poisonous at some level. Not only pesticides, but all chemical compounds have some level of toxicity, and so the expression that something or some compound is "nontoxic" is never strictly accurate. It is usually expressed as the lethal dosage required to kill 50 percent of a population of test animals, such as laboratory rats, mice, or rabbits (see Appendix C for LD_{50} values of most pest control chemicals). This value is often referred to as the LD_{50} (Lethal Dose 50), and it is commonly expressed as the dose of pesticide, expressed in milligrams per kilogram (mg/kg) of body weight of the animal. Thus, if two materials have different LD_{50} values when tested with the same laboratory animal, the material with the lower LD_{50} value is more toxic because a smaller dose was required to give the 50 percent level of mortality. Keep in mind that the LD_{50} is only a reference figure for the professional to use in comparing the relative toxicities of different chemicals.

Hazard is the degree of danger involved in exposure to the pesticide as it is used. Without exposure, no toxicity, risk, or potential risk from a pesticide occurs. When we minimize exposure, we decrease potential hazard and increase the margins of safety related to each specific use of a pesticide. Excepting fumigants and some insecticide dusts such as boric acid, most pesticides are rarely used in their technical form. Most times they are used in diluted concentrations—for example, 0.5% active insecticide mixed with 99.5% water. It would be necessary to use a much greater amount of a diluted pesticide to be exposed to a toxic amount. Also, the level of hazard can be greatly affected by the type of formulation and the application technique used, as well as the care and judgment used in making the application. For example, wettable powders and microencapsulated formulations are absorbed through the skin less readily than oil solutions or even emulsions. Even the most highly toxic chemicals can be used with a low degree of hazard if they are carefully selected (by formulation type), diluted or mixed, and applied so as to minimize exposure to the applicator or other non-target organisms.

A general rule of thumb is that the hazard is a function of toxicity and exposure. Some people use the equation hazard = toxicity × exposure to help remember this relationship.

and the use of appropriate safety equipment. Regardless of the toxicity of pesticides, minimizing exposure to any chemical used, every time it is applied, is good practice and makes good sense.

MINIMIZE EXPOSURE—THE BASIC TENET OF PESTICIDE SAFETY

A continuing concern in the pest control industry is accidental poisoning that may result from exposure to the various chemicals used to manage insects and rodents. Some people think of these chemicals as being dangerous only if eaten or if severe accidental exposure occurs. They fail to consider the other ways by which pesticides may enter the body.

Chemicals are toxic to people and animals in varying degrees depending on the animal, the type of chemical involved, the way the chemical enters the body, the age or condition of the exposed organism, and other factors. Entry into the body may occur in any of three different ways: through the lungs (**inhalation**), through the mouth and into the digestive tract (**ingestion**), and through the skin (**absorption**) (see Figure 4.1).

Inhaling chemicals can be dangerous, and poisoning symptoms can occur rapidly. The lining of the lungs that separates the air from the blood is extremely thin and permits rapid, often complete absorption of the chemical directly into the blood. The lungs are richly supplied with blood, which normally picks up oxygen from the air. It is then pumped to the heart, where the blood is further pumped throughout the body. Note that the lungs, blood, and circulatory system are specifically designed to quickly transfer certain chemicals (usually oxygen) from the outside of the body to all regions within the body.

Dusts, mists, smokes, aerosols, or ultra-low volume (ULV) spray particles and fumigant gases are all formulations that offer the most hazardous exposure via inhalation (see also Figure 4.2). This is largely due to the small particle or droplet size of the pesticide, which is considered respirable. These applications typically involve dispersal of tiny aerosol droplets or dry particles, which are effective for filling rooms to control flying insects, or voids to control crawling pests like cockroaches, ants, or rodents; but these same small droplets or particles can also be breathed into the lungs and may penetrate into the tiny lung passageways where the primary air exchange takes place. Again, this exposure deep into the lungs will lead to direct entry of the pesticide into the blood, which then circulates throughout the body. In extreme cases, especially when oil-based formulations are used (and with inadequate respiratory protection), symptoms similar to pneumonia, such as clogging of the lungs, coughing, and great difficulty in breathing may also occur. Even when the particles are not small enough to go deeply into the lungs, if no respiratory protection is used the particles will lodge in the throat or nose and later be swallowed.

Chemicals ingested through the mouth are usually absorbed much more slowly than those breathed into the lungs. The rate of uptake depends on the type of pesticide involved. In some cases a chemical may pass through the digestive tract and be eliminated from the body before being completely absorbed. Others, such as the organophosphates, may be rapidly and completely absorbed from the digestive tract, while some types may be degraded by the acid conditions in the digestive tract.

All pesticide applicators must be aware that pesticides commonly enter the mouth via two routes: (1) via direct ingestion, and (2) via pesticide residues on the hands if the applicator eats or smokes without first thoroughly washing the hands.

While the skin offers more protection from absorption of chemicals than do the lungs or the digestive tract, there are many factors that make skin absorption a problem to the pest control specialist. The extensive skin surface is the most likely portion of the body to come into contact with a pesticide. Some pesticides and solvents can pene-

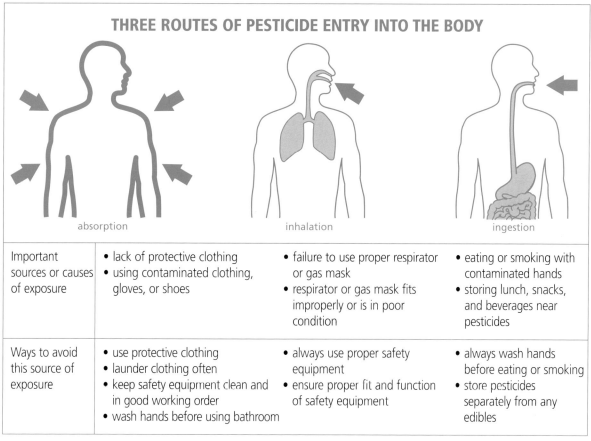

THREE ROUTES OF PESTICIDE ENTRY INTO THE BODY

	absorption	inhalation	ingestion
Important sources or causes of exposure	• lack of protective clothing • using contaminated clothing, gloves, or shoes	• failure to use proper respirator or gas mask • respirator or gas mask fits improperly or is in poor condition	• eating or smoking with contaminated hands • storing lunch, snacks, and beverages near pesticides
Ways to avoid this source of exposure	• use protective clothing • launder clothing often • keep safety equipment clean and in good working order • wash hands before using bathroom	• always use proper safety equipment • ensure proper fit and function of safety equipment	• always wash hands before eating or smoking • store pesticides separately from any edibles

FIGURE 4.1. There are three routes for pesticides to enter the body: via the skin (absorption); via the lungs (inhalation); and via the mouth (ingestion). Careful pesticide application techniques, the use of protective clothing, and common sense minimize exposure to pesticides via these routes. (Provonsha)

trate the unbroken skin rather easily, and all pesticides can readily penetrate cuts and abrasions.

Pesticides will absorb through certain regions of the skin surface more quickly than others. The eyes, genital areas, and underarms are areas of particularly rapid absorption. Never rub the eyes or use the lavatory without first washing any possible pesticide residue off the hands. Also, less absorptive skin surfaces, such as legs and arms, are often exposed for long periods due to pesticide residues on clothing. Therefore, carry extra clean clothing in the service vehicle and change frequently to avoid excessive skin exposure to pesticides.

Different formulations of pesticides can also influence the ease with which the pesticide penetrates the skin. Oil solutions tend to penetrate the fastest, while baits, dusts, wettable powders, suspensions, and microencapsulations are slow to penetrate skin. Some pesticides may be corrosive to the skin, and many liquid forms will be irritating if they get into the eyes or onto sensitive skin. Many of the pyrethroids used for residual control of crawling pests also cause a temporary (several hours) tingling sensitivity of facial skin around the cheeks and eyes when these areas are exposed.

Pesticides that have entered the body by one or more of the three routes mentioned are picked up and distributed throughout the body by the blood. In this way they quickly reach the site of action, which may be the nervous system, kidneys, liver, or lungs. Some may also be stored in fat deposits in cells or body tissues for extended periods before their toxic action occurs.

SAFETY IN THE PESTICIDE-USE CYCLE

The pesticide-use cycle has several aspects, some of which have been mentioned earlier (see also Figure 4.3). The pesticide-use cycle begins with the selection and purchase of the correct pesticides for the pest control task at hand. The pesticides are then transported to the firm's storage location. Pesticide storage is an important consideration for both safety and continued efficacy. Then, since pesticides are frequently purchased in a concentrate form, such as an emulsifiable concentrate, suspension, or wettable powder, they must be mixed properly and safely. From a safety standpoint, application is a key portion of the pesticide-use cycle. Disposal of excess pesticide concentrate or diluted material and

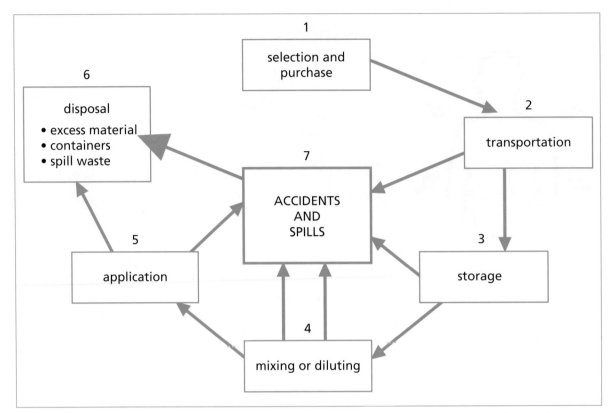

FIGURE 4.2. The pesticide-use cycle. This cycle has at least seven distinct steps. During each step, careful consideration must be given to safety and protection of the applicator, people, non-target animals, property, and the environment. Proper record keeping and compliance with applicable federal, state, and local regulations are necessary throughout the entire cycle.

pesticide containers must also be considered. Occasionally, pest control professionals are also faced with cleanup of pesticide spills.

Pesticide Selection

There are several important considerations in proper pesticide selection (see also Chapter 3). The type of surface to be treated is especially important, since it will affect the residual performance of the pesticide. Staining or chemical reaction with different types of surfaces should also be considered before applications begin. If you are uncertain about the safety of applying a particular material to a surface, it may be best to treat an out-of-the-way portion of the surface as a test. Later, check for staining or other problems before making more extensive applications. Some pesticides may stain or discolor carpets or upholstery only in those areas where strong sunlight is also present; the possibility of interactions between chemicals and sunlight, heat, steam, foot traffic, or other possible factors must be considered. Discolorations also tend to show up after repeated applications to the same areas, which may indicate inappropriate application that is guided by convenience or habit rather

than by inspections and judgment as to true pest locations.

If ULV or some other type of insecticide spray treatment is necessary to give the most effective control, only formulations of nonresidual insecticides registered for this use in the type of equipment and application involved should be selected. Use of residual insecticides in ULV equipment is not permitted for indoor applications because such space spraying would lead to contamination of many surfaces that should not receive such pesticide application.

Safety to non-target organisms, such as cats, dogs, fish, birds, and others types of animals, can be ensured by careful pesticide selection well before applications are made. The presence of house plants should also be considered. Some active ingredients or types of formulations may represent greater potential risk of wildlife poisoning when they are used outdoors, in the landscape. For example, microencapsulated formulations may cause severe bee kills if they are applied to flowering plants. Also, use of some rodenticides may result in danger to pets or wildlife (mammals or birds) from secondary poisoning as they scavenge on dead or dying rodents, or from the availability of the bait outside of the bait station due to bait translocation by the target rodents. The presence of such scavengers, as well as curious pets or children, should also be considered when choosing the specific rodenticide bait form and when placing baits (see Chapter 15).

The tremendous growth in the use of computers and similar electronic technology in a wide variety of household devices and industrial or office equipment represents an additional challenge to pesticide selection. Most spray and dust formulations will damage or even ruin computer and other electronic equipment if they are applied into these complex and expensive machines and onto their microchips and other circuitry. This can make control of cockroaches and certain other crawling insects in such equipment very difficult, as these pests may prefer to harbor inside cash registers, telephones, radios, stereos, smoke alarms, microwave ovens, and other such electronic equipment. Specialized spray formulations or more novel forms of application equipment, such as certain types of baits, are needed for these situations.

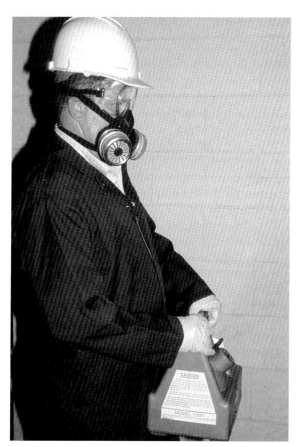

FIGURE 4.3. Proper safety protection to minimize exposure when applying insecticides indoors with ULV equipment (fogging) includes goggles, respirator, coveralls, protective gloves, and safety cap. (Myers)

Medical Tests for Applicators

Persons who work with organophosphate or carbamate insecticides for an extended time during the year (e.g., pesticide applicators or pesticide manufacturers and formulators) have long been advised to consider establishing a regular cholinesterase testing program through their doctor. Such a program would likely consist of an initial blood test at time of hire to determine a person's baseline level of cholinesterase.

Then, when the insecticides are being used regularly, similar tests can be performed on the individual, and these results can be compared with that person's baseline level of cholinesterase. Through this testing procedure, cholinesterase levels during the time of year when exposure to insecticides is greatest are known. When cholinesterase levels are significantly depressed, the doctor may advise that the individual limit or possibly completely avoid exposure to these insecticides until the cholinesterase level returns to near normal.

However, with the cancellation in the United States and other countries of most urban pest management uses of organophosphate and carbamate insecticides, this routine medical monitoring may no longer be necessary. Pest management professionals should seek the advice of their physicians concerning the need, and specific types, of medical monitoring for potentially harmful pesticide poisoning symptoms. Many companies will continue routine medical monitoring of the health of their workers who use chemical pesticides as a precaution, and for liability protection.

Pesticide Transport

Pest management professionals generally do not need to carry large amounts of the commonly used pesticides, and it is good practice to carry only the amount of pesticide needed for a few days of work. There have been a number of changes in federal and state regulations regarding the transportation of pesticides on public roads. These regulations are quite complex, very specific to each state, and change often. Pest management professionals should check with federal and state pesticide and transportation regulatory officials to determine vehicle requirements, restrictions on the amount of pesticide permitted in a vehicle, manifest or vehicle placarding requirements, and any routes where pesticide transport might be limited. Contact the federal Department of Transportation (DOT) office in your state, or the state police, for specific requirements.

A manifest lists the types and amounts of pesticides or other hazardous materials carried in the vehicle; it must be carried during pesticide transport. This manifest must be readily accessible in the cab of your vehicle if requested by an inspector. It must be kept in an approved format, with all the necessary information included on the form.

An approved placard on the side of your vehicle is also required if a fumigant is carried. There are fines for improper transport of pesticides on public highways, making this an important area in which to be well informed and in compliance with all regulations.

There are other practical suggestions that pest control professionals should consider regarding pesticide transport. Pesticides and other chemicals should be carried in a vehicle compartment separate from the driver and passenger compartment (see Figure 4.4). This will prevent pesticides from contaminating the driver's compartment should a vehicle accident or a spill occur. The ideal vehicle for pest management use would have a body completely separated from the driver space, and the pesticide storage compartment would be heated in cold weather and cooled during hot weather. Extra care should be taken in outfitting any commonly available vehicle

FIGURE 4.4. Pest management service vehicles should segregate pesticide concentrates from the driver and passengers, and from application equipment. All compartments should be kept locked for security. (Myers)

to safely carry pesticides, and strict procedures and company policies should also be followed in the routine handling of pesticides within the vehicle.

Chemicals must be handled and stored carefully to avoid spillage and container breakage. All containers at or smaller than 2.5 gallons should be stored in a box or compartment that will not allow them to turn over or bump into other containers. This compartment should be sturdy, lined to prevent container breakage, secured to the floor or the trunk, and clearly labeled. It should also be kept locked at all times to minimize theft or possible entry by children. It should not allow pesticides to freeze during the normal course of the workday (i.e., it should be emptied for overnight storage), nor should it allow them to become too hot. Keep in mind that aerosols can explode if heated above 130°F for even short periods. A bursting pesticide aerosol is a severe hazard, both from the force of the rupturing can and from the pesticide dispersed within the storage compartment.

As a general rule, pesticides carried in a service vehicle should be in their original containers with the original label on them. Some pest management companies, however, premeasure small quantities of pesticide into service containers. Some manufacturers even provide premeasured dose quantities in small containers. These containers must be clearly labeled to identify the pesticide. The label must be securely fastened to the new container carried in the service vehicle (contact your pesticide distributor or state pesticide regulatory agency for details).

If chemicals are spilled inside or outside the vehicle, the spill should first be contained with an absorbent and then cleaned up promptly. Service vehicles should be provided with an absorbent material, such as cat litter or garage floor sweeping compound, to soak up any liquids that may be spilled. Most pesticide distributors now offer special absorbent material for use in pesticide spill situations. Each professional should have a brush or small broom to clean up any absorbent-pesticide mixtures as well as any granules, dusts, or other dry pesticides that may be spilled. A heavy-duty plastic bag or other sturdy container should be available in the vehicle as a receptacle for this waste material. A gallon of water, soap, clean wiping cloths, and towels should also be in each vehicle, so that the professional can remove pesticides from hands or other contaminated surfaces. A clean change of clothing, stored in a sealed plastic bag so it cannot become contaminated before use, should be in the vehicle. A proper fire extinguisher (type ABC) should always be carried in a vehicle. Specific fire extinguishers are required by DOT when the vehicle is classified as a commercial motor vehicle.

In case of a large spill or a vehicle accident involving a spill, the proper agencies may have to be notified. Again, each state has a designated agency for spill reports. A good phone number to keep in the vehicle is the CHEMTREC hotline, (800) 424-9300. It can be called at any time for specific information on procedures in case of pesticide spills or accidents. The manufacturer should be contacted in cases of larger spills; their representatives will know how to properly handle the spill. The MSDS for each product will provide the manufacturer's emergency phone number, and MSD sheets should be carried in the service vehicle.

Pesticide Storage in Buildings

As with pesticide transport, local fire officials and state pesticide regulatory agencies can provide details on state or local regulations regarding the storage of pesticides and other chemicals. Many regulations require a report of the types and amounts of pesticides that are stored. Some areas also require specific types of lists (of materials under storage) to be provided to fire department officials or other state or local regulatory officials for their use and safety in case of a fire or other mishap.

Pesticides should be stored in an area, preferably a room, specifically reserved for this purpose (see Figure 4.5). The room must be securely locked at all times when not in use and should have a sign clearly designating this area for pesticide storage. This sign should say (at least), "Keep Out—Pesticide Storage." Posting approved fire code signs on the outside of this area and the building may also be required (contact your local fire department). The storage area should be kept dry and cool but should never be allowed to freeze. It should be ventilated, but never to other inside areas. It should be constructed or modified to keep the pesticides out of direct sunlight. If possible, fire-resistant construction is best. It should have a cement or some other type of floor that will not absorb spilled materials, and no floor drains. State or local building or fire codes may require that the floor be modified to create a moat that surrounds the pesticide storage area, so that spilled pesticide liquid will be contained within the building. A fire extinguisher should be available nearby, as well as materials to handle any pesticide spills (see the preceding discussion under "Pesticide Transport"). If fire extinguishers are maintained, be sure to provide employee training (an OSHA requirement). Your fire extinguisher supplier or local fire department can often provide this training. Proper storage of fumigants will almost certainly require special facilities.

FIGURE 4.5. Pesticides should be stored in neat, well-ventilated, lighted and secure areas, that are properly identified and placarded, and away from office or other areas where people are routinely located. (Myers)

Store all pesticides in the original, labeled containers in which they were received. Never store them in other containers. All pesticide containers should be checked on a regular basis for any sign of leaks or deterioration of contents. If a pesticide container is damaged, immediately transfer the contents to another container with an identical label.

Solvents must be handled with particular care since many of them are flammable, produce toxic fumes, or both. Flammable and toxic chemicals should always be kept in their original, tightly closed containers or in special solvent containers (properly labeled), and away from any source of excessive heat or open flame. If possible, store them in a separate building with adequate ventilation that promptly removes any fumes produced. If solvents must be stored inside a building where people work, regularly check that the containers are tightly sealed and the ventilation system for the storage room is functioning properly. Liquid pesticides should be stored in separate areas from dry pesticides such as dusts, granules, or baits.

A fire involving pesticides in a storage area or after a vehicle accident creates a health hazard from toxic fumes, poisonous runoff, and leaking or exploding containers. Federal and state laws now require that such storage requires prior notification of local environmental, health, and emergency or fire department officials, so that they are aware of any potential special hazards in case of any emergency. Under such circumstances, do not take any unnecessary risks in attempting to fight the fire. Call the fire department immediately and advise them that pesticides are involved.

Fumigants should never be stored in a building where people work. They should always be kept in a separate building with adequate air circulation to remove any gas that may escape from the containers. This building should be cool and dry, and kept locked. Signs indicating the presence of fumigants should be placed on the outside of buildings. Only properly trained personnel should have access to this storage area. Other regulations and precautions for storing fumigants are beyond the scope of this book, but they should be thoroughly understood by anyone using these materials. Check fumigant labels for specific requirements.

Mixing Pesticides

The purpose of pesticide mixing is generally to take a concentrated form of the pesticide (e.g., an emulsifiable concentrate or a wettable powder) and dilute it to a much less concentrated form for final use. Studies have shown that the greatest exposure of technicians to pesticide often occurs during the pouring, mixing, and other handling of concentrate forms, rather than during application or cleanup phases. Working with concentrated forms of pesticides always requires extra care. Any spill or other mishap with the concentrate increases the exposure hazard. Safety in pesticide mixing should be practiced during all phases of lifting and carrying the container, opening the container, pouring the concentrate, and mixing the material to obtain a uniform mixture in the spray tank (or other device).

Whenever mixing some pesticides, for adequate safety the applicator is required to wear chemical-resistant safety gloves, goggles or a full face shield to protect the eyes in case of splashing, a respirator (especially if working in tight quarters or where dust or wettable powder is being mixed), and adequate protective clothing, including long pant legs and sleeves.

Rubber, polyethylene, neoprene, or other chemical-resistant safety gloves are preferred, and they are generally available through pesticide distributors or catalogs specializing in chemical safety equipment. Some professionals prefer to use disposable gloves, which can be used during the mixing and handling process, throughout the application process, and then discarded. Make sure the disposable gloves are chemical resistant. Any reusable chemical-resistant gloves should be clean and free of punctures. Check the pesticide labels for specifics, as some pesticides may require a certain type of glove be used.

Use both hands when lifting a large, heavy container of pesticide concentrate. If both hands are used, the container is less likely to be dropped, even if the handle breaks. The container is also less likely to bump against other things, since it will be held

higher up, away from the ground, and at waist level. If the material does spill, it typically covers the shoes and pant legs. Therefore, it is important to have these areas protected beforehand and to remove this clothing as soon as possible after such a spill. Rinse water and clean, spare clothing stored in the service vehicle will be useful when spills occur.

Tightly closed containers stored in warm areas sometimes build up pressure, which may cause the material to spray in one's face when opening the lid. Use scissors to open envelopes containing powder, because ripping and tearing envelopes will lead to spillage or flying dust. A respirator can offer an extra measure of protection by preventing inhalation of the most concentrated form of the pesticide powder.

When pouring any concentrate into a measuring device, be sure the device is placed solidly on a level surface. Many pesticides come in containers with measuring lines or other devices to make measuring and pouring easy and less hazardous. The larger 55-gallon drums used for some insecticides and industrial herbicides generally have specialized measuring equipment for pouring off smaller amounts of concentrate.

When adding liquid or dry concentrate to a tank of water, it is usually a good idea to put only half of the final amount of water (or other diluent) needed into the tank before adding concentrate. It is always possible that the material will splash or spray out of the tank and into the eyes when a liquid concentrate is poured for measuring or mixing. This is one important reason to wear eye and hand protection and to have only about one-half of the final amount of the diluent in the tank when the concentrate is added. Practice pouring water from common types of pesticide containers, smoothly and in a controlled manner (to aid in precise measuring), without splashing. As stated earlier, mixing from smaller containers or dose bottles is now more common.

After the concentrate is added, the empty pesticide container or measuring device should be triple-rinsed according to directions on the label, and this rinsate added to the tank. Then, the tank mixture should be shaken or agitated to disperse the concentrate (especially with wettable powders, suspensions, or microencapsulated formulations) before the final amount of water or diluent is added to the tank. Many professionals carry extra water on the service vehicle for rinsing containers, measuring cups, and mixing or stirring devices. They may also have a policy of measuring and mixing all concentrates outside of the customer's premises to reduce possible liability in case of spills. All mixing and measuring equipment should be kept clean and rinsed between uses, and any spills should be cleaned up immediately. Technicians should also be aware that state regulations may require formal reporting of spills involving amounts larger than some minimum level, but in some areas there is no minimum level, so all spills must be reported.

It is important that pesticide dilutions, or mixtures, are mixed correctly to ensure their safe and effective use. This will require careful reading of the label and some knowledge and ability to make basic calculations.

Contamination of Drinking Water Systems

In some pest management operations, such as termite or power spray applications, a hose connected to a drinking water supply system is used to fill the spray tank. Some application equipment, such as proportioning devices, are connected directly to the water supply system. These hoses may dip into the solution in the tank, making a direct connection between the pesticide and the water supply. In all of these situations, a sudden reduction in the water pressure, such as would be caused by a broken hydrant or when one or more other faucets are turned on suddenly, can cause a pesticide to be drawn back into the drinking water supply lines. A related problem can arise in agricultural or urban pest management operations where spray tanks are filled from siphon or pump lines placed into ponds or streams. If the pumping equipment suddenly fails, a backflow might be created, which would cause the contents of the spray tank to flow into the pond or stream.

The best method to prevent this is to not allow the hose to dip into the spray tank solution. Portable backflow preventers are available and must be installed between the hose and the water faucet any time there is a possibility of the hose end contacting the pesticide. These simple devices remain open when water is flowing through the line at a proper pressure, but they close when the pressure drops. This prevents any liquid in the hose from being drawn back into the water supply. Ordinary check valves are not suitable for this use and should not be relied on. Pesticide equipment distributors can provide recommendations. Backflow preventers are mandatory for all siphon lines used to fill pesticide tanks from streams, ponds, or other bodies of water. Remember, the best precaution is to have an air gap between the hose end supplying the water and the surface of the spray tank reservoir.

Another cause of water supply contamination is the practice of attaching a water supply hose to the discharge side of a pump in order to prime the pump. This practice should never be permitted.

When priming a pump, pour water from a separate container into the hose leading to the pump, using a funnel if necessary.

Safe Application

Safe applications begin with reading and understanding the label directions on the pesticide container. Remember that federal and state regulations require that all pesticides be used only according to their label directions. Every pest management firm should have regular training sessions to review the labels for all pesticides used. All sections of each label should be reviewed, and each professional should understand what the various sections mean. There should be no misunderstanding about the proper mixing, application, disposal, cleanup, first-aid, and other procedures for each product. Also, safety training within the firm should include a review of all Material Safety Data Sheets (MSDS) for all pesticides and other chemicals used, and any other OSHA-required safety training.

The label directions generally include the necessary considerations for safe pesticide application under most circumstances. By using care, common sense, and appropriate safety equipment, the applicator can apply pesticides safely. Generally, labels will advise if people or pets need to be removed prior to application, or if other such precautions must be taken. When space sprays are used or flea treatments performed—both involving general treatment of most floor areas—the professional should give the customer specific directions on when to reenter the premises and what procedures or precautions to take before reentering.

Moreover, it is important to consider the presence of any particularly sensitive or ill people in the premises. The company should have strict policies regarding situations such as the presence of infants, children, pregnant women, the elderly, invalids (such as those on dialysis or some other life support), or those identified as chemically sensitive. The use of pesticides indoors, or perhaps even in the yard, where pesticide-sensitive people are present can lead to serious medical problems and lawsuits, so such use should be avoided as a matter of company policy. In general, do not treat with any pesticide in a spray, fog, mist, or dust formulation where someone is ill and under a physician's care or informs you that they tend to be very sensitive to chemicals. Use of baits or traps will generally be acceptable. If a sick person is present, suggest that another date be scheduled for the necessary applications. If this is not acceptable, obtain clearance from the person's physician and be certain that the ill or sensitive person is not present during applica-

Triple-Rinse Method for Empty Pesticide Containers

Containers for liquid pesticide concentrates are not really empty until they have been properly rinsed. Only then can they be disposed of according to label directions. Use the following triple-rinse procedures to remove pesticide residues, use the rinsate in your spray tank, and then dispose of the container:

1. Let the container drain or drip into the spray tank for at least 30 seconds.
2. Fill the container 1/4 full of water (or oil, for oil-soluble materials).
3. Replace cap on container and rotate or shake container to rinse all sides.
4. Drain rinse mixture from container into spray tank.
5. Repeat steps 2–4 two more times before disposing of container.

Alternatively, specialized hose-end attachments are available that will puncture pesticide concentrate containers, such as plastic and metal jugs, and allow power-rinsing of the inside of the jug, which is then drained of rinsate. Repeated use of these units is an alternative way to accomplish triple-rinsing of pesticide concentrate containers.

tion or for an adequate time afterwards.

Labels have sections on special precautions to take when pesticides are used outdoors or applied in such a way that contamination of non-target areas is possible. Spray or runoff must not contaminate any body of water or areas where children, pets, or wildlife might be harmed at a later time.

There has been increasing concern about contamination of underground water systems, either natural or constructed (e.g., wells, cisterns, or drainage systems), with pesticides. Soil treatments with termiticides have particular potential to contaminate underground water systems or subslab and subbasement drainage systems. Pesticides that have any significant likelihood of leaching through soil and into groundwater or running off into surface water after application will usually be classified as restricted-use pesticides, because the potential for such environmental contamination is one of the key reasons for this classification. Some restricted-use pesticides will have specific label directions designed to ensure use that will avoid significant

environmental contamination.

Specialized heating and air-conditioning system designs are also used below some houses. These can also become contaminated during soil termiticide treatment (see Chapter 7). These contamination situations can lead to serious health and safety concerns and to enormous legal liability. Such situations show that a pesticide should never be applied under a slab or foundation, into a crack or void, or anywhere else unless the area where the material will end up can be seen, or it is certain that no harmful effect will be created and that the application is necessary.

Proper Disposal

State pesticide regulatory officials can inform the pest management firm of any special requirements or restrictions on pesticide and pesticide container disposal. Otherwise, the container rinsing and disposal procedures outlined in federal regulations should be followed. These are generally described on the pesticide label. All disposal of pesticides must be done in a manner that will not contaminate any aspect of the environment.

Pesticide disposal has received a lot of attention by state and federal regulatory agencies. Much of this regulation is motivated by a desire to reduce or eliminate the pollution of surface waterways like ponds, lakes, streams, or oceans, and of groundwater. Many regulations of pesticide waste disposal are directed toward large-volume generators of chemical waste (e.g., manufacturers). In general, pest management firms should not encounter disposal problems if label directions and other normal procedures are followed. However, problems may occur when a firm's excess material can no longer be used. Thus, to avoid costly and difficult disposal problems, do not stockpile large amounts of pesticide. Inventory management is crucial.

Empty or partially emptied pesticide containers, excess spray mixtures, dusts, or other final formulations can present disposal problems. Use up all prepared spray mixtures on the job, according to the label. The pesticide label will have specific instructions on proper disposal procedures for empty containers. After triple-rinsing, containers for liquid concentrates, such as emulsifiable concentrates, suspension concentrates, or microencapsulated forms, can be disposed of in a sanitary landfill or recycled through special pesticide container management programs. Rinsate from these rinses should be added to the spray tank and used according to label directions. After rinsing, the containers should be punctured, crushed, or otherwise disabled before disposal. Bags or other containers that contained powders should be thoroughly emptied and disposed of through the municipal trash disposal system.

Disposal by commercial pest control firms of containers containing unwanted, excess, or unusable pesticide is not allowed in the normal municipal trash. Generally these containers are considered hazardous waste if disposal is to be attempted, and only officially permitted firms are allowed to accept, manage, and dispose of hazardous waste from commercial sources. This disposal concern for excess pesticide can be avoided by careful inventory practices (i.e., do not overpurchase), and any excess pesticide should be stored until it can be used. Another alternative is to make arrangements for another certified pesticide applicator to use the material in an approved fashion; in addition, many distributors will accept unopened containers for a refund of the purchase price. There are licensed hazardous waste or pesticide disposal services available in many areas, but their services are usually expensive. Depending on the amounts and kind of excess pesticide, a time limit may be allowed for proper disposal before being in violation of federal or state laws regarding disposal of pesticide waste. If these materials are considered excess, then they are considered waste that must be properly disposed of, and not stored indefinitely. In many areas there are periodic special pesticide disposal programs, often called clean sweeps, conducted by state environmental or agricultural officials. Some may allow disposal of nonagricultural pesticides by users such as pest control operators. Similar programs for homeowners, called household hazardous waste collections or clean sweeps, will generally not allow disposal of nonresidential wastes, such as pesticides from pest control firms, but some (especially those conducted at permanent facilities) will accept both household and small business wastes, including unusable pesticides from pest control firms.

Experience and careful planning allow the completion of most pesticide applications without having excess formulation left as a disposal problem at the end of any job. If some formulation is left over, the excess material could be used at the next appropriate account, assuming the material will not break down in the spray tank or container. Do not overapply the material inside a premises. However, it is always legal to apply a pesticide by using it in a way that is allowed and described on the label. For example, most insecticides labeled for crawling insect control indoors are also labeled for use in controlling ants, ground beetles, crickets, or other insects outdoors. In such situations, these insects are considered occasional invaders (see Chapter 12).

These insecticides are also often labeled for

Less Is Better

Throughout the pesticide-use cycle, a good rule of thumb is that less is better. The less pesticide bought, stored, transported, applied, and disposed of, the better off the firm will be regarding pesticide regulations and other considerations. In general, problems with regulatory compliance will be greatly reduced when the less-is-better philosophy is routinely followed. Also, in case of a fire, accident or other disaster, all manner of problems will be lessened if large amounts of pesticide are not involved. Most firms also now control their inventories at fairly low levels because they do not want to tie up excessive capital resources in stored pesticides or other equipment.

treating exterior surfaces for flying insect control. Therefore, it is perfectly valid to apply excess material onto ground surfaces below shrubs around the perimeter of the structure for control of crawling insects. Another very worthwhile use of excess material (again, if the label permits) is to treat exterior walls around light fixtures to control flying insects, such as ants, beetles, or termites, that are attracted to the lights at night (and then often enter the home to become pests). By using ingenuity and knowledge of the label, many valid, safe, and legal ways can be found for using up small amounts of pesticide left over after a job.

When cleaning pesticide application equipment, such as sprayers and dusters, the cleaning solution should not be washed down a sink or drain, as this will lead to direct contamination of the sewage water. Care must be taken that there is no contamination (e.g., by runoff) of surface or groundwater under or near the disposal area. One legal use of these rinsates is to place them into the termite tank, if the company has such equipment. This is recommended only for dilute rinsate materials.

Pesticide Spills

Pesticide spills can be either small or large, but the first action to take is to limit the size of any possible spill. One step is to limit the amount of active ingredient routinely carried on the vehicle. Carry small containers of only those materials likely to be needed, and limit the total volume to as few days' worth of supplies as practical. As previously mentioned, the local area may have regulations that restrict the amount of pesticide carried without being required to have extra permits and insurance.

The first thing to do with any spill is to **contain** it, as quickly as possible. For small spills of one to two gallons or less, which may be diluted spray material or concentrate, the vehicle should carry enough cat litter or other dry absorbent (e.g., that made for oil spills on garage floors) to be quickly thrown onto the spill. This will stop the spread of the spill and begin absorbing the chemical for later disposal. If the professional is not near the vehicle or doesn't have absorbent available, towels, paper, or some other absorbent material, such as sand and soil, can limit the short-term spread of the spill. If the situation is potentially dangerous to a passerby, a stream, or some other sensitive object, articles like bath towels, cushions from lawn chairs, soil from a flower bed, and so on, can be used to quickly limit the spread of the chemical. Containment must come first. The cost for later replacement of these items will be minor compared to possible environmental contamination, fish and other wildlife kills, lawsuits, and bad publicity.

After the small spill has been contained, use a broom or brush and dustpan to sweep up the absorbent material and other residue from the spill. If necessary and appropriate, wash the site with detergent and water until it is as clean as possible. For indoor areas, soiled carpeting or other items that cannot be cleaned effectively may have to be replaced. Fortunately, dusts and wettable powders will not be absorbed by most surfaces, so these can be cleaned up quite thoroughly with a dustpan and broom. Wear protective gloves, shoes, and clothing when cleaning up a spill. Put all absorbent and other debris in large plastic garbage bags and seal them tightly. Recall that a supply of these bags should be in the service vehicle at all times, ready for situations like this. It may also be best to put protective clothing and any tools that became contaminated in the incident into the trash bag when the cleanup is finished. Remove the bags to the place of business for later disposal. Contact a pesticide distributor or state pesticide regulatory agency for instructions on disposing of all contaminated materials. Most states have detailed regulations concerning nonresidential chemical waste disposal, and specially designated landfills or other treatment facilities to receive waste such as materials contaminated with moderate amounts of pesticide. State or local pesticide regulatory agencies may have requirements for reporting spills or other pesticide-related accidents. Be aware of these requirements beforehand, or check on any such responsibility after the spill.

If the spill is too large to contain readily (e.g., if a termite tank ruptures suddenly, a vehicle accident causes a spray tank to rupture, or a large can of concentrate spills), try first to contain the material with soil, absorbent, or any other means possible. Then, keep people away from the spill area and call (or ask someone else to call) the local police and fire departments. (Always have enough spare change in the vehicle to use in a pay phone in case of any emergency while in the field. Have all the emergency numbers readily available in the vehicle or in a wallet.) During the call, specify to these agencies that a pesticide spill situation is involved. If a vehicle accident results in fire or an obvious high risk of fire, either of which cannot be handled with the vehicle's fire extinguisher, move away from the area. Then, keep others away and immediately call the local police and fire departments. Some spills may be large enough that calls to federal agencies or the national CHEMTREC hotline, (800) 424-9300, are also necessary for instructions and notification.

You should make all reasonable efforts to keep others from being injured by the situation. Most fire departments have special equipment for handling chemical spills and fires. They will want to know what chemicals are involved, so you should be able to quickly provide these names and some information about the potential hazards to firefighters and the public nearby. This is the type of information that should be discussed and learned at the routine safety meetings held at the company.

OTHER SAFETY CONSIDERATIONS FOR PEST MANAGERS

Protective Clothing

Special protective clothing is generally not necessary when the professional is making spot treatments with insecticides or placing most types of rodent baits or traps. However, whenever insecticides are applied in closed spaces, in overhead applications, or under conditions of prolonged exposure, an approved respirator and other protective clothing should be worn. When these chemicals are applied as a fine mist, ULV (fogging), or dust, there is danger of breathing in the particles and contaminating skin and clothing. Wear an approved respirator with the proper cartridges for the type of chemical hazard involved. However, the pesticide label is your direct guide as to what precautions and protective clothing are needed when using the product (see Figure 4.6).

Respirators

Proper respirators might be required when using dusts, mists, pesticides with vapor action, or fumigants. Self-contained breathing equipment is mostly used in fumigation work, as required by labels or

FIGURE 4.6. Common safety clothing and equipment such as coveralls, goggles, knee pads, ear protection, respirator, and safety cap (helmet) should be used when applying pesticides in various situations. (Myers)

other regulations. Consult Chapter 20 for further discussion of safety considerations in the use of fumigants.

Respirators are intended to remove solid and liquid particles from the air breathed by a pesticide applicator. They always contain a filter and some type of absorbent material, such as activated charcoal, so that they can remove some gaseous vapors. However, these respirators are not suitable for working in atmospheres that include high concentrations of gases and vapors, or atmospheres low in oxygen. In these cases, a self-contained breathing apparatus must be used.

Respirator cartridges approved for urban pest management work (i.e., for use when fogging, misting, and dusting) should carry approval stickers from NIOSH, the National Institute for Occupational Safety and Health, for use with pesticides and organic vapors. There are at least two basic types of respirators suitable for pest management work: those that fully cover the face and those that cover only the nose and mouth. Either style of respirator will use similar NIOSH-approved cartridges, although different brands may use cartridges of different sizes or shapes. If a respirator is required, it is often as important to also protect the eyes from contamination with pesticide, so a full-face respirator would be the best choice. Wearing safety goggles in conjunction with a nose and mouth respirator is another option (see Figure 4.7).

Respirator cartridges come with instructions on how often to change them. Immediately throw away old cartridges so that they will not be confused with new ones. Be sure the new cartridges fit properly. Refer to the manufacturer's directions and supplemental information for other details of proper respirator use and maintenance.

Respirators should be cleaned after each use, or at least whenever the cartridges are changed.

Remove the cartridges before cleaning. Wash the respirator in warm soapy water, using a soft brush or a sponge. Rinse it thoroughly, and check for cracks or defects in the rubber or straps. Dry it with a cloth, or let it air dry. Before reinserting the cartridges (or inserting the new cartridges), test the respirator for a tight seal. Replace the cartridges and place the respirator in its carrying case. The best way to store the respirator is in a clean (change it regularly), sealed plastic storage bag. The supply of extra cartridges should also be kept in separate, sealed bags until ready for use. A separate compartment or box in the vehicle should be designated for respirators and other protective clothing, as well as the first-aid kit and other safety items. It is important that these be stored separately and not be exposed to any vapors, spills, dust, or other contamination while in the vehicle. Even though these procedures involving the storage, maintenance, and handling of safety equipment may sound like a lot of effort, the professional depends on these items to work properly and to be a source of protection on the job, not a hazard themselves.

Coveralls

As discussed previously, many pesticides can be absorbed through the skin. This can often occur without irritation, so clothing should be checked frequently for signs of contamination, such as moist spots, stains, or other residues. Never allow pesticide or contaminated clothing to remain in contact with the skin for longer than is absolutely necessary. Remove the clothing quickly when contamination is spotted, and wash the skin thoroughly with soap and water as soon as possible. Contaminated clothing should be laundered before being worn again. Work clothes used during pesticide applications should always be washed separately from other items. Use as much hot water as possible, with

FIGURE 4.7. Different types of respirators, with and without eye protection.

heavy-duty detergent. Prewash spot remover products can help remove heavy deposits or stains. In general, a pest management professional's work clothes should always have long sleeves and pant legs. Specialized protective clothing for most jobs can be regular coveralls, or many distributors carry disposable coveralls (use once and throw away), which are designed for use by pesticide applicators. These often have a special coating that sheds water or oil sprays that might fall on the body, or they may be made of Tyvek™ fabric, which sheds moisture from the outside but allows water vapor to pass through from the inside (and so reduces excessive sweating).

Other Safety Clothing

Pest management professionals often examine baseboards, peer into cracks and crevices and under tables and chairs, and crawl through crawlspaces, closets, and other areas where the lighting is poor. Many other situations make them prone to minor injury by simply bumping into objects. This often leads to head and eye injuries. The nature of pest management work often causes professionals to not look where they are going while concentrating on other details as they move about. Thus, all service vehicles should carry one or two hard hats, or bump caps. In fact, many accounts will require that you wear a hard hat when servicing their facilities. Safety shoes, with toe protection and chemical-resistant, nonskid soles, are recommended. Also, many progressive, safety-minded companies now require their service people to wear safety glasses at all times, even if a person does not need corrective lenses. This is a good policy that should be strictly enforced. Some health insurance carriers may actually require it.

Gloves should be worn to prevent pesticides from coming into contact with the hands. Do not use canvas or leather gloves, because they can accumulate pesticides and hold these residues close to the skin, where absorption will be increased. Select gloves that are made of (noninsulated or insulated) rubber, neoprene, polyethylene, or some other chemical-resistant material. Pesticide distributors generally have gloves suitable for use in pesticide application work. As with respirators, reusable gloves should be washed with soapy water occasionally (inside and out), rinsed thoroughly, checked for any leaks, and stored in separate plastic bags. Most distributors have disposable, tight-fitting safety gloves available, similar to medical gloves. Many professionals like to wear these because they are not bulky and allow the flexibility needed during a pesticide application. Be sure that these gloves meet the chemical-resistant glove requirements of pesticide labels.

Many professionals also carry heavy-duty rubber boots with nonskid soles for use on jobs where there might be excessive moisture or wet and greasy floors. Other situations in which such boots come in handy are on wet lawns and for outdoor work on rainy or snowy days. A final piece of safety equipment that many professionals use is knee pads. These are used primarily for comfort, and they remove any reason for avoiding the many tasks that require kneeling to inspect or treat under objects.

Vehicle Safety

One of the most hazardous aspects of any pest management professional's job is the period spent driving between jobs. Professionals often work under time pressure, and most routes take them through the more crowded portions of urban and suburban areas at peak traffic periods, when traffic is heaviest and accidents are most frequent. Driving skills and vehicle safety should be regarded as high safety priorities. Pest management professionals should be particularly careful to see that their cars and trucks have all necessary safety equipment in good repair. Brakes, lights, windshield wipers, mirrors, and horns should always be in good operating condition. Of course, the greatest safety feature is the driver. The driver must always be wide awake and alert to any driving hazards. Companies that schedule work that pressures service people to move quickly through each job and between jobs are taking a greater risk in maintaining quality service work and technician safety. Safe driving means driving defensively, and this requires that people maintain a calm, unhurried, patient attitude behind the wheel.

Besides the equipment needed to perform pest management work, a number of other safety items should be carried on the service vehicle (see Table 4.1). These include a fire extinguisher rated for all types of fires (i.e., for fire types A, B, and C). Usually this will be a 10- to 15-pound fire extinguisher, which is often mounted in a bracket near the driver's seat. This fire extinguisher should be serviced at regular intervals and never hidden under piles of debris, boxes, or other equipment inside the vehicle. Consult commercial fire extinguisher businesses for recommendations on the best type, installation, and maintenance.

Articles such as absorbent for pesticide spills, several large plastic garbage bags, brooms and a dustpan, protective clothing, spare work clothes, two to three gallons of water (e.g., in plastic milk jugs labeled as water), soap and detergent, clean rags, and towels have been mentioned previously. Another important item is a first-aid kit for medical emergencies. There are many types of first-aid kits available from medical supply houses. Beyond the standard array of bandages, compresses, gauzes, tape, scissors, forceps, and tourniquet, a physician can recommend additional medications to carry in the kit. (Some suggestions are made in Table 4.1.) These can include common drugs such as aspirin, salves or ointments for burns and scrapes, and perhaps specialized first-aid medications for pesticide poisoning incidents (e.g., syrup of ipecac to induce vomiting, and activated charcoal preparations for ingestion). Physicians should be able to advise on specific first-aid procedures relative to any special pesticides that might be used, though most experts now prefer that nonmedical personnel not attempt complicated first-aid procedures (see pp. 88–89). Many companies have designated a company physician, who is occasionally invited to speak at company safety meetings on topics such as first aid for pesticide poisoning incidents. Refer to the labels of the pesticide products for first-aid directions, or consult MSDS. Many companies require weekly, documented inspections of the first-aid kit and all other safety equipment carried in the service vehicle.

A final piece of safety equipment that should be carried in the vehicle is a detailed operating procedure book, outlining all the safety and emergency response procedures the professional will need to follow if problems arise in the field. This operating procedure book should include pesticide labels and an overview of your company's general policies on responsibilities and proper conduct in carrying out all day-to-day operations. In addition to procedures that will serve to protect technicians, there should be clear instructions, backed up with adequate training, on how the technician should respond in cases where the customer's family members, pets, or property are harmed or damaged by misapplications of pesticides or other accidental situations. In some cases the customer may be upset and accusing, or simply be concerned and fearful, that a pesticide poisoning has occurred. The technician may be uncertain as to what happened or may have happened, or convinced that no such exposure has occurred, but the technician must know how to respond correctly to the customer's concerns in a way that will help protect the employer from undue liability.

Safety With Mechanical Equipment

Safety precautions must be observed routinely and documented with all mechanical equipment, both in the shop and on the job.

All moving parts that drive power-driven

TABLE 4.1. Safety-related equipment that should be carried in all pest control service vehicles.

A safety and emergency response guidebook

A fire extinguisher (type ABC)

A first-aid kit, including:
- a one-ounce bottle of syrup of ipecac (one only)
- a small bottle of detergent solution
- a small container of salt (offer a solution of 1/2 teaspoon of salt per quart of water to aid shock victims)
- a pint jar of activated charcoal (available from some pharmacies)
- a shaped plastic airway for resuscitation
- adhesive bandages, compresses, adhesive tape
- a teaspoon
- a blanket (in a sealed plastic pouch)
- tongue depressors
- two small empty plastic jars with tight lids (to mix activated charcoal and collect vomitus for examination by doctor)
- a can of evaporated milk (with can opener)

A pesticide spill control kit, including:
- towels
- rags
- absorbent
- large plastic bags
- brooms and dustpan
- a shovel

Protective clothing (all enclosed in separate, clean plastic bags and tightly sealed), including:
- respirators
- spare respirator cartridges
- goggles
- extra clothing (coveralls)
- a bump cap
- gloves (chemical resistant)
- boots (waterproof and chemical resistant)

A cellular phone

Spare change for emergency telephone calls

An index card listing telephone numbers for local emergency medical services, poison control centers, and CHEMTREC

Clean water (2 to 3 gallons) and detergent to wash hands or other body parts

equipment, such as universal joints, drive shafts, belts, pulleys, and chains, should be covered with protective guards. This reduces the chance of catching clothing or fingers in these parts and provides protection if these parts suddenly fail (and would otherwise fly off the equipment). It is a good practice to assume that all external moving parts of power equipment are hazardous. Install adequate guards *before* an accident occurs, and keep them well maintained. Loose clothing, neckties, rings, and other jewelry should not be worn when working with power-driven equipment that has external moving parts; these items can easily become entangled in moving parts.

Grinding Machines

Each grinding machine used for sharpening tools must be marked plainly with "Do not operate without safety glasses," and a pair of these glasses must be kept on each machine so that it is impossible to overlook them when beginning work. Even when only a small bit of grinding is to be done, a tiny fragment of material thrown off by the grinding wheel can cause serious eye injury. A grinder should be securely fastened to a firm support; chipped or cracked grinding wheels should be discarded; and the speed of rotation should not exceed the recommended maximum. Homemade grinders are extremely dangerous if they lack proper covers, lighting, and tools.

Pumps and Hoses

All pumps used in the shop or on the job should be equipped with a pressure regulator and liquid return bypass. If there is no bypass, the pump may produce a greater pressure than the hose can withstand. Liquid shooting from a ruptured hose not only results in lost material but also can cause serious injury or damage to property and the environment. Serious physical injury can result even if the material in the hose is not poisonous.

The rated working pressure of a hose or spray equipment must equal, or preferably exceed, the maximum pressure that will ever be used in that hose or piece of equipment. Hoses become weakened with use and age, and old hoses often will not withstand high pressure. Hoses should be replaced as they show signs of age or wear.

All valves and gaskets that could leak pesticide must be checked regularly and kept in good repair. Sharp corners or projections that can cut should be filed down, removed, or covered on all pest control equipment.

Tanks and drums should be mechanically pressurized only when they are designed for this purpose, and only when a pressure gauge and safety valve are present and working properly. All tanks that are to be mechanically pressurized should bear the seal of the American Society of Mechanical Engineers (ASME) to indicate that the steel plate used in the tank is without defects and is the specified thickness, that only code-approved materials

are used, that proper welding techniques have been used by experienced professionals, and that all openings and supports are of the correct size. Handheld spray tanks should not be subjected to more than the manufacturer's recommended maximum pressure.

Ladders

The use of ladders is necessary in many kinds of pest management work. Accident records for workers who frequently use ladders show that using ladders is one of the most hazardous aspects of such work. A fall from a ladder, even from a short height, can cause serious injury. Any use of a ladder should include great caution.

The proper ladder should be selected for each job, and professionals should know how to use it safely. If a ladder is too short for the job, the professional may stand on a step much too high for safety. A ladder that is too long may stand too far from the wall against which it is placed, increasing the likelihood that it will slide out from under the professional while in use. This is especially likely if it is used on a hard, smooth floor or other surface, or on surfaces that have sand or other slippery residues. In either case, the wrong-sized ladder can be a very dangerous piece of equipment.

Ladders are commonly made of wood or an alloy of magnesium or aluminum. Wood ladders are generally poor conductors of electricity and are thus safer for use around electrical installations. Metal ladders should always be conspicuously labeled "Do not use around electric wires or equipment," because they are excellent conductors of electricity and can easily be the cause of a fatal accident if they come in contact with an electric circuit. Lightweight ladders sold for household use are not suitable for professional pest management work. Always choose a ladder rated for heavy commercial or construction use.

All ladders should be inspected when first purchased and should be reinspected frequently to be sure that all rungs or steps are tight and that there are no breaks in the side rails. Ladders should never be painted, as paint will cover small cracks and breaks. Wood ladders can be varnished or sealed with a clear wood sealer.

All ladders should be equipped with nonskid feet on the bottoms of the side rails. These feet must be set level on a firm foundation before the ladder is used.

When using any ladder, the top steps or rungs are not for standing. Do not use the top two steps of a stepladder or the top three rungs of a straight ladder. If the ladder is not long enough for you to reach your objective without using these top steps or rungs, a longer ladder is needed. When using a ladder to get to such places as a roof, be sure the ladder extends 3 to 4 feet above the edge of the roof. This provides a portion of the ladder to hang on to when getting on and off the roof.

Your shoes should be clean and dry when you climb a ladder. Hold on to the ladder with both hands while climbing. Do not carry anything in the hands while ascending or descending tall ladders. Use a rope and a bucket or bag to get tools to and from the desired place.

Electric Equipment

Electric power tools can be particularly hazardous in pest management work. All such equipment should be kept in good repair through regular inspection and maintenance.

Use only electric cords of sufficient capacity to handle the necessary current load. Ordinary household extension cords are usually made of No. 18 wire, which is insufficient for most pest management work. This wire is too light and the insulation is not heavy enough to give sufficient mechanical protection to the wire. Only heavily insulated, industrial-grade wire should be used, preferably in a wire size no lighter than No. 14, even in extension cords for a single electric light.

The flat three-wire extension cords commonly available are approved for indoor use only. Cords for outdoor use must have an additional outer covering over the wire to protect it.

Breaks in the wire or insulation should not be repaired or taped over. All breaks should be cut out of the wire, and the cord should be shortened or replaced. Do not splice electric cords. When making repairs on extension cords and light cords, use only heavy industrial-type plugs of a type approved by OSHA. These plugs are usually made of a tough plastic material and are moisture resistant. Each terminal and contact in the plugs has its own recess, so there is no chance of flashover between the wires. They also have no metal screws on the front, which could be shorted out by stray strands of wire, and each has a wire clamp to prevent tension on the connecting terminals. The usual electric plugs sold in hardware stores for household use are entirely unsuitable for professional use.

Be sure the outer insulation of the wire in extension cords and lights extends entirely inside the plugs or sockets, and that the wires inside are tightly attached to the terminals provided. A light socket attached to an extension cord should be well insulated and constructed of heavy metal, rubber, or porcelain. Extension lights used in pest management work should be of heavy-duty construction

and should have a reflector or a wire cage device to protect bulbs. Special rough-service bulbs are available; they do not break as easily as standard bulbs. Both the glass and the filaments inside are more rugged and can take more jarring.

Wiring on electric tools must meet all the standards of size, insulation, and installation mentioned for extension cords. In addition, all electrically driven tools must be wired for three-wire service so they can be easily grounded. Even heavy-duty equipment that is clean and in good repair may short out if not properly grounded. Improper grounding can cause fires and electric shocks.

Grounding Electric Tools. All electric circuits will ground themselves in one way or another. If they are not grounded properly, they may ground themselves through the body of the person holding or contacting the equipment, often with disastrous results. The best method of grounding is a completely grounded three-wire circuit. This electrical service extends all the way from the service entrance to a building, through three-wire circuits to three-hole outlets, and through a three-wire connector from the outlet into the tool you are using. Unfortunately, much industrial and household wiring is still of two-wire type and is not properly grounded. Always assume that any two-hole outlet is not grounded. If the outlet plug has three holes, it may or may not be grounded properly. It is necessary to check the circuit to be sure it is grounded every time that electric tools are used. There are simple devices available that indicate properly grounded circuits simply by plugging them into the receptacle. If the circuit is properly grounded, the electric tool can be directly plugged in with safety, or connected with a three-wire extension cord. If an extension cord is used, place the tester in the outlet end of the cord to be sure the cord is in good condition.

With two-hole outlets or improperly grounded outlets, it is necessary to use various devices in the line to be sure the circuit is grounded properly. The simplest of these is the common adapter. It is equipped with two prongs to push into the receptacle and a three-hole outlet plug on the other end to plug your tool (which has a three-wire connection) into. These adapters are equipped with a short green wire attached to the ground plug opening. A proper ground *must* be made from this wire.

If the wiring of a building is in metal conduits that extend all the way back to the main fuse or circuit breaker box, grounding can be accomplished by loosening the screw that holds the cover on the outlet box and attaching the green wire to it. The best way to create a proper ground is to solder or firmly clamp a 16-gauge copper wire (about 10- to 20-feet long) to the short grounding wire and clamp the other end to the nearest water pipe or to a water faucet. This will ensure a positive ground. The clamp must be secured to bare metal to get a good ground connection. Plastic or PVC plumbing cannot be used as a ground connection, because plastic is usually a nonconductor of electricity.

Use only bare wire to make a ground connection. It can be twisted or solid wire, but it should not be insulated, because insulation will hide any possible break in the wire.

Where multiple tool outlets are desired from one receptacle, a ground connector is used. This is a simple device consisting of a multiple-outlet electric box equipped with a three-pronged plug or a two-pronged plug and a ground wire and clamp. It is rigged in the same way as a two-way/three-way adapter, but it provides multiple outlets in which to plug lights and tools.

Ground Fault Interrupters. The best method of preventing electric shock is by use of **ground fault interrupters**. These devices are designed to break the circuit and shut off the current in a fraction of a second if there is even a tiny short in the circuit. Ground fault interrupters will work even though not connected to a grounded circuit. It is wise, however, to see that the circuit is grounded, as the ground fault interrupter will not provide protection if a drill or other tool directly contacts a hot wire.

When using an electric drill or hammer where there is any possibility of striking a buried object, such as a radiant heating pipe, water pipe, gas pipe, or electric conduit, it is necessary to use an *electric drill stopper* to avoid unnecessary and costly damage. These devices work by shutting off the electric current to the tool whenever the drill strikes any grounded object. They are used by connecting them to a properly grounded circuit and then plugging the drill into the device. They will not protect against electric shock if the drill comes in contact with a hot electric circuit.

Each professional must examine all electric cords and connections, before using them, to make certain that all insulation is sound and that all connections are tight. The power cord should be adequately insulated where it enters the tool. Periodically check that internal wear has not damaged insulation inside the tool. Failure to do this can cause a very serious and unnecessary accident.

Fuses. Most electric circuits now being installed in buildings are equipped with circuit breakers to prevent overloading. Older circuits in homes, however, are often equipped with fuses of the screw-in type. In household wiring, these fuses should never be heavier than 15 to 20 amps. The blowing of a fuse indicates that too heavy a load is being placed on the circuit, with a consequent danger of fire if the fuse does not burn out. Never replace household fuses with anything heavier than 15 to 20 amps, even on a temporary basis.

When using heavy-duty motorized electric equipment, the loads placed on the wiring at the time the equipment starts will frequently burn fuses. This problem can sometimes be overcome by using time-delay fuses, which can withstand a short overload without burning out. Use time-delay fuses of no more than 15 to 20 amps, and then only after an inspection shows the wiring to be in good condition.

It is impossible to overemphasize the need for observing these safety precautions in the use of electric equipment. Electric shocks are sudden and unexpected. Professionals in the crawlspace under a house or standing on a damp floor have little opportunity to save themselves when a shock occurs. Therefore, a high degree of caution and some preventative measures are well worth the time they require.

Prevention of shock should always be the first consideration when working around electricity. Electric shock is one of the most common causes of accidental death to workers in the pest management industry. Management personnel are justified in and, indeed, obligated to insist that employees wear shoes with soles and heels made of some nonconductive material.

If an electric shock should occur, it is very important to remove the victim from contact with the live conductor as quickly as possible. If possible, turning off the source of electric supply is the safest way to do this. Do not attempt to remove the victim from the live wire with your bare hands, because you may become another victim. Use rubber gloves, a dry stick or rope, a heavy-duty dry cloth (such as a coat), or some other nonconductor to keep from coming in contact with the current.

It is most important to apply first-aid measures as quickly as possible in severe electric accidents. Usually the victim will have stopped breathing, so cardiopulmonary resuscitation (CPR) must begin at once. If there is another person present, send that person to call for help, but begin CPR at once. If you are alone, leave the victim and call for help only after breathing has become strong and regular. There are many other injuries, such as burns and fractures, which may occur at the time of electric shock, but medical professionals may never have an opportunity to treat these problems if CPR is delayed. However, situations like this make apparent the need to have a cellular telephone in the service vehicle, so that emergency assistance can be quickly summoned before or during initiation of CPR.

Keep the victim protected from chilling by covering with blankets and by using other sources of warmth if available. If the victim should revive before medical assistance arrives, keep the person quiet, lying down, and warm.

Every pest management professional should be taught how to do CPR, since this procedure is critically important as first aid in cases of drowning, heart attack, inhalation of toxic gases, and many other mishaps. The accepted techniques are well established, and local Red Cross instructors or paramedics are usually available to teach such procedures. This form of safety training should be repeated, and practice sessions conducted, at least annually.

Fire Prevention

Fire is an ever-present danger in many pest management operations. Wood and paper about the shop, flammable solvents and pesticides, and electric- and gasoline-powered equipment all create the potential for fire. Every professional should check the workplace frequently for the presence of fire hazards and should correct any problems. If the local fire marshal does not check the premises regularly, the professional should call the state fire marshal or the local fire department to request an inspection and recommendations for the safety of everyone in the firm.

Uncovered containers of oil and oil-based pesticides, regardless of size, are an open invitation to fire and should not be permitted. Electric circuits should be checked regularly to see that they are not overloaded. Any mass of extension cords plugged into one outlet should be removed. One of the most serious fire hazards in pest management work is the accumulation of oily rags. These should always be washed or discarded promptly and not permitted to remain in service kits or on shelves, even overnight. If this is not possible, they must be kept in tightly closed metal containers since they can very easily start a serious fire by spontaneous combustion. Spontaneous combustion occurs when bacteria in the rags begin to degrade the oily residue. Their metabolic activity produces considerable amounts of heat, which may not escape the center of a rag pile. This can eventually cause the rags to ignite. If the rags are stored in a tightly sealed metal container, the bacteria are deprived of oxygen and cannot produce enough heat to ignite the rags. The best way to control a fire is to prevent it. Close attention to the removal of fire hazards is time and money well spent, because a serious fire

can easily cause injury and property damage that can put a firm out of business.

Smoking should be prohibited in areas where any flammable material is stored or handled. To reduce the chances of fire, storage areas should be well separated from any shop areas where gasoline engines are run or grinders are operated.

Welding on pest management equipment may be hazardous because dangerous fumes can be produced. Before any welding is started, the equipment should be cleaned thoroughly, and all solvents removed. The safest approach is to take the equipment to an experienced welder who will know what precautions should be taken before any repairs are made.

ENVIRONMENTAL PROTECTION

The professional must be alert to avoid contamination of the environment with pesticides. Remember that the environment is all of our surroundings and its many forms of life. Soil, air, and water are all part of the environment, as are all plants and animals. Care must be taken not to permit pesticides to contact any aspect of the environment except those where the pesticides are needed and allowed. Pesticides put in the wrong place, such as on the wrong plant or where the wrong animal can eat them, are pollutants. They may cause serious harm and are unlikely to do any good. Pesticides used properly are an aid to maintaining the environment or to protecting property and public health and thus are beneficial. The best immediate guide to the possible negative effects of a pesticide on the environment is found on the label. Read the label carefully and follow any precautions or directions closely and completely.

Different pesticides act in different ways after they are applied. Some generally break down fairly quickly into harmless products, even though they may be fairly toxic at the time of application. This is why some insecticides applied onto exposed surfaces for flea or cockroach control last for only a few weeks to a few months, and their effective residual capacity for controlling the target pest may actually be much shorter.

Some pesticides—primarily older types such as the chlorinated hydrocarbons DDT and chlordane (which are now banned for use in the United States and many other countries)—are considered bioaccumulators. Over time and with repeated exposure, they can build up to higher and higher concentrations in the bodies of humans or other animals. They may accumulate in the body to such an extent that they harm individual animals or other animals that eat them. Pesticides used cur-

Multiple Chemical Sensitivity (MCS), or Idiopathic Environmental Intolerance (IEI)

In recent years there has been increasing concern among certain segments of the public, the medical community, and the news media about apparent sensitivity to pesticides and other chemicals commonly used in our society. Some people have been diagnosed by their physicians as having multiple chemical sensitivity, or MCS, in which the immune system is thought to have been permanently compromised by previous exposures to chemicals, to the point that subsequent exposures to similar or even dissimilar chemicals may cause a variety of negative symptoms (e.g., headache, fatigue, dizziness, nausea, and/or watery eyes).

Other experts have termed this disorder idiopathic environmental intolerance, or IEI. MCS and IEI do not have any consistent set of symptoms or documented physiological basis, nor any clearly identified cause or causes. Thus, it is a rather controversial topic in the medical and public health communities. Pest management technicians encountering customers who claim to be sensitive to chemicals and pesticides, or who are suffering from MCS, should be extremely careful about any use of pesticides or other chemicals. Nonchemical pest management techniques should be relied on if at all possible, or any pesticide use should occur only after clear, legally enforceable liability waivers have been signed by the sensitive client (and, preferably, in consultation with the client's physician). Then, any pesticide applications should be conducted with great care and only after detailed discussion and explanation with the client. The use of baits or no-odor formulations should be emphasized, with no general or spot applications of residual insecticides. Many pest control firms will refuse to use any pesticides in situations where sensitive persons or MCS patients are involved.

rently are generally considered to have very low or no bioaccumulation hazard.

Persistent pesticides (e.g., some termiticides) break down slowly after being applied and can remain in the environment without change for a long time. This can allow long-term pest control and may be a desirable characteristic if the pesticide does not harm non-target organisms and does not have a tendency to become mobile within the environment (e.g., to leach through soil and into groundwater). Persistent pesticides usually do not react readily with air, sunlight, or heat. They are not easily broken down by microorganisms in the soil

and are only slightly soluble in water. The most notable examples of this type of persistent pesticide are some of those used in termite control, along with some of the pyrethroids used in residual applications for crawling insect control. When placed in the soil, these pesticides persist longer than they would on exposed surfaces, because they are not exposed to sunlight and temperature extremes.

Pesticides applied as power sprays can drift for great distances. Outdoor applications should generally not be made when the wind velocity can carry the pesticide from the target site to an unwanted site. Wind velocities greater than three to four miles per hour can easily carry pesticides into adjacent yards, where they can endanger children, pets, wildlife, or honeybee hives. Drift of insecticide sprays into bodies of water, such as ponds or streams, can cause fish kills or other damage.

Pest control firms that can use industrial herbicides, particularly many of the soil sterilent herbicides, should pay particular attention to the weather so as to avoid making applications immediately before a heavy rain storm. The flushing action of a heavy rain can easily carry the freshly applied material off the target plants or soil, killing plants in areas where herbicidal action was not intended. These chemicals (as well as some insecticides) can also be washed into streams, with harmful effects to fish and other aquatic life. Many soil sterilant herbicides wash off easily from the surface of the soil and should not normally be used on steep slopes (see label precautions).

Soil termiticides are applied in relatively high volumes for subterranean termite control. They are generally applied to limited and protected areas under and around foundations. They bond closely with the soil particles to which they are applied, and they do not disperse significantly through the soil but tend to stay where they are placed. The professional should avoid treating surface soil on slopes (which is not permitted in most label directions anyway), because treated surface soil or the pesticide itself may be washed down the slope and into a stream or pond, where it may injure plants, fish, or other wildlife. Also, do not perform the regular soil treatment used in termite control when wells or cisterns are near; contamination of a water supply will create a serious hazard. Tile drains around homes can lead to the movement of termiticides into bodies of water, though such movement is difficult to ascertain.

The potential to contaminate subslab plenums or heating and air-conditioning ducts has been discussed previously. All termite control professionals must be very careful to avoid this sort of contamination, and the use of effective baits for subterranean termite control may be especially preferred in situations where contamination of adjacent water resources would be a significant possibility if soil treatments were used.

Pest management professionals must be particularly aware of sensitive areas, such as food handling establishments, hospitals, and other locations where young, elderly, or ill persons are located. Careful consideration of all pets and their eating areas must be kept in mind. Pesticides used in or around such areas should be the least toxic and safest of the effective materials available. They should be applied in a manner that avoids contamination or undue exposure.

PESTICIDE POISONING

Pest management professionals should know the basic symptoms of pesticide poisoning and the first-aid procedures appropriate for the chemicals they use. It is important that they know what kinds of sickness might be caused by these chemicals, both for their own safety and in case someone else should suffer some overexposure as a result of pest management activities. Do not try to act as a physician in cases of pesticide poisoning. Rather, immediately perform the first-aid procedures recommended on the label or the MSDS, to help stabilize the victim before medical help is available.

There are two kinds of clues to pesticide poisoning: symptoms and signs. Some are feelings that only the person who has been poisoned can notice—such as nausea or headache. These are symptoms. Other effects, like vomiting, muscle twitches, pinpoint pupils, or passing out, can be noticed by others. These are signs. Therefore, the professional should know:

- what an individual's feelings (symptoms) might mean
- what signs of poisoning to look for in coworkers and others

Pesticides in the same chemical group will cause basically the same types of poisoning symptoms and signs. These may be mild or severe, and either rapid or slow in their appearance (after exposure), depending on the specific chemical involved and the amount absorbed. However, the pattern of illness caused by one type of pesticide chemical is always the same. Having some of the symptoms or signs of pesticide poisoning does not always indicate poisoning, because other kinds of illness can have similar effects. For example, headache and a general feeling of distress and nausea are common symptoms of the flu. It is the pattern of symptoms that makes it possible to tell one kind of sickness from another.

Get medical advice quickly if unusual symptoms begin at work, during or following pesticide exposure, or later the same day. If you suspect a person has been poisoned, do not leave that person alone until either medical help is available or the apparent crisis is well past. Do not let yourself or anyone else become dangerously sick before calling your physician or going to a hospital emergency room. It is better to be too cautious than too late for the medical help to do any good. If at all possible, bring the container or the label of any suspected pesticide involved in the poisoning to the physician or the emergency room personnel. Do not carry the pesticide container in the passenger compartment of the vehicle during the ride to the hospital or doctor's office. Try to have a copy of the pesticide label, the MSDS, and any other facts associated with the poisoning situation.

Symptoms and Signs of Pesticide Poisoning

Organophosphates

These pesticides (e.g., chlorpyrifos, propetamphos and diazinon) act on the nervous system. The signs and symptoms go through stages, in the following order:

Mild poisoning
- fatigue
- headache
- dizziness
- blurred vision
- too much sweating and salivation
- stomach cramps or diarrhea

Moderate poisoning
- inability to walk
- weakness
- chest discomfort
- muscle twitches
- constriction of the pupils in the eye
- earlier symptoms become more severe

Severe poisoning
- unconsciousness
- severe constriction of the eyes (pinpoint eyes)
- muscle twitches
- secretions from the mouth and nose
- breathing difficulty (lungs seem to fill up)
- death (if not treated)

Illness may be delayed a few hours, but if signs or symptoms start more than 12 hours after exposure to the organophosphate pesticide, some other illness besides pesticide poisoning is probably involved. In other cases, repeated exposure to relatively small doses of organophosphate or carbamate insecticides can result in rather sudden pesticide poisoning, even if the last exposure seemed minor. Check with your physician to be sure.

Carbamates

The only carbamates likely to cause illness on the job (e.g., Sevin®, Baygon® and Ficam®) act very similarly to the organophosphates just discussed. They produce the same signs and symptoms, but treatment of carbamate poisoning is usually easier for the physician. For these reasons, carbamates are generally considered safer than organophosphates.

Fumigants and Solvents

Too much exposure to these materials may make a person seem drunk. The signs and symptoms are

- poor coordination
- slurred words
- confusion
- sleep

Repeated exposure to the fumigant methyl bromide has caused permanent internal injury without early signs or symptoms of poisoning. A fatal dose can be absorbed before symptoms appear.

Inorganics

Large single doses of most inorganic pesticides (e.g., boric acid) cause vomiting and stomach pain. The signs and symptoms of poisoning depend on the mineral the pesticide is made from. However, these materials can be quite hazardous because they are generally formulated with a high rate of active materials. There are often no direct antidotes for their toxic effects.

Pyrethroids

Symptoms and signs of pyrethroid poisoning are very rare in pest management work because these chemicals (e.g., resmethrin, permethrin [Dragnet®, Torpedo®, Flee®], cypermethrin [Demon®, Cynoff®, Prevail®], cyfluthrin [Tempo®], and deltamethrin [Suspend®, DeltaDust®]) are generally of low acute toxicity to mammals. Some allergic-type reactions, especially respiratory responses similar to asthma or intense hay fever (irritated and watery eyes, sneezing), can occur. Some of the newer residual pyrethroids can cause tingling or irritation of facial skin for a period of several hours after skin exposure to dust or spray particles. Full face shields and respirators prevent or greatly reduce these symptoms.

Emergency First-Aid Procedures for Pesticide Poisoning

General first-aid instructions for pesticide poisoning are as follows:

1. Give mouth-to-mouth respiration or CPR if breathing or pulse has stopped.
2. Stop the exposure by either washing the pesticide off and removing clothing (skin or eye exposure), removing the victim from the source of vapors or dust (inhalation exposure), or cautiously administering milk or water if the pesticide was swallowed and the person is still conscious and can swallow (ingestion exposure). Do not induce vomiting.
3. Call for medical help.
4. Read the pesticide container or label for further instructions, and save the label for use by the medical responders.

Medical antidotes should be prescribed or given only by a qualified physician or emergency medical technician. These professionals have access to detailed databases on emergency medical treatment for all pesticides, so their treatment of the poisoned individual will be greatly facilitated by access to the labels for the products involved.

For severe skin exposure, remove the pesticide from the skin as quickly as possible. Remove all contaminated clothing quickly. Prompt washing (rinsing for fifteen minutes with lukewarm water, then washing with soap and water) of the contaminated skin may prevent sickness even when the dose or spill is large. Do not forget to clean any pesticide from the hair or from under the fingernails. Wettable powders, emulsions, microencapsulations, and other suspensions are generally easy to remove by thoroughly rinsing with plain water. Solutions of pesticides in oil or other solvents are harder to remove without soap or a detergent. Detergents work better. (Washrooms at the firm's office and emergency field washing facilities should be supplied with detergents rather than plain soap.) Dry the victim and wrap in clean blankets, clothing, or other protective garments before seeking medical assistance.

If a pesticide dust or vapor is inhaled, go to fresh air right away, if at all possible. If you come upon a person who has been overcome by an inhaled poison, such as a fumigant or an inert gas, within a confined space or other area where there is restricted airflow, do not enter that potentially dangerous and life-threatening area unless absolutely necessary. Whenever possible, wait for an emergency medical technician or other responder who has the proper protective equipment to remove and treat the victim. If the victim cannot be removed, open all windows and doors to maximize ventilation with fresh air. Loosen tight clothing. Apply artificial respiration if breathing has stopped. Then, seek medical help as soon as possible, especially if any symptoms arise. Until help arrives, keep the victim quiet and warm, and apply artificial respiration if breathing stops.

If a pesticide is splashed into the mouth or swallowed:

- rinse the mouth with plenty of water
- go, or be taken, to a physician immediately
- do not induce vomiting, vomiting is generally no longer recommended (see label directions)

If a pesticide is splashed into the eyes:

- hold the eyelids open and wash with lots of clean, running, lukewarm water
- continue rinsing for at least 15 minutes
- do not use chemicals or drugs in rinse water

For chemical burns of the skin:

- wash skin with large quantities of lukewarm water, for 15 to 30 minutes
- remove contaminated clothing
- immediately cover burned area with loose clothing or gauze
- avoid the use of ointments, grease, powders, or other drugs
- treat shock by keeping patient prone, warm, and comfortable until medical help arrives

The general aim of first-aid measures is to help prevent further absorption or exposure to the chemical. Speed is essential; start first-aid measures at once. Consult the pesticide label (if available) for instructions on practical first-aid procedures. If other people are available, have them call for medical help immediately. If this is not possible, the nature of the poison and the situation should dictate whether the first action should be a call for medical help or the application of first aid to the victim. Save the pesticide container and a sample of the toxic material for use by the medical personnel when they arrive.

Anticoagulants

Small repeated dosages of anticoagulants (e.g., brodifacoum, bromadiolone, difethialone, diphacinone, and chlorophacinone) are of greatest danger. Vitamin K or K_1 are antidotal but must be administered by a physician (or a veterinarian, in case of pet poisonings). With the second-generation anticoagulants (e.g., brodifacoum, bromadiolone, and difethialone), poisoned animals may have to be monitored closely for several weeks, and Vitamin K_1 may have to be administered repeatedly, depending on the results of prothrombin tests. In severe cases with any type of anticoagulant, a whole blood transfusion may be necessary.

Nonanticoagulants

If the victim has recently (within 3 hours) consumed cholecalciferol (e.g., Quintox®) bait, induce vomiting. Administer 2 to 4 teaspoons of syrup of ipecac followed by large quantities of liquid, or use other methods. Consult a physician or a veterinarian immediately.

The toxic action of bromethalin (Fastrac®, Eaton's Bromethalin®) is caused by the uncoupling of the basic energy conversion process in body cells. Induce vomiting if the bait was recently ingested, and consult a physician (or veterinarian) immediately.

Poison Control Centers

Poison control centers have been established in most states and many local areas to provide information to the public and the medical profession concerning the prevention of and proper response to accidents involving poisonous materials, such as pesticides. These services are available on a 24-hour basis. The pest management professional should contact the local health department or medical society to determine the location and telephone number of the nearest poison control center. Keep this telephone number near your telephone, in your wallet, in your service kit, and posted inside your service vehicle.

In case of a poisoning accident, tell the attending physician the poison involved and, in case the physician does not have the information at hand, how to reach the poison control center. Poison control centers generally provide emergency or other treatment information only to physicians. Laypersons should first call their physician or a hospital, and call the poison control center only if a physician cannot be reached.

As an emergency service to users who need information on first aid in cases of poisoning, most pesticide labels now carry a 24-hour hotline telephone number. This is usually a toll-free number with an 800 area code. Again, check the labels of pesticides you use for these numbers, or for other first-aid instructions.

Pesticide manufacturers in the United States have also set up a 24-hour hotline for emergency information to users and the medical profession. This is called the CHEMTREC hotline. The CHEMTREC hotline can be reached, toll free, in the United States by dialing (800) 424-9300. The CHEMTREC service provides information on proper responses to all pesticide accidents, including poisoning incidents and pesticide spills, and on the location of cleanup teams for pesticide spills.

There is also a National Pesticide Information Center (NPIC) that can be contacted for general information on the health effects, symptoms, and treatment of pesticide poisoning, as well as many other general topics related to pesticides and pesticide safety. The telephone number for this service is (800) 858-PEST (858-7378), or it is available through the Internet at **http://npic.orst.edu/**. This website also lists the Human and Animal Poison Control Centers available in the United States (at **http://npic.orst.edu/emerg.htm**).

SUPPLEMENTARY READING MATERIAL

Ellenhorn, M. J., and D. G. Barceloux. *Medical Toxicology: Diagnosis and Treatment of Human Poisoning.* New York: Elsevier, 1988. 1,512 pp.

Goldfrank, L. R., ed. *Toxicologic Emergencies: A Complete Handbook in Problem Solving.* New York: Appleton-Century-Crofts,1982. 432 pp.

Lewis, R. J., Sr. *Sax's Dangerous Properties of Industrial Materials.* Vols. 1–3. New York: Van Nostrand Reinhold, 1992.

Purdue Pesticide Programs series documents: E-62, *Pesticides and Personal Safety* (15 pp.); PPP-21, *Pesticides and Container Management* (11 pp.); PPP-25, *Pesticides and Applicator Certification* (15 pp.); PPP-26, Pesticides and Their Proper Storage (2 pp.); PPP-27, *Pesticides and Commercial Vehicle Maintenance* (2 pp.); PPP-28, *Pesticides and Spill Management* (2 pp.); PPP-30, *Pesticides and Wildlife* (39 pp.); PPP-35, *Pesticides and Water Quality* (57 pp.); PPP-37, *Pesticides and Material Safety Data Sheets* (34 pp.); Purdue University Cooperative Extension Service, West Lafayette, IN 47907.

Recognition and Management of Pesticide Poisonings. 5th ed. Washington, D.C.: U.S. Environmental Protection Agency, 1999. EPA-735-R-98-003. 243 pp.

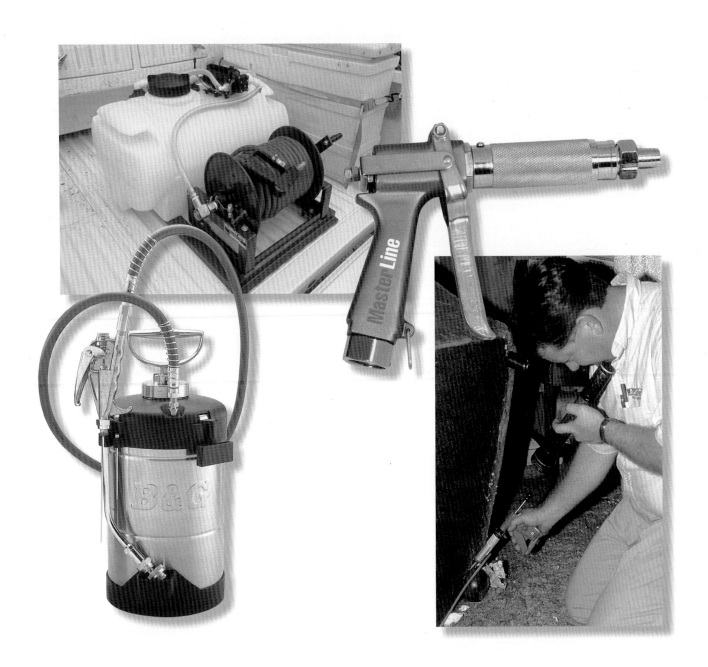

CHAPTER 5 | Equipment

Regardless of how well trained and knowledgeable a pest management professional may be, effective pest management cannot be achieved unless the professional is backed up with high-quality, dependable equipment. It is essential to know how to choose the equipment best suited to each job and how to use it properly and safely to obtain the best results.

Generally, it is wise to buy the best equipment available. Downtime due to faulty equipment can be expensive to the overall company operation, as well as annoying to your clients. Moreover, cheap equipment can be potentially hazardous to people and the environment because it may not provide adequate safety features, or might break during use, causing a pesticide spill. Using cheap or "make do" equipment can result in injuries, and possibly even lawsuits. Simply stated: With pest management equipment, you get what you pay for—it pays to use and maintain quality equipment.

Quality in equipment means not only good, durable construction, but also good design that gives it a professional appearance. Moreover, good equipment must be maintained and thus, *kept* looking professional. The reaction customers have to a pest management service and the professional is often influenced by the appearance of the equipment. Dirty, unkempt, or malfunctioning equipment is certain to reflect negatively; good, attractive equipment presents a professional image, and helps instill confidence in the client.

This chapter has three objectives: (1) to acquaint the professional with the basic types of pest management equipment and to help him or her understand how they function; (2) to assist the professional in selecting the proper tool for a specific job; and (3) to provide information on equipment maintenance to ensure safe, economical, and efficient use of each piece of equipment.

To reach these objectives, this chapter is divided into the following topics:
- Equipment for Applying Pesticides,
- Vacuum Devices and Other Specialized Equipment,
- Equipment for Conducting Inspections, and
- Equipment Maintenance.

Equipment specific to termites, flies, rodents, urban wildlife, birds, and safety are discussed within their respective chapters.

Certainly, there are many different types of pest management equipment and each type may have different models. This chapter focuses only on the **basic models** of each equipment group. New equipment technology and improvements to existing equipment are ongoing, so even a well-equipped professional needs to periodically re-examine equipment in order to profit by new developments. To keep up to date, all pest management professionals must review current trade magazines and equipment information brochures, attend educational conferences and seminars, and visit and talk with their local suppliers. These sources of information are essential in operating a profitable company in today's competitive climate.

EQUIPMENT FOR APPLYING PESTICIDES

Equipment for applying pesticides can be placed into four general groups:

1. Bait Applicators
2. Sprayers
3. Equipment for applying aerosols and "fogs"
4. Dusters

Bait Applicators

Over the past decade or so, baits have become one of the most widely used formulations for the control of cockroaches, termites, ants, and some occasional invaders (see Chapters 6, 7, 9, and 12). As a result, new bait application technology is continuously emerging. A host of products are now available that make baiting efforts convenient, effective, and professional.

The most popular baits used today are formulated as gels, powders, granules, and solid composites. These formulations are packaged primarily in four ways: (1) as ready-to-use, disposable syringe-style cartridges that the applicator merely squeezes to apply to the bait; (2) as pressurized gels in cans (similar in appearance to an ordinary aerosol can) in which the baits can be applied directly from the can; (3) as prepackaged 30 g and bait tubes, (depending on the brand) that are loaded into an applicator, and (4) within tamper-resistant bait containers.

Bait applicators (also referred to as bait "guns") are available in several different models. Each of these guns basically achieves the same purpose, but differences exist in design, durability and style as well as the amount and calibration of the bait to be delivered. Some professionals prefer to not use bait guns at all and use the prepackaged disposable bait syringes. Others use the inexpensive plastic guns that have utility for relatively short periods of baiting. One of the biggest issues with gel baits for most professionals is being able to control bait leakage. Bait leakage is a concern relative to wasting bait, baiting convenience (having to constantly use a rag), and the safety issues of not having bait drip onto surfaces and/or floor.

To avoid some of the problems associated with the inexpensive bait applicators, some professionals prefer more sophisticated bait applicators (Figure 5.1). Some bait applicators are adaptations of medicine injectors that are used in the animal health industry. Professionals that use bait guns as a major component of their baiting programs appreciate the high-quality durability and performance features of this level of applicator. High-quality bait applicators allow for precise baiting doses, virtually no leakage, and help to avoid underbaiting and overbaiting—important cost and safety issues for any pest management company.

Various dispensing tips on the guns allow the professional to administer baits into various types and sizes of cracks and crevices under different circumstances that in turn provide for effective placement into areas where the bait is most likely to be encountered by the target pests such as cockroaches, ants, or termites.

Some bait guns offer a variety of useful accessories such as plastic and metal tips, extension tips, and flashlight attachments. Another accessory, the bait holster (or pouch) can be worn on the belt for easy carrying and storage of the applicator. A holster also enables the professional to work more effectively. Because the PMP frequently needs to have his or her hands free while performing routine pest control work—especially for crack and crevice baiting operations (e.g., moving boxes, furniture, disassembling equipment, etc.). This results in needing to lay the equipment down "momentarily." The more this is done, the greater the chance of leaving the bait gun behind on the job. Like a flashlight holder, the bait applicator holster helps to minimize the chances of losing the bait gun. Holsters also present a professional image to clients. Most holsters are designed with pouches to hold and store the different tips, and storage pouches to hold bait tubes.

Exterior Insect Bait/Monitoring Stations

In addition to the bait stations that are specifically designed for subterranean termite control (see Chapter 7), various **exterior** stations are available that are designed to be used for nontermite pest baiting and/or monitoring programs. These stations can provide valuable services for both the residential and commercial market especially since many professionals now offer quarterly service options to the homeowner.

The stations can be baited with liquid, granular, and/or gel baits (see Figure 5.2). Such baiting options offer good management strategies for insect pests such as ants, cockroaches, termites, crickets, and other occasional pests. Some stations are designed to be "multipurpose," meaning that they can be used for either baiting and/or as pest monitoring stations. For general insect monitoring insert sticky glue boards into the stations. Some models also allow the stations to be both baiters

FIGURE 5.1. A high-quality bait applicatior with a 30 g syringe containing a gel bait. For effective bait applications for cockroaches, small amounts of bait are carefully applied using crack-and-crevice tips as close to cockroach harborage as possible.

FIGURE 5.2. Exterior bait/monitoring stations for pests other than, or in addition to, termites can provide an excellent urban IPM tool for pest professionals.

FIGURE 5.3. Recent models of compressed-air sprayers come equipped with important applicator and safety features that are important for regulatory and label compliance purposes.

and termite monitoring devices containing various types of wood strips and even termite attractants (refer to Chapter 7, and to the discussion in this chapter on termite baits).

Sprayers

Sprayers vary from the hand-pumped flit gun with a tank capacity of as little as one cup to large hydraulic machines powered by gasoline engines having tanks that can hold several hundred gallons of pesticide formulation. All sprayers have several basic characteristics in common. There is usually a tank, a method of pressurizing the liquid, a pesticide delivery line within the tank leading to a control valve, and another delivery line leading from the control valve to a nozzle. All other items found on any sprayer, whether it is the simplest of flit guns or the most complicated of power sprayers, are merely accessories and are incidental to this basic design.

The majority of sprayers and sprayer systems used in structural pest management operations are of three general types: (1) handheld compressed air sprayers and related sprayers, (2) large-volume sprayers ("power rigs"), and (3) electric mid-volume sprayer systems.

Handheld Compressed-Air Sprayers

The handheld compressed-air sprayer (see Figure 5.3), is one of the "workhorses" of everyday pest management equipment. To this day, this sprayer remains one of the most widely used pieces of equipment in the industry, although bait guns and various other tools have reduced the reliance on sprayers as the primary pesticide application tool.

In addition, the handheld sprayer is probably the single piece of equipment the general public most

readily associates with a pest management professional. A thorough understanding of the compressed-air sprayer—its basic construction, how it works, how to maintain it, and how to make repairs—can save time, money, embarrassment, and even lawsuits.

Components. Three major parts make up the compressed-air sprayer: (1) the tank, (2) the pump unit, and (3) the applicator wand and hose. (Refer frequently to Figure 5.4).

The **tank** forms the body of the sprayer. Tank capacities range in size from 1/2 gallon to 3 gallons. The tanks on professional-level tanks are made of stainless steel to resist the corrosive nature of many pesticides formulations. The tank serves two purposes: (1) it is the reservoir for the spray mixture, and (2) it acts as a pressure chamber. A **discharge tube** is attached on the inside of the tank. The air pressure inside the tank forces the spray mixture through this tube and into the hose.

The **pump unit** consists of a *pump cylinder* containing a *plunger rod* and various soft *gaskets* and *valves*. The pump unit is hand-operated to generate air pressure inside the tank.

The **applicator wand** is comprised of the *valve trigger* and the *nozzle*, and is connected to the tank via a synthetic-rubber (usually neoprene) **hose** that acts as the delivery tube from the tank to the applicator wand. Some wands have a stubby-nose design, but most sprayers today have an **extension tube** between the valve and the nozzle. The extension tube provides reach when applying pesticides into and behind objects, cabinets, etc. It also helps

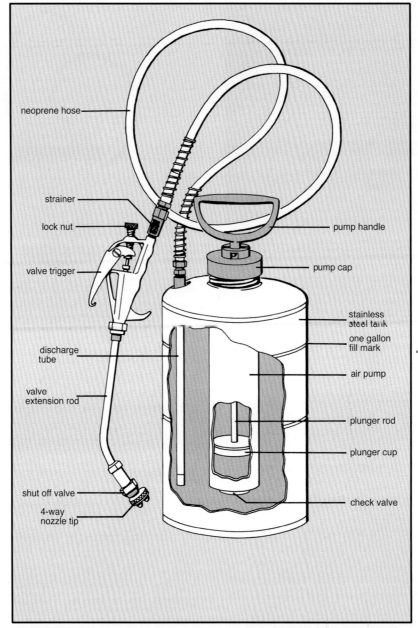

neoprene hose

strainer

lock nut

valve trigger

discharge
tube

valve
extension rod

shut off valve

4-way
nozzle tip

pump handle

pump cap

stainless
steel tank

one gallon
fill mark

air pump

plunger rod

plunger cup

check valve

FIGURE 5.4. The major parts of a compressed-air sprayer. A pressure gauge and/or regulator are also important accessories to the sprayer. (Provonsha)

to reduce splashback of pesticides onto the applicator's hands and body. Extension tubes are now available in lengths varying from 9 to 60 inches to meet the various needs for treating overhead and out of reach areas. Some manufacturers offer telescoping applicator wands for convenience.

The **nozzle** is the smallest component on the sprayer, but it plays a large role in applying the pesticide safely and in the right doses. Much of the effectiveness of a pesticide application depends on the proper functioning of the nozzle. Nozzle tips are designed to give specific shapes of spray at a set pressure. Most nozzles on the handheld sprayer

offer a four-way "multitip" that can produce two different flow rate *pin-stream* spray patterns and two *flat-fan* spray patterns (see Figure 5.5). The applicator can easily change from a pin stream to a fan spray by merely rotating the tip. The appropriate nozzle opening for each particular situation should always be carefully considered to produce the safest and most effective spray pattern (see Figure 5.6).

Pin-stream nozzles produce solid streams of spray and are used to spray insecticides into various cracks and crevices, or in some cases, to project a solid stream of spray. Specialized nozzles are avail-

FIGURE 5.5. Most nozzles on the handheld sprayer offer a four-way multitip that can produce two pin-stream spray patterns and two flat-fan spray patterns. The applicator can easily and quickly change from a pin stream to a fan spray by merely rotating the tip.

able with one pin-stream orifice adapted to permit the use of a plastic or metal **crack and crevice extension tube**. This is an extremely useful nozzle as it permits the professional to apply pesticide **directly** into cracks and crevices with little worry of spilling or splashing pesticide on surrounding surfaces. Various crack and crevice tips may also be available that allow for precise pesticide applications into areas where they will not contaminate surfaces, foods, or people.

Flat-fan nozzles produce a fan-type spray pattern. These patterns provide an even coat of spray on flat surfaces such as a wall, and may also be used to apply pesticide into a crack wherever there is room enough for such application. It should be noted, however, that liquid dispersed into a crack using a fan pattern usually will not penetrate as deeply into the crack as it will when applied as a pin stream. On multitip nozzles, the smaller fan opening typically produces an 80 degree **fine-fan** spray pattern; the larger orifice produces a 50 degree **coarse-fan** spray pattern. The latter nozzle delivers more than twice as much spray per minute as the fine spray nozzle. See Table 5.1.

Table 5.1. The amount of spray delivered from a sprayer depending on the nozzle orifice selected.

Pattern	Spray Angle	Ounces of Spray Per Minute @ 20 psi
Coarse fan	50 degrees	14.08
Fine fan	80 degrees	6.40
Broad pin stream	straight	8.96
Fine pin stream	straight	4.48
C & C straw	Straight	3.84
Aerosol tip straw	straight	7.04

The application wand and pump unit contain various soft gaskets and valves that can be referred to as **"sprayer software." This software is critically important to the proper functioning of the sprayer.**

When sprayer software becomes worn or broken, or is improperly installed, the sprayer will malfunction or constantly leak. Sprayer software must be inspected and replaced regularly (refer to sprayer maintenance discussion). Many plastic components of today's sprayers are constructed with highly durable plastics (e.g., Viton®) that provide relatively long life. Such durability is especially important for the check valve on the bottom of the pump unit and for the seat gaskets used at the nozzle tips.

Daily use. Proper daily use of the sprayer is critical for effective insect control, safety, and for keeping the sprayer in good repair long term. The following discussion concerns the **key basics** for effective and safe daily use of the sprayer.

Correct **filling of the sprayer** is important to achieve a good mixture of water and insecticide. Whenever a sprayer is filled, the following tips are important:

- Use clean water; allow the faucet to run for a several seconds before collecting.
- Never place the pump unit of the sprayer on the ground where it will collect dust, dirt, and possible contaminants that may clog the sprayer. Also, the pump unit may leave an undesirable residue of pesticide on the floor.

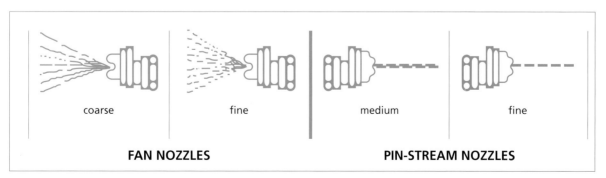

FAN NOZZLES — coarse, fine

PIN-STREAM NOZZLES — medium, fine

FIGURE 5.6. The spray patterns produced by the fan and pin-stream orifices on a four-way nozzle tip.

How a Compressed-Air Sprayer Works

The tank should be filled with liquid to about 75% of its capacity. The remaining space allows for a compartment of air. This air supplies the pressure that is applied to the tank mixture via the pump unit. When the plunger of the pump is stroked, air is forced through a check valve at the base of the pump cylinder into the tank. The air rises through the liquid to the top of the tank. As more air is pumped into the tank, the air becomes compressed and exerts pressure back onto the liquid. The amount of pressure that builds up in the tank is measured as pounds per square inch, or psi. When the discharge valve on the applicator wand is opened, liquid is forced through the discharge tube into the delivery hose to the application wand and out through the nozzle. Most sprayers today utilize a no-drip feature allowing the valve to shut off the liquid at the nozzle tip.

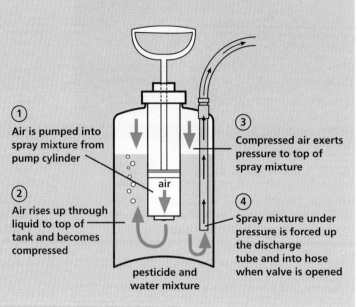

1. Air is pumped into spray mixture from pump cylinder
2. Air rises up through liquid to top of tank and becomes compressed
3. Compressed air exerts pressure to top of spray mixture
4. Spray mixture under pressure is forced up the discharge tube and into hose when valve is opened

air

pesticide and water mixture

- Unless otherwise directed by insecticide label directions, mix insecticide concentrates into the sprayer by first filling the tank about 1/4 full with water; then add concentrate, and then add remaining water to the tank.
- Fill the tank to only 3/4 of its total capacity. (Most sprayers will have a one-gallon indentation mark on the tank). The remaining 25% of space comprises the essential air pressure chamber and should not be filled with liquid.
- Gently shake (agitate) the filled sprayer to ensure proper mixture of the pesticide and water. (With most pesticides, the sprayer should be agitated periodically throughout the day. Some pesticides require more frequent agitation than others. Check the label of the specific pesticide).

Pressurizing the sprayer. Establishing and maintaining correct pressure on the sprayer are important for not only obtaining good insect control, but for safety and other reasons as well. For example:

- Sprayer pressure affects the *amount* of insecticide applied, and the *type* of pesticide coverage. Too much or too little pressure often causes spotty and uneven coverage—that, in turn, results in poor insect control.
- High pressure is seldom necessary. Furthermore, excessive pressure may increase the hazards to the applicator and to the public because

of the possibility of hoses bursting under pressure. Also, insecticide particles at high pressures tend to bounce off the intended surface. Not only does this waste the insecticide, but the pesticide may drift onto other people, objects, food, or food-preparation surfaces.
- Continual excessive pressure on the sprayer also causes premature wear and damage to the sprayer software.
- In some food facilities, regulatory agencies allow no more than 20 psi of pressure to prevent unnecessary pesticide drift into the air.
- Some insecticide labels dictate the particular pressure that is appropriate for an application against a specific pest.

Therefore, using the correct pressure on a sprayer is very important. As such, the professional should be able to accurately measure the pressure in the sprayer at all times. Some sprayers offer accessories such as pressure regulators (see discussion below). Sprayers can also be equipped with a pressure gauge. A pressure regulator and gauge allows the professional to control and monitor the pressure in the tank at all times. Not only is this important to prevent using excessively high pressures, but also to monitor the pressure drop in the tank while the pesticide is being sprayed.

Selecting the correct pressure for the sprayer varies according to the type of insecticide application. For example, for crack and crevice treatments, pressures of 10 psi and lower are most effective. Achieving pressures in this range requires only two to four strokes of the pump handle with a full one-gallon sprayer.

General and spot treatments are most often performed using either the fine or coarse fan nozzle openings. A general, effective operating pressure for fan spray applications is between 20 to 25 psi. This pressure produces a uniform spray pattern. Fine fan applications at these pressures would be used to apply a fine residual spot treatment at the base of wall. At slightly higher pressures (e.g., 25 to 35 psi), a coarse fan application can be used to treat along outside foundation walls. To achieve 20 to 25 psi in a one-gallon sprayer when full requires from 9 to 11 strokes of the pump handle depending on the condition of the sprayer's software.

Daily maintenance tips for the handheld compressed-air sprayer.

- At the beginning of each workday, fill the sprayer with a little water and run a check to see that all components are working properly. This practice will ensure safe and accurate spray applications while on the job and help minimize any expensive downtime and potential accidents. If there is a malfunction with the sprayer and the cause isn't obvious, refer to Appendix F, Troubleshooting The compressed-air Sprayer.

- Always **release the pressure** from the sprayer if it is not to be used for one hour or more (e.g., during lunch hour). Hoses and gaskets deteriorate if chemicals are left in a sprayer under pressure for prolonged periods.

- Using different types of insecticide formulations (e.g., wettable powders, encapsulated pesticides, suspension concentrates, emulsions, etc.), may require using separate sprayers. Switching from a wettable powder to an emulsion, for example, may clog the sprayer unless it is thoroughly cleaned after use. Moreover, some insecticides, such as the encapsulated formulations, require using large mesh filter screens. Carefully follow all directions as provided by the chemical manufacturer.

- Never pick up or carry the sprayer by the hose. This will stress and eventually cause breaks in the hose.

- The supporting springs at both ends of the hose must always be kept in place to prevent crimping and breakage of the hose.

- Never allow a sprayer to remain in a vehicle for prolonged periods, (e.g., overnight), during

freezing temperatures. Severe damage to the tank, hose, and application wand can result.

- On the vehicle, keep a sprayer repair kit containing all necessary software, extra hoses, etc., as well as the tools needed for on-the-job repairs. Repair kits are available from supply distributors.

- Nozzles that become clogged on the job require special care. Nozzle tips are usually made of brass, which is a relatively soft metal; thus, they are easily damaged. Great care must be taken to see that the hole in the tip is not deformed or enlarged to any degree while being cleaned, since this will produce dramatic differences in spray patterns. Therefore, never use metal objects such as a knife, wire or pin to clean the nozzle. Unclog a nozzle by either backflushing with water, or by using a soft bristle. A baby's toothbrush with a pen clip can be kept in a shirt pocket to provide quick on-the-job repair of a clogged nozzle tip.

- Always attempt to calculate how much spray will be needed for the day's work to avoid having excess insecticide at the end of each day. This precaution will save on chemical costs and eliminate the need to dispose and/or store insecticides. Ideally, all insecticide should be used up on the job.

- Some sprayers contain a safety lock nut. When this is tightened, it prevents the trigger from being accidentally activated and discharging pesticide. This device is especially useful when operating the sprayer in residences.

- At the end of each workday, release all pressure, rinse the sprayer, and flush the hoses.

Wiping Cloth

One of the most important pieces of equipment associated with the on-the-job use of the sprayer is a **clean wiping cloth**. As long as the cloth is clean, it can be carried in a convenient pocket or tucked under the belt. If pesticide splashes into the face or elsewhere on the skin, it can be wiped off immediately to minimize the danger from the contact. Such a cloth is also readily available for wiping up pesticide leaks, drips or spills from floors and other surfaces thus preventing damage or unsightly smears that would be objectionable to the customer. When the wiping cloth has been soiled by pesticide, it must not be used as a wipe cloth or even carried in the hand or pocket because skin absorption of the pesticide can easily occur. Soiled wiping cloths should be discarded.

Accessories

Several sprayer accessories are available that permit the professional to perform customized applications. A few of these accessories and add-ons are discussed here, but more are constantly being developed and added.

As mentioned, using the correct pressure on a compressed-air sprayer is an important practice for the PMP. Some models offer both **pressure regulators** and **pressure gauges** with the sprayer. Regulator kits can also be purchased and easily added on to existing sprayers.

The regulator controls the output pressure and the gauge monitors the tank pressure. Using a sprayer equipped with a constant low pressure output system as achieved with a regulator is important for four reasons: (1) economy: less pesticides are wasted with low pressure applications; (2) improved pesticidal application and control; (3) safety by avoiding drift and runoff from excessive pressures, and (4) proper calibration. Applying the correct amount of liquid pesticide is vital with today's emphasis on regulatory and label compliance.

Finally, because there is variation among sprayers due to the condition of the sprayer; different pesticide formulations, (which recommend different application pressures) and different tank sizes, pressure regulators and gauges, keep the PMP informed of the sprayer output pressures at all times instead of having to guess by stroking the pump handle.

Various **nozzle tips** enable the professional to change from flat-fan to pin-stream spray, from crack and crevice to aerosol applications with a simple twist of the nozzle tip.

Crack and crevice tips are available as plastic, stainless steel, or brass. Plastic offers some flexibility, but it tends to break. Metal tips offer more durability, but caution is needed when a metal tip is used near electrical areas where the tip might inadvertently contact electrical wiring. Certain tips offer four-way dispersal of liquids for treating various voids.

Even when using crack and crevice tips to treat various crevices and voids, the pin stream of liquid may not sufficiently penetrate or thoroughly cover the surface of the crack to leave a residue on the surface that the insect pest travels. To improve this, some tips and systems are designed that disperse the liquid in a crack and crevice application from a simple pin stream to an aerosol-type application, providing better penetration and coverage within crevices and small voids. It is important to note however, this is not the same as an aerosol application. These new tips can be attached to standard sprayers and operate as low as the standard operating pressures of 20 psi or higher when needed.

Lacquer Applicators

Some pesticide or liquid formulations (e.g., lacquers) are too thick to be applied with standard nozzles and tips. Professionals that use lacquers often simply use paint brushes and apply these formulations by hand in the same manner as one paints a surface. In this way, the "painted-on" pesticide allows for a smooth film of liquid to be applied without the threat of splashback or excessive runoff.

Backpack or Knapsack Sprayers

Backpack sprayers have tank capacities ranging between 2 and 5 gallons (see Figure 5.7). To avoid excessive and unwieldy weights, most professionals do not exceed the 3-gallon capacity. Backpack sprayers are designed to be carried on the person's back to distribute the workload and to allow for continuous spraying of large areas without having to constantly refill the sprayer. Backpack sprayers are used for applying herbicides and/or insecticides to lawns, fencerows, around building perimeters, orchards, etc. They may also be used for indoor pesticide and disinfectant spray applications, such as in large commercial food facilities and warehouses.

Most backpack sprayers use a specialized hand-operated lever (also referred to as LOKs: Lever-Operator Knapsacks) to prime a "piston pump" to pressurize the sprayer. The pump may be mounted on the outside or inside of the tank. Depending on the model, pressures can be generated up to 150 psi, although the maximum working pressure on most backpack sprayers is usually between 40 and

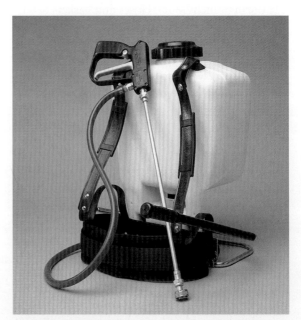

FIGURE 5.7. Backpack sprayers offer the pest management professional a convenient sprayer for exterior pesticidal applications, especially for residential sites.

75 psi. With these pressures, solid-stream sprays can be directed up to 25 feet if needed. Some models offer a battery-powered pump to eliminate the need to prime the pump at all.

Because the backpack sprayer is not the choice for precision applications using low pressures (such as crack and crevice applications), only two types of nozzles openings are usually available—flood jets and cone nozzles. Some models offer both cone and pin-stream nozzles.

The cleaning and maintenance of backpack sprayers are similar in principle to those described for the handheld sprayer. However, as with all equipment, the owners manual should be consulted.

Foam Applicators

In the past, foam applicators or "foamers" have been mostly used for termite control efforts. But in the last few years, foaming equipment has become available as inexpensive, portable, handheld units that are popular for applying foams into various hard-to-reach structural voids and other areas. New professional level handheld foamers are available that are similar in appearance to other portable sprayers (see Figure 5.8). Other less-elaborate hand-pump foamers are also common. Some manufacturers offer battery-operated foamers.

Most PMPs today consider foamers standard liquid application equipment. This is because foamers can provide good residual coverage into a multitude of hard-to-reach nooks and crannies (e.g.; wall voids, soffit voids, concrete block, etc.) for the control of carpenter ants, termites and other cryptobiotic pests.

Perhaps the greatest utility of the portable handheld foamers is for treating the various components of floor drains and the numerous crevices associated with floor tiles in commercial food-serving establishments. These "microenvironments" are among the primary breeding locations used by drain flies, fruit flies and phorid flies. Foam applications of insecticides or bioenzymatic products can be used as foams to coat these microenvironments in combating persistent small fly infestations (refer to Chapter 11 for more details on this approach).

Large-Volume Sprayers

The **large-volume sprayer** is the second broad type of sprayer used in the pest management industry. The large-volume sprayers are often referred to as "power sprayers," "spray rigs," and "termite rigs" depending on their use (see Figure 5.9). Many variations exist with power sprayer systems. As a result of recent technology, it is now possible for PMPs to customize the basic spray rig to fit the specific

FIGURE 5.8.Portable handheld foamers have become important tools for today's PMP for treating into various structural voids for ants and termites, drains in commercial facilities for small flies (e.g., drain flies, fruit flies, etc.), and other uses.

needs of the company and its operations. This section focuses on the power sprayers used for large-volume spray operations such as industrial site perimeter treatments, termite control, weed control, and lawn/shrubbery pest management.

Components. The basic power sprayer system is comprised of five major components (see Figures 5.9 and 5.10):

Tank
Pump and motor
Hose
Applicator/Nozzle
Accessories
   • strainers
   • pressure gauge
   • air-gap device
   • pressure regulator
   • flow meters
   • agitators
   • pressure-relief valves

The **tanks** of the larger volume sprayers have been improved upon dramatically in recent years. These tanks range in capacity from 50 to 250 gallons. Most tanks used for termite control/lawn spraying operations are 100-gallon capacity, although some rigs utilize a "dual system" of two 50-gallon tanks. The tanks are made of fiberglass or polyethylene, which are resistant to the corrosive properties of pesticides. Most tanks are now translucent to facilitate viewing the level of liquid in the tank. The tank should have large openings for easy filling and cleaning, as well as provision for straining during filling.

FIGURE 5.9. An example of a large-volume power sprayer unit, often referred to as a "spray rig." Note the important air-gap device emerging from the top left-hand side of the tank.

Similarly, it should contain large drains and other outlets that are sized to the pump capacity. If a dual-tank system is used, the plumbing should provide for agitation and adequate withdrawal rates in both tanks. All tanks should have a gauge to show the liquid level. External gauges should be protected to prevent breakage. Most tanks contain a shutoff valve for temporarily holding liquid pesticide while other sprayer parts are being serviced.

Every tank must contain an air-gap device, or a backflow preventer. In many states, these devices are now required by law.

The **pump** is used to generate hydraulic pressure (i.e., pressure created by fluids) to the pesticide directly in the line rather than pressurizing the tank. There are many different types of pumps varying in size and capabilities. The basic principle of operation among the most commonly used pumps is the same. In each case the discharge of liquid occurs as a rapid succession of separate and distinct slugs of liquid that are entrapped and pushed out of the pump by mechanical action. Gasoline or electric **motors**, ranging in power from 3/4 to 7 horsepower (hp) are used to drive the pumps, although most professionals employ the 5.0 and 5.5 hp motors.

Matching the right pump for the job is important. Two factors must be considered: (1) the amount of pressure that will be needed for the various spraying operations, and (2) the types of pesticide formulations (e.g., emulsions, wettable powders, or both) that will be used in the large-volume sprayer. Jobs that require high-pressure/large-volume applications (e.g., tree spraying operations) require powerful pumps, such as the large models of the piston or roller pumps. If a large-volume sprayer is used for only termite control (low-pressure applications), the smaller models are adequate.

The types of pumps most commonly used in pest management operations are: (1) **roller**, (2) **piston**, and (3) **diaphragm**.

Roller pumps are among the least expensive and most widely used pumps in the industry. They pump moderate volumes of liquid, 8 to 30 gallons per minute (gpm), at low to moderate pressures (10 to 300 psi). Roller pumps are available equipped with from five to eight rollers. The more rollers, the more power to the pump. The smaller roller pump models are often used for termite control because they produce the desired low pressures, are economical, and are easily repaired. The recommended operating pressure, for example, for most operations in termite control is less than 50 psi at the nozzle.

For large spraying operations, the six or eight roller pumps operate at pressures up to 300 psi. The rollers are available in different materials such as nylon, Teflon, or rubber. The choice of roller material depends upon what type of chemical is to be used. Some rollers, for example, wear rapidly in wettable powders (but are replaceable). The pump case is usually cast iron or a nickel alloy. Stainless steel models provide outstanding performance for use with wettable powders, but are relatively expensive. Roller pumps are appropriate for emulsions, soluble powders, and other nonabrasive pesticide formulations.

Piston pumps are the most durable of the various power pumps; they are also more expensive. They deliver low to medium volumes (2 to 25 gpm) at low to high-pressures (20 to 600 psi.) Piston pumps are used for high-pressure sprayers or when

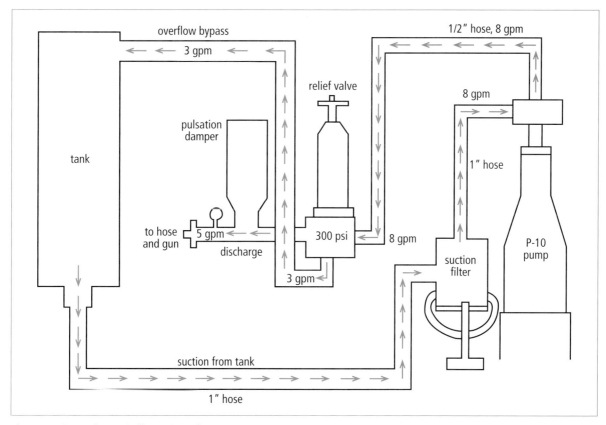

Figure 5.10. A schematic illustration of a power sprayer rig.

both low and high pressures are needed. The smaller models such as the "twin piston" pump are commonly used in termite control operations.

The cylinders of piston pumps are iron, stainless steel, or porcelain lined. The pump casing is usually iron. The piston cups are replaceable and are made of leather, neoprene, or nylon fabric. These materials make the pump abrasion-resistant and capable of handling various types of pesticides, including wettable powders, for many years. When piston pumps do fail however, they usually do so quite rapidly. Thus, when using piston pumps, it is wise to carry a spare pump on the truck to avoid costly downtime.

Piston pumps also create a pulsating or throbbing action that can be damaging to gauges, valves, hose fittings, and other parts. When pulsation is a problem, it is necessary to have a **surge tank** in the line to reduce the force of the pulsation. A surge tank is a small chamber containing air. It is placed in the discharge line between the pump and the control valve and serves to cushion the peak of the pulses produced by the pump so a more even and regular flow is available at the nozzle.

Diaphragm pumps are used when most of the work involves only low-volume, low-pressure applications because diaphragm pumps deliver low volume (1.4 to 10 gpm) at low to moderate pressure (10 to 100 psi). They withstand abrasion from

wettable powder mixtures much better than roller pumps because the spray mixture does not contact any moving metal parts except the valves. The rubber or neoprene diaphragm may be damaged by some solvents. The pump case is usually iron.

The small diaphragm pumps have enjoyed a recent resurgence with the new portable systems used in treating crawlspaces and attics. They are also being used on portable carts for various indoor treatments using 3- to 7-gallon tanks

Hose. The hose of large-volume sprayers is a vital part of the system. Hoses must be long enough for the purpose intended, be of sufficient diameter to carry an adequate flow of liquid, and be made of materials that will not be deteriorated by the pesticides.

It is important that only high-quality hose is used and that it is maintained in good condition. Cheap or worn-out hoses may suddenly burst on the job and pesticides may spill or splash onto people, property, or contaminate the environment.

Quality power sprayer hoses are usually made of polyvinyl chloride (PVC) and are capable of withstanding working pressures of up to 600 psi or more. PVC hoses are lighter in weight than rubber hoses, but they tend to stiffen in cool weather.

Hoses used in termite/lawn spraying operations usually have an inside diameter of 3/8-inch or 1/2-inch. For high-volume, high-pressure spraying operations, it is necessary to use a heavy-duty hose with diameters of 3/4-inch to 1.0-inch. Heavy-duty hoses are quite stiff and heavy, and are can be laborious to work with.

When choosing hose size, it should be remembered that the smallest opening in the spray line determines the actual capacity for delivery—regardless of the size of the hose. Thus, if a 1/2-inch inside diameter hose is used with couplings having an inside diameter of 1/4-inch, the delivery rate of the hose will be that of only a 1/4-inch hose. Therefore, it is important to match hoses and couplings properly to deliver the desired volume of spray.

Finally, hose length is also an important consideration. Most professionals use between 150 to 300 feet of hose, which provides extra lengths when it is needed. **Hose reels** enable the professional to handle and manage long lengths of hose. Reels are operated either by hand cranks or by electric rewind motors. The motor-driven reels are valuable on large spray rigs where the hose is wound and unwound many times a day (such as in lawn spraying programs) as they save time and reduce physical exertion and therefore can also help keep the number of worker's compensation claims low.

When purchasing hose for power-spraying operations, the professional should consult with a knowledgeable supplier and describe the pesticides, equipment, and types of operations for which the hose will be used.

Nozzles used on large-volume sprayer systems vary considerably according to the type of spraying operation. For termite control, nozzles may be specialized, such as the subslab injector or the trenching rod (refer to Chapter 7). For lawn and shrubbery spraying operations, "spray guns" are commonly used (see Figure 5.11). Most spray guns have adjustable nozzles that operate on the same principle as those described for the handheld compressed-air sprayers. However, there are some important differences.

Nozzles of power spray guns are made up of four major parts: the nozzle body, the cap, the strainer (screen), and the tip. Successful large-volume spraying depends on the correct selection, assembly, and maintenance of the nozzles.

The **nozzle body** holds the strainer and tip in proper position. Several types of tips that produce a variety of spray patterns may be interchanged on a single nozzle body made by the same manufacturer.

The **nozzle strainer** is placed in the nozzle body to screen out debris that might clog the nozzle opening. The type of nozzle strainer needed depends on the size of the nozzle opening and the

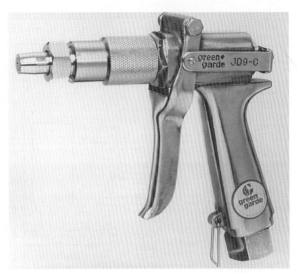

FIGURE 5.11. A versatile nozzle for large-volume liquid spraying applications.

type of chemical being sprayed. The cap is used to secure the strainer and the tip to the body. The cap should not be overtightened.

Nozzle tips break the liquid pesticide into droplets. They also distribute the spray in a predetermined pattern and are the principal element that controls the rate of application. Nozzle performance depends on: (1) nozzle design or type, (2) operating pressure, (3) size of the opening, (4) discharge angle, and (5) distance of nozzle from the target.

Nozzle patterns for large-volume spray guns and applicators are of three basic types: solid stream, fan, and cone.

Solid-stream nozzle patterns may be used under high pressure to spray a distant or specific target, such as pests in trees. With low pressure, the solid-stream nozzle is used in termite control applications (with subslab injectors and application rods), and for applying termiticides in a solid stream into holes or through slabs.

Fan nozzle patterns from spray guns may be of different types such as regular flat fan, even flat fan, or a flooding fan pattern. Fan nozzles are used mostly for uniform spray coverage of surfaces, for example, applying herbicides or fertilizers to ground areas.

Cone nozzle patterns are used where penetration and coverage of plant foliage or other irregular targets are desired. They are most often used to apply fungicides and insecticides to foliage, although some types are used for broadcast soil applications of herbicides or fertilizers.

Accessories. Filtering is done in sprayers by **strainers**. Pesticide mixtures must be filtered to remove dirt, rust flakes, and other foreign materials from the liquid in this tank. Proper filtering protects the working parts of the sprayer from undue wear and avoids time loss and uneven application caused by clogged nozzle tips.

Filtering should be progressive within the system with the largest mesh screens in the filler opening and in the suction line between the tank and the pump. They should be keyed to the size of the nozzle opening. Total screen area should be large enough to prevent pump starvation. A smaller mesh strainer is usually placed in the pressure line between the pump and the pressure regulator. The finest mesh strainer is placed nearest the nozzle. Instruction manuals should be consulted for correct strainer size and placement within the sprayer system. Strainers should be cleaned regularly or during use to prevent them from becoming clogged. Damaged or deteriorated strainers should be replaced.

Pressure gauges monitor the function of the sprayer system. They must be accurate and have the range needed for the particular types of spraying operations. For example, a 0 to 100 psi gauge with 2-pound gradations is adequate for most low-pressure sprayers.

Gauges should be checked frequently against an accurate gauge to ensure accuracy. Excess pressure will destroy a gauge. If a gauge does not zero, it should be replaced. Gauge protectors can be used to guard against corrosive pesticides and pressure surges.

The **pressure regulator** controls the pressure and, indirectly, the quantity of spray material delivered by the nozzles. It protects pump seals, hoses, and other sprayer parts from damage due to excessive pressure.

The bypass line from the pressure regulator to the tank should be kept fully open and unrestricted and should be large enough to carry the total pump output without excess pressure buildup. The pressure range and flow capacity of the regulator must match the pressure range that will be used and the capacity of the pump. Pressure regulators used in pest management operations are usually one of two types: spring-loaded bypass valves and unloader valves.

Spring-loaded bypass valves open or close in response to changes in pressure, diverting more or less liquid back to the tank to keep pressure constant. These valves are used with roller, diaphragm, and small piston pumps.

Unloader valves work like a spring-loaded bypass valve when the sprayer is operating. However, when the nozzles are shut down, they reduce strain on the pump by moving the overflow back into the tank at low pressure. These valves are used on the larger piston and diaphragm pumps.

Flow meters are a valuable accessory to a modern large-volume sprayer systems. As these meters display the amount of chemical pumped, they enable the professional to accurately monitor not only chemical flow, but also the total amount of chemical applied for any particular area or job. For example, these meters can measure the amount of termiticide injected into each hole for subslab applications. Some models can accommodate a flow range of 3 to 30 gallons per minute, and are available for low-pressure operations (max. 50 psi) or for high-pressure operations (600 psi). Ideally, flow meters should be attached near the nozzle, instead of at the pump, to provide accurate chemical output at the time and point of application. Calibration should be checked frequently. Some solvents can affect accuracy of the mechanism.

Every large-volume sprayer must have agitation to keep the spray material uniformly mixed. If there is too little agitation, the pesticide will be applied unevenly. If there is too much agitation, some pesticides may foam and interfere with pump and nozzle operation. The type of agitation necessary depends on the pesticide formulation to be used. There are three basic types of **agitators**: (1) bypass agitators, (2) hydraulic (jet action) agitators, and (3) mechanical agitators.

Soluble powders and liquid formulations such as solutions and emulsions require little agitation. Bypass agitation is sufficient for these formulations. **Bypass agitation** uses the returning liquid from the pressure-relief valve to agitate the liquid in the tank. The return must extend to the bottom of the tank to prevent excessive foaming. Bypass agitation is insufficient for wettable powders or in tanks larger than 55 gallons.

Hydraulic agitation is required for wettable powder and flowable formulations in small tanks and for liquid formulations in 100-gallon or larger tanks with roller, piston, or diaphragm pumps. Hydraulic agitation is provided by the high-pressure flow of surplus spray material from the pump. The jet or jets are located at the bottom of the tank. The agitator is connected to the pressure side of the pump. Jet agitator nozzles should never be placed in the bypass line. The pump and tank capacity and operating pressure determine the minimum jet number and size.

Wettable powder formulations are best mixed and kept in suspension with **mechanical agitation**. The mechanical agitator usually consists of flat blades or propellers mounted on a shaft that is placed lengthwise along the bottom of the tank. The paddles or propellers are rotated by the engine to keep the material well mixed. Mechanical agitators are usually found only on large high-pressure hydraulic sprayers.

Every sprayer must have a method of turning on and shutting off the flow of liquid to the nozzle. This is accomplished by **control valves** placed in the line. There are many different kinds of control valves: some are turned, some are squeezed, and some are bent to cause them to operate. A quick-acting control valve is usually preferred because it shuts off immediately when the handle is released and thus prevents leakage from the nozzle, especially when the valve is located close to the nozzle.

Slow-acting control valves are ordinarily closed by rotating the valve stem resulting in a slow but positive shutoff. This type of valve is frequently used in the lines of power sprayers, although a quick-acting valve should be used at the nozzle end of the line. Spray guns usually have a quick-acting valve.

In all large-volume spray equipment, shutoff valves should be provided between the tank and the hose so pressure can be shut off from the hose without shutting down the engine or motor driving the spray rig. If there is not a valve in this position, then each time it is necessary to replace hose, clean a strainer, or replace a spray tip, the entire rig must be shut down.

Electric Mid-Volume Sprayers

With the advent of the borate treatments for termite and other wood-destroying organisms (see Chapters 7 and 8) and an increase in perimeter treatment services, the smaller portable electric spray systems that offer mid-volume liquid applications have become popular in the pest management industry.

These systems are usually comprised of 15-, 25- and 30-gallon tanks equipped with small, 12-volt electric pumps powered by a battery, (or wired to the truck's battery or electrical system), a 100 foot, 3/8-inch hose, pressure gauges and adjustable bypass units. (see Figure 5.12). These systems are used for treating joists, sill plates, and rafters inside crawlspaces and attics, as well as for the occasional exterior perimeter treatments when more than a handheld sprayer or backpack sprayer is needed. Because of their small size and light weight, they can be included on standard pest routes (i.e., non-termite control) on the smaller trucks. This provides greater versatility for any particular route, and the expensive costs of the larger trucks carrying the full-size termite rigs can be avoided.

Innovations have also occurred with the mid-volume sprayer systems relative to "skid platforms" that facilitate a PMP being able to mount and remove a "rig" on a vehicle on a "as-needed" basis.

Specialty Power Spraying Systems

Some spray equipment for large and mid-volume

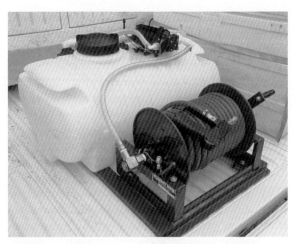

Figure 5.12. Mid-volume sprayer systems provide portability and compactness for performing perimeter treatments and small termite jobs. (Myers)

applications have become specialized to provide a portable, all-in-one concept of the conventional "spray rig" systems. In the past, these systems have been referred to as "closed-mixing" and "proportioner spraying" systems. Newer technology has produced systems referred to as "inline injection" systems. Although these systems have been around for about the past 20 years, only recently has the technology been improved to a point where they have become more widely used by companies that perform numerous termite and lawn spraying programs.

Depending on the particular system used, inline injector systems may contain most of the sprayer components necessary for termite, weed, and ornamental spraying operations (including backflow prevention, ground and wall-foaming capability, etc.). They may or may not utilize a tank and/or a motor system. Using specialized "pesticide injection devices," inline injector systems automatically inject the insecticide concentrate into the flow of incoming water. Water can be obtained directly from a hose hook-up at the job site that is connected to the portable spray system. In this way, the insecticide is proportioned and mixed inline into the water diluent and then pumped out of the unit. In this way, the professional need not have to bother with mixing operations or have contact with the concentrate. The threat of pest concentrate spillage is also reduced.

When tanks are used, these portable systems typically utilize 30- or 50-gallon tanks. Some models are set up on skids that can be mounted and dismounted on the service vehicle on a daily basis or as needed. Because of their portability and compactness, inline injection systems can also used on smaller models of pickup trucks.

The inline mixing of the concentrate for inline injector system must be 100% reliable. The new technology that ensures this reliability is considered by some to be relatively expensive. The expense may be offset in the ability to use smaller service vehicles, less pesticide wastage, better safety factors, convenience, and other advantages. Some inline injection system companies offer leasing options to offset the initial expense of the high-tech equipment.

Equipment for applying aerosols and "fogs"

Machines that convert liquid formulations into very small, fine droplets (aerosols) are known as aerosol generators. Some machines are also referred to as "foggers."

Some confusion exists regarding the different types of aerosol generators such as the difference between mist machines and fog machines. Part of the reason lies in the fact that many of the aerosol generator machines in use today can be adjusted so they produce both a "fog-type" spray and a "mist-type" spray. Yet some machines use trade names such as "fogger," while another machine that produces the same type of spray may use the name "mist blower." To further add to the confusion, some machines are advertised as "cold fog generators," "hot fog generators," "ULV fogger", and so on.

A clear understanding regarding the terms "fogs," "mists," "aerosols," ULD, ULV, etc., is essential to choose the right type of equipment to perform a specific task. Therefore, a brief, simplified discussion of the different types of liquid insecticide sprays and the composition of each follows.

Liquid Insecticide Sprays

Different types of liquid insecticidal sprays are categorized according to the size of the particle (droplets) that makes up the spray as it is applied by a particular piece of equipment. Generally, it is the size of the opening in the nozzle through which the liquid is forced that determines the insecticide particle size.

No spray nozzle will break a liquid pesticide into completely uniform droplets; some will be large; some will be small, and some will be in-between. Droplets are measured in **microns**. One micron is 1/1,000 of a millimeter or about 1/25,000 of an inch. For comparison purposes, the diameter of an average human hair is about 100 microns and an average raindrop is more than 4,000 microns in diameter.

Thus, insecticide spray droplets can be listed according to their size (diameter of the droplets) in microns with the largest droplets first, proceeding towards the smallest droplets, as follows:

Type of Spray	Droplet size (microns)
coarse sprays (largest droplets)	400 and larger
fine sprays	100 to 400
"mist" aerosols	50 to 100
"medium-sized" aerosols	5.0 to 50
"fog" aerosols	0.1 to 5.0
smoke	0.001 to 0.1
vapors (smallest droplets)	less than 0.001

Coarse sprays are mostly made up of relatively large droplets measuring 400 microns or more in diameter. Because these droplets are so large, they do not float in the air, and fall quickly to the ground. Coarse sprays are produced with coarse spray nozzles or solid-stream nozzles. Such sprays have limited use in indoor household pest management. The spray patterns used in tree spraying programs would all be coarse sprays.

Fine sprays contain droplets ranging between 100 and 400 microns. Fine sprays are useful in making insecticide applications indoors or outdoors. Fine sprays are produced by the common one-gallon sprayer using the smaller fan nozzle at about 20 to 30 psi. Like coarse sprays, fine spray droplets fall to the ground rather quickly.

Aerosols are droplets ranging between 0.1 and 100 microns, which actually is a very broad range of particle sizes. In fact, discussions of all the different types of aerosols can be very confusing. For the purpose of presenting a practical discussion of aerosol generator equipment, the aerosols are grouped into a convenient size category of: "mist aerosols," "medium-sized aerosols," and "fog aerosols."

Mist aerosols are relatively large, ranging between 50 and 100 microns in diameter. Mists are usually produced from liquids when the liquid is forced through fine nozzles by high-pressure pumps, high-speed mechanical rotors, or by atomizers. Mists aerosols are still relatively heavy and will not float in the air unless carried by some type of strong air currents, such as a brisk wind. Otherwise, mist aerosols settle too rapidly leaving a wet film on horizontal surfaces.

Medium-sized aerosols measure between 5 to 50 microns in size. A common "aerosol can" produces aerosol droplets of about 20 to 30 microns in size.

Fog aerosols make up the lower end of the aerosol particle range measuring between 0.1 to 5.0 microns in size.

Smokes contain droplets of 0.001 to 0.1 microns, although some particles may be larger. A large portion of pesticides dispensed through thermal fog generators contain droplets in the fog-smoke droplet size category.

Vapors are very tiny particles less than 0.001 micron in diameter. Examples of vapors are the pesticides liberated from plastic strips, or the vapor produce by common moth balls.

By using different types of equipment, the same insecticide can be applied as different types of sprays. For example, when a pyrethroid insecticide is applied using a standard one-gallon hand sprayer with a fan nozzle orifice at 15 psi of pressure, the droplets emerging from the sprayer are relatively large and fall into the category of a coarse spray. When the pyrethroid is packaged as a canned aerosol insecticide, it will be applied as a medium-sized aerosol.

FIGURE 5.13. Canned insecticides provide convenient methods for applying insecticides. These cans can be installed into pouches that are worn on the professional's belt.

Aerosols and Fogs

For the purposes of this chapter, the aerosol generators and similar equipment are categorized as follows:

Pressurized Aerosol Containers (PACs)
Pressurized Liquid Sprays (non-aerosols).
Pressurized Bait Dispensers
Mechanical Aerosol Generators (MAGs).
  • Aerosol Generators for Void Treatments
  • Cold Foggers (ULD/ULV and Mist machines)
  • Thermal Foggers

Pressurized aerosol containers (PACs). The simplest example of pressurized aerosol containers is a can of insecticide which might be purchased in a supermarket by a homeowner. The professional, however, has access to additional and more sophisticated types of canned insecticides (see Figure 5.13). Most PACs used by professionals are purchased and used in a prepressurized and ready-to-use formulation.

Pressurized aerosol containers range in size from two ounces to several pounds and can be multifunctional. They may produce coarse sprays, any one of the aerosol types of spray, or even dusts. Some insect growth regulators (IGRs) are available in pressurized can format, as well. The pressures under which the pesticide formulations are packaged can vary from 25 to 80 psi. Some canned formulations are highly specialized for applying pesticides directly into cracks and crevices and structural voids. Others are designed to produce fog or mist types of applications into open air spaces.

Most insecticides packaged in cans contain a liquid formulation together with some type of non-toxic gas that acts as a propellant to eject the insecticide when a valve is opened. Some of the canned insecticides do not contain any solvents or emulsifiers as do the liquid sprays applied from sprayers. When canned insecticides are applied, their gas propellant quickly evaporates leaving the insecticide in the air, on a surface, or in a crack or crevice.

Valves and nozzles on canned insecticides vary considerably from small combination pushbutton valves and nozzles, to hand-operated valves connected to a finely machined nozzle by a hose or extension tube. The valve in all instances must be a quick-seating type that closes automatically when pressure is released to avoid wasting pesticide.

Prepressurized container insecticides offer several advantages:

• convenient and easy to use;
• no mixing and handling of concentrated toxicants;
• the potential for any environmental contamination is minimized because (1) less insecticide is applied compared to that applied from sprayers and (2) no excess insecticide is left over in need of disposal;
• some PACs are capable of delivering the insecticides deeper into crevices and wall voids than insecticides applied from conventional sprayers because their propellant gases carry the insecticide into these areas.

But unless canned insecticides are used carefully and correctly, they are easily overused and wasted, resulting in expensive insecticide applications. Over the course of a month, and perhaps many routes, such wastage can amount to a significant amount of money lost. The wastage associated with PACs can be minimized with proper training and careful inventory practices.

Pressurized aerosol containers produce aerosols that typically range in droplet size between 20 to 30 microns, although some products may produce smaller droplets. Aerosol droplets of this size float in the air for short periods of time before falling to the ground.

Some of the propellants used to force the insecticide out of the can are flammable. Part of the propellant, in liquid form, mixes with the pesticide formulation, and the remainder fills the head space above the liquid in the form of gas. As the pesticide is forced from the container, it is propelled through a small expansion chamber before reaching the nozzle. Here the gas in the formulation expands rapidly to partially break up the pesticide before it is ejected through the nozzle where complete expansion takes place. Generally, the larger the expansion chamber and the smaller the nozzle orifice, the smaller the particle size of the final aerosol.

Pest management professionals use PACs for different types of insect control operations. For example, the larger-sized PACs are commonly used for flying insect control in large enclosed spaces. Smaller, more portable, one-pound cans are often used to discharge an aerosol that will flush insects (e.g., bed bugs, cockroaches) insects hiding in cracks and crevices, within voids, equipment and furniture or provide quick knockdown of wasps and other stinging insects.

Small plastic extension tubes that serve as nozzles are available to attach to the valve of some pressurized containers. With these tubes it is possible to inject aerosol particles (or liquid sprays) directly into cracks and crevices.

There are also pressurized cylinders that are specifically designed for applying cold fogs. These cylinders are pressurized as are normal canned aerosol containers with some minor modifications in how they operate. These cylinders are also equipped with extension hoses and extension tubes that can be used to inject the finely divided particles into cracks and into wall voids.

Pressurized liquid sprays. For many years, insecticides that were packaged into cans produced only an aerosol type of spray. And thus, the term "aerosol" is often used when discussing any spray (especially insecticides) that originate from a can.

Today, pest management professionals also have access to pressurized liquids for use as sprays. These sprays are packed in cans very similar to those producing aerosols; however, they are not aerosols because the nozzle on these types of canned insecticides produces a coarse wet spray similar to what is produced using a hand sprayer with a pin-stream opening. Pressurized liquid

sprays deposit a thin film of pesticide directly on a surface rather than a fine droplet that floats in the air. Most pressurized liquid spray cans utilize a compressed gas such as carbon dioxide, nitrous oxide, or nitrogen to produce the pressure needed to propel the liquid insecticide out of the can.

Some pesticide and equipment manufacturing companies have developed specialized types of canned insecticides and/or specialized application equipment resulting in **canned insecticide systems**. With these systems, a professional can apply either aerosol-type insecticides (for space treatments, fogging operations or flushing), or pressurized liquid spray pesticides separately or simultaneously through specialized application nozzles

Pressurized canned baits. Some baits are formulated into pressurized cans. In this way, the amount of bait applied is control by pressing the nozzle tip as compared to the "estimated squeezing" or pushing that is needed with bait guns and bait syringes.

Mechanical aerosol generators (MAGs) for void treatments. Often, it is desirable to be able to deliver flush-and-kill insecticides to inaccessible or difficult-to-reach structural areas such as the voids of walls, ceilings, floors, cabinets, as well as certain types of utility voids. To meet this need, manufacturers developed specialized aerosol generation machines for void and crack-and-crevice treatments (e.g., Micro-Injector®, Actisol) (see Figure 5.14).

These devices incorporate two lines to the nozzle assembly to achieve deep penetration. One line pumps the concentrated insecticide in very small amounts into a swirl chamber, the other line propels blasts of air into the chamber. The higher velocity and volume of air aerosolizes the insecticide and forces it out of the tip. It is important to note that void treatment MAGs are not designed for conducting "space treatments" of large open

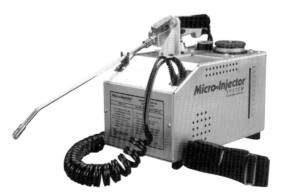

Figure. 5.14. A mechanical aerosol generator (MAG) designed for delivering aerosols into voids and other deep spaces.

spaces (although some labels permit space treatments with these units on a relatively small open areas). Space treatments are best conducted using ULD/ULV machines which will be discussed.

Some of the larger models of MAGS are mounted on carts. But most professionals use the lighter and more portable units that can be hand-carried into a facility. Long or telescoping flexible hoses provide for convenient access to work in and around commercial equipment and access the various voids and harborages.

Void treatments using MAGs are best for pest infestations where the pests are harboring deep inside cabinets; walls; ceilings or equipment; various voids inside commercial kitchens in restaurants, schools, hospitals; and the like (e.g., carpenter ants, stinging insects, cockroaches, bed bugs, brown recluse spiders, etc.).

Mechanical aerosol generators offer some advantages over the prepackaged aerosol cans and systems mentioned earlier. First, air provided by an air compressor within the unit is the propellant used to deliver the aerosol which provides savings when a lot of commercial work is conducted. Second, these machines are capable of delivering the aerosols deep into the various voids and cracks and crevices. And third, these units project a professional high-tech image to commercial clients.

Cold foggers (ULD/ULV machines). Cold foggers (also called *cold aerosol generators*) break liquid pesticides into aerosol droplets ranging in sizes between 1 and 30 microns, although some cold foggers can be adjusted to produce droplets ranging into the mist size (15 to 60 microns). Usually the liquid is broken down by using some type of mechanical action. For example, some machines propel the liquid into spinning discs and rotors; other machines utilize extremely fine nozzles combined with high pressure, while a few machines use strong blasts of air.

Cold foggers are used in the pest control industry to apply pesticides, disinfectants, deodorants, and germicides in enclosed spaces of warehouses, hospitals, restaurants, farm facilities, and residences. They are also used outdoors for mosquito/fly control programs.

Perhaps the most commonly used cold fogger in urban pest management today is the **ultra-low dosage**, or **ULD line of equipment** (also referred to as **ULV, ultra-low-volume** in outdoor spraying operations).

The concept of ULD treatments using a cold fogger involves distributing a very small amount of concentrated insecticide solution over a relatively large area. In other words, an ultra-low dosage of

insecticide is applied. For example, a 3% synergized pyrethrins formulation can be applied at a rate of 0.5 to 1.2 fluid ounces into an area measuring 1,000 cubic feet. To do this, cold fogger machines use special nozzles to break up the insecticide solution into billions of tiny droplets.

The aerosol droplets produced by a cold fogger will range in size between 1 to 30 microns. The most effective droplets are those from the 5 to 15 micron range. Droplets of this size remain airborne for periods of 2 to 6 hours and are carried by air currents. Eventually these tiny floating droplets contact most of the insects that are exposed to the surrounding air currents. The droplets attach to the hairs and setae on the bodies of exposed insects, accumulate and eventually work their way into the insect's body.

Cold foggers are available in varying models and sizes. Some models of ULV machines deliver the pesticide directly from a nozzle on the machine; others have flexible extension hoses that can be used to make application of fine particles at a distance from the machine. The smaller handheld models are powered by electricity and are commonly used indoors in commercial facilities such as restaurants, hotel kitchens, and a wide range of commercial storage rooms. The larger models (see Figure 5.15) are typically powered by gasoline and are mounted on wheel carts or trucks. These models are often used for outdoor spraying programs. Indoors, they are commonly used for space treatments of large warehouses and similar operations.

Cold fogging machines are helpful in providing knockdown of flying insects (flies, gnats, mosquitoes, etc.), and crawling insects (cockroaches) that are exposed to the cold fog at the time of spraying. However, there is considerable doubt as to the effectiveness of cold foggers in controlling overall infestations of crawling insects such as cockroach-

Figure 5.15. An ultra-low-volume (ULV) machine used for conducting space treatments in large open spaces such as distribution warehouses.

es, or grain moths and beetles in food warehouses if these machines are used alone.

The synergized pyrethrins or synthetic pyrethroid pesticides used in these machines do an excellent job of flushing some crawling insects from certain types of insect harborage. For example, the insects that are flushed out by small aerosols particles are usually using surface harborage areas such as the cracks and crevices on the edge of a table. But because small aerosol droplets will go only where air currents will carry them, most aerosol droplets will not penetrate into deep cracks and crevices, wall and cabinet voids, deep equipment voids, closed boxes, closed cabinets, or any other areas where air currents don't readily travel. Simply stated, fogging (cold or thermal) treatments alone will not effectively control cockroaches. Nor can space treatments effectively control an infestation of grain moths or beetles infesting a grain warehouse because insecticidal fogs cannot reach the developing stages of the pests.

Therefore, when attempting to provide more than control of the available insects (during the time of the treatment), residual sprays or additional programs (where permitted) are recommended to supplement fogging operations. Where residual sprays are not permitted, a wet spray of synergized pyrethrins or synthetic pyrethroids applied by a handheld sprayer should be used so that insects driven out by fogs will have to walk on the wet pesticide. This combination of treatments will produce better control of pests than the use of a fogging operation alone.

Proper calibration of cold fogging equipment is critical. If aerosol droplets are too large, they settle out of the air too rapidly; if too small, they will be deflected around the target insect rather than hitting and sticking on it. Therefore, the operating directions for cold fogging machines and the labels of the specific pesticides for these machines must be strictly adhered to. Improper use of some of these machines can result in explosions or fires; pesticide contamination; and/or oil-residue damage to furniture, surfaces, and equipment.

Applicators not thoroughly experienced with cold fogging equipment often feel the need to see a fog or cloud being produced from the machine to be convinced a pesticide is actually being applied. However, when cold fogging equipment is calibrated correctly, the pesticide droplets should not be visible except under certain types of refractory light. Running a cold fogging machine at a setting that produces a visible fog defeats the effectiveness of the machine, while also creating the potential for various hazards.

The following are important procedures to follow when cold fogging machines are used indoors:

- The appropriate respirator must be worn when operating cold fogging equipment.
- Prior to treatments, any building occupants must be informed that they will need to evacuate the area to be treated for several hours following treatment. All pets (dogs, cats, birds) must be removed. All green plants must be covered or removed. All aquariums must be disconnected and covered.
- All exposed foods and utensils must be stored or removed.
- Food contacting surfaces should be covered.
- All doors, windows, and other openings to the outside should be closed and locked. Cold fog applications are not effective in well-ventilated rooms. Also, they are less effective if made at temperatures lower than 50º F.
- If the target pests are infesting cabinets, drawers, and other such areas, the cabinet doors and drawers should be kept wide open.
- Pilot lights and any other open flames must be turned off, as well as ventilation systems, fans, and blowers.
- Before treated buildings are reoccupied, they must be ventilated by opening windows and doors.
- After treatment, any food contact surfaces that were exposed during fogging should be thoroughly washed.
- When using cold fogging machines in potentially hazardous areas such as flour mills, gas engines cannot be used. Electric motors must be explosion-proof.

Mist machines. An example of a mist blower is the common electric paint sprayer. These mist machines and others contain a tank holding the liquid and an air-mix nozzle. The unit can be activated with air under relatively high pressure to force the liquid through a very small nozzle opening. The principle involved is the same as in a handheld compressed-air sprayer except much less pressure is used when spraying with the hand sprayer.

Mist machines (such as mist blowers), were once widely used in the pest control industry. However, these machines have been replaced by ULD equipment or the specialized compressed-air sprayers with the aerosol nozzle tips. Large, motorized mist blowers may still be used in some mosquito control programs and fruit orchard spraying programs.

Thermal foggers. Thermal foggers create a insecticide fog by introducing an oil-based insecticide formulation into a chamber that is heated to a temperature sufficient to cause immediate vaporization of the oil. Thermal foggers (also referred to as thermal aerosol generators) are the "true foggers" of pest control equipment because the majority of the aerosol droplets produced by thermal foggers are in the fog-size category.

The heat source used to vaporize the oil in fog generators is produced either by a flame in a heat chamber, by an electrically heated chamber, by steam velocity ejection, or by using the exhaust stream of a jet or internal combustion engine.

Larger foggers put out large volumes of fog at a rate of 30 to 60 gallons per hour and are usually used for large-scale outdoor work, such as mosquito control. Under certain conditions they are also used indoors to treat large buildings, such as warehouses.

Smaller, portable foggers put out smaller quantities of insecticide (5 to 15 gallons per hour) and are used for treatment inside buildings and for smaller areas outdoors.

Pesticide droplets produced by fog generators are very small, ranging in size between 0.2 and 10 microns. For this reason, fogs have the ability to penetrate between leaves of vegetation and they float in the air long enough to kill mosquitoes, gnats, and other small flying insects that use vegetation as harborage.

It is important to note that a pesticide fog produced by a thermal fogger behaves in the same manner as does the small aerosol droplets of cold fogging equipment. Thus, fogs move only on available air currents. Any exhaust air current leaving the building will also take the fog out of the building. Also, fog particles do not move against the inside of cold exterior walls.

Outdoor fogging operations for flying insect control are done most effectively when the vehicle carrying the fog machine is not moving in excess of 10 miles per hour and when the wind velocity is not above 5 mph. Winds greater than this blow the pesticide out of the area too fast, which results in poor insect control.

Some of the same recommendations made for using cold foggers also applies to thermal foggers. A few additional safety considerations:

- When used indoors it is possible for these machines to build up a sufficient concentration of insecticidal fog in the atmosphere to cause explosions. Thus, pesticide must not be injected into closed spaces using a thermal fogger (containing oil diluents) in an amount exceeding 1 gallon of pesticide per 50,000 cubic feet of enclosed space. Any amount greater than this may create an explosive mixture.
- Before treating with a thermal fogger, all open flames must be extinguished. Also, electric switches must not be turned on or off while there is fog in the air.
- Both large and small thermal fog machines become extremely hot during operation. The operator must be careful not to contact the heated portions of the fog machine or to allow any objects to contact these areas.
- Some thermal fog machines intermittently and unexpectedly project a flame from the nozzle. The nozzle of thermal foggers must be kept away from any combustible materials or appliances.

Dusters and Granular Applicators

Dusts and granular formulations of insecticides are widely used in the industry. Indoors, dusts are used for controlling cockroaches, silverfish, carpenter ants, and other insect pests that hide in cracks and crevices and wall voids inside buildings. Outdoors, granular contact insecticides and granular formulations of baits are used as general-purpose treatments for a wide variety of perimeter pests such as ants, millipedes, ground beetles, crickets, and others. Therefore, the equipment used for applying dusts and/or granules should be selected carefully and used properly.

The equipment used to apply dusts are referred to as "dusters." However, granular pesticides and some rodenticide tracking powders are also commonly applied using duster equipment. Thus dusters have evolved into serving pest professionals as multipurpose applicators. Dusters are of two broad types: (1) **hand dusters** and (2) **powered dusters**. Certain equipment is also used specifically for applying only granular insecticides or granular bait formulations and this equipment is referred to as **granular applicators**.

Hand Dusters/Granular Applicators

Hand dusters are used to apply dusts, granular insecticides, and occasionally tracking powders. For dusts, hand dusters are used to introduce small quantities of dusts in thin layers into cracks and crevices and various wall, cabinet bases and/or equipment voids. There are three types of hand dusters: (1) bulb dusters; (2) bellows duster and (3) plunger dusters. Depending on the type and model, hand dusters can hold from 4 to 64 ounces of dust or granular insecticides.

The smaller **bulb** and **bellows dusters** hold up to 4 to 8 ounces of material. The dust is ejected when the bulb or bellows is squeezed—forcing the dust out of the duster in a dust-air mixture (see Figure 5.16). Some professionals prefer using a bel-

Figure 5.16. A bellows hand duster. Note that the spout of this duster is the top area of the duster. By gently squeezing the duster, a fine dust-air mixture can be applied to cracks and crevices. (Myers)

lows-style hand duster while others prefer a bulb-style or a modified bulb-style duster. Hand dusters are available with various types of extension tips that enable the professional to get the dust into deep wall voids and other hard-to-reach areas.

The bulb-style duster is often modified to be used as a **granular applicator** by removing the screen and by either removing or shortening the nozzle tip to permit the granules to flow out of the bulb smoothly (see Figure 5.17). One of the more valuable accessories to the bulb duster/granular applicator is an inexpensive "filler funnel" that allows for rapid filling of the bulb duster without spillage or loss of materials. Several of the manufacturers of granular insecticides and baits package their granular product into containers that are designed to allow the product to be shaken out of the container saving the need for a separate piece of equipment. And some manufacturers also offer their own applicators (e.g., "snuffers") to be used with their products.

The larger **plunger dusters** can be used to apply dusts, granules, and tracking powders. Depending on the model, plunger dusters can hold from 14 to 64 ounces of material. The forward action of the plunger forces a current of air down a tube, carrying dust with it as it leaves the nozzle. The amount of material applied will vary according to how vigorously the plunger is pumped and the location of the material within the top or bottom of the duster's cylinder. Plunger dusters come equipped with extension tubes and various nozzle tips.

Because plunger dusters can hold more material than the bulb/bellows dusters, they can be used on larger-size jobs without having to refill frequently. However, it is more difficult to maintain

Tips for the proper use of hand dusters for applying dust and granular insecticides

Applying insecticidal dusts in paper-thin layers is the key for the dusts providing maximum effect. In fact, many crawling insects are actually repelled by thick layers of dust. To achieve fine, thin layers of dusts, the following tips are helpful:

- Fill the duster no more than 2/3 full.
- When dusting, keep the spout above the level of the dust inside the duster.
- Continuously shake the duster in a gentle manner between each squeeze to create the desired air-dust mixture.
- Place pebbles or small ball bearings in the hand duster to aid in breaking up clumps of powder and agitate the entire contents of the duster. This helps in applying the very fine layer of dust necessary for good insect control.
- When dusting around electrical outlets or appliances with dusters containing metal spouts, place a small section of rubber or plastic tubing over the metal tip to avoid contacting electrical wires. Some commercial dusters are equipped with only plastic spouts. Others provide plastic extension tubes that can be placed over the metal spout.
- Always keep the screen on bulb dusters in place as

these help to maintain the fine dust consistency.
- Duster should not be left in vehicles overnight during cold temperatures. Chilled dusts do not float as well as warm dust.

It is also important for the dust inside the duster to remain dry, otherwise the dusters constantly become clogged. To prevent clogging, a few simple steps should be followed:

- Placing the tip of the duster in a moist spot should be avoided as the duster may suck up water and debris.
- Ream out the spout occasionally using a small piece of stiff wire will clear a clogged duster.
- It is best if separate dusters are used for granular insecticides and insecticide dusts. This is also true for using hand dusters for rodenticide tracking powders. If the same duster is to be used for different formulations, the duster must be thoroughly cleaned.
- Store hand dusters in tight, dry containers or plastic "zipper" bags.
- Each duster container should be properly labeled as to the contents of the duster.

Figure 5.17. Bulb-style "dusters" can be easily modified for use as a granular insecticides/ baits applicator. (Myers)

control of the quantity and accurate placement of the pesticide with plunger dusters than with the smaller bulb style dusters.

When large amounts of granules need to be applied (e.g., around the perimeter of large commercial accounts), portable hand-cranked whirly seeders (the same devices that are used to seed and fertilize turf areas) can be used. These devices can be worn around the neck and the granules or baits can be distributed while walking.

Battery-powered dusters

Powered dusters have changed markedly during the last few years because of the increased use of dusts. Handheld dusters are now available that contain rechargeable batteries to provide power for automatic applications of dusts and fine granular applications.

These dusters can be used to make precise applications to wall voids, cracks and crevices, cabinet voids, and other hard to reach or out of reach areas under continuous pressure without having to refill or recharge the duster. Some models come equipped with various types of extendable plastic hoses or tubes that allow for convenient treatment of overhead bee and/or wasp's nests (see Figure 5.18).

Extension dusters and bee poles

The extension duster/granular applicator is another type of "duster" that is used to treat overhead, out-of-reach areas without having to climb ladders. Extension dusters are equipped with lightweight aluminum telescoping poles, to facilitate treating up to 20 feet away. These dusters are invaluable for treating overhead bee/wasp nests, carpenter ants, cockroaches and silverfish in attic and soffit voids, tree cavities, etc. Some models contain handy scrapers for removing wasp nests.

Depending on the model, the dust chamber may be located at the top of the tubing or at the base with the plunger. Some extension dusters are also available in various power-driven models.

Bee poles enable a professional to treat out-of-reach overhead areas for bee nests without the use of a ladder. Bee poles are usually telescoping aluminum poles containing a prepressurized aerosols at the end of an extendable poles. The aerosols are activated by release cords to activate the release valves on the aerosol.

Extension dusters and bee poles not only save time in treating aerial nests by eliminating the need to install and climb ladders, but are considerably more welcomed by the technician assigned to eliminate an aerial bee nest from the comfort of the ground instead of dodging active bees 25 feet up on a ladder!

The use of extension dusters and bee poles also helps to minimize the costs associated with worker's compensation claims when employees fall from ladders attempting to dodge dangerous insects or over-reaching in attempts to access difficult-to-reach areas.

Safety training and on-the-job awareness is critical when using extension dusters and bee poles. Applicators must be aware of electrical lines at all times when using these, or any other telescoping pest control equipment.

SPECIALIZED PEST MANAGEMENT EQUIPMENT

Pest elimination/cleaning equipment

Several pieces of ordinary cleaning equipment have become adopted and sometimes modified by the

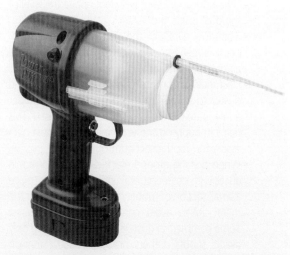

Figure 5.18. A handheld, battery-operated hand duster. Several models are available with a wide range of accessories for making versatile dust applications.

pest management industry to enable them to be used to eliminate pest infestations. This equipment can be used to directly remove pests from their harborages or kill the pests within their harborages with the use of heat and/or steam. Such equipment fits nicely into the IPM approach because it offers effective techniques for those situations where chemicals may be undesirable or unallowed.

Vacuums are now considered by most professionals to be essential pest management equipment—especially for those situations where little or no pesticide applications are warranted.

For years, vacuums were used primarily as a cleaning supplement to chemical pest control procedures. But new technology has enabled vacuum devices to be used for removing and/or reducing pest populations of German cockroaches, fleas from carpets, bed bugs, spiders, ladybug beetles, wasps, ants, psocids, cluster flies, fabric pests, and other pests (see Figure 5.19).

Vacuums used for pest management procedures must be equipped with HEPA (NP 100) filters (high-efficiency particulate air) that eliminate the allergenic airborne insect fragments, other arthropod allergens (house dust mite), as well as various pathogenic microorganisms. For example, because the HEPA filter filters down to 0.3 microns, these filters are used in facial respirators to protect against Hanta virus and other possible pathogens while working in crawlspaces and similar environments.

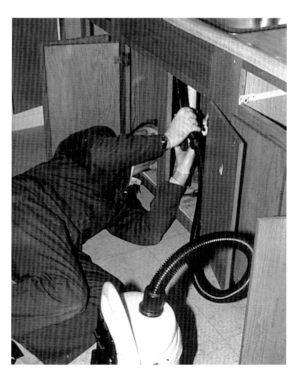

Figure 5.19. Vacuums can be used to suck a wide range of urban pests from their harborages; they provide an excellent nonchemical tool.

Various accessories and model types enhance the usefulness of vacuum devices.

Backpack vacuums are available that enable the professional to work hands-free operation. A wide selection of attachments, such as the crack and crevice micro units, enables the professional to reach pests in difficult and hard-to-reach locations, as well as being able to clean computers, and other office machines.

Some professionals employ hair dryers or industrial strength hand-heaters to first flush cockroaches and bed bugs out of their crevices and suck up the pests as they run out trying to avoid the heat. In sensitive accounts such as schools, nursing homes, hospitals, and public office buildings, the flush/vacuum systems combined with trapping, monitoring and baiting programs have become the standard cockroach treatment regime.

Other general uses and advantages of vacuum devices in urban pest management include the following:

- Removal of breeding mediums for insect pests such as stored grain pests, fabric pests.
- Quick removal of indoor ants nests, cluster fly masses, ladybird beetle masses, etc.
- Direct removal of fleas from carpeting (must be done on a daily basis).
- Easy monitoring of infiltrating pests in food plants (i.e., by examining the catch of the vacuum device).
- Quick removal and clean up of rodent droppings and rodent contaminants (shredded nests, hairs).
- Clean insect light trap catch pans and lights.
- Provide a means to conduct nonchemical pest management operations in chemically sensitive environments.
- Remove pests from various appliances, machines, and sensitive electronic equipment.

Spider brush. One of the most widely used piece of equipment by pest management professionals with residential routes is the **spider brush**. Spider brushes are merely modified cleaning brushes installed on poles to facilitate overhead removal of spiders and their webs. The brush must be cleaned after each use and all captured spiders destroyed.

Steam/vapor machines. High temperatures are used in different programs to kill structural pests (e.g., heat treatments in food plants to kill stored product pest infestations). Similarly, portable steam-generating equipment is becoming increasingly popular to treat drain flies, bed bugs and mites in mattresses, stored product pests, fleas, mites, and other pests.

Pestproofing Equipment

One of the essential principles of urban IPM is pest exclusion. As such, more emphasis is being placed on pestproofing materials and equipment.

This topic in itself is would require a full chapter to discuss it thoroughly. But as an overview, the important pestproofing equipment for the pest management professional involves the use of sealants, anti-pest tension strips, screens, netting, and other appropriate equipment.

Sealing operations can have tremendous impact on denying many pests entry into buildings (e.g., cluster flies, ladybugs, yellowjackets, etc.). Sealing various cracks and crevices around equipment and walls indoors can help corral cockroaches away from sensitive areas and into areas that are easily accessible during a service visit. Effective heavy-duty sealant compounds and sealant/caulking guns are available for those who perform exclusion services on a serious level.

New technology in door brushes is effective in denying pests entry into commercial facilities and should always be offered as part of a total IPM program by professionals. New technology has produced door brush systems that are easily installed and easily replaced, much in the same manner as is done with automobile windshield wipers. The brushes come in many different styles and sizes to fit all the different types of doors within commercial establishments including dock plates.

Hardware cloth and screens play an obvious and important role in pest denial operations. Screens of various mesh sizes and materials are available for nearly any structural situation. However, a professional must be knowledgeable regarding mesh sizes relative to the specific pests needing to be excluded. Screens and mesh sizes must also be fitted so as to be compatible with the air-flow requirements of commercial accounts.

Various specific materials for rodent and bird and wildlife proofing are discussed within their respective chapters (see Chapters 15–17).

Steam/vapor machines employ low-pressure water vapor at temperatures of about 220° F. Such temperatures in direct contact or close range to arthropods are lethal. Thus, steam/vapor machines can be used to nonchemically eliminate the breeding sources and maggots of small flies in dirty drains and other microenvironments. Steam machines can also be used to treat for bed bugs in mattresses, fleas in carpeting, small patches of grain moths or beetles. Additionally, steam/vapor machines can be

used as an "add-on" service by pest professionals to clean drains, remove feces and fecal marks, clean the hard-to-reach areas beneath commercial sinks and other low-lying equipment, etc. When decaying organic materials and the food clutter that commonly accumulate in these areas are removed any pests occupying these areas are eliminated.

Computers/Electronic Data Processing Equipment

Perhaps more than any other piece of equipment discussed in this chapter, the potential of computer hardware, software, customized company networking programs and the Internet all represent the most exciting frontier in this new millennium.

Computer equipment and a wide variety of portable hardware and software systems are now standard operating equipment for up-to-date pest management companies. For example, handheld personal data managers (PDM) and electronic clipboards are being used by technicians on-the-job for inspections, routing, record keeping, situation analysis, and a wide range of client-specific functions.

Scanning devices with bar code technology and readers are used for data gathering and record keeping of many pest management devices such as exterior termite bait stations, interior and exterior pest monitoring stations, interior mouse trapping programs (for large warehouse accounts), insect light traps, etc. (see Figure 5. 20). The accompanying software to the various PDMs is developing at a frantic pace providing very impressive high-tech capabilities for the average pest professional—even

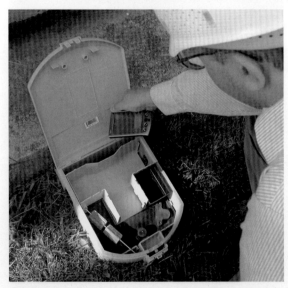

Insert Figure 5.20. Bar coding of equipment can be used for quick scanning using various types of handheld personal data managers (PDMs).

for those that aren't necessarily "computer savvy."

The Internet now provides PMPs everywhere with the ability to gather immediate access to updates on virtually any aspect of pest management, such as downloading pesticide labels, MSDS, equipment updates and specifications and so forth. The Web can also be used to update memberships, register for meetings and conventions, join pest management chat rooms, and review the current issues of the industry's magazines.

But perhaps one of the most powerful aspects of the Web is that it offers a PMP an opportunity to become quickly informed on issues of periodical importance. For example, by accessing the websites of the Centers for Disease Control (**www.CDC.gov**) or the particular state board of health's, a pest professional can obtain updates and background information on important health-related issues (e.g., West Nile virus, Hanta virus, food poisoning, etc.). Or, a pest professional can download up-to-date biology and behavior information on virtually any important urban pest species simply by accessing any one of a dozen entomology departments from around the country.

EQUIPMENT FOR CONDUCTING PEST CONTROL INSPECTIONS

The inspection is the most important phase of any pest management operation. To be effective in solving a pest problem, the professional must correctly identify the pest, the locations and extent of the pest infestation, and the structural and/or environmental conditions that may be conducive to encouraging the pest problem. Consequently, certain equipment is necessary for conducting professional-level pest inspections, which includes being able to gain access to structural areas and equipment voids to verify the presence of pests, install a control device, or make a possible treatment.

Flashlight

Although simple in form and function, the flashlight is probably the most important piece of equipment in the pest management industry. Many insects, rodents, and other pests are secretive by nature. They hide in inaccessible or difficult-to-reach areas, and/or are active at times when people are inactive (i.e., at night). As such, the professional must often venture into and inspect areas that are poorly lighted such as attics, basements, and crawlspaces. Moreover, he or she must have visual access to many nooks and crannies above, below, and within all kinds of equipment and storage items. Rarely do such areas contain enough light to expose hiding pests or evidence of their presence. Thus, the flashlight is essential in all pest management operations. When used properly, it can make the difference between successfully solving a pest problem or overlooking a critical aspect of the problem and having to make several callbacks and facing disappointed clients.

Tips for Selecting and Using Flashlights for Pest Management Operations

Flashlights are available in a wide variety of models (see Figure 5.21). However, for pest management operations, a flashlight classified as heavy duty is required. Cheap, homeowner flashlights are not adequate. The two most important factors to consider when selecting a flashlight for professional use are durability and light intensity. The professional's flashlight must withstand constant abuse, day in, day out, and still perform. It must also produce a strong beam of light (e.g., 15,000 or more candlepower) to adequately illuminate pests or pest signs in darkened areas.

Flashlight body and lens. The body casing of the professional's flashlight must be resistant to breakage because it is likely to be dropped in the course of everyday working conditions. The casing should also be waterproof and corrosion resistant. For these reasons, heavy-gauge plastic, rubber, or metal are the preferred materials for the body casing.

Long-handled bodies can hold more batteries (and thus produce more power), but are bulkier and more difficult to carry, handle, and balance than the shorter bodies. Body color is also a con-

Figure 5.21. The flashlight is the most important inspection tool. Models that are compact, bright, lightweight, and highly durable are most popular with pest management professionals.

sideration. Bright yellow or orange bodies are easier to retrieve if dropped in a dark area than are solid-black flashlights.

The lens of the professional's flashlight should be made of shatterproof plastic, not glass (many food and pharmaceutical facilities do not permit the use of flashlights that are not shatterproof/explosionproof).

Bulbs. The bulb must deliver a bright concentrated beam of light. Halogen bulbs produce extremely bright light and are the choice of many professionals, even though they are more expensive than standard bulbs.

Power source. Flashlights can be powered either by standard disposable batteries or by rechargeable batteries and recharging units. Because the average life of a two-cell flashlight is approximately two to three hours of continuous use, batteries require regular replacement to maintain the strength of light necessary for professional inspections. Standard batteries, however, provide advance warning of power exhaustion because they begin to dim prior to power exhaustion.

Some rechargeable flashlights can be charged via a charge holder plugged into a vehicle's power source. The flashlight can then be recharged "on the road" while driving between accounts. The drawback to rechargeable flashlights is that they die rather suddenly, and the professional may be caught in a dark attic or crawlspace without a light.

Overall, it may be wise for the professional to have access to two types of flashlights. The standard two-cell flashlight will serve the needs of the professional in accounts and situations where only cursory types of inspections and pesticide applications are required (e.g., maintenance work in residential accounts). In cases of loss or breakage, these flashlights are not expensive to replace. Some facilities such as the larger industrial plants, or situations such as large, dark, crawlspaces or attics, will demand extremely bright and powerful light. For these instances, the use of the "ultra" powerful (e.g., 75,000 candlepower) flashlights may be required.

Whichever type of flashlight is used, extra flashlights and parts (batteries, bulbs), should be carried on the vehicle to allow for battery and bulb wear and the occasional loss of the flashlight.

A **flashlight holder** that can be attached to the belt of the professional is a wise accessory. The holder serves to protect the flashlight when it's not in use. Flashlights stuffed into back pockets tend to fall out, breaking the lenses and sometimes expensive halogen bulbs. A holder also helps reduce the occurences of leaving the flashlight in the vehicle or

at a work site. Finally, a flashlight kept neatly and safely in a holder presents to the public a far more professional image of our industry than does a flashlight that sticks or hangs out of a technician's back pocket.

Flushing Agents

A flushing agent (containing pyrethrins or another insecticide that stimulates insects) is an essential inspection tool because it forces cryptobiotic insects (e.g., cockroaches, carpenter ants, bed bugs, silverfish, etc.) from their hiding spots. In many cases, it is impossible to physically see into the harborages of these pests such as hollow table legs, light sockets, wall crevices, cabinet and wall voids, and so forth. Flushing agents can reveal if insects are present in these and other inaccessible harborages. Cans of flushing agents can be kept in beltpouches for convenient and hands-free inspections when needed.

Hand Mirrors

A small, metal hand mirror enables the professional to see underneath, on top of, and behind equipment and objects. And, by reflecting the flashlight beam off the mirror, the inspector can gain visual access into many out-of-sight areas such as the inside corners of equipment, furniture, and air ducts. A furnace inspector's metal mirror with a telescoping handle (available through pest control suppliers) permits even greater capabilities for viewing into difficult-to-see areas above or below arms reach.

Utility Tools

A small, portable tool set containing a few types of screwdrivers and ratchets permits the professional to disassemble various inspection plates, ventilator grills, and access panels for inspection and/or treating purposes. Some brands of pocketknives and "multitools" come equipped with various knife blades, screwdrivers, and forceps that can serve as convenient utility tools.

Utility inspection tools can be kept in a **tool pouch** (see Figure 5.22). And, like the flashlight, the "inspection tool pouch" can be worn on a trouser or utility belt, making the tools conveniently available to the professional when they are needed.

A **ladder** is a valuable inspection tool for management programs involving carpenter ants, mice, roof rats, birds, and cockroaches. A ladder kept on the service truck facilitates a professional's ability to inspect suspended ceilings, cathedral ceilings, outdoor roof areas, and other overhead areas when

Figure 5.22. Access tools such as a screwdrivers, tack puller, thin-blade spatulas, and others of personal choice can make the difference between successfully accessing the primary pest source or missing it completely and facing expensive callbacks.

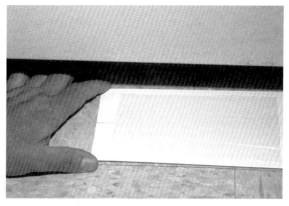

Figure 5.23. An inexpensive sticky monitoring trap. When placed correctly, monitoring traps can provide quick feedback on the presence or absence of pests, their severity, and the pest's population distribution. (Myers)

necessary. For safety reasons, chairs should never be used as substitute ladders.

Monitoring Traps

Monitoring traps have become one of the most important tools in urban IPM evolution and movement. These devices can be used as tools to alert the professional as to the severity of an insect infestation as well as to where insect "hot spots" may exist. They can also provide clues as to the direction the insects are traveling, helping to narrow down the source of the infestation. Monitor traps can record the presence or absence of pests and/or the numbers of pests before and after a control program. By utilizing the monitor traps in this fashion, the overall effectiveness of the program can be demonstrated to both the professional and to the client.

Monitoring traps are available as inexpensive cardboard sticky traps that are meant to be disposable after only several days or weeks of time (see Figure 5.23). Some of these traps come flat and are folded into various size traps. Others come pre-assembled and ready for immediate placement.

More elaborate and multifunctional monitoring/bait stations, comprised of tamper-resistant plastic into which small sticky pads or even baits, are also available (see Figure 5.24). These monitoring stations can be reused for many years and provide a very professional image of IPM to the client. These traps cost more than the disposable cardboard monitors, but will withstand the expected contact by employees at the work site, cleaning operations, and items falling or being placed on them. The more

sophisticated traps are best suited for facilities where formal urban IPM programs are essential such as schools, food and pharmaceutical plants, biotech firms, zoological gardens, etc. In some cases, certain models of mouse traps containing sticky boards can also serve this function (refer to Chapter 15).

In addition to the sticky monitoring traps, pheromone **monitoring traps** also can also be used for various stored product and fabric pests (refer to Chapters 10 and 11).

Insect Identification and Collection Tools

A hand **magnifying lens** should be considered an essential on-the-job tool for every pest professional (see Figure 5.25). The hand lens can often aid in identifying to species pests such as ants, small flies, wood-destroying beetles, grain beetles, and moths. For example, because some ant species respond to baits while others do not, keying out the ant properly is essential. A hand lens can also aid in differentiating between insect, rodent, toad, bat, and other

Figure 5.24. Pest monitoring traps are essential tools for any urban IPM program. Many models are available to fit a variety of needs depending on the job site.

Insert 5.25. A hand lens is an essential on-the-job pest identification tool. (Myers)

animal fecal pellets. When on-the-job identification is not possible, plastic vials (e.g., empty medicine vials, film canisters, etc.) can be used for collecting insect specimens for positive identification at a later date (or for inclusion into insect collections).

For professionals requiring more than a simple hand lens but not wanting to invest in a formal scientific microscope, field macroscopes are available that provide good resolutions and relatively high magnifications (e.g., **www.rfinterscience.com**)

Removable adhesive **labels** are useful on inspections for recording specimen collections. These labels are also useful for marking pest hot spots and structural problems, and for dating bait containers, etc. These labels are available in many shapes and colors from office supply stores.

Inspection Diagrams and Reports/Building Plans

Taking a few moments to construct an **inspection diagram** that presents an overview of the structure and surrounding buildings and areas can be extremely useful in helping to solve pest problems. In some cases, inspection diagrams need not be more complex than just an outline of the building and its surrounding environment. Such an overview often helps to see the "big picture" clearly and thus, to be able to consider all the factors inside and outside the account that may affect the pest problem. Diagrams also are invaluable in helping to recall details if needed at a later time.

Currently, sophisticated computer portable writing tablets are available. These "electronic clipboards" allow for reports and diagrams to be professionally transcribed from the professional's own handwriting or "scribbles" on the job to a highly

polished appearing document when downloaded and printed out at the office. Like the handheld scanning devices, such electronic tablet tools are likely to become indispensable for general pest management, as well as termite inspections and graph generating.

It is a pest professional's responsibility to provide feedback to clients on the status of a pest problem, as well as all the conducive conditions affecting the pest problem. **Inspection reports** should list the specific pests present, the extent of the infestation, the control tools and chemicals to be used, structural deficiencies in need of the customers attention, and so on. Inspection reports can help to protect both the professional and the customer. (Some examples of inspection reports are provided in Chapter 18).

For pest management operations in large or complex buildings (hospitals, high-rise condominiums, schools, etc.), **building plans** enable a professional to visualize floors and rooms above, below, and on all sides of problem areas. Building plans also help to illustrate the overall layout of the buildings, utility lines, heating/cooling ducts, shaft connections, pipe chases, and so on. Such information can help to pinpoint areas within the building complex that are warm and humid. This, in turn, can aid in identifying high-activity areas of insects that require such environments (e.g., pharaoh ants, cockroaches, silverfish and others). Building plans are also valuable for determining potential entry points of pests into buildings and possible "migration paths" of pests from one part of a building to another. Finally, building plans can serve as a checklist to organize large pest management programs and help to ensure all pertinent areas of the building complex receive attention.

Miscellaneous Inspection Equipment

Equipment carrying cases are available from various suppliers for transporting various pest management equipment. Some professionals employ heavy-duty cloth pocketed belts that fit snugly around a sprayer. Other professionals simply use heavy-duty buckets and pails. Various types of plastic boxes are also available in a wide assortment in the typical mart-style store.

Cameras are especially useful inspection tools for both residential and commercial facilities where it is important to document situations and/or areas that may need correction by the client. Inexpensive **digital cameras** are now available that enable any professional to take photographs that can be downloaded into electronic files and directly incorporated into reports. Some homeowners and commercial clients (e.g., food, pharmaceutical, biotech plants, etc.) often do not allow any photographs to be taken on their premises. Always seek permission prior to using any camera on the job. It is important to keep in mind that digital images are usually not acceptable as evidence for litigation cases as the images are easily edited.

For inspections involving wood-destroying insects such as termites, wood-boring beetles, and carpenter ants, **moisture meters, humidity meters, sound-detection devices, fiberoptic telescopes,** and **movement detection devices** are all useful inspection equipment.

The **moisture meter** (see Figure 5.26), can pinpoint moisture problems within a structure that may lead to or be the cause of insect infestations or wooden structural deficiencies. Many wood infesting insect pests often seek wood or structural environments with relatively high levels of moisture and humidity. Moreover, high levels of moisture in wood and wall voids commonly lead to various wood-destroying fungi. (For additional information regarding the use of moisture meters, refer to Chapter 8).

Humidity meters are also available that can measure the humidity level of an area. Although this may seem excessively specialized to some, keep in mind that several important pest groups (e.g., termites, ants, stored product pests, etc.) occupy those areas inside structures and structural components that provide them with relatively high levels of humidity. Thus, such devices, similar in concept to the moisture meter can help a professional to focus their attention on those areas more vulnerable to pest infestations.

Figure 5.26. A moisture meter can pinpoint moisture problems that may lead to or be the cause of insect infestations or structural deficiencies within a structure.

Sound detection devices can be used to actually hear structural pests at work inside wooden members or wall voids. In some cases, a common stethoscope (available at most drug stores) can be used for insects such as carpenter ants. For termites and other smaller wood-destroying insects, there are fairly sophisticated sound-detection devices available that amplify the sounds of any movement made by these insects, or even the sounds of the termite worker's mandibles chewing on wooden fragments.

Movement detection devices became known to the pest management industry in about 2001. This technology allows for detection of even the smallest of movement of insects or animals inside any type of substrate (e.g., wood, concrete, sheetrock) or within any type of structural void or ground cavities.

This technology is rather unique in that the microwave detectors can be very specific about the animal making the movement inside a wall (e.g, a termite vs a mouse). Moreover microwave equipment is effective in penetrating concrete or wood ranging from 3 to 5 inches/7.5 cm to 12.7 cm in thickness even if there is an air space of 2 feet /0.6 m separating two substrates. In this respect, this technology far exceeds the technology of using sound-detection devices. Considering the potential for callbacks, re-treatments and the litigation associated with WDO work and inspections, microwave inspection equipment certainly has strong possibilities for providing professional assistance. Movement-detection devices utilize microwave technology and are likely to become available in different formats over the next several years.

Fiberoptic telescopes can be used by pest professionals for seeing into various types of wall, floor, ceiling, and equipment voids. Some scopes permit viewing into various inaccessible spaces with only 0.5 inch/1.2 cm diameters with resolutions ranging from 0.75 inch/1.9 cm to 12.0 inches/30.5 cm with 40-degree views. Lamps attached to the fiberoptic telescope provide light for the void. Such telescopes can provide valuable insight into many structural areas and help to pinpoint (or confirm the absence of) termites, ants, urban wildlife, moisture and mold problems.

A **portable drill** can serve as an important treatment tool for pest management operations. A drill enables the professional to gain access into wall, cabinet, ceiling, and equipment voids for the purpose of injecting dusts or other types of insecticides. In fact, the operation of drilling and dusting is probably one of most effective methods of long-term control of crawling insects that live deep in cracks and crevices or voids, or for accessing carpenter ants, or bees and wasps in soffits, and walls, etc. Some of these areas are often impossible to treat without first drilling an access hole.

A **pocket-sized tape recorder** can serve as an important "note-taker" during termite or sanitation inspections.

EQUIPMENT MAINTENANCE

Equipment must be kept clean and in good repair at all times. Moderate, continuous, preventive care will maintain equipment in good condition if performed in advance of problems. When purchasing new equipment, be sure to obtain from the manufacturer or supplier all available information on its construction, maintenance, and operation.

Instruction manuals and diagrams that show the construction of equipment must always be retained and organized in a binder. These documents should be accessible so that when repairs or replacement parts are necessary, the binder can be easily referred to. With each new piece of equipment, the manufacturer's instructions should always be carefully followed. Instruction manuals provide the most up-to-date and specific maintenance instructions. It is prudent for the professional to periodically review the manuals for specific care and maintenance instructions.

The following discussion provides additional general guidelines for proper equipment maintenance. Weekly cleaning and maintenance of the one-gallon hand-held sprayer is discussed in Appendix G.

Large-Volume Sprayers

Many of the same principles for maintaining and cleaning the handheld sprayer also apply to the large- and mid-volume sprayers. However, improper maintenance of the larger units can be especially troublesome or costly.

Large-volume sprayers must be cleaned regularly, not less than once each week if they are in regular use. Sprayers that are not regularly used, or are used with a variety of chemicals, should be cleaned with detergent and water after each use. In areas, where spray rigs may be down for several months due to the winter, the motor's oil should be changed, gaskets checked and replaced. The entire system should be flushed, including the tank. After this washing, clean water should be used as a rinse. Many PMPs in the colder regions of the country winterize their rigs with antifreeze.

Special care must be given to the **strainers**. These are located at different places on different sprayers, such as at the discharge tube, at the discharge valve, and at the nozzle. Strainers are cleaned by removing them and backflushing with water in the reverse direction from the normal flow of pesticide. Where this does not remove all extraneous material on the screen, it may be necessary to soak the screen in a solvent that will dissolve the pesticide that has been used. If a screen has been damaged or if it is impossible to clean thoroughly, discard it and replace it with a new one.

Valves must always be maintained in good repair. They should open easily and rapidly, should shut off quickly and tightly, and should not leak. Packing gaskets in the valve should be made of materials that are resistant to the chemicals being used and should be replaced as frequently as required to prevent leakage. When it is necessary to take a valve apart, the gaskets should be replaced at the same time.

Nozzles require special care. Much of the effectiveness of a pesticide application depends on the proper functioning of the nozzle. Nozzle tips are designed to give a specific shape of spray with a specific kind of droplet at a set pressure. The hole in a nozzle tip should be cleaned out either by backflushing or with a bristle or copper wire that is much softer than the material in the tip itself. Great care must be taken to see that the hole in the tip is not deformed or enlarged while being cleaned.

If pesticides in the spray tank need to be changed, flushing the tank and lines out thoroughly with several rinses of clean water ensures that all of the previous pesticide has been removed. With some formulations, it may be necessary to neutralize the tank using ammonia. Check all labels for proper directions. In all cases where changing from one pesticide to another, be sure to remove and clean all strainers and be sure to flush the lines and hoses out completely each time a chemical change is made.

When cleaning any equipment, remember that it is illegal to flush pesticide residues into sewer systems. This applies to both the original solution and to the wash water that is dilute pesticide. Arrangements must be made either to collect this material until it can be disposed of properly or to disperse it into an area where there is no possibility of it harming people or animals, or of contaminating the groundwater supply. Many companies have disposal sumps at their place of business.

When cleaning spray lines, one important principle should be kept in mind: If there is a continuous open passage from the tank through the nozzle tip and there is pressure in the tank, pesticide will come out the nozzle when the valve is opened. If pesticide does not emerge, there is an obstruction in the system. To correct obstructions, it is best to first check the nozzle tip for blockage. Next, without the nozzle tip in place check the spray valve to see if everything is working at this

Equipment Storage

Special attention must be given to sprayers in the wintertime because freezing can destroy pumps, tanks, and spray lines. All sprayers, (including hand sprayers), must either be thoroughly cleaned and all water removed, or they must be stored in warm areas even for as short a period as overnight; remember, freezing can occur in just a few hours.

As a general rule, when cleaning any pesticide application equipment for storage, it is important that all traces of pesticide be removed. When cleaning and preparing power sprayers for winter storage, it may be necessary (after cleaning), to add some oil or antifreeze to the line and run it through the tank and pumps so as to be certain there will be nothing in these lines or pumps that can freeze.

point. If the spray still does not come out the end, check backward at each point—through the spray valve, through the strainer, through the hose, and in through the tank outlet. Eventually the blockage will be located.

Hoses should be carefully inspected for any breaks, particularly at the points where the hose is fastened to any couplings. The hose should be replaced when breaks are found. Hose should never be carried or stored with sharp kinks in it. This practice will cause breaks, not only in the outer covering, but in the inner liner as well. On larger sprayers with hose reels, the hose reel should be spring loaded to avoid unnecessary wear on the hose.

Pumps should never be operated at speeds or pressures above those recommended by the manufacturer. Because pumps depend on the spray liquid for lubrication and removal of the heat of friction, they can be damaged if run dry or with restricted inlet or outlet. Plunger or piston parts on pumps must be maintained in good condition to prevent loss of efficiency in pumping. The rods and pistons that move the cups must move freely and easily; they should be well lubricated. On any equipment that contains either bearings or gears, these parts must be kept clean and properly lubricated at all times.

In general, it is wise to use **electric motors** a size larger than what is required for any given application because this will give maximum power without overloading. Thus, if a 1/4 horsepower motor is necessary, use a 1/3 horsepower instead. All electric motor-driven equipment must be wired to a three-wire circuit with the third wire always grounded when in use. Motors should be oiled or greased regularly, except those with sealed bearings. Period-

ically, they should be taken apart, cleaned, and the brushes replaced if there is any excessive sparking when the motor is in operation. Special attention must be given to electric cords. These must always be heavy duty and must be checked carefully for any breaks in the insulation or plugs. Electric cords must never be patched with tape. If there is a break in the wire or insulation, remove the broken portion completely and reattach the good wire portion properly to the plugs.

Gasoline engines do not normally require a great deal of care beyond keeping oil at a proper level in the crankcase. Determine the correct weight of oil to use, keep it at the full level during operation, and change it after the number of hours running time recommended by the manufacturer. Gasoline engines of the type generally used on pest control equipment are usually best serviced in a shop recommended by the manufacturer. Except for small adjustments, it is good practice to have an engine rebuilt each year rather than send it in for a series of repair jobs. Such rebuilding will usually eliminate the need for repair during the operating season and will result in lower maintenance costs in the long run. Unless you are an expert mechanic, you should not tamper with the carburetor or make other adjustments on the engine once it has been rebuilt.

In general, complicated mechanical repairs are best left to qualified mechanics. For minor repairs, every professional should carry a **tool kit** to help keep equipment operational. In most cases the kit need only be a wrench, a pair of pliers, and a few screwdrivers. However, termite professionals usually require a more elaborate list of tools for on the job repairs. In either case, repair tools are best kept handy by being on the truck and kept organized. Downtime trips back to the shop for a tool to make minor repairs are expensive.

Both small and large companies should maintain a **well-equipped repair shop** at its place of business. The shop should contain sufficient good quality tools to perform more extensive repairs than can be accomplished on the job.

Dusters

Dusters should be emptied frequently and cleaned thoroughly, being careful to remove all caked or hardened dust. The tubes should be cleaned by running a stiff wire or write brush through them to scrape the side of the tube as much as possible. Special care should be taken to see that all screens and other small openings are clear. When dusters are put in storage, first remove all dust and clean thoroughly.

Foggers

Some foggers require special attention. The high degree of heat in thermal foggers causes a carbon formation from the pesticide formulation that must be removed regularly so it will not interfere with the normal flow of pesticide through the machine. Remove carbon immediately after each use of the machine before it has had time to harden or to build up into a thick layer. It is especially important not to damage any portion of the heat chambers or any small orifices that may be present.

Using Equipment Properly

The information in this chapter should give the professional a survey of the types of equipment that are available. The discussion of maintenance in this chapter and in the appendix should be of value to the user in keeping his equipment in good working order thus avoiding the expensive and embarrassing problems of on-the-job equipment failure. Although this information is important, what is even more important is *how the equipment is used*. The best professional would be hampered seriously if forced to use a substandard sprayer, but there is no sprayer available that is so perfect that it can make up for the mistakes of someone who does not use it properly.

In many of the chapters that follow, there will be considerable emphasis placed on the habits of insects and the application of chemicals for insect control. One of the most important considerations in such an operation is the determination of how much pesticide is to be applied and how well this application is made. To excel in this phase of pest control, the professional must understand the capabilities and limitations of each piece of equipment being used for any particular pest control operation.

Applicators sometimes find themselves in situations where they are pressed for time. The common response in such a situation is to "work a little faster." But to do so may not be the wisest course to follow. For example, when using the handheld sprayer at a certain pressure and with a certain nozzle, a specific amount of pesticide will be applied over a given time period. If the professional sprays an area at a more rapid rate, there will be less pesticide applied to the area because it will have taken less time to spray the area.

It is wise to attempt to establish a spraying technique that will result in applying the amount of pesticide for an area as prescribed by the particular insecticide label. Thus, it is good practice to determine how long it takes to spray a measured area with the sprayer properly used. By measuring the amount of liquid applied for this time and area, it will be possible to estimate the average rate of application per minute. This will vary somewhat among different individuals and equipment, and each person should work it out for himself. It is not feasible to make detailed measurements of every job that is done, but an occasional series of such "test plots" should help each person have a better understanding as to the type of spray applications he is likely to be making on the job.

Matching the appropriate equipment to the specific job is an important decision, and should be carefully thought out prior to beginning the work. Occasionally, there is temptation to take on a large-scale operation even though there is not appropriate equipment on hand. Experiences of this kind are often disastrous (in terms of labor costs versus cost of purchasing or operating equipment) because it becomes necessary to try to substitute manpower for machine power in order to finish the job. For example, the one-gallon hand sprayer is not appropriate for many outdoor lawn spraying programs unless such programs involve only a few spot treatments. Each job should be approached on the basis of what must be accomplished and what equipment will be needed.

The same sort of consideration is needed when using other equipment such as fogging machines. Small, electrically operated fogging machines are adequate for treating relatively small enclosed spaces, but they are woefully inadequate for any sort of large-scale outdoor use. Larger, truck-mounted models are necessary for such work. For example, when attempting to distribute pesticide over large areas to combat insects such as mosquitoes, a large fogging or misting machine would be needed because it is the best equipment for this type of operation.

When using spray equipment, the professional must understand the function of pressures in a spray system. As a general rule, pressure should be constant for any given spray application. In using power sprayers, professionals sometimes increase sprayer pressure in attempts to spray a greater distances. But pressure does not greatly increase the distance to which spray can be projected out of any nozzle because the length or height of a column of spray is a function mostly of the volume that is being delivered rather than the pressure that is behind it.

When spraying large areas, use higher-volume delivery nozzles to cover more space at the same speed of application. It is unwise and unsafe to increase the pressures since it has little effect on volume and may result in more splashing and breaking up of the spray into fine particles that, in turn, may drift and damage premises, cars, ornamentals, etc.

These few examples should be sufficient to emphasize that the successful professional must learn to evaluate equipment on the basis of the job that it is designed to do. He must learn how to operate this equipment in a safe and efficient manner. To do this, equipment must be in proper working order at all times.

SUPPLEMENTARY READING MATERIAL

Barile, J. "Equipment" In: *Mallis's Handbook of Pest Control.* 9th.Ed. S. Hedges (ed.). Mallis Handbook and Training Technical Committee. Cleveland. OH. 2003.

Bennett, G.W., J.M. Owens, and R.M.Corrigan. *Truman's Scientific Guide to Pest Control Operations.* Advanstar Publications. Cleveland. OH. 1997. 520pp.

Brakeman, L. Upgrade or perish. *Pest Control.* Vol. 70 (5) 42-47 (2002)

Brehm, W. L. "Care and Maintenance of the One Gallon Stainless Steel Sprayer." *Pest Control.* 36 no. 5. (1968).

Cassens, D. L. "Using Electric Moisture Meters." *Pest Control Technology.* 7 (2):15,16,46. (1979).

Cornwell, P. *The Cockroach.* Vol. II. Insecticides and Cockroach Control. St. Martins Press. New York. NY. 1976. 557 pp.

Ebeling, W. *Urban Entomology.* Univ. of Calif. Los Angeles. 1975. 695 pp.

Gitlin, R. "High tech technicians exude professionalism." *Pest Control.* Vol. 69 : (5). S8-S11. (2001)

Gooch, H. "Pest control in the computer age." *Pest Control.* Vol. 67 : (9). 53-55. (1999)

Gooch, H. "Simply scan for success." *Pest Control.* Vol. 66 : (1). 50-52. (1998)

Harbison, B. "Coming into focus: Using digital cameras in pest control." *Pest Control Technology.* 29 (4): 66, 68, 72, 74 (2001).

Hedges, S. 1995. "Vacu-cide: Killing cockroaches with suction." *Pest Control Technology.* Vol. 23 (6); 28-32.

Katz, H. Equipment. Pages 941-988 in: *Mallis's Handbook of Pest Control.* 7th Ed. K. Story (ed.). Franzak and Foster. Cleveland. OH. 1990. 1152 pp.

Mallis, A. *Handbook of Pest Control.* Franzak and Foster Company. Cleveland. 1982. 1101 pp.

Mix. J. "Will handheld computers herald a coming change for our industry?" *Pest Control.* Vol. 67:(4). 76-78. (1999)

Snell, E. J. "Equipment" Pages 1187-1248, In: *Mallis's Handbook of Pest Control.* 8th. Ed. S. Hedges (ed.). Mallis Handbook and Technical Training Company. Cleveland. OH. 1997. 1456 pp.

Snyder, T. "Vacuums are vital to IPM." Parts 1&2. *Pest Control.* Vol. 68. Nos. 5/6 (2000)

Stanbridge, D. "Microwave technology makes insect detection easy." *Pest Control.* Vol. 71 (2):42,44. (2003).

Truman, L. C., and W. L. Butts. *Scientific Guide to Pest Control Operations.* 2nd. Ed. Purdue University/Pest Control Magazine, Cleveland Co. 1967. 187 pp.

CHAPTER 6 | Cockroaches

Cockroaches are among the most common insects. Based on fossil evidence, cockroaches are known to have been present on Earth for nearly 350 million years. Their sizes vary considerably; some species were up to several inches long. Some biologists consider insects to be one of the most successful groups of animals to ever inhabit this planet, and cockroaches (often referred to as roaches) are one of the most adaptable and successful insect groups. They have been able to survive many changing environments over millions of years. There are approximately 3,500 species of cockroaches worldwide, with about 70 species found in the United States. Their presence in nearly every part of the world and in a wide range of habitats demonstrates that cockroaches are truly an outstanding success story in nature. Many of the same outstanding biological characteristics that make them so successful in nature can also make them some of the most difficult pests to control. Cockroaches, especially German cockroaches, are some of the most commonly encountered household insect pests in much of the United States, and many other areas worldwide. Fortunately, effective control technology and pest management understanding are now available to allow consistently high levels of cockroach control for most species, and in most situations.

Only a few of the cockroach species found in the United States routinely enter and infest our dwellings. The most common of these are the German cockroach, American cockroach, oriental cockroach, brownbanded cockroach, smokybrown cockroach, Australian cockroach, brown cockroach, woods cockroach, field cockroach, and Asian cockroach. Of these species, the first five probably represent 95 percent or more of all cockroach management concerns in and around buildings. In some parts of the country, one species may be more important than another. Certain other species may

infest homes or other buildings but will generally be found in very localized situations or only under other unusual circumstances.

The most common cockroach pest species can be distinguished from each other by use of the pictorial key in Figure 6.1. This key is used in the same manner as the key to the orders of insects found in Chapter 2.

COCKROACH DAMAGE AND HEALTH IMPLICATIONS

The presence of cockroaches is often detected by their damage or by the fecal matter, called frass, they deposit. These clues can aid in diagnosing a cockroach problem. Cockroaches may eat such things as glue or paste (especially from animal-based materials), starch, and certain colors of dyes. As a result, items such as stamps, envelopes, and bindings of older books, draperies, and occasionally wallpapers may show signs of feeding. The size of the mandible marks and the apparent degree of vigor with which the insects have fed can be indications of the type of cockroach that did the damage. The size and shape of fecal droppings are also clues to the cockroach species involved.

The most important aspect of cockroach damage derives from their habit of feeding and harboring in damp and unsanitary places, such as sewers, garbage disposals, and damp and unsanitary areas of kitchens, bathrooms, and storage areas indoors. Filth and germs from these sources are spread by the cockroaches onto food supplies, food preparation surfaces, dishes, utensils, and other surfaces. Cockroaches contaminate far more food than they eat. Diseases transmitted as a result of these habits include various forms of food poisoning or gastroenteritis. These same habits, along with the smell imparted by any significant level of infestation, are

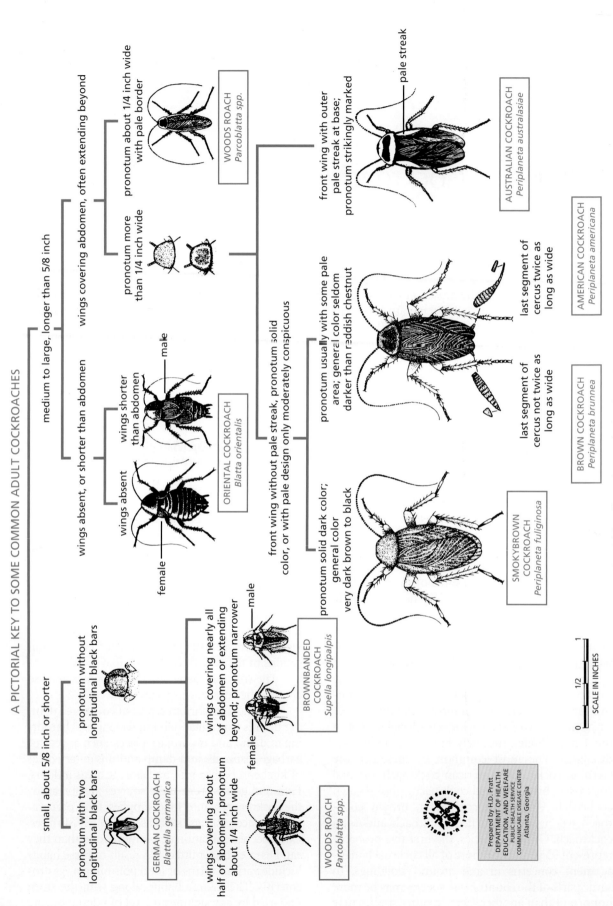

FIGURE 6.1. A pictorial key (from the CDC) of eight cockroach pest species.

why people are so disgusted and repulsed by the mere presence of cockroaches. For many people, personal disgust and the social stigma attached to cockroaches result in a complete lack of tolerance for any cockroaches in their home or elsewhere. For others, the presence of cockroaches constitutes an important source of health-threatening allergens and can even trigger life-threatening asthma attacks. However, studies have found that some people have a less severe attitude about cockroaches, such that low levels of cockroach presence and an occasional sighting may be acceptable. These attitudes, or tolerances, about cockroaches are often context specific, so that little or no cockroach presence may be acceptable indoors, while some low or moderate levels may be acceptable in the landscape. In either case, a carefully considered and executed management program will be necessary.

Cockroaches produce odorous secretions from various points in their bodies, and these secretions can affect the flavor of foods. When cockroach populations are high, these secretions may result in a characteristic odor in the general region of the infestation. Disease-producing organisms, such as bacteria, have been found on cockroach bodies. Although several digestive diseases have been transmitted experimentally, different forms of gastroenteritis appear to be the principal diseases transmitted by cockroaches. These include food poisoning, nausea, abdominal cramps, vomiting, diarrhea, dysentery, and other illnesses. The organisms causing these diseases are carried on the legs and bodies of cockroaches and are deposited on food and utensils as cockroaches forage. Cockroaches also carry a wide variety of protozoa and other microorganisms inside their bodies, some of which may occasionally be involved in the spread of disease to humans. Cockroach excrement and cast skins also contain a number of allergens to which many people exhibit allergic responses, such as skin rashes, watery eyes, and sneezing. For some very allergic people, and particularly for those who also have a chronic lung disease such as asthma, allergic attacks to cockroach allergens can be very serious and even life threatening. All forms of contact with cockroaches should be kept to a minimum. For the most part, however, cockroaches usually are not associated with severe illnesses or disease outbreaks, though they are nearly universally detested.

GENERAL BIOLOGY AND BEHAVIOR OF COCKROACHES

Most cockroaches are tropical and subtropical in origin, generally living outdoors. They are mostly active at night, during which time they forage for food, water, and mates. They may be seen in the daytime, particularly when a heavy population is present or when some other form of stress is placed on the population. Such stresses include lack of food or water, exposure to pesticides (particularly pyrethrins or pyrethroids), and exposure to predators, such as ants. Cockroaches ordinarily prefer a moist environment, and most species also prefer a relatively high degree of warmth for areas where they will be active. Some tropical cockroaches feed only on vegetation. However, chewing mouthparts enable cockroaches to feed on a wide variety of materials we produce, consume, shed, or excrete. They are especially fond of starches, sweets, grease, and meat products, but they will also eat a great variety of other materials, such as cheese, beer, leather, bakery products, starch in book bindings, glue, hair, flakes of dried skin, dead animals, and plant materials. They can generally be considered to scavenge on the fallout of human activity in structures and in unsanitary areas, such as garbage cans or piles, sewage systems, and septic tanks. This understanding can be helpful to the technician when recommending sanitation procedures to place stress on infesting populations.

Cockroaches usually orient to protected **cracks and crevices** that provide a warm and humid environment. Some species, such as the American and oriental cockroaches, gather in large groups on open walls in protected places or in open areas outside. While they are often found in groups in their daytime hiding or resting areas (called harborages) and can be found feeding in groups at night, cockroaches are not social insects, as are the ants, some bees and wasps, or termites. Cockroaches generally forage individually for food and otherwise behave in a largely individualistic or nonsocial manner. Thus, although cockroaches are not social insects, they do often form aggregates.

The general shape of a cockroach is familiar to everyone. They are oval and flat bodied, which enables them to squeeze into all types of cracks and crevices. A shield-like covering called a pronotum projects forward over the head; their mouthparts are of the chewing type and are oriented downward and slightly toward the rear of the body. With their long, spiny legs they can run rapidly over most surfaces. Specialized pads in their tarsi allow them to easily scale glass windows or walk across a ceiling.

Besides their ability to move around inside and outside, and the fact that some species are good fliers, cockroaches are well known for moving to new areas via "hitchhiking." Because they prefer to hide in cracks and crevices in the daytime, they are frequently moved about by people or in products shipped around cities or across the country. Careful inspection of furniture, clothing, or other goods coming into a home or other facility may reveal cockroaches hiding in these items. Careful observations by pest management professionals and researchers have shown surprising numbers of German cockroaches entering such facilities as hospitals, restaurants, zoos, and supermarkets by these routes (every day, in some cases).

Cockroaches develop by a gradual metamorphosis that consists of three stages: **egg, nymph,** and **adult** (see Figure 2.2). The female produces an egg capsule, called an **oötheca,** which contains two rows of eggs. The egg capsules of a few common species can be identified by use of the pictorial key in Figure 6.2. Nymphs hatch out of the egg capsule by working together to break a seam along the top of the egg case. When the seam splits open, the tiny nymphs emerge to begin their life. The nymphs generally resemble adults in appearance and behavior but are smaller, do not have wings or wing pads, and frequently have a somewhat different color. Newly molted nymphs are white but will darken to the normal color within a few hours. Some people mistakenly think these recently molted individuals are albino cockroaches. Nymphs undergo a series of molts; with the last molt, the wings (if they exist

Pennsylvania woods roach

1) Oötheca curved in an inverted half-moon shape; usually contains 16 eggs on each side. Normally found outdoors under bark of old logs and stumps—Pennsylvania woods roach.
1') Oötheca straight, at least on the bottom side. Normally found in buildings 2

Brownbanded cockroach

2) Oötheca 1/4 inch or less in length; no more than nine eggs on each side—brownbanded roach.
2') Oötheca 1/3 inch or more in length 3

German cockroach

3) Oötheca slender, about 1/3-inch long; light brown. Top and bottom sides parallel; contains 12 to 24 eggs on each side. Carried by the female until a day before hatching—German cockroach.
3') Oötheca purse shaped, not slender; length greater than 1/3 inch; dark brown to black 4

Oriental cockroach

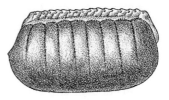

American cockroach

4) With eight eggs on each side—oriental cockroach or American cockroach.*

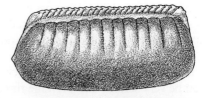

Smokybrown cockroach

4) With 12 eggs on each side—smokybrown cockroach. **

*The oötheca of these species are quite difficult to separate with accuracy.

**The oötheca of the brown cockroach may key out at this point. It is difficult to distinguish between oöthecae of these two species.

FIGURE 6.2. A pictorial key of oötheca (egg capsules) of some common cockroaches. (Provonsha)

FIGURE 6.6. In homes, German cockroaches are most commonly found in kitchens, other areas of food storage or consumption, and bathrooms. (Shuster and Provonsha)

in that species) are fully formed and the sexes are easily distinguished. Wings of the adults may be long and functional, or short to almost nonexistent. In some species, males are winged, but females have only small wing pads. Adults may or may not fly, depending on the species and environmental factors. The length of time required for the eggs to hatch, for the nymphs to develop, and for the life span of the adults will also vary (within each species) due to temperature, humidity, the quality of their diet, and other environmental conditions.

German Cockroach
Blattella germanica (Linnaeus)

The German cockroach is the most economically important urban pest. It is the most common cockroach species in houses, apartments, restaurants, hotels, and other institutions throughout the United States. In some southern areas, larger cockroach species, such as the smokybrown cockroach

or other *Periplaneta* species, can be a more common problem. The oriental cockroach or some other species may also be more common in certain situations, especially infesting around or under the premises and frequently moving indoors. However, the German cockroach is by far the most common and important species infesting our homes and institutions. In some areas it may still be referred to as the croton bug.

Adults are pale to medium brown and about 1/2- to 5/8-inch long. *German cockroaches can be distinguished from other roaches by the two dark stripes on the anterior, dorsal portion (pronotum) of the thorax* (see Figures 6.3 and 6.4, following page 254). Adults of both sexes have well-developed wings, but they never fly. Males are easily distinguished from females by the slender, tapering shape of the abdomen. German cockroach nymphs resemble the adults except that they are smaller, wingless, and darker in color, often being nearly black. A single light stripe running down the middle of the back is the most prominent marking on the younger German cockroach nymphs (see Figure 6.5, following page 254).

Adult females carry the egg capsule protruding from the rear of the abdomen until the eggs are ready to hatch (see the cover photos for this chapter and Figure 6.4, following page 254. Females carrying egg capsules are called gravid. The egg capsule is light brown in color, about 1/3-inch long, more than twice as long as wide, and shows about sixteen external divisions or segments on either side. The nymphs may break open the capsule while it is still attached to the female, or she may deposit the capsule in crevices and other protected locations where the young will be able to find food and harborage when they emerge. The German cockroach is the only common house-infesting species that carries the egg capsule for such an extended period. Capsules removed from the female more than a couple of days before the normal hatching time will be less likely to hatch unless they remain under conditions of high humidity. This may also be true for gravid females that are killed by an insecticide within several hours to one day or more before the time the egg capsule would normally have hatched. The embryos in the newly formed egg capsule require a reasonably steady flow of water, usually from the adult female, to prevent death from desiccation, or drying out. Again, if the humidity is high (greater than 70%),

Why the German Cockroach Is So Successful as a Pest

As mentioned previously, the German cockroach is the most commonly encountered of the house-infesting species in the United States. It is also generally the most persistent and difficult to manage. The reasons for this are somewhat complex, but an understanding of some of the factors involved is basic to the practice of successful pest management. First, the German cockroach has a larger number of eggs per capsule than the other species that infest structures. Second, it also has the shortest period to develop from hatching until sexual maturity, so populations of German cockroaches will build up faster than those of other species. These factors combine to produce what entomologists call a high reproductive potential.

Third, German cockroach nymphs have a better chance of surviving than do those of other species, because the female carries the egg capsule during the entire time that the embryos are developing within the egg. This results in the nymphs avoiding many hazards of the environment that may affect eggs that remain detached and isolated prior to hatch. Thus, more nymphs are likely to hatch, and a higher reproductive potential is likely.

Fourth, German cockroach nymphs are smaller than those of most other cockroaches, so they are able to conceal themselves in many places inaccessible to individuals of the larger species. In fact, in a commercial kitchen, there may be literally thousands of cracks and crevices that young cockroaches can hide in and remain protected. German cockroach nymphs also tend to stay close to each other and often close to the female at the time of hatching, creating a tendency for a high local population density. They also respond to an aggregation pheromone associated with their frass, which has the effect of increasing the level of aggregation, or clumping, of individuals in the population.

These biological factors, combined with its very adaptive feeding habits and other behaviors, give the German cockroach, compared to other cockroach species, increased chances for survival and for persistently maintaining high populations.

Moreover, several additional factors have contributed to the success of the German cockroach. The high reproductive potential of this species can significantly affect its ability to develop resistance to insecticides. During the late 1950s and the 1960s, insecticides such as DDT and chlordane were widely used to control German cockroaches. In many cases, some individuals of German cockroach populations exposed to these insecticides survived. Because these cockroaches reproduce so quickly, survivors were able to pass the ability to survive exposure to DDT and chlordane to following generations. Over many generations, large portions of populations can become resistant to insecticides. It is possible within a single town or city to find populations of cockroaches that are resistant to a particular insecticide, and others that are susceptible to the same insecticide. Similar patterns of resistance have developed in this species in relation to certain organophosphates, carbamates, and pyrethroids that have been extensively used since chlordane and DDT were abandoned. Each population's history of insecticide exposure over many generations will determine the levels of resistance to various insecticides. Currently, baits based on some of the newer toxicants like abamection, fipronil, imidacloprid and hydramethylnon are allowing professionals to achieve very consistent and effective control of this species, but resistance to even these toxicants is inevitable.

desiccation may not occur, and the egg capsule can survive for up to a few days after premature dropping or death of the female.

Adult females can produce from four to eight egg capsules in their lifetime. Each capsule contains 30 to 48 eggs. It usually takes 20 to 30 days from the time of initial formation of the first egg capsule until it hatches, with this time generally being shorter under warmer temperature conditions (greater than 25°C). Formation of the next egg capsule usually begins within a couple of weeks.

There are 6 or 7 nymphal stages, called instars, before the molt into the adult stage. The number of nymphal instars may increase under certain environmental conditions (poor diet, low temperatures, etc.), or if appendages, such as legs or antennae, are lost during the earlier nymphal instars. In the latter case, extra instars will occur to allow regeneration of these missing body parts. Completion of the nymphal stage under room conditions requires 40 to 125 days, depending on environmental conditions (diet quality, crowding, temperatures, etc.). Adult German cockroaches can live up to a year, but most will die from various causes long before that time.

Nymphs have habits similar to those of adults. They are active mostly at night but hide in dark crevices during the day. If German cockroaches are seen during the day, the population is probably so large that the available cracks are already full, or food and moisture are in such short supply that daytime foraging is necessary. Such behavior indicates that the population is under considerable stress. This species usually hides in areas close to moisture and food, which means the cockroaches are generally found in kitchens and other food areas (see Figure 6.6). They prefer to rest on wood rather than on metal or other smooth surfaces. Large infestations do occur on metal surfaces when there are few other surfaces available. Examples are on submarines or in large modern food-processing plants and kitchens with stainless steel equipment and wall panels.

The German cockroach is a general feeder but is particularly attracted to fermented foods and beverage residues (e.g., beer spills). If water is present, adults can live about a month without food, but young nymphs will die of starvation within 10 days. Without food or water, the adults die in less than two weeks. Most stages become very stressed if deprived of food or water for more than a couple of days. Stressed cockroaches tend to wander or forage for resources aggressively, even during abnormal periods, such as the daytime.

Infestations are sometimes found in areas not generally suspected of harboring German cockroaches, such as dresser drawers in bedrooms. German cockroaches found scattered through non-food areas of a home or building is usually a sign of a very heavy infestation or of the repellent effects of insecticide applications elsewhere in the facility. Cockroaches in these areas will find food scarce but can feed on scattered crumbs, soiled clothing, some types of exposed glue used in furniture, or some cosmetic products. German cockroaches can also be found outdoors during warm months, often around garbage receptacles. This, too, is usually a result of a heavy infestation indoors.

Some of these uncommon patterns of infestation are more understandable in the light of recent research on the normal movement patterns of German cockroaches within and between urban apartments. While most German cockroaches, and especially the younger nymphal stages, probably do not forage more than a couple of feet from their preferred harborage under field conditions, detailed field research has shown that some individuals can be quite mobile within structures. Up to 10% (or more) of the adult German cockroaches in a moderately to heavily infested apartment can move into or out of the kitchen area within a week's time. Adult males (see Figure 6.3, following page 254) appear to be the most mobile stage, followed by nongravid adult females (see Figure 6.7) and large nymphs; gravid females probably rarely leave the harborage. Similar rates of movement have also been measured between adjacent apartments. Movement between apartments usually does not occur unless the two adjacent apartments share common plumbing. Thus, exclusion of German cockroach movement

FIGURE 6.7. Adult female German cockroach, showing abdomen slightly wider than wings, and much broader than abdomen of male (as shown in Figure 6.3, following page 254). (Myers)

into the wall voids that house plumbing connections, or careful treatment of those areas with insecticides (e.g., dust formulations), will greatly aid in maintaining adequate control in multifamily dwellings and other large, complex structures, such as hospitals and motels. This understanding of life-stage-specific levels of movement and foraging suggests that the youngest nymphs in the population may not be readily controllable except by the most thorough crack and crevice applications, and that they may be particularly susceptible to secondary poisoning (following bait application) due to their coprophagy (eating of frass, or excrement, of others) within harborages. Similarly, since gravid females do not appear to forage or feed much at all, they may be the most important and difficult portion of the population to control.

The German cockroach is a relatively active species; many individuals in the population move around readily within structures. They travel from one location to another and can pass through very small openings. They are also regularly carried from place to place in such things as bagged potatoes and onions, beverage cartons, grocery bags, food carts, other food packages, handbags, and the folds of clothing. The pest management professional must look very closely to find all the places in which cockroaches may be living, and he or she must try to determine how cockroaches might be transported into the premises. It may not be possible to eliminate all the German cockroaches in a structure at any one time if a steady flow of cockroaches is being carried into the premises via people, food shipments, or other routes. Further, the use of some repellent insecticides such as pyrethrins and pyrethroids may scatter cockroaches widely throughout a building. If all the scattered, or satellite, populations are not found and treated, reinfestation of treated areas will occur.

American Cockroach
Periplaneta americana (Linnaeus)

The American cockroach is also known as the waterbug, flying waterbug, and, in some areas of the southern United States, the palmetto bug. It is the largest of the common species, growing to 1-1/2 inches or more in length. It is reddish brown with a pale brown or yellow border on the upper surface of the pronotum (see Figure 6.8, following page 254). Both sexes have well-developed wings, but those of the males extend beyond the abdomen.

The female drops her egg capsule within a day after it is formed. Sometimes it is dropped in a suitable location, such as near a food source, or in a protected area. In the southern United States, this will frequently be outdoors on moist and decaying wood or other substrates. At other times the capsule may be glued to a relatively hidden surface with secretions from the female's mouth. The egg capsule is dark brown, symmetrically shaped, and about 5/16-inch long (length usually less than width). Egg capsules are formed at the rate of about one per week until from 15 to 90 capsules have been produced. Each capsule contains 14 to 16 eggs. At room temperature, nymphs will hatch out in 50 to 55 days. In the process of hatching, nymphs will molt and leave their first cast skins in the egg case.

Young nymphs are grayish brown, and each will molt 9 to 13 times before reaching maturity. After the first few molts, nymphs become more reddish brown in color (see Figure 6.9, following page 254). The time required to complete the nymphal stage varies from 160 to 971 days. Under ideal conditions an adult female can live up to 14 to 15 months, but males live for a somewhat shorter period. However, in natural populations, many factors reduce the average life span of American cockroaches.

When indoors, the nymphs and adults are usually found in dark, moist areas of basements and crawlspaces as well as in and around bathtubs, clothes hampers, floor drains, pipe chases, and sewers. In basements they are usually found in corner areas high on the walls or in floor drains. In the North, this cockroach is commonly associated with steam heat tunnels. In northern areas where steam heat tunnels are not found, the American cockroach is restricted primarily to large institutional build-

ings, greenhouses, and facilities like zoos. The American cockroach is also common around the accesses to sewers, near garbage, and on the underside of the metal covers of large sump pumps in boiler rooms. American cockroaches have also been observed migrating from one building to another during warm months in the northern United States.

In the South, this cockroach is abundant in alleyways, yards, hollow trees, and palm trees. Recent studies in Florida have shown that American cockroaches, along with other *Periplaneta* species and other outdoor cockroaches, are generally associated with trees, shrubs, and woodpiles in landscapes. They especially prefer moist, shady areas. Sometimes they are found under roof shingles or flashing, or even in the attic. Similar studies in Texas have shown that American and smokybrown cockroaches often prefer moist, shady areas of ground cover, which are often found around foundations and near swimming pools. The automatic sprinkler systems for irrigating these areas of turf and ground cover provide particularly attractive and favorable living conditions for cockroach populations. When conditions are unfavorable, American cockroaches and other outdoor species may move indoors.

American cockroaches feed on a variety of foods, but decaying organic matter seems to be preferred. They also feed on book bindings, manuscripts, clothing, or glossy paper, if they contain starch. Syrup and other sweets are also attractive. The adults can survive two or three months without food, but only about a month without water.

The adults have well-developed wings but seldom fly, unless temperature conditions are above 85°F, at which point they can be very active flyers. They are capable of gliding long distances and will cover considerable distances if they take off from a tree or rooftop. In the South and as far north as Kentucky, American cockroaches have been reported to fly short distances.

Oriental Cockroach
Blatta orientalis Linnaeus

The oriental cockroach is also referred to as the waterbug, black beetle, or shad roach. It is found in all parts of the United States.

Total length of this cockroach is about 1-1/4 inches for the female and 1 inch for the male. The female has small, functionless, rudimentary wings called wing pads. The male's wings cover about three-quarters of the abdomen (see Figure 6.10, following page 254). Neither the male nor the female can fly. Adults are very dark brown or nearly black and usually have a somewhat greasy sheen to their body. Females are broader and heavier looking than males.

The female carries an egg capsule for about 30 hours, after which it is either dropped or attached to a protected surface near a food supply (they are not glued to surfaces). Females will produce an average of eight capsules, each containing 16 eggs, which will hatch in about 60 days under room conditions.

Nymphs molt from seven to ten times, and the nymphal stages usually take several months to a year to complete development. Unlike the other house-infesting species, the oriental cockroach generally has a seasonal developmental cycle. The peak number of adults usually appears in late spring or early summer. The number of adults in the population is generally quite low by late summer and early fall, due to natural mortality and the hatching of nymphs. Few live adults are usually found in the population throughout the year, but if nymphs have not reached maturity by late fall or early winter, their development seems to slow considerably, and maturity is not reached until spring.

The nymphs and adults have similar habits and are found associated with decaying organic matter indoors and out. They can be found in yards, beneath leaves, in dumps, in crawlspaces, in the mulch of flower beds, or in landscape retaining walls. They are also common in high-moisture areas such as sewers, water meter enclosures, drains, and dark, damp basements. Both nymphs and adults are sluggish and are usually located at or below ground level indoors. They are seldom found on walls, in high cupboards, or in the upper floors of buildings. They are commonly found in bathtubs because they have difficulty walking on or up smooth surfaces due to their small tarsal pads (especially between the hooks of their pretarsal claws).

Oriental cockroaches feed on all kinds of filth, rubbish, and other decaying organic matter. If water is available, they can live for a month without food, but they die within two weeks without water. In many areas oriental cockroaches are generally found outdoors during warm weather. In periods of drought there may be considerable movement into structures, apparently in relation to humidity gradients. As cold weather approaches, or sometimes during unseasonably cool periods, a similar migration indoors may occur. There may be considerable group movement within heated structures during cold weather, particularly if some areas of a building are maintained at warmer temperatures than other areas.

Brownbanded Cockroach
Supella longipalpa (Fabricius)

This is one of the smaller cockroaches, rarely being more than 1/2-inch long. It is light brown and can

be readily distinguished from the German cockroach by the presence of two lighter, transverse bands running from one side to the other across the base of the wings and abdomen in adults, and in the same position on the nymphs (see Figure 6.11, following page 254). These bands may be somewhat irregular or broken and are more apparent on the young (see Figure 6.12, following page 254) and the females than on the males. The female has a broader body than the male (compare at Figures 6.11 and 6.13, following page 254). Both males and females are quite active, and the adult males fly readily when disturbed. All stages may jump when attempting to escape. They frequently occur in the same buildings as the German cockroach. Professionals must be very careful to identify this species correctly, as control techniques are different for the two species because of their very different distribution and behaviors within structures.

A female brownbanded cockroach (see Figure 6.13, following page 254) carries her egg capsule for a day or two and then attaches it to a protected surface. The egg case is purse-shaped, light brown in color (see Figure 6.14, following page 254), and cemented in place, usually to the side or under surfaces of infested objects. The egg capsule is about 3/16 inch long, with length less than twice the width, and shows about eight external divisions or segments along either side. Females will produce about 14 egg capsules during their adult life, each containing about 18 eggs. These hatch in 50 to 75 days, depending on temperature. Under room conditions, nymphs mature in about 160 days. Adults may live up to 10 months.

Nymphs and adults are generally found on ceilings, high on walls, behind picture frames and light fixtures, or near motors of refrigerators and other appliances. They are also found in light switches, closets, and furniture. They do not require as close an association with moisture sources as the German cockroach. This helps explain why they are commonly found in rooms other than the kitchen or bathroom. These cockroaches strongly avoid light and are not normally seen during the day.

The brownbanded cockroach prefers feeding on starchy materials. However, it can be found feeding on almost anything and has been known to chew on such nonfood materials as nylon stockings, presumably for the residues of body oils and skin flakes.

When making an inspection for brownbanded cockroaches, look beneath tables and chairs, dressers, and chests. Look also behind pictures, along picture moldings, on rough plaster walls and ceilings, and most especially on the ceilings and upper walls of cabinets, pantries, and closets. No room should be left uninspected, nor should any piece of furniture (wood, metal, or upholstered) if its construction provides shelter. Look for tiny black droppings, attached egg capsules, or cast skins where they have fallen from above onto shelves or ledges.

These cockroaches are more often found in homes, apartments, hotels, and hospital rooms than in stores, restaurants, and kitchens. They are very common in institutional buildings. They are frequently transported in furniture and will rapidly spread throughout an entire building. They have long been abundant in the southern states but are now found as far north as Canada. In the cooler northern states they are generally found in the warmer parts of buildings.

Smokybrown Cockroach

Periplaneta fuliginosa (Serville)

Smokybrown cockroaches are closely related to the American cockroach but are distinguished by their slightly smaller size, being slightly more than 1-inch long, and uniform mahogany color. They do not have any lighter coloration around the edge of their pronotum, as do adult American cockroaches. Both males and females have wings longer than their bodies (see Figure 6.15, following page 254). Young nymphs have long antennae, which are white at the tip.

Females lay a dark brown to black egg capsule, which contains 24 eggs. Each female produces about 17 capsules, and they are usually glued to a surface, although occasionally they may be found lying loosely on the ground or floor. Their life cycle is similar to that of other *Periplaneta* species, except that the average adult life span is less than that of the American cockroach. In a protected area, smokybrown cockroaches will live for about 200 to 300 days at room temperature.

This cockroach is restricted in its distribution within the United States. It is common throughout central Texas and eastward, along the Gulf Coast, throughout Florida, and up the eastern seaboard. It is the most common species of cockroach encountered in some parts of the South, and it is now known to be present in some areas of southern California. It is not generally found in the northern United States except when accidentally brought in.

Normally, this cockroach feeds on plant material (especially in greenhouses), but it can feed on almost anything that other cockroach species feed on once inside a dwelling. It is commonly found living in wood shingle roofs and in gutters, where it feeds on decaying organic matter. In attics, it is typically found living at the roofline.

Nymphs and adults enter buildings in a number of ways. They can be brought into the house with firewood or anything else that is stored outside, in garages, or in other storage areas. They can enter around doors and windows, through ventilation ports under the eaves of a house, or through any other small cracks or crevices that lead inside. Many homes with brick facades are built with regularly spaced weep holes in the brickwork; cockroaches and many other insects can enter wall voids via these weep hole accesses. They can also move

Domestic vs Peridomestic Species

Some species of cockroaches, such as the German and brownbanded cockroach, are strictly (or nearly so) indoor, or domestic, pest species in the United States. When the pest control professional encounters these species infesting homes or other facilities, it is important to understand that control procedures need be focused only indoors. Pesticide treatments or other management procedures outside of the premises, such as in landscape areas, will rarely be necessary.

However, the other species of cockroaches are often called peridomestic because their infestations usually originate and have ongoing focus in areas around (landscapes or neighborhoods), under (crawlspaces), or above (attics) the premises (the indoor, domestic, areas) that the pest control professional has been retained to protect. Effective control or pest management procedures for these peridomestic species, and in these specific infestation situations, should therefore include close attention to the outdoor component of these infestations. It is in these areas where environmental modifications, such as the removal of trees, woodpiles, mulched areas, or other ground covers may be important pest management steps that will limit the potential for these cockroach species to persist and to continuously reinfest the premises.

However, it is important to note that in more-northern areas of the United States or in many other cooler and more-temperate areas, some of these species, such as American or oriental cockroaches, that may be distinctly peridomestic in warmer areas will not demonstrate a significant presence in landscape, crawlspace, or other strictly outdoor situations adjacent to the infested premises. For successful short- and long-term control of cockroaches, it is important for the professional to understand whether an infestation is peridomestic or domestic under the situations actually being faced, and to respond accordingly.

onto roofs and gutters and eventually into the structure. Smokybrown cockroaches move in and out of buildings to forage more than do American cockroaches and most other outdoor species.

Woods Cockroaches
Parcoblatta spp.

The term *woods cockroach* covers a number of cockroach species, usually of the same genus and having similar habits. The species most generally described is the Pennsylvania woods cockroach, *Parcoblatta pennsylvanica* (DeGeer). Woods cockroaches are small, usually not more than 2/3-inch long. Adults are dark brown, with the sides of the thorax and the front half of the wings margined with yellow (see Figure 6.16, following page 254). The wings are longer than the body in the male, while those of the female cover only 1/3 to 2/3 of the abdomen.

The males are generally strong fliers, whereas the females do not fly. The Pennsylvania woods cockroach is widely distributed in the eastern, southern, and midwestern United States, up to Canada.

Egg capsules are produced during the warmer months and are deposited loosely behind the loose bark of dead trees, fallen logs, or stumps. Woods cockroaches rarely breed indoors. Nymphs and adults are usually found outdoors beneath loose bark in woodpiles, stumps, and hollow trees (see Figure 6.17, following page 254).

These cockroaches often become a problem when infested firewood is brought indoors. They will wander about the house without congregating in any particular room. They can be especially troublesome during the mating season, which is often May and June. Male woods cockroaches are strong fliers and will come from considerable distances, often in large numbers. They are readily attracted to lights at night and accidentally gain entry indoors. Large numbers may also be found in the rain gutters of homes. Woods cockroaches feed primarily on decaying organic matter.

Australian Cockroach
Periplaneta australasiae (Fabricius)

The Australian cockroach is similar in appearance to the American cockroach but is rarely more than 1-1/4 inches long. It is reddish brown and can be distinguished by prominent yellow stripes along the outer front edge of either wing, and by a prominent dark spot in the center of the pronotum (see Figure 6.18, following page 254). Well-developed wings in both sexes extend to the tip of the abdomen.

Adult females drop their egg capsules in cracks, crevices, or other hidden areas shortly after they are formed. The eggs hatch about 30 days after the egg capsule is dropped. There are approximately 24 eggs per capsule, but only about two-thirds of this number usually hatch. Egg capsules are symmetrical, brown, elongated (the length is more than twice the width) and about 1/2-inch long. Egg capsules are dropped at about 10-day intervals and not glued to surfaces. The nymphs are strikingly marked with distinct splotches of yellow on the dorsal side of the thorax and abdomen. Nymphs move about under loose bark and in moist decaying vegetation, as do the adults.

This cockroach is found chiefly in the southern United States, but it has been found in greenhouses, zoo buildings (especially where plant material and humid conditions are prevalent), and houses in the northern states. It feeds predominantly on plant materials, although it will feed on various starchy materials in homes.

Brown Cockroach
Periplaneta brunnea Burmeister

Brown cockroaches are generally distributed in the southern United States, from Florida to Texas, but they have been found as far north as Philadelphia, Pennsylvania, and Columbus, Ohio.

The brown cockroach resembles the American cockroach, except it has a broader body and less distinct, or sometimes virtually no yellowish markings on the thorax. It is a dark, reddish-brown color with well-developed wings in both sexes, but not as long in the males as in the male American cockroach. The last segment of the cercus is short and blunt when compared to that of the American cockroach (see the cockroach key, Figure 6.1). Brown cockroaches occur indoors and outdoors, where they are found under the bark of trees and in sewers, garbage heaps, crawlspaces, and similar places. In southern states, this cockroach is associated with trees, particularly palm trees. The brown cockroach normally feeds on plant materials.

Egg capsules contain an average of 24 eggs each. The egg capsule is normally glued on a wall near the ceiling, usually in open places in either homes or commercial buildings. Indoors, the cockroach seems to prefer sticking the egg capsule to cement or plaster, rather than wood. Outdoors, placement of the egg capsules is similar to that of the American cockroach.

Field Cockroach
Blattella vaga (Hebard)

This is a small cockroach, slightly smaller than the German cockroach. It is very similar to the German cockroach but can be distinguished by a blackish area on the front of the head, extending from the mouthparts to between the eyes. This blackish area on the front of the head can be very faint, appearing more tan in color, in some individuals. The adults have a different color pattern than do German cockroaches on the upper surface of the abdomen (below the wings). This species was probably introduced from Central Asia, but its distribution in the United States is from California to Texas. The field cockroach feeds largely on decomposing vegetation and is common in irrigated areas. It normally lives outdoors and occupies areas under stones, clumps of earth, and similar locations. Occasionally, however, it wanders into homes during dry parts of the year.

The female carries the egg capsules until they are ready to hatch. The capsules are normally dropped outdoors. When these cockroaches come indoors, they wander about on the walls and floors during daylight hours and make no attempt to hide in dark cracks, as German cockroaches do.

Asian Cockroach
Blattella asahinai Mizukubo

This species is native to certain areas in Southeast Asia and appears to have been introduced to the United States through the port of Tampa, Florida. It is established in the Tampa, Lakeland, and St. Petersburg areas of Florida, and its distribution as a common pest has slowly expanded throughout most of central Florida. It has the potential to spread to other areas of the southern United States with similar year-round climate conditions. It is very similar in appearance to the German cockroach, but it has very different behavior. It prefers to infest shaded and moist areas in landscapes, grassy areas, and ground covers. It typically becomes most active just at dusk, remaining so for a few hours thereafter. Adults will fly quite readily and for relatively long distances. They will fly to lights at night. Because they will enter homes, these cockroaches are a particular nuisance when they fly inside and into TV screens and onto people. They are also a considerable nuisance when they fly into backyard barbecues and other patio events in the evening.

This species is quite susceptible to all the insecticides typically used for cockroach control. The limits of its ultimate geographical spread within the United States are difficult to estimate at this time, but it may spread to other warm and moist regions of the gulf coastal states and California.

COCKROACH MANAGEMENT
Understanding basic cockroach biology and behavior is essential to the professional who attempts to manage cockroaches. Also, the more that is understood about cockroaches, the greater the likelihood of success on those occasions when standard management methods do not work or cannot be used. However, in some cases, it may be practically impossible to achieve total elimination due to various circumstantial factors unless a relatively broad-reaching (and thus expensive) program is implemented. Managing a cockroach infestation to a tolerable level is more realistic in such cases.

Consistent and effective cockroach management requires a considerable degree of planning and organization to develop a multifaceted program that includes the following steps: **inspection and survey, treatment** (often involving the use of multiple insecticide formulations, plus nonchemical techniques applied indoors or around the premises), **client education**, and **follow-up**. It is important to keep adequate records throughout this process. Record keeping is necessary to satisfy legal or regulatory requirements in some states and also organize and implement an effective program. This attention to detail and record keeping is especially helpful when the initial management efforts are not satisfactory. Additional steps may be needed to modify the program to eliminate any surviving cockroaches.

Before proceeding with a general discussion of these steps, it is important to understand the main objective of a cockroach management program. That objective is to manage a cockroach infestation to the lowest possible level consistent with client expectations. In many cases, and especially for infestations indoors, this means total elimination, while in other situations or contexts a pest management approach that achieves only significant reductions will be acceptable. This is what most clients who call professional pest management firms expect, whether or not these objectives are stated in the contract or agreement under which the service is provided. Whichever objective is pursued, a reasonably detailed program should be planned, explained to the customer, and executed.

The necessary program steps are outlined and discussed in the following sections, with the greatest detail given for German cockroach management. Management programs for other species indoors will usually be conducted in a similar manner to those for German cockroaches, except that certain aspects of the behavior of other species should be taken into account. Some other species that are peridomestic in their distribution and behavior will also require substantial attention to outdoor insecticidal treatments and other management measures. Details of these outdoor application procedures are discussed in the sections for each species.

In most cases, cockroach management should

be proposed as more than a one-time treatment. Very rarely will elimination be possible with one treatment or with the use of only one type of insecticide in the cockroach management program. (A possible exception to this statement is the use of fumigation to eliminate all cockroaches and other pests from a structure; however, fumigation alone will not leave any protection against reinfestation, so it is rarely done except as part of a broader, long-term program.)

Pest management firms that offer one-visit cockroach management, and clients who settle for this, should understand that the objective of such a program can be accurately stated as to provide only a treatment. Such treatments usually lead to only temporary reduction in the infestation, but not to effective long-term management or elimination. Pest management firms should provide a higher level of service than just spray, bait, or even a combination treatment. Most clients turn to professionals for their knowledge and expertise to design and conduct a safe and effective cockroach management program. Otherwise, there are over-the-counter insecticide products readily available to consumers. In fact, these consumer products include versions of most of the insecticides commonly used by professionals, but most consumers lack the equipment, knowledge, experience, and techniques to use these insecticides with greatest effectiveness.

Inspection and Survey

The primary goal of a cockroach inspection is to locate as many cockroach hiding places, or harborages, as possible, as a means to determine necessary and proper insecticide treatments and other management activities. It is also important to note safety considerations, such as the location of pets and the presence of small children

In many specialized or difficult accounts, proper inspection includes preparation of a **diagram** of the indoor and outdoor areas where the program will be conducted. This diagram should include notes on all cockroach sightings, areas where frass was spotted, conditions that are conducive to cockroach presence, sanitation problems, locations of sensitive areas (e.g., areas with pets, children, handicapped people, sensitive people, or sensitive equipment), and other treatment considerations.

For highly complex situations, and where a heavy infestation exists, a series of diagrams and extensive notes may be necessary. This leads to the necessary customization of the various insecticide applications and other management efforts, helping to ensure a successful result with the greatest

safety and a minimum number of re-treatments. Such forms and record keeping are also important for accounts involving regulatory inspections and potential lawsuits.

The tools required to conduct a professional cockroach inspection include a heavy-duty flashlight, a mechanic's mirror (to allow inspection of difficult cracks and crevices), a flushing agent (e.g., pyrethrins), and screwdrivers, pliers, and other hand tools to open equipment panels or gain access to other possible cockroach harborage areas (see Figure 6.19). Knee pads and a bump cap are useful when inspecting areas that are dark or difficult to reach, sometimes called dead spaces, which cockroaches often prefer. For additional information on inspection tools, refer to Chapter 5.

When conducting a cockroach inspection indoors, especially for German cockroaches, it may be important to spend time either sitting on the floor or crawling around. This will allow a different perspective on all the available cockroach harborages. If all inspections (and treatments) are made from a standing position, important harborages, sanitation considerations, and other factors are likely to be overlooked. Keep in mind that a cockroach crawls around with its head and antennae less than 1/2-inch from the floor, wall, or other surfaces. Thus, an inspection made by a person whose head and eyes are five to six feet above the floor does not permit a view of the world in which the cockroach lives. It has often been said about cockroach man-

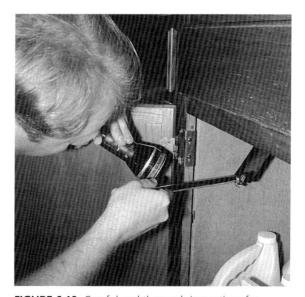

FIGURE 6.19. Careful and thorough inspections for cockroaches are critical to success of the overall control program, as all harborages must be located for later focus of insecticide and noninsecticidal treatments. Many technicians use a mechanic's mirror as an aid during inspections indoors, and a strong flashlight is also essential. (Myers)

agement that "You need to think like a cockroach." In many ways, this is especially good advice for the inspection and survey phases of the program. In addition to a floor-level perspective, an above-floor-level perspective is often required. Thus, a ladder can be an important tool for proper inspections and treatments. This is especially true in commercial establishments, such as restaurants and supermarkets, which often have suspended or high ceilings.

Keep in mind the behavior of the cockroach species involved and, if necessary, include an inspection of affected outdoor areas. Trees, shrubs, ground covers, mulched areas, locations near food and water sources (e.g., pools and pet dishes), woodpiles, trash receptacles, door and window casings, roof areas, clogged rain gutters, and other possible harborages should be inspected, if necessary. Attics, garages, and crawlspaces should be considered for some species, particularly in regions with warm, moist climates.

Nighttime inspection is another good technique that will occasionally be necessary in difficult infestation situations. When the cockroaches are normally out and foraging at night, whether indoors or outdoors, you can gain a much better idea of where they are harboring and traveling. A type of yellow filter, available from pesticide and equipment suppliers, can be put over the flashlight lens to allow searching for German cockroaches without startling them. Their presence and movement can then be monitored more effectively, with less disruption of normal behavior. In this way the professional can observe and trace cockroach movement to overlooked or unseen harborage areas.

A cockroach **survey**, using **trapping techniques**, is sometimes necessary to determine the extent of an infestation, because even a thorough inspection will not reveal all the cockroach harborages or where they are foraging most actively at night. Surveys are particularly useful in large, complex accounts, and especially where there is a moderate to heavy level of infestation. A second advantage to surveys comes when the survey is repeated in the exact same manner some time after the management program is implemented, because the surveys can be used as a basis for estimating the program's effectiveness. This can be especially useful when the goal is total elimination, or zero cockroaches. The accuracy and validity of such program estimates will depend on the pretreatment and post-treatment surveys being conducted thoroughly and in exactly the same manner.

Professionals sometimes resort to intensive surveys after trying and failing with one or more inspections and treatment regimens for cockroach control. In general, when a cockroach problem persists despite thorough treatments, a survey can assist in at least narrowing down the areas that may be serving as sources of infestation or that are not receiving proper insecticide treatment. Once the last few remaining harborages are identified, final elimination of the cockroach infestation will often follow.

Cockroach surveys involve the use of **sticky traps** placed at strategic locations within the structure or in the landscape (for outdoor species). Whenever possible, place survey traps either against a wall or in a corner of a floor, a shelf, or a drawer. Cockroaches have a behavioral trait known as thigmotaxis, which means that they prefer to have the side or top of their body touching another object. Thus, they prefer to walk along walls and close to furniture, and to hide in cracks and crevices during daylight hours when not foraging. Traps placed even a couple of inches from a wall, or from the sidewall of a cabinet or drawer, may not be found nearly as readily by the cockroaches as those placed against walls or other objects.

Most commercially available traps come complete with bait to encourage cockroaches to enter. One night of trapping with a sufficient number of trap locations will usually provide enough information to design a much more complete and effective management program. If survey results are low on the first night, and a significant infestation is suspected, it may be necessary to reposition some of the traps and survey for a second or third night to locate some harborages more precisely.

When traps are picked up, record the numbers captured in each trap and make notes on the diagram or floor plan you prepared during the inspection phase. Also, notice the position and direction in which captured cockroaches were heading. These observations can give important clues regarding the location of nearby cockroach harborages. Use this survey information to direct further inspections, trap placements, or insecticide applications. Be sure to use the same type and brand of trap for follow-up surveys. Even sticky traps vary widely in their ability to capture various stages.

Some researchers and pest management professionals also use spatial analysis software programs with their computers to enter trap catch data, along with spatial diagrams of the interior layout of the rooms that include locations of furnishings, appliances and other relevant features. These analyses provide contour maps that help the professional locate and focus on infestation "focal points" or "hot spots."

Sanitation

The first aspect of the treatment phase is **sanitation**. Sanitation efforts will help to eliminate food, moisture, and harborage available to the cockroach population, thereby stressing cockroach populations, which will lead to better control results. Sanitation involves not only various types of cleaning procedures to remove food and water sources, but also the elimination of cockroach harborages by caulking or similar structural repairs.

Of course, sanitation should be practiced for general public health reasons. In commercial facilities, it is generally mandated by public health codes applicable to restaurants and other food handling facilities. It is interesting to note that research fails to show that sanitation alone can substantially reduce German cockroach numbers where high levels of cleaning, caulking, and other sanitation procedures have been applied to cockroach-infested apartments. Other research indicates that insecticide applications provide greater initial control and have better residual action where proper sanitation procedures are first applied and then routinely followed. These latter observations are supported by researchers who have noted that grease and other typical forms of soiling on household or commercial kitchen surfaces can substantially decrease the residual action of insecticide spray applications. Rigorous sanitation also causes stress on German cockroach populations, so they will forage more actively and may be controlled more readily by insecticide applications, and especially by bait applications. Some laboratory studies have also shown that starved German cockroaches are more susceptible to insecticides.

In general, all sanitation deficiencies should be noted during the inspection and survey. Recommendations should be made and reinforced with the client (commercial or residential) to correct these problems, and continuously monitored thereafter. Some pest management firms conduct all aspects of a necessary sanitation program, at extra cost, as part of the overall program for commercial clients. Others have devised ways to encourage or force these clients to follow up on needed sanitation procedures. Very often, high-quality programs that guarantee cockroach elimination will include in their guarantees a requirement that the client must adhere to rigid sanitation standards.

Pest management professionals who are unable to gain client assistance with sanitation considerations, and are, therefore, unable to provide satisfactory cockroach management, are in effect selling insecticide treatments and not pest management or elimination programs. Clients who do not understand the importance of sanitation to the overall program, or who will not implement reasonable and necessary sanitation recommendations, will either be forcing the professional into excessive

reliance on insecticide treatments or should expect to continue having a cockroach problem. Pest management firms that have a policy of canceling accounts with such unresponsive customers, after first doing everything possible to educate them to these needs, will generally be better off in the long run. A policy of canceling accounts with such customers will result in gaining a reputation as a serious and highly professional pest management firm, and will help build and maintain morale among the professional service staff in the field.

Other Nonchemical Control Methods

We have already discussed caulking and screening as part of the sanitation effort to eliminate harborages. These procedures are also effective to prevent cockroach movement between rooms or floors of a structure, or to keep invading outdoor species from entering the premises. These are called **exclusion techniques**. Other exclusion techniques are the use of sticky barriers (e.g., rodent glue board adhesive or special insect trap adhesives) to prevent cockroaches from climbing the legs of tables or other furniture. There are also Teflon aerosol formulations that leave a dry, powdery film on treated surfaces. If properly applied on vertical surfaces, these films can be effective cockroach barriers. Such techniques may be especially useful under special situations where no pesticide can be used. Some items that cannot be treated with insecticides (e.g., in food-handling facilities) can be routinely bagged in sealed plastic garbage bags each evening to prevent cockroaches from using them as harborage or contaminating them.

Use of **heat** greater than 120°F for several hours, or cold at 0°F for 60 minutes or at 32°F for several hours may also be practical with German cockroaches to effectively control them in situations where insecticides cannot be used or no residues are permitted. For example, when portable items, such as toasters, clocks, or books, cannot be treated with insecticide, they can be placed inside sealed plastic garbage bags and stored in a freezer overnight.

While the use of **traps** was stressed for survey purposes, they can also be used as part of the treatment program. However, they are incapable of removing a significant portion (i.e., more than 90%) of the population when used alone.

Recently, **vacuum cleaners** specially designed for indoor pest control have been marketed for direct physical removal of cockroaches from their immediate harborages in an attempt to reduce cockroach populations (especially domestic species like the German and brownbanded cockroaches).

Cockroach Control in Food-Handling Establishments

Only those residual insecticide formulations that bear directions on their labels for such use can be used for pest control in food handling establishments. Typical labels bear wording such as "Food areas: limited to crack and crevice treatment only.... Applications of this product in the food areas of food handling establishments, other than as a crack and crevice treatment, are not permitted." Before the professional can determine which insecticides can be used for control in these areas, the term **residual insecticide**, as defined by the EPA, must be understood.

Residual insecticides are those products applied to obtain insecticidal effects lasting several hours or longer and applied as general, spot, or crack and crevice treatments. Residuals include common insecticides such as certain organophosphates, carbamates, and pyrethroids. Pyrethrins and some other pyrethroids are usually thought of as nonresidual materials, but certain formulations with higher than normal concentration and applied as coarse sprays can provide insecticidal effects lasting several hours or longer, so they are considered residual by the EPA.

There are four types of residual applications recognized by the EPA: general, barrier, spot, and crack and crevice. Each may be used in certain areas of food-handling establishments.

General treatment is application to broad expanses of surfaces such as walls, floors, and ceilings, or as an outside treatment. This is permitted only in nonfood areas using only those insecticides so registered.

Barrier treatment is usually considered the application of pesticides to thresholds and other entrances, the foundation, and the soil adjacent to the foundation. Read the label, because some pesticides contain explicit instructions for this use. Some outdoor insects or related pests may become invaders or nuisances when populations build up outdoors and then attempt entrance to the premises. A barrier treatment with residual sprays, dusts, or granules may be beneficial in controlling such pests.

Spot treatment is application to limited areas on which insects are likely to walk, but which will not be in contact with food or utensils and will not ordinarily be contacted by workers. Such areas may occur on floors, walls, and the bases or undersides of equipment. For this purpose, a spot should not exceed 2 square feet. In the past, this application method could be used only in nonfood areas. However, some insecticides have received EPA approval for label directions permitting spot applications in food areas.

Crack and crevice treatment is the application of small amounts of insecticides into cracks and crevices in which insects hide or through which they may enter a building. Such openings commonly occur at expansion joints, between different elements of construction, and between equipment and floors. These openings may lead to voids, such as hollow walls, equipment legs and bases, conduits, motor housings, or junction or switch boxes. Spray, dust, or bait formulations (loose granular or gel) can all be applied by use of the crack and crevice method. It permits the use of products in food areas as long as the insecticide is placed only into cracks and crevices. It does not permit treatment of open or exposed surfaces.

It is important to note that residual insecticides may be applied when food establishments are in operation unless the label of the product being used specifically indicates that all operations must be stopped at the time when applications are made.

When using **nonresidual insecticides** (defined as those applied to obtain insecticidal effects only during the time of treatment) as **space treatments**—by aerosol, mechanical aerosol, or ultra-low volume (ULV) or fogging treatments—the application should be made while the food-handling establishment is not in operation and exposed foods are removed or covered. Also, food contact or handling surfaces should be cleaned before use. However, the use of nonresidual insecticides as **contact treatments**, which means hitting the target pest with a wet spray for immediate insecticidal effect, can be done while the establishment is in operation. Both space treatments and contact treatments are considered general insecticide applications.

Vacuum cleaner treatments can reduce cockroach populations but do not eliminate them because cockroaches tend to rebound in three to four weeks after such treatments. The flushing-and-vacuuming technique may be very useful in control programs where high cockroach numbers are present initially. Also, hard-to-reach gravid females may be more vulnerable to being caught by the flushing-and-vacuuming technique than by other control methods.

Many types of electrical or mechanical devices are marketed for cockroach (and other pest) control, including electromagnetic, sonic and ultrasonic, and microvibrational and electromechanical devices. To date, no valid scientific studies have shown any of these devices to be effective at repelling, sterilizing, killing, or otherwise affecting cockroaches or their behavior in a way that can be used effectively in a management program. Therefore, none of the devices currently in the marketplace are recommended. Professionals are cautioned to view any new devices with great skepticism until reliable, published scientific data from at least several qualified and unbiased sources are made available.

Lastly, there are a number of predators, parasites, and disease organisms present in nature that act to naturally limit the size of cockroach populations. This is called biological control. Some types of wasps lay their eggs in cockroach egg capsules, especially capsules of the *Periplaneta* species and the brownbanded cockroach. The wasp larvae eat the contents of the cockroach egg capsule. Spiders can also serve as cockroach predators. Microorganisms, such as ycasts and other bacteria, can provide substantial population reduction or suppression under some limited circumstances. The entomopathogenic fungus *Metarhizium anisopliae* (Metchnikoff) has shown potential for management of German cockroaches in the laboratory, although this has not been demonstrated in any field tests. The slow speed of action, low levels of control, and inconsistency of results experienced with biological control renders these approaches of little use in most urban cockroach management programs (and especially indoors, where elimination of cockroaches is generally required). In the future, however, some of these biological control agents might be useful for control of peridomestic species in outdoor situations, where modest levels of population suppression may be acceptable.

Insecticidal Control Methods

In spite of the most rigorous sanitation and nonchemical control procedures, cockroach management will eventually require the use of carefully selected and conducted **insecticide applications**. Remember that, whenever possible, these applications should be made in conjunction with, and complementary to, the other appropriate sanitation and nonchemical procedures discussed above. Taken as a whole, these treatment procedures, when directed by careful inspection, surveys, and use of your experience and judgment, will constitute integrated pest management (IPM). This integrated approach should involve looking at the big picture while examining all aspects of the cockroach's behavior and the structural or other environmental factors that affect the management program. This approach ensures that maximum control is obtained with the greatest safety and efficiency.

Perhaps the most basic principle for applying insecticides against cockroaches is this: Regardless of the type of insecticide or formulation used, insecticide placed directly into or near cockroach harborages will produce far better control than insecticide placed where cockroaches will only walk over or

encounter it occasionally. Thus, the professional should search for, locate, and treat harborages.

There are a number of very effective cockroach bait formulations available for use indoors or outdoors. Indoors, there are gel, paste, aerosol foam, granule or bait-station formulations of abamectin, fipronil, imidacloprid, hydramethylnon or boric acid that will very effectively control German cockroach infestations—IF they are placed into or very near all the harborage areas that contribute to the infestation (see Figure 6.20). Similarly, there are granular bait formulations available that will effectively control peridomestic cockroach species when applied to areas in the landscape or the home (e.g., attics or crawlspaces) where those species harbor and forage.

Typical insecticide application techniques used with residual insecticide spray or dust formulations indoors are crack and crevice, spot, and general. Outdoors, barrier treatments are also used. These techniques are discussed in Chapter 5. Remember: To prevent misapplications, always check the label before applying an insecticide.

Chapter 3 contains a discussion of the various insecticide formulations used in pest management. Residual spray formulations made from emulsifiable concentrates (EC or E), flowable microencapsulations (FM or ME), suspension concentrates (SC), wettable powders (WP or W), and oil or water solutions (S), along with ready-to-use aerosols, are available for use against cockroaches. Dusts (D) and baits, along with ULV or aerosol formulations of nonresidual insecticides, are also available. During the inspection phase of the cockroach management

FIGURE 6.20. Precise application of cockroach gel bait with bait gun. Note: Use gloves to protect from exposure to insecticide and cockroach frass and allergens, and use a flashlight when applying in poorly lighted areas. (Myers)

program, take note of the types of surfaces and other conditions present, and choose insecticides and formulations accordingly.

In general, formulations such as wettable powders, microencapsulations, or suspensions will give better residual action against cockroaches on porous surfaces, such as unpainted wood, particle board, concrete or paper, and latex-painted or vinyl surfaces. Emulsifiable concentrates are generally used where no visible residue can be allowed, or where long residual action is either unwanted or impossible, and more moderate residual action will be acceptable. Little or no residual action can be expected where treated surfaces are exposed to excessive heat or moisture in commercial kitchens, laundry rooms, and some bathrooms. Use of residuals in either a crack and crevice or spot treatment mode around sources of heat and steam will not give significant residual action, so consider the use of nonresiduals (e.g., aerosols) applied into such cockroach harborages and baits placed nearby, where any surviving cockroaches will find them. Voids that will remain dry are usually best treated with dusts or residual aerosols (with crack and crevice tips). If other areas require treatment, this should generally be done with nonresidual aerosol or ULV applications. Baits can be placed in other areas where cockroaches are expected to forage, and they are generally effective when applied to nearly any type of interior surface. ULV treatments with nonresidual insecticides are frequently used to supplement thorough crack and crevice and void treatments, and these combination treatments are often called clean-out treatments.

There are many types of bait guns, bait stations or other bait application devices, sprayers, dusters, and other equipment available for use in applying insecticides for cockroach management. Compressed-air sprayers, aerosol insecticide systems, and hand dusters are most commonly used. Power sprayers are often used in outdoor applications, while power dusters and ULV equipment can be used for certain indoor applications. Chapter 5 discusses this application equipment in more detail.

Client Education and Follow-Up

There is much that the client can do to assist in the overall cockroach management program. Educate the client as to why sanitation is important to the total pest management program. In addition, explain a few of the program's details to the client and establish good communication with the client. It is much easier to deal with a client who understands the reasoning for what must be accom-

plished. A client who understands some of these details, including the thoroughness of the effort and the progress being made, will be more likely to maintain a long-term relationship with the firm (see Figure 6.21). Good customer relations and communication also help avoid accidents, pesticide contamination, or other problems.

Important aspects of the cockroach management program include continued inspections, occasional surveys, and necessary insecticide applications to maintain the highest possible degree of cockroach management. Do not fall into a routine of using only certain types of insecticide applications without doing the inspections and whatever else is necessary to find any and all remaining cockroach harborages. If insecticide applications and other activities in an account become too routine, the cockroaches will adapt to them and avoid the treatments. Keep in mind that a pest management firm is hired to eliminate pests, not to apply pesticides.

One of the hardest aspects of the professional's (and the supervisor's) job after satisfactory cockroach management or elimination is achieved is to maintain the necessary level of alertness and intensity in each account so that cockroach infestations do not rebound. Avoid the common cycle of initial clean out followed by a period of complacency, followed by an emergency need to do another clean out. Long-term control of cockroaches requires unrelenting effort. From the start, think of the management program as a continuing process that requires a constant and high level of vigilance. After satisfactory management has been achieved, rely more on inspection and survey and less on a routine

FIGURE 6.21. Customer or client education is an important step in cockroach pest management (and for other pests), as a means to enhance safety and follow-up sanitation or other measures that will assist the program. (Myers)

of insecticide treatments. Frequent clean-out treatments should not be necessary if the program is properly designed and there is adequate attention to inspections, surveys, sanitation, incoming sources of infestation, and necessary insecticide treatments.

The success of the very best pest management firms lies in their ability to be organized, thorough, and consistent about the details and execution of a cockroach management program. The other key to long-term success is to remain vigilant and do all the follow-up work necessary to keep the cockroaches from returning in any significant numbers. Good cockroach management takes considerable on-the-job experience and knowledge of cockroach behavior. It also requires a strong dedication and persistence to demand of yourself the effort and discipline to be very thorough in all aspects of the job. If any aspect of the program is ignored for long, cockroaches (especially German cockroaches) are so prolific that infestations will develop rapidly and undo all the work it took to achieve control at the start of the program.

German Cockroach Management

Much of the preceding discussion on where cockroaches will harbor was written particularly with the German cockroach in mind. This species is most commonly found near sources of food, water, and warmth indoors. This is particularly true of the small nymphs. The larger nymphs and adult males are known to range more widely inside infested buildings. Adult females forage for food and water in a manner similar to the males, except after the egg capsule is formed and is being carried. During this time they will leave the harborage to forage very little, if at all, except perhaps to obtain water.

When inspecting for German cockroaches, **thoroughness** is very important. Check places such as cracks and crevices within or between items of construction; under the tops of tables; behind and under sinks; in cabinets; in the motor compartments of refrigerators and soft drink dispensing machines; underneath the bases of kitchen equipment or pallets set on the floor; in switch boxes and fuse boxes; underneath cafeteria counters and soda fountains; in food carts; in cash registers and telephones; in vegetable bins; around meat counters and checkout stands; under meat cutting blocks; and almost anywhere else conditions are favorable. It is impossible to list all the places where German cockroaches may live and hide—they will vary depending on the exact situation of each infested premises—so the professional must inspect thoroughly and use judgment and experience to find all harborages.

Occasionally, previous insecticide applications may have scattered the German cockroaches into many different, and even relatively unfavorable, harborages. This makes inspection and management more difficult. In such cases the use of traps in a detailed survey will often be the only way to find all the scattered harborage locations and allow for adequate insecticide application and other management procedures.

Most German cockroach populations became resistant to chlorinated hydrocarbon insecticides years ago, and many still are. There are no chlorinated hydrocarbon insecticides labeled in the United States for use against any cockroach species. Studies of German cockroach populations collected from field locations have increasingly shown significant levels of resistance to most of the organophosphates and carbamates, and to synergized pyrethrins or the pyrethroids. However, it is important to understand that the field strains chosen for most of these resistance studies were selected because pest management professionals or homeowners had reported significant problems in controlling these strains with insecticides. Therefore, insecticide resistance was suspected, and the results of the research confirmed those suspicions. Resistance should generally be one of the last explanations considered (or blamed) for insecticide failures in the field. Experience has shown that incomplete or improper insecticide application is usually the cause of control failure.

In recent years, the availability of an increasingly effective array of bait products has allowed a much greater level of German cockroach control, often to the point where this pest is more readily and easily controlled or eliminated than in any past times since the advent of synthetic organic insecticide sprays. Thus, this species is now considered by many professionals to be of secondary importance as a household and commercial or institutional pest, typically behind the several household ant pest species.

Several very effective **bait** products are available which contain fipronil, abamectin, imidacloprid, hydramethylnon or boric acid as their active ingredient. Abamectin is available in granular, gel and spray foam formulations, while fipronil and hydramethylnon are available in containerized baits or gel formulations for German cockroach control, and imidacloprid as a gel. Often, very high and acceptable levels of control can be achieved with careful and thorough use of baits alone. Like any chemical control technique, however, resistance resulting in lack of control is likely. To delay the onset of resistance, professionals should consider rotating their use of baits in accounts where German cockroaches are problematic. To enhance the efficacy of baits, professionals should also remember that bait placement, primarily in cracks and crevices, and not on exposed surfaces is the key to controlling German cockroaches since most cockroaches do not travel far from their harborage (see Figure 6.22).

The residual spray or dust insecticides most frequently and effectively used for German cockroach control are pyrethroids such as deltamethrin, lambda-cyhalothrin, cypermethrin and cyfluthrin; organophosphates such as chlorpyrifos, propetamphos, and acephate; and the inorganic dust boric acid. However, in the United States and certain other countries, virtually all indoor uses of the organophospate and carbamate insecticides are no longer allowed so residual spray and dust formulations of the pyrethoids or other insecticides are the primary alternatives to use of the bait products. Many of these residual insecticides are available in a variety of formulations, including emulsifiable concentrates, wettable powders, suspension concentrates, dusts, and flowable microencapsulations.

Nonresidual insecticides can be used in aerosol or ultra-low volume applications, or they are sometimes added to residual sprays to give flushing and quick knockdown action. These include synergized pyrethrins or various pyrethroids. Use of insect growth regulators (IGRs) in managing German cockroach infestations is discussed at the end of this chapter.

Crack and crevice treatments with baits (gels, powders, granules or foams) or residual insecticides are usually best for German cockroach management since they result in the insecticide being placed exactly where the insect spends most of its time (hiding). They also result in safer, more controlled applications. There are many types of specialized cockroach bait applicators for indoor use, designed to allow precise bait placement.

FIGURE 6.22. German cockroach nymph feeding on insecticide gel bait that was applied into joint between wood molding elements. (Myers)

For residual spray applications , use a fine pinstream nozzle or one equipped with an extension tube. Aim the insecticide directly into the crack as deeply as possible, so the insecticide will penetrate and deposit within the crack or void and behind the crack or crevice. Avoid any splashing or spraying of the material out of the crack and onto exposed surfaces, especially in food handling establishments or in areas where children or other sensitive people might become exposed. With a compressed air sprayer, any pressure from about 8 to 15 psi will be adequate, while somewhat higher pressures are generally used for fan spraying. Crack and crevice injection treatments are sometimes conducted using higher-pressure equipment that produces fine, aerosol-like spray or mist particles, but such applications should be only of properly labeled nonresidual insecticides. Crack and crevice applications of residual insecticides should be applied only as low-pressure sprays, such as those produced by a compressed-air sprayer or by specially designed pressurized aerosols fitted with crack and crevice tips. If a spot treatment is needed, use a flat-fan nozzle, but first be sure the material is labeled for such application in the location involved (e.g., in a food-handling establishment, such as a restaurant kitchen or grocery store).

Special care must be taken when it is necessary to treat near dishes, glassware, or cooking utensils. Before treating, always remove these items from the treatment area and cover them with material such as polyethylene or a clean cloth. Never contaminate dishes or other food contact surfaces, such as countertops in kitchens and dining areas, with insecticides. Do not rely on the customer to wash dishes or other food contact surfaces. Either be certain not to contaminate them, or wash them yourself after treatment.

Dusts are one of the most effective types of residual insecticide application for German cockroach control. When applied in dry areas, they typically provide longer-lasting results than sprays. They should be used to supplement residual sprays and baits. Dusts should be applied to cracks and crevices and to wall and cabinet voids, using a hand duster (see Figure 6.23). A power duster or plunger duster can be used to treat larger voids, such as attics or crawlspaces. Hand dusters should have plastic tips on them, so that the tip will not conduct electricity if it is used near electric outlets, conduits, or equipment. For more information on the proper use of dusts and dusters, refer to Chapter 5.

ULV applications of nonresidual insecticides are frequently used to supplement applications of residual insecticides. The term *clean-out* is often applied to the practice of using ULV applications of

FIGURE 6.23. Application of insecticide dust into void below kitchen cabinets, using bellows-type hand duster. (Myers)

a nonresidual insecticide immediately after applying a residual insecticide. These ULV applications are also sometimes referred to as *fogging*. This two-treatment approach gives a higher level of initial control than if either the residual or nonresidual approach is used separately. In some areas the use of residual insecticides may be prohibited or inadvisable, so nonresiduals and baits may be the only available options. In these latter situations, be sure to use the ULV treatment first, and then apply baits after the premises have been thoroughly ventilated. This will minimize contamination of the baits with repellent pyrethrins or pyrethroids. In other situations, where the residents or clients are very concerned about the safety of any spray application techniques, the use of nondirected general applications, such as with ULV fogging equipment, will not be acceptable, so only crack and crevice and bait applications are permitted.

It is important to keep in mind that a properly conducted insecticide treatment program for German cockroach management requires careful consideration as to the choice of both insecticide ingredient and insecticide formulation. Select the most appropriate formulations and combinations of materials for each situation. These decisions are based on many factors, such as label restrictions, type of surface to be treated, non-target species present (pets or plants), client preferences (such as concerns about the sensitivity of children or others to insecticides), past insecticide usage patterns in the account, and other factors. The key to the control of German cockroaches (or any pest) is to integrate all the management tools available—inspections, sanitation, exclusion, and other nonchemical techniques—to minimize insecticide applications. A pattern of excessive insecticide use may lead to contamination, accidents, regulatory enforcement citations, and other problems. Always be careful not to

become too complacent or disrespectful about the potential hazards of the pesticides you use. Keep in mind that the objective is to manage or eliminate the cockroaches with the maximum level of safety for you, the client, and the environment.

American Cockroach Management

In larger urban buildings, American cockroaches are found in dark, damp, and warm places. They frequently congregate in groups in more-or-less open spaces, rather than in cracks and crevices. They are often found near steam pipes or in sewers, grease traps, floor drains, pipe chases, damp basements, and similar places. They are also common in the sanitary and storm sewers of most cities.

As with German cockroach management, it is important to do a thorough inspection. A trap survey may be necessary in difficult or special situations before any management procedures are attempted. This includes infestations originating in the landscape outdoors.

In the southern portions of the United States, American cockroaches are often peridomestic pests commonly found in the landscape (e.g., treeholes) along with other larger cockroach species, and they can readily move inside during nighttime foraging (see Figure 6.24). Movement indoors often increases during periods of cold, extremely hot and dry weather, or excessive rainfall. In these cases, it is important to treat, eliminate, or modify (to make uninhabitable) all outdoor areas where these peridomestic cockroach populations are focused. Keep in mind that American cockroaches and other peridomestic species can also be harboring around rain gutters and within soffits at the roof line, or in attic areas and crawlspaces.

Perimeter or barrier treatments using residual pyrethroid insecticide formulations to prevent cockroach entry into buildings will also often be helpful, but their residual effectiveness will be quite limited (usually to 1 week or less). Identify where the cockroaches are harboring and moving around in the landscape, and focus insecticide applications in those areas. The effect of these treatments will be primarily to kill only the cockroaches in the treatment area, and then others will move back to these areas from adjacent, untreated areas of infestation (if available) within a few days. Gel baits applied to outdoor sites harboring peridomestic cockroaches are highly effective; and in areas of the country where cockroaches' natural enemies are present, baits will conserve natural enemies whereas sprays may kill them and result in a resurgence of the cockroach population. Also, recent research shows that some other pests (such as Argentine ants or

FIGURE 6.24. Infestations of American cockroaches and other "peridomestic" species often have a substantial, or even primary, component which originates from infested areas outdoors. These outdoor sources of infestation must be located and properly treated or eliminated (non-chemical habitat modifications) to ensure success in the overall cockroach pest management program. (Myers)

slugs) may become more numerous after some perimeter treatments because they appear to feed on the carcasses of cockroaches and other insects killed by the perimeter spray. One important note: Do not treat firewood piles with residual sprays. Instead, use baits, such as scatter baits of certain organophosphates, carbamates or other active ingredients in these areas, or have the customer remove the wood.

Exclusion techniques, such as caulking or sealing various cockroach entry points, will also be effective in reducing the problem indoors. To prevent cockroaches from entering through weep holes in exterior brick facade, insert small squares of window screening into the holes, using a putty knife. This prevents insect entry yet still allows for air exchange, for which the weep holes are intended. Excessive and widespread insecticide applications in the landscape will not usually be necessary, but properly focused sanitation, exclusion, and insecticide treatments will offer consistent and effective results.

American cockroaches can be controlled by the use of sprays, dusts, or baits. Residual insecticide sprays applied into infested areas will control American cockroaches slowly, but effectively. Indoor surfaces are most effectively treated with wettable-powder, suspension, or flowable microencapsulated formulations. This is especially true for basement and other utility areas where bare concrete or other porous surfaces are present. Residual sprays of pyrethroids are recommended. American

cockroaches and other larger, peridomestic cockroach species are not known to have significant resistance to any group of insecticides currently registered and available for their control. Be sure to treat around floor drains where American cockroaches are harboring, and try to use window screening or some other method to physically prevent them from entering the building.

Insecticidal dusts are also very effective. Dust applications should be made to voids and other indoor harborage areas that will remain dry. Do not apply dusts to wet or damp areas. In some situations, American cockroaches can be killed by the use of nonresidual, quick-knockdown insecticides. Nonresiduals are usually applied either with aerosols, ULV sprayers, or foggers.

American cockroaches will also feed on commercially available baits containing abamectin, fipronil, imidacloprid, hydramethylnon, sulfluramid, chlorpyrifos, trichlorfon, propoxur, or boric acid. It is important to remember that sufficient numbers of bait locations should be used. For outdoor applications in landscape situations, the use of scatter baits labeled for these species and locations should be strongly considered. Mulched areas below landscape plantings should be a focus for such scatter bait treatments.

When insecticide spray applications to plants, such as trees, ground covers, or grassy areas, are necessary outdoors, use only formulations that are safe for use on plants. In these situations, wettable powders, suspensions, or microencapsulated or emulsifiable concentrate sprays of the residual materials already listed are generally appropriate. For applications to the sides of houses, door and window jambs, and other exterior surfaces, microencapsulated formulations, suspensions, or wettable powders are preferred over emulsifiable concentrates. These applications are frequently called perimeter or barrier treatments, and they are further discussed, along with various physical exclusion techniques, in Chapter 12.

Oriental Cockroach Management

Indoors, oriental cockroaches prefer dark, moist areas, such as under porches and in crawlspaces, basements, and floor drains. They may be found outdoors in abandoned cisterns, water valve pits, bark mulch under shrubs around the foundation, stone walls, and garbage and trash dumps. Oriental cockroaches are often found in cooler places than are typical for the other large species of cockroaches, such as *Periplaneta* spp. For example, they can overwinter in protected landscape areas of colder regions in the United States.

Oriental cockroaches can be controlled with the same types of insecticidal sprays and baits used for the American cockroach. However, the damp situations in which this cockroach is normally found will typically decrease the long-term effectiveness of residual insecticides, cause baits to mold (reducing their effectiveness), and often prevent the successful use of dusts.

Because oriental cockroaches often move into dwellings in large numbers, a perimeter or barrier treatment is recommended when cockroaches are found living outside. Research on the movement of oriental cockroaches under, around, and into homes from harborages in crawlspaces and cinder block foundations has shown that these cockroaches frequently move into the home along plumbing (e.g., up through the floor from underneath the crawlspace) and under door or window jambs. Thus, carefully treat these areas with insecticides and/or physically prevent such invasion by caulking or screening.

Brownbanded Cockroach Management

Brownbanded cockroaches prefer somewhat warmer, drier conditions and places than do German cockroaches, and they are usually found widely dispersed throughout houses or other buildings. Like the German cockroach, they are almost always found only indoors, so they are not considered peridomestic except perhaps in the warmest and most tropical areas of the United States. Unless a control program is thorough, these cockroaches can be difficult to manage because they live as individuals and small groups in such widely scattered locations. A thorough inspection of the premises is a must for brownbanded cockroach management, with special attention to available harborages in upper areas within rooms.

Sprays or dusts (e.g., of products recommended for German cockroach control) should be thoroughly applied to such places as inside bureaus, on shelves in clothes closets, in ceiling light fixtures, and behind valances above windows. Professionals must learn the hiding places of this cockroach.

Many professionals use contact, nonresidual insecticides in fogging or ULV machines to treat the whole area inside the house. When using this technique, be sure to remove all drawers and open all closet doors so the application will better penetrate cockroach harborages in these areas. The building should be closed for at least two to three hours after application to ensure adequate results.

Under some limited conditions, brownbanded cockroaches have been managed with programs that include releases of a relatively common oöthe-

cal parasite, *Comperia merceti* (Compere), along with limited use of pesticides. However, this approach is not suitable for most homes and commercial or industrial facilities, where there may be low tolerance for the release and presence of parasitic wasps, or where a higher level of control (or even elimination) is demanded over shorter time frames than can be obtained with such biological control techniques.

Smokybrown Cockroach Management

This peridomestic cockroach can be controlled with the residual sprays and baits recommended for American cockroaches. However, the extent and thoroughness of treatments must often be greater, since this cockroach is typically more active in its movements and will usually be found living in and around the inside and outside of a building. Individuals or groups of smokybrown cockroaches may be found in almost any room of a building as well as in and around crawlspaces, garages, attics, flower beds, trees, shrubs, trash or garbage receptacles, woodpiles, railroad crossties, and just about any other place where they can hide. They move about readily, going in and out of buildings. It should be noted that the smokybrown cockroach is highly susceptible to desiccation, more so than the other cockroaches discussed in this chapter. For that reason it is common to find breeding populations in areas of the home where excessive moisture exists, such as in attics where water has leaked in from the roof. Corrective measures to alleviate moisture problems will often reduce smokybrown cockroach infestations.

Often it is necessary to treat outside areas with power sprayers to get thorough coverage of the areas in which these cockroaches hide, and of the areas where they may be entering the home or building. Dusts are effective in attics and crawlspaces, and they may be applied with power dusters. When treating exterior surfaces of the home or building, use wettable-powder, suspension, or microencapsulated formulations to obtain the most effective residual performance on these difficult porous surfaces. In addition, it is often necessary to dust cracks on the outside of the building and to dust in the cracks of wood shingle roofs. Be sure not to miss any points on the exterior where these cockroaches may be entering, as these applications will be the most effective toward reducing the numbers making it into indoor areas.

In addition to harboring in attics where excessive moisture from leaky roofs is present, professionals should also check rain gutters for the possibility that smokybrown cockroaches are living in debris trapped in the gutters. There are various insecticide baits available for use against other outdoor cockroaches, crickets, millipedes, and other crawling insects. These can also be useful to control the smokybrown cockroach. Put gel or paste baits near entry points and scatter baits (waxy formulations will be best in damp areas) into ivy or mulched areas (e.g., pine needles, bark chips, or straw; see Figure 6.25). Similarly, treat treeholes, which are a favorite harborage, and treat outbuildings (with ULV foggers or baits). Do not fill treeholes with concrete or other materials thinking this will eliminate the harborage site. This measure will frequently exacerbate the problem by creating more harborage space. Concrete and other materials separate and pull away from the treehole, creating cracks and crevices that actually create harborage, resulting in higher cockroach populations.

In general, successful smokybrown cockroach management requires planning and thoroughness. It also requires use of more types of applications than any other type of cockroach management. Fortunately, once adequate results have been achieved in and around a home, the reproductive potential of this species is low enough (compared to the German cockroach) that its numbers will not rebound quickly. However, if one or more groups of smokybrown cockroaches are left unaffected by the effort, or if they cannot be eliminated from adjacent property, adequate control and customer satisfaction may be difficult to obtain. In many areas of the southern United States, smokybrown cockroach management is very frustrating in heavily wooded neighborhoods because of the many cockroach population reservoirs that are present, but frequently difficult to find

or treat effectively. These situations and frustrations, which are often shared among neighbors or in neighborhood associations, make this species a good candidate for area-wide approaches to control. This type of service approach should be considered by pest control firms in some areas, particularly in the southern United States.

Woods Cockroach Management

Woods cockroaches are usually only occasional invaders of houses or other premises. They are difficult to manage with insecticides inside the house because the infestation originates outdoors. At times they may be numerous in crawlspaces under a house. In these situations a thorough treatment with a residual insecticide spray or dust will be effective for their control. Woods cockroaches are common in woodpiles, so firewood should be stored away from the house to reduce their movement inside (see Figure 6.26). Because the males fly to lights at night, the use of residual insecticide sprays around doors, windows, porches, patios, and any other areas where outside lights are located will be especially effective; consideration should be given to manipulating the lighting so as to avoid attracting these pests and other night flying insects.

Field Cockroach Management

Field cockroaches are found living on decomposing vegetation and under stones or clumps of soil. They come into homes only during drier portions of the year, to get moisture. They can usually be controlled by removing decomposing plant material from the area or, when necessary, by spraying or dusting infested indoor areas with direct-contact insecticides.

Australian Cockroach and Brown Cockroach Management

These peridomestic cockroaches can be controlled with the usual nonchemical and chemical techniques. Use residual insecticide sprays, dusts, or baits in a manner similar to that discussed for the American cockroach. Since these species are more common in tropical and semitropical areas, pest control professionals should consider any palm trees in the landscape (or nearby) to be sources of infestation and the focus of insecticide treatment (especially with scatter baits among the fronds, adjacent to the tree trunks).

Asian Cockroach Management

Asian cockroaches present a rather difficult pest management challenge for professionals and

FIGURE 6.25. Mulched areas in landscape plantings are commonly infested by peridomestic cockroach pest species such as smokybrown and Asian cockroaches. (Myers)

FIGURE 6.26. Other common sources of infestation for peridomestic cockroach pests such as woods and oriental cockroaches are firewood piles (shown) or stone walls in landscapes. (Myers)

homeowners in the affected areas. Typically, these cockroaches are primarily an outdoor pest problem, but they do readily enter the home and can establish an infestation inside. The adults are strong fliers and are attracted to exterior and interior lighting and/or other light-colored surfaces and areas around a home. Management efforts should begin with raking and the removal of any leaf litter or other items that provide harborage to these roaches in the landscape (for example, mulched areas as shown in Figures 6.24 and 6.25). Then, if possible, bright lights shining through windows from inside or from exterior fixtures near doorways should also be eliminated or their brightness reduced. Besides removing buildup of decaying plant material that may be providing these insects food in the landscape, efforts should be undertaken to remove other food sources near the home, like pet dishes and garbage cans. Exclusion techniques, such as caulking, weatherstripping, and screening of weep holes in brick facades, should be considered. Insecticide applications, such as residual sprays at entry points into the structure, may be helpful. In the landscape, cockroach scatter baits can be applied to those areas where these cockroaches are harboring. When available, waxy formulations that are less susceptible to rapid spoilage under moist landscape conditions are preferred. Spray formulations labeled for cockroach control outdoors can also be used in these areas. In general, treat for Asian cockroaches as you would other peridomestic cockroaches, that is, find and treat outdoor breeding sites.

OTHER TECHNIQUES IN COCKROACH MANAGEMENT
Built-In Pest Control

Extensive treatment of wall voids, attics, crawlspaces, and other voids with **dust formulations** of boric acid or other inorganic insecticides has long been recognized as a very useful strategy to eliminate, or at least limit, cockroach and other pest problems in structures. Such treatments are most conveniently done during the building's construction, but they can also be done by careful and thorough application after construction. In general, as long as these dusts remain dry, they will effectively kill cockroaches in the treated voids.

IGRs (Insect Growth Regulators)

Chemicals that mimic, and disrupt, function of the cockroach's natural juvenile hormone, such as the juvenoid IGRs hydroprene (Gentrol®) and pyriproxyfen (Archer® and Nylar®), are useful in cockroach management. While they can be thought of as merely another type of insecticide, their action is quite different from that of traditional insecticides, which generally affect the nervous system. When used properly, these juvenoid IGRs will sterilize a high proportion of the adult cockroaches that survive other insecticide applications and management efforts. While they may kill some immature cockroaches, their most important action is to prevent surviving immatures from becoming reproductively capable as adults. However, since the adults present at the time of IGR application will not be sterilized, it is important to use these IGRs in conjunction with an effective conventional residual insecticide. This can be done as a combination spray, or by use of an IGR fogger and a separate bait or residual spray treatment. The strategy of using juvenoid IGRs in conjunction with applications of conventional bait or spray insecticides is based on the concept that the conventional insecticides will fairly quickly remove susceptible individuals from a population, while the juvenoid will hinder development and reproduction among any survivors.

In some situations, such as chronically infested apartment housing or other accounts where any form of spray or bait application may not be permitted because of customer preference, small, specially designed pads impregnated with hydroprene, called point sources, can be placed similarly to containerized cockroach bait stations. These units will emit, by a process of sublimation, hydroprene that will spread within the room, up to 75 square feet, according to the manufacturer. The hydroprene has a high affinity for greasy or oily residues on surfaces in areas such as those frequented by cockroaches, or for the greasy layers on the cuticles of the cockroaches themselves. Thus, the cockroaches in the area near the device will be exposed repeatedly over time, and sufficiently high levels of sterility within the population not controlled by the other insecticides used in the control program can be achieved to allow superior long-term German cockroach control. Follow label directions regarding the number of these units to use per unit of infested area.

In general, the treatment program involving conventional insecticides should be designed and implemented (with any repeat applications necessary) to provide one to two months of 80% or greater control for the added effect of the IGR to be of significant value to the overall management program. Applications of the IGR, by whatever forms or methods, should be repeated at intervals determined by ongoing monitoring of the cockroach population with sticky traps, with reapplications made whenever 80% or fewer of the adult female cockroaches captured do not show severely twisted or crinkled wings, which indicate sterility (see Figure 6.27). In cases where there are few adult cockroaches present in the trap sample, so that a calculation of the proportion of females sterilized is difficult, repeated and/or expanded applications of the juvenoid IGR should be considered at intervals of anywhere from wo to four months, depending on the specific situation, conditions, and previous experience with the intensity of infestation. In most situations of chronic German cockroach infestation and poor building maintenance and sanitation, this level of juvenoid IGR pressure (i.e., more than 80% twisted-wing adults in sticky-trap monitoring) against the population's ability to rebound must be maintained.

In general terms, juvenoid IGRs restrict the high reproductive potential of the cockroach population. Because this reproductive potential is a key aspect of the success and persistence of cockroach populations (especially German cockroaches), these IGRs provide a substantial advantage to the pest management professional in many circumstances. Even under very difficult and chronic infestation conditions, programs incorporating proper use of an IGR will generally result in a very high level of control, because most remaining adults will not be capable of reproduction. The use of other conventional insecticides can then often be reduced. However, it is important to understand that juvenoid IGRs are only useful additions to cockroach management programs; they may permit the use of fewer applications of conventional insecticides, spaced at longer intervals, over the long run. These products are not effective tools when used

FIGURE 6.27. German cockroaches showing moderate to severe (as here) wing twisting or crinkling due to juvenoid insect growth regulator (IGR) exposure will not be able to reproduce. IGR applications can be a significant aid to effective, long-term German cockroach pest management under difficult conditions that otherwise contribute to chronic infestations. (Myers)

alone, and their added benefit to the overall control program will generally not become apparent for several weeks after the first application.

Juvenoid IGRs have less utility in intensive cockroach management and elimination programs that rely on frequent and thorough applications of conventional insecticides, such as in restaurants, food plants, or healthcare facilities. On the other hand, they are particularly valuable in management programs for multifamily housing units or in other situations with chronic cockroach problems where frequent and costly insecticide applications are not practical. They might also be useful in situations where applications of conventional insecticides are less desirable or not permitted for whatever reason, such as in some zoo buildings, pet stores, or animal research facilities (and then only if the IGR will not harm desirable invertebrates within those facilities). In multifamily housing units and other complex structures, it is important to use the juvenoid in every unit, so that nonsterile cockroaches will be less likely to invade juvenoid-treated units. Hydroprene is not recommended for outdoor use in spray applications because it degrades in the outdoor environment. Pyriproxyfen has some ability to persist in outdoor situations where it is exposed to light, moisture, and other environmental factors, but the professional should consult product label directions closely for any precautions and prohibitions concerning applications outdoors.

Representative materials from a second group of IGRs, called chitin synthesis inhibitors, are registered for use against cockroaches and other crawling insects in some parts of the world. To date, however, this group of IGRs is known to structural pest control in the United States only by use of the benzoylphenyl urea compounds, hexaflumuron and noviflumuron, in subterranean termite baits (Sentricon® and Recruit®); while the juvenoids previously listed (along with methoprene, or Precor®) have many other uses, such as for control of fleas, ants, and stored product pests, and as larvicides for mosquitoes and other aquatic insect pest species. Recent research has shown that noviflumuron can control German cockroach populations much faster than the juvenoids IGRs, since it can effectively kill nymphs by preventing them from molting, and cause sterility of adults. As with any other type of chemical control technology, there is a high likelihood that resistance to these IGRs will evolve within German cockroaches over time.

Fumigation

Fumigation, usually with sulfuryl fluoride (Vikane®), is another practice occasionally used in cockroach management for restaurants, buses, and certain other situations. This technique may seem rather radical, but it is legal, can be done safely, and has been found to be a practical alternative for some situations. Fumigation provides immediate elimination of a cockroach population. However, since it provides no residual control for new cockroaches that are likely to enter the premises, fumigation will not take the place of a traditional cockroach management program. For accounts where the expense of fumigation is feasible, it may be wise to substitute fumigation for the initial clean out, and then continue with a traditional cockroach control program.

SUPPLEMENTARY READING MATERIAL

Appel, A. G., and L. M. Smith II. "Harborage Preferences of American and Smokybrown Cockroaches for Common Landscape Materials." *Environmental Entomology* 25 (1996): 817–24.

Atkinson, T. H., P. G. Koehler, and R. S. Patterson. *Catalog and Atlas of the Cockroaches (Dictyoptera) of North America North of Mexico.* Entomological Society of America, Miscellaneous Publication no. 78. Lanham, Md.: 1991. 86 pp.

Bell, W. J., and K. G. Adiyodi, eds. *The American Cockroach.* New York: Chapman and Hall, 1981. 525 pp.

Cornwell, P. B. *The Cockroach: A Laboratory Insect and an Industrial Pest.* London: Hutchinson & Company, 1968. 391 pp. Cornwell, P. B. *The Cockroach: Insecticides and Cockroach Control.* New York: St. Martin's Press, 1976. 557 pp.

Ebeling, W. *Urban Entomology.* Los Angeles: University of California, 1975. 695 pp.

Gould, G. E., and H. O. Deay. *The Biology of Six Species of Cockroaches Which Inhabit Buildings.* Lafayette, Ind.: Purdue University, 1940. 31 pp.

Mallis, A. *Handbook of Pest Control.* 6th ed. Cleveland: Franzak & Foster, 1982. 1,101 pp.

Roth, L. M., and E. R. Willis. *The Biotic Associations of Cockroaches.* Smithsonian Miscellaneous Collections, vol. 141. Washington, D.C.: 1960. 470 pp.

Rust, M. K. "Managing Household Pests." *Advances in Urban Pest Management.* Ed. G. W. Bennett and J. M. Owens. New York: Van Nostrand Reinhold, 1986. 399 pp.

Rust, M. K., J. M. Owens, and D. A. Reierson, eds. *Understanding and Controlling the German Cockroach.* New York: Oxford University Press, 1995. 450 pp.

Scott, H. G., and K. S. Littig. *Household Insects of Public Health Importance and Their Control.* Atlanta: U.S. Department of Health, Education, and Welfare, Communicable Disease Center, 1959. 33 pp.

Smith, L. M., A. G. Appel, T. P. Mack, G. J. Keever, and E. P. Benson. "Comparative Effectiveness of an Integrated Pest Management System and an Insecticidal Perimeter Spray for Control of Smokybrown Cockroaches." *Journal of Economic Entomology* 88, no. 4 (1995): 907–17.

Willis, E. R., G. R. Riser, and L. M. Roth. "Observations on Reproduction and Development in Cockroaches." *Annals of the Entomological Society of America* 51, no. 1 (1958): 53–69.

Wright, C. G. "Life History of the Smokybrown Cockroach." *Journal of the Georgia Entomological Society* 14 (1979): 69–75.

CHAPTER 7 | Subterranean Termites

The management of termites is a major portion of pest control work over a large part of the United States. Many pest management companies do only termite management, while most companies that manage other household pests also do termite management. In no other aspect of pest management do so many variables affect the type of work to be done and the results of the control operation as in termite management.

Termite management specialists must be knowledgeable in building construction, termite biology and behavior, the proper and safe use of chemicals, the use and maintenance of equipment, and safety. Termite management specialists must use considerable judgment in the performance of every job.

The order Isoptera consists entirely of termites, which are primitive insects closely related to cockroaches. Termites harbor one-celled organisms in their digestive tracts, and these organisms convert cellulose into substances the termites can digest. In nature, termites help to convert dead wood and other organic materials containing cellulose to humus. From this standpoint, termites are very beneficial animals. Only when people began building with wood in the natural home of the termite did the termites start feeding on buildings.

Termites are social insects. This means there is a division of labor among the different types of individuals, called castes. (Most ants, bees, and wasps are also social insects. See Chapter 9 for more information on them.) Nearly all termite species have reproductive and soldier castes. In many termite societies, there is also a distinct worker caste, but in most of the more primitive species, the typical duties of the workers (nest building, food gathering, and feeding of the reproductives and soldiers) are handled entirely by the nymphs. Even in species with workers, the older nymphs may do some of the work.

Workers and nymphs of subterranean termites (family Rhinotermitidae) perform all of the work of the colony and are the forms that do all of the damage to structures. Soldiers serve only to defend the colony against enemies. They cannot eat wood. They, together with the reproductives, are fed by the workers. Both workers and soldiers are eyeless and therefore blind.

Winged adults are referred to as the primary reproductives (often called swarmers). They emerge from the colonies on colonizing flights during certain seasons of the year. After these flights, a male (king) and female (queen) will pair up, lose their wings, and construct a small cell in the soil. There they will mate, lay eggs, and rear the first group of workers. In colonies where these primary forms are no longer present, supplemental (or secondary and tertiary) reproductives, without pigmentation or functional wings, occur, often in large numbers. Secondary reproductives form from nymphs, and possess eyes and wing buds, while tertiary reproductives form from workers and lack eyes and wing buds.

Each termite colony is self-supporting and essentially independent of other colonies, although recent research suggests closely related colonies may share workers during parts of the year.

LIFE HISTORY

The stages in the life history of subterranean termites are essentially the same for the various species of concern to the pest control specialist. Refer frequently to Figure 7.1 as you read the following paragraphs.

Termites develop via gradual metamorphosis from eggs laid by the primary or supplementary reproductives. Larvae hatch from the eggs and undergo several molts through which different individuals develop into one of the various castes (see Figure 7.2, following page 254). Four different castes can develop from larvae: workers, soldiers,

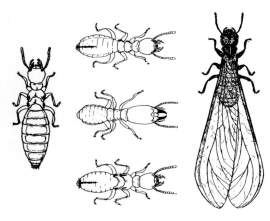

FIGURE 7.1. Representatives of the castes of the eastern subterranean termite, *Reticulitermes flavipes* (Kollar). *Right:* The winged (alate) primary reproductive. These alate forms are the familiar swarmers that often give the first indication that a structure is infested. *Middle row, top:* The sexually underdeveloped worker. The members of this caste are the individuals that do the actual damage. Note the complete lack of wing pads. *Middle row, center:* The soldier is greatly modified in head structure and serves a completely specialized function in the division of labor within the colony. It works solely in the defense of the colony and cannot feed itself. *Middle row, bottom:* A nymph, or developing reproductive (either primary or supplementary). Note the lengthened wing pads, which are usually the first indication of the development of these reproductives. Left: A functional supplementary reproductive. Female supplementary reproductives are thought to be the most important of the reproductive individuals in the subterranean termite colony.

winged (primary) reproductives, and supplementary reproductives. (See Figures 7.3 and 7.4, following page 254.)

In new colonies, larvae from the first small batch of eggs usually all become workers. Nymphs and soldiers are not normally produced until later egg laying.

In the species where a distinct worker caste occurs, **workers** are the most numerous individuals in a termite colony. They, along with the nymphs, perform all of the work of the colony—feeding the other castes, grooming the queen, excavating the nest, and making the tunnels. In the process of making nests and tunnels and ingesting food, they chew and eat wood, thus causing the destruction that makes termites economically important. Workers are usually light colored and do not have wings or any specialized structures.

Soldier termites serve specifically to protect the colony from its enemies. Their heads are large, quite hard, and have much larger mandibles than are found in the other castes. When openings are made into termite workings, the soldiers gather with their large heads and strong mandibles facing outward and protect the colony from invaders

Supplementary reproductives (see Figure 7.11, following page 254.) of both sexes are wingless or have only very short, nonfunctional wings, although tertiary forms have no wing buds. These reproductives are developed as needed and quickly replace a primary queen who is injured or dies. They also usually develop in addition to the primary queen and become the most important source of eggs in the colony. Supplementary reproductives, with a group of males and workers, may become isolated from the main colony and can establish a new colony, thus spreading the original infestation without being visible above ground at any time.

Primary reproductives (swarmer termites) are the caste most often seen by homeowners. They have fully developed wings and eyes. The winged adults are usually much darker than the other members of the colony. All four wings are the same

Swarming to Start New Colonies

At certain times of the year numerous small, immature, nymphal termites from mature colonies molt into larger nymphs with wing buds. Sometime later these individuals molt into sexually mature males and females called swarmers, or alates. Swarmers have two pairs of long narrow wings of equal size, thus describing the name of the order of classification to which termites belong—Isoptera; "iso," meaning same, and "ptera," meaning wing. Unlike other termites in the colony, swarmers are dark colored, almost black in some species.

During the spring, and often triggered by a combination of warm temperatures and rain, swarmers, which are both male and female, leave the nest in large numbers by taking flight from specially constructed mud tubes built a half inch or so above the substrate in which the termites are living and feeding. Termites continue to swarm throughout the warm season, although less frequently than during the spring. Colonies normally swarm only once per season, but may swarm twice or more; second and later swarms generally do not match the intensity of the first swarm. In warm parts of structures they will even swarm during the winter, although this is rare. Reticulitermes species typically swarm during the day, while Formosan termites swarm at night. Swarm flights are brief and swarmers are not good flyers. Often, they are transported by the prevailing winds. Typically, they do not fly very far before landing on the ground, but if winds are strong swarmers can be carried great distances before reaching the ground.

Colony Budding

If one or both of the primary reproductives die or if a part of the colony becomes isolated (i.e., is cut off from the primary reproductives), then supplementary reproductives may be produced. Supplementary reproductives help expand the foraging territory of termite colonies and often aid in the formation of new colonies. As a colony increases in size, groups of foragers may form satellite-like colonies, or areas of concentrated activities. Over time some of these groups may become physically separated from the rest of the colony and the primary reproductive (queen), resulting in the production of supplementary reproductives in the isolated group. This separation can result from a dramatic weather event (e.g., a flood) that separates termites, by cutting termites off by soil disruption, perhaps during construction, or by the application of a termiticide that results in the separation of termites in a structure from nestmates in the soil. After the separation, worker termites in the separated group may produce supplementary reproductives which may then allow establishment and growth of a new colony

length and extend more than the length of the body beyond the tip of the abdomen. Although functional workers develop in a few months, it usually requires 12 months of progressive colony growth for swarmer termites to occur. Both male and female reproductives leave the colony in great numbers (swarms), usually in the spring or fall. Some species swarm in both spring and fall.

These swarms are often the first visible indication that termites are present. Environmental conditions must be just right before termites will swarm. The temperature, moisture (both within and outside the colony), light conditions, and even barometric pressure influence swarming activities. As a general rule, swarmers emerge on warm, sunny days when the humidity is high (e.g., often on days following rain showers).

After a brief flight, the wings are broken off, and males and females pair and attempt to establish a new colony. They are particularly defenseless at this time, and most die or are killed by their natural enemies, or they succumb to dessication and other environmental factors. Each surviving pair makes a small cell in which they mate and lay eggs. Although this is the classically stated example of termite reproduction, there is an unfortunate tendency to overemphasize the importance of the primary queen. An exception is the Formosan termite, where the colony depends on the queen to produce eggs, and there is a tendency to not form secondary reproductives, even when the queen dies.

Actually, it is the supplementary reproductives that are responsible for the production of most of the eggs within a colony after it has become established. In a colony of 1 million individuals, the queen may have laid as few as 10,000 of the eggs. The supplementary reproductives are responsible for the remainder.

Swarmer termites are often confused with flying or swarmer ants. Since ants are often seen swarming in and around buildings, it is important to distinguish between the two so that appropriate control recommendations can be made. There are three ways to separate termites from ants. First, ants have a very thin waist between the thorax and the abdomen, while termites are broad waisted. Second, termite wings are all the same size and shape, whereas the forewings of the ant are larger, longer, and of a different shape than the hindwings. And third, termite antennae are straight; ant antennae are elbowed (see Figure 7.5).

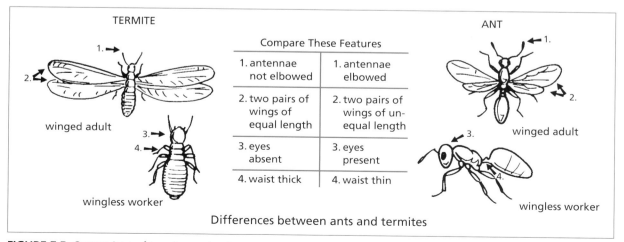

FIGURE 7.5. Comparison of termites and ants.

THE TERMITE AND ITS ENVIRONMENT

Termites require specific environmental conditions to survive (see Figure 7.6). Most times moist soil or other moist environments provide these conditions. **Moisture** is critical to termite survival because all castes except the swarmers are soft-bodied insects that lose water rapidly upon exposure to dry air. Thus, an available moisture source is critical to termites. Because of this, termites construct tubes (called **mud tubes**) that pass over exposed areas. Termite tubes serve to (1) conceal the termites, (2) provide the termites a moist environment, and (3) protect the termites from their enemies (ants). Termites maintain contact with the soil unless there is a constant aboveground source of moisture. The negative response to light that termites exhibit is intimately involved with keeping the termite in a concealed environment and may have come about as a response to the need to conserve water.

On occasion, freestanding shelter tubes will be built straight down from the infested wood toward the ground if they are in a protected area, such as a crawlspace under a house. This usually occurs after a colony has become well established and feeding has progressed some distance from the initial shelter tun-

Mud Tubes

Termites build shelter tubes to protect them from the desiccating effects of air and to protect them from natural enemies, such as ants. Shelter tubes are constructed of soil, particles of wood, and other debris held together with glue-like saliva and liquid anal secretions. The humidity inside an active shelter tube is high, and helps protect termites from desiccation. The tubes also serve as a physical deterrent to ants, the main enemy of termites.

There are many types of shelter tubes, including access tubes between the soil and food resources located aboveground (the most common), exploratory tubes which branch numerous times, but ultimately dead end, drop tubes which typically extend down to the soil from wood members in a crawlspace or other suspended wood, and swarm tubes. Swarm tubes are short, and built by worker termites to facilitate the flight of swarmers.

It is important to be able to determine the difference between active and inactive shelter tubes. When an active tube is opened often, but not always, termites will be found inside. The soil which makes up an active tube is dark in color and looks and feels moist. In comparison, an inactive tube made with the same soil will crumble when opened, is lighter colored, and dry.

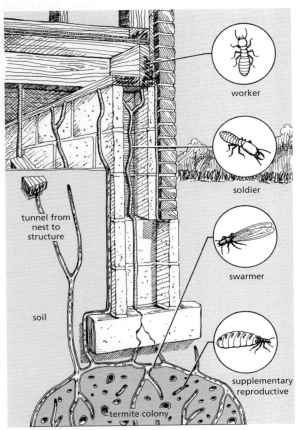

FIGURE 7.6. The environment of the subterranean termite. (Provonsha)

nel. In this way, the colony can obtain the necessary moisture without having to travel great distances.

The retention of moisture is not the only important factor associated with water in the life of the termite. The warm, moist conditions that prevail within the closed system of the nest provide an ideal site for the growth of microorganisms, particularly fungi, which provide a source of protein and vitamins essential to the termite. The accumulation of termite fecal material in the nest, in turn, helps to promote the growth of the fungi.

The most striking facet of this intricately interdependent system is the delicacy with which it is balanced. It is not uncommon to discover the remains of a termite colony that is slowly being crowded out by the growth of fungi that has for some reason progressed at such a rate that the termites could not keep up with it. If sudden temperature shifts or other factors result in the accumulation of water within the galleries, the termites may literally drown.

Each autumn the termites in the temperate zone normally respond to the gradual decreases in temperature by moving downward in the soil, where the

Colony Structure

Termites are social insects that live in groups called colonies. Some scientists view the colony not as a collection of individuals but as a single living entity whose parts (i.e., individual termites) work together towards the survival and reproduction of the whole (i.e., the colony).

The colony structure of subterranean termites has typically been thought of in terms of what we know about colony structure in other social insects, such as ants, that is a single, centralized colony in the soil from which workers forage in search of food and water. Colony structure in subterranean termites likely does not "fit" the ant colony model of sociality, where there exists a central, immobile site (nest) containing the greatest concentration of the social group. It is more likely that subterranean termite social groups are decentralized, and follow a loose pattern in their movement activity. The colony is thought to forage, or concentrate their activity, in different locations at different times via a network of extensive subterranean tunnels, and are nearly always on the move. Termite foraging activity might be concentrated in one section of their territory at one point and just days or weeks later might shift their activity to yet another section of their foraging territory, or might expand the size of their present foraging territory altogether.

necessary conditions of temperature and humidity can be maintained. In the spring, the colony then responds to increased temperatures and moisture in the soil above and again moves upward. In structures where warmth and moisture are present in winter months, termites may be present above ground the year round.

The type of soil has a great effect on the ability of subterranean termites to flourish. Subterranean termites generally prefer a sandy soil over a clay soil. However, they will survive in many types of soil.

Feeding

Subterranean termites have preferences in the type of wood they will eat. The eastern subterranean termite prefers slash and loblolly pine, while the Formosan termite prefers sugar maple and slash and loblolly pine (see Table 7.1). Although woods like redwood, cypress and juniper are less preferred by termites, no wood is completely immune to attack. The condition of the wood is also important. Decayed wood is eaten faster and preferred

over sound wood (see Table 7.2). Termites working in the wood facilitate decay by increasing the moisture content. Thus, termite damage is usually associated with decaying wood.

TABLE 7.1. Feeding (mg/8 weeks) on 11 species of wood by the Formosan termite, Coptotermes formosanus, and the eastern subterranean termite, Reticulitermes flavipes. (From Smythe and Carter, 1970)

Wood	C. formosanus	R. flavipes
Loblolly pine	381	493
Slash pine	367	270
Sugar maple	455	113
Western larch	167	181
Black walnut	74	59
Redwood	43	37
White oak	22	20
Black cherry	12	18
Bald cypress	19	17
Douglas fir	107	14
Ponderosa pine	20	14

TABLE 7.2. Feeding (mg/8 weeks) by the eastern subterranean termite, Reticulitermes flavipes, on five species of decayed and nondecayed wood. (From Smythe et al., 1971)

Wood	Decayed	Nondecayed
Sugar maple	726	438
Loblolly pine	706	436
Slash pine	701	508
Western larch	669	335
Ponderosa pine	660	333
Average	692	410

The major species of subterranean termites in the United States consume wood at approximately the rate of 2 to 3% of their body weight each day. Factors affecting consumption include the environmental conditions, size of the termite, and size of the colony. The average, mature colony of eastern subterranean termites contains about 60,000 to 1 million workers, while a Formosan termite colony contains 350,000 to 2 million workers. Under ideal conditions, an eastern subterranean termite colony of 60,000 would consume about 5 grams, or 1/5 ounce, of wood each day, while a Formosan termite colony of 350,000 would consume 31 grams, just over 1 ounce (see Table 7.3). It would take the eastern subterranean termite colony approximately 118 days to consume a 1-foot length of 2 × 4 pine, while the Formosan colony could consume the same board in 19 days. Thus, Formosan termites are usually more destructive than native subterranean termites.

TABLE 7.3. Consumption of wood by theoretical colonies of the Formosan termite, Coptotermes formosanus, and the eastern subterranean termite, Reticulitermes flavipes. (From M. I. Haverty, "Termites," Pest Control, May 1976, 12–17, 46, 47, 49)

	C. formosanus	R. flavipes
Wood consumption rate (mg wood/gram of termite/day)	33.2	23.4
Weight of worker (mg)	3.79	2.50
Wood consumption/termite/day (mg)	0.89	0.083
Estimated number of workers/colony	350,000	60,000
Wood consumption/colony/day/(g)	31.04	4.98
Days to consume 1 board foot of pine*	38	236
Days to consume 2 x 4 in. board, 1 ft. long	19	118

*This calculation assumes that pine weighs an average of 0.5 g/cc, with 2,359.7 cc/board foot or 1,179.9 g/board foot.

Properties of Wood

Wood is an ideal building material. Weight for weight, it is stronger than steel. It is a renewable resource, and trees can grow in a wide variety of sites and climatic conditions, making it readily available and cost effective to produce. Different woods offer a wide range of color, texture, density, strength, workability, and other characteristics.

Types of wood can be generally divided into two groups: softwoods and hardwoods. Softwoods are cone-bearing trees with needles or scale-like leaves, such as the pines, firs, and cedars. Hardwoods are oaks, cottonwoods, elms, tupelos, and other trees with broad, mainly deciduous leaves. These terms do not refer to the actual density or hardness of the wood as both groups contain wood varying from hard to soft.

Each year trees put on a layer of new wood just under the bark and appear as growth rings in cross sections of the trunk. Each ring is composed of an initial zone of thin-walled cells called springwood and a later zone of summerwood consisting of thicker-walled cells. The newest annual rings nearest the bark and colored white are known as the sapwood. The sapwood is the physiologically active part of the stem through which sap is conducted and food is stored. As cells of the sapwood die and age, extractives are deposited in the cells, changing them into heartwood. Heartwood is normally darker than sapwood, but colors vary among species.

Communication in the Colony

For social insects, communication is needed to maintain efficient social integration and division of labor. The most basic means of communication among termites is via chemical (pheromone) communication. In fact, each colony develops its own characteristic odor. Any intruder, be it a termite from another colony, an ant, or any other natural enemy, is instantly recognized as foreign when it enters the colony. An alarm pheromone is secreted by the colony, and this triggers the soldier termites to attack and kill the intruder. The intruder is then walled off from the colony with fecal matter. If a hole in the termite workings occurs, it is immediately patched by the workers.

Sound is another means of termite communication. Termite soldiers and workers bang their heads rapidly on the surface of their mud tunnels or wood galleries when the colony is disturbed. The vibration of the surrounding surface is perceived by others in the colony, and they too take up the banging activity. This activity serves to mobilize the colony defenses just as do the alarm pheromones mentioned earlier.

One of the primary means of communication is via trophallaxis, which is the mutual exchange of nutrients and the transfer of food between colony members. Trophallaxis permits the efficient movement of nutrients within the colony, enhances recognition of colony members, distributes chemicals involved in caste regulation, and transfers cellulose-digesting protozoans. Termites exchange food from both the mouth and the hind gut. When termites shed their skin during moltings, they also lose their hind gut contents, including the protozoa they need for digesting wood. To get a new supply of protozoa, they must feed from the hind gut of other colony members. The feeding of the queens and soldiers by the workers is also a form of trophallaxis. In addition to serving as an exchange of food and nutrients, trophallaxis helps in the recognition of nestmates and distribution of chemicals involved in caste regulation.

Worker termites forage continuously for new sources of food. They also forage randomly in many locations throughout their foraging territory, looking for food. When a foraging termite worker finds a source of food, it recruits others to the food source by laying a chemical (pheromone) trail. The more foragers that find the food and return with it to the colony, the more intense the pheromone trail becomes. As the food source is depleted and the foragers no longer deposit the pheromone, the trail deteriorates and eventually is abandoned.

The proportion of the castes in the colony is

Foraging

The foraging territory of *Reticulitermes* species may cover 0.5 acres, and workers may forage 260 linear feet from one spot to the next. Formosan termites have been shown to forage a linear distance approaching 330 feet and cover 1.5 acres of foraging territory. Typically, however, subterranean termite foraging territories are much smaller and foraging distances less. It appears that there may be geographic differences in the size and numbers of colonies found. In some areas, such as the southern United States, *Reticulitermes* are thought to be characterized by fewer colonies, but on average the colonies are larger than those found in the southern United States. It should be noted that the foraging territory, and linear foraging distance, of subterranean termites is dynamic, and thus constantly changing during their daily quest for cellulose-based food resources.

also regulated chemically. For example, soldiers and reproductives produce chemicals that are distributed to other colony members by trophallaxis. These chemicals inhibit the production of additional soldiers and reproductives. Termites may react to a high level of soldier-produced chemical by killing some of the soldiers. Thus, the needs of the colony are met, and the proper balance of the different castes is maintained. In most subterranean termite colonies, nymphs can molt into alates or supplementary reproductives; workers can change into soldiers, nymphs, or supplementary reproductives; and nymphs that have begun developing wing buds may actually lose them with additional molts and return to the worker stage. All of these changes are chemically regulated within the colony, depending on its needs. For example, high levels of juvenile hormone in the colony will result in the production of soldiers; low levels result in nymphs.

SUBTERRANEAN TERMITES OF NORTH AMERICA

The large majority of termite damage that occurs in the United States is caused by subterranean termites. However, in certain specific areas, nonsubterranean species may be the principal problem. Several species of the genus *Reticulitermes* comprise our most important and widespread group of subterranean termites. These termites are very destructive, as they will damage building timbers and contents, fence posts and utility poles, and, occasionally, living plants.

The **eastern subterranean termite**, *Reticulitermes flavipes* (Kollar), is thought to be the most common and widely distributed termite in North America. It is found north to Ontario, Canada, south to Florida, and west to Arizona and Utah. Swarming begins as early as February in the southern states and as late as May or June in the colder areas. In addition, late fall swarming from September to November may also occur. Swarms have occurred every month of the year where colonies are associated with heated slabs.

The **light southeastern subterranean termite**, *Reticulitermes hageni* Banks, occurs north to the District of Columbia, south to Florida, and west to Texas and Kansas. Swarming occurs from August to October in the northern part of its range, and from October to February in Florida.

The **southeastern subterranean termite**, *Reticulitermes virginicus* Banks, is found north to Philadelphia, south to Florida, and west to eastern Texas and Oklahoma. Swarming flights occur in May or June, with some fall flights in October and November.

The **Pacific Coast subterranean termite**, *Reticulitermes hesperus* Banks, is the most destructive subterranean termite on the West Coast. This termite excavates galleries similar to those of the eastern subterranean termite, spotting the wood with dirty, yellowish-brown fecal spots. Shelter tubes are built, but less commonly than by the eastern termites. The Pacific Coast termite is found north to British Columbia, south to western Mexico, and east to Idaho and Nevada. It is a slow-developing species, with the flight of reproductives not usually occurring from new colonies until after the fourth year.

The **arid land subterranean termite**, *Reticulitermes tibialis* Banks, is found north to Oregon and Montana, south to western Mexico, east to Indiana, and south to Missouri, Arkansas, and Texas. Much of this distribution overlaps that of the Pacific Coast subterranean termite; however, the arid land subterranean termite is the species found in the drier portion of the area.

Another subterranean termite that has been found in the continental United States, as well as in Hawaii, is the **Formosan subterranean termite**, *Coptotermes formosanus* Shiraki. Since 1965, this termite has been found in several cities along the Gulf of Mexico and Atlantic coast. The number of infestations already located, the evidence of large and widely dispersed swarms, and the fact that some infestations appear to have been active for years, suggest that this termite is now firmly established on this continent. Although this termite is found mainly in tropical regions, it has moved into more temperate areas via the shipment of infested wood and wood products.

The Formosan subterranean termite is one of the world's most aggressive and economically important species of termite, and it has been reported to cause more damage to structures in Hawaii than any other wood-destroying insect. This termite represents an extreme economic hazard in all areas where it becomes established. Although subterranean in nature, this termite is quite active when free of soil contact, if enough moisture is present to support the colony. Control of this termite is often more difficult than control of other subterranean species.

However, the principles of management, application techniques, and recommended insecticides are the same as those discussed later in this chapter. Additional steps may be necessary, such as removing moisture sources above ground and spot treating with termiticide, removing secondary nests from wall areas, or, in extreme cases, fumigating the aboveground portions of a structure where well-established colonies are present.

A new subterranean termite, *Coptotermes havilandi*, has been found in Miami, Florida. This species is considered to have as much potential for damaging structures as the Formosan subterranean termite.

In addition to the members of the genera *Reticulitermes* and *Coptotermes*, the soldierless nasutiform and desert termites are subterranean in habit. Of these, only the **desert termite**, *Amitermes wheeleri* (Desneux), damages buildings. This species is distributed from southwestern Texas through Arizona and Nevada to California. In nature, it lives in dead trees, stumps, and cactus plants, and it is a strong flyer that invades buildings in desert areas.

INSPECTIONS FOR SUBTERRANEAN TERMITES

When called to a building in which a subterranean termite infestation is suspected, a pest management specialist must be able to determine whether termites are actually present. Sometimes an active infestation is obvious. Other times the problem may be difficult to see, requiring a great deal of effort, situation awareness, and the use of specialized techniques and information to reach the correct diagnosis.

It is most important that termite management specialists (including inspectors) know and understand building terms, such as crawlspace, footing, joist, and so forth. Appendix H contains definitions of these frequently used terms and diagrams identifying structural members. A knowledge of these terms is helpful in understanding the following discussion of inspection and treatment for subterranean termites.

The termite inspector must know the species (and its habits) in the specific locality in order not to miss any possible sign of infestation. The inspector must be able to recognize the signs of damage to know whether termites are present and, if so, to evaluate the extent of the infestation.

In making the inspection, a good, bright flashlight must be used. The inspector must look at each potential trouble spot closely. Often this means crawling into crawlspaces and other nonbasement

Inspection Tools and Detection Devices

A proper inspection also requires tools for peering into dark areas and for probing and tapping wood. A bright flashlight will be required for a visual assessment. Making sure the flashlight has strong batteries might seem obvious, but is still worth mentioning. While an inspector is crawling beneath a cluttered and convoluted crawlspace is not a good time for a flashlight to quit. Reflecting the flashlight beam off an inspection mirror can be helpful for shining light into hard to see areas, especially those that might be too small for the flashlight to access. The mirror itself can be used to see around or under obstructions.

Inspection of wood members can be done by tapping with a small hammer or a screwdriver handle to listen for hollow sounds associated with damaged wood. It might also be possible to hear the sound of falling dislodged feces or the sounds of disturbed soilders. For probing wood, a penetrating tool such as an ice pick, a penknife blade, a screwdriver, or a small pick will be needed. For deeper penetration, a tool such as the knife blade may leave less visible marks, though some wood types may require the use of heavier tools for proper penetration. A hand lens and sample vials can help with identification and collection of any termites or termite signs (discarded wings, frass, etc.) found during the inspection.

Various electronic detection devides are also available to help with termite inspections. Because termites generally require a certain level of moisture, a moisture meter can be a useful tool for assessing areas and conditions conducive to termite activity. A borescope or fiberoptic instrument can be used to look into otherwise inaccessible areas. While acoustic devices such as a stethoscope can be used to listen for termite activity, it often takes considerable practice to effectively recognize the sounds of termite movement.

areas. A satisfactory view usually cannot be obtained from a distance greater than a few feet. For this part of the inspection, the inspector should wear a pair of coveralls, a bump hat, and gloves. The inspector also needs to measure the structure accurately. A steel tape, a folding rule, and a rolling measuring device are essential tools for every inspection.

The presence of swarmers or their shed wings almost invariably indicates that there is a termite infestation. To do a proper job, however, the specialist must not only determine the point from which the swarmers came, but also locate all exposed tubes and damaged wood.

The workings of subterranean termites differ from those of all other wood-destroying organisms. These termites remove only the soft layers (spring wood) within the annual rings of the wood grain, penetrating the hard layers only to get from one soft layer to another. This frequently leaves a damaged piece of wood looking very much like the pages of a book. The most distinctive feature of subterranean termite damage is the presence of a **brown mudlike material** that lines the galleries in an irregular pattern. (see Figures 7.7 and 7.8, following page 254.)

Subterranean termites travel constantly from their nests in the ground to the wood, or to the other cellulose-bearing material upon which they feed. They make these trips only inside wood or in the mud tubes that they construct. Single tubes, when they are built in the open, are about the diameter of an ordinary lead pencil. (see Figures 7.9 and 7.10, following page 254.)

Termites may excavate the wood so that only a very thin layer of wood is left on the surface between their cavities and the outside. When this layer is broken, they will cover the hole with the same material used to make their tubes. This mixture of soil, feces, and saliva is also frequently used to cover the crack between two boards so that the termites can move about in a protected environment.

As a general rule, subterranean termites are found at or near ground level. They occasionally occur above the level of first-floor windows, especially in the warmer areas of the country. An inspector must thoroughly examine all of the underparts of a house, including the basement and crawlspace walls, supporting piers and beams, sill plates, floor joists, and subfloors. Particular attention must be paid to all places where concrete steps, porches, or concrete slabs join with the structure.

Cavities in the wood that are not visible from the surface can be detected by tapping on the wood and listening for the hollow sound of damaged wood. Occasionally, it is possible to detect a ticking sound made by the disturbed soldiers within the

wood. Tapping does not usually require a heavy object but can be done by using a small hammer or even by thumping the surface of the wood with the knuckles.

Cavities can also be detected by probing the wood with a tool, such as a screwdriver, awl, geologist's pick, or pocketknife. Some specialists prefer to probe deeply, thus making deep, visible marks in the wood. A thorough inspection can be made by using the small blade of a penknife to probe the wood, leaving scarcely visible marks in the wood. The sharp blade will penetrate deeply and will detect cavities in the wood as easily as will the larger tools. In some types of construction, however, the use of heavier tools may be necessary.

Live termites in mud tubes or within wood is, of course, certain evidence of their presence. Failure to find live termites, however, does not necessarily mean that they are not present in the structure. An inspector must be able to distinguish the difference between new and old workings. As a general rule, old mud is dry and brittle and breaks away easily. Fresh workings will be moist.

In addition to termite-detecting dogs, a number of gas detectors and sound detectors have been

Termite-Detecting Dogs

Dogs are now being used by some pest management specialists in the detection of termites. Beagles, properly trained and working with a certified handler, can add to the termite inspector's ability to find hidden, active infestations. The handler/inspector is a key part of this inspection team.

Formal conditioning of dogs usually begins when they are a year old or younger. They can be trained to detect not only termites, but also powderpost beetles, wood borers, and carpenter ants. The dogs are also trained to go under low objects, up onto roofs, and into dark areas, such as crawlspaces.

Once the dog has been trained, the handler must be carefully selected. This individual should be a well-trained termite inspector, and also someone who can properly handle and care for the dog and become familiar with the cues and responses the dog gives when it detects an insect infestation. The handler must maintain the dog in a working posture, using specific commands during the inspection process.

Termite-detecting dogs can be used for initial inspections, quality control (with follow-up inspectors), follow-up inspections after treatment, and annual renewal inspections. They can also have distinct public relations and marketing advantages for the pest control firm.

marketed to aid in termite inspections. All of these methods have limitations and need further research and development to improve their detection capabilities.

Inspections should also ascertain any risk of contamination should a termiticide need to be used. Wells, springs, cisterns, and so forth can be contaminated by termiticide applications. If any of these are present in or near the structure, termite management must be conducted with special care. Alternative methods of successful management, using limited amounts of insecticides or no insecticide at all (e.g., mechanical alteration), generally require more labor and are more expensive. However, it may be necessary to employ these methods to avoid a contamination problem (see the discussion of contamination later in this chapter).

THE INSPECTION REPORT

To present the results of a termite inspection to the client as well as have a work plan for the treatment, it is necessary to make an adequate **diagram** of the building to be treated together with a sufficient description of the structure and the problems to be solved. See Appendix I for more information on the use of graphs in termite control.

A well-designed inspection form offers many advantages because it allows the inspector to include all pertinent information. Such a form should include cross-ruled paper on which a diagram of the structure can be drawn to scale. This drawing should include the type of construction, all crosswalls, stairways, doorways, porches, stoops, and other parts of the structure that will affect the method of treatment. It is most important that it be drawn accurately and to scale, because this may reveal blind areas, which are often sites of severe infestation and damage.

Each place where live termites are found should be clearly indicated on the diagram. All existing damage, inaccessible areas, and other unusual situations should be indicated. In addition, details of construction should be shown, including the materials of which the outside walls and foundations are made (e.g., concrete block, stone, etc.), and whether the foundation extends below grade; the places where it will be necessary to drill through the concrete floor, such as in doorways, stairways, supporting walls, porches, sidewalks, and driveways; whether the building has a basement or a crawlspace or is a concrete slab on grade; the location where ventilators should be installed; the conditions that may be conducive to termite attack (such as improper grade); and other pertinent information. Individual companies may prefer to include addi-

tional items or may find that local conditions are such that additional information is necessary.

PREVENTION

The most effective and economical time to implement termite prevention techniques is during the planning and construction process. Whether pre- or post-construction, limiting favorable food (wood), moisture, and shelter conditions to termites can prevent or help eliminate infestations.

A majority of structural termite infestations are associated with contact of wood to the ground. Structural wood in contact with the soil provides termites with food, shelter, moisture, and entry into a structure that is difficult to detect. Exterior wood should be at least 6 inches (15 cm) above ground level, and may require regrading or pulling soil or mulch back from the foundation to eliminate wood-to-ground contact. Timbers in crawlspaces should be at least 18 inches (46 cm) from the ground. Wood in door frames, stair carriages, wood posts, etc. should be cut off at the bottom and be supported by a concrete base. If wood-to-soil contact is unavoidable, wood can be treated with a preservative. However, termites can enter through cut ends and cracks in treated wood and are also able to build tunnels over the wood surface.

Wood, cardboard, paper, or other cellulose materials in the soil can attract termites to a structure. These materials should not be buried in fills during the construction process. Mulch and wood chips can also attract termites by providing both a food source and favorable moisture conditions. Pea gravel or crushed stone may serve as a substitute for mulch, but if mulch is used it should not be allowed to contact wood siding or framing of doors or windows. Firewood, landscape timbers, compost piles, and other cellulose material stacked close to a structure attract termites and provide a hidden point of entry. To prevent infestations, these materials should be stacked as far from the structure as is practical. Dense vegetation should not be allowed to grow against the siding and foundation of a building. Shrubs, vines, and trellises make inspection difficult and can trap moisture, increasing conditions favorable for wood decay and termites.

High moisture conditions around a structure can contribute to a termite infestation. In addition to reducing vegetation in contact with the building, soil around a structure should be sloped so that surface water drains away from the structure. Proper installment and maintenance of gutters, downspouts, and splash blocks and proper positioning of lawn sprinklers or irrigation systems to avoid pooling water will reduce soil saturation.

High humidity in crawlspaces can also lead to problems. Plumbing or appliance leaks can lead to damp wood and soil conditions in this area, and areas of crawlspaces beneath potential trouble spots should be inspected and any leaks or problems repaired. In some climates or areas, soil conditions themselves may contribute to crawlspace humidity. Polyethylene sheeting can be placed over soil in a crawlspace to reduce evaporation from the soil and condensation on structural timbers. Adequate ventilation can further reduce moisture problems. A vent area of 1 square foot (0.1 m²) per 150 square feet (14 m²) of crawlspace area is required for most building codes. Total vent area can be reduced in crawlspaces with a vapor barrier.

Plumbing leaks can also lead to favorable termite conditions inside a structure and may allow a colony to survive above ground with no soil contact. Roof leaks or inadequate drainage can also cause this problem. Water leaking into wood areas below the roof or standing water on the roof surface potentially lead to wood decay or other moisture problems that can be conducive to termite infestation. Special attention should be given to flat or low-pitched roofs where drainage problems may be more frequent.

Certain types of construction are conducive to termite attack. Dirt-filled porches are susceptible to termite attack, because such construction joins the exterior wall of the building above the top of the foundation and in close proximity to structural timbers. Attached planter boxes also bring soil in close proximity to structural timbers and should be separated from the foundation by at least 3 inches (8 cm). Foam insulation and stucco used near the foundation may serve as a route of entry into a structure as termites may tunnel behind or through such materials to reach wooden structural members.

Use of termite-resistant woods may be another nonchemical alternative for subterranean termite prevention; California redwood, red cypress, and red and yellow cedar have all been shown to have some level of termite resistance. Certain extractive chemicals present in the wood may be distasteful or hazardous to termites. However, with time these chemicals lose their potency or are lost from the wood, making these woods more susceptible to termites.

TREATMENT OF SUBTERRANEAN TERMITES

It would be difficult to list and describe every detail for the different treatments available for the management of subterranean termites. **Soil treatment** is the principal method used in control, and widely

varying types of construction, even within small regional areas, make it necessary for the termite management specialist to think in terms of the principles of management involved in each situation and to adapt management methods to fit the situation. Using **baits** for termite management is another method that involves different considerations, while **physical barriers**, such as metal screens, is a third method requiring another set of considerations.

Chemical Treatments

Sometimes, the application of a chemical barrier will be sufficient for subterranean termite control. Other times, factors involved with a particular structure will dictate that nonchemical methods be employed in conjunction with the chemical methods to obtain suitable structural protection. For times when chemical barriers are inadvisable or impractical, the use of baits and/or nonchemical methods alone must be used. Which chemicals and techniques are used will depend on several factors, including the availability of pesticides, the area of the country, the type of construction, the characteristics of the soil substrate, the unique attributes of the structure, and to a lesser extent, the species of subterranean termite in question.

Two main strategies for chemical deterrents are used in termite control. Depending on the circumstances, the approaches may be used alone or together as part of a management program. In the first strategy, chemical deterrents, such as borates and pressure treatments, applied directly to structural wood cause the wood to become repellent, toxic, and/or unusable by the termites. Treating the wood during the construction process provides the most effective and economical use of direct wood treatment, because it provides the best opportunity for maximum coverage of the wood surfaces. Though termites may gain access to the structure or structural members, they are unable to use the treated wood as a food source once they get there. With chemical soil barriers, on the other hand, the strategy is to deny termites access to the structure altogether. As with wood treatment, application of the barrier as part of the construction process, generally before the foundation is laid, provides the most effective and economical control. Both of these chemical methods will be discussed in more detail in sections to follow.

Repellency vs Toxicity

Termites forage throughout the soil substrate. Suitably applied, chemical soil barriers will prevent termite foragers from reaching the wood and other cellulose material in a structure. There are two main ways chemical barriers keep termites from accessing structures. The first is through repellency. Termites foraging through the soil will encounter the chemical barrier and are compelled to change the direction of their foraging. Currently, the pyrethroid types of soil barriers operate in this way. Though the chemicals are toxic to the termites, the repellent nature of the chemicals makes it less likely that the termites will forage into the treated soil, and mortality is low. Other chemical barriers are not repellent in nature. These prevent termites from accessing the structure by not only killing the foragers that contact the treated soil, but also by killing other individuals they may contact in the colony.

Fipronil and imidacloprid soil termiticides are also nonrepellent, but the lethal action on the termites is slower. Because the death is slower, the chances are increased that foraging termites will temporarily survive the initial contact with the treated soil and contaminate nonforaging nestmates when they return to the nest. Although imidacloprid termiticide ultimately causes the termites to die, the death is often brought about by disorientation, starvation, and increased susceptibility to soil pathogens caused by the action of the imidicloprid. Although it is more slow-acting, the toxic effect of fipronil is more direct.

Termite baits are not chemical barriers in the same sense, but they also rely on slow-acting chemicals by killing termites that consume treated cellulose bait materials. These toxins also are passed on to nonforaging nestmates and cause their demise. The use of termite baits relies on an ongoing process of inspection to identify new termite activity in the area of a structure. This concept is different than that of liquid chemical barriers, and requires a great deal of persistence on the part of the pest management professional.

Soil Treatment

The major objective of the specialist in soil treatment for subterranean termite control is to establish a **chemical barrier** between the termite nest, usually in the ground, and the wood in a structure. In buildings under construction this is accomplished by keeping wood out of contact with the ground and by pretreating the soil below the foundation with insecticide to establish a chemical barrier. (Pretreating will be discussed separately.) In buildings already constructed, the barrier is made either with termiticides or by modifying the existing structure to make a mechanical barrier.

A complete termite management program may involve any of the following basic steps: (1) mechanical alteration, (2) soil treating, (3) foundation treating, and (4) wood treating. Any given termite control job may involve one, several, or all of these steps, depending primarily on the type of construction encountered. In many cases, adequate termite control can be achieved without involving all four types of treatment.

Mechanical alteration involves modifying the structure to provide a barrier that cannot be penetrated by termites, or to eliminate conditions that are conducive to termite invasion. For example, the use of concrete or metal barriers, the removal of cellulose debris, the elimination of moisture near or in the structure, the establishment of sufficient ventilation of the infested area, and the elimination of wood-to-soil contact are all effective methods of mechanical alteration.

Soil treating consists of the application of termiticides to the soil under and adjacent to a building to create an impervious chemical barrier. A continuous barrier should be established along the inside and outside of the foundation, under slabs, and around utility entrances.

Foundation treating is the application of termiticide to a foundation to make it impervious to termites. The objective is to place termiticide in all cracks at the footing as well as through cracks in the foundation wall, which may lead to the ground outside. Treating the inside of hollow concrete block walls is another example of foundation treating.

Wood treating is the application of insecticides directly to wood to eliminate existing termite infestations or to make the wood impervious or resistant to termites.

As a general rule, the first three methods are used in termite control practice, with wood treating being a pretreat or supplemental measure. Pressure-treated wood is frequently used in the construction of buildings and provides effective termite control if it is used for all wood construction, at least to the ceiling level of the first floor. Spraying insecticides on wood already in place provides only surface protection and doesn't penetrate to the center of the wood, where it is most needed. In badly damaged wood, insecticide can be injected into the cavities made by termites. This will provide better control than will a brush or spray application.

The remainder of this termite management section discusses the procedures to use for various types of building construction. It is important to remember that foundations can be of three general types: (1) slab, (2) basement, and (3) conventional (crawlspace). Each of these types of construction has structural features that require specialized attention to establish a physical or chemical barrier that prevents termite entry into a building. For example, treatment outside the structure may involve trenching and treating or rodding to treat the soil on the outside of the foundation, rodding beneath slabs, or vertical drilling and treating of outside slabs, stoops, or porches. Treatments inside may involve trenching and treating the soil along foundation walls in crawlspaces, vertical drilling and treating slab foundations, rodding around bath traps and other utility openings, or treating wood directly. The examples that follow will outline the procedures to use in controlling subterranean termites for these and other elements of construction.

Brick Veneer on a Frame House

As a basic type of construction that includes many of the elements to be considered in termite control work, we will consider the foundation and wall of a brick veneer house in which the brick veneer extends below grade (see Figure 7.12). This construction and its possible variations occur in a large proportion of the houses throughout the country. In this illustration, points of probable infestations are through cracks in the brick mortar below grade on the outside and through tubes on the face of the foundation on the inside.

In most situations, termites can be controlled in

brick veneer walls via termiticides alone. In one method, the soil adjacent to the foundation would be removed to within about 1 foot above the footing (a process called **trenching**). As the soil is replaced, it should be treated with termiticide at the rate of 4 gallons per 10 linear feet for each foot of depth from grade level to footing. The termiticide can also be carried to the level of the footing by injecting the insecticide through a long pipe inserted at 1-foot intervals (see Figure 7.13). This procedure is called rodding. Many specialists use a combination of trenching and rodding, especially if the footing is very far below grade level. Many termiticide labels specify trench and rod applications.

When mechanical alteration has been used (see the following discussion), it is not necessary to treat the void behind the brick veneer. Where insecticide treatment has been used, however, this is an essential step in control, and it can be accomplished in two ways. Holes can be drilled through the box sill between each pair of joists from the inside or through the mortar joints of the bricks on the outside. Termiticide is then introduced through these holes at labeled rates. Where the holes are drilled through the mortar joints, they are plugged with mortar after treatment.

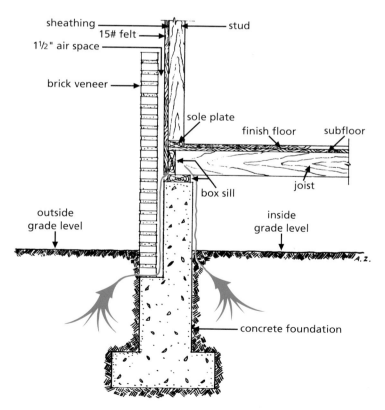

FIGURE 7.12. Brick veneer construction covering wood sheathing and extending below the sheathing and below grade level. Avenues of termite access are indicated by the heavy arrows in the soil. (NPMA)

FIGURE 7.13. Injection of termiticide into the soil, using a hollow treatment rod. (Myers)

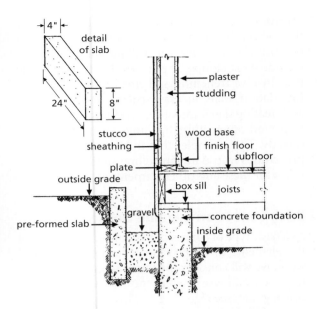

FIGURE 7.14. An example of construction in which sheathing is sealed off by a poured-concrete foundation.

Since the foundation in this case is made of poured concrete, it will not require any treatment unless it has been cracked. Existing cracks in the foundation should be drilled and termiticide injected into the hole. The drilled hole should then be firmly and completely plugged with concrete.

The soil along the foundation wall in the crawlspace should be treated with insecticide in the same manner as the soil outside. Overall treatment of the soil in the crawlspace of the structure is not permitted. Only soil next to walls and posts should be treated.

Mechanical alterations can be used on the outside by (1) removing the lower courses of brick to above the grade line, filling the void with mortar, and replacing the brick; or (2) lowering the grade on the outside to below the brick and retaining it with a wall built out from the building or by constructing a gutter (see Figure 7.14). A poured concrete flash wall barrier is often used in this situation on the West Coast.

If the foundation wall shown in Figure 7.12 were made of concrete block, it would be necessary to treat the hollow voids in the center of the blocks, since termites use these voids to gain access to wood. Holes are drilled, usually through the mortar joints and above grade level, at least every 18 inches, then termiticide is injected at the labeled rate.

Dirt-Filled Concrete Porch on a Frame House

This is a common type of construction throughout the country, and the principles involved apply to stoops and poured outside slabs at ground level, such as sidewalks and driveways (see Figure 7.15).

Treatment of the concrete foundation wall adjacent to the porch is carried out as with the brick veneer wall. However, if the wall is constructed so that voids exist, then the treatment required will be the same as that discussed for the concrete block foundation.

Soil contact where the porch joins the house should be eliminated by tunneling along the foundation wall and removing the dirt. This is usually done by removing a portion of the porch wall at either or both ends and installing an access door. Soil removal can also be accomplished by knocking out portions of the foundation wall from inside the crawlspace and then excavating soil from beneath the porch.

Where the tunneling leaves the porch poorly supported, it is necessary to install supplementary support, such as masonry piers. The soil along the outside of the foundation wall is then treated at the rate of 4 gallons of chemical per 10 linear feet, and the remainder of the accessible soil under the slab is flooded at the rate of 1 gallon of chemical per 10 square feet.

Some specialists feel that the entire area under the porch should be flooded sufficiently to treat all the soil under the porch. Others do not feel this is necessary. If all of the soil is treated, termiticide is applied either by driving grouting rods horizontally under the slab or by drilling vertically through the porch slab at intervals along the porch foundation and at sufficient other points to ensure all the soil under the porch is reached.

In the case of poured concrete slabs, sidewalks,

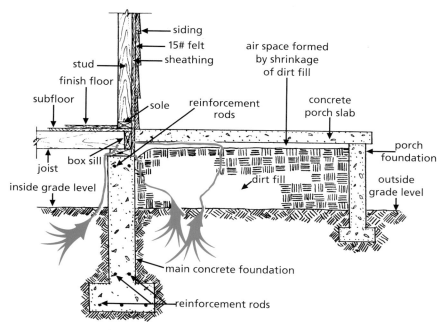

FIGURE 7.15. A common type of construction that involves a dirt-filled concrete porch attached to a frame house. Avenues of termite access are indicated by the heavy arrows in the soil. (NPMA)

and driveways, the critical areas under them can be treated with insecticide either by drilling down through the surface of the slab close to the building or, where possible, by drilling horizontally through the inside wall immediately under the slab.

Slab Floor Construction

This type of construction is used extensively throughout the country (see Figure 7.16). Due to the hazard of drilling through heat pipes or ducts, electric conduits, and plumbing embedded in the floor, it may be advisable to treat from the outside by drilling through the foundation wall. Previous treatment practice consisted of drilling the floor and flooding the fill underneath with insecticide in addition to the necessary foundation treatment and soil treatment outside the foundation. Appendix J contains information on the vertical drilling of slabs. Mechanical alteration is not usually necessary with this type of construction.

Standard practice in many areas of the country consists of drilling holes through the outside foundation walls below the level of the slab floor. Long rods are then introduced horizontally through these holes, and the entire area under the slab is thoroughly treated with insecticide at a rate of 1 gallon per 10 square feet. To drill the holes and introduce the treating rods, it is often necessary to dig a trench outside the foundation to provide room to work. It is not always necessary to drill all of the foundation walls of the building. Where the

treatment rods can be pushed all the way under the floor from one side, a thorough treatment can be made. The foundation wall itself, the ground outside the foundation wall, and any porches, patios, driveways, or other outside slabs are treated as described in previous examples.

See Appendix K for more information on the treatment of slabs for termite control.

Other Situations

The same principles involved in the preceding examples apply to treating many situations.

One of the most common problems in the management of subterranean termites involves situations in which wooden members extend through the concrete in the basement floor. Supporting posts, stair risers, and door frames are common examples. To correct this, cut the wooden members at least 4 inches above floor level, then remove the portion that extends through the floor. The soil underneath should be thoroughly treated with termiticide, and then concrete poured into the hole and into a form extending to the remaining portion of the wood member, so as to support it properly. In the case of stairways, it is advisable to make the entire lower step out of concrete, if possible. It is generally undesirable to attempt to treat buried wooden supports by chemical means alone.

Basement foundation walls (see Figure 7.17) need to be treated by drilling a row of blocks near the footing and then pressure treating. This can be

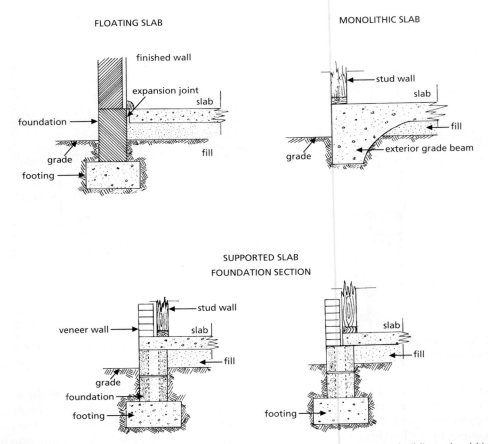

FIGURE 7.16. The three types of slab floor construction of frame houses. Slab construction buildings should be pretreated with termiticides during construction. (NPMA)

done from the interior. If the wall is not accessible due to paneling or some other physical barrier, the block can be drilled below the window or at grade level from the outside. Be aware of any leakage from the blocks, and be prepared to clean up any liquid immediately. Avoiding leakage from treatments applied high up the foundation wall is the main reason why drilling the wall from the inside down close to the footing is often recommended. Repair all drill holes following treatment.

Where termites are coming into a building through a cellar or basement floor, it is necessary to drill the floor and introduce termiticide into the soil underneath (see Figure 7.17). This is usually done along cracks in the floor, around (not in) floor drains, by furnace pads, and around the perimeter of the floor. In the case of small cracks, the holes can be drilled directly through the crack. Next to walls and furnace pads, the holes should be drilled far enough from the wall to just miss any footing that may be present.

Concrete block partition walls that extend down through the basement floor present a special problem. Ideally, they should be cut off above the floor, and a concrete curb placed under them. In practice, this is both expensive and difficult to do. Usual practice is to drill holes through the floor on both sides of the wall and treat the soil underneath.

Basement windows, with or without outside window wells, are another problem. Normally, the window sills are close to the ground. If the sills are made of wood, they provide a good source of food for termites as well as being subject to rot. Ideally, wooden sills should be replaced with concrete. Walls with voids in them should be treated with termiticide, starting as close as possible beneath the window to ensure thorough coverage. The ground outside the window should also be treated. Ideally, window wells should be floored solidly with concrete, but they may be treated with termiticide by rodding next to the foundation.

In some parts of the country, houses are built off the ground on supporting piers of brick, stone, concrete, concrete block, or wood. Concrete piers create no particular hazard. Those of brick, stone, or concrete block, however, are usually hollow and provide termites with an easy route of access to the wood above. Ideally, these should be filled solidly with concrete. In practice, the hollow centers are drilled, and the voids treated with termiticide.

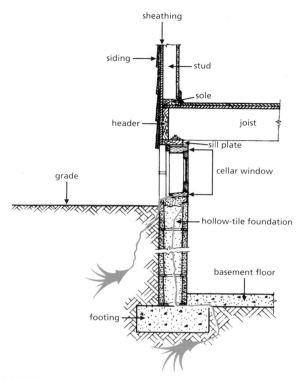

FIGURE 7.17. An example of a concrete block foundation with basement window. Avenues of termite access are indicated by the heavy arrows in the soil. (NPMA)

Wooden porches with outside ground contact should have all wood cut off above ground level, and supporting concrete placed under it. Wherever possible, wooden piers should be removed and replaced with concrete or set on a concrete footing that extends at least four inches above grade level. Where this is not possible, holes should be drilled through the wood to the bottom of the post so the ground underneath can be treated with termiticide. The soil all around the base of the pier should also be treated.

With most of the termiticides now in use, it is not necessary to take any particular precaution for the protection of ornamental plantings. Water emulsions generally will not harm plants. However, always check the label of the insecticide you are using.

The design of a structure does not alter the basic principle of subterranean termite control: Create a barrier (mechanical or chemical) that will prevent termites living outside the structure from entering and using a building for food. The number of specific situations involved in construction are almost infinite in number, but the termite management specialist can get effective control if he or she always proceeds on the basis of this principle.

Special Situations

Several types of construction are extremely difficult (and occasionally impossible) to treat for termites. For example, **plenum housing** is impossible to treat with a termiticide because of problems with vapors entering the living space of the building. The plenum concept uses the area under the subfloor (crawlspace) as a giant heating-cooling duct. There are no vents or access doors in the foundation; thus, termiticide odor can be circulated with heated or cooled air throughout the structure. Therefore, conventional liquid termiticide treatment is not recommended. Termite baits (discussed later) may be an option for treating plenum housing.

Buildings with **cisterns** or **wells** in the crawlspace or near the foundation on the outside are common in many parts of the East, Midwest, and South. It is often difficult to effectively manage termites where cisterns or wells exist without contaminating the water supply. Mechanical alteration and direct wood treatment should be relied on as much as possible, even though the cost may be high. If soil treating is done, it should be done only sparingly and carefully.

If conditions are such that there is no hazard of treated soil being washed or otherwise carried into the well or cistern, the soil adjacent to the foundation may be physically removed, treated, dried, and returned as backfill. To further ensure against contamination, polyethylene sheeting may be placed in the trench prior to replacing the backfill. Also, it is advisable to have the water tested for the pesticide you plan to use before and after the soil is treated.

Voids in foundation walls should not be treated where there is any chance that the insecticide might make its way into the water supply. If an effective chemical barrier cannot be applied to the soil on the inside or outside of foundation walls using the already-described techniques, mechanical barriers should be installed, and annual inspections should be conducted to check for termite activity.

Another common type of construction that requires special consideration in treating for termites involves houses with heating systems under or imbedded within the concrete slab of the structure (see Figure 7.18). The accidental introduction of a termiticide into ducts can result in a serious contamination of the air that flows through these ducts and into living quarters. Applying termiticide under or around the ducts must be done carefully. Greatly reduced pressure (less than 30 pounds at the nozzle tip) or gravity (percolation) methods should be used.

The use of the subslab injector should be limited. If holes are drilled in the interior slab, knowledge of the exact location, directions of the system, and depth and width of the duct are important. If possible, the pest management specialist will want to get

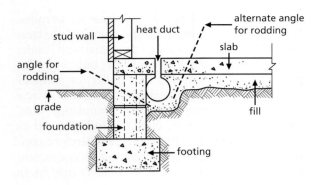

FIGURE 7.18. Rod treating adjacent to a perimeter heat duct.

the chemical under the ducts (see Figure 7.18). Reducing the pressure will keep the termiticide from backing up into the duct. Rodding from the outside by drilling the foundation and running a rod in under the duct work may be the best treatment procedure. Again, knowing the depth of the duct in or under the slab is essential so that the drill or rod does not puncture the duct. Horizontal rodding under the slab is the correct procedure where radiant heat pipes are embedded in the slab of the structure.

When treating structures with subslab heat ducts, it is also essential to periodically check during treatment and immediately after treatment for signs of contamination. The heating system should be turned on and checked for odors. If an odor is present, shut off the unit and determine why the odor is present. Odors could be coming from the moist, treated soil beneath the slab. If this is the case, the odors will usually not be strong and should persist for only a day or two. Charcoal filters in heat registers can be used to minimize this odor.

If a strong odor persists, there is probably a termiticide deposit in a duct. This must be cleaned out. An industrial wet vac is the best method to get any liquid material out of the ducts, and charcoal filters should be used over heat registers. Removal of the deposit may require expertise in chemical deactivation. Termiticide manufacturers all have deactivation and odor control information available, and they should be contacted for up-to-date recommendations.

TERMITE CONTROL EQUIPMENT

One of the greatest mistakes made in the choice of termite equipment is choosing tools that are not heavy enough for the job. Termite control is heavy, industrial-type work. Wherever possible, heavy-duty equipment should be used to make the work as easy as possible and to prevent expensive, time-consuming breakdowns on the job (see Table 7.4).

The basic piece of equipment on any termite job is a tank and pump system used to introduce termiticides into the soil, wall voids, and other areas to be treated. Small gear, roller, or positive displacement pumps driven by electric motors or gasoline engines, such as those described in Chapter 5, are the types most commonly used. Pumps force the termiticide through a hose that must be resistant to the termiticide being used and that must have a sufficiently rated breaking strength to operate safely at relatively high pressures.

At the end of the hose, various types of applicators with valves are used to apply the termiticide. These include rods, subslab injectors, or guns. Rods

How to Avoid Contaminating Drinking Water Systems

Liquids can be drawn into water pipes by siphon action or back pressure. Accidental contaminations of entire residential districts have occurred when the drinking water line had a sudden drop in pressure while a sprayer or tank of termiticide was being filled with water from a hose connected to a resident's faucet. The drop in water pressure siphoned the termiticide into the public water supply system. Basic precautions and training will aid in avoiding this kind of mishap. For example, water hoses must be kept out of contaminated water, water should always be poured into priming pumps, and backflow preventers should be used to prevent the contamination of water supplies. These precautions are discussed in Chapter 4.

Backflow preventers should be installed on the end of the hose connected to the faucet any time water is being used from private or public systems to fill pesticide tanks or equipment. It must be located between the water source and the pesticide tanks. Backflow preventers vary substantially in the level of protection offered; thus, preventers meeting your particular needs should be selected. These can be obtained from pest management suppliers or from plumbing supply houses. Advice on local codes and requirements can be obtained from plumbing or health inspectors.

Additional good practices in protecting water supplies include (1) never permitting a water hose or faucet to extend into the insecticide or the rinse water when filling a spray tank or rinsing insecticide equipment, and (2) never connect the discharge side of a pump to a water supply. If a pump must be primed using an external source of water, pour water from a pail directly into the pump.

FIGURE 7.19. A subslab injector used to inject insecticide under pressure into an area beneath a slab. When the handle on the side is thrust downward into position, the rubber gasket immediately above the tip is thrust outward, making a tight seal against the side of the hole.

3- to 6-feet long can be used to apply termiticide into the soil next to the foundation wall. Various smaller rods are used to inject insecticide into the voids of walls and through concrete slabs.

Subslab injectors (see Figure 7.19) are used to force termiticide into holes through concrete slabs to the fill underneath. This device is essential because it seals the hole around the application rod; considerable back pressure is frequently encountered, making it difficult to inject a sufficient quantity of chemical. A tapered rubber stopper around the applicator rod can also be used.

It is frequently necessary to drill holes through masonry construction. Small holes can be drilled with carbide-tipped rotary bits in an ordinary electric hand drill. Star drills, or punches, hand driven by sledges of two to four pounds, are also used.

Various sized drills and rotating hammers are used to drill holes through concrete. Large holes are drilled using electric or compressed-air hammers (see Figure 7.20). As a general rule, rotating hammers drill faster than the nonrotating types, because dust is removed from the hole mechanically as it is drilled. Carbide-tipped drill bits are more expensive than steel drills but cut faster and require much less sharpening.

Air hammers have the advantage of rapid drilling speed even with large-diameter drills, and the hammer itself is usually of relatively light weight (making work less tiring for the specialist). Electric hammers of comparable specifications usually are heavier and drill more slowly than air hammers. Because they do not require the use of a heavy air compressor, they are more portable than air hammers, and they create less dust.

A termite specialist must be equipped with extension cords for the operation of electric hand

tools and to extend good lights into dark basements and unexcavated areas. Every termite specialist should thoroughly review the sections in Chapters 4 and 5 that pertain to electric lights, extension cords, and drills.

Application tools are continually being developed and improved. Better soil injection equipment, especially injection tips and flow meters, more practical for termite control, is being produced. More versatile foam application equipment (see the discussion on foam termiticides later in this chapter) is now available.

Many other tools are necessary in termite control work (see Table 7.4). These tools and their selection are left to the individual specialist or company, and with new technologies continually entering the marketplace, specialists must keep abreast of these developments and decide which ones best fit their company's needs.

TERMITICIDES FOR SUBTERRANEAN TERMITE CONTROL

Examples of termiticides used for soil treatment include **cypermethrin**, **chlorphenapyr**, **fenvalerate**, **fipronil**, **imidacloprid**, and **permethrin**. Any of these can be used to establish a chemical barrier that is lethal or repellent to termites. Label directions for these materials should be followed closely for the concentration and rate of application to be used. The judgment and experience of the termite specialist is important when selecting the termiticide and method of application that best suits the particular type of construction and the soil condition. Again, follow label directions carefully, and be familiar with current industry practices and appli-

FIGURE 7.20. An electric rotary hammer used to drill into a slab. (Myers)

TABLE 7.4. Typical termite control equipment and accessories for one truck.

100 gal tank	Mop and mop bucket
10 gpm pump	Saw—keyhole
3 hp motor	Saw—crosscut
Hose reel	Small sledgehammer
Treating 3/8" hose (100–200 ft)	Heat gun for tile; tile cutter
Shutoff valve	Crowbar
Subslab injector, side injector tip, flanged treating tip	Rake
Backflow preventor	Shovel
3/4" hose to refill tank (25–50 ft)	6' extension rods (for subslab treating)
Measuring container	Clean rags
Can of gasoline	First-aid kit
Funnel	Spare can of oil
Kit maintenance tools	Extra spark plug
Electric rotary drill for wall voids	Extra hose washers
Electric hammer for concrete floors	Package of vents for foundations
Bits for drill and hammer	Mortar mix or cement
Extension cord—heavy-duty three-wire type	Trowel
Grounding box	Termiticide
Grounding tester	Respirator
Two pairs of coveralls	Fire extinguisher
Pair of heavy gloves	Safety glasses or goggles
Pair of light plastic gloves	Bump hat
Heavy-duty flashlight	Dustpan
Extra batteries for flashlight	Poison control center telephone number
Broom	Spill cleanup absorbent
Termiticide label	

cable state laws that affect termiticide usage. Special-use termiticides (see discussion of wood treatment later in this chapter) can also be used to treat structural wood that is infested with termites.

Managing Termite Re-treatments

There are many factors that determine how well a soil treatment will perform. The termite management specialist must use all the technical information available to create a chemical barrier that will protect the infested structure for as long as possible. This can be accomplished by (1) following label directions on properly mixing the termiticide in the tank; (2) keeping low pressure (about 25 psi) at the treatment nozzle; (3) keeping the flow rate low, about 1 to 2 gallons per minute; (4) adjusting treatment spacings to maximize distribution of the termiticide—space about 12 to 24 inches apart for slabs, using a short rod so that the injection rod is no more than 2 inches below the slab, trench and rod every 9 to 12 inches around the perimeter of the slab, and drill and treat block voids for the lower three courses of block; (5) foaming voids under critical areas that contain a void; and (6) eliminating aboveground moisture sources that termites can use to sustain themselves.

It is most important that retreatments be handled promptly. Use other experienced termite specialists to review the situation and make recommendations. Implementation of high-priority recommendations for retreatment should occur as quickly as possible. If several retreatments at the same property do not solve the problem, it may be necessary to open the problem area to determine the cause. Appendix L contains additional details on termite re-treatments.

Pretreating

In recent years, the treatment of buildings under construction has become a standard procedure in many parts of the country, both for slab-on-ground and basement construction. The termiticides just listed can also be used in pretreatment. The toxicant must be applied to the soil with such thoroughness and uniformity that it provides a barrier to all routes of termite entry. Other methods of pretreating are discussed toward the end of this chapter.

Pretreatment should be carried out only when favorable conditions prevail. Wet or frozen soil should not be treated because there is likely to be considerable surface flow of the termiticide from the site of application. If the treated areas will not be covered immediately, precautions must be taken to prevent contact or disturbance of the treatment by people or animals.

PERIODIC INSPECTIONS FOR ALL TERMITE JOBS

Most termite contracts contain some provision for periodic inspections to monitor the success of the termite control treatment as well as manage any recurrence of activity. These inspections are made either annually or semiannually, depending on the species of termite, environmental factors, and state regulations affecting termite control in any particular region.

These inspections must be as complete and thorough as the original inspection. An inspector will normally need all of the equipment used on the original inspection, with the exception of a measuring device. Where crawling is necessary, the specialist should carry a pair of coveralls, gloves, a bump hat, and, of course, a good, strong flashlight.

The inspector should look very closely for small signs of termite presence, because any infestation that has occurred in the year or 6 months since the last inspection is not likely to be as conspicuous as the original damage. The inspector must be very careful to check all wood near grade level and to crawl and inspect all crawlspaces at close range.

TERMITE BAITS

An alternative (in some cases supplementary) control methodology to soil-applied termiticides is the use of termite baits. A number of bait products, including different active ingredients and baiting systems, are available to the termite control specialist.

Baits take advantage of the social nature and foraging behaviors of subterranean termites. Foraging worker termites consume the bait and then share it with the rest of the colony, resulting in a slow colony decline and, depending on the active ingredient, eventual elimination. Below-ground monitoring stations (without any active insecticide) are usually used to establish a feeding site for the foraging termite workers, and then the baited stations are installed. These are often placed every 10 to 20 feet around the perimeter of the building, 2 feet out from the foundation (see Figure 7.21). The number and placement of bait stations vary depending on the product used, the characteristics of the site, and the

FIGURE 7.21. Termite bait station being inspected for the presence of termites. (Myers)

amount of termite activity. Baits generally consist of cellulose-based material impregnated with an IGR or a slow-acting toxicant. The bait is usually placed inside a child-resistant housing.

Other baiting strategies include interceptive baiting, in which aboveground bait systems are placed in the path of the termites (in mud tubes or in areas of wood damage and termite presence), so that the termites come in direct contact with the bait. The termites then feed on the bait and recruit other colony members to feed at the station, so that a more immediate colony elimination can be obtained (as compared to placing baits in the soil around a structure).

Examples of active ingredients included in termite baits are hexaflumuron and noviflumuron (insect growth regulator), sulfluramid, hydramethylnon, avermectin, and *Metarhizium anisopliae* (a fungus). Some of these termiticides can be used as stand-alone bait treatments, although in many instances of infestation, a supplemental soil insecticide may need to be used to provide a prompt and continuously effective control. Perimeter soil treatments and spot treatments to infested areas, used in conjunction with baits (while taking care to avoid contaminating bait placements with soil termiticide), can usually satisfy a customer's desire for an immediate solution, and allow time for the bait to provide suppression or long-term colony elimination.

As with any technology, there are advantages and disadvantages to the use of termite baits compared to the use of liquid termiticides. One advantage is ease of use. The drilling of structural concrete is not required, and the termite control specialist most often does not have to enter the structure to install bait stations. The toxicant is distributed from a point source, as compared to soil drenching with liquid termiticides; thus, baiting is a more environmentally friendly method of termite control. The active ingredients in baits are generally less toxic than those in soil insecticides, which adds to their environmental friendliness. Termite baits will usually be the treatment of choice for customers who are chemically or odor sensitive, have heat ducts beneath or within slab foundations have plenums, have wells, cisterns or springs beneath or close to foundations, or have rubble foundations. New markets are now open to pest managers, since monitoring systems can be sold to property owners who do not currently have termite infestations but are fearful of them. In some cases no chemical is applied until there is a need, making this a more environmentally sound approach.

There are several disadvantages to termite baits. Bait programs are usually more expensive and may require continuous monitoring after colony elimination or suppression has been attained. The major disadvantage is the length of time it takes a bait to eliminate a colony. With liquid termiticides, control is more immediate; with baits, control may take several months to a year, depending on a number of factors (such as soil type, geographic location, the season, availability of alternative food sources, etc.) that limit termite foraging. Baits cannot easily be put under slabs or in wall voids where termites often occur. Thus, damage may continue to occur until the entire colony is eliminated. Elimination of the colony may not actually be achieved; colony suppression is more likely, and this is satisfactory as long as damage does not recur. How much damage will occur during the period after initial treatment, and who assumes liability for this product limitation, are questions that must be carefully considered and resolved between the pest management company, the bait manufacturer, and the customer. In many cases, customers may find the idea of continuing damage to be unacceptable, and soil treatment may be desired. In a real estate transaction, it is difficult to issue a wood-destroying-insects report when termites might be active for an extended period after treatment. Contracts and reports must clearly define limitations and responsibilities when baits are used. Finally, the absence of termite activity in bait situations may not mean the colony has been eliminated; since termites are sensitive to physical disturbance, it may mean that placing the bait in the station caused the termites to abandon the site and forage elsewhere.

Research reported by different bait manufacturers is variable; therefore, a good understanding of research results and how the bait is to be used will be important when selecting a bait.

Baits are certainly another useful, innovative tool for termite management. However, they should be viewed as an addition to existing termite management methods and not necessarily a replacement for them.

OTHER MANAGEMENT METHODS

Physical barriers, such as **stainless steel mesh** and **sand barriers**, may have utility in subterranean termite prevention and management. When properly installed, mainly during preconstruction, stainless steel mesh has been found to be an effective barrier to subterranean termites. Research has also shown these exclusion barriers to be effective. Cost may be a disadvantage.

Termite shields are installed on a structure as a physical barrier to direct termite invasion and function mainly as an aid in termite detection. They force the termites to build tubes around or over the shield obstacle, thereby making the insect's progress more noticeable. Shields consist of metal sheeting extending across the entire top of a foundation wall. Some termite shields have a protruding edge that extends 2 inches (5 cm) or more at a downward 45° angle. Termite shields must be properly installed to adequately function in termite inspection. Proper installation includes joining and securing shields properly to the foundation wall and to adjacent shields.

Sand, **granite**, or **basalt** may have some utility in preventing termite entry into structures. These barriers consist of specific particle sizes that cannot be penetrated by termites, when properly installed. The particle size distributions are such that the larger particles of sand are too big for termites to move, and the smaller particles that fill the gaps within the larger particle matrix prevent termites from penetrating these spaces. To date, these barriers have been used mainly in Hawaii during preconstruction of structures and utility poles for protection against the Formosan termite. Many variables impact the effectiveness of sand barriers, but when used in conjunction with other methods of termite management, mechanical barriers may have utility. In addition, these barriers may become more acceptable as the use of integrated pest management grows.

Plastics impregnated with toxic or repellent insecticides are used in the same way as the above described physical barriers. The insecticide provides additional protection.

Biotermiticides, such as fungi, nematodes, bacteria, and so forth, still need further research and development to maximize their potential. *Metarhizium anisopliae* has been used by injecting the product into galleries, infested walls, and other moist areas where the humidity accelerates the fungal growth. Several forms of nematodes have been sold for the suppression of termites. Nematodes are applied to the soil or directly into mud tubes. Field tests have not shown satisfactory levels of effectiveness, but further research may result in efficacious uses.

The use of **borates** (disodium octaborate tetrahydrate), in several formulations, to penetrate into wood has shown potential in preventing infestations. Results in eliminating existing infestations have been variable; thus, the use of borates for controlling established infestations must be evaluated on a case-by-case basis.

Properly pressure-treated wood, whether treated with borates or some other wood preservative,

Wood Treatment

Application of various termiticides to wood can result in very effective treatments that can be remedial and/or preventive in nature. As with soil barrier treatments, the treatment of wood before a structure is completed has the greatest preventive potential. A preventive benefit can come from the use of pressure-treated lumber, or it can come from the use of products such as borates during the construction process.

Many materials can be used in the treatment of wood, but borates have some particular advantages as a preventive and remedial material. Borates are generally low in toxicity, nonstaining and odorless, as well as being a fairly naturally derived material. Borates are easily absorbed into wood, generally penetrating to a depth of 1/8 to 1/4 of an inch in typical structural wood. Penetration to this level will generally deter termites from feeding on the treated wood.

Though borates should not be used as a substitute for good construction practices or needed chemical treatment and mechanical alterations, they can be an important tool in the termite management arsenal.

Borate treatment of wood can also be helpful for areas where traditional termiticide treatments cannot be made, such as for areas where wells, springs, etc., are present. Though they may not be enough on their own for such situations, borate wood treatments can be used in combination with other management methods such as termite baits.

will kill termites that feed on the wood. Borate-treated wood should be used for interior uses only, since it can not tolerate wetting. Using treated wood in construction is more expensive, but should be used where there is a high risk of termites being able to access wood. When damaged wood has to be replaced, treated wood should be used.

Foam formulations of soil-applied termiticides are a means of delivering termiticide to areas difficult to reach with liquid formulations. Foams penetrate hard-to-reach cavities and voids (where rocks or other debris, or ridges on the bottom of the slab, may block the flow of the termiticide, where there are cracks in the soil surface, etc.), and they improve termiticide distribution in soils. The most difficult area to achieve uniform and continuous insecticide distribution is under slabs, where the termite management specialist is unable to see the actual deposition of the termiticide.

Foam applications are a tool that can reduce corrective treatments, especially under slabs. The liquid termiticide is combined with air to create uniform, small-diameter bubbles. The foam carries the liquid termiticide in the spaces between the bubbles. The fact that foam is less dense than liquid enables it to disperse uniformly. The foaming agent delays collapse of the bubbles, providing more time for the insecticide to reach desired areas. Underneath a slab, gravity deposits most of the liquid on the soil, with a small portion of the residue on other surfaces (such as the underside of a concrete slab) in the treated areas. Surfactants in the foam improve penetration of the chemical into the soil; thus, a more uniform and continuous residual barrier is established.

Foam machines can be portable and mounted on a pull cart or they can be truck mounted or connected to the termite rig. Water, foaming agent, and the correct concentration of termiticide are pumped through the machine which uses a compressor to add the desired volume of air. This mixture passes either through a screen or an expansion tube inside the machine to create the foam. Foam can be produced in a range of consistencies depending on what is needed for the job. In general, the larger the void beneath a slab, the more air-laden the foam should be. Many factors will influence this consistency, including the type of termiticide, foaming agent, and foam machine used.

Calibration of the equipment is needed to ensure that the desired concentrations of termiticide are being applied to the soil. Calibration can be conducted by timing the application of a measured amount of liquid to see how long it takes to dispense the amount as a foam. Alternatively, a foam application can be timed as it dispensed into a bucket or liquid measuring device, then the amount of material is measured after the foam has drained down to liquid. Spray defoaming agents can be used to speed this process.

Foam applications will always require a longer time to dispense the same amount of material than a liquid application. To avoid contamination of interior surfaces during foam treatments, care must be taken to watch for the emergence of foam through other drill holes, cracks, or expansion joints. A final important consideration is when a combination of liquid and foam applications are to be made, the applicator must be certain the resulting applications together do not exceed the legal application concentration.

Foam treatments do not replace other soil applications—they supplement these applications, so that gaps left by conventional treatments can be successfully treated. Foams are being used to treat, or re-treat, critical areas, such as unevenly filled porches, that liquids might not reach or cover uniformly. Foams may be used in initial treatments to ensure the most complete termiticide barrier in critical as well as hard-to-reach areas, thus avoiding the treatment failures that may occur with soil-applied termiticides.

SUPPLEMENTARY READING MATERIAL

Beal, R. H, J. K. Mauldin, and S. C. Jones. *Subterranean Termites: Their Prevention and Control in Buildings.* U.S. Department of Agriculture, Home and Garden Bulletin 64. Washington, D.C., 1983. 36 pp.

Haverty, M. I. "Termites." *Pest Control.* May, 1976, 12–17, 46, 47, 49.

Krishna, K., and F. M. Weesner, eds. *Biology of Termites. Vol. I.* New York: Academic Press, 1969. 598 pp.

Krishna, K., and F. M. Weesner, eds. *Biology of Termites. Vol. II.* New York: Academic Press, 1970. 643 pp.

Moore, H. B. *Wood-Inhabiting Insects in Houses.* U.S. Department of. Agriculture, Washington, D.C., 1979. 133 pp.

National Pest Management Association. *Approved Reference Procedures for Subterranean Termite Control.* Dunn Loring, Va.: NPMA, 1994. 150 pp.

Weesner, F. M. *The Termites of the United States.* Dunn Loring, Va.: NPMA, 1965. 70 pp.

CHAPTER 8 | Nonsubterranean Termites and Other Wood-Destroying Organisms

Wood-destroying organisms other than subterranean termites cause millions of dollars in damage to wood products each year. These organisms and their prevention and management are discussed here.

NONSUBTERRANEAN TERMITES

Termites other than subterranean termites are divided into two groups: **drywood** and **dampwood termites**. Of these, drywood termites are the most common, although dampwood termites may be found frequently in some limited areas.

Drywood Termites
Family Kalotermitidae

Drywood termites generally live (feed and nest) in undecayed structural wood that has a very low moisture content. Unlike subterranean termites, they do not require any contact with the soil to live. Thus, they can seriously damage not only buildings, but also movable wooden objects, such as furniture. Estimates of treatment costs per year are more than $400 million. In the United States, drywood termites are found in a narrow strip from Virginia to Florida on the Atlantic coast, along the Gulf of Mexico, Arizona, Utah, from Mexico to northern California on the Pacific coast, and Hawaii (see Figure 8.1, following page 254).

A male and female pair (called alates) work their way into the wood chosen for the nest. The opening through which they enter the wood is sealed with a plug of brown cementlike material about 1/8-inch in diameter. Behind this plug they excavate a chamber where the queen lays the first eggs. The nymphs (referred to as larvae by some termite specialists) that hatch from these eggs go through a more complex metamorphosis (several larval/nymphal stages) than do subterranean ter-

mites before becoming soldiers and reproductives. These nymphs perform the work of the colony; there is no distinct worker caste, as with subterranean termites.

During the swarming season, nymphs make round holes 1/16- to 1/8-inch in diameter through which the reproductive forms leave the wood. When swarming is completed, these holes are plugged in the same way as the original entrance holes.

Damage done by drywood termites is entirely different from that caused by subterranean termites. These termites cut across the grain of the wood, excavating large chambers connected by small tunnels (see Figure 8.2, following page 254). The chambers and tunnels being used by the colony are kept clean. Excreta and other debris are

Drywood Termites—Growth In Importance

The distribution of *I. Minor* is influenced by the continued urbanization of the southwestern United States. As urbanization of the southwest continues, the importance of drywood termites in general as structural pests is expected to increase. In coastal cities of southern California, evidence of drywood termites was found in 70% of structures surveyed. Inland, drywood termites were reported from 50% of all structures surveyed. Older neighborhoods had a higher incidence of drywood termite evidence than did newer neighborhoods simply because they had been exposed for a longer period of time. In Florida, only about 10% of homes less than 10 years old would be expected to show signs of drywood termite infestation; 30% of homes 10 to 20 years old; and 60% of homes older than 20 years.

stored in unused chambers or cast out through small openings in the wood surface. These small openings are sometimes called kick-out holes.

Excretal pellets are a distinguishing characteristic of nonsubterranean termites. These pellets are hard and have six distinct concave surfaces on the sides; only the ends are rounded (see Figure 8.3, following page 254). Certain anobiid beetles also eject pellets from wood in which they feed. These pellets can easily be distinguished from those of drywood termites because they have rounded, convex surfaces.

Entrance into wood is usually made from a crack or crevice that the termites can enter before boring into the wood. This may be a crack in the wood itself, the joint between two pieces of wood, or even the space underneath roofing or sheathing paper.

Because of their ability to live in wood without soil contact, nonsubterranean termites are frequently carried in infested furniture and other wooden objects into geographical areas where they are not normally found. For this reason, pest management professionals should be aware of their habits so as to recognize them when they appear.

Drywood termites may attack wood products of all kinds. Structural timbers and woodwork in buildings as well as furniture and other wooden objects may be damaged. Although serious damage is done to buildings and other wood products in some areas of the United States, these termites are usually less injurious than subterranean termites simply because they are less widespread.

The **dark western drywood termite**, *Incisitermes minor* (Hagen), is the most destructive drywood termite in this country. It is found from California to Arizona and Utah, as well as southern costal areas. It causes extensive damage to structures as well as to piled lumber, furniture, and telephone poles. It may infest any dry wooden portion of a structure, from the foundation to the roof.

Small swarming flights occur from April through November on warm sunny days. Winged adults are dark brown with reddish heads and about 1/2-inch long. The white, soft-bodied nymphs remain in the galleries and are not seen unless the wood is broken open.

The **light western drywood termite**, *Marginitermes hubbardi* (Banks), is found from California to Arizona. It is also referred to as the southern drywood termite. This termite has very similar habits to the dark western drywood termite but prefers drier conditions and higher temperatures, and it flies in midsummer at night.

The **West Indian rough-headed powderpost drywood termite**, *Cryptotermes brevis* (Walker), is of considerable commercial significance in the United States. It occurs in the southern costal areas from Florida to Louisiana, where it is found inside buildings. Furniture being moved to other parts of the country is often found to be infested. The head of the soldier is unusually shaped (black and plug-like) and serves as a good means of identification for this species (See Figure 8.4). This termite is especially destructive to woodwork and to furniture because it destroys the interior of wood, leaving a paper-thin layer of wood or paint on the outside.

Three other species of drywood termites are most often found in the southeastern part of the United States. The **light southeastern drywood termite**, *Incisitermes snyderi* (Light), is found from South Carolina to Florida and west to Texas. It is the most injurious species of drywood termite in that area. A second drywood termite, *Incisitermes schwarzi* (Banks), is a common species in southern Florida, but it is not found in structures. The **dark southeastern drywood termite**, *Kalotermes approximatus* Snyder, occurs along the Gulf coast west to New Orleans and on the Atlantic coast north to southern Virginia. It rarely attacks wood in structures, posts, and utility poles.

Rottenwood and Dampwood Termites
Families Kalotermitidae, Termopsidae, and Rhinotermitidae

This group contains some of our largest termites, with alates as much as 1-inch long with wings. Dampwood termites do not require contact with the soil to obtain moisture; however, wood with a high degree of moisture is needed. They are usually associated with wood decay.

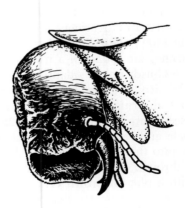

FIGURE 8.4. The head of a soldier powderpost termite. Note that the mandibles point downward rather than forward, as in other termites. This peculiarly formed head functions defensively by physically obstructing holes opening to galleries. (Provonsha)

They plug openings into the wood and excavate large galleries, as do drywood termites. They do not, however, keep the galleries clean. Their pellets can be found throughout their tunnels in infested wood, although many of the six-sided pellets are discarded from the galleries through small openings in the surface of the wood. However, the pellets are only slightly six sided, and they lack the longitudinal ridges that give drywood termite pellets their characteristically sculptured appearance.

The **Pacific dampwood termite** (sometimes referred to as the rottenwood termite), *Zootermopsis angusticollis* (Hagen), is the largest of our native termites. It is also the most economically important termite of this group. The distribution of this termite is from British Columbia to Mexico. It occurs most commonly in the cool and humid coastal areas. This termite is a significant pest at low altitudes along the coastal areas of Washington and Oregon. According to Snyder, although termed a rottenwood or dampwood termite, this species can survive for long periods in dry, sound wood.

Occasionally, colonies of this termite are carried to other parts of the country in shipments of lumber, but it has been unable to establish in these areas. There is no true worker caste. The work of the colony is carried on by the immature soldiers or reproductives. Winged forms are light brown, with dark-brown leathery wings. Nymphs are white to cream colored, with a darker abdomen. Swarms of these termites are sometimes small, numbering only 50 to 60 individuals from a single colony. Swarmers are attracted to light and are common about streetlights at night in summer.

The **desert dampwood termite**, *Paraneotermes simplicicornis* (Banks), is found in the southwestern states from western Texas to California. It differs from other dampwood termites in being subterranean in habit. It attacks only buried wood. This termite is of horticultural importance because it can attack the underground parts of shrubs and young trees. It is particularly troublesome in residential areas and citrus groves in the desert areas it inhabits. It is also found in fence posts, baseboards, and door frames.

The **Florida dampwood termite**, *Prorhinotermes simplex* (Hagen), is found in the southeastern counties of Florida and in the Keys. It lives naturally in damp (but solid) logs near the coast and is an occasional pest of buildings in the limited area where it is found. It is not subterranean by nature, although it may enter logs beneath the soil.

There are several other dampwood termites that are found occasionally in buildings, but they are not very common. More complete information on them can be found in the selected references listed at the end of the chapter.

NONSUBTERRANEAN TERMITE INSPECTION

Nonsubterranean termites are found in wood within almost any part of a structure and in wooden furnishings of all kinds (see Figures 8.5 and 8.6, following page 254). When performing an inspection, systematically inspect all exposed and accessible wood, especially on perimeter walls, on the exterior and interior of the building. It is important to inspect all accessible parts of the attic and crawlspace, if present. Drywood termites are typically found in dry wood. Dampwood termites require wood that has a considerable amount of moisture. Drywood termite infestations are often found around the perimeter of buildings and where wood is joined together. Large, well-established infestations, however, commonly extend over central areas of structures.

When inspecting for dampwood and drywood termites, it is necessary to look not only for visible damage, but also for the plugs (kick-out holes) in entrance and exit holes. The inspector should look particularly for the characteristic fecal pellets pushed out from the termite galleries. Soundings of the wood should be made, the same as for subterranean termites. Tapping the wood will cause a hollow sound where there are internal galleries. Or, sound-detection devices (stethoscopes or sound amplification devices) can be used to determine if active termites are present. Wood can be probed with tools such as an ice pick, screwdriver, or the blade of a penknife to discover termite damage and live termites in their galleries.

Other evidence of infestation includes visible flights of adults, shed wings, and surface blisters (that result from galleries close to the surface of the wood).

Detection Is Difficult

The greatest limitation to drywood termite control remains detection of colonies in wood and determination of the extent of infestation. Determining the location and extent of infestation is difficult, especially in older homes where there may be more than one colony present. Drywood termite colonies grow very slowly, typically consist of only a few thousand individuals, and show no outward signs of infestation other than the production of periodic swarmers and the presence of fecal pellets. They do not produce mud tubes like subterranean termites since their entire life, outside of swarming, is spent inside the wood on which they are feeding. Since they do not need contact with soil; soil is not found in their galleries.

Shelter tubes made of pellets and chewed wood cemented together occasionally serve as a bridge or passageway from one piece of wood to another. Cementlike walls may partition off large chambers or close large openings to conserve humidity.

Sometimes live swarmers or shed wings from swarmers are the first evidence of an infestation. Therefore, it is important to keep in mind the following wing characteristic that quickly separates subterranean from nonsubterranean termites: Nonsubterranean termite wings have **crossveins** between the costal vein, which forms the anterior margin of the wing, and the radius vein, the second-most-anterior vein originating from the wing base (see Figure 8.7). These crossveins are lacking in the wings of subterranean termites (family Rhinotermitidae).

When inspecting for nonsubterranean termites, a diagram should be made of the building, indicating all places where termites are present and where treatment must be made.

TREATMENT FOR NONSUBTERRANEAN TERMITES

Treatment for **drywood termites** consists principally of (1) structural fumigation or (2) wood treatment. The direct wood treatment method (used for local treatment, such as wood injection) should be used only in the case of limited infestations. Extensive infestations should be controlled by fumigation or heat. Whole-structure treatment usually involves fumigation, while partial (compartmental) treatments can be accomplished with heat.

Structural Fumigation

Fumigation is done with **sulfuryl fluoride** (Vikane™), as an example. The entire building is covered tightly with a gastight cover, and the gas is introduced. Vikane has the advantage of rapid and uniform dispersion within the temperature range for climates where drywood termites are found. Such fumigations should be done only by profes-

FIGURE 8.7. A drywood termite wing. Note the crossveins between the two veins running along the front margin of the wing. These crossveins are not found in the wings of subterranean termites.

sionals thoroughly trained in the use of fumigants. Detailed directions, as well as instruction, can be obtained from manufacturers of the gas being used. Chapter 20 provides additional information on fumigation.

Direct Wood Treatment

To prepare for the use of a liquid, aerosol, or dust formulation, holes are drilled into the infested timbers through the termite galleries, using a 1/2-inch drill in larger timbers and smaller drills elsewhere. Insecticide is then forced through these holes, to be dispersed through the galleries. The use of liquid insecticides, such as **borates** (disodium octaborate tetrahydrate), controls drywood termites when active galleries and access points in infested wood are pressure injected. **Drione®** is an example of a dust used. Dusts should be injected into the termite galleries in small amounts. Too much dust will plug the galleries, and the termites will wall off and thus isolate these areas.

When treating limited infestations, aerosol and liquid formulations are used most often. After an insecticide has been injected into wood, the openings should be plugged with wooden dowels.

Other Methods

Other methods of drywood termite control being used on a more limited basis, and still in need of further research and development, include **heat fumigation**, **extreme cold**, **electrocution**, and **microwaves**. For heat treatments, structures are tarped as they would be for conventional fumigation. Hot air is generated by specialized heaters and blown into the covered structure, or a section of the structure, until temperatures reach a constant 140 to 150°F. Fans are used to circulate the heated air and to achieve uniform temperatures within the area being treated. Theoretically, timbers within the treated area will reach 120°F; after 35 minutes at this temperature, termites will be dead. Thermocouples, or temperature probes, are used to selectively monitor heated timbers. This can be quite an expensive process in treating an entire building, because of the prolonged time needed to achieve the needed temperature. Heat fumigation is more practical and economical for areas of manageable size with exposed timbers, and where items that may be damaged by heat can be easily removed.

Liquid nitrogen has been used to create −20°F temperatures for at least 5 minutes for localized treatment of termites. Only limited areas can be cooled to this temperature at one time. Covering the surfaces surrounding the treatment area with insulating mats increases the efficiency of the treatment and reduces condensation. Many variables influence the efficacy of cold treatments; thus, further research is needed.

Electrocution by delivering high-voltage and high-frequency electrical energy to targeted sites in timbers, using a handheld unit, has been used. Spot treatments for drywood termites or powderpost beetles are made by delivering the electric charge to the infested wood. Theoretically, the termites will be shocked and killed by the passing current. Drilling holes into wood and/or inserting copper wire into drill holes improves the passage of current into infested areas. The devices are designed to avoid structural damage and electrocution of the management specialist. As with other localized treatments, identifying all infested areas within a structure is essential to eliminate all of the termites.

Units producing electromagnetic energy at microwave frequencies have also been used on a spot treatment basis to eliminate drywood termites from structural timbers. The high-energy zone is very limited, so heat-vulnerable items usually do not need to be removed from the structure. However, this distance limitation on microwave transmission means that treatment areas are very localized; thus, infestations and their boundaries must be precisely identified to achieve control.

Heat fumigation, extreme cold, electrocution, and microwaves involve complex technologies that management specialists in some geographic areas will want to consider. Consumer preferences, applicator safety, liability, economics, efficiency, and effectiveness are considerations for each company in deciding which control methods best suit their needs.

Dampwood termites, when they are in wood not in contact with the ground, are controlled by the same methods used for drywood termites. Where there is ground contact, structural changes to eliminate moisture may be necessary, together with ground treatment as recommended for subterranean termites. However, control consists primarily of eliminating the moisture problem in the wood, and often involves replacement of damaged and/or moist wood.

When drywood termites infest furniture, insecticides can be injected into their galleries, or the furniture can be fumigated. Drywood termites infesting furniture can also be killed by holding the furniture for 1-1/2 hours in a chamber heated to 150°F, or for 4 hours in a chamber heated to 140°F. Kilns or special vaults equipped with heating units are used for this purpose. Cold may also be used to control these termites. In northern climates, infested furniture and crates may be moved outdoors, while refrigeration chambers can be used in warmer areas. Exposure at

a temperature of 15°F for 4 days will kill termites in wood. Care must be taken to determine if cold or heat will damage the articles involved.

There are a number of measures that should be considered for **prevention** of nonsubterranean termite infestation. All lumber, especially secondhand lumber, should be carefully inspected for evidence of infestation before being used for construction purposes. Infested lumber should be treated. Do not use moist or moisture-damaged wood. In existing buildings, all doors, windows (especially attic windows), and other ventilation openings should be screened with 20-mesh noncorrodible metal wire cloth. Screening will prevent the entrance of winged termites into areas where colonies can be established. Chemically treated wood can also prevent attack. Lumber treated with wood preservatives can be purchased in many areas. Wood from trees that are naturally resistant to termite attack can also be used. Wall voids can be lightly dusted with an insecticidal dust, such as Drione, to control exploring swarmers. Protection of exterior wood surfaces with paint is also of value. An appropriate number of coats will fill many of the cracks and openings into wood used by termites to gain entrance. Larger cracks and joints can be filled with putty or plastic wood. Of course, the use of steel, concrete, brick, or stone in construction instead of wood offers the best protection against nonsubterranean termites. However, use of these materials will not prevent attack of wooden materials inside unless all entryways are properly sealed.

OTHER WOOD-DESTROYING INSECTS

Many other insects in addition to termites infest and seriously damage wood. Many of these, such as the various bark beetles and round- and flat-headed borers, are found alive most frequently in unseasoned wood. The pest management professional is usually most concerned with those insects that damage seasoned lumber. These insects include representatives of the orders Hymenoptera and Coleoptera. Hymenoptera (horntails and carpenter ants and bees) that damage wood will be discussed in Chapter 9. The groups discussed in the following sections are all members of the order Coleoptera (beetles), the larvae of which excavate burrows in wood. The characteristics of the damage done to wood by these insects are generally sufficient evidence to identify the insects to their family, but positive identification to genus or species requires examination of the insect itself.

Characteristics of damage caused by common wood-boring insects in buildings are shown in Table 8.1.

TABLE 8.1. Characteristics of damage caused by common wood-boring insects.

Insect Type	Shape and Size (inches) of Exit/Entry Hole	Wood Type	Age of Wood Attacked*	Appearance of Frass in Tunnels	Reinfests Structural Timber
ambrosia beetles	Round, 1/50–1/8	Softwood and hardwood	New	None present	No
lyctid beetles	Round, 1/32–1/16	Hardwood	New and old	Fine, flourlike, loosely packed	Yes
bark beetles	Round, 1/16–3/32	Bark/sapwood interface	New	Fine to coarse, bark colored, tightly packed	No
anobiid beetles	Round, 1/16–1/8	Softwood and hardwood	New and old	Fine powder and pellets, loosely packed; pellets may be absent and frass tightly packed in some hardwoods	Yes
bostrichid beetles	Round, 3/32–9/32	Softwood and hardwood (bamboo)	New	Fine to coarse powder, tightly packed	Rarely
horntail or wood wasp	Round, 1/6–1/4	Softwood	New	Coarse, tightly packed	No
carpenter bee	Round, 1/2	Softwood	New and old	None present	Yes
round-headed borer	Round-oval, 1/8–3/8	Softwood and hardwood	New	Coarse to fibrous, mostly absent	No
flat-headed borer	Oval, 1/8–1/2	Softwood and hardwood	New	Sawdustlike, tightly packed	No
old house borer	Oval, 1/4–3/8	Softwood	New and old	Very fine powder and tiny pellets, tightly packed	Yes
round- or flat-headed borer, wood machined after attack	Flat oval, 1/2 or more; or irregular surface groove, 1/8–1/2	Softwood and hardwood	New	Absent or sawdustlike, coarse to fibrous; tightly packed	No

*New wood is defined as standing or freshly felled trees and unseasoned lumber. Old wood is seasoned or dried lumber.
Source: M. P. Levy, A Guide to the Inspection of Existing Homes for Wood-Inhabiting Fungi and Insects, U.S. Department of Housing and Urban Development, Washington, D.C., 1975.

Powderpost Beetles

The term **powderpost beetle**, used in the broad sense, applies to any of three closely related families (Lyctidae, Bostrichidae, and Anobiidae) within the superfamily Bostrichoidea. The common name is appropriate because the larvae of these beetles reduce timbers to a mass of very fine, powderlike material. The adults do very little actual damage to wood, serving primarily a reproductive function (see Figure 8.8). There are certain differences in structure, behavior, and nutrition among these groups, and these differences have led to the separation of the families discussed in the following sections.

Among the many different kinds of insects that attack wood and wood products, the destructiveness of powderpost beetles is second only to that of termites. Powderpost beetles cause millions of dollars worth of damage in the United States each year. They infest and reinfest dry seasoned wood, with

the interior of such wood (usually the sapwood only) being completely riddled with holes or galleries and packed with wood dust or frass. Pinhole openings, often called shot holes, perforate the surface of infested wood. The size of these holes varies, depending on the family and species of the beetles involved. Both hardwoods and softwoods are attacked, although the family Lyctidae is specific to hardwoods. (Examples of hardwood are ash, oak, walnut, and pecan. Softwoods include pine, fir, and some maple.)

Powderpost beetles infest flooring, studs, girders, and other parts of buildings, as well as lumber, crating, paneling, furniture, tool handles, gunstocks, and many other wood articles. Infestations are often built into structures as a result of using infested lumber, and these beetles are frequently brought into homes in infested firewood. Beetles that attack softwoods often fly into crawlspaces beneath build-

Beetles, and Those That Damage Our Structures

Beetles belong to the order Coleoptera, the largest of the insect orders, having over 30,000 U.S. species in more than 100 families. Most beetles have four wings; the front pair, called elytra, are thickened, leathery, or hard and brittle, and they usually meet in a straight line down the middle of the back. They cover the thin, membranous hind wings which are folded under the front wings when at rest. The order name, Coleoptera, means "sheath wings" and refers to the characteristic front wings.

Among wood-boring beetles, the larvae are all yellowish-white with dark mandibles (jaws) and sometimes with other dark areas of structures. This stage is always found inside the wood and is rarely seen, except for the larger species, even when damaged wood is split open. The larval stage is responsible for almost all damage done to wood by beetles.

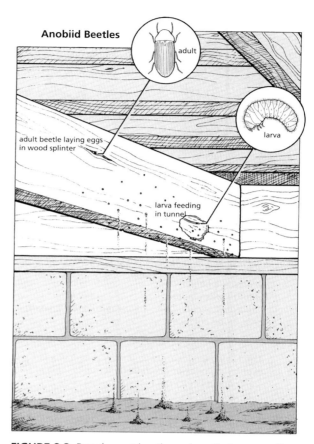

FIGURE 8.8. Powderpost beetles reduce timbers to a fine, powderlike material; hence their name. This illustration shows an adult and larva from the Anobiidae family. (Shuster and Provonsha)

ings and lay eggs on exposed wood there. The first evidence of infestation is usually piles of very fine sawdust on or beneath wood and small holes in the wood surface. At that point, infestations may have been present from 3 months to 3 years or more, depending on the species involved, environmental conditions, and type of wood attacked. In hidden areas, such as crawlspaces, serious damage may be done before the infestation is discovered.

True Powderpost Beetles
Family Lyctidae

Adult lyctid beetles lay their eggs in the surface pores of wood. The eggs are long and cylindrical, rather than round as with many other insects. Larvae bore into the wood as soon as they hatch. Larvae are white with dark brown heads and mandibles. The front end of the body is larger than the back and bears three minute pairs of legs. Lyctid larvae can easily be identified by examining the last pair of spiracles, which are much larger than the others (see Figure 8.9).

Larvae live in the wood, creating galleries (tunnels) as they eat the wood. When the larvae are nearly full grown and ready to pupate, they bore near to the surface of the wood and pupate. Adults bore out through the surface soon after pupation, pushing a fine, powdery wood dust out of the wood as they emerge. Adult activity is greatest in early spring. They are inactive in the day, concealing themselves in cracks and holes in the wood. At night, they become active, are attracted to lights,

and may be seen crawling on windowsills, floors, and furniture.

Adults are flattened and reddish-brown to black in color (see Figures 8.10 and 8.11, following page 254, and Figure 8.12). They are small beetles, varying in size from 3/32- to 7/32-inch long. The basal segment of the antenna is quite long (as long as the second and third combined), and the antenna bears a club consisting of only two segments. The body is somewhat flattened, and the head is distinctly visible from above (which is not the case in most species of the other two families of powderpost beetles).

There are certain similarities in both habit and structure between lyctid and bostrichid beetles. Thus, at one time they were all placed in the family Bostrichidae. It is interesting to note that there are also physiological similarities between the two groups. For example, neither beetle can digest cellulose; hence, this material passes through the digestive tract of the larva virtually untouched and accounts for the large amounts of powdery frass left by the beetles. Since the carbohydrate content of wood is a

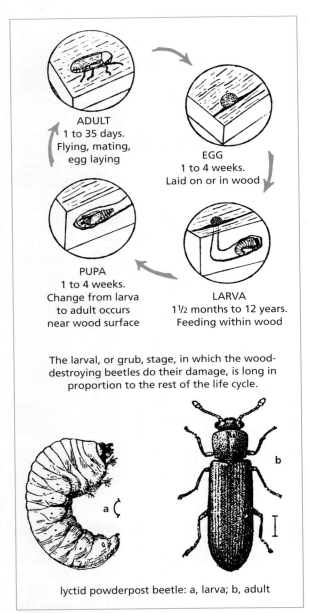

ADULT
1 to 35 days.
Flying, mating,
egg laying

EGG
1 to 4 weeks.
Laid on or in wood

PUPA
1 to 4 weeks.
Change from larva
to adult occurs
near wood surface

LARVA
1½ months to 12 years.
Feeding within wood

The larval, or grub, stage, in which the wood-destroying beetles do their damage, is long in proportion to the rest of the life cycle.

lyctid powderpost beetle: a, larva; b, adult

FIGURE 8.9. The typical life cycle of a lyctid powderpost beetle.

limiting factor in the development of these beetles, it is advantageous to the females to find wood with a high starch content on which to lay their eggs.

It has been shown that females of some lyctid species can actually select favorable wood by a so-called tasting process. Wood that has a low starch content and less than 6% moisture content is seldom attacked. Lyctids are nearly always found infesting the sapwood of hardwoods, especially those that have been inadequately seasoned. Common examples are implement handles made of ash and oak, and flooring or furniture made from oak, maple, walnut, and other hardwoods. Only hardwoods have pores, which are necessary for the female to lay eggs.

Some hardwoods, such as ash, elm, oak, pecan, and walnut, are more readily attacked because of the presence of very large pores. Only the sapwood layers of hardwood are eaten, since the required starches are present. If the starch content is less than 3%, the wood will not be attacked.

Bamboo, which is attacked by some lyctids, is technically classified as grass, but it meets the requirements necessary for lyctid attack. Occasionally, bamboo furniture, baskets, screens, and so forth may be infested. Lyctids can complete a life cycle in one spring and summer season if temperature, starch content of the wood, and moisture conditions are good. However, they usually require a year to complete development when they are in wood that has been built into a structure. This is primarily because of the dryness of the wood. In an unoccupied or poorly heated building, they often reinfest available hardwood for many generations.

Lyctid damage is characterized by the presence of extremely fine, flourlike powder falling from the

Important Lyctid Powderpost Beetles

The **southern Lyctus beetle**, *Lyctus planicollis*, is found throughout the United States and parts of Mexico, but is most common in the southern and Gulf Coast states. This species is dark brown to black and 1/4-inch in length. Closely related to the southern Lyctus beetle is the **western Lyctus beetle**, *L. cavicollis*. This beetle is also found throughout the United States, but is more common on the West Coast. Adults are rusty, red-brown in color, approximately 1/8-inch, and commonly infest firewood, furniture, and building materials in California and Oregon.

The **brown Lyctus beetle**, *L. brunneus*, and the **European Lyctus beetle**, *L. linearis*, are distributed worldwide. They are both dark brown and have glossy, reddish-brown wing covers. Similar in size, the European Lyctus beetle is 1/8- to 1/4-inch in length and the brown lyctus beetle is 1/5-inch in length. The European lyctus beetle occurs more commonly in the eastern United States than in the western states, and has been reported in ash, hickory, oak, cherry, walnut, poplar, and locust. The brown lyctus beetle infests bamboo, oak, and elm.

The **velvety powderpost beetle**, *Trogoxylon parallelopipedus*, has a body that is rusty red-brown to black in color, and covered with fine yellowish hairs, giving it a velvety appearance. It occurs throughout the United States and may infest ash, hickory, oak, and bamboo.

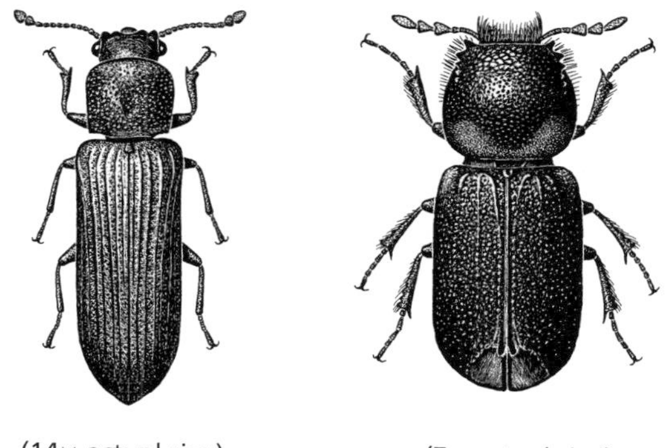
(14× actual size)
(7× actual size)

FIGURE 8.12. Two of the insects referred to as powderpost beetles in the broad sense of the term. Left: *Lyctus planicollis* (LeConte), one of the true powderpost beetles of the family Lyctidae. Note the two-segmented antennal club typical of the members of the family. Right: *Scobicia declivis* (LeConte), a so-called false powderpost beetle of the family Bostrichidae. Note the more cylindrical body shape and the three-segmented antennae characteristic of most members of this family. (Provonsha)

surface holes (see Figure 8.13, following page 254). The frass left by other wood borers usually contains pellets and has a coarse texture and a tendency to stick together. When inspecting damage, be sure to distinguish old damage from active beetle infestations. Newly formed holes and frass are light in color and clear in appearance; old holes and frass are dark in color.

There are 66 known species of Lyctidae, of which 10 are known to exist in the United States. Only six of these are of major importance. They are *Lyctus brunneus* Stephens (brown lyctus beetle); *L. cavicollis* Le Conte (western lyctus beetle); *L. linearis* Goeze (European lyctus beetle); *L. opaculus* Le Conte; *L. planicollis* Le Conte (southern lyctus beetle); and *Trogxylon parallelopipedum* (Melsheimer). In addition to these established species, others are periodically discovered infesting wooden articles shipped into the United States.

False Powderpost Beetles

Family Bostrichidae

The economic importance of the bostrichid beetles in houses is much less than that of the other two powderpost beetle families. Most of the hardwoods attacked are not those commonly used for interior floors, woodwork, and trim. Most of the species do not reinfest wood after it is seasoned, so the damage is limited to that inflicted by one generation. However, this damage can be considerable because of the speed and completeness of their attack on portions of wood having a high starch content (sapwood portion of the wood),

Adult bostrichid beetles bore into wood to lay their eggs, which is different than other powderpost beetle families. Mature larvae are curved and wrinkled, lack hairs on the body, and possess three pairs of short legs. The mandibles are not toothed on the inner margins and the front half of the body is larger than the back half.

Most bostrichids are larger than beetles from the other families of powderpost beetles. Consequently, their entrance and exit holes are larger (more than 1/8-inch). These holes do not contain frass, but the galleries do. The frass is tightly packed, tends to stick together, and is meal-like (contains no pellets).

Upon emerging from their pupal skins (usually in spring of the year), adults bore to the surface of wood. Adults vary from 1/8- to 1-inch long and are dark brown or black in color. The body is cylindrical (except that of *Polycaon stouti*) with a much-roughened thorax, and the antenna bears a club of three distinct and separate segments. The head is usually not visible from above (see Figure 8.12).

Bostrichids are unable to digest cellulose and do not have "partnerships" with organisms that are capable of digesting cellulose. They are dependent on the starch and other nutrients in the wood they infest. There are a considerable number of species in this family, and they attack a wide range of materials. They are most commonly encountered in hardwoods, but certain bostrichids commonly infest softwoods and sometimes become important pests in softwoods. Although primarily a pest of seasoned wood, some species occasionally will be found in unseasoned wood.

The **bamboo powderpost beetle**, *Dinoderus minutus* (Fabricius), is commonly encountered in the United States. It is a small (about 1/8-inch long), cylindrical brown beetle that is a pest primarily of curtains, ornaments, and furniture made from bamboo. It is also found in stored grain products and spices (see Figure 8.14, following page 254).

Polycaon stouti (Le Conte) is a larger black bostrichid (about 3/4-inch long) found infesting hardwood lumber, furniture, and other wood products in the western United States (see Figure 8.15). Occasionally, it is found in other parts of the country in furniture that has been moved from the West Coast. The adults differ from other bostrichids in that the head is visible from above.

The **lead-cable borer**, *Scobicia declivis* (Le Conte), is a cylindrical, reddish-brown beetle, about 1/4-inch long (see Figure 8.12), that attacks the lead sheathing of aerial telephone cables. Where the sheathing is penetrated, moisture enters, and a short circuit can occur. The beetle also attacks solid

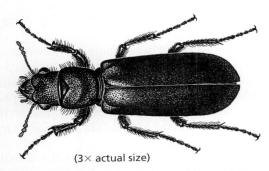

FIGURE 8.15. Black polycaon, an atypical bostrichid. (Provonsha)

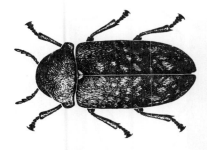

FIGURE 8.17. The deathwatch beetle, *Xestobium rufovillosum* (De Geer). (Provonsha)

wood, with larvae feeding on the wood for about 9 months before pupating. It is found along the U.S. Pacific coast.

The **red-shouldered bostrichid**, *Xylobiops basilaris* (F), is a cylindrical black beetle, about 1/4-inch long, that has patches of red at the base of the elytra. Although it may infest log cabins, rustic furniture, and structural timbers, it is more of a nuisance than an economic pest, because it emerges from dead or dying trees in great numbers.

Ranging in size from 1/4- to 1/2-inch, the **Oriental wood borer**, *Heterobostrychus aequalis*, is brownish-black in color and has a prothorax with several projections. The elytra have several rows of deep puncture marks, and toward the rear, the wing covers are curved inward creating a concave area. These beetles are found in several areas in Florida and as far north as North Carolina. They may also be found in items imported from India and Southeast Asia. Packing cases, boxes, plywood, furniture, and lumber are commonly infested, and it has been found infesting 35 species of trees.

Furniture and Deathwatch Beetles

Family Anobiidae

There are a number of species of Anobiidae encountered as wood borers in structures in the United States. Three species are among the more well known and economically important: *Anobium punctatum* (De Geer), the **furniture beetle**; *Xestobium rufovillosum* (De Geer), the **deathwatch beetle**; and *Euvrilletta peltata* (Harris). The furniture beetle is found primarily in the eastern half of the United States, and although named the furniture beetle, it also infests structural timbers. The deathwatch beetle is found throughout the United States (see Figure 8.16, following page 254, and Figure 8.17). It attacks building timbers in poorly ventilated areas where moisture tends to collect. Its common name is derived from the ticking sound that the adult makes inside infested wood, a sound that is audible in the hush and stillness of night. The sound is actually a mating call.

Euvrilletta peltata (see Figure 8.18) is a serious pest in crawlspace timbers in the southeastern United States. Infestations may become so serious that a loss of structural strength to sills, joists, and subflooring areas can occur. Tables 8.2 and 8.3 summarize comparative information on the three powderpost beetle families.

Anobiid beetles lay their eggs in cracks and crevices of seasoned wood. As soon as they hatch, young larvae burrow into the wood, where they will live and tunnel for a year or more. When mature, they burrow toward the surface of the wood where they pupate. After emerging from the pupal skin, the adults bore to the surface of the wood and escape.

Mature larvae of anobiids are slightly curved (C-shaped), wrinkled, and have tiny hairs on the body. They have three pairs of short legs. Their mandibles are usually toothed on the inner edge. Larvae of the various species vary from 1/4- to almost 1/2-inch long.

Adults are small beetles, usually less than 1/3-inch long. They vary from red to blackish-brown. The dorsal view of the thorax provides a fairly distinctive characteristic for identification of many of the members of this family. The widest point of the thorax is slightly forward of the base, which tapers

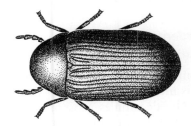

FIGURE 8.18. *Euvrilletta peltata* (Harris). This is a brown to reddish-brown beetle clothed with fine yellow hairs. (H. L. Sweetman, *Recognition of Structural Pests and Their Damage*, by permission of Wm. C. Brown Co., Inc.; drawing by Provonsha)

TABLE 8.2. Comparative biological information on the three families of powderpost beetles.

Characteristic	Family		
	Lyctidae	Bostrichidae	Anobiidae
Size	1/12–1/5"	1/8–1"	1/8–1/3"
Shape	Flattened	Cylindrical, roughened	Oval, compact pronotum
Color	Brown to black	Brown to black	Reddish brown
Head visible from above	Yes	No	No
Antennal club	2 segmented	3-4 segmented	None
Egg placement	Deposited in pores of hardwoods	Female bores into wood to lay eggs	Laid in cracks or old exit holes in wood
Required moisture content of wood*	6–30 %	6–30%	13–30%
Average life cycle	1 year	1 year	1–3 years

*Wood found in structures is considered dry with a moisture content less than 20 percent.

Source: M. P. Levy, *A Guide to the Inspection of Existing Homes for Wood-Inhabiting Fungi and Insects*, U.S. Department of Housing and Urban Development, Washington, D.C., 1975.

slightly backward and toward the midline, giving the thorax a rough, diamond-shaped outline. The pronotum forms a hood over the head, and when viewed from above, completely conceals the head. Also the tibia on the leg of an anobiid does not have spurs as are found on Lyctid and Bostrichid beetles.

Unlike termites, some of the anobiids are able to digest wood without the aid of cellulose-digesting protozoa. Although the growth of certain fungi within the burrows may serve as a source of protein and increase the rate of development of the larvae, it is known that some species can complete the life cycle on a steady diet of cellulose alone, due to the presence of an enzyme that converts the cellulose to useful nutrients.

Anobiids infest all types of seasoned wood (both hardwoods and softwoods), although they usually are more serious pests of the sapwood of softwoods. As a result, infestations are common in crawlspaces

TABLE 8.3. Timbers attacked by common wood-boring insects.

	Unseasoned	Seasoned	Softwood	Hardwood	Sapwood	Heartwood
lyctids		+		+	+	
bostrichids	−	+	−	+	+	
anobiids		+	+	−	+	−
round-headed borers	+		+	+	+	
old house borers		+	+		+	
flat-headed borers	+	−	+	+	+	+
wharf borers		+	+	+	+	+
scolytids	+		+	+	+	+

Note: + means yes; − means occasionally.

Source: M. P. Levy, *A Guide to the Inspection of Existing Homes for Wood-Inhabiting Fungi and Insects*, U.S. Department of Housing and Urban Development, Washington, D.C., 1975.

and basements, because most framing lumber in buildings is pine. Cabinets, furniture, and woodwork are also infested. Infestation is characterized by small, round holes on the surface, with fine to coarse powder sifting from them. This frass is characterized by the bun-shaped pellets within the mass.

The life cycle takes one or more years, depending on the species involved and environmental conditions. The adults emerge in greatest numbers from April through July and will reinfest wood if the moisture content of the wood is high enough. In crawlspaces, reinfestation occurs most frequently where ventilation is poor and humidity is absorbed by the wood members. Attics and wall voids are rarely infested, because ventilation and temperature control remove moisture. If a house has no problem with excess moisture in the basement or crawlspace, has central heating and cooling systems, and does not remain closed up or unoccupied for long periods, widespread, extensive damage by anobiid beetles is unlikely.

Long-Horned Beetles, or Round-Headed Borers

Family Cerambycidae

Species in this family (more than 1,200 species recorded in the United States) feed as larvae on living trees, recently felled trees and logs, and seasoned lumber. Indoors, the only species of major economic importance that can reinfest dry, seasoned wood is the old house borer. Some species that begin their development in dying trees, logs, or unseasoned lumber are able to complete their development as the wood seasons. The adults of these borers will emerge from the wood after it has been incorporated into a structure. They will not reinfest the wood because of its dryness, but they are of great concern to property owners who find them or evidence of their activity (see Figure 8.19, following page 254).

Another common source for these beetles indoors is from **firewood** brought indoors. Sighting of adult beetles can lead to a false impression of structural attack. Thus, firewood should be brought indoors only when it will be used soon thereafter.

The beetles of this family lay their eggs in cracks or crevices in bark or on the surface of rough-sawn timbers. The larvae are wood borers.

Mature larvae are large, varying from 1/2- to 3- or 4-inches long. The body is long and narrow and a light cream color. The rear portion of the head is partly drawn into the body, so that only the mandibles and other mouthparts are easily seen. Larvae are called round-headed borers.

Adults are large, conspicuous beetles varying in length from 1/2- to 3-inches long. They can be easily distinguished from other beetles by their long, thin antennae, which may be longer than the body; thus, adult beetles are called long-horned beetles. Many species have conspicuous markings on the wing covers.

The most common structural pest of this family, and the only one that commonly infests houses and other structures, is *Hylotrupes bajulus* (Linnaeus), the **old house borer**. Larvae hollow out extensive galleries in seasoned softwood (e.g., pine). The old house borer is frequently a pest of newer structures, although it is found in older buildings. It is well established along the U.S. Atlantic coast, but infestations have been reported as far west as Louisiana and Minnesota.

Adults are about 3/4-inch in length and grayish-brown to black in color, with two white patches on the elytra. The dorsal surface is densely covered with light-colored hairs. On the pronotum there are two black, shiny bumps. When these bumps are surrounded by long, grey hairs, the result is an owl-like appearance (see Figure 8.20, and Figure 8.21, which follows page 254).

The life cycle of the old house borer ranges from 3 to 12 years, although it can be considerably longer if environmental and nutritional conditions are favorable. Because this beetle has a very long life cycle and can infest the same piece of wood again and again, it may be many years before serious structural damage is recognized. The exit holes of emerging adults do not occur in very large numbers until the infestation has been established for several years. This, along with the fact that larvae will do extensive feeding without breaking through the surface of the wood, make it necessary to inspect infest-

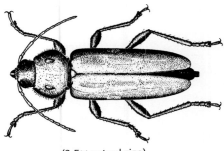

(2.5× actual size)

FIGURE 8.20. The old house borer, Hylotrupes bajulus (Linnaeus). This large beetle is quite destructive to seasoned softwoods, in which the larval stages construct extensive galleries packed with powderlike frass. It is one of the long-horned beetles of the family Cerambycidae. (Provonsha)

ed wood very carefully to detect old house borer damage. Rough wood being examined should be probed or struck to detect weakness or the presence of boring dust. If exit holes are present, they will be broadly oval and about 1/4- to 3/8-inch in diameter.

Like a number of other members of this family, the old house borer is able to digest cellulose. Because carbohydrates are readily available to this insect, the limiting nutritional factor appears to be the supply of protein. Larval development is more rapid in wood infested with wood decay fungi because these fungi are a source of protein for the larvae.

Bark and Timber Beetles
Family Scolytidae

The scolytids are small, cylindrical beetles with elbowed antennae that bear a large expanded club (see Figure 8.22). The club (except three small genera) appears to consist of a single segment that is much wider than the preceding segments. The larvae do not have legs.

There are a number of species of the family Scolytidae that may be of concern to the pest management professional. Bark beetles excavate extensive galleries immediately beneath the bark on the surface layers of wood. Timber beetles, on the other hand, excavate tunnels within solid wood. Some timber beetles derive nourishment directly from the wood. Others feed on fungi that they cultivate within the galleries. The eggs are deposited within the galleries. These beetles are often (but not always) associated with wood from trees that are either dead or dying, before the wood is processed.

Bark beetles may create problems in log cabins, park shelters, and similar structures made of roughhewn wood in which the bark is left intact or in which small areas of bark are left in place. Other

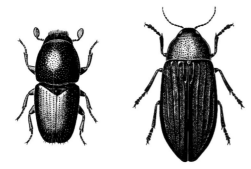

FIGURE 8.22. *Left:* A scolytid beetle. Note the elbowed antennae with the compact club. *Right:* The buprestid beetle is more than 3/4-inch long and usually metallic in color. (Provonsha)

common sources of bark beetles are rustic lawn and porch furniture and firewood brought indoors during winter.

Timber beetles are sometimes troublesome when they emerge from improperly seasoned wood used in hardwood floors or in decorative paneling. Although the emerged beetles may be a nuisance for a short time, they cannot reinfest the dried wood or bark, and they cause no loss of strength to the wood from which they emerge.

Ambrosia beetles are another group of beetles belonging to the scolytid family and the family Platypodidae. They are so named because their larvae feed only on ambrosia fungus, which grows in moist, usually green, wood. The adult beetles introduce the fungus spores into their tunnels, and wherever the fungus grows, the wood is stained blue, black, or dark brown. These stains around the tunnels and holes are the key to identifying ambrosia beetle damage. This damage is sometimes confused with powderpost beetle damage, even though the stains are very evident. It is important to know the difference, because powderpost beetles can reinfest wood in structures, and ambrosia beetles cannot.

If live ambrosia beetles are found indoors, the most likely source is firewood that has been recently cut. Since their attack ends before or shortly after wood is brought indoors, no control is needed.

Wharf Borer
Family Oedemeridae,

The **wharf borer**, *Nacerdes melanura* (Linnaeus), adult is about 1/2-inch long, resembles the long-horned beetles in general appearance, but does not belong to the same family. It may be yellow to light brown with the tips of the wing covers, the legs, and the underside of the body black. The body is densely covered with short yellow hair. The wing covers

each bear four lengthwise raised lines (see Figure 8.23, and Figure 8.24, which follows page 254).

The larva is about 1-inch long, narrow, and cylindrical. It bears wartlike swellings on the upper side of the last two segments of the thorax and the first two segments of the abdomen. There is a similar swelling on the underside of each of the third and fourth segments of the abdomen.

This insect's common name is derived from one of the places it is commonly found. It can be a serious pest in pilings and wharves, where the larvae excavate extensive galleries, weakening the timbers and providing excellent sites for invasion by rot organisms. Wharf borers may be found in buildings in which poor drainage or faulty plumbing accounts for the presence of very moist wood, especially pilings. It is also a problem in wood lying on damp ground (especially in crawlspaces) and wood that has been buried beneath the soil. Wharf borers have been found in association with redevelopment activities in which old buildings are torn down and some of the old wood has been buried.

The wharf borer is commonly found along the Atlantic and Pacific coasts and near the Great Lakes. It has also caused damage and annoyance in other areas across the United States. Whether the larvae do serious damage in structures is debatable because the wood on which they feed is moist and usually already decayed. The presence of the borer, however, does compound the problem. In addition, thousands of adults may appear suddenly after emerging from wood and create a nuisance in their attempt to escape from the structure. Swarming occurs primarily in the summer months.

Flat-Headed, or Metallic, Wood Borers
Family Buprestidae

Active infestations of flat-headed borers are rarely seen in structures, but wood damaged by the larvae is often encountered. If adults happen to emerge within buildings, they will not reinfest structural timber.

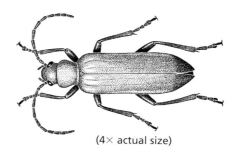

(4× actual size)

FIGURE 8.23. The wharf borer, *Nacerdes melanura* (Linnaeus). (Provonsha)

Adults are hard-shelled, boat-shaped beetles having bright colors and a metallic luster giving rise to the common name metallic wood borers (see Figure 8.22, and Figure 8.25, which follows page 254). Usually the elytra are ridged or roughened. They are strong fliers and actively seek weak or injured trees to infest in the spring and summer months.

The larvae are white to yellow, legless grubs that have a conspicuous widening and flattening of the thorax just behind the head (thus the name flat-headed borer). They tunnel in and under the bark and eventually move into the sapwood and heart-wood of dead or dying trees. Most buprestids feed until winter, pupate, and emerge in the warmer months through an oval exit hole. The larval tunnels are broadly oval, being about three times as broad as high, and are tightly packed with fine frass.

Other Wood-Infesting Beetles

Another group of beetles that does not contribute to significant structural damage but should be recognized, is the family Curculionidae, the **weevils**. These beetles are sometimes called snout beetles because their head is prolonged into a distinctive snout. They are small, about 1/8- to 1/5-inches long, and black to reddish-brown in color. The elytra are heavily pitted. Larvae are whitish, grublike, legless, and approximately 1/8-inch when full grown.

The female excavates holes in the wood or uses cracks and crevices to deposit her eggs. The larvae bore primarily with the grain in some species, but may take a more random route with other species. Adults and larvae may both be found feeding in the galleries. Adults leave exit holes when emerging from the wood approximately 1/16-inch in diameter or elongate, irregularly shaped holes 1/16- to 1/12-inch in diameter. Frass is very fine and powdery with tiny pellets and is packed in the galleries. The damage is similar in appearance to anobiid beetles but the pellets, frass and tunnels are much smaller.

Wood-boring weevils are not common and do not cause significant amounts of damage, but may cause confusion if detected, because of their unusual appearance. There are a few species of weevils that will attack seasoned wood, but they are most often found in wood that is damp or slightly decayed. They attack hardwoods, softwoods, and plywood, and occur in all parts of the country. Moisture control is the best solution for these weevils in most cases.

The **telephone pole beetle**, *Micromalthus debilis*, is the only member of the beetle family Micromalthidae found in the United States. Adults are only about 1/16-inch in length. Antennae are 11-segmented, the first two segments of which are longer than the final nine segments. The head is wider than the prothorax and the prothorax narrows where it meets the elytra. The body color varies from light to dark brown.

Relatively little is known about the telephone pole beetle's biology, but what is known is unusual for the insect world. Until recently, only female specimens of this beetle have been collected. The females are "parthenogenetic," or are capable of reproducing without mating. Even more bizarre, these beetles are "paedogenic," meaning that the larvae are capable of producing larvae or eggs prior to maturing into adults. Maturation of larvae seems to occur at the same time in a particular infestation, with beetles emerging by the thousands.

The telephone pole beetle commonly infests rotting oak or chestnut logs. High moisture content is a prerequisite for proper development. It is reported to infest wood that is ultimately used inside buildings. Some of the more common infestation situations include telephone poles (hence its nickname) and wood paneling in bank vaults. This beetle is native to North America and is occasionally transported to other countries. Infestations are best resolved by vacuuming up emerging beetles and eliminating moisture problems in wood.

PREVENTION OF WOOD-BORING BEETLES

Most of the procedures that will prevent attack on wood before it is used are the responsibility of those who harvest, mill, or store the wood. Those who use wood must take precautions to reduce the chances of building an infestation into structures, furniture, and so forth.

Although the pest management professional is usually called in after an infestation is suspected, it is important that this person be a knowledgeable consultant to the lumber and construction industries, as well as to consumers, on the prevention of wood-boring beetles. Steps that can be taken to prevent beetles from infesting buildings include:

- inspecting wood prior to purchase
- using properly kiln- or air-dried wood
- sealing wood surfaces
- using chemically treated wood
- ensuring good building design

These preventive measures all have limitations; however, they should still be considered as management tools where no beetle attack has yet occurred.

Although careful visual inspection of wood is essential, some infestations may not have progressed to the point where they can be detected. Using kiln- or air-dried wood in construction is one of the least-expensive and most-practical preventive measures. Still, there are a few beetle species that can survive and reinfest wood that has been properly dried. Sealing wood surfaces with varnish, shellac, or paint eliminates the habitat necessary for egg laying, but it is usually not feasible to seal the surfaces of structural timbers. Using chemically treated wood (e.g., treated by fumigation, wood preservatives, or insecticides) will provide beetle-free wood, but using such treated wood is usually cost prohibitive. In addition, fumigation will not protect the wood from a future infestation. Using good building design and practices, such as proper ventilation, drainage, and clearance between wood and soil, will tend to reduce the moisture content of wood in a structure, creating less-favorable conditions for beetle development. Central heating and cooling systems also speed up the wood-drying process.

INSPECTING FOR WOOD-BORING BEETLES

Periodic inspections are needed to determine the condition of wood and to locate any evidence of attack by wood-destroying beetles. It is necessary to visually examine all exposed surfaces of wood (painted and unpainted) and to sound or probe them for evidence of internal damage.

The homeowner or building occupants should be interviewed, since they may have noticed some evidence of the beetle attack, whether it be actual beetles, holes in wood, or frass. This is essential information, especially inside a house where the inspector might look for hours without discovering any evidence.

Evidence of beetle attack is much more pronounced and more easily detected in attics, crawlspaces, unfinished basements, and storage areas. The signs are more likely to be undisturbed, and the absence of finishes on the wood leaves more wood surface that has been exposed to reinfestation.

Damage caused by beetles that do and do not reinfest wood is often very similar. Thus the inspector needs to collect beetles, larvae, frass, wood samples, or any other evidence that can be more closely examined with good light and magnification. Only in this way can positive identification of the attacking beetles be determined. Since the beetles do not cause damage very rapidly, a delay in treatment will not result in any harmful consequences, and positive identification often prevents unnecessary treatment.

The inspection will also help to determine whether the infestation is still active. To be certain that the infestation is active, the inspector should try to find fresh frass, which is the color of newly sawed wood, or live larvae or adults in the wood.

Information that will assist professionals in identifying any evidence discovered during an inspection is found in Tables 8.1, 8.2, and 8.3.

MANAGEMENT OF WOOD-BORING BEETLES

Nonchemical

Alteration of environmental conditions might one day be the only procedure necessary to eliminate some infestations of wood-boring beetles. No wood-destroying beetles in buildings develop rapidly in wood that is dry. If the use of vapor barriers, ventilation, and central heat can dry wood and keep it dry, the use of other management measures may not be necessary. This would not be a rapid means of management and probably would not completely replace others. Regardless of the method used, it is wise to recommend that every effort be made to reduce the moisture content of the wood to be protected to below 20 percent. **Moisture meters** can be used to determine the moisture level in the wood.

Where economical and practical, infested wood should be removed and replaced. This is only practical in limited infestations. Wood adjacent to the wood removed must be carefully inspected to be certain that it is free of beetles.

Electric current treatment and heat treatment, as discussed for drywood termite management, have uses in some wood-boring beetle infestations. Every situation should be evaluated before making a decision on the treatment method or combination of methods to be used.

Chemical

There are certain similarities in management strategies recommended for the control of wood-boring beetles, but in many instances specialized techniques are required. Although the pest management professional may find these pests in a variety of situations, the nature and extent of the required treatment can be determined by keeping certain aspects of their life histories and habits in mind.

If it can be determined that the damage in a particular instance was caused by one of the true powderpost beetles, it will be necessary to concentrate management activities on articles made of hardwoods. In most cases, this will involve a thorough application of insecticide to all exposed hardwood surfaces.

If the infestation involves either bostrichid or

anobiid beetles, the scope of the treatment is altered to some extent. Unless the professional can make a definite species determination and thereby establish the various woods subject to attack, it must be assumed that softwoods, as well as hardwoods, are endangered by the pest. In addition to determining the type of wood being attacked, each problem must be analyzed in light of the severity of infestation, possibility of reinfestation, the area of the structure being attacked, the speed of control needed, and the cost the property owner can bear.

Residual insecticides approved for use against wood-boring beetles are effective when applied properly. In the past it was thought that oil formulations resulted in better control than water-based emulsions because of greater penetration into wood, but this is not the case. Furthermore, oil solutions present a possible fire hazard, greater expense, greater hazard and discomfort to the applicator, and danger of damaging plants near the treatment area.

To obtain the best results, the professional must combine knowledge of the beetles with knowledge of insecticides. The most difficult problem encountered in such treatments is getting the insecticide to the insects, concealed and well shielded in their burrows. Although a material with a long residual life would kill the beetles shortly after they emerge, it is desirable to kill them in their tunnels so they will not mar the surface of the wood with emergence holes. The best penetration into the tunnels is obtained by using a fumigant, but the danger in handling these materials and the fact that they have no effective residual life limits their usefulness. Residual sprays provide effective control in most cases. Sprays should be applied at a low pressure (to reduce splashing), using a flat-fan nozzle to obtain thorough coverage. A compressed-air sprayer can be used to inject insecticide directly into the galleries made by beetles. Penetration into certain finishes (paint, varnish, water-repellent stains, etc.) is limited, and repeated injections into exit holes is necessary.

In treating finished wood, such as furniture or flooring, it is best to use an oil solution to avoid spotting or in any way changing the appearance of the finish. Even with the oil solution, it is best to apply a small amount to an out-of-the-way area and allow it to dry before making a complete treatment. The oil carrier may have a solvent action on some wood finishes. Therefore, keep all objects off treated areas for about 24 hours or until all stickiness has disappeared. Do not allow any surface to be walked on or handled until it is thoroughly dry. Insecticide should be applied to the entire surface of the infested wood using a flat-fan nozzle at low

Wood Preservation Using Borates

Borate-based wood preservatives (disodium octaborate tetrahydrate) may be used as a preventive residual treatment on wood. Borates are toxic to wood-boring beetles, decay fungi, and many termites species, but are not considered significantly hazardous to humans or livestock. They should be applied at a stage of construction when access to all wood members is available. Treated wood should not be exposed to excessive moisture to prevent leaching. Through time, the disodium octaborate tetrahydrate diffuses deep into the wood, providing long-term protection. This penetrating ability also makes borate treatment to beetle-infested wood a good option.

pressure, or by using a soft-bristled paint brush. If there are only scattered patches of infestation, treat only the infested boards. Avoid overtreating (e.g., if the solution runs off or puddles), particularly on hardwood floors laid over asphalt paper or asphalt-based mastic. The asphalt will be dissolved by excess oil and may bleed through the finished floor. Any excess solution should be wiped up immediately. Be careful not to mar the surface if the finish has been temporarily softened by the spray.

Homeowners should be informed that residual applications take time to work, and that they can expect to see more emergence holes and frass produced. However, activity will cease in time as reinfestation ceases.

When it is impossible to control powderpost beetles via insecticidal sprays, it is necessary to resort to fumigation. For example, fumigation is necessary when the beetles have moved into walls and other inaccessible areas. Thus, the entire building is covered with gasproof tarpaulins and fumigated with a gas, such as sulfuryl fluoride (see product labels). Such fumigations should be done only by professionals thoroughly trained in the use of gases. Detailed directions, as well as instruction, can be obtained from the product manufacturers. Chapter 20 of this book discusses fumigation in more detail.

If the **old house borer** is to be managed, management programs involve only the treatment of softwoods to which this pest is restricted. Infestations of this beetle often involve extensive excavations, and larvae may be considerable distances from the obvious points of infestation. If the infestation is too widespread for spot treating with residual sprays, fumigation may be necessary. Other **long-horned beetles** require no management.

The presence of **ambrosia**, **bark**, and **timber beetles** is an incidental occurrence, and the number of beetles emerging is generally small. Such situations seldom require treatment because reinfestation is rare, although the killing of emerging beetles using some type of knockdown insecticide is sometimes desirable.

Buprestid beetles also do not require management because, like the long-horned beetles and bark beetles, they infest dead or dying trees before the wood is processed, and if they do emerge after construction, they do not reinfest the seasoned wood.

Wharf borer management, in situations where replacement of structural members is not necessary, requires the use of a wood preservative either alone or in combination with an insecticide. The fungicidal properties of these materials will combat the rot organisms that are virtually always associated with this insect. The toxicant should be injected into the infested wood under pressure. Replacement of damaged lumber should be done only with pressure-treated lumber. It is also important to remember that the correction of excessive moisture in infested wood is a prerequisite to any use of insecticides. If emerging adults are creating a nuisance, repeated use of a quick knockdown contact spray, such as synergized pyrethrins, will result in effective management.

When wood-boring beetles infest furniture or other movable articles, one of the most effective and rapid means of management is vault fumigation. If a vault is not available, infested articles can be wrapped in tarps and then fumigated. Another proven tactic is to subject the infested materials to dry heat, as mentioned earlier in this chapter. This type of treatment must be approached with caution, since it may result in warping of the wood or damage to the finish. Rustic furniture can be dipped in solutions of appropriately labeled insecticides.

WOOD DECAY

Decay of wood in buildings is a problem in moist, humid parts of the United States. Moisture in some form is necessary for the growth of fungi that cause rot. A fungus sends minute threads, called mycelia, through damp wood, taking its food from the wood as it grows. The visible body of the fungus is on the outside surface of the wood. This is called the fruiting body, and, when mature, it produces millions of tiny spores (seeds) that are present in the air and soil.

Two major types of fungi can attack wood: (1) **surface molds** and (2) **rot fungi**. Fungi that color the wood green, grey, pink, orange, black, or blue are called surface molds, mildews, and sap or blue stain fungi. They do not reduce the strength of the wood they grow on. The decay or rot fungi either bleach wood or make it brown and crumbly. They do reduce the strength of the wood and can be as destructive as termites and other wood-destroying insects (many of which are also attracted to moist wood).

The surface molds and stain fungi grow more rapidly than decay fungi and often appear on wood during construction. Fungus growth will not continue after construction if the wood dries out. However, the presence of stain fungi indicates that conditions at one time were suitable for decay, and an inspection using a moisture meter should be conducted to see if the wood is still moist enough to support decay fungi.

Most decay fungi grow only on wood subject to wetting by contact with moist soil, rain, or faulty plumbing. The fungus, Poria incrassata, however, can actually conduct water directly to wood and thus cause severe damage to wood even though the wood is not exposed directly to moisture (see Figure 8.26, following page 254).

It is most important to point out that the application of fungicides or insecticides to fungus-infested wood or soil will not stop the wood decay. Only by eliminating the moisture source can wood decay be completely controlled. Therefore, the application of chemicals by pest management professionals is of minor importance in fungus management. The first step in correcting a fungus condition is to determine the source of moisture and eliminate it if possible. All badly rotted wood should be removed and replaced with sound, dry

Decay Fungi Common in Structures

White rot gives wood a white bleached appearance. The strength of the wood decreases gradually until it becomes spongy to the touch and stringy when broken.

Brown rot turns wood brown and breaks it into brown cubical pieces with cracks perpendicular to the wood grain. It is the principal cause of building decay in the United States, and it causes rapid loss of strength in infested wood.

Water-conducting fungi (*Poria spp.*) are recognized by papery white-yellow mycelial fans and dirty white to black rootlike structures, called rhizomorphs, that can conduct water up to 25 feet from a moisture source to the wood. Thus, this fungus can attack wood that other fungi cannot, and it can destroy large amounts of wood in 1 to 2 years.

lumber. When it is not possible to eliminate the source of moisture entirely, the replacement lumber should be pressure treated with a wood preservative before installation. Treated wood should also be used where the timber will contact the soil or be driven into the ground.

When wood is used in the construction of a building, it should be well seasoned, so that it does not contain enough natural moisture to support decay fungi. Wood should not be used in those parts of construction where it can be moistened by wet soil. In extremely wet or humid areas, construction lumber is frequently treated with preservative chemicals to prevent fungus damage.

Wood in unventilated crawlspaces under houses is subject to much dampness. Condensation of water after evaporation from soil is the most common source of liquid water and subsequent decay problems in homes. The pest management professional can do much to relieve this situation by providing proper drainage and ventilation, installing a vapor barrier, and treating the wood.

Condensation— Its Role in Wood Decay

Condensation is free water or ice extracted from the atmosphere and deposited on any cold surface. The term *relative humidity* is a means of describing the amount of water vapor held by air. If water vapor is injected into air in an amount greater than the air can hold at that temperature, then the excess condenses into visible droplets.

In recent years, the shift in building practices—larger homes that are more airtight—has led to additional condensation problems. Energy conservation practices have increased the airtightness of buildings. Also, emphasis has been placed on the installation of humidifiers in heating units to create a more comfortable environment; however, the likelihood of moisture problems in wood has also increased. Finally, improperly installed insulation may contribute to moisture problems.

There are numerous sources of water vapor in buildings. Moisture produced from mopping floors, washing clothes, cooking, baking, and so forth, lead to an estimated 1 pound of water per day being introduced into the air of an average home. A poorly ventilated crawlspace may produce up to 100 pounds of water per day per 1,000 square feet. These moist environments are favorable for the survival and reproduction of decay fungi, termites, and other moisture-loving insects.

Measuring wood moisture (see Figure 8.27, following page 254) with a moisture meter is an important method to determine:

- whether wood has a moisture content (20% or above) that will lead to decay
- small changes in the moisture content of wood, to demonstrate the success of a moisture management program over time
- the likelihood of infestation or reinfestation by wood-boring insects
- whether fungi seen on the wood surface are still actively growing

The electric resistance of wood decreases as its moisture content increases. This is the basis for the operation of portable moisture meters. They measure the resistance between two needles inserted into wood and give a direct readout of moisture content. The higher the meter reading (decreasing electric resistance), the higher the amount of moisture in the wood. Moisture meter readings can be affected by the wood species involved, moisture distribution, grain direction, chemicals in the wood, weather conditions, and temperature. Thus, directions and information supplied with the meter must be understood and followed to ensure accurate readings.

Water should drain away from a properly constructed building. This is accomplished through proper grading, roof overhang, and the use of gutters, downspouts, and drain tile. Proper grading should be taken care of before construction and is usually an expensive task if done later. The other methods should be used to move water away from the foundation walls. It is also important that condensation (e.g., from air conditioners) be properly drained. Indoors, dehumidifiers should be used where moisture in the air is likely to be a problem.

Proper ventilation in crawlspaces can be obtained by installing 1 square foot of opening for each 25 linear feet of wall. These openings should be located so as to provide cross ventilation. The opening should be unobstructed. Where screening, wire mesh, or louvers are used, the total opening should be greater than 1 square foot per 25 feet of wall.

Attic vents are recommended at the rate of 1 square foot of vent for every 150 to 300 square feet of attic floor space. Vents should be located both near the ridge and at the eaves to induce airflow. Where louvered openings cannot be used, globe ventilators, fan exhaust ventilators, or special flues incorporated in a chimney may be best. Inlet openings under the cornice or roof overhang are required in all cases. Flat roofs where the same framing is used for ceiling and roof require openings

Toxic Mold

Some fungi can be harmful to humans through the production of toxins and allergens. Those that produce allergens in fungal spores or hyphae (vegetative parts) can trigger allergic reactions and asthma attacks in sensitive individuals, and cause "hay fever" in persons who are not allergic to them. *Stachybotrys chartarum*, "toxic black mold," is a greenish-black, wet-looking surface mold that develops on wood which has been very wet for at least two days. It is suspected as the causal agent in certain acute lung conditions, and also causes allergic reactions in sensitive individuals.

This funcus is not a wood-destroying organism, and pest management professionals are not usually qualified to inspect for, identify, or remediate this fungus. All of these steps require a lot of special expertise and lab support.

between each joist. Any opening provided should be screened and protected from the weather.

Installation of a vapor barrier on the soil surface of unexcavated areas will cause soil moisture to condense on the barrier and return to the soil rather than condense on the floor and joists above. Adequate barriers can be made by covering the soil with roofing paper or 4-mil to 6-mil polyethylene sheets. Proper installation of these barriers is essential; a small portion of the soil surface should be left uncovered. This will allow wood in the crawlspace to dry slowly, minimizing warping and cracking. Inspection 1 to 3 weeks after installation will allow for proper adjustments of the vapor barrier so that the wood can slowly recover from the excess moisture.

When moisture problems result from poorly constructed or poorly maintained buildings, these problems have to be corrected before wood decay management can begin. Such problems as faulty roofing, siding, plumbing, and so forth, usually require the services of other specialists. If the source of moisture is removed and the wood dries out, decay will be stopped.

SUPPLEMENTARY READING MATERIAL

Bennett, G. W., and J. M. Owens, eds. *Advances in Urban Pest Management*. New York: Van Nostrand Reinhold, 1986. 399 pp.

Hickin, N. E. *The Insect Factor in Wood Decay*. London and New York: Hutchinson, 1963. 336 pp.

Krishna, K., and F. M. Weesner, eds. *Biology of Termites*. Vol. I. New York: Academic Press, 1969. 598 pp.

Krishna, K., and F. M. Weesner, eds. *Biology of Termites*. Vol. II. New York: Academic Press, 1970. 643 pp.

Levy, M. P. *A Guide to the Inspection of Existing Homes for Wood-Inhabiting Fungi and Insects*. U.S. Department of Housing and Urban Development, Washington, D. C., 1975. 104 pp.

Mallis, A. *Handbook of Pest Control*. Mallis Handbook & Technical Training Co. 1997, 1,453 pp.

Mampe, C. D., ed. *Wood Decay in Structures and Its Control*. Dunn Loring, Va.: NPMA, 1974. 28 pp.

Moore, H. B. *Wood-Inhabiting Insects in Houses: Their Identification, Biology, Prevention and Control*. U.S. Department of Housing and Urban Development, Washington, D.C., 1979. 133 pp.

Weesner, F. M. *The Termites of the United States*. Dunn Loring, Va.: NPMA, 1965. 70 pp.

Williams, L. H., and H. R. Johnston. *Controlling Wood Destroying Beetles in Buildings and Furniture*. USDA leaflet no. 558, Washington, D.C., 1973. 8 pp.

CHAPTER 9 | Ants and Other Hymenopterous Pests

Ants are among the most successful of insects, and many pest control firms consider them the most important household pest in terms of business opportunity…and challenge. Like termites, they are social insects and live in colonies. However, ants evolved this social behavior separately from termites, and these two groups are not closely related. Ant colonies include a collection of workers, one or more reproductives, eggs, larvae, and pupae. Ant colonies build structures called nests, which typically require much effort by the worker ants in the colony to maintain. Many species prefer to nest in the ground; others will be found in wood, such as dead logs, fence posts, hollow trees, or even wood within structures. When ants nest in wood, their damage will usually be much less than that caused by termites, because ants will only hollow out a nest gallery. Unlike termites, ants do not eat wood and cannot digest cellulose. Nests afford the ants considerable protection from their enemies, some protection against extremes of weather, and some proximity to their food, water, and other resources. There is practically no food item (besides cellulose) that will not be eaten by some species of ant, and most species will eat a variety of foods.

GENERAL CHARACTERISTICS

Ants usually have distinctly elbowed antennae, in which the first segment, closest to the head, is called the scape (see Figures 9.1 and 9.2). It is followed by a series of much smaller segments, and in some species the last two or three segments are enlarged into a more or less recognizable shape referred to as a club.

The first one or two segments of the abdomen, where it attaches to the thorax, are much smaller than those that make up the rest of this body region, which is called the gaster. This typically gives ants

their rather thin-waisted appearance (see Figure 9.1). This thin waist is properly known as the abdominal pedicel. The pedicel may consist of one or two segments, and each segment is somewhat enlarged on the upper surface. This enlargement may vary in shape from a slight hump to a rather high, flattened, plate-like structure. When trying to identify ants, it is very important to become familiar with the shape and segmentation of the pedicel, which is sometimes called the node. It is an important characteristic used to separate ant species and identify ants from other types of insects.

Adult male and female ants of many species are winged, as are adult termites. In ants, the front pair of wings are always longer and wider than the hind pair. When at rest, they extend only slightly beyond the tip of the abdomen.

The mandibles are the most conspicuous of an ant's mouthparts. They are supplied with well-devel-

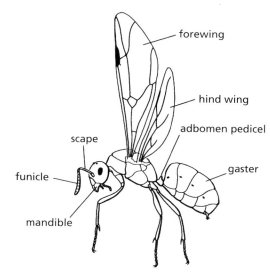

FIGURE 9.1. An illustration of an ant, showing body parts. (Provonsha)

FIGURE 9.2. Adult worker ants, showing elbowed antennae typical of ant workers. (Myers)

oped musculature and, in the workers, are used to carry and break up food, to excavate nests in wood or the ground, and to attack or defend the nest from enemies.

Ant antennae are especially important organs for the senses of taste and touch, and they have many sensory cells and spines. They are thus useful for detecting and tasting food. Ants are known to use a number of chemical pheromones to communicate between individuals within the same colony, and these are also sensed primarily through the antennae. These may be trail pheromones, sex pheromones, alarm pheromones, or other types, and they are generally produced by specialized glands located in the abdomen. Many of these pheromones are actually blends of different chemicals and are deposited or used in very tiny amounts. Often, as ants from different colonies or the same colony encounter one another in the field, various antennal touching and stroking behaviors occur between the different ants as a form of recognition. Thus, the antennae through which these mechanical and chemical communication signals are received are very important to ants.

Most structure-infesting ants either do not have the ability to sting or retain it only to a limited degree. However, many ants from the tropical regions, some of which have been introduced into the United States, are particularly serious pests because of their ability to sting. This sting involves piercing of the skin with the ovipositor, a structure located in the tip of the abdomen of females. Venom secreted by a gland associated with the ovipositor not only creates rapid, intense pain but also may cause serious, even life-threatening, allergic reactions in some people.

Distinguishing Ants

Though most ants are easily recognized, there are a few other insects that strongly resemble ants. Some of the winged ants also resemble winged termites, and it is very important for pest management professionals to make this distinction correctly in the field when inspecting premises where a flight of swarmers has emerged. The four characteristics to positively distinguish winged ants from winged termites in the field are as follows:

- The front pair of wings on ants is noticeably larger than the hind pair, while all four wings on termites are nearly the same size.
- Termite wings are not clear but have a milky, translucent appearance. Most ant wings will appear quite clear when held up to light.
- Ants usually have a thin-waisted appearance, because of the modified abdominal segments called the pedicel. Termites have a broad-waisted appearance, because they have no pedicel.
- Ant antennae are elbowed and have the first segment elongated into a scape. Termites have straight antennae, and all the segments are beadlike.

The thin waist and elbowed antennae are also good characteristics to help identify winged or nonwinged ants from other small insects of otherwise similar appearance. A hand lens is often needed to see these characteristics in the field. Many professionals also have dissecting microscopes at their offices to help positively identify insect specimens, as an aid to deciding the most appropriate control strategy in each situation.

BIOLOGY

Ants have a complete metamorphosis comprised of four stages: **egg**, **larva**, **pupa**, and **adult** (see Figure 9.3). Eggs are almost microscopic in size and vary in shape according to species. Larvae that hatch from the eggs are very soft, pear or gourd shaped, legless, and off-white in color. The head and mouthparts are at the narrow end of the body. Adult workers that tend the nest will move the eggs, larvae, and pupae around within the nest and feed and groom the larvae. After several days to some weeks of feeding, during which time several molts are completed, the larvae will enter the pupal stage. Pupae resemble an adult ant but are soft, white, and do not move about or feed. In some species, all of the pupae are naked, while in others, they are enclosed in silk cocoons. In still others, some pupae

FIGURE 9.3. Four stages of the ant life cycle are shown, including (from left to right) egg, larva, pupa, and adult. (Myers)

may be naked while others will be in cocoons. Pupae, especially those in cocoons, are often called "ant eggs." When an ant colony nesting in the soil or under a stone or board is disturbed, worker ants can be seen scurrying about carrying these pupae, but close inspection will reveal that the smaller larvae and the very tiny eggs are also being carried out of sight, away from the intruding source of danger. Eggs and small larvae are often stuck together and moved as a single clump.

Adults require several days to attain complete maturity after emergence from pupae. During this period the body of the adult hardens and attains mature color. From 4 to 8 weeks, or sometimes more, are required for development from the egg to the adult stage. This development time varies according to environmental factors, such as temperature, food abundance, and disturbances.

Ants live in colonies and have a well-developed caste system for the division of labor between adult forms. In many common species, the colony is established by a newly mated queen, who sheds her wings and digs a small gallery or seeks a small cavity under a stone, a piece of bark, or some recess within a structure to start the nest. The queen seals herself in this cell and remains nearly dormant while the first group of eggs develop in her body. When mature, the eggs are laid and hatch in the sealed nest cell. Inside her body, the queen's flight muscles are reabsorbed to provide energy for this long period before workers will be available to forage for food and feed the queen along with the rest of the colony. The queen nurses and feeds the first group of larvae until they pupate. Workers developing from these first eggs are always undersized due to the relatively small food supply available to them. Workers of the first brood dig an opening out of the nest gallery and begin to forage for food, both for themselves and the queen. With an additional supply of food available,

the queen is then able to lay more eggs. Workers, all sterile females, care for the new eggs, larvae, and pupae in each succeeding generation.

The success rate for colony founding is very low due to environmental extremes, competition within species, predation, and other factors. Successful colonies of many species often take more than one season to develop populations large enough to even be noticed. It will often take a year or two for colonies to develop to the point where substantial numbers of new males and queens are formed. These are usually winged forms called alates, or **swarmers**, which are capable of reproducing. As the colony develops, these alates leave the nest at suitable times to mate. Queens then establish new colonies. Mature colonies will continue to produce groups of swarmers as well as sufficient numbers of workers to keep the colony healthy and well protected, sometimes for many seasons. In some species there may be multiple queens in a mature colony, while others will have only one queen laying eggs. If the queen should die at some time after the colony has become well established, a worker or one of the other female reproductives can sometimes begin to produce eggs and take over this function in the colony. Mating with a male reproductive is required for viable eggs to be produced by this new queen.

Ant colonies normally have three distinct adult castes: workers, reproductive females (queens), and reproductive males. As stated earlier, **workers** are sterile females and may vary considerably in size. When all the workers in a colony are basically the same size, the colony is called monomorphic. When different sizes are present, the colony is termed polymorphic. Sometimes the division of labor, such as nest tending, defending, or foraging, will be assumed by workers of these different sizes. Some workers will have specific tasks suited to their specially adapted features. In other species or situations, younger workers tend the nest or do other tasks closer to the colony, while the older workers serve as foragers.

Queens are generally the largest individuals in the colony. Unmated queens usually retain their wings, while the mated queens do not. After development of the first group of eggs, the queen is cleaned, fed, and otherwise cared for by the workers, so her primary function becomes egg laying. However, for colonies with only one producing queen, she also produces pheromones that serve to maintain her dominance over the colony and coordinate colony development and function. Where there are multiple queens contributing to reproduction within a colony, patterns of pheromone production and effect will be more complex.

Males perform no function other than to

inseminate potential queens. In those species that have winged queens, males will also have wings. The male dies within a few days of mating. Mating may take place in the nest, on the ground, or in the air. Adult males do not remain in the nest long, and many are killed by predators and the elements without mating.

FEEDING HABITS

Some ant species feed on a wide variety of food items, while others typically feed on a rather narrow range of foods. Food preferences may also change significantly during the course of a season, especially for outdoor species, or depending on the specific needs of the colony. Periods of high egg production typically require foraging ants to bring back proteins to the queen or queens, while at other times foragers may prefer to gather sugars or greases for their own energy needs or to promote larval growth.

Adults are unable to ingest hard, solid food particles. They ingest only liquids, which are sucked from the food material, or smaller particles in suspension. However, they can carry large food items in their mandibles, with or without help from other workers. The youngest larvae must be fed on liquids, and liquid food is used for all larval instars in some species. In many other species, older larvae are fed small food particles, which they are able to ingest. Foraging ants bring food or water back to the colony and pass it to other nest-tending workers by a mouth-to-mouth process called trophallaxis. Nest-tending workers then pass the food to larvae or the queens. Workers may stimulate larvae to regurgitate liquid food for use within the colony. Thus, there is often a rather complex pattern of food transfer, or flow, within the colony. The direction of this flow is basically toward the larvae and reproductives. Because of this food flow, ant baits that include a nonrepellent and slow-acting toxicant in a suitable food bait formulation are very useful and effective. Foraging workers will feed on the bait and not be killed before they pass it along to other colony members, allowing complete colony kill.

In nature, many ants obtain energy-rich sugar by feeding on the sugary honeydew excreted by aphids or other sucking insects on plants. Some ants tend, and even defend, these other insects as a food resource. Thus, controlling honeydew-producing insects on plants inside the home or around the foundation may be an important factor in decreasing the presence of such ants inside.

Dead insects, earthworms, and other organisms are frequently scavenged. Live insects may be preyed on. Indoors, dead flies and gnats can be found on windowsills and in light fixtures, so these are good areas to place ant bait or to apply a residual insecticide spray or dust. Some ants, such as leaf-cutting ants, actually cut, strip, and carry away plant leaf tissue. This leaf material is carried into the nest mound and used as a substrate to grow fungi, on which the ants feed. Other ants typically gather seeds as food.

To date, no universally effective ant bait has been developed. This is because there are so many pest species, with variable food preferences and highly discriminating feeding behaviors. The feeding preferences of any particular colony infesting a premise will also vary depending on the season, the nature of the other food resources available, and many other factors. Development of a truly universal ant bait is an unlikely prospect, but advances in bait formulation technology for ants have been made and this is an active area of research for bait manufacturers and urban entomology researchers.

ECONOMIC IMPORTANCE

Ants may affect us adversely by stinging or biting; invading and contaminating food; nesting in lawns, golf courses, or within premises; stealing seeds from seed beds or feeding on germinating seeds; defoliating or gnawing into plants and plant products; fostering other injurious insects (e.g., aphids or scale insects on ornamental plants); gnawing holes in various types of fabrics; removing rubber insulation from telephone wires or other equipment; killing young poultry, birds, livestock, or game; simply annoying humans and animals with their presence; and possibly transmitting certain human diseases after crawling over sputum, feces, carrion, and so forth. Some carpenter ants can cause serious structural damage to wooden structures. However, only a small number of all the ant species are damaging or medically significant due to their stinging behavior, and require control because of these factors. Most species are neutral or nondamaging, and some are beneficial predators on other pests (e.g., red imported fire ants depress tick populations in many areas). Thus, control programs are usually necessary because ants are simply a nuisance that homeowners or others do not want to accept. Apart from their economic importance, the ants are considered by some experts to be the most important group of living organisms in terrestrial habitats, from an ecological perspective.

IDENTIFICATION OF PEST SPECIES

Because of the wide variations in feeding and other habits of different ant species, their successful management often requires exact identification of the species involved. This knowledge allows the professional to gain accurate information about the species from reference books or other sources, to better understand its behavior, where it is probably coming from, and what type of bait material it should respond to. Most ant keys are designed for use with specimens of the workers, or foragers, but not the winged forms. The pictorial key in Figure 9.4 allows tentative identification of most common household pest species. Refer to specific descriptions in this chapter to help further determine the species involved. The key is designed as an aid in identifying common structure-infesting ants, but it does not include every ant species that can be found around buildings, or the many ants that may be found outdoors in lawns or other areas. Pest management professionals should be aware that some 30 or more ant species have been observed in and around structures, of which most can be considered pests.

MAJOR PEST SPECIES
Carpenter Ants
Camponotus spp.

Carpenter ants are among the most conspicuous of ants found in and around homes, being large and typically blackish or very dark bodied. Foraging workers have rather large mandibles with which they can bite or give a strong pinch. Workers vary greatly in size from 1/4- to about 3/4-inch long. Many species are black, perhaps with some faintly grayish bands on the abdomen; others may have some brown or reddish coloration along with the black, so that they appear distinctly two-toned (see Figures 9.5 to 9.9, following page 254). Two dozen species are known in the United States, and various species occur throughout the United States, with one or two primary pest species in the Midwest and Northeast, and one or two primary species along the West Coast. In the western states, the same species found in the East and Midwest typically occur at higher altitudes, while other species are found nearer to sea level. About 13 other species that infest buildings may be encountered. Depending on the species, some may be common, but most are not often seen inside homes.

Carpenter ants will establish nests in a number of different locations. Outdoor sites include stumps, hollow logs, telephone poles, fence posts, or other similar large pieces of wood. Wood that is moist or partially decayed is preferred by many species, especially in the northeastern United States; however, cracks, crevices, and other cavities may be used to start a nest in sound wood. Ants may be carried into homes in firewood or enter and

establish colonies via other routes. Often ants move into a building solely to feed. Among the other methods, foragers often simply enter homes via tree limbs or wires that touch the house. Therefore, the nest, which is the source of infestation, may or may not be in the home itself. Most often, the primary nest, where the queen is located, will be away from the home or other infested structure, while nests located within the structure will be secondary, or satellite nests, where no egg-laying queen is present. Indoor nests may be found in hollow doors, windowsills, porch substructures, roofs, baseboards, fireplaces, shingles, or other naturally hollow areas. The nest may also be just a hollow pipe with several hundred ants in it. In wooded areas where many carpenter ant colonies may be present around an infested home, more than one satellite nest, associated with different primary nests (and thus separate colonies), may be encountered. These biological factors can complicate and frustrate control programs.

Carpenter ants excavate nest galleries in wood. These galleries somewhat resemble the work of termites but can be distinguished by their entirely clean and almost sandpapered appearance (see Figure 9.10). They are frequently hollowed in moist or unsound wood, although carpenter ants can burrow in sound wood. Carpenter ants do not use wood for food. Carpenter ants cut galleries with the wood grain and prefer to follow softer areas of the wood. The galleries are generally smooth and clean—hence the name carpenter ant. Some of the harder wood layers often remain as walls separating the many tunnels. Openings are cut in these walls at frequent intervals to provide passageways for movement from section to section of the nest gallery. Access to the outside may be through natural cracks or openings in the wood. Sometimes, however, the ants cut special openings, which are called **windows**.

Winged reproductive forms swarm primarily in the spring, but they may also do so at other times of the year. Under some conditions, winged males may appear indoors as early as warm spells during February or March; but the females tend to emerge later. Once new colonies begin to mature, several sizes and forms of adult ants will be found in the nest. There is usually only one egg-laying queen per colony. The colony is said to be mature when winged reproductives, or alates, are formed. This takes three to six years for most colonies, at which time 2,000 to 3,000 (or more) individuals will be present. There is seldom any further increase in numbers, due to the constant drain of the many swarmers produced each year. Alates may be produced at any time, but usually develop in the late summer. They swarm after spending the winter in

A PICTORIAL KEY TO COMMON HOUSEHOLD ANT WORKERS

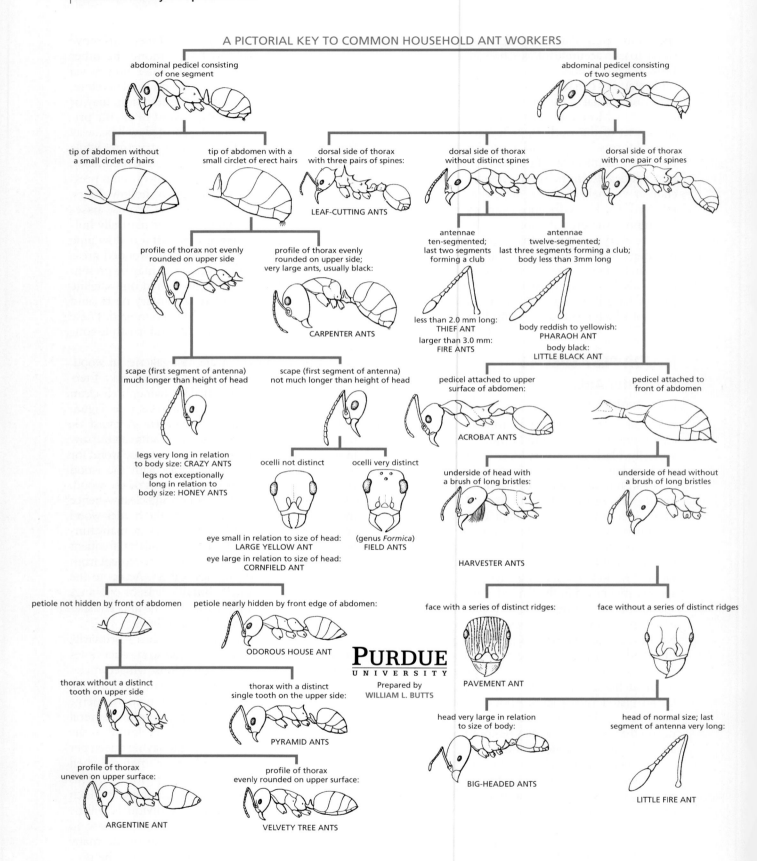

FIGURE 9.4. A pictorial key to common household ant workers. (Purdue; drawing by Provonsha)

FIGURE 9.10. Carpenter ant damage as nest galleries in wood. Note clean galleries, which contain no mud-mastic material typical of subterranean termite damage to wood. (Myers)

the nest. From 200 to 400 winged individuals may be produced each year in a mature colony.

The carpenter ant diet includes a great variety of both animal and plant foods. These ants will feed on other insects, living or dead, and nearly anything people eat. Aphid honeydew is particularly attractive. Many sweets and meats found in kitchens and storage areas are fed on, including syrup, honey, jelly, sugar, meat, grease, and fat.

Foraging ants will travel 100 yards or more from the nest for food, and they may wander throughout the house. Workers can lay down trail pheromones, at least on major foraging trails, but they are often seen scattered about and foraging without any noticeable effect of a trail pheromone. Food may be carried back to the nest, but more often is taken into the crop near to where it is found. Later, it is regurgitated in the nest for use by the queen, developing larvae, or the nonforaging workers.

Carpenter ants are of economic importance because of the damage they do to structures, the food they contaminate, and their unsightly and unwanted movement inside and outside of buildings. Their nesting activities can weaken building structures, although not usually as seriously as termites. This damage can often be considered primarily a symptom of water damage and wood decay, as they usually will not extend galleries far beyond this softened wood and into the sound wood of structures. This is particularly true for species found in the eastern and midwestern United States, but *Camponotus modoc* has been observed to do substantial structural damage in the Pacific Northwest.

Argentine Ant
Linepithema humile (Mayr)

The Argentine ant is a severe pest in the southern United States and in California (and in many other

parts of the world), although isolated occurrences have been reported in more northern areas of the United States. In areas of heavy infestation, it may be found in practically every home.

Workers are 1/12- to 1/8-inch long and are light to dark brown in color (see Figure 9.11, following page 254). Queens are much larger, being up to 1/6- to 1/4-inch long. Many fertile queens are present in each nest. Mating usually takes place inside the nest, so winged forms are not usually found. In addition to laying eggs, queens also clean and feed themselves and are active in feeding and grooming immatures.

Nests are typically located in moist soil next to or under buildings, along sidewalks, or beneath boards and plants, and they are usually near sources of both water and food. Occasionally these ants may nest within a structure or other locations not typically considered soil related, such as under a bathtub set above a slab-on-grade foundation, under the cracks or expansion joints of slabs, under insulation in an exterior wall void, and in potted plants or flower boxes. Argentine ants prefer sweet foods, principally sugars, syrup, fruit juices, secretions of plants, and honeydew. Workers forage for food along regular paths extending out from the nest and branching out to explore every portion of an area. Foragers may enter houses in large numbers, particularly when conditions outside the building become too wet or too dry. Their foraging range is often sufficient that the nests may be located on properties adjacent to the client's yard and home, thus complicating effective control efforts (that typically rely on eradication of colonies at the nests).

This ant is well adapted to urban and suburban environments and will persist where other species do not thrive. It may be the only ant species present in many locations. Workers are very aggressive and often eliminate other ants in an area. However, different Argentine ant colonies can coexist in the same area, so the number of colonies per unit area may be quite high. Other research on the genetic relatedness (or variation) between Argentine ants in certain regions has suggested that colonies of this species may be extremely large, and cover large areas—even referred to as "super colonies." Effective control or suppression of Argentine ants in such regions can be very difficult.

Fire Ants
Solenopsis spp.

Many of the ants of this genus are called fire ants because their venom, injected by a stinger, causes intense irritation and may cause severe reactions and even death in especially sensitive people. Fire ants are very active and aggressive and may kill young wildlife or produce sores and nausea in humans. Four species are commonly found as pests in the United States: the southern fire ant, *Solenopsis xyloni* McCook; the fire ant, *Solenopsis geminata* (Fabricius); the red imported fire ant, *Solenopsis invicta* Buren; and the black imported fire ant, *Solenopsis richteri* Forel.

The **southern fire ant** (*S. xyloni*) is found in the southern states, from the Atlantic coast to California. The abdomen is brown to black, and usually the head and part of the thorax are yellow or reddish. Workers are 1/15- to 1/4-inch long (see Figure 9.12, following page 254). Nests usually occur in loose soil, although they may also occur in the woodwork or masonry of houses. Nest entrances may be craters in the ground scattered over an area of from 2 to 4 square feet or under boards and stones, by a tuft of grass, in cracks in concrete, or underneath houses. Foragers collect a variety of foods, including meat, grease, butter, nuts, seeds, and vegetables.

The **fire ant** (*S. geminata*) is also found in coastal areas of the southern United States, particularly in Florida. Workers are highly variable in color and have habits similar to those of the other fire ants.

The **red imported fire ant** (*S. invicta*) is an important agricultural, urban, and suburban pest that typically nests in the soil and makes characteristic earthen mounds. It is found in the coastal plain area of the southern states, from South Carolina along the Atlantic coast into northern and central Florida, across the southern states, and into much of the eastern half of Texas. It is also established in the urban and coastal areas of Southern California. Its northern distribution is limited by the severity of winter conditions, such that it is not found in areas where moderate to hard frosts are common during winters. Its presence in lawns, parks, cemeteries, athletic fields, and similar areas brings it into direct conflict with people, where its aggressive stinging behavior makes it intolerable in most situations. When mounds of this species are disturbed, workers appear to boil or swarm out of the ground in very aggressive defensive behavior. They will sting any intruding animal repeatedly. Workers are dark reddish-brown in color and may be found in two basic sizes, called major and minor workers, which are 1/15- to 1/4-inch long (see Figure 9.13, following page 254). Typical yards contain several mounds, and larger yards may contain several dozen.

S. invicta has been found to have either one reproductively active queen per colony, called a monogynous colony, or many reproductively active queens, termed a polygynous colony. Each mound may be inhabited by a separate colony (which will typically be a monogynous colony), or one colony may occupy several distinct mounds, which are connected by underground foraging tunnels. In some areas the home range of large polygynous colonies can be very difficult for researchers to determine, and the ranges of individual colonies can overlap. Thus, some researchers consider that from genetic, behavioral, and territorial perspectives, the concept of distinct colonies has become blurred. Control may be more difficult in areas where multiple-queen colonies are found.

Large colonies can have up to 300,000 to 500,000 workers that forage over an area with a radius of more than 100 yards. Fire ants are both predators and scavengers, attacking and killing other insects and small animals or feeding on dead animals. They also feed on honeydew, certain parts of plants or plant secretions, and other sweet materials. Occasionally, this species will nest inside homes or institutional buildings such as hospitals or nursing homes, especially in the winter under bathtubs (which often have access to bare soil through the slab, under the tub), next to hot water heaters, or near other sources of warmth. Colonies have been found nesting and foraging on the upper floors of hospitals or other such buildings.

The **black imported fire ant** (*S. richteri*) is similar to the other three fire ant species in behavior but is a darker brown color. It is now restricted to a small area around the northern end of the border between Mississippi and Alabama. Once quite common in the southern United States, it has been displaced by competition from the preceding species (especially *S. invicta*).

Thief Ant
Solenopsis molesta (Say)

This is one of the smallest household ants, being from 1/25- to 1/15-inch long. Workers vary in color from yellow to dirty brown and have a two-segmented antennal club (see Figure 9.14, following page 254). Thief ants are found over most of the United States. They often live in nests of larger ants, where they may feed on the larvae of their hosts, thereby earning their common name. Their chief foods in homes are greasy materials, such as cheese and meats, although they occasionally feed on sweets. Bacon, ham, and other prepared meats are especially attractive to thief ants. They may feed on stored seeds and dead animals.

This ant is so small that it may often escape notice around kitchen sink and cabinet areas. Unobservant people may complain about the flavor of food without realizing that it is infested with thief ants. The ant usually comes in from outdoors, but it may nest in cracks and crevices of walls or cabinets and commonly beneath tile countertops in kitchens. They can be very persistent and difficult to control.

Pharaoh Ant
Monomorium pharaonis (Linnaeus)

Pharaoh ants are light yellowish to reddish-brown in color, with workers measuring 1/15- to 1/12-inch long (see Figure 9.15, following page 254). They are found in localized regions throughout most of the United States and parts of southern Canada. They have become a common pest in many areas and an important source of business for pest management firms. Pharaoh ants can be easily distinguished from thief ants by the presence of three segments in the antennal club. They are an important ant pest in homes, apartments, hotels, grocery stores, restaurants, hospitals, nursing homes, and other facilities throughout much of their range. Their small size, which enables them to get into almost anything, and their very wide food preferences combine to make pharaoh ants difficult to eliminate from structures in many cases.

Nests are rarely found but occur between walls, under floors, above ceilings, behind baseboards and switch plates, in old trash, in folded bathroom linens, or outside in gardens and along walks (see Figure 9.16). Pharaoh ants nest on porous substrates in warm places near furnaces, heat ducts, and hot water pipes that are also near moist conditions or open sources of water. Ants range widely from their nests, usually over established trails marked by trail pheromones. Workers are frequently seen trailing along windowsills, countertops, and baseboards.

In the warmer climates of the southern United States, pharaoh ants are frequently found foraging and nesting on the outside of buildings or in adjacent landscape areas. This is especially true in humid regions or where other sources of constant moisture, such as sprinkler systems and evaporative cooling units (e.g., on rooftops), are present. Under such circumstances, inspections and control programs must be extended beyond the interior portions of the building. In areas where severe winters and cool or cold nights during the summer prevail, pharaoh ants are unlikely to be found foraging and nesting outdoors.

Pharaoh ants will feed on such a diverse array of materials that use of the term *food preferences* seems inappropriate. However, substances like syrups, fruit juice, honey, jelly, cakes, pies, greases, dead insects, or meats and blood are frequently fed on. In hospitals they will often feed on blood and other bodily fluids, medical waste, or intravenous feeding fluids.

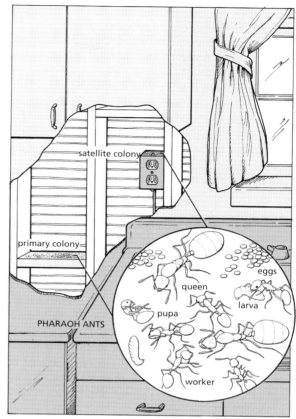

FIGURE 9.16. While pharaoh ants are typically found foraging in kitchens or other areas where open water (moisture) and food sources are available, their nests may or may not be close by to these resources and are rarely found by the pest control professional. (Shuster and Provonsha)

Even though several very effective bait formulations are available for pharaoh ant control, this ant can be very persistent and difficult to control. It has a tendency to appear suddenly in various places within a structure. Its tendency to forage over wide areas and to nest in well-protected or -hidden areas contributes to control difficulties. In addition, attempts to control this species with spray or dust applications indoors, or the occurrence of other forms of stress on the colony or colonies, will frequently cause the colonies to split into subcolonies that scatter to other locations within the structure. This behavioral process is called **budding** and is commonly observed of this species, which makes it an especially difficult pest to control.

Pharaoh ant colonies may be very large, with tens or hundreds of thousands of workers and many queens. Moderate- to large-sized colonies will frequently bud to form numerous subcolonies, as a queen or queens and a group of workers carrying brood will move away from the larger colony and begin a new colony unit. This colony may or may not become a distinct unit, as workers may switch between different colonies or subcolonies.

The mature sexual forms are winged but do not fly, so swarms are never seen. Mating occurs in the nest and throughout the year. Occasionally, when a particularly good food resource is found, especially close to the nest, some queens can be seen traveling to and from the food location. Typically, however, the queens remain in the nest and are not seen or, importantly, cannot be controlled without use of an effective bait that the foragers must bring back to the nest and feed to the queens.

Little Black Ant
Monomorium minimum (Buckley)

This is a very small (1/15-inch long), jet-black ant found in all states (see Figure 9.17, following page 254). Nests are normally located outdoors in relatively open areas. These ants will also nest in rotten wood, woodwork, and masonry of buildings. Colonies have multiple queens and may become very large. Most of their feeding is on plant secretions, but they will occasionally invade houses in search of food. Once inside, they feed on sweets, meats, breads, grease, vegetables, and fruit.

Big-Headed Ants
Pheidole spp.

The soldiers of these ants, which are workers that serve strictly a defensive function, have exceptionally large heads in relation to their body size—hence the common name for these ants (see Figure 9.18, following page 254). The minor workers do not have enlarged heads but can be recognized by the shape of their heads, which narrow abruptly behind the eyes (see Figure 9.19, following page 254). These ants are found in warmer and drier sections of the United States and have very similar habits to fire ants. Nests are found in exposed soil or under cover, and in rotting wood. They rarely nest indoors but may invade homes to forage for food. They prefer meats, grease, and breads. They superficially resemble fire ants but can be distinguished from them by the presence of twelve segments in the antenna, with a three-segmented antennal club.

Pavement Ant
Tetramorium caespitum (Linnaeus)

This is a small (1/8- to 1/6-inch long) blackish-brown ant, with paler legs and antennae (see Figure 9.20, following page 254). The abdomen is all black. Readily visible on the head and thorax are parallel lines or ridges that do not differ in color from the cuticle but give the cuticle a grooved texture (see Figure 9.21, following page 254). There is a pair of small spines at the back of the thorax, and the body has a sparse array of small hairs all over it.

The pavement ant is common throughout the Atlantic coastal region and midwestern United States, and along the West Coast. It is an occasional pest in the southern United States. Nests are usually found outdoors under stones, next to buildings, and under cracks of pavement, although they are occasionally found in walls, under floors, and in insulation. Pavement ants can be a particular nuisance around homes with slab-on-grade construction. Foragers enter buildings through cracks in the slab and similar openings. This slow-moving ant enters buildings in search of food, with greasy and sweet materials being preferred.

Little Fire Ant
Wasmannia auropunctata (Roger)

This small tropical ant has become established in Florida and in California. It is about 1/15-inch long and reddish in color, and it characteristically moves around slowly. These ants are sensitive to cold, appearing only in the warmest weather. Their sting is very painful.

In the United States, little fire ants are rarely a serious household pest, being encountered by homeowners usually outside, most often in citrus trees and landscaped areas. They usually nest in exposed or covered soil, rotten wood, plant cavities, and trash, but only occasionally inside houses. When foraging indoors they prefer foods such as fats, peanut butter, and other oily materials.

Harvester Ants
Pogonomyrmex spp.

Harvester ants are comparatively large, red (see Figure 9.22, following page 254) to dark brown, or blackish ants (see Figure 9.23, following page 254) that range from 1/4- to 1/2-inch long. They can be recognized by the long hairs that form a "brush" under their heads. These hairs are used to clean their legs and antennae, carry water, and remove sand during excavation of the nest. Harvester ants are most often found in warmer and drier regions of the West and South, but one eastern species, found in Florida, may be encountered. They are normally found in fields or in lawns, where they clear large areas of vegetation around their nest openings and gather seeds that they store in their burrows. They will only rarely invade the home. Their severe stings make them pests when they occur in lawns, parks, or athletic fields.

Leaf-Cutter Ants
Atta spp.

Leaf-cutter ants remove foliage from vegetation and carry it back to the nest. Leaf fragments are chewed and added to large underground fungus gardens that provide the colony's food. It is quite possible for them to remove all of the leaves or needles from a tree in a single night. In the United States, leaf-cutter ants occur in Texas (where they are called cut ants), Louisiana, and Arizona. The reddish or rust-colored workers range from 1/12- to 1/2-inch in length (see Figure 9.24, following page 254), but the winged reproductives can be 1-1/4 inch or longer. The dorsal part of the thorax has at least three pairs of spines.

Leaf-cutter ants nest in well-drained sand or loamy soils. Mounds are formed in the shape of a large funnel. The nest is often 10- to 12-feet deep and may cover 1/4 acre. This nesting behavior also results in these ants being called town ants in some areas. They never nest indoors but may enter houses while foraging, often to carry away seeds. Workers travel well-defined trails that may extend some distance from the nesting area. Since the colony remains in one spot for several years, the foragers may be found traveling some distance from the nest.

Acrobat Ants
Crematogaster spp.

Ants of this genus hold their abdomen over their head and thorax when excited—hence the common name of acrobat ants. They range in color from yellowish-brown, to red-and-black, to black; and have a heart-shaped abdomen that is flattened on the upper side and curved below (see Figure 9.25, following page 254). They are not normally found in households but may wander inside from time to time in search of food. Some species in this genus may be found in decayed or partially decayed wood and in such wood inside homes. They are seldom found in sound wood.

Odorous House Ant
Tapinoma sessile (Say)

The odorous house ant is a common household pest distributed nearly throughout the United States. It is a particularly common problem along the West Coast, Atlantic coastal and New England regions, and in the midsouthern region of the United States. Workers are 1/12- to 1/8-inch long and brownish-black in color (see Figure 9.26, following page 254). This ant is frequently confused

with the Argentine ant but can be easily distinguished by its darker color and the fact that the front of its abdomen overhangs and hides its flattened petiole. This ant gives off a very characteristic, pungent, and unpleasant odor when crushed.

Nests are located in a great variety of situations both indoors and outdoors. Outside, nests are usually shallow and found underneath a board or stone. Indoors, these ants frequently nest in walls and underneath floors. Colonies are large and usually contain many active queens. Workers forage along regular trails, and the food habits of odorous house ants and Argentine ants are similar. Odorous house ants tend to move indoors late in the year when honeydew, one of their primary foods, becomes less abundant. Honeydew availability may also be reduced at other times, such as during and just after periods of excessive rainfall. These ants may then range more widely for food, often causing them to enter homes.

Velvety Tree Ants
Liometopum spp.

Velvety tree ants are pests principally in California. They are easily identified by their glistening, velvety-black abdomen, red thorax, and brownish-black head (see Figure 9.27, following page 254). Their nests are located in old tree stumps, in cavities in trees, under tree bark, beneath stones on the ground, and, occasionally, within the walls or attics of homes. Foragers commonly enter homes, where they contaminate foods in the kitchen and seek other insects for food.

The California velvety tree ant, *Liometopum occidentale* Emery, is distributed widely throughout the state of California. It occurs in the foothills and mountains of southern California, and at lower levels in northern California. Foragers travel along trails and constantly ascend and descend trees, such as oaks and poplars, often at a considerable distance from the nest.

These ants tend honeydew-producing insects, such as aphids or scale insects, and also kill and eat other insects. They often invade picnic or outdoor barbecue areas, contaminating food, stinging people, and, when crushed, producing a foul odor similar to that of the odorous house ant. Their sting is quite painful, and the pain may persist for some time.

Pyramid Ants
Dorymyrmex spp.

These ants are common in the southern United States and in California. They vary in color from uniformly dark brown to brown with a reddish tint. Workers have a distinct single tooth on their thorax, which causes the thorax to form a pyramid shape that gives these ants their common name (see Figure 9.28, following page 254). Workers are 1/15- to 1/12-inch long and are commonly found in gardens and flowerbeds. They often tend aphids on ornamental plants, feeding on honeydew, but also frequently enter homes along distinct foraging trails.

Field Ants
Formica spp.

The many species and varieties of these ants infest fields, lawns, and gardens throughout the United States. Their length varies from 1/8- to 1/4-inch, and they may be brown, black, or reddish or have combinations of these colors (see Figure 9.29, following page 254). Foragers prefer sweet foods but will also feed on other insects as predators or scavengers. Nests are commonly built as earthen mounds along fences, sidewalks, flowerbeds, and in lawns.

Field ants are most likely to be pests of recreational areas. When infestations are heavy, individuals may wander into homes in search of food. The Allegheny mound builder, *Formica exsectoides* Forel (see Figure 9.30, following page 254), builds large mounds of earth during its nesting activities. This species is seldom found in the home but has caused fire ant scares in the northeastern states. Other common species of field ants are relatively large and black, resembling the carpenter ant. Pest management professionals must be careful in making identifications between field ants and carpenter ants.

Some field ants capture the larvae and pupae of other ants and raise them in their own nests. The emerging adults become slaves for the field ants. Thus, field ants are sometimes called slave ants.

Crazy Ant
Paratrechina longicornis (Latreille)

This ant is found in scattered locations in all states. Workers are about 1/10-inch long and dark brown in color (see Figure 9.31, following page 254). Their legs and antennae are much longer in proportion to the other parts of their body compared to what is normal for other house-infesting ants.

The crazy ant has become an important household pest along much of the Gulf coastal region of the United States, and in Arizona. In the northern United States it is more common indoors than outdoors because it cannot survive outdoors during cold winters. Its habit of seeming to run aimlessly about the room accounts for its name. Crazy ants nest in small cracks, crevices, and voids inside, and

they wander throughout the building searching for food. They prefer to feed on animal matter, grease and other insects, but will readily eat sweets of all kinds.

False Honey Ant
Prenolepis imparis (Say)

This ant is widely distributed throughout the United States. The shiny workers vary in color from light to dark brown and are about 1/8- to 1/6-inch long (see Figure 9.32, following page 254). They are not usually troublesome in homes and spend most of their time close to the ground. They typically nest in clay soils in well-shaded areas. Coarse earthen pellets usually surround the nest entrance. Within the nest certain workers are fed large quantities of sugary liquids by other workers who forage; these liquids are stored in the greatly distended abdomens of the "honey pot" ants and regurgitated to other colony members as required.

Cornfield Ant
Lasius alienus (Foerster)

This abundant ant is an important pest in homes in the northern United States and especially in the Pacific Northwest (see Figure 9.33, following page 254). As its name indicates, it is a common ant in cornfields. In homes it prefers sweet substances, while outside it also feeds on dead and live insects, plant sap, and honeydew. Common nesting sites include in rotting logs and stumps, under stones, and in exposed soil. It often builds small craters in lawns. This ant is the most common nuisance ant pest of picnics in its range.

Large Yellow Ant
Acanthomyops interjectus (Mayr)

This ant, which is common from New England to the Midwest, is also known as the citronella ant because of the citronella-like odor given off when the ant is crushed. This is the most dependable characteristic for field identification of this species. Workers are reddish yellow to reddish-brown in color and about 1/5-inch long (see Figure 9.34, following page 254). Winged reproductives swarm in basements and around house foundations in early spring and are frequently mistaken for termites. Outdoor nests are found in old logs and stumps and under stones. This ant may bring large piles of dirt to the surface of the ground at the entrance to its nest, either outdoors or indoors, which frequently causes homeowners great alarm. Aside from the debris created, however, this ant does no harm. Workers feed on the honeydew produced by subterranean aphids and mealybugs, and they will not be encountered foraging indoors.

Ghost Ant

Tapinoma melanocephalum (Fabricius)

This is a small to tiny ant (1.5 to 2mm long) that has a very characteristic pale, whitish abdomen, legs and antennae; but very dark-colored head and thorax (see Figure 9.35, following page 254). This species has become an important household pest throughout much of Florida and Hawaii. These ants can develop very large colonies, with many queens, and colonies can divide or split through a budding process similar to the pharaoh ant and white-footed ant. They generally nest outdoors under mulch, rocks, boards or other items, or under loose bark of tress and in lumber and firewood piles. Removal of these nesting areas will aid control programs. Finding all the nest areas and treating them directly with insecticide spray or soil drench can achieve satisfactory control. These ants may also respond to some baits.

White-footed Ant

Technomyrmex albipes (French Smith)

This pest species was introduced to Florida sometime before the mid-1980s, but has since become a significant pest in the central and southern parts of that state. It is also known from Oahu in Hawaii, and its spread from these areas is likely (perhaps aided by association of colonies with root balls of nursery plants). Workers are medium to small ants (2.5 to 3mm long), black to dark brown in color, but with distinct yellowish-white tibia and tarsi on each leg—thus appearing "white-footed" (see Figure 9.36, following page 254). This ant does not bite or sting, or cause any structural damage, but many homeowners consider it a nuisance due to their frequent foraging in kitchens, bathrooms and around exteriors of homes or buildings. This ant is primarily a honeydew feeder, so it will nest in soil, mulched areas or aboveground locations around landscapes, and then tend aphids, scales, or mealybugs on plants. However, they are also known to occasionally nest within homes.

White-footed ants appear so successful, and a difficult nuisance to control around homes, because colonies of this species frequently become very large—with upwards of 2 to 3 million individuals. Interestingly, research has shown that about one-half of the colony is fertile, reproductive females, called intercastes, that are inseminated by wingless males. Winged reproductives swarm and leave the colony typically in July or August in south Florida. After colony formation, the dealated queen is eventually replaced by the reproductively capable workers (intercastes). As colonies grow larger they can occupy many nest sites interconnected by foraging trails, or divide to form new colonies by budding.

The very large colony size, multiple nesting sites, and aggressive foraging around and into homes make this ant difficult to control. Research has shown that thorough baiting programs, guided by careful inspections and observations of foraging trails and likely nesting areas, will provide the best possible suppression. Since the ants respond best to sweet, liquid baits, these must be replenished regularly in order to remain attractive to foragers. Control of honeydew-producing pests on landscape plants can also aid in suppression. Pest management professionals should be aware that these ants also feed on dead insects, so they may also respond to protein-based baits. If these ants are foraging or nesting in wall voids or attics, use of residual dusts may be necessary.

ANT CONTROL

Proper procedures for ant control in and around homes or other buildings depend greatly on the species of ant involved, the extent and nature of the infestation, and location of the nest or nests used by the infesting species. Proper identification of the ant species in each situation will help the professional to determine where to begin the search for the source of the trouble—the nest or nests—and to understand whether it is likely there may be multiple nests for separate colonies, or satellite nests for one colony. Occasionally, the professional can note certain characteristics of the nest, or aspects of the ants' behavior, that aid identification of the particular species. For example, a carpenter ant infestation can be confirmed by the presence of wood shavings thrown out of the galleries.

The first step in ant control in or around homes or other buildings is to conduct a **thorough inspection** of the premises to determine which species are present (one or more may be involved) and, if possible, all the nest locations. Sometimes, a survey program with nontoxic baits is necessary to determine where ants are nesting. Useful survey bait items may include a simple sugar solution (i.e., 10% sucrose, as table sugar, in distilled water, where the moisture itself may also serve as an attractant in situations where it is otherwise scarce), honey or honey/water solutions, jelly, peanut butter, bits of fresh meat (e.g., hamburger or liver), freshly killed insects (e.g., crickets or mealworms, available in many pet stores), or bacon grease. More than one type of item (e.g., a sweet and a grease) is often used to ensure a response by the ants. In some cases, many survey bait locations may need to be checked and possibly moved on repeat visits, over several days. A **diagram of the premises** and notes of ant sightings should be made to guide proper and thorough treatments at a later stage in the control program.

If an ant colony is established within the structure, killing the exposed workers seldom gives permanent relief because the queen or queens in the nest will continue to produce more workers. A chemical barrier, or perimeter treatment, may be effective for some ant species nesting outdoors that are invading the building for food, but it may not be very effective at all for other species. However, this barrier will be temporary because workers from the nest, or from other nests, will again invade the building when the chemical residue becomes ineffective. Colony eradication will provide longer-term relief, so it is important to remember that the first priority of ant control is to locate the nest or nests and treat them directly, to eradicate them through effective use of baits, or to use one of the newer nonrepellent residual insecticide sprays (e.g., fipronil) that can provide general suppression of ants and often colony kill.

In the case of pharaoh ants, it is very rare that the professional is able to locate and gain direct access to the usually numerous nest locations. Finding carpenter ant nests may be very difficult and time consuming even when freshly killed insects are used as survey baits. The task may also require some carpentry skills to open void areas to locate the colonies and allow effective insecticide treatment. Specific management procedures for carpenter and pharaoh ants will be discussed separately, following discussion of general recommendations for managing other ant species in and around homes or other structures.

Species That Nest Indoors

Certain ant species are more likely than others to nest inside structures. The thief ant, pharaoh ant (see the later section on control of this species), odorous house ant, and crazy ant are examples, but experienced professionals will encounter occasional situations where some of the other species discussed here may nest indoors. Eradication of such ants is much more likely if the foraging workers can be traced to the vicinity of the nest or nests, and if all forms of chemical or nonchemical treatment are then focused on the colonies in those nests. This is the function of the inspection and survey phase of the control program.

Baits have become the primary tool used by many professionals for effective, efficient and safe ant control in and around homes or other accounts (see Figure 9.37). They will often be especially desirable for use as the primary control tool where children or pets are present, though their use may need to be supplemented by focused applications of residual or nonresidual insecticide sprays or dusts. A number of commercial bait formulations are available that contain abamectin, hydramethylnon, fipronil, imidacloprid, sulfluramid or boric acid as the active ingredient, and each may be effective for colony kill of only certain species. These active ingredients are formulated in a variety of bait bases and forms. Bait bases include sugars, greases, soy or other vegetable oils, protein from various sources, and other proprietary formulations. The bait product form will vary from coarse particles that are typically offered to foragers in discrete piles, as small dabs of gel, as paste applied with specialized syringe-like guns, or in discrete child-resistant plastic stations similar to those used for cockroach baits.

Whichever form is used, the objective is to have the foraging ants feed on the bait and carry it back to the colony, where the active ingredient is transferred and kills the queens and brood (larvae) of the colony. Thus, bait placements should be made as near as possible to all the nest areas and along all ant foraging trails identified during the inspection and survey baiting phases of the program. Where sulfluramid, abamectin, fipronil, imidacloprid or hydramethylnon baits are used, effective elimina-

FIGURE 9.37. Baits have become a primary ant control tool for pest management professionals. Bait products containing any one of several active ingredients are available, and most actives are formulated into different forms (e.g., liquid, gel, foam or solid granules) and with different bait bases to stimulate feeding (e.g., sweet, grease, oil or protein). Myers

tion of the colony and foraging ants will often be observed within a few days to two weeks if the ants forage on the baits aggressively. Boric acid and juvenoid (methoprene, fenoxycarb or pyriproxyfen) baits typically work much more slowly, requiring up to several weeks or more of continuous exposure and feeding.

When using baits, other competing food sources should be removed if possible. The repellency of residual insecticide sprays can cause ants to avoid baits placed in those treated areas. The professional should be aware of this possibility. However, ants may not respond to the bait because the food bait base of the product is unattractive to the ant species involved. Also, if the baits are stored with other pesticides or volatile chemicals, they may become tainted with chemical residues that could render them repellent to ants. Ants are typically very discriminating about the food items they will feed on, and the food preferences of individual colonies will vary due to location-specific factors or at different times of the year when they are active (seasonality). Any avoidance can be especially frustrating because success in the form of complete colony kill relies on a strong feeding response to the bait by foraging ants.

When residual or nonresidual insecticide treatments must be made indoors, whether as the primary control tool or as a supplement to bait use, professionals may misjudge the situation in attempting to locate and treat the nest or nests. Worker ants may sometimes be appearing and disappearing at a rapid rate at one or two points beneath a baseboard, behind a sink, or under a cabinet, but the nest may be in the wall or in the bottom void of a kitchen cabinet some distance from the point of entry. Applications only at the points where workers are seen may be quite ineffective if the workers can find alternative routes to and from the nest and their food sources. It is good practice to apply insecticide dust into all cracks and crevices for several feet on each side of the places where the ants are seen. This often means that applications are required beyond the specific rooms where ant foragers are a problem. It is often helpful to drill small holes to allow treatment into any voids where colony activity is suspected. Dust or crack and crevice aerosol formulations of residual insecticides such as bendiocarb, silica aerogel, or pyrethroids (like cyfluthrin and deltamethrin) are available and effective for use against household ants. When made into the nest area, these applications will generally eradicate the entire colony quite rapidly.

In addition to direct treatment of nest galleries or other voids with dusts, it may be appropriate to apply crack and crevice or spot treatments with a residual spray in areas where the ants have been seen entering, exiting, or traveling, such as along baseboards, around door moldings, and in the cracks or crevices in those elements. Many of the commonly used **residual insecticides** labeled for controlling other indoor crawling insects, like cockroaches, are also labeled for ants. In general, wettable powder and microencapsulated formulations will provide superior residual performance on porous surfaces, compared to emulsifiable concentrates. However, emulsifiable concentrates generally create fewer concerns with visible residues when used indoors. Aerosol formulations of these residual insecticides are also available.

If these treatments are supplementary to the primary reliance on baits, the spray or dust applications should generally be made in places, or at a later time, so that they do not interfere with active foraging on the baits due to repellency. Some residual insecticides labeled for ant and other crawling insect control, such as imidacloprid, fipronil and chlorfenapyr, will have low or no repellency to the ants. This can be an advantage when they are used along with ant baits. Conversely, the repellency of pyrethroids is often an advantage when a "barrier" treatment is desired.

Efficient ant control may be obtained with one treatment or set of treatments when the appropriate combination of these management and control procedures is carefully applied following a thorough inspection. All insecticide applications should include full consideration of the ants' behavior and the likely locations of their nests and food resources. However, follow-up visits and inspections should be scheduled, and supplementary treatments made if required by continued ant presence. Baiting programs generally depend on follow-up service visits for success. The need to repeat other forms of treatment generally indicates that the nest, or all the nests, were not located and properly treated the first time. An undetected outdoor source for the infestation is another possibility.

Species That Nest Outdoors

Except for the species mentioned in the previous section, the remainder of the ants discussed earlier in this chapter are more likely to nest outdoors than indoors. They become pests by becoming an intolerable nuisance when they forage inside for food, or when they occur in sufficient numbers that they interfere with various outdoor activities. Species capable of stinging are a particular nuisance in and around homes, and may present a serious medical risk to people allergic to their stings. Whenever possible, it will be helpful to find the nest or nests when attempting to control these species. Nests will usually be in the ground but may be concealed under stones, boards, slabs or sidewalks, or in stumps or logs. They may also be in aboveground locations such as in trees or in voids within the exterior walls, behind rain gutters, or in attics. When the nest or nests are found, they should be treated directly with an insecticide.

For nests in soil, a spray or **drench of a residual insecticide solution** will generally be most effective, but dusts can be forced into the nest galleries. Wettable powders or insecticidal granules are sometimes applied to the nest area and then thoroughly watered in. Up to several gallons of drench may be required on large mounds of established colonies, but only 2 quarts to 2 gallons on smaller colonies. Some professionals use termite rods to inject the chemical into deep soil nests (e.g., for fire ant or field ant control). For some mound-building species, it may be advisable to scrape off or break up the mounds just before treatment.

Effective baits, containing the active ingredients mentioned below for fire ant baits, are also available for outdoor use against many ant species. These may be granular baits that can be scattered in areas where the ants are foraging, or placed out in specialized bait stations that are designed to protect the bait from outdoor conditions (and prevent access by children or pets). Liquid and gel baits, whether sugar-based or oil-based, will generally need to be offered to the ants within bait stations, though most gels can be applied into protected places such as on the exterior of buildings or tree trunks. Some stations are designed to allow use of two or more types of baits simultaneously, which can improve results when more than one pest ant species is present or the ants' food preferences are shifting. Reliance on baiting may be necessary when the nests cannot be located and treated directly, or it may be the most effective strategy for some species and under the conditions present. When baits are used, other supplementary insecticide applications to visible mounds or likely ant access points into the structure may be appropriate. Care should be taken when baits applications are followed by use of spray, dust or granular applications that there is sufficient time (a few days) or distance between the applications so that foraging ants are not repelled from the areas where the bait was applied. As mentioned above, some active ingredients used in residual spray or dust formulations for ant and other crawling insect control will have little or no repellent effect, while others, such as the pyrethroids, will be highly repellent.

In addition to treating ant nests or mounds, or the use of baits, exterior surfaces such as walls, door or windowsills, and any other entry points used by the ants should be treated with a residual insecticide. It is important to treat all potential runways, such as pillars and steps, and other routes such as tree limbs, vines, shrubs, telephone wires, and door or window moldings that ants might be using to gain entry. The soil surface along the perimeter of the building should also be considered for treatment with the residual insecticide. Residual treatments of wettable powders or microencapsulated insecticides will be more effective on most exterior surfaces, while emulsions or granular formulations will be effective for soil treatment. Some newer residual materials, such as fipronil, are nonrepellent and appear to be especially effective for general suppression of ants because workers contaminated with the active ingredient will bring it back to the colony's nest area, where total colony kill can be obtained (sometimes within days).

The length of effective residual action, either for killing ants that crawl on treated surfaces and are sufficiently exposed or for repelling them when synthetic pyrethroids are used, will vary with the species involved and the environmental factors that normally degrade such residues outdoors (e.g., heat, sunlight, rain, wind, dustiness, etc.). However, the most effective residual treatments on exterior surfaces of buildings probably do not last more than 4 to 6 weeks under the warm-season conditions when ant species invading indoors from the landscape are most active and troublesome. Frequent retreatments may be particularly necessary to allow effective control of highly aggressive and adaptable species, like the Argentine, white-footed, crazy, and red imported fire ants. Some professionals have also found that these perimeter treatments can create or exacerbate control problems with some ant species when highly repellent pyrethroid insecticides are used, due to scattering and incomplete control of the ants and their colony units. In other situations and for other species (e.g., carpenter ants), the repellency of residual deposits of pyrethroid insecticides can be a useful tool in the overall program. As mentioned previously, other residual insecticides labeled for ant control are nonrepellent (e.g., fipronil), and have shown to be an important tool for pest management professionals faced with difficult ant pest situations. To maximize the duration and level of effectiveness for residual barrier spray treatment, instruct the homeowner to irrigate thoroughly the day before the treatment is applied, and then to avoid irrigation for as long as possible thereafter.

If the ants are also feeding on honeydew on trees, shrubs, or other plants adjacent to the house, it may be beneficial to the ant control program to treat the plants involved for control of the aphids, scales, or other sucking pests. This will serve to both remove an ant food source and kill ants that may crawl onto the plants before the insecticide residue deteriorates. Be careful when treating around foundation plantings, turf, or other plant material to select only insecticides labeled and safe to use on plants, and remember that such treatments to turf and ornamental plantings may require special applicator certification and licensing.

When ants are scattered and numerous in a lawn or garden, or around a patio area, and quick eradication of all foragers is required (e.g., before a party in the customer's yard), or where colonies are very large (particularly with the Argentine ant or one of the fire ants), a **broadcast treatment** of the yard is often necessary. This can be done with either a spray or granular formulation of an appropriate insecticide. Remember to irrigate after applying granular insecticides, to release the active ingredient from the granules. Such broad-scale treatments should be conducted several hours to a day or more before the property will be used for a party, athletic event, or other purpose, so that the insecticide will be thoroughly dry and adhered to the soil, turf, or other plant material before people will be exposed to it. This will greatly decrease or eliminate the potential for any significant exposure of people or pets to the insecticide. In some cases where several days to a couple weeks are available prior to the event for which ant control or suppression is required, broadcast treatment with a granular, food-based bait formulation may be timely and effective (and preferred, due to lower risk of hazardous exposure).

Individual mounds or larger outdoor areas infested with red imported fire ants can be treated with one of several commercially available **fire ant baits**. Bait formulations of hydramethylnon, sulfluramid, abamectin, imidacloprid, fipronil, spinosad, pyriproxyfen, fenoxycarb, or methoprene are available. However, baits with the latter three juvenoid active ingredients will control colonies rather slowly, taking up to several weeks for visible results. This may not be acceptable to the customer. In such cases, other insecticide treatments, such as individual mound drenches or a broadcast treatment, may be necessary. However, in some situations it will be impractical for each mound to be treated, so an areawide bait program should be considered. This can be followed up several days later, after the ants have fed on the bait and it has a chance to affect the reproductives and brood, with drench treatments on visible mounds. If only bait is used, the customer should be advised not to expect quick results in terms of areawide fire ant suppression. Certain aerosol injection formulations are registered for rapid control of fire ant mounds. Individual mounds can be treated by inserting a long spray wand into the mound and activating the aerosol to fill the nest galleries with fine aerosol droplets.

Leaf-cutter ant mounds can be especially large, with extensive galleries extending deeply and widely into the soil. Some of the methyl bromide products labeled for fumigating or sterilizing soil prior to replanting turf, ornamentals, or vegetables can be used to fumigate these mounds. In conjunction with this, residual sprays or dusts can be applied to the major trails used by the foragers. Professionals should seek the advice of state or local entomology experts for proper procedures to follow in controlling these ants.

Species That Nest Under Slabs or Sidewalks

Ants nesting under slabs or sidewalks can create some particularly difficult control challenges. Species such as pavement ants, red imported fire ants, large yellow ants, and Argentine ants are commonly found outdoors nesting under stones or sidewalks. If these ants will respond satisfactorily to one or more of the commercially available bait formulations, control should be achieved fairly quickly. Alternatively, effective treatment of their nest sites in such situations may require use of power spray equipment and termite rods. Sometimes, the colony may establish a nest near the edge of a foundation slab, from which the foragers will move inward along plumbing and electrical entries or through cracks and expansion joints in the foundation. Subslab heating systems provide these ants with other points of entry and conditions under the slab that generally favor continuous ant activity throughout the winter. It is often necessary to treat all baseboards and any other points where the ants are entering through the slab. Some drilling of the slab and subslab for treatment, similar to what is recommended for subterranean termites, may occasionally be necessary. This may be required where the ants are not nesting along the perimeter of the slab but may be anywhere underneath it. However, subslab heating or air-conditioning ducts should not be contaminated. Rather, it may be necessary to use a commercially available bait material placed into the ducts, monitored routinely, and replenished with fresh bait as needed (perhaps daily or two to three times per week). All bait should be removed after control has been achieved.

In basements, spot treatments with residual insecticide should be applied to areas where ants are entering. This becomes difficult and may be ineffective if the basement has been finished with paneling or if ants are nesting in a concrete block foundation wall. Voids in such a wall must be treated, usually with a dust formulation. If dust or liquid cannot be forced from the top, holes must be drilled at various points along the wall for this purpose. Many professionals prefer to treat insulated voids using an aerosol insecticide fitted with a specialized crack and crevice or injector-type applicator. If ants are nesting in the soil adjacent to a basement wall or below the basement floor, soil treatment with termite rodding equipment may be necessary (as discussed earlier for ant colonies below slabs).

Carpenter Ants

Effective management of carpenter ants has benefited from the development of effective commercial ant bait formulations that can work reliably under many situations. If the carpenter ants are not responding adequately to the baits, or an alternate control approach is preferred, success will depend on finding the ants' nesting galleries and treating them directly, to eliminate the entire colony at its source or sources.

When carpenter ants are found foraging inside a structure, their colony or colonies may be nesting within the building or somewhere outside. The main nest, where the reproducing queen is located, will usually be found outdoors, away from the home, except when a constant source of moisture is available inside. Ants from individual colonies may also be distributed between two or more satellite nests, located inside or outside. Eliminating colonies outside may be just as important as eliminating a colony (probably a satellite colony) already established inside a building. Colony elimination outdoors is often the only effective way to prevent ants from entering the structure. Under certain circumstances an entire colony might also migrate from one nesting site to another, such as from a tree outside to some structural timbers inside. In addition to such relocations, colonies may be established by newly fertilized females that fly in, or by the introduction of infested materials, such as firewood, into the home or garage.

A **thorough inspection** is important in carpenter ant management. The entire structure and adjacent grounds should be inspected since more than one colony will often be present, or a colony may have one or more satellite nest sites (e.g., the main nest in a stump outside and a subcolony nest in the structure). The steps of a successful inspection include an interview with the residents; an inspection indoors; an inspection outdoors; detection by sound; and, often, the use of freshly killed insects, such as crickets or mealworms, as survey baits.

The initial interview of the client is important. Information should be obtained on where ants have been seen, where ants are most prevalent, patterns of their movement, and whether swarmers or sawdust-like material have been seen. If there are or have been moisture problems in the structure, it is important to know where, since carpenter ants will often nest in these areas.

Besides inspecting in areas where ants have been seen traveling in highest numbers, the most important places to inspect indoors are areas of the wooden structure associated with high moisture. Critical areas to inspect include plugged drain gutters, poorly fitted or damaged siding and flashing, wood shingle roofs, hollow porch posts and columns, attached wooden patios, and leaking door or window frames. Other susceptible areas include wood in contact with the soil, wood in areas of improper ventilation (which will have a high moisture content), and wood scraps in crawl spaces or under dirt-filled slab porches. Moist wood, especially if it has been partially decayed and softened by fungi, is preferred by carpenter ants for nesting. It is easier for the workers to physically remove shreds of softened wood from the inner walls of the nest gallery as it is hollowed out and enlarged.

Carpenter ant satellite colonies are occasionally found nesting in perfectly dry environments inside hollow veneer doors and other void areas. They may be found nesting in a cavity in insulation above a ceiling, or in a wall void. In many of these cases, a gallery is not hollowed out of the wood, but the ants merely find and use existing cavities.

Signs of carpenter ant activity indoors include (1) piles of wood debris or dead ants ejected from the colony; (2) windows, or small openings, to the nest; (3) ants foraging in kitchens, pantries, and other storage areas for food; (4) swarmers; and (5) damaged timbers. The wood debris usually has a shredded quality, because ants must tear shreds of wood from gallery walls using their mandibles. This sawdust should not be confused with ordinary sawdust or the much finer, powder-textured frass of powderpost beetles. Many times, these shreds will not be visible, because they are deposited by the worker ants in some void area, such as between walls or in unused nest galleries. Pieces of dead worker ants and other insects may be mixed with this shredded wood debris. Windows may not always be present, since ants can also use existing cracks or separations between trim boards. Carpenter ants usually forage more outdoors than indoors and are also usually more active at night. However, foragers commonly move indoors in the spring after they first become active and when it is too cool for extensive foraging outdoors. Swarmers often become trapped and die around windows and in spider webs of basements and crawlspaces. Inspection of out-of-the-way places usually reveals these swarmers. The surface of damaged wood often appears very solid, but damaged areas can sometimes be located by sounding the timbers.

Outdoor inspection should include a thorough inspection of the structure's exterior as well as the grounds. Carpenter ant workers forage extensively and may travel as far as 100 yards from their nest. They generally forage individually above ground, but foraging trails have been observed and reported below ground or at the soil level underneath grass. These ants commonly nest in trees and stumps and use branches and vines to travel from tree to tree or to gain access into structures. Carpenter ants may nest in living trees but are usually associated with the dead heartwood portion of the trunk or a large limb (and especially with dead limbs). They will typically enter through a knothole, scar, dead area, or crotch in the limb. Stacks of firewood and logs, stumps, fence posts, railroad ties used in the landscape, wooden portions of attached porches or patios, and other similar places are also potential nesting sites. As with an indoor inspection, it is important to look for areas on the outside of the structure where moisture problems exist or may have existed. Piles of shredded wood near timbers or near posts, firewood, stumps, or trees are evidence of a nesting site.

Use of **sound-detection equipment**, such as a stethoscope, is sometimes helpful in locating nests. An active colony will produce a distinct, dry rustling sound that intensifies if the colony is disturbed. The sound, thought to be a form of communication, is made by the worker ants with the mandibles but is not related to the chewing or removal of wood. This rustling noise is occasionally quite loud but usually will be more easily detected when conditions are still. If a suspicious timber is found, the inspector should rap heavily on the timber and then press an ear (or a stethoscope) to the surface to listen for activity. In cases where some carpentry is necessary to allow eradication of carpenter ant nests and (possibly) repair of leaks and other moisture conditions that encouraged infestation, the client will appreciate the use of tools like a stethoscope to pinpoint ant activity and reduce the extent of expensive repairs needed thereafter.

Entomology researchers have shown that carpenter ant colonies can often be rather easy to locate by offering freshly killed insects, such as crickets or mealworms (commonly available at pet food or fishing supply stores), to foraging carpenter ants. These insects used as survey baits are easy to handle and transport if they are immobilized by chilling (in a refrigerator or ice chest), and they can be killed by simply cutting each of them into two to three pieces with scissors immediately before placement. The best sites to place these insect pieces out as survey bait will be where foragers have been noticed in the highest numbers during previous phases of the inspection, or based on interviews with the residents. Since such freshly killed insects are highly desired by the carpenter ants (or other ant species) as a protein source, they will quickly begin to carry these insect pieces away—back to the nest or nests. Such survey baiting should be started just before dusk and continue into the early nighttime hours. Generally, when the carpenter ants begin to respond, significant numbers will arrive at the survey bait sites within 15 to 20 minutes or so. Then, the ants returning to the nest locations can usually be easily observed and followed with the aid of a flashlight. This procedure should be used until all the nesting sites are located.

Protection of structures from carpenter ants requires destruction of the ants in all colonies in and around the structure. This is often difficult in residential areas where ants are nesting on properties near to that of the customer. For many years, there has been a trend to build homes, and entire neighborhoods, on heavily wooded lots. Such locations are ideal for carpenter ants, so there may be several colonies on a moderate-sized lot, and ants from many other colonies may be foraging in or around a home. Reinfestation of favorable sites on such wooded lots will be certain and rapid, so carpenter ant problems may be perennial for some homeowners.

Elimination of high-moisture conditions and replacement of decayed wood aid in carpenter ant management, helping to prevent future infestations by the ants and wood-destroying fungi. Some professionals offer this service to their customers. The importance of these procedures should be discussed with the customer, and their necessity stressed. However, unless the nest is physically removed, insecticides must be applied to control carpenter ants.

Bait products containing most of the delayed-action toxicants mentioned previously in this chapter are available for carpenter ant control, and they are available primarily in granular or gel forms. These baits can effectively reduce the numbers of foraging workers and eradicate colonies under many infestation situations. After sufficient inspection to locate all carpenter ant foraging trails and areas, these locations should be baited and necessary follow-up inspections and treatments planned. When the ants respond aggressively to the baits, formulations containing abamectin, hydramethylnon, fipronil, imidacloprid or sulfluramid should provide substantial reduction in presence of foraging ants within 2 to 3 weeks (some re-treatments may be needed during that time). The following treatment guidelines describe strategies for use of other, nonbait insecticidal approaches, which may be used if baiting strategies are not preferred or they do not provide satisfactory control. Some professionals may also combine use of baiting with other these forms of insecticide treatment.

Insecticide spray or dust applications should be made directly into the nest galleries, in the general vicinity of the nest, and into its openings or approaches where foraging ants have been active. Many insecticides are labeled and effective for carpenter ant control. Residual materials frequently used for the control of other crawling insect pests indoors are preferred. After the nest or nests are found, carpenter ants are usually not difficult to control, because they are quite susceptible to insecticides.

If entrances to the nest are found, they can often be enlarged slightly so that insecticide can be introduced. Although injection of water-based sprays into the nest galleries can be effective, such applications may further contribute to wood decay problems. **Dust formulations** are preferred for treating carpenter ant nest galleries, because deep penetration and distribution of the dust into the galleries is generally obtained. Aerosol formulations applied via crack and crevice tips have similar advantages and will be effective.

Insecticide should be applied to reach as much of the areas inhabited or traveled by the ants as possible. To whatever degree is practical, the extent of the galleries should be determined by careful inspection and the use of listening devices prior to treatment. Then it is often advisable to drill 1/4- or 3/8-inch holes at about 12-inch intervals in the infested timbers to intercept the various cavities and galleries of the nest. Void areas of the construction may be drilled into and accessed in the same manner. Dust or aerosol insecticides should be applied using a tip that fits tightly into the holes, and the insecticide should be forced into and throughout the ant nest galleries. Holes may then be sealed by hammering in pieces of wooden dowel of the appropriate size.

In cases where it is impossible to find the nest, a more general treatment of the premises may be necessary. The outside of the foundation should be treated with appropriate residual materials, as should the base of trees, fences, and shrubs and the sides or other exterior surfaces of the house, where ants have been seen foraging or entering the home. This should be done with a cone or fan nozzle so that complete coverage is ensured. Wettable powder, suspension concentrate, or microencapsulated formulations will generally give the most effective residual performance on the wide variety of surfaces outdoors. Tree branches touching the structure should be cut back to prevent foragers from using them to travel and gain access into the home. Special attention should be paid to treatments on and around exterior surfaces where telephone and electric wires connect to the building and might allow carpenter ant entry. Most of the residual pyrethroids will be very effective for killing and/or repelling carpenter ants in these types of applications.

Indoors, baseboards and door frames where the ants have been seen traveling should be treated with a residual insecticide. If there is a full basement or crawlspace, the mudsill (the board that lies on the top of the foundation) and any structural timbers between it and the subfloor should be thoroughly treated with a general application of a liquid residual insecticide. Inaccessible attic areas should also be thoroughly treated with a dust insecticide if any ant activity has been detected there.

Some pest management firms attempt to manage carpenter ants with extensive use of residual insecticide applications to many surfaces inside and outside the structure, and with minimal attempt at locating the nest or nests. Since the source of the problem is not treated directly and eliminated, these extensive residual applications often have to be repeated. While this strategy may ultimately be effective in some cases, it essentially relies on very extensive insecticide use, with its potential risks. It may also require more total service time due to callbacks than would a careful, but successful, inspection and direct nest treatment using more conservative insecticide applications. A careful and systematic inspection by an alert and experienced professional, supplemented by the use of survey baiting and followed by focused insecticide applications (to the nest or nests), is the most efficient approach to carpenter ant control. Nests are sometimes found quickly, and the problem rapidly eliminated. At other times, this approach may take considerable time over more than one visit. Of course, the nest galleries may never be found, so extensive use of residual insecticides may ultimately be necessary.

Another consideration in the choice of basic carpenter ant management strategies is that some professionals find it difficult to price their work and still remain profitable and competitive. The time required to do inspections is hard to predict and will sometimes be extensive. Thus, some professionals find it easier to estimate the time and materials needed if they skip inspections and depend on extensive insecticide treatments to kill off foragers and (hopefully) eliminate the colony over a longer time period. However, this approach will often require multiple services, and it may take some weeks to eliminate the problem. Such jobs are expensive even when properly conducted. Placing emphasis on **locating and directly treating nests** will usually provide a quicker and neater result and will generally be more satisfying to both the professional and the customer. In these days of high public consciousness and concern for the potential negative effects of pesticides, methods that are effective and rely on minimal pesticide use should be preferred. This approach also stresses the value of experience and knowledge of carpenter ant behavior, instead of just providing a specialized spray service.

Pharaoh Ants

This species is a common and widespread pest in the United States, and despite the availability of effective baits that can provide fairly rapid colony kill, these ants can be considered one of the more difficult pest management challenges by professionals. When pharaoh ants are positively identified as the pest species in a home or other premises, their efficient and effective management requires comprehensive baiting procedures. Control using liquid insecticides or dusts indoors should not be attempted, as this will rarely be effective and generally causes the ant colonies (there will often be several) to move. Liquid or dust applications may even stimulate colonies to divide, or bud, resulting in an increased number of more widely scattered colonies.

Pharaoh ant control should be attempted as an organized and systematic program, to which sufficient time and labor must be devoted to ensure necessary attention to detail and follow-up. The level of effort required to obtain complete elimination in pharaoh ant management programs means these programs can become fairly expensive, especially for large institutional clients. Up to several months may be required for total elimination of pharaoh ants. Estimating the resources needed for pharaoh ant control can be a difficult problem for some situations, especially where this species is heavily infesting a large and complex structure, such as a hospital or hotel.

Baits containing boric acid or juvenoids like methoprene, fenoxycarb and pyriproxyfen are rather slow-acting toxicants. However, baits containing hydramethylnon, abamectin, fipronil, imidacloprid or sulfluramid are generally preferred because they are faster acting and can result in elimination of pharaoh ant colonies within a few days.

The first step in a pharaoh ant control program is to **interview the residents** or workers who inhabit the structure and are in a position to give much useful information on ant sightings. Then, many professionals put out a large number of **survey bait stations** to determine, as closely as possible, where the ant colony or colonies are located. Since this survey step alone requires time and expense and may not be necessary if very thorough toxic bait placement will be done anyway, many experts recommend skipping this survey baiting phase. However, in some complex situations or where toxic bait placement may be restricted for some reason, survey baiting may be necessary to locate the foraging areas and nest locations of active colonies within the structure. A reasonably **detailed map** or **diagram** of the premises should be made, and all bait station locations and other important notes marked on it. Record information on this diagram about observations and client reports of ant foraging activity. Include data on the location of active survey bait station locations (dates and numbers of ants at the station). Many professionals use two or more copies of the diagram and color-coded notes to distinguish various types of observations or the relative intensity of ant activity in different areas.

A number of considerations about pharaoh ant behavior should be kept in mind as guides to proper survey or toxic bait placement. Pharaoh ants prefer warmer and moister conditions than many other types of household ant pest species. Their nesting and foraging behavior will usually cause them to focus their activities near sources of moisture, such as sink areas, dishwashing equipment, water fountains, windows where moisture condenses during cold seasons, aquaria, house plants, and so forth. Also, while they will forage for liquid and semi-liquid sources of sugars, they also need protein to maintain brood production within the colony. Thus, they will frequently be found foraging on dead insect carcasses, especially those of flies and gnats, which typically collect on window ledges and around light fixtures. In situations where active cockroach or other insect infestations also occur inside, these sources of protein may be ample.

In hospitals, protein sources such as blood, intravenous diet fluids, vomit, or fluids around wounds provide pharaoh ants with many excellent food resources. (Some of these foraging behaviors in healthcare facilities may constitute a medical hazard, because pharaoh ants can carry pathogenic bacteria on their bodies. This factor has the potential for the spread of infections among patients and will be of concern to the Infection Control staff.) Add to this various foods, such as sweets and soda or greasy items like potato chips, that visitors bring into the facility, and it is easy to see how even careful housekeeping may not adequately restrict pharaoh ant access to food resources.

Any special efforts that the client, either a homeowner or a facility's janitorial staff, can make in the way of sanitation and removal of food and water sources will aid the initial and long-term pharaoh ant control program. These efforts will force the ants to focus more actively on survey or toxic baits. The client should also be informed of the various steps in the program, its overall complexity, and the time required for complete elimination. In this way, the client is more likely to be patient, and more willing to assist with sanitation and reporting of any ant sightings.

Survey baits of sweet substances, such as sugar, corn syrup, honey, or various jellies, mixed with distilled water will be attractive to pharaoh ant foragers as long as the baits stay moist and do not crystallize. When mixing these baits, use enough water to make the mixture the consistency of syrup (e.g., 10% sugar by weight). It may be necessary to heat these mixtures to obtain uniform consistency, but be sure they have the proper consistency. Pharaoh ants seem to respond to the moisture in the bait as much as to the energy value of the sugars present. Also, foragers can transport liquid and semi-liquid foods back to the nest area (in their crops) much more easily than solid materials. Small plastic pill bottle caps (e.g., those used by pharmacists) or pieces of aluminum foil serve as good bait stations. In situations where ants are foraging actively, many ants will be seen within 1 to 2 hours trailing to and from baits placed near nest areas. Visit these survey bait stations frequently, perhaps after 2 to 4 hours or at least within the next day. Take notes on the activity at various stations, replenish the baits, and move the stations around as necessary to more closely determine the location of all areas of ant activity. Time spent in this survey phase of the program may be an important asset to overall success.

Commercial ant baits should be placed in areas where pharaoh ants were noted foraging during the inspection and survey periods. If no survey baiting was conducted, it is best to assume that all rooms or other areas within the structure should be carefully and thoroughly baited. Commercial baits formulated with hydramethylnon, abamectin, or sulfluramid are preferred for efficient and rapid control of pharaoh ant infestations. The ants will generally feed on them aggressively for 1 to 2 days, after which time little or no further ant activity will be seen. Survey baiting is usually required after control appears to have been achieved, to ensure that all ant activity has been eliminated.

If boric acid baits are used, they should be replaced frequently so they remain fresh and moist as long as ants continue to forage on them. Again, small bottle caps, pieces of aluminum foil, or similar items can be used as bait stations for these baits. If foraging ants are responding aggressively to the boric acid baits, substantial control will be noticed over the first 1 to 2 weeks of the control effort. Intensive baiting should be conducted for at least 2 weeks. Thereafter, survey and insecticidal baits should be used to monitor continuing ant activity at 1 to 2 week intervals for several weeks. Not until all evidence of ant activity has ceased for several weeks, during which a number of survey baitings are conducted, should the infestation be considered eliminated. In large facilities where the initial infestation was extensive, total control is often not achieved for several months to a year. Thus, the use of boric acid baits has generally been replaced by the newer and more efficient baits previously discussed.

In warm and moist areas of the southern United States, pharaoh ant colonies may be located outside, and foraging workers can be readily found on the roof, on exterior walls, or around the perimeter of the building. These colonies can be associated with exterior wall surfaces or various areas of the foundation, such as under the slab, attached steps and sidewalks, or under the bark mulch of foundation plantings. They might also be associated with rooftop ventilation equipment if sources of moisture are present. These colonies, or the sub colonies budding off from them, can readily reinfest the interior portions of the structure where intensive baiting has been conducted. Thus, inspections, surveys, and baiting or insecticide spray applications should be conducted in these situations.

Research has shown that exterior baiting of pharaoh ants is very important to successful overall control in areas where outdoor nesting and foraging is common. Thus, professionals might choose to use the loose, granular form of one of the baits labeled for control of imported fire ants outdoors. These baits should be readily accepted by the pharaoh ant foragers outdoors, and they are capable of providing rapid colony destruction.

Since such outdoor sources of pharaoh ants can contribute to reinfestation of the structure at any time in the future, care should be exercised regarding any control guarantees in southern states. In addition, pharaoh ant colonies may be carried into structures in any area of the United States, at any time. Sources of infestation, such as inside shipments of packaged food, laundry, and houseplant pots or via many other routes, have been recorded.

OTHER HYMENOPTEROUS PESTS

Other members of the order Hymenoptera, besides the ants, can become serious pests in and around our parks, homes, or other structures. The pest management professional will encounter these pests from time to time, especially during warmer periods of the year. Some are pests primarily because people are disturbed by their presence, while others are important because their presence in or near inhabited structures represents a true health and safety risk to people and pets.

Various wasp species display different habits. Some are social and live in colonies, while others are solitary. Social bees and wasps develop colonies similar to those of ants. These colonies have a queen that produces all the eggs, workers, and brood. The social wasps that will be discussed belong to the family Vespidae and include the paper wasps, hornets, and yellowjackets.

Solitary wasps do not have a colony group. The adult female builds a cell for each egg that she lays and provisions each cell with insect or spider prey for the larva to eat. There are several families of solitary wasps, but the species most commonly encountered by pest managers belong to the family Sphecidae. These include the mud daubers and digger wasps.

As with bees, female wasps have their ovipositor, or egg-laying structure, modified into a stinger. Wasps differ from bees in that most feed their young on animal matter, such as insects, spiders, or meat particles, and not on pollen. Bees also have hairy bodies, while wasps tend to have smooth and apparently hairless bodies. Professionals will occasionally be called on to control colonies of social bees, such as honey bees (family Apidae) or bumble bees (family Bombidae). Carpenter bees (family Xylocopidae) resemble large bumble bees but have solitary nesting behavior.

The most common hymenopterous pest species that may harm people directly include certain bees and wasps. In contrast to most of our North American ants (except fire ants and harvester ants), these bees and wasps are frequently dangerous because of allergic response to their painful stings. Stinging behavior is generally a defensive reaction, which can occur either when the colony is threatened near the nest area or the individual bee or wasp is trapped and threatened. Foraging wasps of some species are more likely to sting people at some times of the year than others. For example, yellowjacket workers are more apt to sting people during the latter part of their annual cycle, in August or September, for much of the northern part of the United States.

The stinging process includes injection of rather potent venom. For some species, especially from the family Sphecidae, the venom serves the function of paralyzing or subduing prey, but stings of these wasps are not dangerous to people. The venom of the vespids and the social bees is a defensive material used to drive off intruders when the nest is threatened. In addition to causing intense pain, vespid wasp or social bee venoms contain proteinaceous materials that can cause severe allergic reactions in some individuals. Some people may even go into shock and die of suffocation as their lungs fill with fluid after being stung by a social bee or social wasp. Fortunately, the percentage of our population allergic to these venoms is quite low, probably less than 1 percent.

Wasps and bees are considered beneficial insects in most circumstances. Control measures are justified only on the basis of problems these insects may be causing in each given instance. Control usually becomes necessary when a nest is located in a poor location relative to the safety, comfort, or other interests of people. There will usually be little need to control a hornet nest high in a shade tree or a paper wasp nest on a high, remote eave of a house. In these locations, the colony is unlikely to be disturbed by the activities of people or pets near ground level. However, when social wasps or social bees are nesting in locations such as under the front steps of a home, in a school playground, or near the pole supporting a clothesline, an imminent hazard is created, and control is warranted.

Wasps, Hornets, and Yellowjackets
Family Vespidae

The most dangerous species of stinging Hymenoptera are wasps of the family Vespidae. A useful characteristic that aids in field identification of vespid wasps is that they fold their wings lengthwise when at rest, making the wings seem only half as wide as they actually are. They also hold their wings separately, often parallel to the body, when at rest.

These wasps are social insects that build nests of a paper-like material, called carton, which is a mixture of wood fibers and the salivary secretions of the female wasps. In northern, temperate regions of the world, new colonies must be founded each year, because only the mated queens from the previous year's colonies overwinter (see Figure 9.38). Queens are inactive during the winter, hiding in protected niches under tree bark or in stonewalls, attics, and other sheltered places. In early spring, overwintering **queens**—called **foundresses**, since they establish, or found, the new nests and colonies each year—visit exposed wood surfaces, such as raw and weathered wooden fences or siding, or dead tree limbs where the bark has sloughed away. They chew away wood fibers and combine them with salivary secretions to form the paper-like carton for nest construction.

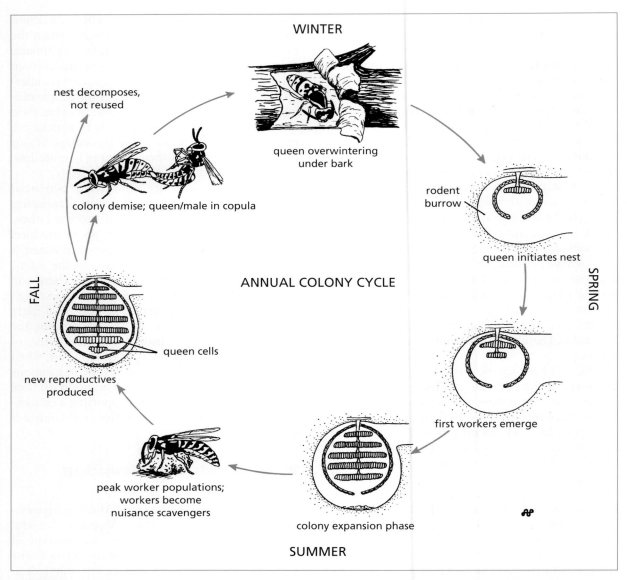

WINTER

nest decomposes,
not reused

queen overwintering
under bark

rodent
burrow

queen initiates nest

colony demise; queen/male in copula

FALL

ANNUAL COLONY CYCLE

SPRING

queen cells

new reproductives
produced

first workers emerge

peak worker populations;
workers become
nuisance scavengers

colony expansion phase

SUMMER

FIGURE 9.38. Yellowjacket and hornet colonies in the United States usually have an annual life cycle. The paper nest constructed during the season by a colony is not reused. Underground nests will quickly decompose after the season is over, while aboveground nests may persist for some time. The typical annual colony cycle for these social wasps is shown in this series of illustrations. (Original drawing by Provonsha; reprinted with permission from Wilson, Bennett, and Provonsha, 1977)

The nest is begun by the foundress as she builds a small number of cells and places an egg in each. After the eggs hatch, larvae develop within the cells and are completely dependent on the queen for food. The queen forages outside the nest and brings food back to the larvae, caring for them in this way until pupation occurs. Food for the larvae is protein, usually in the form of caterpillars or other insects. Adult wasps feed on liquids such as nectar, honeydew, and juices from the bodies of insects fed to larvae. After the first sterile female workers emerge, these workers take over nest building and brood rearing, and the queen stays on the nest. Workers are

adult females as far as the structural features of their bodies are concerned, but they do not mate.

Only one egg-producing queen will be present in the colony. The workers protect and maintain the nest, forage for food and water, and care for the immature stages, or brood (i.e., the eggs, larvae, and pupae). Adult males and newly produced queens leave their parent colony during late summer into early fall. The colonies die off, and only the newly mated queens will find a protected location to overwinter.

If the overwintering queen is able to survive the winter (many do not), she will try to start a new nest and found a new colony during the next spring. Besides failure to overwinter, many queens are killed and replaced by other queens of the same species during the early nest-founding period of each season. Thus, there is much competition, and various forms of mortality throughout each season limit the number of successful colonies in any given area. Seasonal weather trends, such as excessive moisture or dryness and excessively cold or harsh overwintering conditions, can also affect wasp population trends across different regions of the country. For example, excessive rains and wetness during the spring are generally thought to decrease colony survival in ground-nesting yellowjackets.

Paper Wasps
Polistes spp.

Wasps of the genus *Polistes* (see Figure 9.39) build rather simple nests, usually consisting of only one tier or layer of cells. The cells open downward and are not covered. Collectively, this layer of cells is called a comb. Nests are usually suspended beneath horizontal surfaces, commonly hanging from the eaves of houses and beneath window ledges or porch roofs (see Figure 9.40). Polistes nests are rather small, rarely more than 6 to 8 inches in diameter, so there are seldom more than 100 to 200 workers on the nest at any one time.

Hornets
Vespa and *Dolichovespula* spp.

Some of the most universally recognized and fear-provoking social wasp nests are the large grayish brown carton structures often seen hanging from a tree or bush. These nests generally resemble very large, inverted teardrops or bloated soccer balls (Figure 9.41). The wasps that build such nests are commonly referred to as hornets but are considered yellowjackets by entomologists. The nest consists of

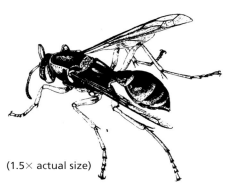

(1.5× actual size)

FIGURE 9.39. A single-comb paper wasp, Polistes spp. (USDA)

several tiers of carton cells, each similar to the single tier of the *Polistes* nest in appearance. A continuous paper envelope surrounds the whole nest. There is a single opening at the lower tip of the nest. As the nest approaches its final size, the new combs are built below the level of this opening, which will then be positioned on the side of the nest.

The **bald-faced hornet**, *Dolichovespula maculata* (Linnaeus), is moderately large and has whitish (*D. maculata* and others) or yellowish (*D. arenaria* and others) markings on the front of the head, between the eyes. The basic color of the body is black, with white markings on the thorax and abdomen (see Figure 9.42). Aerial nesting yellowjackets in the genus *Dolichovespula* can be distinguished from the ground- or structure-nesting yellowjackets of the genus *Vespula* (discussed later) by the noticeable separation between the lower margin of the eye and the base of the mandible.

The **European hornet**, *Vespa crabro germana* Christ, is the largest paper wasp and the only true hornet present in the United States. Its body is brownish and marked with orange. This species was introduced along the Atlantic coast and has extended its range slowly into the midwestern states. It does not build exposed nests but nests in natural cavities, such as hollow logs or stumps, or in cavities within buildings.

Yellowjackets
Vespula spp.

Several species of social wasps known commonly and by entomologists as yellowjackets are the smallest of the common vespids at about 1/2-inch long (see Figure 9.43). Most species typically build their nests underground, so workers will come and go from the nest via an earthen tunnel that ends in a hole at the soil surface. Underground nests are often started in an abandoned mammal burrow or a similar underground cavity. The nest is expanded initially to fill the cavity, and then the cavity is enlarged as the colony develops. Particles of earth and small stones may be piled up around the opening of a burrow that houses a large colony of an underground nesting species. Yellowjackets will often use available openings at or near ground level. Yellowjackets, for instance, have built extensive nests within the voids of concrete block foundations or below railroad ties used in landscaping around patios.

A species that commonly nests in structures has spread widely across the northeastern and midwestern regions of the United States. It is also established in the western United States, in Washington, Idaho, and California. This is the **German yellow-**

FIGURE 9.40. Polistes nest. (Sweetman) (Provonsha)

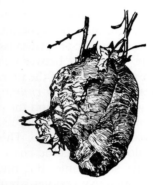

FIGURE 9.41. A bald-faced hornet nest. (USDA)

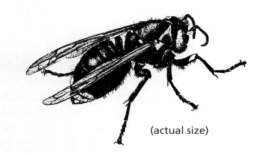

(actual size)

FIGURE 9.42. A bald-faced hornet worker. (USDA)

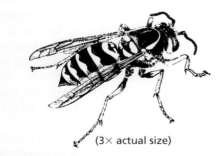

(3× actual size)

FIGURE 9.43. A yellowjacket worker.

jacket, *Vespula germanica*, which apparently was introduced from Europe into the northeastern United States. German yellowjackets are often found nesting in wall voids, attics, or crawlspaces, and they use some available hole or crack in the exterior facing of the building as an entry point.

Whether in the ground or within a wall void, yellowjacket nests are made of carton and resemble the bald-faced hornet nests described earlier. As many as several thousand workers may be produced in a colony in one season. Colonies in certain areas of California and southern Florida will persist for more than a year, so are called perennial. These colonies ultimately develop more workers than typical annual colonies. Some species of *Vespula* forage nearly exclusively on live prey, such as flies, caterpillars, and other insects, while other species forage strongly for meat from carcasses, garbage, and picnic tables to feed developing larvae. Yellowjackets also forage on sources of sugars or other carbohydrates, such as beer, fruit (e.g., sliced watermelon), and sweet beverages at picnic sites. Workers may also obtain sugars from the honeydew of aphids or scale insects. As new queens are produced in the colony in late summer, they demand sugars from the workers, which then forage aggressively for honeydew and other sources of sugar. The tendency to scavenge at human food sources puts these yellowjackets in frequent conflict with people in picnic areas, parks, backyard patios, and so forth. This conflict becomes particularly acute in the late summer and early fall, when the number of workers out foraging is at its peak, and some of their other sources of meat, prey, and sugars are declining.

Yellowjacket workers tend to be somewhat unpredictable in their response to humans who approach the nest. Often, a person approaching the

The Dominulus

The dominulus paper wasp, *Polistes dominulus* (Christ), has spread westward over the past 20 years from New England states to the Great Lakes. It resembles yellowjackets with its yellow and black striping on the abdomen, and confuses professionals when they first encounter this wasp on its exposed paper nest. Unlike other *Polistes*, dominulus wasps may reuse and add to nests built in previous years. They are very active on their nests and can detect human activity at some distance (up to 20 feet away), but are not aggressive in defending their nests until the intruder gets close to the nest. It also outcompetes native species of *Polistes* in areas where it becomes established.

nest is completely ignored, but sometimes a person simply walking nearby will be stung. Most serious stinging incidents occur when the nest is accidentally disturbed. Humans are usually ignored by yellowjacket workers away from the nest, so stinging incidents under such circumstances are usually caused by accidental trapping of the worker against some part of the body (e.g., between folds of clothing, under an arm or leg, or in the mouth when swallowing a beverage from a container that contains a foraging yellowjacket). Many experts consider yellowjackets to be the most dangerous of the social Hymenoptera in the United States, because of the insect's nesting and foraging behavior and the potential for its venom to induce severe, life-threatening allergic responses in certain sting victims.

Nonsocial, or Solitary, Wasps
Family Sphecidae

Sphecid wasps include only solitary nesting species. This means that a single female builds a nest, or several distinct nests, often with several or many cells each. No carton is used in these nests. Each cell is provisioned with live prey, usually another type of insect or a spider. An egg is laid on the prey before the cell is sealed. When not flying, sphecid wasps can be distinguished from vespid wasps at a distance because they do not fold their wings and hold them separately but lay one on top of the other in a flat position on top of their bodies.

Pest management professionals in many areas receive excited calls from homeowners who find their lawns being dug up by hornets. True hornets do not excavate burrows in the ground, but a number of sphecid wasps are known to do so. The species most often mistaken for a hornet is the cicada killer, *Sphecius speciosus* (Drury). It is a large insect, up to 2-inches long (see Figure 9.44). The body is black and strikingly marked with yellow, so that its general appearance bears some resemblance to a large hornet. The female wasp excavates a large burrow about 1/2-inch in diameter. Soil is thrown out of the burrow, leaving a small but unsightly mound of dirt at the entrance. The cell is provisioned with food, such as spiders, caterpillars, cicadas, and other insects that have been stung and paralyzed. The female then deposits an egg on the food and seals the cell. These are not social insects, so each burrow is the result of efforts by a single female. The only real damage done by cicada killer wasps is to lawns or flower beds, and to the psyches of anxious homeowners and their family members. Female wasps will not sting unless they are handled, but their sting can be painful. Similar problems and behaviors are sometimes observed from a large black wasp of the genus *Chlorion*.

Certain sphecid wasps construct their nests of mud and are commonly known as mud daubers (see Figure 9.45). They are frequently observed visiting the edges of mud puddles during the summer, where they obtain mud to make their nests. Their mud nests are often found plastered among the rafters of attics, garages, or outbuildings, or on the sides of buildings (for example, see Figure 9.46). Mud daubers typically prey on spiders. The chances of being stung by a mud dauber are rather remote, but their nests should be approached with some caution. One problem associated with mud daubers' nests is often neglected; the insect or spider prey in these nests, along with the wasp larval and pupal cast skins, can support a population of dermestid beetles, such as the cabinet and carpet beetles. Some dermestid infestations of homes originate in these wasp nests, so they should be removed and destroyed after control is achieved.

Bees
Families Apidae, Xylocopidae, and Bombidae

Certain species of bees can become pests in and around homes. Some species are important primarily because of their ability to inflict stings, while others may also cause structural damage as a result of their nest-building activities.

Honey Bees
Family Apidae
Apis mellifera Linnaeus

Apart from the Africanized honey bee, which has become established in certain parts of Texas and is considered a pest by beekeepers and in other situations, the wild or domesticated European honey bees can become a serious pest when they establish a nest in or on a structure. The most serious problems result when a swarm of honey bees locates a small opening or openings in an exterior wall, down a chimney, or behind some faulty flashing of a home and then nests in a wall void or some other interior area.

Honey bees may be various shades of yellow, black, brown, or orange, with the head, antennae, legs, and a portion of the abdomen being dark (see Figure 9.47). The body is covered with light-colored hairs, thickest on top of the thorax. Worker bees are usually about 2/3-inch long. This is a social species with three adult castes: queens (only one lays eggs in each colony), drones (males), and workers (sterile females). Individual colonies may have 20,000 to 50,000 bees.

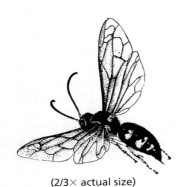

(2/3× actual size)

FIGURE 9.44. A cicada killer wasp.

(1½× actual size)

FIGURE 9.45. An adult mud dauber wasp. (Provonsha)

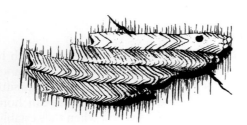

FIGURE 9.46. A mud dauber wasp nest. (Sweetman)

(2½× actual size)

FIGURE 9.47. A honey bee. (USDA) (Provonsha)

Social behavior is highly evolved in the honey bee. In addition to feeding the larvae, workers also amass reserve supplies of honey, which can be used as food by all the members of the colony during periods of adverse conditions. Unless the nest has been built in an unfavorable area, the colony can survive throughout the winter, so these bees are not limited to annual reestablishment of colonies.

Honey bee nests consist of many wax cells constructed by the worker bees. As with yellowjackets and the nests of other social wasps discussed previously, these masses of cells are called combs. However, while some of these cells are used to house the immature stages (eggs, larvae, and pupae), others serve as storage sites for honey. If honey bees become well established within the wall voids of a house, large amounts of wax and honey may collect within the wall. As long as the bees are active, the workers keep the air moving inside the nest by fanning with their wings, so the temperature remains below the melting point of the wax. If the bees are killed, this form of air-conditioning ceases to function. In warm weather or if the interior of the house is kept warm, the wax within the wall void may then become soft enough to melt, allowing the honey to seep out of the storage cells and create a mess. If a sufficient amount of honey is inside the walls, enough may be absorbed by plaster or similar porous wall material that an unsightly and virtually permanent stain may appear on the inside wall.

Another problem inherent to such situations is that the presence of honey in the wall void will attract foraging worker bees from other honey bee colonies. Other insects, such as various flies, ants, and beetles, will also be attracted to the nest site and may later infest other materials inside the home. Thus, there may be a continuous supply of bees or other pests around the house, even though the original colony was destroyed. It is important to advise the homeowner to completely remove the nest as soon as possible after the colony is controlled, even if this requires substantial expense for carpentry and repairs.

Africanized honey bees are similar to the common wild and domesticated honey bees of the United States in appearance, except that they are slightly smaller in size on average (so specialists should be consulted for certain identification of specimens suspected to be the Africanized strain). However, Africanized honey bees are quite different in key aspects of their behavior. First, they are more aggressive than the other strains of honey bees, so they gradually displace other strains in regions where the Africanized strain becomes established. Second, colonies of Africanized bees are much more likely to abscond, or change location, than the domesticated honey bees. Third, Africanized honey bees are much more aggressive in attacking animals, including humans, that disturb the colony. Workers from the nest will attack in great numbers, stinging the threatening animal or human, and the attack will persist much longer than that of non-Africanized honey bees. The defensive zone of attack around Africanized honey bee nests is up to 100 feet when people, pets, or other animals are actively moving about (e.g., children playing) or working with power equipment; virtual direct contact with the nest is needed to provoke other domestic and wild strains of honey bees in the United States. Some Africanized honey bee attacks result in the death of the unfortunate victim, which has led to this strain of honey bees being called killer bees.

The expected range of Africanized honey bees in the United States should ultimately be limited to southern and coastal parts of California, Arizona, New Mexico, Texas, Louisiana, Mississippi, Arkansas, and Georgia; all of Florida; and the eastern seaboard up to the very southern part of Virginia. Some seasonal spread north and inland of this zone will also occur, but the severity of winters in those areas bordering the expected range should kill off colonies in most years.

Carpenter Bees
Family Xylocopidae
Xylocopa spp.

Carpenter bees resemble large bumble bees but have very different nesting behavior. They bore long tunnels into wood and divide these tunnels into cells where individual larvae will develop. While several to many females may be nesting in wood of the same structure or other site, each is acting in a solitary fashion, as these are nonsocial bees.

The common eastern species, *Xylocopa virginica* (Linnaeus), resembles many of the bumble bees closely enough that it is often confused on casual observation. This carpenter bee is black in color and marked with areas of yellow hair, but the dorsal sides of the abdominal segments (except for the apparent first segment) have no areas of yellow hair. In bumble bees, at least some of these abdominal segments will have yellow hair on their dorsal surfaces (see Figure 9.48). Other species of carpenter bees, from other genera, may be black, green, or somewhat purplish in color, and they are variously marked with whitish, yellowish, or reddish hair. The dorsal surface of the abdomen is also generally bare in these species.

The typical carpenter bee gallery has an entrance hole on the wood surface and continues

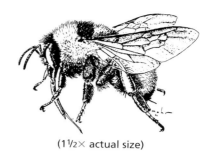

(1½× actual size)

FIGURE 9.48. A bumble bee. (Mohr) (Provonsha)

inward for a short distance. It then turns sharply upward and runs in the same direction as the grain of the wood. The female provisions the galleries by inserting a ball of pollen on which an egg is laid. Live prey, such as insects or spiders, are not used. The female then closes the cell by placing a mass of wood pulp in the gallery. A series of cells are constructed as the bee works backward, out of the gallery. Females often enlarge existing galleries or use old ones, so very complex gallery systems can be developed over a number of years. These galleries are often made in the siding or window trim of homes, and in such cases the structural strength of tunneled timbers may be reduced.

Carpenter bee nests are usually not difficult to locate. Some of the more common sites chosen within buildings include siding, eaves, wooden shakes, porch ceilings, window sills, doors, and so forth. They will also nest in telephone poles, fence railings or posts, and even in lawn furniture. Many types of wood are selected for nesting, but softer woods are preferred. Unpainted or well-weathered wood is much more susceptible to attack than hardwood or well-painted timbers. Another sign to look for in locating carpenter bee galleries is the yellowish or brownish excrement stains created on the side of the home, below the entrance holes to the galleries.

Carpenter bees complete one generation per year in most areas of the United States. Tunnels are prepared and eggs laid in the spring. Larvae and pupae develop in the closed cells in early summer. Adult bees emerge in late summer and return to the same tunnels to hibernate for the winter months. In the spring, the adults mate and the females lay eggs, completing the cycle.

The abandoned nests of carpenter bees are frequently infested by any number of secondary pests, including dermestid beetles, dried fruit moths, and other scavengers that will feed on unused pollen and nectar. Certain wasps, ants, and bees will also be found in old galleries, using them as shelter and nesting sites.

Bumble Bees
Family Bombidae
Bombus spp.

Bumble bees are social insects that generally nest underground (see Figure 9.48). They do not make holes or tunnels in wood but will nest in abandoned mouse burrows under piles of grass clippings or leaves, stones, logs, or other such locations. They seldom become a problem of consequence except in situations where the nests are established close to a sidewalk, near a building foundation, or in some other location where conflict with people or pets is inevitable. A number of species may be commonly encountered, some of which are more likely to sting people than others. Whenever the nest area is directly threatened, bumble bees will attack and sting the intruder as a defensive reaction.

Other Wasps
Horntails
Family Siricidae

Horntails are medium- to large-sized wasps that may emerge from wood that has been in a building for only a few years. Infestations begin in dying trees or in recently felled logs. The female wasp deposits eggs in the wood using her hornlike ovipositor. Larvae bore about in both the sapwood and heartwood layers, making tunnels 1- to 2-feet long. Tunnels are packed with dust-like frass and cast skins from each larval molt. Pupation occurs close to the wood surface, and the new adult emerges and uses its strong jaws to chew out of the wood or almost any building material that may have been used to cover the wood. Emergence holes are about 1/4-inch in diameter. The presence of these holes in walls, floors, or trim may cause concern to the homeowner.

Nearly all horntail infestations are associated with softwoods, such as pine, fir, and spruce, although horntails occasionally emerge from hardwood logs of firewood. Under normal conditions horntails take 2 or 3 years to complete their life cycle. They usually are found in low-cost, rough timbers that were salvaged from diseased or fire-damaged trees. Such wood is seldom kiln dried (which would have killed any eggs or larvae present).

Horntails do not infest lumber after it has been cut, and they usually occur in small numbers. Therefore, treatment of the wood is seldom justified. Homeowners should be informed of the nature of the problem and advised to merely kill horntail wasps that emerge (e.g., with a general-purpose household aerosol insecticide).

Cockroach Egg Parasites

A number of families of the order Hymenoptera include species that are parasites on the eggs of cockroaches. Among these, tiny adult ensign wasps from the family Evaniidae have a peculiar form of abdomen that is held up over the thorax almost like a flag. After the wasp lays its eggs inside cockroach oöthecae, the larvae feed on and kill the cockroach embryos. Adult wasps later emerge and may be seen in homes, especially those infested with oriental or American cockroaches. Ensign wasp presence within a home is nearly always an indication that an infestation of cockroaches is also present. Since they are parasites of important pest species, these wasps could be considered beneficial, but the professional will usually be asked to eliminate both the wasps and the cockroaches.

Certain members of the wasp family Eupelmidae also frequently parasitize brownbanded and American cockroaches. These insects are very small (1/12- to 1/6-inch long) and are quite difficult to identify. If very small hymenopterous insects are found in a home, and if they have no recognizable veins in the wing and seem to jump into the air when they begin to fly, it is quite possible that they may be cockroach egg parasites. Inspection of the premises for cockroaches is indicated, and specimens of these wasps may have to be sent to a qualified entomologist for positive identification.

CONTROLLING WASPS AND BEES
Social Species

Vespid wasps, such as paper wasps (*Polistes* spp.), hornets, and yellowjackets, are active outside the nest during the daylight hours. Nearly the entire colony is in the nest during the evening and nighttime hours, although some workers may be stranded away from the nest and will not return until morning. Control measures for hornets and yellowjackets should be attempted during the nighttime hours when the whole colony is in or on the nest. *Polistes* nests can usually be treated during the daytime, because these wasps are not as aggressive in their nest protection behavior as hornets and yellowjackets.

There are many insecticides labeled for controlling vespid wasp colonies when applied into or onto the nest. The difficulty involves making the treatment without being stung. If applications must be made during the day, the professional should use protective equipment such as boots, heavy coveralls, veiled headwear, and heavy gloves. A very good investment for professionals doing bee and wasp control work is a good wasp suit (see Figure 9.49).

FIGURE 9.49. Technician making insecticide application while wearing a full bee suit for protection from possible bee or wasp attack. (Myers)

Many traditional suits used by beekeepers will not offer sufficient protection against wasps, and particularly aggressive attacks by bald-faced hornets. This equipment should be carefully secured in such a fashion that wasps cannot slip under cuffs or other areas of the clothing. When working around yellowjackets and bald-faced hornets many professionals wear an extra layer of heavy cotton work clothes under the wasp suit so no stings can penetrate through the clothing. Use plenty of masking tape wrapped around the bottoms of pant legs and sleeves and around the collar. If these stinging insects get under the protective suit, a very dangerous situation can arise in terms of basic safety due to falls or other accidents, especially if the technician is working high above the ground on a ladder.

For *Polistes* nests, an aerosol spray of one of the many fast-acting wasp killer aerosols will quickly kill all workers present on the nest. These contain propoxur (Baygon®), permethrin, or some other pyrethroid insecticide. Some of these aerosols can be applied via use of a long pole, where the can is positioned at the top of the pole and activated by use of a lanyard. Otherwise, it is often necessary to use a ladder to reach nests for treatment and removal. A slower-acting insecticidal approach is to apply a dust of carbaryl (Sevin®) directly onto the exposed nests. Carbamate insecticides are very toxic to all hymenopterous insects, and there are dust applicators now available with long tube sections that allow applications to bee or wasp nests under eaves at roofline, or up in trees (see Figure 9.50). After the colony has been killed with the initial insecticide application, the nest should be scraped or knocked

down and removed so as not to attract dermestid beetles at some later time, and to keep wasp pupae from possibly reestablishing the worker force. After nests are removed, be sure that a spray or dust residue of a residual insecticide is left in the nest area to ensure that any worker wasps not present at the time of initial treatment will be killed later.

The most difficult problems in wasp control are generally those that involve large aerial nests of yellowjackets (including bald-faced hornets) and ground or structural nests of yellowjackets. Aerial nests are often not readily accessible from the ground. It would seem that the easiest way to treat such a nest would be to spray it from the ground with a power sprayer, but this is generally not advisable. The force of the spray stream will often break open the carton nest envelope and scatter the nest and excited wasps in all directions. Although the nest will be destroyed and many wasps eventually killed, a number of workers will escape and continue to cause problems for your client on the following morning. The absence of the nest and presence

FIGURE 9.50. Technician applying insecticide dust to paper wasp nest using a specialized duster with very long applicator tube. Since paper wasps (*Polistes* spp.) are typically not very aggressive at defending their nest, and the technician is relatively far from the nest, a bee suit is not necessary for added protection from stings (though it would be advisable when treating bald-faced hornet nests). (Myers)

of insecticide seems to aggravate these stragglers, so they will have a greater tendency to attack and sting nearly any moving object.

Control of aerial nests of hornets and yellowjackets from a ladder should be attempted only while wearing a full wasp suit or equivalent protective clothing. If ladders are needed, this work should be conducted only using heavy-duty ladders in good condition and proper ladder safety procedures (see Chapter 4). Treating or removing aerial wasp, hornet, or yellowjacket nests is no time to be using a flimsy, unsafe ladder. A specialized aerosol formulation or a dust application, directed into the nest opening, should be used for fast wasp knockdown and killing action. A liberal amount of material should usually be applied, up to one large can of aerosol or 3 to 4 tablespoons of dust. Within a few hours, or certainly by the next day, all the colony members should be killed by this initial application. Before nest removal on the next day, a few seconds of aerosol spray should be directed into the nest entrance to be certain all wasps have been killed. The nest should then be removed, if possible.

Aerial wasp nests can even be removed, intact and without the use of insecticide, if the professional wears protective clothing and simply slips a large, heavy plastic garbage bag over the nest and removes it (sealing the bag after the nest is free of its attachment point). A quick dusting of the nest area will serve to kill, over the next day or so, any stragglers not removed with the nest. This removal need not be dangerous as long as a full wasp suit is worn and carefully sealed. Goggles or eyeglasses are necessary when working around a bald-faced hornet's nest, to prevent the hornets from spraying venom through the veil of the wasp suit and into your eyes. After the nest is secured in the garbage bag, the colony can be killed by simply leaving it in the sunlight or some other warm area, because wasps cannot withstand high temperature conditions for any length of time. Alternatively, the nest can be frozen in a freezer for a day or so, or burned in an incinerator.

Control of ground-nesting yellowjacket nests can often be done safely and efficiently during the daytime (see Figure 9.51), but it will generally create fewer safety concerns when scheduled at night. The nest entrance should be located during the daytime and marked in some way for easy and precise location in the evening. When the nest is approached at night, it is a good idea to have the available light (e.g., a spotlight or flashlight) set and focused on the nest from a distance, off to the side. Do not hold it in your hand because it may attract attacking wasps. Again, it is safest to wear protective clothing. Approach the nest slowly and carefully. The quickest and surest way to kill the colony is to

FIGURE 9.51. Technician making liquid insecticide application into yellowjacket ground nest. Since this was a daytime application, a full bee suit was worn for protection from possible wasp attack, but the suit may not be necessary for applications made at dusk or dark. Application of insecticide dust formulations are an especially effective alternate choice for bee and wasp colony control. (Myers)

have a hand duster, loaded with carbaryl, bendiocarb or one of the pyrethroid dusts, in one hand, and a large piece of rag or steel wool in the other. The rag or steel wool is held near the entrance hole, and several large puffs of are quickly applied directly into the hole. As the dust is being applied, the hole should be tightly sealed with the rag or steel wool. More dust can be applied onto the area around the nest entrance to kill any workers that may return the next morning.

Yellowjacket nests in structures should be controlled in a similar manner to those below ground, except that the nest entrance should never be plugged from the outside. If constrained workers cannot escape to the outside, they may locate a way to escape toward the inside of the home or structure, creating a possible stinging threat for people inside. The nest entrance can be approached at night, and a dust (carbaryl, bendiocarb, or pyrethroid) or aerosol spray (synergized pyrethrins or a fast knockdown pyrethroid) can be applied into the entry hole. A follow-up visit the next day is needed to ensure that all yellowjacket activity has ceased. The carton nest should be removed if it is accessible or the homeowner advised to do so, even if some carpentry is necessary. As with honey bee nests within wall voids, yellowjacket nests can become an important source of carpet and other dermestid beetle infestations for the home, so the nest should be removed whenever possible.

Much of the success of treatment for a honey bee infestation in a house or other structure is dependent on steps the professional should take prior to insecticide application. The professional should explain the situation to the customer in detail, making sure the client is aware of the possibility of the undesirable aftereffects of odor and staining from melting wax, honey, and rotting bees. The professional should also realize it is quite impossible to guarantee that bees will not return unless the nest and the honey are removed and the entrance hole sealed.

In most cases, a dust formulation of carbaryl, bendiocarb or one of the pyrethroids should be chosen for treatment of voids within the walls. (If large amounts of liquid insecticide are used, spotting or staining of inside walls with insecticide will likely result.) Dust should be blown into the entrance hole used by the bees. If the nest can be reached by drilling a hole into a wall, treatment can be made from inside, without the use of protective clothing or a ladder, which may be necessary for outside applications. However, the possibility of forcing bees into indoor areas and creating a safety hazard should be considered. It is best to treat at night when the bees are less active, and to wear protective clothing. Follow applications into the entry hole with residual insecticide spray or dust treatments to surfaces around the nest entrance.

One treatment will usually be sufficient, but a second treatment may be necessary a few days later. As with treatment of yellowjacket nests in structures, the honey bee nest entrance must not be sealed until all the bees are dead. Then, all openings in the vicinity of the nest entrance should be caulked and painted. Professionals are often called to remove wild honey bee swarms from exposed situations outdoors, particularly during the spring. At the center of this mass of bees will be a queen, which all the other bees will follow. Swarms often cause quite a lot of fright and disruption in public areas. While swarms can be killed with appropriate aerosol sprays or insecticidal dust applications, or by placing the whole swarm in a large plastic garbage bag, many professionals keep a list of local beekeepers just for such situations. Beekeepers will usually remove swarms and place them into beehives for use in producing honey.

In areas where Africanized honey bees are known to be present, pest control professionals should approach the control of any honey bee swarms or nests with great caution. Control of these bees should be undertaken only after completing specialized training. State agricultural agencies can provide or arrange for such training. A full bee suit made of heavy-grade material should be worn at each job and carefully sealed at all possible bee access points. Care should be taken before insecticide application is made to be sure all residents, neighbors, and onlookers, who might be considered

by the bees as a threat, are out of the area or safely indoors. Africanized honey bees are not resistant or especially difficult to kill with insecticides, so the materials and techniques just discussed for bee and wasp control can be used effectively.

Bumble bee nests can be controlled using the same procedures described for underground nests of yellowjackets.

Nonsocial, or Solitary, Species

Cicada killers can be efficiently controlled by treatment, with either a liquid or dust formulation, of the lawn areas where the wasps are burrowing. Residual insecticides such as are used for ant and other crawling insect control outdoors will provide effective control, usually within a day or so. Direct applications of carbaryl, bendiocarb, or pyrethroid dust into the burrows can also be made.

Mud daubers are not aggressive about defending nests under construction. However, protective clothing should be worn. A residual insecticide liquid or dust application to the mud nests and the surfaces in the immediate area will provide effective control. Then, scrape away and remove the nests, if possible.

Carpenter bees can be controlled by use of the same insecticidal dust or aerosol treatments recommended for controlling wasps or other bees. Apply these insecticides into the gallery entrances and then plug the holes securely with pieces of wooden dowel coated with carpenter's glue. Drilling and treating the infested wood is usually not necessary, and galleries can be plugged immediately because bees that might be inside the gallery will not be able to bore their way out of the gallery before succumbing to the insecticide. The holes should not be sealed with caulk or other such soft materials, because they may be penetrated by emerging bees later that season if all the larvae or adults are not killed by the insecticide. Wood surfaces in the vicinity of the gallery entrance holes can be treated with a residual insecticide after the holes have been treated and sealed, to control any bees that may return to the area. Use of protective clothing may be advisable while treating and plugging gallery holes even though female carpenter bees, like other solitary species, are not aggressive at defending their nests.

Cockroach parasites may be annoying to the homeowner if they occur in sufficient numbers. However, these wasps cannot sting people. They can be controlled by space treatments of synergized pyrethrins or other nonresidual insecticides labeled for this type of application. Control of the cockroaches these wasps are parasitizing is necessary to achieve long-term elimination of these wasps. Make a careful identification of the cockroach species involved (there may be more than one) and consult Chapter 6 of this book for cockroach management procedures.

SUPPLEMENTARY READING MATERIAL

Aho, T. "Ant Bait Specifics Yields Control for PCOs." *Pest Control* 64, no. 4 (1996): 48, 54–55.

Akre, R. D., A. Greene, J. F. MacDonald, P. J. Langdolt, and H. Davis. *Yellowjackets of America North of Mexico.* U.S. Department of Agriculture, Agricultural Handbook no. 552. Washington, D.C.; 1980. 102 pp.

Edwards, R. *Social Wasps: Their Biology and Control.* Sussex, England: Rentokil Limited, 1980. 398 pp.

Granovsky, T. A. "Effective Ant Surveys and Pricing Can Generate More Dollars." *Pest Control 63,* no. 4 (1995): 40–43, 48.

Granovsky, T. A., and H. N. Howell. "A Practical Approach to Controlling *Monomorium pharaonis* (L.), Alias Pharaoh or Sugar Ant." *Pest Management* 2, no. 5 (1983): 11–14.

Granovsky, T. A., and H. N. Howell. "Texas A&M Research Team Develops New Pharaoh Ant Control Technique." *Pest Control Technology* 11, no. 3 (1983): 30, 32, 34, 62.

Gulmahamad, H. "Argentine Ant: The Genghis Khan of the Ant World." *Pest Management* 14, no. 6 (1995): 8–15.

Hedges, S.A. *Pest Identification Series, Volume I: The Ants.* Pest Control Technol. Media Group. available on the Internet at http://www.pctonline.com/store/

Hedges, S. A. *Field Guide for the Management of Structure Infesting Ants. 2nd Edition.* Cleveland: GIE, Inc. Publishers, 1998. 289 pp.

Hedges, S. A. "The Great (Ant) Bait Debate." *Pest Control Technology* 24, no. 4 (1996): 32–33, 36, 38–39, 101.

Hedges, S. A. "IDing Ants Made Easy." *Pest Control Technology* 23, no. 5 (1995): 36–39.

Hedges, S. A. "Pavement Ant Control in Commercial Buildings." *Pest Control Technology* 23, no. 5 (1995): 50–51, 54, 56, 58.

The Hive and the Honeybee. Hamilton, Ill.: Dadant & Sons, 1975. 740 pp.

Klotz, J. H., B. Reid, L. Hansen, and S. Klotz. "Ecology to Control Carpenter Ants." *Pest Control* 64, no. 6 (1996): 46, 48, 50.

Klotz, J. H., and D. F. Williams. "Ant Baits: A Case of Fatal Attraction." *Pest Control* 63, no. 10 (1995): 82–84.

MacDonald, J. F. *Biology, Recognition, Medical Importance and Control of Indiana Social Wasps.* Purdue University Agricultural Experiment Station Bulletin no. 219. 22 pp.

Smith, E. H. "Controlling Those Pharaoh Ants in Hospital Areas, Part I." *Pest Control* 51, no. 11 (1983): 46, 82.

Smith, E. H. "Controlling Those Pharaoh Ants in Hospital Areas, Part II." *Pest Control* 51, no. 12 (1983): 42.

Smith, M. R. *House-Infesting Ants of the Eastern United States: Their Recognition, Biology and Economic Importance.* USDA/ARS Technological Bulletin no. 1,326. Washington, D.C., 1965.

Structure Invading Ants of Florida. University of Florida Publications. Gainesville, 1995. 16 pp.

Univ. of California Statewide IPM Program. *Key to Identifying Common Household Ants.* available on the Internet at http://www.ipm.ucdavis.edu/TOOLS/ANTKEY/

Univ. of California Statewide IPM Program. *Pest Management Guidelines: Ants in the Home & Landscape.* available on the Internet at http://www.ipm.ucdavis.edu/PMG/PESTNOTES/pn7411.html

Wilson, E. O. *The Insect Societies.* Cambridge, Mass.: Harvard University Press, 1971. 548 pp.

Wilson, G. R., and M. J. Booth. "Pharaoh Ant Control with Insect Growth Regulator in Hospitals." *Pest Control* 49, no. 3 (1981): 14–15, 19, 74.

CHAPTER 10 | Stored Product Pests

The pests of stored products are so numerous that it is impossible to discuss all of them in a single chapter. The aim of this chapter is to discuss only the major insect pests found in mills, warehouses, processing plants, homes, and retail stores. Vertebrate pests are discussed in later chapters.

The stored product insects of concern to the professional exist under very specific conditions. They are usually found living in products such as dried fruits, spices, flour, bran, peas, dried vegetables, dried flowers, grain, milled cereal products, dog food, nuts, candy, macaroni and spaghetti, cheese, and other similar items.

Stored product pests contaminate—and thus eliminate for human consumption—far more food than they eat. They are most important as pests of stored grain, damaging about 10% of the world's grain production. Stored product pests also are important in the household and retail stores as "pantry pests" that find their way into packaged cereals, spices, and other foodstuffs.

Many stored product insects feed generally on all types of dried vegetables and animal matter, while others have more definite food preferences. Certain stored product pests originate in crops still growing in the field, while others infest food products during processing and storage. Stored product pests may fly into buildings from the outside, come from secluded areas indoors, or migrate into uninfested items from infested sources, such as food refuse that collects in cracks and crevices. They can also be carried into a building on materials other than food products, such as furniture, rugs, and bedding, as well as in or on almost any product of plant or animal origin. For example, some home decorations use dried flowers or grain, which can become infested by stored product pests. The professional must be alert to these alternative sources of infestation when inspecting homes and offices.

Most pests of stored products are of tropical or subtropical origin. As a result, they live and reproduce best under warm conditions. With only a few exceptions, they cannot live for long at low temperatures, and they usually do not hibernate. Almost all of them are adapted to living on foods with a very low moisture content, although mites and psocids are exceptions, and require a comparatively high moisture content. Very few stored product pests can live and breed at temperatures above 95°F, and most do not lay eggs at temperatures below about 60°F. Certain insects and mites, however, can breed at temperatures of 40°F to 50°F if moisture conditions are suitable; spider beetles, which may be serious pests in the northern parts of the United States, are quite active at these temperatures.

In mills and warehouses, it is essential to **inspect** regularly for the presence of stored product pests. The first consideration in the prevention of infestation is to have all grain, cereal dust, and other debris in which insects can breed removed (i.e., proper sanitation), as well as pointing out to the owners of the premises that finished products kept too long in storage can be a prime source of infestation to the entire area. Infested goods should be removed from the premises as soon as possible to prevent spread of the infestation to uninfested merchandise. These and other preventive and corrective measures will be discussed in greater detail later in this chapter.

Insects of stored products can be separated into four groups according to their feeding habits. *A knowledge of the feeding habits of these pests, some knowledge of their biology and behavior, and the ability to identify the pests are invaluable to the pest management professional.*

• **Internal feeders**—These insect larvae feed entirely within the kernels of whole grain and palletized product and thus may remain undetected until adults emerge from the kernels. Examples: rice weevil, granary weevil, lesser grain borer, and Angoumois grain moth.

- **External feeders**—These insects feed on the outside of the grain. They may also chew through the outer seed coat and devour the inside. These are known as external feeders. Examples: Indianmeal moth, drugstore beetle, flat grain beetle, cadelle, khapra beetle, and cigarette (or tobacco) beetle.
- **Scavengers**—Scavengers feed on grain only after the seed coat has been broken, either mechanically or by some other insect. Examples: confused flour beetle, red flour beetle, Mediterranean flour moth, and sawtoothed grain beetle.
- **Secondary pests**—Secondary pests feed only on materials that are deteriorating, damp, and have some mold growth present. Some of them feed on mold rather than the food product. Examples: yellow mealworm, foreign grain beetle, some grain mites, and psocids.

Occasional exceptions to these feeding habits may be found; however, as a general rule, each of these insects will feed as indicated.

Adults of most of these insects can be identified by the use of the descriptions and the key in Figure 10.1, and the larvae by the use of the key in Figure 10.2.

INTERNAL FEEDERS
Rice Weevil
Sitophilus oryzae (Linnaeus)
Order Coleoptera; Family Curculionidae

The rice weevil is also known as the black weevil. Adults are reddish brown and about 1/8-inch long. There are four light red or yellow spots on the wing covers, and the punctures on the pronotum are round (see Figure 10.1, and Figures 10.3 and 10.4, which follow page 254). This weevil is widely distributed due to grain and food distribution. It can fly and frequently infests grain both in the field and in storage. *The rice weevil is probably the most destructive pest of stored grain.*

The legless larva has a short, stout, whitish body and tan head. When viewed from the side, the body appears to be more or less straight in outline on the underside and semicircular on the backside. The top surface of each of the first three abdominal segments has two transverse creases, so that the segment is divided into three subsections (see Figure 10.2, and Figure 10.5, which follows page 254).

Both adults and larvae feed on a wide variety of grains. The female bores a hole in a grain kernel, deposits a single egg in this depression, and seals the hole with a gelatinous fluid. She may lay as many as 300 to 400 eggs in her average lifetime of 4 to 5 months. The larval and pupal stages are spent inside the grain (see Figure 10.5, following page 254), with the adult emerging through an irregular exit hole on emergence from the pupal skin. These exit holes are usually the first sign of grain damage, and by this time serious damage may have been done to the entire lot of grain (see Figure 10.7). The egg, larval, and pupal stages may all be completed in as little as 26 days under favorable temperature and moisture conditions. Because both the larvae and the adults feed on the seed kernels, the grain is completely damaged beyond any use.

Infested grain that does not have any damage visible to the naked eye can be detected by staining techniques that make the gelatinous egg plugs visible. Grain to be examined is immersed in a solution of acid fuchsin for 2 to 5 minutes, after which excess stain is removed by washing in tap water.

The tiny egg plugs, which are about the size of an ordinary pin prick, show up a bright cherry red, and feeding punctures and mechanical punctures are light pink. A stain of gentian violet can also be used. With this stain, egg plugs are purple. Although it is seldom found in materials other than whole grain or seeds, this beetle has been recorded from solidified milled products, such as macaroni and caked flour.

Granary Weevil
Sitophilus granarius (Linnaeus)
Order Coleoptera; Family Curculionidae

This chestnut brown or black beetle closely resembles the rice weevil. It is easily distinguished, however, because it has no markings on its back, has no functional wings, and the punctures on the pronotum are oval (see Figures 10.3 and 10.4, following page 254). The granary weevil has become so specialized that it has no functional wings and thus is dependent almost entirely on humans for its distribution. It is found breeding only on grain in storage. The granary weevil is more common in the northern states than southern states, but it is found in all parts of the country.

The granary weevil larva is similar in appearance to the rice weevil, but usually the first four abdominal segments bear two transverse creases on the top side (see Figure 10.2). Both larvae and adults feed on whole grain, such as oats, wheat, rye, and barley that has not been milled. They occasionally infest beans and nuts, as do rice weevils.

Granary weevil adults are resistant to cold

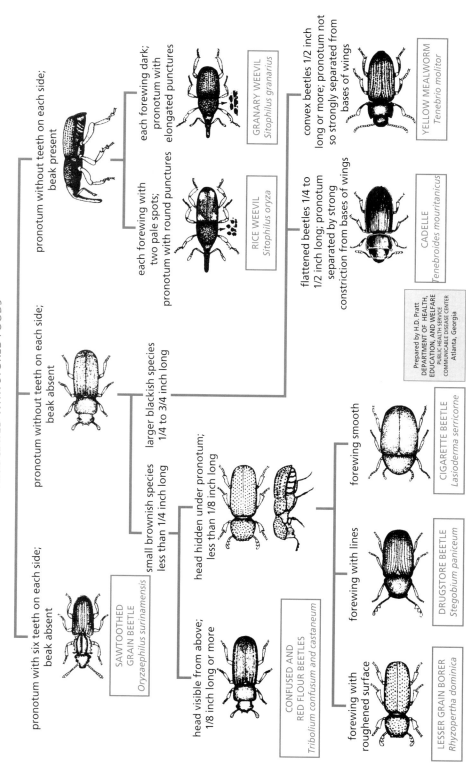

A PICTORIAL KEY TO SOME COMMON BEETLES
ASSOCIATED WITH STORED FOODS

pronotum with six teeth on each side; beak absent

SAWTOOTHED GRAIN BEETLE
Oryzaephilus surinamensis

pronotum without teeth on each side; beak absent

small brownish species less than 1/4 inch long

larger blackish species 1/4 to 3/4 inch long

head visible from above; 1/8 inch long or more

head hidden under pronotum; less than 1/8 inch long

CONFUSED AND RED FLOUR BEETLES
Tribolium confusum and castaneum

forewing with roughened surface

LESSER GRAIN BORER
Rhyzopertha dominica

forewing with lines

DRUGSTORE BEETLE
Stegobium paniceum

forewing smooth

CIGARETTE BEETLE
Lasioderma serricorne

pronotum without teeth on each side; beak present

each forewing dark; pronotum with elongated punctures

GRANARY WEEVIL
Sitophilus granarius

each forewing with two pale spots; pronotum with round punctures

RICE WEEVIL
Sitophilus oryza

convex beetles 1/2 inch long or more; pronotum not so strongly separated from bases of wings

YELLOW MEALWORM
Tenebrio molitor

flattened beetles 1/4 to 1/2 inch long; pronotum separated by strong constriction from bases of wings

CADELLE
Tenebroides mouritanicus

Prepared by H.D. Pratt
DEPARTMENT OF HEALTH, EDUCATION, AND WELFARE
PUBLIC HEALTH SERVICE
COMMUNICABLE DISEASE CENTER
Atlanta, Georgia

FIGURE 10.1. A pictorial key to adults of some of the more common beetles that infest stored grain and other food products. (Courtesy U.S. Public Health Service, Communicable Disease Center, Atlanta, Georgia)

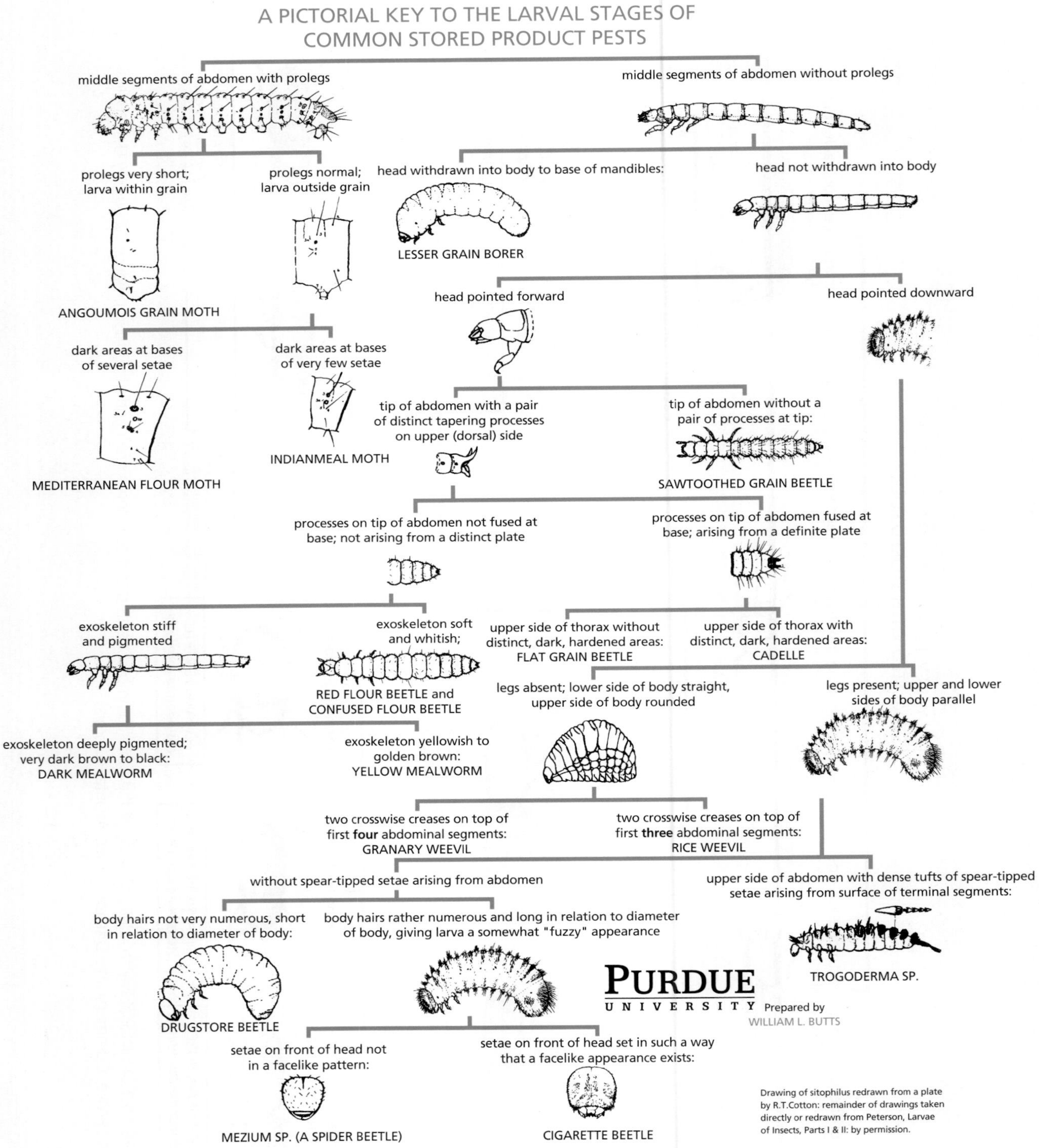

FIGURE 10.2. A pictorial key to the larval stages of some of the more common insect pests of stored grain and other food products.

FIGURE 10.7. Typical damage by two stored grain pests. *Top:* An ear of corn damaged by the Angoumois grain moth. Note the rather regular circular outline of the emergence holes. *Bottom:* Shelled corn and wheat damaged by the rice weevil. the outline of the holes in the kernel is more irregular than those made by the Angoumois grain moth.

weather and may hibernate through the winter. Adults vary greatly in size, differing in this respect from most insects. Adult size usually depends on the size of the grain kernel. Large kernels produce large adults. The female drills a hole in the whole grain, buries a single egg in it, and seals the hole with a gelatinous plug in the same way the rice weevil does. Egg plugs can be easily detected using the dye technique described in the section on the rice weevil. Each female may lay up to 250 eggs. Larval and pupal development take place inside the grain. On leaving the grain, the adult leaves an irregular, easily visible hole in the seed coat. Adults live an average of 7 to 8 months.

Angoumois Grain Moth
Sitotroga cerealella (Olivier)
Order Lepidoptera; Family Gelechiidae

The Angoumois grain moth is next in importance only to rice and granary weevils as a pest of stored grain. It is frequently encountered in homes, warehouses, and stores. It is distributed throughout the country, but is particularly important in the southern, eastern, and central states.

In most cases, the Angoumois grain moth attacks only whole kernels of corn, wheat, and other grains and seeds. It is sometimes found in homes, emerging from decorative ears of corn or decorative boxes containing seed. Bird seed and cereal baits for rodents are subject to infestation if they contain whole kernels. Unusual infestations have been reported in cornmeal, flour, cashew nuts, hulled chestnuts, and dry, minced onions.

Eggs are laid on or near grain either in the field or after harvest. Upon hatching, the minute, white larvae (see Figure 10.2) bore into the kernels of grain and feed on the inside. When mature, the larva eats its way to the outer portion of the grain, leaving only a thin layer of the outer seed coat intact. Pupation takes place just under the seed coat. When the adult emerges from the grain, it pushes aside the thin layer of seed coat, leaving a small trapdoor covering its exit point from the kernel (see Figure 10.7). The adult is small (wing spread about 2/3 inch), yellowish white, with pale front wings. The hind wings are characteristically pointed and fringed (see Figure 10.6, which follows page 254, and Figure 10.8).

Lesser Grain Borer
Rhyzopertha dominica (Fabricius)
Order Coleoptera; Family Bostrichidae

The lesser grain borer is a dark brown, cylindrically shaped beetle that is about 1/8-inch long. The head is nearly hidden by the thorax when viewed from above (see Figure 10.9, following page 254).

The larva is thick bodied, cylindrical, and grublike. It resembles the larva of the drugstore beetle, but the lesser grain borer larva has the head retracted into the thorax to about the level of the mandibles (see Figure 10.2, and Figure 10.10, which follows page 254). Also, the body diameter of the lesser grain borer larva is largest in the thoracic region, in contrast to the drugstore beetle larva, which is largest in the abdominal region. Body setae (hairs) are very short on lesser grain borer larvae.

This insect represents a transitional form insofar as its feeding habits are concerned. The eggs are laid either singly or in clusters in the grain mass, and larvae may enter the kernels and develop within, or they may feed externally in the flourlike dust that accumulates from the feeding of the adults and their fellow larvae. Pupae may be found either within the hollowed out grain (see Figure 10.10, following page 254) or outside in the grain dust. Both larvae and adults may bore into articles such as books and wood. The life cycle from egg to adult averages about 58 days.

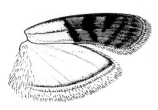

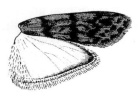

FIGURE 10.8. Wing patterns of some common moths that are pests of stored products. Top: The Indianmeal moth; note the light basal area of the wing and the much darker coloration from near the middle to the tip. Center: The Mediterranean flour moth; note the zigzag black lines that run across the wing. Adults are quite difficult to separate from a number of similar species. Bottom: The Angoumois grain moth; note the narrow, fingerlike extension of the leading edge of the tip of the hind wing. This characteristic is helpful in distinguishing this moth from other moths associated with stored products.

EXTERNAL FEEDERS
Drugstore Beetle

Stegobium paniceum (Linnaeus)
Order Coleoptera; Family Anobiidae

The drugstore beetle is a brown, cylindrical beetle about 1/8-inch long. The adult closely resembles the cigarette beetle but does not have the hump-backed appearance of that beetle. The drugstore beetle has **distinct longitudinal lines** on the wing covers, which the cigarette beetle lacks (see Figure 10.1, and Figure 10.11, which follows page 254). Adult drugstore beetles are good fliers.

The larva is about 1/8 inch in length, grub-shaped or C-shaped, and near white in color. The mouthparts and the underside of the head are brown. There are numerous short, colorless setae on the head and body. There are no distinctive pigmented markings on the body, and the mouth opening is directed approximately downward (see Figure 10.2, and Figure 10.12, which follows page 254).

In the home, the drugstore beetle feeds in flour, breakfast cereals, red pepper, or almost any food it can find. One of the most commonly infested materials is kibbled dog food. It has even been found in such items as books, wheat treated with strychnine, and pharmaceutical products (thus the name drugstore beetle).

Cigarette, or Tobacco, Beetle

Lasioderma serricorne (Fabricius)
Order Coleoptera; Family Anobiidae

The cigarette beetle is the most important pest of stored tobacco. It may also be a serious pest of items such as books, flax tow, cottonseed meal, rice, ginger, pepper, paprika, dried fish, crude drugs, seeds, pyrethrum powder, and dried plants.

Adults are light brown, about 1/8-inch long, and fly readily. The head is bent downward, so the beetle has a distinct **hump-backed appearance** (see Figure 10.1, and Figure 10.11, which follows page 254). The female lays about 30 eggs over a period of about 3 weeks in newly harvested tobacco or other susceptible food items. The adults are good fliers and are most active during the early evening hours unless temperatures are below 65°F. During the day they hide in dark places. Even though they are strong fliers, their primary means of spreading is via infested materials transported by humans.

The cigarette beetle larva resembles the drugstore beetle larva, but the body hairs of the cigarette beetle are considerably longer, giving it a more fuzzy appearance (see Figure 10.2, and Figure 10.12, which follows page 254). The color is near white throughout, except for a distinctive group of yellowish-brown markings on the front surface of the head. The lower margin of the head is colored, and a series of four spots are arranged just above this area in such a way that a pattern suggestive of a little clownlike face is formed. Larvae feed on dried tobacco leaves, causing great damage.

Cadelle

Tenebroides mauritanicus (Linnaeus)
Order Coleoptera; Family Ostomatidae

The cadelle, also known as the bread beetle and the bolting cloth beetle, can be found in rice and flour mills, in grain stored on farms, and in country elevators. It is commonly found in such packaged materials as ground cereals, corn, oats, nuts, spices, and fruits, as well as in whole grains.

Both larvae and adults gnaw through sacks and even through wooden boards, thus leaving openings large enough for other insects to enter. Adults are shiny black and about 1/3-inch long (see Figure

10.1). The pronotum is separated from the wing bases by a strong constriction, which is useful in identification.

The cadelle larva is strikingly marked and is one of the most easily distinguished of the stored product pest larvae (see Figure 10.2). It is about 5/8-inch long when full grown and is dirty white in color. It has a dark brown head, and the mouth opening is directed forward. The prothorax has a dark brown hardened plate that covers most of the top surface of the segment. The second and third segments of the thorax have a pair of distinct brown spots on the top surface of each. The last segment of the abdomen has a dark brown plate on top, from which two distinct projections arise. Although a number of beetle larvae would fit this description, the cadelle is the only one of these likely to be found in stored grain and food products.

Eggs are deposited at random in flour or in crevices of food materials. A female will lay from 10 to 60 eggs in a batch and may lay as many as 3,500 in a lifetime.

The larvae feed on almost all grains as well as on flour, meal, bread, dried fruits, and similar foods. They also seriously damage tobacco by boring into it. In grain, the larvae often eat only the germinal portion of a grain, then move to another grain. In this way they damage a very large number of kernels. Moreover, cadelle damage provides the means of entry for other stored product pests that cannot penetrate the seed coat on their own.

Both adults and larvae may be active in the winter, but they hibernate when the temperature gets too low.

Trogoderma, or Cabinet Beetles
Trogoderma spp.
Order Coleoptera; Family Dermestidae

Prior to its being discovered in California in 1953, the **khapra beetle**, *Trogoderma granarium* Everts, had not been known to occur in the United States. Since this insect is one of the most serious pests of stored grain, a general investigation of grain storage facilities in the southwest was carried out, resulting in numerous subsequent records of infestation. It has now been reported in all areas of the country.

Two members of the genus *Trogoderma* are well-known pests in this country: *T. ornatum* (Say), the **cabinet beetle**, and *T. inclusum* LeConte, the **larger cabinet beetle**. These two beetles are similar in appearance; most specimens have well-defined areas of light brown markings on their very dark elytra (see Figure 10.13, following page 254). A distinctly indented notch on the inner margin of the eye of the larger cabinet beetle serves as a means of

separating the two species.

In contrast to these species, the khapra beetle does not have well-marked areas of light coloration on the elytra (some specimens show a confused, indistinct mottling). In this respect it is quite similar to another species, *T. glabrum* (Herbst), which is widely distributed in the United States. It is extremely difficult to separate individuals of the two species. All pest managers, especially those located near ports of entry and airports, should be alert to the possibility of encountering the khapra beetle. If there is any suspicion of a khapra beetle, the insects should be sent for identification to experts familiar with this group of beetles.

Trogoderma variabile Beal (the **warehouse beetle**) is a widely distributed pest of stored cereal grains and other food products. *T. variabile* is a variable species morphologically, and it is not improbable that many of the older records of *T. inclusum* as a pest of stored products may actually have been *T. variabile* infestations. The warehouse beetle has been recorded from a number of sites in which it was present in cereal baits containing anticoagulant rodent poisons.

The larvae of the genus *Trogoderma* are similar to each other in appearance (see Figure 10.14, following page 254). When full grown, they are about 1/4-inch long and about 1/8-inch wide at the middle of the body. The body is tapered slightly at both ends and is yellow to medium brown, and the last three or four abdominal segments bear dense clumps of darker colored setae that have very distinctive spear-shaped tips. Both larvae and adults of this genus are very difficult to identify. Larvae and any adults without distinctive markings should be submitted to an expert for identification.

Control of *Trogoderma* may require fumigation. Only licensed fumigators should be involved in this work.

Indianmeal Moth
Plodia interpunctella (Hubner)
Order Lepidoptera; Family Pyralidae

Adults of the Indianmeal moth have a wingspread of about 3/4-inch. The front wings are tan on the front third and reddish-brown with a coppery luster on the back two-thirds (see Figure 10.8, and Figure 10.15, which follows page 254). The mature larva is about 1/2-inch long and a dirty white color with a sometimes greenish or pinkish tint. The larva feeds on all kinds of grains and grain-based products, seeds, powdered milk, dog food, crackers, candy, nuts, chocolate, dried fruits, and virtually all other dried foodstuffs around the home. This moth is the most commonly found stored product moth in the home (see Figure 10.16, following page 254).

Larvae, when ready to pupate, leave their food supply and wander about in search of a suitable place in which to spin their white silken cocoons and pupate. During this period, they are frequently noticed by the homeowner and mistaken for clothes moth larvae. It is important that the pest management professional be able to distinguish between the larvae of clothes moths and the Indianmeal moth to make proper recommendations and treatment for control. The Indianmeal moth is found in most any stored food product, feeds in or near a tunnel-like case with frass incorporated into it, and leaves extensive webbing matted over the surface of food products on which it feeds.

Adults, too, are frequently mistaken for clothes moths. The distinctive markings on the wings of the Indianmeal moth separate it from clothes moths. Adult Indianmeal moths live less than 2 weeks, are nonfeeding, and chiefly fly at dusk in the early evening. During the day they prefer to rest in poorly lighted areas. If disturbed, they fly in an irregular zigzag pattern.

The larvae of these moths are rather difficult to identify, but reference to the pictorial key (see Figures 10.3, and 10.17 following page 254) should be helpful in making determinations.

SCAVENGERS

Confused Flour Beetle

Tribolium confusum Jacquelin duVal
Order Coleoptera; Family Tenebrionidae

The confused flour beetle is a pest primarily in the northern states. The adult is reddish-brown and about 1/8-inch long (see Figure 10.1, and Figure 10.18 which follows page 254). It is often confused with the red flour beetle, but the antenna of the confused flour beetle is gradually enlarged to form a four-segmented club, whereas the antenna of the red flour beetle enlarges abruptly to form a distinct three-segmented club (see Figure 10.19, following page). The small size of the confused flour beetle enables it to work its way inside many sealed containers. It feeds on a wide variety of foodstuffs and is a particularly important pest in flour. It is also commonly found in cereal products, peas, beans, dried fruits, spices, and other similar materials.

The adults of confused flour beetles do not fly. They may live as long as 3 years. Each female can lay as many as 300 to 400 eggs in her lifetime.

The larva is somewhat cylindrical in body shape and about 1/8- to 1/4-inch long (see Figure 10.2). It is yellowish-white in color except for the darker mandibles and the pair of projections that arise from the last abdominal segment. There are no distinct darkened areas on the top side of the body segments. The head is flattened, so the mouth opening is forward.

Red Flour Beetle

Tribolium castaneum (Herbst)
Order Coleoptera; Family Tenebrionidae

The red flour beetle is primarily a pest in southern states. It is very similar in appearance and habits to the confused flour beetle. Adults can fly, which probably accounts for the much more frequent appearance of this beetle in farm-stored grain.

The red flour beetle, confused flour beetle, sawtoothed grain beetle, and Indianmeal moth are the most important pests of stored foods in retail stores and homes.

Flat Grain Beetle

Cryptolestes pusillus (Schonherr)
Order Coleoptera; Family Cucujidae

The flat grain beetle is the smallest of the common grain-infesting insects. Adults are flattened, oblong, reddish-brown, and about 1/16-inch long. The antennae are slender and are about two-thirds as long as the body.

The larva is a little less than 3 millimeters long. The abdominal segments are about one-and-a-half times as wide as the thorax, and the last segment of the abdomen bears a pair of distinctly sclerotized, hooklike structures joined at the base. These processes and the head are brown in color, in contrast to the remainder of the body, which is nearly white.

Sawtoothed Grain Beetle

Oryzaephilus surinamensis (Linnaeus)
Order Coleoptera; Family Cucujidae

The sawtoothed grain beetle is found in such foods as breakfast cereals, flour, dried fruits, macaroni, dried meats, chocolate, and others of a similar nature. It is small enough that it can readily penetrate tiny cracks and crevices to get into packaged foodstuffs. When left undisturbed, a large population will develop rapidly.

The adult is a small brownish beetle about 1/8-inch long. It is easily identified by the six sawlike projections on each side of the thorax (see Figure 10.1). The adult may live and breed for as long as 3 years. It does not fly.

The female lays 50 to 300 white, shiny eggs. They are laid either singly or in small masses in crevices in the food supply, although they are also laid freely in such items as flour.

The larva is less than 1/8-inch long and is long and narrow in body form (see Figure 10.2). The head is somewhat flattened, and the mouth opening points almost straight ahead rather than downward. The antennae are about as long as the head. The last segment of the abdomen is tapered and there are no large dorsal projections. The body is dirty white, and each abdominal segment bears a yellowish plate on the top side.

The larva nibbles on finely divided food particles because it cannot feed on large particles, such as whole grain. For this reason, this beetle and its larvae are frequently found along with other insects that feed on larger grains.

The **merchant grain beetle**, O. mercator, is similar in appearance and habits to the sawtoothed grain beetle but is found in warmer climates. To separate these two beetles, one must examine the small projection on either side of the head, behind the eyes (see Figure 10.20 following page 254). The sawtoothed grain beetle projections are curved and wide, whereas the merchant grain beetle projections are pointed and narrower. A behavioral feature used to distinguish the two species is that the merchant grain beetle flies, whereas the sawtoothed grain beetle does not.

Mediterranean Flour Moth
Ephestia kuehniella Zeller
Order Lepidoptera; Family Pyralidae

The Mediterranean flour moth is a pest in the home and in food-processing plants such as feed mills. It infests such items as flour, nuts, chocolate, beans, and dried fruits. Adults have a wing expanse of about 1 inch (see Figure 10.21, following page 254). The front wings are a pale grey with wavy black lines running across them. The hind wings are a dirty white. It can be distinguished from the Angoumois grain moth via the hind wings, which are rounded at the tips rather than pointed, as in the Angoumois (see Figure 10.8). The Mediterranean flour moth is most easily recognized by its characteristic pose when resting. The front of the body is raised, giving the wings a distinct downward slope with the tip of the abdomen protruding up between them. None of the other house moths have this characteristic pose.

Females lay their eggs in accumulations of flour or other milled products. The larvae hatch in a few days, and when mature, they measure about 1/2-inch long. They are white to pink, with a few small black spots on each body segment, from which the body hairs arise (see Figure 10.2).

The larvae spin silken threads as they move about. These threads fasten particles together in a dense mat that is very characteristic of this insect. Larvae are often found away from the infested product, seeking a crack or crevice in which to pupate.

Species closely related to the Mediterranean flour moth include the tobacco moth (or chocolate moth), *Ephestia elutella* (Hubner); the almond moth, *Cadra cautella* (Walker); and the raisin moth, *Cadra figulilella* (Gregson). All are found throughout the United States and are similar in appearance and biology. They may also be found in similar habitats feeding on similar stored products. However, the tobacco moth is a serious pest of tobacco and is not often found in homes, the raisin moth prefers dried fruits and often infests these fruits outdoors while they are drying, and the almond moth prefers nuts and dried fruits and is primarily a warehouse pest.

SECONDARY PESTS
Yellow Mealworm
Tenebrio molitor (Linnaeus)
Order Coleoptera; Family Tenebrionidae

Adults of the yellow mealworm are shiny dark brown or black, about 1/2-inch long, and most common in the northern states (see Figure 10.1, and Figure 10.22, which follows page 254).

Larvae are active and are found in all sorts of unusual places in addition to breakfast cereals, macaroni, and feed mills. This larva is the "golden grub" sold as fish bait in many parts of the country. When full grown, it is a little over an inch long (see Figure 10.2, and Figure 10.23, which follows page 254). The body is elongate, cylindrical, and has a harder body wall than the larvae of most other stored product pests. The body has a shiny yellow or light brown appearance, with only a few scattered setae.

Mealworms (adults and larvae) are usually found in dark, damp places in spoiled grain products. In residences, they are commonly found in basements or at soil grade level. The adults are easily confused with ground beetles, but examination of the hind leg reveals five tarsal segments on ground beetles and only four on mealworms. Also, a behavioral difference is that mealworm adults are slow moving, while ground beetles move rapidly.

Adult mealworms live only 2 to 3 months. Each female lays about 275 eggs, which hatch into larvae that grow to 1-1/4 inches long. The insect may remain in the larval stage for up to 600 days, depending on temperatures.

Dark Mealworm

Tenebrio obscurus (Fabricius)
Order Coleoptera; Family Tenebrionidae

The dark mealworm is similar in habits and appearance to the yellow mealworm. Adult dark mealworms are the same size as yellow mealworms, but dark mealworms are dull black. Dark mealworm larvae are dark brown, as compared to the shiny yellow to light brown yellow mealworm. The insect is found throughout the United States.

MISCELLANEOUS STORED PRODUCT PESTS

Many other pests are found in stored products. The corn sap beetle (family Nitidulidae) is very common in mills and warehouses in the South, infesting stored grain and flour (see Figure 10.24). Spider beetles (family Ptinidae) commonly infest flour, meal, seeds, and similar products (see Figure 10.25, and Figure 10.26 which follows page 254). Psocids (order Psocoptera), or book lice, are tiny, pale-colored insects that occur in great numbers on flour and in grain (see Figure 10.27, and Figure 10.28, which follows page 254). Bean and cowpea weevils (family Bruchidae) are found throughout the United States and infest all types of stored beans and peas (see Figure 10.29). Foreign grain, rusty grain, and square-necked grain beetles are members of the family Cucujidae, a family of small reddish-brown beetles usually found infesting grains in poor condition (see Figure 10.30, and Figures 10.31 and 10.32, following page 254). A number of other flour beetles (family

Tenebrionidae), similar in biology and feeding habits to the red and confused flour beetles, are occasional pests of grain and grain products. Included in this group are the broadhorned, depressed, long-headed, slenderhorned, and smalleyed flour beetles. Moths of minor importance include the meal, rice, and wax moths (family Pyralidae), the European grain moth (family Tineidae), and the brown house moth (family Oecophoridae). The red-legged ham beetle (family Cleridae) is a cosmopolitan, shiny blue-green beetle, infests dried meats, and is a pest primarily in meat processing and storage areas (see Figure 10.33, and Figure 10.34, which follows page 254). Grain mites (order Acarina) frequently occur in large numbers in grain and flour (see sidebar). They are very small and a pale grey color (see Figure 10.35). The cheese skipper (family Piophilidae) is a small, bluish-black fly that is an important pest of cheese and cured pork.

MANAGING STORED PRODUCT PESTS IN FOOD-HANDLING ESTABLISHMENTS

Management of stored product insects must be accomplished from the time the raw products are grown until they are consumed. In the fields and in farm storage, management is usually the farmer's responsibility. However, pest management services are always required in food-processing plants, warehouses, retail stores, homes, and other food handling establishments. On occasion, these services may even be needed in bulk storage facilities.

Commercial food-handling establishments must now comply with the high standards of sanitation and pest management expected by the public and enforced by such regulatory agencies as the U.S. Food and Drug Administration; the Meat and Poultry Inspection Program of the U.S. Department of Agriculture; and state or local food and drug, health, or agriculture agencies. Each food industry has its own good-manufacturing practices that the pest management professional must comply with. To do this, a general knowledge of sanitation and pest management are of utmost importance (see Chapter 18).

Stored product pest management includes the use of insecticides, but if other methods, such as sanitation, insectproofing, proper storage practices, monitoring, and insect electrocutors, are used successfully, the amount of insecticide needed may be reduced significantly. Since the use of insecticides in food-handling establishments is limited, the use of other pest management methods becomes even more important.

Review the entire facility layout with management. Interview the manager for past history of inspections, citation problems, storage practices,

Grain Mites

Grain mites infest most food materials. In severe infestations, grain mites and their shed skins may accumulate on the floor at the bases of sacks of grain or other food, resulting in a characteristic minty odor. Damage to food products occurs as a result of mite feeding, contamination of the food product by the mite and its cast skins, and an off-flavor imparted by the pest. Human exposure to grain mite infestations in food can also result in a form of dermatitis known as baker's itch.

These mites are widely distributed, quite prolific under favorable (warm and humid) conditions, and are represented by a number of mite species in several families. Species identification is for the specialist, although managing these pests does not vary much from species to species (good sanitation, frequent inspection, good ventilation of storage areas, and maintain relative humidity at less than 60%).

receiving inspection procedures, return product policy, vehicle and equipment inspection procedures, coopering and railcar preparation procedures, and any other items important to the specific type of operation being inspected. With this background information in hand, all areas of the facility and surrounding grounds can be thoroughly inspected.

Pest management in food-handling establishments includes the following steps:

- **Inspection** of exterior grounds and all areas of the establishment (both interior and exterior areas). Monitoring tools, such as various kinds of traps, are useful in determining the status of infestations.
- **Identification** of the pests that are present and

conditions that are conducive to future infestations.
- **Application** of stored product pest management techniques:
  1. **Good housekeeping** (including sanitation and storage practices)
  2. **Exclusion**
  3. **Other nonchemical measures,** including traps, air curtains, etc.
  4. **Insecticidal measures**
- **Evaluation** of the program to ensure that all phases are operating to the satisfaction of the pest control company and the establishment management.
- **Establishment** of a good communication system with management.

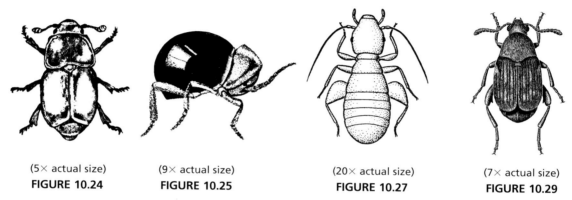

(5× actual size)
FIGURE 10.24

(9× actual size)
FIGURE 10.25

(20× actual size)
FIGURE 10.27

(7× actual size)
FIGURE 10.29

FIGURE 10.24. A corn sap beetle. Note the short elytra (front wings), clubbed antenna, and absence of distinctive markings on the body. (USDA; *Hinton Bulletin of Entomology*; and Sweetman, *Recognition of Structural Pests*) **FIGURE 10.25** A spider beetle, *Mezium americanum* Laporte. Note the somewhat spiderlike outline of the body. These beetles are active at rather low temperatures and are often serious pests in cooler climates. (USDA; *Hinton Bulletin of Entomology*; and Sweetman, *Recognition of Structural Pests*) **FIGURE 10.27.** A psocid. These small, wingless insects often occur in large numbers in grain that has become moist and in which mold is becoming established. (USDA; *Hinton Bulletin of Entomology*; and Sweetman, *Recognition of Structural Pests*) **FIGURE 10.29.** A bean weevil, *Acanthoscelides obtectus* (Say), from the family Bruchidae. (Provonsha)

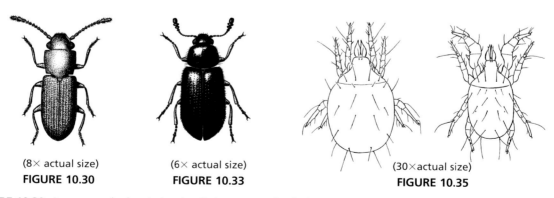

(8× actual size)
FIGURE 10.30

(6× actual size)
FIGURE 10.33

(30×actual size)
FIGURE 10.35

FIGURE 10.30. A squarenecked grain beetle, *Cathartus quardicollis* (Guerin-Menevill), from the family Cucujidae. This group of grain-infesting beetles is composed of species less than 3 millimeters in length and reddish-brown in color. (NPMA and Sweetman, *Recognition of Structural Pests*) **FIGURE 10.33.** A red-legged ham beetle, *Necrobia rufipes* (De Geer). This is a shiny bluish-green beetle with reddish legs. (NPMA and Sweetman, *Recognition of Structural Pests*) **FIGURE 10.35.** Grain mites. These tiny whitish arthropods sometimes become extremely numerous in situations in which grain or other food products are stored under warm and humid conditions. (NPMA and Sweetman, *Recognition of Structural Pests*) (Provonsha)

Sanitation as a service is rapidly expanding for the pest management industry. In this chapter, we will consider the aspects of sanitation of immediate benefit in managing stored product pests. However, Chapter 18 provides detailed information on sanitation, related inspection services, and pest management.

A sanitation program should be documented and continually updated to ensure the removal of product residues that attract stored product pests and provide breeding areas. The facility must be constantly monitored so that new defects, such as holes and cracks in walls, are sealed before allowing pest entry or becoming pest harborages. Doors and windows must be checked to ensure that they remain pestproof. Any conditions favoring pest infestations must be brought to the attention of the facility management for correction.

Proper storage and stock rotation are essential in food-handling establishments. All items should be stored up off the floor (usually on pallets) and at least 18 inches away from walls, to allow for proper inspection and treatment. The oldest stock should be the first rotated out of storage, and food stock should be rotated with nonfood stock. All torn bags should be removed and the area cleaned up immediately. Ventilation is also important to keep food

Sanitation for Food-Processing Equipment

One of the most frequent sources of stored product pest infestations in food plants is within the food processing equipment. This is because processing equipment may contain hundreds of voids and nooks and crannies which provide ideal microhabitats (good temperatures and humidity) for small insects. And these are also the areas where food residues from processing constantly accumulate. Unfortunately, because of the hidden nature or inaccessibility of these cracks and crevices, such infestations often go undetected until an infestation develops.

Therefore, frequent inspection and cleaning of all processing equipment within the food plant is paramount to control stored product pests. Some food plants replace certain metal cover cleaner plates on the equipment with sturdy plexiglass plates. This enables a thorough inspection into inaccessible parts of the equipment without disassembling the equipment. If vacuum cleaners are used for removing food residues from inside equipment, they should be emptied after their use. Otherwise the contents may serve as breeding grounds for various type of insect pests.

Food Handling Terms Defined

- **Food-handling establishment.** An area or place other than a private residence in which food is held, processed, prepared, and/or served. (Held includes displayed for sale as well as stored.) Such places include restaurants, lunchrooms, catering facilities, cafeterias, bars and taverns, private clubs, military messes, officers and NCO clubs, eating facilities in plants and office buildings, mobile catering units, airlines, ships, drugstores, confectionery stores, dairy product stores, bakery product stores, drive-in movies, school lunchrooms, colleges and universities, hospitals, federal and state prisons and jails, and homes for the aged, orphaned, and handicapped.
- **Food.** The EPA's definition is the same as the FDA's: (1) articles used for food or drink for humans or other animals, including pet food, birdseed, and feed for cattle, horses, swine, poultry, etc.; (2) chewing gum; and (3) articles used for components of any such article.
- **Nonfood areas.** This term includes garbage rooms, lavatories, floor drains (to sewers), entries and vestibules, offices, locker rooms, machine rooms, boiler rooms, garages, mop closets, and storage areas (after canning or bottling).
- **Food areas.** This term includes areas for receiving, serving, storage, packaging (canning, bottling, wrapping, boxing), preparing (cleaning, slicing, cooking, grinding), edible waste, storage, and enclosed processing systems (mills, dairies, edible oils, syrups).

moisture content low.

Vegetation that is too close to a building can attract insects and vertebrates that may eventually become pests outdoors as well as indoors. These pests can gain entry through any naturally occurring openings (plumbing, electrical, vents, etc.) to the exterior. Outside lighting must also be managed so that night-active pests are not attracted to the building. Sodium vapor lights are the least attractive to insects, and they should be placed as far from the building as is practical. Where light is needed near a building, such as for security, place the light where it will reflect off the area rather than placing it immediately above the area. Mercury-vapor lights are very attractive to insects and should not be used within 150 feet of a building.

Inspecting all incoming materials is essential. In addition, all incoming vehicles should be checked to make certain they are thoroughly and regularly cleaned and disinfested. Spilled product around loading docks, railroad tracks, and other transportation areas must be immediately cleaned up. Paving these areas will assist in cleanup.

Other noninsecticidal pest management measures for stored product pests include **physical exclusion**, **light traps**, **controlled temperatures**, **modified atmospheres**, and **pheromones**.

Physical Exclusion

As noted, food-handling establishments need to be pestproofed to deny access to the facility and to eliminate harborages. In addition, doors in food-handling establishments should be equipped with self-closing devices. If doors are used for ventilation, tight-fitting screens (20 mesh) should be installed. All overhead truck doors and railcar doors should remain closed except when in use. Exterior overhead doors equipped with inflatable dock cushions or folding dock covers can prevent pest entry while these doors are being used. Airdoors or plastic curtains can be used to help prevent pest entry. All of these exclusion devices must be kept in good working condition at all times.

Light Traps

The distance at which an insect responds to a light trap is determined by lamp type and trap design, in addition to the visual acuity and nature of the specific insect. Most insects do not respond to light traps more than 100 feet away. House flies respond at 20 to 25 feet, with a significant increase at 12 feet. Even at 12 feet, it will take up to 7 hours for 90% of the flies to respond, and 36 hours for a 99% response.

Several other factors must be considered. Light traps should be placed about 50 feet apart; however, use good judgment to determine best locations. Ceiling-hung traps are necessary for night-flying insects, such as those found in loading dock areas. These traps should be mounted 8- to 12-feet high, perpendicular to and above door openings. Light traps for flies and other stored product pests should be placed down lower, about 5 feet from the floor. Look for bottleneck areas that insects must pass through, and place traps close to these areas. In food processing areas, use only low wall mounts and keep the traps at least 5 feet from open product so that contamination will not occur. It is also important to use nonelectrocuting light traps in food areas, to avoid food contamination that can occur with electrocuting light traps (i.e., insects "explode" when they hit the electrical grid). It is also important that traps not be placed in direct sunlight and that they not be placed where their attractive light shines directly outdoors (and attracts insects to the building).

Electrocuting light traps (with UV lamps behind an electric grid) are best for use in areas of high insect pressure. They come in wall, ceiling, and portable types. Insects are attracted by the UV light, come in contact with the electric grid and are killed, and then fall into collecting pans below. Nonelectrocuting light traps also use UV lamps to attract insects, but they trap the insects on glue boards. This type of trap is better for use in identifying insects, less expensive to purchase and operate, but is limited in the number of insects it will hold. Some trap systems combine both types, using low voltage to stun insects, which then drop onto glue boards. This type can be used in food-processing areas.

Controlled Temperatures

Both low and high temperatures are used in selected situations. Insects are cold blooded; their body temperatures closely follow that of their environment. When temperatures are lowered, insect activity decreases until all activity stops. Further decreases in temperature result in death. The quicker the drop in temperature, the better the kill. Generally, temperatures below freezing for 3 to 5 days are sufficient to kill most stored product pests. Similarly, as temperature increases, activity increases to a point where some vital biological process is inhibited and activity ceases, or the insects die. Temperatures at 120°F to 150°F for 2 hours will kill many pest insects. Controlled temperatures are especially useful during the storage of some products and can be used in homes to kill insects in small quantities of stored product (by placing the infested produce into a freezer or oven using the just-mentioned recommendations). A knowledge of product chemistry is necessary since extremes in temperatures may adversely affect some food components.

Heat sterilization of food-handling facilities is being used more frequently as greater restrictions are placed on fumigants. Using either portable heaters or heating equipment already present in a facility, the building temperature can be raised to **between 120 to 150°F for approximately 24 hours**. The idea is to provide enough time for the heat to penetrate and kill insects in all the cracks, crevices and voids throughout the treated space. All heat-sensitive equipment and other articles prone to damage must be removed first.

Special heat "sterilization" machines are available. These are designed to produce hot air, steam or electricity to disinfest foods before they are packaged. This can be accomplished by exposing the product to 122°F temperatures for one hour; however, this sterilization process does not prevent reinfestation. The different life stages of insects have different tolerance levels for heat; eggs and adults are most sensitive, larvae less so, and pupae least sensitive.

The use of infrared heat for the control of surface infestations on packaged bakery products has also been successful. Starting with an exposure temperature of 50°F, the surface temperature of the product can be raised to between 140 to 150°F within 20 seconds. This is sufficient to kill any life stages of insects present without harming either the product or packaging.

The use of **cold** can also be used to control certain stored product pests. For example, all stages of the sawtoothed grain beetle are killed when exposed to temperatures of less than 5°F for 24 hours. Cold does not kill all insects however; some insects, or at least some stages of certain insects are resistant to cold temperatures. Some food plants store highly susceptible foods such as flours and corn meals under refrigeration until the food is needed. Products stored within a deep freeze for at least four days will kill most stored product pests.

Modified Atmospheres

This method of stored-product pest management involves changing the existing atmosphere in a storage facility to one that is lethal to insects. The facility is purged with carbon dioxide (CO_2), nitrogen, or the combustion gas products from a modified atmosphere generator. CO_2 is preferred over the other gases because of generally faster insect kill, lower cost, less stringent sealing requirements for storage structures, and less influence on performance caused by slight fluctuations in concentration. However, for some pests, such as internal feeders, a 60% CO_2 atmosphere must be maintained for at least 14 days.

Controlled atmosphere may also be combined with certain electrotechnologies (heat sterilization to about 30°C) and fumigation (phosphine concentrations of around 165 ppm, reduced from the usual 850 to 1,500 ppm). Carbon dioxide is used at 6 to 19% to replace oxygen in the stored product (bulk grain), and infesting insects become more susceptible to the other control methods. This combination of technologies is receiving additional research attention; thus, its ultimate utility in stored product pest management is yet to be determined.

Pheromones

Pheromones (naturally occurring chemicals produced and released by insects) are used in stored product pest management as effective tools for monitoring infestations. Appropriate quantities of synthetic pheromone are placed in traps to detect and evaluate pest infestations. Traps are checked periodically to aid in formulating an effective pest management program.

There are two principal pheromones, aggregation and sex, used to attract others of the same species. Aggregation pheromones are usually produced by males of long-lived insects, and both sexes often respond. Examples are the lesser grain borer, red, and confused flour beetles; weevils; flat and rusty grain beetles; and sawtoothed grain beetles. Sex pheromones are usually produced by females of short-lived insects to attract males of the same species. Examples include the warehouse beetle, carpet beetles, khapra beetle, cigarette and drugstore beetles, Indianmeal moth, Mediterranean flour moth, tobacco moth, and Angoumois grain moth. Several trap types containing pheromones (and sometimes a food bait) are available.

Pheromone traps have several advantages. They can be placed in equipment and areas that shelter pests, do not require additional expense to operate, work 24 hours a day, will detect low populations (often before management knows there is a problem), and are easier to count, because traps are species specific.

Trap placement and maintenance are essential in using pheromones successfully. Indoors, traps should be placed 30 feet away from doors and in corners or on support posts in areas where insects have been noted, sanitation is poor, or there is a high potential for reinfestation. Receiving areas usually meet these criteria. Protect the traps from dust, moisture, and damage. For crawling insects, place the traps from floor level to 6 feet off the floor. Traps for flying insects are usually placed 6 to 9 feet off the floor. Use a grid pattern 25 to 50 feet apart to start, remove traps not catching anything, and concentrate traps in areas of insect activity. For monitoring, use one trap per 30,000 to 100,000 cubic feet of space. For mass trapping, use one trap per 3,000 to 10,000 cubic feet.

Outside, pheromone traps can be used to catch insects before they enter a facility. Place traps about 50 feet apart and use only at temperatures above 65°F, since pheromone activity is temperature dependent. As noted for indoor use, traps outdoors must be protected from the elements.

Summary

With increasing regulatory and consumer concerns about the use of chemicals in and around food products, nonchemical control measures will become increasingly important in pest management programs. Since it is unlikely that any one

Using Insecticides in Food-Handling Establishments

Only those residual insecticide formulations that bear directions on their labels for such use can be used for pest control in food-handling establishments. Typical labels bear wording such as "Food areas: limited to crack and crevice treatment only.... Applications of this product in the food areas of food-handling establishments, other than as a crack and crevice treatment, are not permitted." Before the professional can determine which insecticides can be used for control in these areas, the term **residual insecticide**, as defined by the EPA, must be understood.

Residual insecticides are those products applied to obtain insecticidal effects lasting several hours or longer and applied as general, spot, or crack and crevice treatments. Residuals include common insecticides such as synthetic pyrethroids. Also included are synergized pyrethrins. These are usually thought of as nonresidual materials. Certain formulations with higher than normal concentration and applied as coarse sprays provide insecticidal effects lasting several hours or longer and are therefore considered residual by the EPA.

There are three types of residual applications recognized by the EPA: general, spot, and crack and crevice. Each may be used in certain areas of food-handling establishments.

General treatment is application to broad expanses of surfaces such as walls, floors, and ceilings, or as an outside treatment. This is permitted only in nonfood areas using only those insecticides so registered.

Barrier treatment is usually considered the application of pesticides to thresholds and other entrances, the foundation, and the soil adjacent to the foundation. Read the label, because some pesticides contain explicit instructions for this use. Some outdoor insects or related pests may become invaders or nuisances when populations build up. A barrier treatment with residual sprays, dusts, or granules may be beneficial in controlling such pests.

Spot treatment is application to limited areas on which insects are likely to walk, but which will not be in contact with food or utensils and will not ordinarily be contacted by workers. Such areas may occur on floors, walls, and the bases or undersides of equipment. For this purpose, a spot should not exceed 2 square feet. Until recently, this application method could be used only in nonfood areas. However, some insecticides have received EPA approval for label directions permitting spot applications in food areas. This wordage will appear on the labels of other insecticides as more data are collected.

Crack and crevice treatment is the application of small amounts of insecticides into cracks and crevices in which insects hide or through which they may enter a building. Such openings commonly occur at expansion joints, between different elements of construction, and between equipment and floors. These openings may lead to voids, such as hollow walls, equipment legs and bases, conduits, motor housings, or junction or switch boxes. The crack and crevice treatment includes the use of sprays, dusts, or baits. It permits the use of products in food areas as long as the insecticide is placed only into cracks and crevices. It does not permit treatment of surfaces.

It is important to note that residual insecticides may be applied when food establishments are in operation unless the label of the product being used specifically indicates that all operations must be stopped at the time when applications are made.

When using **nonresidual insecticides** (defined as those applied to obtain insecticidal effects only during the time of treatment) as space treatments (aerosol, ULV and fog treatments), the application should be made while the food-handling establishment is not in operation and exposed foods are removed or covered. Also, food handling surfaces should be cleaned before use. However, the use of nonresidual insecticides as contact treatments (which means hitting the target pest with a wet spray for immediate insecticidal effect) can be done while the establishment is in operation. Both space treatments and contact treatments are considered general insecticide applications.

chemical or nonchemical method will provide lasting pest control, the integration of methods and materials that best meet the criteria of each individual job should be considered. Thus, the integration of nonchemical methods and technologies—as replacements for, or companions to, chemical applications—will reduce the chemical inputs into most pest management programs without compromising the quality of the program.

PEST MANAGEMENT IN FOOD-PROCESSING AND -SERVING ESTABLISHMENTS—USING PESTICIDES

The principles and practices of inspection, sanitation, and facility maintenance for properly managing pests apply to all food-handling establishments. The installation of insect light traps and electrocutors, in areas where food will not be contaminated, will provide some insect control, and more importantly, they can be used to monitor pests in the facility. Pheromone and baited traps are also useful for detecting infestations before they become serious problems. The use of monitoring devices makes possible a more precise timing of insecticide treatments.

The use of pesticides in and around food processing and serving establishments is restricted as a result of the 1972 amendment of the Federal Insecticide, Fungicide, and Rodenticide Act. This is especially true in food areas of food-processing and -serving establishments. Applications of most residual insecticides are limited to the cracks and crevices only. Food areas include places where food is exposed during receiving, storage, preparation, processing, and serving. It does not include dining areas, where food is under the control of the person eating it.

Crack and crevice treatment includes the use of sprays, dusts, or baits. It permits the use of such products only into cracks and crevices. It does not permit treatment of surfaces. Liquid insecticides must be applied under low pressure and with great care to avoid splashing or runoff, which might lead to contamination of the exposed surfaces of the building or equipment. When dusts or baits are applied into cracks or voids, care should be taken to avoid leaving any of the material on exposed surfaces. If nonresidual contact sprays or space sprays are used, care should be taken not to treat food areas when food is exposed, and to avoid leaving any of the material on exposed surfaces that may come in direct contact with food or food products. These applications can be made only when the food service establishment is closed.

Insecticides that are registered for crack and crevice treatment in food areas and that do not have specific instructions to the contrary may be used while the establishments are open and in operation. However, care must be taken to avoid any contamination of food. A few of the residual insecticides are also labeled for use as spot treatments in food areas; their labels will specify when and where they can be used.

The **insect growth regulators (IGRs)** disrupt normal development of the insect and prevent the immatures from ever reaching the adult reproductive stage. Cigarette beetles, for example, have been effectively controlled by the use of IGRs. Care must be exercised in the use of IGRs because they are known to be volatile and capable of migrating from the treated area to other areas in the building which may be insecticide sensitive. As with all pesticides, labels must be carefully followed.

In nonfood areas (loading docks, storage areas, locker rooms, offices, etc.) of food establishments, more liberal use of residual insecticides is permit-ted. In each case, the label of the product you use must describe the pests to be controlled, the places that can be treated, the concentration that can be used, and the method of application. Labeled residual sprays may be used to treat surfaces in nonfood areas, as long as the sprays do not come in contact with food containers.

In commercial food-processing and -serving establishments, special sanitation problems may exist. To manage stored product pests in these accounts, it is essential that the premises be cleaned of any loose food materials that may be lodged on the floor, the walls, and the ceiling. Residues of food allowed to accumulate will provide harborage for many insects. If the management of an establishment will not clean up this debris, the pest management professional is well advised not to enter into an agreement, particularly if elimination of the insects must be guaranteed.

PEST MANAGEMENT IN WAREHOUSES

In warehouses, the first step in managing stored product pests is to ensure that there is a sanitation program in place and operating. Then the professional must conduct an inspection and monitoring program to locate possible sources of infestation and identify the insects involved. All infested material must be removed from the premises, unless the warehouse is to be fumigated.

Insects on the outside of packaged materials can be killed using a contact spray containing an insecticide with relatively low toxicity to humans, such as pyrethrins or certain pyrethroids. After the debris has been cleaned up and the infested material has been removed, the storage areas can be sprayed with residual sprays labeled for indoor use. The application should be made to any areas that could possibly harbor insects. Particular attention should be paid to cracks and crevices from which debris cannot be thoroughly removed. If there is any likelihood that the room will be used for bulk storage of loose grain, a protective insecticide treatment should be used.

If there is a minor infestation in returned goods which must be held in the warehouse for a period of time, the infested material must be stored in one area of the warehouse only and must be stored away from walls and off the floor on pallets. The area should then be treated at regular intervals with one of the labeled insecticides. The insecticide can be applied with a pressurized aerosol or ULV machine to obtain maximum penetration through the space between the containers in the stack. Prior to the space treatment, however, a residual application to the floors and to the walls up to the maximum height of storage can be made using appropriately labeled insecticides. If exposed food products are present, application will probably be limited to crack and crevice treatment. The need to repeat this residual application will depend on both the type of surface being sprayed and the length of residual of the insecticide being used. Timing may be on a monthly, bimonthly, or even a quarterly basis. The pest management professional should check conditions carefully so as to have an effective residual working at all times. The residual and space treatment program is effective only if the storage area is cleaned out initially and an infestation is not introduced after the program has started. During this program the building must also be kept clean, so that untreated dust and debris do not accumulate. As a standard method of warehouse maintenance, this system is excellent.

Other good pest prevention and management practices include moving out the oldest materials first, holding incoming materials for inspection, and treating buildings periodically with labelled residual sprays, especially when areas are emptied of their stores. See Chapter 18 for further discussion of pest management in food-processing facilities.

PEST MANAGEMENT IN RETAIL FOOD STORES

In retail food stores, managing stored product pests depends on prompt removal of infested material. Again, the pest management professional would be very unwise to attempt control of storage pests until this has been done and a thorough sanitation program is in place. After this, an application of a contact spray of low toxicity should be made to kill any adults or larvae that may be exposed. This application should be made with a pressurized aerosol or ULV machine using pyrethrins or pyrethroids labeled for this use. Make applications to as many surfaces in the area of infestation as possible, taking extreme care not to contaminate food items in the store. If any food items are not in tight containers, be sure they are completely covered with a protective material, such as a plastic sheet, before treatment. In nonfood areas, residual sprays may be used. Residual sprays of appropriately labeled insecticides can be used in food areas as crack and crevice treatments and, in some cases, spot treatments. Chapter 19 includes a more detailed discussion of pest management for supermarkets.

MANAGING STORED PRODUCT PESTS IN HOMES

The source of a stored product pest infestation in a home is usually confined to areas where foods are stored, such as the kitchen. The entire infestation may be isolated within a single cabinet or a single box of material. Before any control can be attempted, the source of infestation must be found and eliminated. This is not always easy to do, but it is essential. Look very carefully into all cracks and crevices where food debris may be accumulating, inside containers of such things as cereals, beans, peas, flour, dried fruits and spices, and any other material in which insects may live and complete their life cycle. Do not overlook the possibility that a sealed container may be infested on the inside and be loose enough to allow insects to escape. Also check under cabinets and open or accessible wall voids for spillage, such as of pet food, which may harbor pests. Pet foods and birdseed may be a source of infestation, and they may be located in a room other than the kitchen.

After removing infested material, remove the contents of drawers and cupboards in the area,

Prevention of Stored Product Pests In Homes

The following procedures will help homeowners prevent infestations in pantries and kitchens:

- Purchase dried food in packages that can be used up in a short time. Keep foods in storage less than 2 to 4 months, if possible.
- When purchasing packaged food, be certain that the containers are not broken or unsealed. Check the packaging date to be assured of the freshness of the food. Packages with clear plastic or wax paper coverings should be checked for the presence of insects. (Foods are sometimes infested before being brought into the home.)
- Store dried foods in insectproof containers, such as screw-top glass, heavy plastic, or metal containers. This will prevent entry or escape of insects. Ordinary metal kitchen canisters are generally not tight enough to exclude insects. Some plastic containers with tight-fitting lids may be acceptable. Cardboard, paper, or plastic wrapping will not prevent insect infestation. Use older packages before newer ones, and opened packages before unopened ones.
- Store dried foods in a home freezer to prevent pests from developing.
- Keep food storage areas clean and do not allow crumbs or food particles to accumulate, because exposed food will attract insects. Cleanliness and proper storage also are important in areas where pet food and birdseed are stored.

thoroughly vacuum and clean these areas, and spray all cracks and crevices and other insect harborages with standard residual materials labeled for this use. After the insecticide has dried, cover all drawer bottoms and shelves with paper to avoid having food or food containers come in contact with the residual. It may take several days for insects not actually contacted during the treatment to come in contact with the residual and be killed. The homeowner should be advised of this fact, so that the pest management professional will not be making unnecessary return trips immediately after completing the job.

The application of insecticides for the control of pests in or around food requires considerable care on the part of the pest management professional. It is essential that no insecticide of any type come in contact with food products. No insecticide should be considered as nontoxic or suitable for use directly on any food product. When shelves are treated, food products should not be replaced on them until the insecticide is completely dry, and shelf paper should then be placed on the shelf to protect the food from direct contact.

SUPPLEMENTARY READING MATERIAL

Baur, F. J., ed. *Insect Management for Food Storage and Processing*. Saint Paul, Minn.: American Association of Cereal Chemists, 1984. 384 pp.

Bennett, G. W., and J. M. Owens, eds. *Advances in Urban Pest Management*. New York: Van Nostrand Reinhold, 1986. 399 pp.

Cotton, R. T. *Pests of Stored Grain and Grain Products*. Minneapolis: Burgess Publishing, 1963. 318 pp.

Ebeling, W. *Urban Entomology*. Los Angeles: University of California, 1975. 695 pp.

Mallis, A. *Handbook of Pest Control*. 7th ed. Cleveland: Franzak & Foster, 1997. 1152 pp.

Monro, H. A. U. Manual of fumigation for insect control. FAO Agricultural Studies, No. 79. 1969. 382 pp.

Monro, H. A. U. *Pests of Stored Products*. London: Hutchinson, 1966. 234 pp.

National Pest Control Association Sanitation Committee. *Sanitation and Pest Control Floor-Level Inspection Manual*. Vienna, Va.: NPCA, 1972. 22 pp.

Schoenherr, W. *A Guide to Good Manufacturing Practices for the Food Industry*. Danville, Ill.: Lauhoff Grain, 1972. 8 sections.

CHAPTER 1

FIGURE 1.5. Head of a cockroach, showing chewing mouthparts. (Myers)

FIGURE 1.6. Piercing-sucking mouthparts of the stable fly. (Myers)

FIGURE 1.8. Sponging mouthparts of a fly. (Myers)

HOUSE FLY—MOUTH

FIGURE 1.9. The sponging organ, the labellum, located at the end of the mouthparts of the house fly. (Univar)

FIGURE 1.10. Siphoning mouthparts of a moth. (Myers)

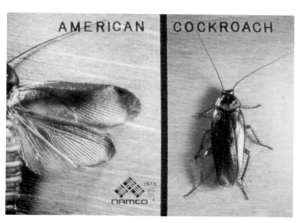

AMERICAN COCKROACH

FIGURE 1.12. Wings of the American cockroach. Forewing and hindwing in the spread position and in resting position, with hindwings hidden beneath the leathery forewings. (Univar)

CHAPTER 2

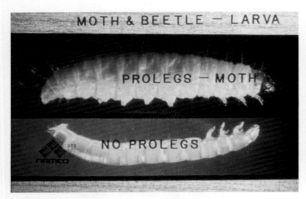

FIGURE 2.5. Examples of larvae. Top: Moth larva with abdominal prolegs. Bottom: Beetle larva lacking abdominal prolegs. (Univar)

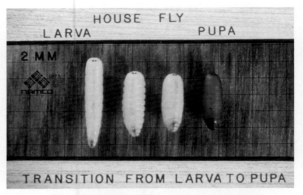

FIGURE 2.6. Stages in the life cycle of a house fly. (Univar)

CHAPTER 6

FIGURE 6.3. Adult male German cockroach, surrounded by excrement pellets called "frass". (Myers)

FIGURE 6.4. German cockroaches. Left: Mating. Right: A female carrying an egg capsule. (Univar)

FIGURE 6.5. Nymph of the German cockroach (right). Note the light stripe that runs lengthwise down the top of the thorax. This characteristic distinguishes the nymph of this cockroach from those of other common species such as the brownbanded cockroach on the left. (Univar)

FIGURE 6.8. Adult American cockroach. (Myers)

FIGURE 6.9. American cockroach nymphs of different instars. (Myers)

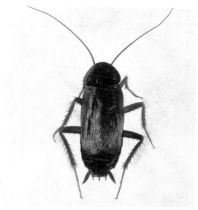

FIGURE 6.10. Adult male Oriental cockroach. (Myers)

FIGURE 6.11. Brownbanded cockroaches. Left: last instar nymph. Right: Adult male. Note the two light, transverse bands across the base of the wings. (Univar)

FIGURE 6.12. Brownbanded cockroach nymph, showing two light-colored transverse bands across the thorax. (Myers)

FIGURE 6.13. Adult female (left) and nymph of the brownbanded cockroach. Note that female's wings are much shorter than the abdomen. (Myers)

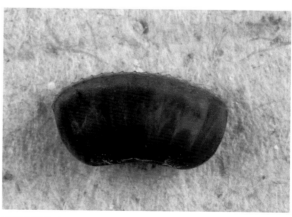

FIGURE 6.14. Egg case, or oötheca, of the brownbanded cockroach. (Myers)

FIGURE 6.15. The adult smokybrown cockroach. (Univar)

FIGURE 6.16. Adult male Pennsylvania woods cockroach. (Myers)

FIGURE 6.17. Pennsylvania woods cockroach nymph. (Myers)

FIGURE 6.18. Australian cockroach adult. (Myers)

CHAPTER **7**

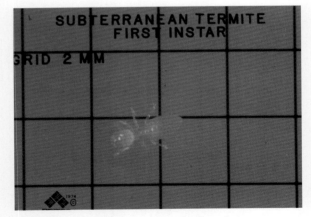

FIGURE 7.2. The first instar nymph of a subterranean termite. (Univar)

FIGURE 7.3. A subterranean termite soldier. Note the large head and jaws, which are used in protecting the colony. (Univar)

FIGURE 7.4. A subterranean termite primary reproductive (swarmer). This form emerges from the colony to disperse and start new colonies. (Univar)

FIGURE 7.7. Evidence of termite damage to books. Note the mastic-like (mud) deposits. (Univar)

FIGURE 7.8. Example of subterranean termite damage to wood. Note that the soft layers of the annual rings have been eaten, and that the hard layers remain. (Univar)

FIGURE 7.9. Examples of termite tubing; a close-up view of an earthen tube. (Univar)

FIGURE 7.10. Shelter tubes that hang from floor joists to the ground. (Univar)

FIGURE 7.11. One supplementary reproductive termite (light colored with short wings) shown among many worker termites and one fully winged primary reproductive. (Myers)

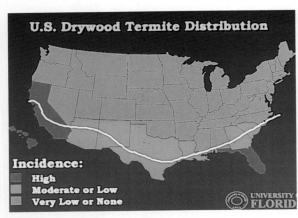

FIGURE 8.1. Distribution of drywood termites in the United States. (Univar)

FIGURE 8.2. Typical drywood termite damage. Note that the galleries are extensive and that they cut across several annual rings. (Univar)

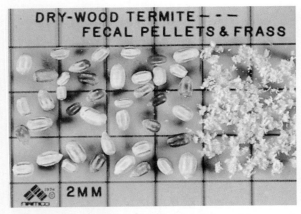

FIGURE 8.3. Drywood termite fecal pellets and frass. Often, these materials are pushed out of the galleries. These pellets are important in diagnosing an infestation. (Univar)

FIGURE 8.5. Primary drywood termite reproductive that has emerged from the colony. (Myers)

FIGURE 8.6. Drywood termite nymph and soldier. (Myers)

FIGURE 8.10. Powderpost beetle from the family Lyctidae. (Univar)

FIGURE 8.11. Lyctid powderpost beetle and its emergence hole. (Myers)

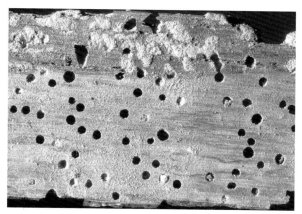

FIGURE 8.13. Damage from powderpost beetle infestations over a several-year period. (Myers)

FIGURE 8.14. The bamboo powderpost beetle. (Univar)

FIGURE 8.16. The deathwatch beetle. (Univar)

FIGURE 8.19. An adult beetle from the family Cerambycidae. (Univar)

FIGURE 8.21. The old house borer, the only long-horned beetle that infests structures. (Univar)

CHAPTER 8

FIGURE 8.24. The wharf borer. (Myers)

FIGURE 8.25. One of the metallic wood-boring beetles. (Univar)

FIGURE 8.26. Wood decay that has occurred as a result of moisture problems. (Univar)

FIGURE 8.27. A moisture meter used in determining potential problems with wood decay. (Myers)

CHAPTER 9

FIGURE 9.5. Black carpenter ant worker, *Camponotus pennsylvanicus* (DeGreer). (Myers)

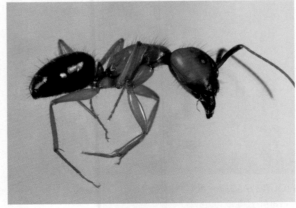

FIGURE 9.6. Florida carpenter ant worker, *Camponotus floridanus* (Buckley). (Myers)

FIGURE 9.7. Western carpenter ant worker, *Camponotus modoc* (Wheeler). (Myers)

FIGURE 9.8. Carpenter ant worker, *Camponotus herculeanus* (L.). (Myers)

FIGURE 9.9. Carpenter ant worker, *Camponotus vicinus* (Mayr). (Myers)

FIGURE 9.11. Argentine ant worker. (Myers)

FIGURE 9.12. Southern fire ant worker. (Myers)

FIGURE 9.13. Red imported fire ant worker. (Myers)

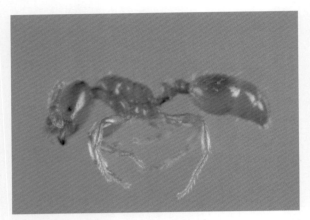

FIGURE 9.14. Thief ant worker. (Myers)

FIGURE 9.15. Pharaoh ant worker. (Myers)

FIGURE 9.17. Little black ant worker. (Myers)

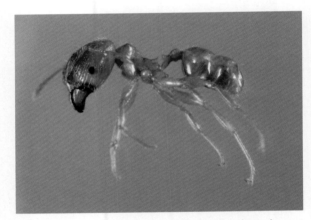

FIGURE 9.18. Big-headed ant soldier, with enlarged head. (Myers)

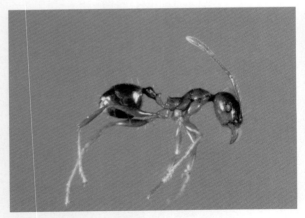

FIGURE 9.19. Big-headed ant worker. (Myers)

FIGURE 9.20. Pavement ant worker. (Myers)

FIGURE 9.21. Front view of pavement ant worker head, showing characteristic grooves running from base of mandibles to top of head. (Myers)

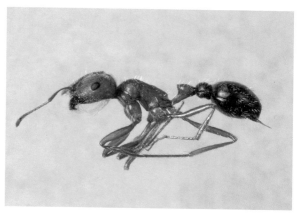

FIGURE 9.22. Red harvester ant worker. (Myers)

FIGURE 9.23. Black harvester ant worker. (Univar)

FIGURE 9.24. Leaf-cutter ant worker. (Univar)

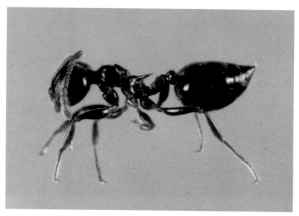

FIGURE 9.25. Acrobat ant worker. (Myers)

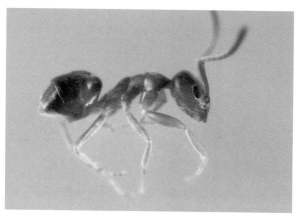

FIGURE 9.26. Odorous house ant worker. (Myers)

FIGURE 9.27. Velvety tree ant worker. (Myers)

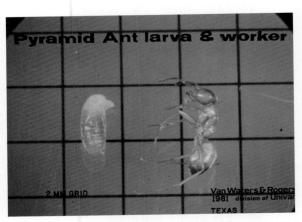

FIGURE 9.28. Pyramid ant worker (right) and larva. (Univar)

FIGURE 9.29. Field ant worker (*Formica* spp.). (Myers)

FIGURE 9.30. Allegheny mound builder ant worker (*Formica exsectoides* Forel). (Myers)

FIGURE 9.31. Crazy ant worker (note elongated legs and scape of antennae). (Myers)

FIGURE 9.32. False honey ant worker. (Univar)

CHAPTER 9

FIGURE 9.33. Cornfield ant worker. (Myers)

FIGURE 9.34. Large yellow ant worker. (Myers)

FIGURE 9.35. Ghost ant worker. (Myers)

FIGURE 9.36. White-footed ant worker. (Myers)

CHAPTER 10

FIGURE 10.3. A comparison of the rice and granary weevil adults, showing characteristics red markings on the wing covers of the rice weevil. (Univar)

FIGURE 10.4. Whole body comparison of rice and granary weevil adults. (Univar)

FIGURE 10.5. Rice weevil larvae shown inside wheat kernels that have been split open. Severe damage may be done before infestation is detected, since there is little external evidence of an infestation. (Univar)

FIGURE 10.6. Angoumois grain moths. (Univar)

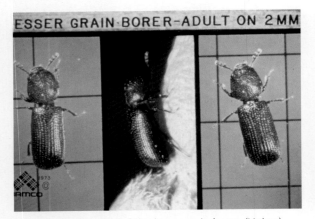

FIGURE 10.9. Adults of the lesser grain borer. (Univar)

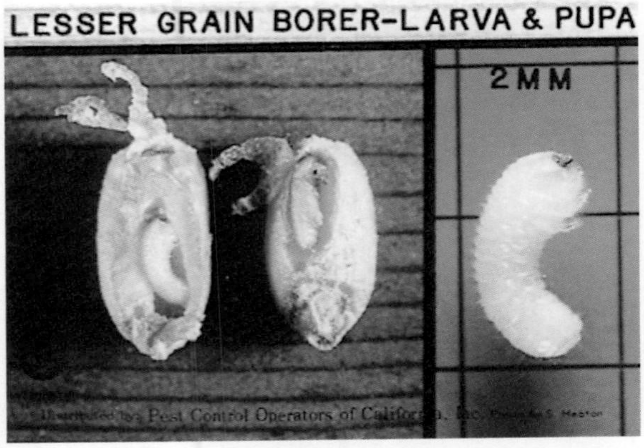

FIGURE 10.10. Left and Right: Lesser grain borer larvae. Center: Pupa. (Univar)

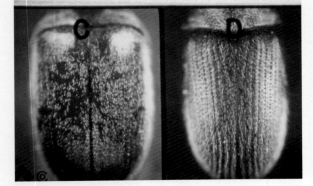

FIGURE 10.11. Comparison of adults of the cigarette and drugstore beetles. Note the longitudinal lines on the wing covers of the drugstore beetle, which are lacking on the cigarette beetle. (Univar)

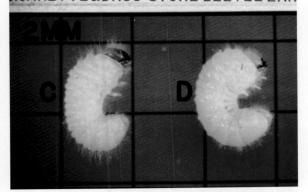

FIGURE 10.12. Comparison of the larvae of cigarette and drugstore beetles. Note the longer body hairs on the cigarette beetle. (Univar)

FIGURE 10.13. Comparison of the adults of one of the *Trogoderma* spp. with a black carpet beetle adult. Note the areas of reddish-brown markings on the elytra, which are lacking on the black carpet beetle. (Univar)

FIGURE 10.14. Larva of the black carpet beetle. (Myers)

FIGURE 10.15. The Indianmeal moth. (Myers)

FIGURE 10.16. Indianmeal moth adult on corn. (Myers)

FIGURE 10.17. The larva of the Indianmeal moth. (Myers)

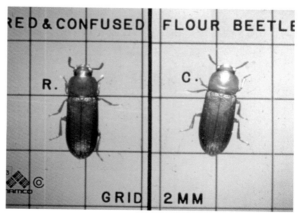

FIGURE 10.18. Red and confused flour beetles. (Univar)

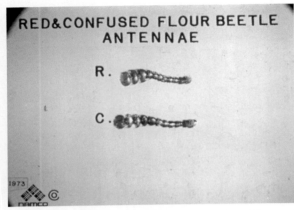

FIGURE 10.19. Comparison of red and confused flour beetle antennae. Note the distinctly three-segmented club of the red flour beetle, as compared to the gradually enlarging segments of the confused flour beetle. (Univar)

FIGURE 10.20. Comparison of the sawtoothed grain beetle and the merchant grain beetle. (Univar)

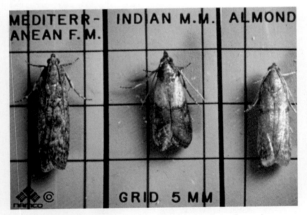

FIGURE 10.21. Comparative color patterns of moths commonly found infesting stored products. (Univar)

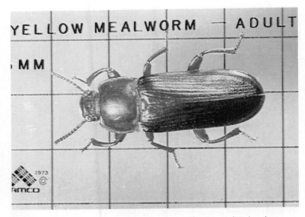

FIGURE 10.22. An adult yellow mealworm. (Univar)

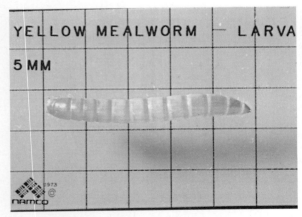

FIGURE 10.23. The larva of the Indianmeal moth. (Univar)

FIGURE 10.26. A spider beetle. (Myers)

FIGURE 10.28. A Psocid or book louse. (Univar)

FIGURE 10.31. The rusty grain beetle. (Myers)

FIGURE 10.32. The foreign grain beetle. (Myers)

FIGURE 10.34. The red-legged ham beetle. (Univar)

CHAPTER **11**

FIGURE 11.2. Adult cat flea. (Myers)

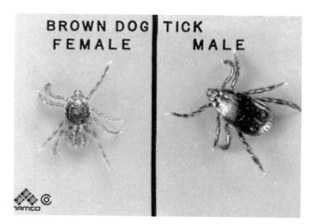

FIGURE 11.6. Brown dog ticks, female and male. Note that the scutum, the sclerotized shield on the upper side of the body, covers the entire upper surface in the male but is restricted to a much smaller area on the anterior half in the female. (Univar)

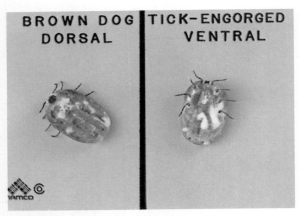

FIGURE 11.7. Engorged brown dog tick females. As the female feeds on a host and become engorged with blood, she becomes four to five times larger than normal. (Univar)

FIGURE 11.10. Head louse (notice tarsi modified into claws for tightly grasping hair). (Myers)

FIGURE 11.11. Crab louse, or pubic louse (notice tarsi modified into claws for tightly grasping hair). (Myers)

FIGURE 11.12. A chewing louse, also commonly called a bird louse. (Myers)

FIGURE 11.19. A common bed bug seeking a feeding site on its human host. Feeding occurs during the night, usually while the host is sleeping. During the day, the bed bug remains hidden off the host (see Figure 11.20). (Myers)

FIGURE 11.21. Adult bat bug. (Myers)

CHAPTER **11**

FIGURE 11.22. Close-up of head and thorax of adult bat bug, showing the longer hairs and broader shape of the wing pads at the inner margin, as compared to the bed bug (compare to Figure 11.19 and see also distinction between bat and bed bugs at lower left of Figure 11.18). (Myers)

FIGURE 11.23. Masked hunter, also called the kissing bug, is capable if inflicting a painful bite and wound when handled. (Myers)

FIGURE 11.24. Wheel bug. (Myers)

FIGURE 12.2. Adult clover mite on plant leaf, note very long front pair of legs. Clover mites usually have dark red colored bodies, with the front legs a pinkish tinge. (Univar)

FIGURE 12.3. Millipede. (Myers)

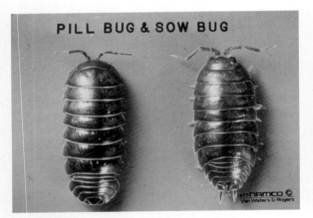

FIGURE 12.5. Pillbug (left) and sowbug. (Univar)

FIGURE 12.7. Garden slug. (Myers)

FIGURE 12.9. Cricket. (Myers)

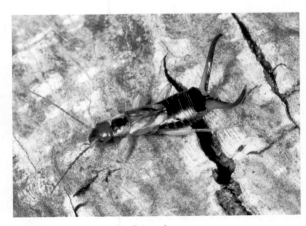

FIGURE 12.10. Earwig. (Myers)

FIGURE 12.14. Strawberry root weevil, note relatively short proboscis, or snout bearing mouthparts, for a weevil. (Univar)

FIGURE 12.16. Ground beetle; note head and mouthparts are visible from above. (Myers)

FIGURE 12.18. Multicolored Asian lady beetle. This species varies widely in color and number of spots on wing covers (elytra), but the black or very dark M-shaped marking on the thorax (above the wings) is characteristic. (Myers)

FIGURE 12.19. Mass of multicolored Asian lady beetles on a window ledge. Notice the variation in coloring and number of markings (dots) on wing covers. (Myers)

FIGURE 12.21. Foreign grain beetle. Note relatively square shape of thorax and antennae with three-segmented club. This beetle is quite small at 1/10th to 1/8th inches long, and its larval stages develop on fungus or mold deposits that can form inside walls when excessive moisture and condensation occurs due to faulty ventilation of those spaces. (Myers)

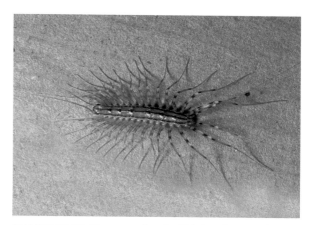

FIGURE 12.25. House centipede. This is a fast-moving centipede that commonly infests areas within homes that are rarely disturbed, such as basements, attics and closets. However, individuals will occasionally be sighted in other areas during the day, or especially as the centipedes hunt for prey at night. (Myers)

FIGURE 12.27. House spider, with eggs sacs. This is one of the spiders responsible for cobwebs that appear in the main living areas of the home. (Myers)

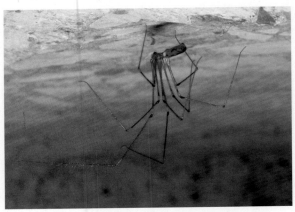

FIGURE 12.28. Cellar spider. As the name implies, this species is most common where cool, damp conditions prevail, such as in basements, but it may be found elsewhere in the home. It also is responsible for cobwebs found in homes. (Myers)

FIGURE 12.29. Jumping spider. These spiders are relatively fast moving, and are agile jumpers that may be hard to catch. They are commonly found around the base of window and door casings, where they feed on insects that collect on sills or the floor. (Myers)

FIGURE 12.30. Agrarian sac spider, also commonly known as the yellow sac spider. This species can get fairly large, at an inch or more across, and is typically found in basements, garages or around patios of homes. (Myers)

FIGURE 12.31. Black widow spider, note distinctive red hourglass shaped marking on underside of abdomen, against overall black color. (Myers)

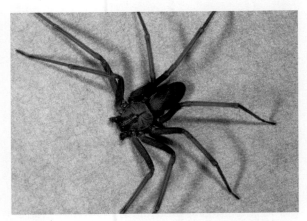

FIGURE 12.32. Brown recluse spider. Note characteristic fiddle-shaped marking on top of cephalothorax, and visible fangs. At full size, this species is 1 to 1-1/2 inches across when viewed from above. (Myers)

FIGURE 12.33. Close-up view (from above) of eye pattern and fiddle-shaped marking characteristic of the brown recluse spider. (Myers)

FIGURE 12.34. An adult of the smaller European house spider, *Tegenaria domestica*. (Univar)

FIGURE 12.35. Tarantula spider. These venomous spiders are common in landscapes around homes in hot and dry areas of the southwestern United States, from central Texas and west. They may come indoors to escape extreme heat, or at night while hunting for crawling insects or other prey. (Univar)

FIGURE 12.36. Silverfish. In homes, these primitive insects are most commonly found in rarely disturbed areas like attics, basements or closets, or under bathroom fixtures at floor level. (Myers)

FIGURE 12.38. Close-up photo of a springtail. (Univar)

FIGURE 12.39. Adult book louse, or psocid. (Univar)

FIGURE 12.41. Adult and larva of the hide beetle. (Univar)

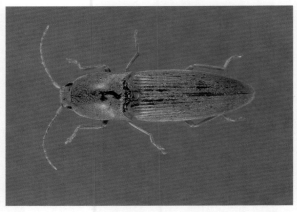

FIGURE 12.42. Click beetle. These are commonly found in homes during the summer because they are attracted to lights and enter around door or window jams. (Myers)

FIGURE 13.2. Adult webbing clothes moth, note characteristic tufts of light red or rust color hairs extending from the top of the head. (Myers)

FIGURE 13.4. Larva of the webbing clothes moth. (Myers)

FIGURE 13.6. Close-up of larvae of the casemaking clothes moth, which are hidden inside the two white silken cases. Head of the lower, rightmost larva is just visible as it slightly protrudes from the left end of the silken case. (Myers)

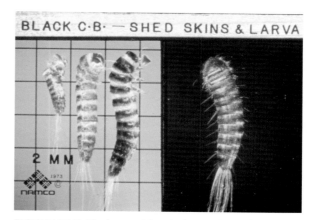

FIGURE 13.7. Black carpet beetle larvae. Note the distinctive carrot shape of the body and the long tail bristles. (Univar)

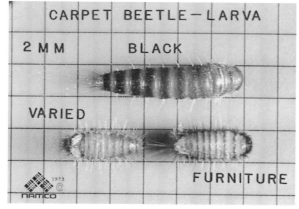

FIGURE 13.9. Comparison of the black, varied, and furniture carpet beetle larvae. The head of the varied carpet beetle is narrower than the posterior end. The larvae of the furniture carpet beetle is torpedo shaped, with the head region wider than the rear. (Univar)

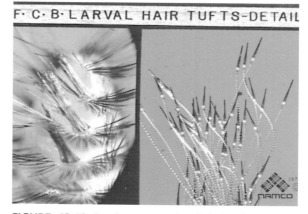

FIGURE 13.10. Furniture carpet beetle hair tufts and detail of the spear-shaped hairs (termed haustisetae). Haustisetae are found on all members of the genus *Anthrenus* and the genus *Trogoderma*, and the size, shape, and construction of these setae are very useful in positively identifying larvae. See the explanation in Figure 13.5 for more details. (Univar)

CHAPTER **13**

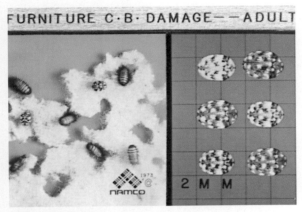

FIGURE 13.11. Furniture carpet beetle larvae, larval feeding damage, and adults. (Univar)

FIGURE 14.5. The house fly and the little house fly. Note the size difference. (Univar)

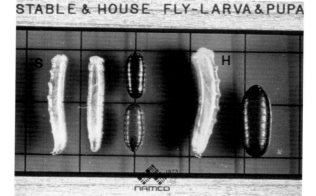

FIGURE 14.6. The larval and pupal stages of the stable fly and the house fly. (Univar)

FIGURE 14.7. House fly sponging up liquefied food. (Univar)

FIGURE 14.8. Piercing-sucking mouthparts of the stable fly. (Myers)

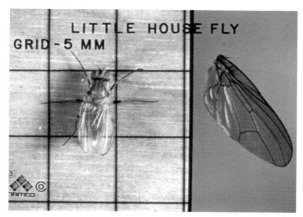

FIGURE 14.9. Little house fly. (Univar)

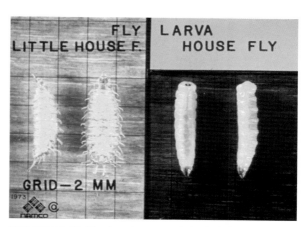

FIGURE 14.10. The larval stages of the little house fly and house fly. Note the prominent lateral processes on the little house fly. (Univar)

FIGURE 14.11. One of the flesh flies. (Myers)

FIGURE 14.12. One of the blow flies. (Myers)

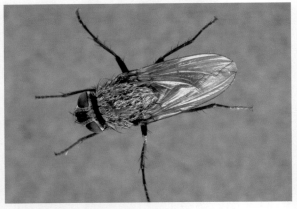

FIGURE 14.14. The cluster fly. Note golden hairs on the thorax. (Myers)

FIGURE 14.16. A fruit fly. (Univar)

FIGURE 14.18. A phorid or humpbacked fly. (Myers)

FIGURE 14.20. The cheese skipper. (Myers)

FIGURE 14.21. A horse fly. (Myers)

FIGURE 14.22. A deer fly. (Univar)

FIGURE 14.24. A moth fly. (Myers)

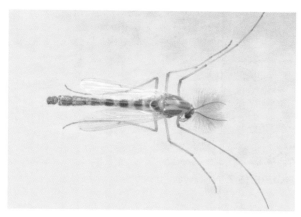

FIGURE 14.27. A midge. (Myers)

FIGURE 14.31. An Aedes mosquito. (Myers)

FIGURE 14.36. A fungus gnat. (Myers)

CHAPTER 15

FIGURE 15.4. The house mouse. (Myers)

FIGURE 15.6. A Norway rat. Note the thick, heavy body and the small, close-set ears. (Univar)

FIGURE 15.7. A Norway rat with a litter of pups.

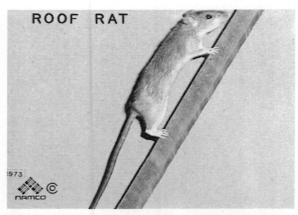

FIGURE 15.8. A roof rat. Note the long tail and more slender body than the Norway rat. (Univar)

FIGURE 17.1. The big brown bat.

FIGURE 17.5. A meadow mouse (vole). Note the snubby nose, flattened ears, thick body, and short tail.

FIGURE 17.6. The eastern mole. Note the large front paws, fleshy nose, and lack of any visible eyes and ears. (Myers)

FIGURE 17.11. A pocket gopher pushing soil out of a burrow.

FIGURE 17.19. A thirteen-lined ground squirrel.

FIGURE 17.21. A woodchuck, also called a groundhog. Woodchucks are the largest of the squirrel family.

FIGURE 17.23. An opossum. (Myers)

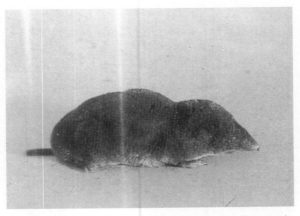

FIGURE 17.24. A short-tailed shrew. Note the elongated, furry snout and the lack of visible eyes and ears. Shrews are not rodents; they are related to the mole.

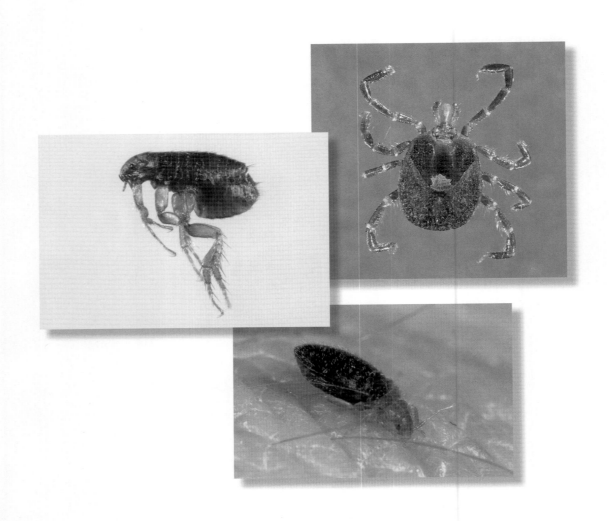

CHAPTER 11 | Fleas, Ticks, and Other Ectoparasites

Many of the arthropods discussed in this chapter will feed directly on humans or other warm-blooded animals. An organism that lives in or on another organism and obtains nourishment during all or part of its life from it, without directly causing its death, is generally known as a **parasite**. The organism from which the food is obtained is known as the **host** of the parasite. Parasites that feed from the external surface of the host are known as **ectoparasites**, and only ectoparasites will be discussed in this chapter. Parasites that live and feed within the host's body are called **endoparasites**.

Many of these ectoparasitic pests are blood feeders, while others feed on other body fluids. Some of these parasites carry disease-causing organisms, such as bacteria, protozoans, rickettsias, or viruses, from one host to another. When parasites perform this function, they are called **vectors** of disease. Public health entomology is the science that deals with the relation of insects and other arthropods to the causation of disease in humans by the transmission of organisms that are responsible for such pathological conditions. The arthropods involved may be the causal agents themselves (e.g., pubic, or crab, lice) or vectors (e.g., certain mosquitoes that vector encephalitis). An important goal of public health entomology is prevention and, if possible, eradication of human diseases related to arthropod transmission and causation.

FLEAS

Order Siphonaptera

Fleas are pests of humans and their domestic animals all over the world. While most fleas prefer nonhuman hosts, many can and do feed readily on humans when infestations are heavy or when other hosts are not available.

Fleas are small, wingless insects that average 1/12- to 1/6-inch long but can vary from as small as 1/25- to 1/3-inch long (see Figure 11.1, and Figure 11.2, which follows page 254). When viewed from the front, head on, the adult flea's body is narrow from side to side. This allows it to move readily between hairs in an animal's fur (or in the nap of carpeting) into very narrow areas, such as crevices and folds of upholstery, or even below flooring and into subflooring areas. The flea body is also covered with spines that project backward, making it well adapted for moving forward between the hairs or feathers of the host's body. These same spines make removal of the flea, by shaking or scratching, rather difficult. Adult fleas have piercing-sucking mouthparts to penetrate the skin of the host and suck blood. Their long, powerful legs permit them to jump as high as 7 to 8 inches vertically and as far as 14 to 16 inches horizontally. These considerations should be kept in mind when flea management programs are planned.

Fleas have a complete metamorphosis. The smooth, rounded, light-colored eggs are about 1/50 of an inch in diameter, only large enough to be barely seen. They are frequently laid on the host animal, but may be laid by adults that have fallen to the ground (e.g., into carpeting or the host's bedding). Since flea eggs are not attached to the host, those laid on the host will fall off and hatch on the ground, in nests or bedding, or in carpets, upholstery, or cracks in the floor. A female flea will lay a few eggs each day until she has laid up to 200 to 400. Depending on the temperature and humidity, these eggs will hatch in anywhere from 2 days to a week, but most will hatch within 2 to 3 days under favorable conditions. Cat fleas feeding undisturbed on cats can live up to 3 weeks or more on the host.

Flea larvae (see Figures 11.1 and 11.3) are small, active, maggot-like creatures. Each has 13 body seg-

FIGURE 11.1. In homes, fleas are common pests of humans and their domestic animals. (Shuster and Provonsha)

ments and chewing mouthparts, but no legs. They feed on all types of organic debris, and develop particularly well when they can feed on the feces of adult fleas, which contain undigested or partially digested blood. This explains the frequently observed presence of blood in the guts of flea larvae. The larva grows through three instars in about 1 week or up to several months, depending on environmental conditions and food availability. A mature third instar larva will be about 1/8- to 1/6-inch long, and 1/64-inch wide.

These larvae are rarely seen in the field by homeowners or pest management professionals, unless a very close and thorough inspection is made. They frequently become entwined within the carpet and resist the pull of a vacuum cleaner. The mature larva spins a cocoon for pupation. This cocoon becomes covered with grains of sand, lint, dust, or other debris from the substrate, so it is well camouflaged in the substrate. If temperatures are favorable (greater than 70°F), within about 7 to 10 days the adult flea develops within the cocoon, but the adult may not emerge immediately.

Many adult fleas emerge from the pupa within 7 to 14 days after the cocoon is formed, but some

will remain in a pre-emerged adult state, from which they may not emerge for several months to a year later. Warmth and mechanical signals (e.g., the weight of a pet's paw actually stepping on the cocoon) will trigger emergence. This phenomenon helps to explain the situation where vacationers, or people who move into a new home or apartment, are besieged by hungry fleas within several hours after returning to their home or moving into new premises. Hungry adult fleas may have been present for some time in the premises, or many may have been stimulated to emerge from cocoons by the sudden presence of host animals. Adults are ready to feed and mate very soon after they emerge from the pupal cocoon.

Fleas such as the cat flea generally require rather warm (70 to 85°F) and humid (greater than 50% relative humidity) conditions to develop substantial infestations, either indoors or out. The larvae are particularly sensitive to temperature and moisture extremes, especially excessive dryness. Thus, flea problems seem to peak in the spring, summer, and fall seasons, when these environmental conditions are common indoors and out. However, the "flea season" can be year round in many regions, especially in the South. Conversely, fleas cannot survive outdoors under the hot and dry conditions present in many regions of the United States during the summer season. However, specific conditions in each yard can allow flea development, so the professional must be alert while making inspections and subsequent insecticide applications. Fleas will generally be concentrated in pet resting areas outdoors because the substrate in such areas will receive a fallout of fecal material (containing blood for the larvae to feed on) from adult fleas feeding on the pet.

Fleas are important as carriers of parasites or disease organisms. Pest management professionals

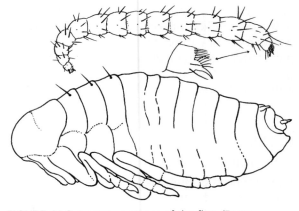

FIGURE 11.3. Immature stages of the flea. (From Peterson, Part II of *Larvae of Insects*, lithographed by Edwards Brothers, Ann Arbor, Mich., 1971)

should know how to identify each of the common species and understand details about its habits. If a flea species that can transmit plague or typhus is encountered, the professional should notify local public health authorities immediately. These officials can determine whether a significant medical hazard exists for the public. Characters used for flea identification are not difficult to master, although practice with a hand lens or use of a dissecting stereomicroscope is required to make positive identifications. The pictorial key in Figure 11.4 allows identification of most species commonly encountered in urban pest management situations.

Cat Flea
Ctenocephalides felis (Bouche)

Dog Flea
C. canis (Curtis)
Family Pulicidae

Cat fleas and dog fleas are two very similar species that occur throughout the United States. **Cat fleas** are by far the more commonly encountered of the two species in pest management work in and around homes (see Figure 11.2, following page 254). **Dog fleas** are usually found on wild (or feral) hosts, rather than on domestic pets. Both species prefer dogs or cats as hosts, although they may be found on

a wide variety of other animals, including rodents and livestock. The role of wildlife hosts such as raccoons, opossums, skunks, and feral cats or dogs, which are present in significant numbers in many urban and suburban communities across the United States, as sources of cat flea infestation that is frequently transferred to pet cats and dogs should be recognized by pest control professionals and public health officials. In particular, infestations on feral hosts may be very important to the cat flea's ability to survive and overwinter in the more temperate regions of the United States, so infestations can resume and reestablish on many domestic pet hosts each spring. Cat fleas prefer locations where dust and organic debris accumulate, and they are commonly found in houses, under buildings, and, if temperature and humidity conditions permit, in yards. Both flea species are intermediate hosts of the internal parasite (endoparasite) **dog tapeworm**, *Dipylidium caninum* (Linn.), which is common in both cats and dogs. When playing near infested pets, children can become infected with this tapeworm by accidental ingestion of fleas that carry this endoparasite.

Customers calling about fleas will see small dark insects that jump. These insects may be biting people, and there will usually be a dog or cat living in the home or apartment. Severe problems often occur when people return from vacation to a home that is infested with particularly hungry fleas, some

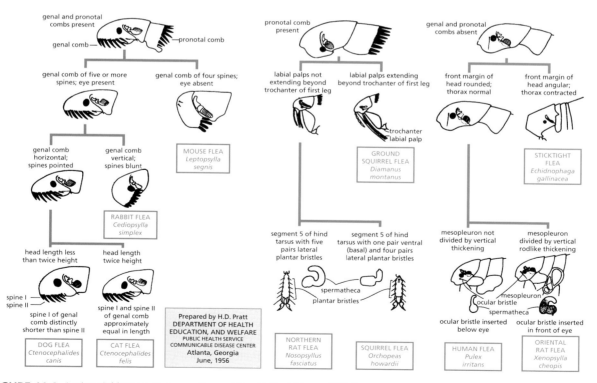

FIGURE 11.4. A pictorial key to common fleas of the United States. (CDC)

of which will have emerged from cocoons only after the people and their pets return.

The typical skin reaction to flea bites on humans is formation of a small, hard, red, slightly raised, itching spot. Bleeding may occur. The single puncture point caused by the flea's mouthparts is generally apparent in the center of each spot. Thus, close inspection reveals a small reddish bump with a more pale, flesh-colored center. While some people do not experience such skin reactions to flea bites, welts distinguish flea bites from the bites and stings of most other arthropods, or from irritations resulting from other causes. Ants and spiders leave two marks when they bite. Fire ant stings typically result in red spots that turn to small, hard, pale or flesh-colored bumps after a couple of days. There will usually not be a red perimeter to the bump, as is common with flea bites. Mosquitoes, bees, wasps, and bed bugs leave a much larger swelling or welt. However, the degree of reaction to the bite will vary from one individual to another.

Human Flea

Pulex irritans (Linnaeus)
Family Pulicidae

The human flea is found throughout the United States and is not uncommon in homes on the Pacific Coast. It can survive on human hosts exclusively but is regularly found on swine and occasionally on dogs. This flea has been infected with plague in the laboratory and shown to be capable of transmitting the plague bacteria, although it is not a normal carrier of disease.

Oriental Rat Flea

Xenopsylla cheopis (Rothschild)
Family Pulicidae

The oriental rat flea is the chief carrier of the causal organisms of bubonic plague and murine typhus. It is most common in seaport towns, where it has been introduced on both Norway and roof rats, but is well established throughout most of the United States. It is one of the most abundant rat fleas across the southern United States and in southern California. Rats are the preferred host for this flea species, although it does occasionally bite people.

Northern Rat Flea

Nosopsyllus fasciatus (Bosc)
Family Ceratophyllidae

This flea commonly infests rats and mice throughout the United States and is the most common rat flea in the northern states. It may transmit plague

organisms from one rat to another, but it does not usually bite humans.

Sticktight Flea

Echidnophaga gallinacea (Westwood)
Family Pulicidae

The sticktight flea is a prominent pest in the southern and southwestern United States, where it is primarily found on poultry but also attacks other animals, including people. Adult female fleas attach firmly to the host, forming severe ulcers on the head or neck of domestic fowl; on the ears of dogs, cats, and rats; and on almost any part of people. While adult females remain attached to the host throughout their life, the larvae feed on organic matter on the ground. Therefore, all stages can be found in poultry yards and surrounding buildings. This flea can be infected with plague or murine typhus. However, since females normally live on only one host, this species' importance as a vector of these diseases is reduced.

European Mouse Flea

Leptopsylla segnis (Schonherr)
Family Leptopsyllidae

This flea is commonly found on rats in the Gulf Coast states and in California. It is found less commonly on the house mouse in the same areas. These fleas can become a problem for humans indoors when heavy infestations of rats and mice occur in buildings.

Diamanus montanus (Baker)
Family Ceratophyllidae

This is a flea commonly found attacking ground squirrels throughout much of western North America. It is responsible for transmitting many of the plague cases to people in the southwestern United States.

Flea Control

The cat flea was once a common urban pest throughout much of the United States that provided much business for pest management professionals who service residential accounts. However, with the availability of several very effective on-animal flea control products, which are dispensed primarily by veterinarians, flea control in and around homes is only an occasional concern for those firms today.

The first significant new veterinary product marketed for flea control in the United States was Program™, which incorporated the chitin inhibitor IGR, lufenuron, into pills fed to dogs or liquids added to the diet of cats. Other products, such as Advantage™ and Frontline™, which contain the insecticides imidacloprid and fipronil, respectively, are formulated for spot-on or spray application to the pet's coat. The pyrethroid insecticide, permethrin, has also been marketed as spot-on products for flea and tick control on pets. Formulations of the juvenoid IGR, pyriproxyfen, are also available for on-host applications such as sprays, dips, shampoos, and spot-on. The chitin inhibitor and juvenoid IGRs control flea populations by preventing the hatching of flea eggs by exposing the fleas to IGR in the host's blood or in the fur. These IGRs are not insecticidal to the adult fleas. The products containing imidacloprid, fipronil and permethrin actually kill the adult fleas within a few hours to a couple of days after they get onto the host, and before they can lay eggs. Thus, when used according to directions, these products can effectively prevent most flea infestations from becoming established in the home, so there should be little need for supplemental premise treatments.

When IGR products are used, there may be an occasional need for supplemental insecticidal control of adult fleas that bother the pets or people in the home, usually by use of a flea collar or nonresidual spray. These modest supplemental insecticidal applications are usually not needed with imidacloprid and fipronil products, because the troublesome, biting stage of the flea life cycle is directly killed on the pet hosts (which will be the primary object of any adult fleas that may be introduced).

In the rather infrequent cases of significant initial flea infestation—where people are being bitten throughout the home and yard—pest control professionals will be needed to provide flea control through premise treatments.

Consistently effective flea control off the host should also incorporate the use of insect growth regulators as a foundation for the program, onto which the use of adulticides will generally be added. Consistent and effective flea management in and around homes typically requires a carefully organized and executed program. An important component of this program will be cooperation of the homeowner in maintaining proper sanitation and continued flea control on the pet, presumably with one of the highly effective products discussed earlier. Much of the difficulty in controlling fleas through premise treatments is due to failure to adequately plan and implement thorough and detailed programs. A critical factor in each program's success is the professional's ability to communicate with customers (pet owners) and enlist their aid. Another reason for management failures is inadequate insecticide application, where some important areas are missed by oversight or because the spray pattern of the application equipment is incomplete (e.g., due to worn out parts or clogged nozzles). All aspects of each program must be organized and thorough to ensure consistently good flea management.

The following sections discuss the typical steps in a detailed cat flea control program based on premise treatments.

Field Identification

The first step is to determine positively that the pest problem involves fleas and that the species involved is the cat flea. Never make either assumption, and be sure to contact local public health officials if one of the flea species that can transmit human diseases is encountered.

Inspection

Many professionals find that use of a pair of white athletic socks (laundered between uses) is a practical and essential method for making a proper flea inspection. While wearing the white socks (without shoes), look for sites where high numbers of fleas are concentrated. Fleas will be visible on the white socks. Use a diagram or floor plan of the premises, along with other notes, to locate these problem areas. Sample rooms by walking through them for a couple of minutes (per room) with the white socks on. Sample all upholstered furniture that might harbor fleas, by tapping your feet on these potential flea hot spots. Note difficult areas to treat, such as cement or tile floors, crawlspaces where rodents may be contributing to the flea problem, and areas where the cats or dogs often sleep, lounge, or travel throughout the residence. Remember that cats often sleep or lounge on upper shelves or other such areas inside, on higher ledges and vantage points on the exterior of the home, or behind furniture. Dogs usually lie on the floor or on furniture. When inspecting indoors, be sure to check each room on all floors, and do not forget the closets or basement areas.

Next, **inspect outdoor areas** where pets spend time to determine if fleas are present. Inspect pet lounging areas and kennels, in garages, below wooden frame steps and porch areas, and in crawlspaces (if pets or rodents can enter).

An important aspect of the inspection process is to **interview the customer** to learn all relevant facts about the pet's habits and where fleas have been noticed. The presence of any infants, who may be sensitive to insecticide-treated carpets and so forth, and the presence of any particularly valuable or potentially sensitive carpeting or upholstery fabrics should also be noted. Note any existing carpet or upholstery stains, before insecticide treatments begin. Be sure to take notes during this interview and during all other parts of the inspection phase of the program. These will help guide the treatment phase of the program and will be particularly useful in guiding any follow-up treatments that may become necessary. Carefully and thoroughly written notes, especially regarding any existing carpet stains or other damage, will also be useful in case the customer makes a false damage claim at some later time.

Customer Education

Begin by reassuring customers that this problem is by no means unusual and is controllable with their cooperation. Be sure to stress that **customer cooperation** is essential to the overall success of the program. They will probably be upset and frustrated with their situation, but you will need them as an ally in this program, not as a hindrance. Discuss the basic details of the flea life cycle and the steps of a thorough, safe, and effective flea control program. Tell the customer that, if pets are present, they should be treated with one of the effective on-animal flea control products. There should be no surprises for the customer before, during, or after the program.

When explaining the flea life cycle, be sure to emphasize that control of the pupae present at the time of treatment is very difficult and will likely be incomplete, so some adult fleas will emerge for at least several days to a couple of weeks after treatment.

An important initial part of the program is removal of all unnecessary clutter and debris indoors and outdoors; such clutter could interfere with thorough insecticide application. This should be followed by a thorough vacuuming of all floor, upholstery, and other indoor areas where fleas have been found. Generally, the vacuum cleaner bag should be disposed of after this initial vacuuming. All pet bedding should be laundered or discarded, as appropriate. Most of this preparation work will be the customer's responsibility, before the treatment phase (though some pest control firms include thorough vacuuming prior to insecticide treatment as part of their program). Since this preparation will take some time and effort, you should not plan to do any treatments until these steps are completed. This will require making an appointment for a return visit within a day or two. If these important initial sanitation steps are not done satisfactorily, the professional's ability to obtain rapid and effective flea control, without a high probability of expensive callbacks, is in jeopardy. A critical decision will be necessary on whether to proceed, insist on greater sanitation efforts, or, in some cases, abandon the job.

At the least, the customer should be informed of any concerns, and any guarantees that might have been made may have to be altered.

Explain the basics of all treatment procedures and be prepared to discuss the chemicals that will be used. Questions and concerns about the safety of the necessary extensive indoor and (possibly) outdoor applications will likely come up. In general, all people and pets should be away from the premises during any applications and should not reenter treated areas for 1 to 2 hours or until all sprays have thoroughly dried. This will greatly decrease any chance of toxic exposure or slipping accidents on wet or damp surfaces. Any other cleaning operations after the insecticide treatment should be delayed at least 24 hours, or longer if possible. This is especially desirable where wettable powders, dusts, or microencapsulated formulations are used, because these formulations tend to give slower knockdown and kill of fleas. Cleaning will decrease the level of insecticide residues and reduce the effectiveness of these treatments.

Explain again that some adult fleas will appear for up to 2 to 3 weeks after the initial treatment but should be controlled by residual action if they do not gain access to an untreated pet host (in which case continued efforts to control fleas on the pets should be stressed). Explain any follow-up treatments or preventive treatments that will be made.

Be certain the customer understands what to do about flea control on the pet. Pest management professionals should not include treatment of pets as part of their offerings, because of the liability involved and conflicts with the proper role of veterinarians. If the homeowners handle this chore, be sure to remind them to read all label directions on the products used and to repeat treatments as needed. If a veterinarian is involved, try to determine what treatment regime is being used on the pet and how your management should supplement this. Cats, especially kittens, are more sensitive to insecticides than are dogs. In all these cases, customer education, communication with the veterinarian (if necessary), and customer care to keep children and pets off sprayed surfaces until they are completely dry are essential to helping avoid pesticide poisoning incidents. However, studies have shown that after insecticide residues on carpets or grass have dried, the potential for significant exposure (of pets or children) through "dislodgeable" residues on those treated surfaces is very low.

Treatments

Besides treatment of fleas on the pet, insecticide applications are required indoors and, frequently, to selected areas outdoors. Remember, be sure that no people or pets are on the premises during treatment or until all spray residues have dried. All possible flea harborage areas should be treated, including carpeting, other floor areas, pet resting areas, and upholstered furniture. Be sure to spray the lower 12 to 18 inches of drapes or furniture, as well as other areas (above floor level) where the inspection and pet habits indicate flea presence. When using a compressed-air sprayer with a flat-fan spray nozzle, be sure that the spray pattern is consistent from edge to edge. To produce a fine, even spray pattern with these sprayers, they should be kept at low but consistent pressure (about 10 psi) by stopping frequently to pump the sprayer. Keep in mind that the spray liquid must penetrate into the nap of carpets or into the many cracks and crevices where flea larvae and adults hide. Recent research has shown that control of flea pupae is greater when low spray pressures of 7 to 10 psi or slightly higher are used, which appears to allow the spray residue (when applied at sufficient concentration and volume per unit area—consult product labels) to soak down into the nap of the carpet rather than to bounce off (as it does when sprayed at higher pressure).

Anyone familiar with dog behavior knows that dogs generally shake violently whenever they awake from sleeping. This behavior causes any flea eggs deposited in their fur to fly in all directions, often hitting walls and falling behind sofas or other furniture. As stated before, dogs frequently lounge on furniture, and cats tend to lounge under or behind furniture or in other remote areas of the home. Other research has shown that all stages of the flea life cycle are concentrated in those areas where pets prefer to lounge and travel indoors, in large part because those areas receive a fallout of fecal droppings from the adult fleas feeding on the pets. These droppings then become available to flea larvae in the substrate. Thus, while flea infestations tend to be concentrated in certain areas, they will often be quite scattered inside homes. Premise insecticide treatments must therefore be thorough. Be sure to move furniture to allow easy and thorough treatment behind and below each piece. Remove cushions from upholstered chairs and sofas, and treat the undersides of the cushions and the areas below or behind them. Do not treat surfaces of cushions that will later be exposed to the people or pets.

Before treating carpeted, upholstered, or any other surfaces, the possibility of staining these surfaces needs to be considered. Many modern carpets, upholstery fabrics, and wall coverings are not particularly sensitive to most water-based sprays, but some modern carpet dyes have shown sensitivity to certain insecticides. Specifically, some red dyes are sensitive to acidic spray solutions; so reddish or brown carpets may tend to turn a pale yellow, blue, or green color. Of course, insecticides formulated and labeled for use indoors tend to be safe on most surfaces, but experience and caution are important in avoiding problems. When in doubt, it is always a good idea to treat out-of-the-way spots, wait a few days before checking for staining problems, and then proceed with necessary treatments. Keep in mind that sunlight or wear from foot traffic can interact with the spray residue to contribute to the staining process under some circumstances.

Various insecticide formulations are available for spraying indoors, including emulsifiable concentrates, wettable powders, microencapsulations, and aerosols. Emulsions are generally preferred for treating carpeting because they allow for better penetration of the active ingredients down into the nap of the carpeting, without leaving visible residues. Wettable powders and microencapsulated formulations will generally give superior residual activity on noncarpeted surfaces. However, these latter formulations may leave undesirable visible residues on some surfaces.

Formulations of permethrin and other pyrethroids are available for residual use indoors. Some product labels may not allow general or broadcast applications for flea control indoors, but rather direct the applicator to treat only spots where fleas are most prevalent. Use of these residual insecticides is often followed by use of ULV or aerosol applications of nonresidual synergized pyrethrins or pyrethroids. These are intended to give rapid knockdown of all adult fleas present. In addition, the insect growth regulators (IGRs) methoprene or pyriproxyfen are often combined with the residual or nonresidual insecticide applications to give an added dimension of long-term control (120 days or more) of immature flea life stages.

These IGRs affect flea larvae, causing them to die during molting or by developmental failure in the pupal stage. IGRs generally stop production of adult fleas within the home but are not active on pupae existing at the time of treatment. Therefore, some adults are likely to emerge for up to 2 to 3 weeks after treatment and must be controlled by effective residues of a conventional residual insecticide or via repeated applications of nonresidual insecticides. When spraying carpets for flea control indoors, be sure to use the full recommended volume of insecticide dilution per unit of carpet area. Limit the pressure in the compressed-air sprayer to 10 to 15 psi or lower, consistent with an even spray

Flea Problems Where No Cats or Dogs Are Present

Flea infestations can occur even where there are no obvious animal hosts on the premises. When pets have been removed, such as during vacation periods or when a home or apartment is vacated, flea larvae will continue to develop. When people return to the premises, the pre-emerged and emerged but starved adult fleas will feed vigorously and often cause severe irritation.

Raccoons, bats, squirrels, or other wild animals nesting in or near the home may also be the primary hosts for the fleas involved. When rats or mice are eliminated from a building, any flea populations they supported will frequently begin feeding on people. It may be a good idea to spray or dust for flea control as a precautionary measure following some rat or mouse management programs.

pattern, and use a flat-fan nozzle giving a good, even spray pattern. Do not leave untreated areas between spray swaths while treating. Be especially certain to treat areas where the pets spend a lot of time lounging and where they prefer to travel. Move furniture if necessary, and also remember to treat the bottom 12 to 18 inches of drapes or wall coverings, and inside closets (if necessary, based on the results of the inspection). As much as possible, apply the material so as to get it down into the nap of the carpeting, to reach those areas where the flea larvae and adults hide. Thorough vacuuming before treatment tends to make this process easier, and some professionals even rake thick shag or heavily matted carpets before treating.

Outdoor areas that require treatment should be sprayed with formulations of the just-listed residual insecticides that are labeled for outdoor use. Treat all perimeter areas of the home and the yard, and especially any kennels or other pet runs. Keep in mind that cats will often move up into vines or onto ledges on the sides of homes or on the roof.

Follow-Up Inspections and Treatments

These should be explained to the customer in advance. Some firms prefer to attempt flea management with a single, thorough program of treatments, especially when they are supplemental to the use of the more effective on-host treatments available through veterinarians. The policy of other firms is to strongly recommend a more extended program. Single-treatment programs will generally have lower cost to the customer and usually result in less pesticide use in and around the home.

However, these programs will sometimes result in callbacks for retreatment. This is generally an added expense to the pest management firm, an expense that can be very burdensome in some situations. Extended programs generally require more sales training, involve repeat visits for inspections and follow-up treatments, and generally allow firm guarantees even for difficult situations.

TICKS

Order Acarina; Suborder Ixodida

Ticks are the largest and most conspicuous members of the order Acarina and are practically the only members of the order that can be identified without the aid of a microscope. They differ from mites in a number of external body features. The most easily seen features are the **spiracular plates** (also called **stigmatal plates**), which surround the external openings of the respiratory system. These plates are rather broad and well developed, and they are located just outside the bases of the third and fourth pairs of legs.

All ticks feed exclusively on the blood of vertebrates. There are two families of ticks that contain most of the species in the suborder (see Figure 11.5). These are the **Ixodidae**, or **hard ticks**, and the **Argasidae**, or **soft ticks**.

Hard ticks have the capitulum, where the head and mouthparts are located, exposed, and easily visible from the top view. The upper side of their body also bears a distinctly sclerotized shield, or scutum. This structure covers most of the upper body surface in the male, but is restricted to a much smaller area, immediately behind the capitulum, in the female. When a female becomes completely engorged with blood, her abdomen increases to many times its normal dimensions, and the scutum will then appear to be extremely small in relation to the body size. Males do not become so large when engorged.

In soft ticks, the body has a rather nondescript saclike shape. The front portion of the body extends forward, above, and beyond the base of the capitulum, so that the capitulum is concealed when the tick is viewed from above. Soft ticks do not have a scutum on the upper side of the body, and the exoskeleton is rather leathery in texture, with a distinctly roughened surface.

Life Cycle and Habits

Ticks have four stages in their life cycle: egg, larva, nymph, and adult. Mating usually occurs while adult ticks are on the body of the host animal. The female then drops to the ground and deposits her eggs. Adult female hard ticks feed only once and lay

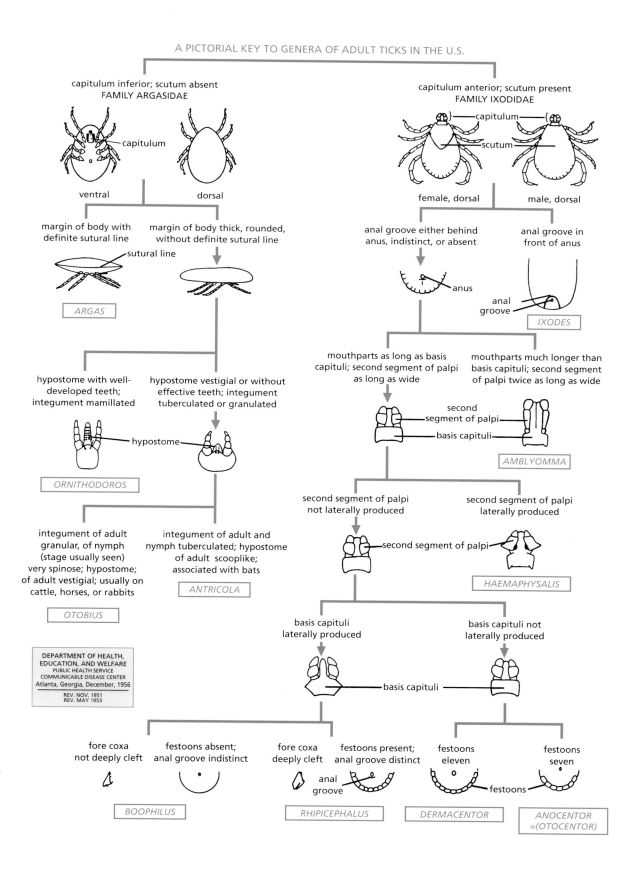

FIGURE 11.5. A pictorial key to genera of adult ticks. (CDC)

one large batch of eggs, often containing as many as 10,000 or more eggs. Some adult female soft ticks will feed several times and lay 20 to 50 eggs after each meal. Depending on such conditions as temperature and humidity, larvae will hatch from the eggs in anywhere from 2 weeks to several months.

The first immature-stage larvae, which are sometimes called seed ticks, have only six legs. These larvae must find and attach themselves to a host to get a blood meal. After obtaining this blood meal, they usually drop to the ground, shed their skin, and emerge as eight-legged nymphs. Larvae of some ticks that feed on only one host remain on the host to molt. Because of the difficulty of finding a suitable host, larvae can withstand long periods without feeding.

Nymphs resemble the adult in that they have eight legs. They do not, however, have a genital opening. Like the larva, the nymph must be able to live without feeding for long periods of time until it finds a suitable host. After finding a host and feeding, the nymph molts and becomes an adult. Hard ticks have only one nymphal instar, while soft ticks may have several. A few ticks, such as the cattle tick, *Boophilus annulatus* (Say), have only one host and molt on it, leaving the host only to lay eggs.

Adult ticks may require several days of feeding before they are able to reproduce. Male hard ticks usually die soon after mating, and females die soon after laying their eggs. Adult soft ticks are generally longer lived, and egg laying is a periodic activity of the female.

Since they cannot run, hop, fly, or move quickly, ticks must climb onto an appropriate object, such as tall grass or weeds, or up onto fences and sides of buildings to wait for a suitable host to pass by. When they detect vibrations and chemical cues, such as host odors or exhaled carbon dioxide, they fall from their perch and hope to snag or attach onto a passing host (e.g., a mammal with a fur coat). Ticks are also capable of detecting shadows cast by a passing host. These tick behaviors are important to understand and recognize to make thorough and effective applications of acaricides for tick control. These behaviors also explain why ticks crawl up exterior or interior surfaces of homes and often lodge in cracks and crevices below shingles, clapboard siding, window moldings, and so forth. In these latter cases, the professional must understand this aspect of tick behavior and carefully inspect and treat all these cracks and crevices.

Most ticks will feed on blood from a wide variety of animals, with a few tick species feeding on only one kind of host. In some tick species the immature stages will feed on different hosts than do the adults. Reptiles, amphibians, mammals, and birds are all vertebrates that ticks may parasitize. Migratory songbirds regularly spread ticks across wide regions of the United States as they move about en route to their seasonal habitats. Most ticks spend the bulk of their life on or near the ground, waiting for a suitable host animal.

Certain ticks carry the causal organisms of such diseases as Rocky Mountain spotted fever, Lyme disease, babesiosis, erlichiosis, typhus, rickettsial pox, relapsing fever, tularemia, Colorado tick fever, and Texas cattle fever. Another health threat posed by certain ticks attacking humans and other animals involves a poorly understood condition called tick paralysis. This occurs during the feeding process when the host is afflicted with a paralytic condition that develops gradually and may result in death. Paralytic symptoms disappear rapidly upon removal of the tick, and there seem to be no serious aftereffects. Most of the tick problems that pest management professionals encounter are in and around homes, and some will involve the disease-carrying species such as *Ixodes* spp. Only those species likely to be encountered by the professional around homes or other structures are described in this chapter. The pictorial key in Figure 11.5 allows identification of other ticks to the genus level. The reader should refer to the selected references at the end of the chapter for specific identification and more complete information on those ticks that transmit disease.

Hard Ticks
Family Ixodidae

Brown Dog Tick
Rhipicephalus sanguineus (Latreille)

This is one of the most widely distributed ticks in the world, and there are records of its occurrence on a number of hosts. By far the most common host is the domestic dog, and the brown dog tick is virtually restricted to this host in the United States. There are occasional collection records of people and domestic cats as hosts, but these records are generally for instances where there has been close contact with infested dogs. In other parts of the world, this tick seems to have a somewhat wider range of hosts. Under normal circumstances in North America, all feeding stages of the tick feed on dogs. The adults commonly attach to the ears and between the toes, and the larvae and nymphs are often found in hair along the back. While these developmental stages are often found on the indicated host body regions, they are not restricted to these regions and may be found on practically any part of the dog's body.

When individuals of each feeding stage

Vectors of Lyme Disease
Ixodes scapularis and *Ixodes pacificus*

Lyme disease is caused by a spirochete (a type of bacteria), called *Borrelia burgdorferi*, that affects humans and their pet dogs, as well as a number of wildlife species. In the eastern and midwestern United States this disease organism is vectored principally by a hard tick, *Ixodes scapularis*, which commonly attacks white-tailed deer and various rodent species. The vector in Pacific coastal areas is *Ixodes pacificus*, which has a similar biology. This disease was first recognized and reported as a cluster of cases that occurred around Lyme, Connecticut, in 1975. Since then, three areas in the United States are now identified where this disease organism is known to be endemic, or occurring naturally. These are areas of the Northeast (in coastal areas from northern Virginia to southern Maine), the northern Midwest (Minnesota and Wisconsin), and the West (parts of California, Oregon, Utah, and Nevada). Most cases occur in the northeastern United States, but cases have been reported in at least 49 states, and federal health agencies (CDC) report that Lyme disease accounts for more than 95% of the reported vector-borne illnesses in the United States. Lyme disease is also an increasingly common diagnosis for pet dogs in these U.S. endemic areas.

Symptoms of Lyme disease can be severe, including acute headache to more serious nervous system impairment, symptoms resembling rheumatoid arthritis, expanding red rash on or near the tick bite, low-grade fever, abdominal and joint pain, dizziness, and stiff neck. Most of the cases occur during the summer, because this is the time people are out hiking in areas infested by the tick vector, which is active then, and might be bitten by an infected tick. Persons living in or visiting the Lyme disease areas who develop these symptoms after receiving a tick bite should consult their physician and explain that they received a tick bite and suspect Lyme disease. Effective treatments for the disease are available to physicians.

Ixodes scapularis and *I. pacificus* have a rather complex 2-year life cycle. Eggs are deposited in the spring, and the tiny larvae emerge several weeks later. They feed once during the summer, usually for 2 days on the blood of small mammals, such as field mice. The following spring, larvae molt into nymphs, which also feed once (for 3 to 4 days) during the summer, either on field mice or larger mammals, such as dogs, deer, or humans. It is the nymphal stage of these ticks that is most likely to attack and bite humans. These nymphs will then molt into adults in the fall. Adults attach themselves to a host, usually the white-tailed deer, where they mate. The adult male ticks then fall off the host and die, and the females obtain the blood meal necessary for successful egg production. In areas where Lyme disease is highly endemic, such as the northeastern United States, upwards of 80 to 90% of the *I. scapularis* ticks collected in the field have the causal organism *(B. burgdorferi)* in their bodies.

Since Lyme disease and any tick management programs directed at vector populations are public health concerns, pest management professionals will rarely become involved in such programs. However, the principles of tick management will be much the same for these Ixodes vectors of Lyme disease as for other ticks discussed in this chapter, if the professional is called on to control these ticks near wooded areas, in yards, or at urban and suburban parks.

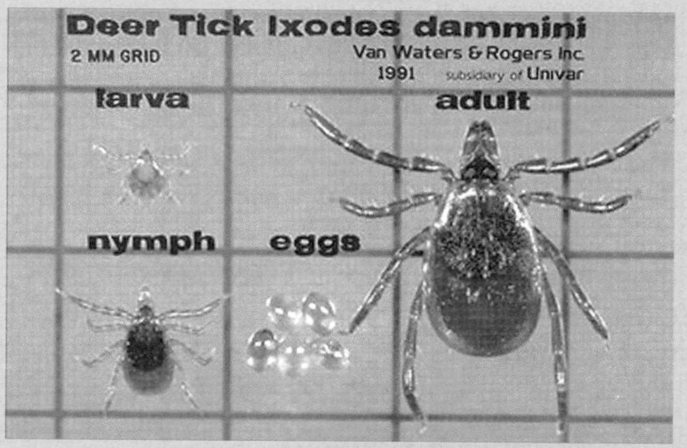

Life stages of the deer tick, now called *Ixodes scapularis*, which is the primary vector of Lyme disease in much of the United States. A very similar and closely related species, *I. pacificus*, is the primary vector in Pacific coastal areas. Stages shown are the egg, larva, nymph, and adult. (Univar)

become fully engorged, they drop from the host and seek some protected situation in the immediate surroundings. For this reason, all tick life stages may be found behind baseboards, around window and door moldings, or in furniture. Couple this behavior with the climbing behavior of newly hatched larvae or other stages that have not obtained a blood meal recently, and one can understand why nearly all cracks and crevices in an infested premise must be carefully treated to obtain complete and adequate tick control. Homeowner calls usually occur in the late summer and fall, when ticks are encountered crawling on carpeting, walls, and sometimes furniture.

Brown dog ticks can be found outdoors in the southern United States during any time of the year, but they are found active outdoors only during the warm months in the northern United States. It is generally believed that this species cannot overwinter in the more northern United States except within a heated structure.

Adult males are flat, about 1/8-inch long, and uniformly red-brown, with tiny pits scattered over the back. They do not enlarge upon feeding, as females do (see Figure 11.6, following page 254).

Before feeding, adult females resemble the males in size, shape, and color (see Figure 11.6, following page 254). As they feed, females become engorged and swell to 1/2-inch long and 1/4-inch wide (see Figure 11.7, following page 254). The legs, mouthparts, and shield area behind the head remain red-brown, but the enlarged portion of the body becomes gray-blue to olive. The red-brown color is distinctive, and no other tick normally encountered by the professional will be uniformly red-brown.

Egg laying begins about 3 days after the engorged adult female drops from the dog. She may deposit as many as 5,000 eggs in places such as between boards, under plaster or carpeting, or in other cracks and crevices. The eggs usually hatch in about 3 weeks, although up to several months may be required under particularly cool or dry conditions. After hatching, the larvae wait for a dog to attach to. They can live up to 8 months while waiting for a host. Once on the host, the larvae feed for about 3 days and then drop off. Molting occurs about 1 week after the blood meal, and nymphs emerge to climb vegetation or vertical surfaces to again wait for a host. The second feeding will last about 4 days, after which the nymphs again drop off, to molt into the adult stage. Adults can live up to 1-1/2 years without feeding, but they must feed before mating. After mating, the female completely engorges herself with blood and then drops off the host to lay eggs.

A home can become heavily infested if the family dog picks up ticks from an infested residence, boarding kennel, open field, or similar place where other infested dogs have been present. Of course, another infested dog may visit the residence, during which time some ticks may drop off. In this case, the home and yard may become infested even though a dog is not generally kept there. Dogs do not become infested with brown dog ticks by direct contact with other dogs. Ticks feeding on a dog drop off and molt before they resume host-seeking behavior and attach to another dog.

American Dog Tick
Dermacentor variabilis (Say)

Dogs are the preferred host of adults of this tick species, but these ticks will also feed readily on many other large animals. Larvae and nymphs of this species feed virtually exclusively on small, wild rodents. Newly hatched larvae are yellow with red markings near the eyes, while engorged larvae are slate gray to black. Nymphs are similar in appearance to the larvae but have four pairs of legs instead of three pairs. Adults are generally brown but become slate gray when engorged.

This tick is a vector of the causal organism of Rocky Mountain spotted fever and is one of the species commonly involved with tick paralysis.

This species is the most widely distributed tick of this genus in North America and is the most commonly encountered by pest management professionals. It occurs throughout the eastern and central United States. See Figure 11.5 for characteristics that can be used to distinguish this tick from the brown dog tick and other species.

Rocky Mountain Wood Tick
Dermacentor andersoni Stiles

As its common name suggests, this species is encountered throughout the Rocky Mountain region, where it is the principal vector for Rocky Mountain spotted fever. It is commonly involved with cases of tick paralysis. Larvae and nymphs are generally found on small wild rodents, and the adults on larger mammals. However, cases are known where all three life stages have been found on medium-sized mammals, such as jackrabbits.

This species is a common problem for campers and other vacationers in areas within its normal range.

Groundhog Tick
Ixodes cookei Packard

Both nymphs and adults of this species may attack humans. They are most common in the New England states, where they are found in summer cottages around areas frequented by groundhogs.

Soft Ticks
Family Argasidae

Common Fowl Tick
Argas radiatus Raillet

This tick, known also as the chicken tick and the blue bug, is a soft tick common in poultry houses in the southern and southwestern United States. It may injure or even kill chickens, and it may attack humans. It can be controlled in chicken houses and bird roosting areas by application of residual materials (to be discussed) that are also labeled for use in the areas involved. *Argas persicus* (Oken) is another fowl tick that is relatively rare in the United States.

Relapsing Fever Tick
Ornithodorus turicata (Duges)

This group of soft ticks, which transmit the causal organisms of relapsing fever, are sometimes found in buildings in the western and southern United States. Control may be obtained with materials used for control of the fowl tick.

Tick Management

To make it more difficult for ticks to get on the body, individuals walking in tick-infested areas should avoid sitting on the ground or on logs in areas with brush and long grass. Repellents containing DEET can be applied directly to the skin, while those containing permethrin are generally applied to socks and trouser legs. However, total protection, especially for extended periods, is difficult to maintain with these repellents. When people are in areas where ticks are numerous, they should always examine their bodies closely at least twice each day, and remove any ticks that may be present.

The only species likely to become numerous or established in homes is the brown dog tick. This is primarily because all feeding stages of this tick commonly feed on the domestic dog, which is typically allowed indoors.

Nonchemical tick management procedures should be considered and implemented along with chemical procedures. Some nonchemical techniques that help reduce tick problems include keeping grass and weeds cut short in tick-infested areas. This increases chances of tick desiccation during the summer, discourages alternative hosts, such as rodents, and lessens the amount of plant material that may need acaricide treatment. Removal of clutter and debris on the property will also discourage rodent populations, as will removal of any nesting material left by rodents. Removal of bird nests in and around structures will reduce the number of ticks, especially of soft ticks. Fencing of yards and leash laws prevent dogs from straying into tick-infested fields, woods, and parks. However, where deer populations are high in urban or suburban areas, populations of the deer ticks that are vectors of Lyme disease are also likely to be high in yards, parks, schoolyards, cemeteries, and golf courses, and around ponds and along streams. Screening and sealing house entry points used by other tick hosts, such as squirrels, raccoons, chipmunks, and bats, will also reduce tick problems in and around the home. Sealing cracks and crevices where ticks can hide, both inside and on the exterior

of the home, will aid in management. Regular examination and grooming of pets (especially dogs), and frequent cleaning of their bedding, is also strongly recommended.

Residual sprays of several residual pyrethroids are labeled and generally quite effective for tick control. Not all materials, or all formulations, will be labeled for indoor use, so product labels should be consulted. Some dust formulations of these residual materials, or of silica aerogel (e.g., Drione®), are also available and may be preferred in some situations that are difficult to treat with a spray. Nonresidual products are generally formulated as space sprays. These contain pyrethrins or pyrethroids and may be useful to supplement residual treatments. They can be effective either by direct contact or when sublethal dosages stimulate ticks to move about, so that they will be more likely to encounter surfaces that have been treated with residual materials.

Infested pet bedding should be carefully washed or disposed of. The area around the pet bed should be carefully and thoroughly treated. All tick life stages can usually be found in cracks and crevices in the infested structures. Since ticks can go without feeding for such long periods, and since the period that they remain concealed may be longer than the residual life of the acaricide chemicals applied, the effectiveness of these treatments may depend on the thoroughness of application. The professional must be careful to thoroughly treat all crevices where ticks are harboring to be sure acaricide reaches places where ticks are concealed. Other areas needing particular attention include baseboards, doorway and window casings, and the edges of carpets. During warm weather, outdoor areas frequented by the dog should be treated. This includes the yard, doghouse, and crawlspace. Since turf, shrubs, and other vegetation will require treatment, use spray formulations labeled for use on such plants to avoid plant damage. When treating the yard, be sure to treat all fences, siding, plant material, and so forth up to several feet above the ground.

It should be explained and emphasized to the owner that the dog must be treated if the infestation is to be eliminated. However, such treatments are a job for the veterinarian or pet owner, not the pest management professional. Among the effective flea control products discussed previously, those containing fipronil (Frontline®) or permethrin are also effective for tick control on dogs. Pet shops and other retail outlets generally carry liquid washes (dips or shampoos) or dusts appropriate for pet owners to use on pets. Many of those products contain permethrin, which will either kill or repel ticks effectively. However, as discussed previously in relation to flea control programs, professionals should be cautious about what insecticides are being used to control ticks on the pet and in the home or yard areas, and they should avoid potentially harmful overexposure of the pets to insecticides.

In some areas, particularly in the southern United States and areas where the deer ticks that vector Lyme disease are common, ticks other than the brown dog tick may infest lawns, shrubbery, and crawlspaces under buildings (see Figure 11.8). It will usually be unnecessary for the pest management professional to treat the entire landscape; so one way to determine the extent and locations of tick presence on the property is to sample using a drag cloth. Use a white pillowcase or larger cloth, and simply drag it slowly along on the grass, and brush it up onto foliage within 1 to 3 feet of the ground. Stop occasionally to check the cloth for ticks (some may be very small), and note infested locations on a diagram of the property to guide acaricide treatments and any follow-up sampling. Such records will also aid longer-term tick management programs for customers who want this service, and they can assist design and communication of the need for other nonchemical tick management methods (e.g., mowing grass, removal of brushy areas, fencing to keep

FIGURE 11.8. Deer tick numbers in landscapes of homes in wooded or partially wooded residential areas are usually highest along the boundries between turf and areas with trees or shrubs that offer daytime cover for deer and other tick hosts. Monitoring of tick populations by drag cloth sampling (see text) should guide applications of acaricides for tick control in these areas. (Myers)

deer away, etc.). Areas where ticks are found should be thoroughly treated with one of the already-mentioned acaricides. Shrubbery up to a height of 2 to 3 feet should be sprayed. If possible, grass and weeds should be kept mowed in wooded areas, vacant lots, and fields. These areas may require treatment with an acaricide. Yards bordering these areas may also require frequent acaricide treatment, especially along edges adjacent to wooded or brushy areas.

LICE
Orders Anoplura and Mallophaga

Members of the insect orders Anoplura and Mallophaga are known collectively as lice. All known members of both orders are wingless parasites of warm-blooded animals, but lice from the two orders differ considerably in structure and feeding habits. Anoplurans have sucking mouthparts and feed on blood, while mallophagans have chewing mouthparts and feed on skin scales and secretions. Both orders display gradual metamorphosis in their development.

Because all lice are parasitic and spend virtually their entire lifetimes on the host, the pest management professional is seldom directly involved in the actual process of louse control. In practically every situation encountered, successful louse control involves direct treatment of the host animal. The responsibility for such treatments belongs to physicians or veterinarians, depending on the host involved. Lice are considered in this chapter so that the professional will be able to identify those occurring on people and have a basic understanding of their biology and behavior in order to deal with customer concerns about these parasites. In some northern areas with very cold climates, certain lice species may be found on dogs, and especially those with thick, long fur.

Sucking Lice
Order Anoplura

The order Anoplura is a rather small one, containing approximately 500 species, three of which are parasites of humans. The antennae have no more than five segments, the head is narrower than the thorax, and the thoracic segments are fused with the abdomen and cannot be moved independently (see Figure 11.9). In practically all species where the life history has been studied, the eggs, immature stages, and adults are all found on the host. Only mammals are parasitized by sucking lice. The adult female attaches eggs to the hair of the host, and both the immatures and the adults suck blood from the host.

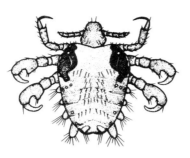

FIGURE 11.9. Body and pubic lice, both greatly enlarged.

Body Louse

Pediculus humanus humanus Linnaeus

This species and the head louse have been the subject of spirited controversy among experts on the classification of these groups. Biologically, there are two rather distinct patterns of behavior within the body louse species, and many authorities feel that this is actually a complex of two species.

The body louse (see Figure 11.9) is important from the standpoint of its activities as a parasite, but it can be even more harmful to humans as a vector of typhus and relapsing fever. Circumstances that cause large numbers of people to be crowded together under unsanitary conditions are most favorable to the rapid development of large body louse populations, which accounts for the ever-present danger of typhus outbreaks in such situations.

Body lice tend to remain on the host's body only during the actual feeding process. When not feeding, they will typically move into the host's clothing, where they will often be concealed in folds or seams. Associated with this behavior is the habit of placing eggs on garment fibers instead of attaching them directly to the host's body hair. This egg placement behavior is a unique habit that does not occur in other sucking lice.

Body lice can be transferred between hosts on bedding that has been recently used by an infested person. People sleeping or huddling together in their clothing also increase opportunities for the spread of body lice.

Control requires treating the body, clothing, and bedding of the infested person. Treating the premises is seldom called for. Pest management professionals should not treat humans or their clothing. Recommendations for control should be left to medical or health department personnel. These lice can usually be controlled by laundering or dry-cleaning infested garments and bedding. In 125°F water, the adults are killed in 5 minutes and the nits (eggs) in 10 minutes. Frequent changes to properly laundered clothing will eventually end an infestation, without insecticidal treatment.

Head Louse

Pediculus humanus capitus De Geer

Head lice are the species most commonly encountered by the pest management professional, as outbreaks of this species are relatively common in schools (see Figure 11.10, following page 254). School systems in the United States generally have ongoing programs of surveillance for head louse infestations among schoolchildren, and pest management professionals may be called on to consult in these public health programs.

The typical head louse rarely exceeds a length of 1/3-inch, and its body wall is generally slightly tougher and more deeply pigmented than that of the body louse. All stages of the life cycle normally occur on the host, as the eggs (called **nits**) are attached directly to host hair. Sometimes, globules of hair spray are mistaken for head louse eggs. This louse can be spread by the shared use of personal items, such as hats, hairbrushes, combs, wigs, or towels. Control of this species involves direct treatment of the host and is usually considered a medical problem. Most pharmacies have insecticidal dusts and shampoos available for louse control. One application may suffice, but repeat treatments are sometimes necessary. As with body lice, laundering of hats or other clothing items in warm water (greater than 125°F for 10 minutes), or dry-cleaning, will kill all stages of head lice. No insecticidal treatment of these items should be conducted. Treatment of other surfaces, such as shelves in cloak or locker rooms, may not be necessary if on-host control procedures are properly conducted and supervised by public health personnel.

Crab Louse, or Pubic Louse

Pthirus pubis (Linnaeus)
Family Pediculidae

Crab lice are parasites of humans and, while usually associated with the pubic and perianal regions, they may be found on body hair of any region (see Figure 11.11, following page 254). All life stages occur on the host, and the eggs are attached directly to host body hairs. This insect does not move around much on the body of the host, and it may remain stationary, with the mouthparts inserted into the skin, for several days at a time. Transfer of pubic lice between individuals is nearly impossible except as a result of contact between the body regions where these lice are typically found (i.e., during sexual intercourse). Crab lice are unable to survive more than a few hours, or at most a day, off a host. Therefore, transfer of crab lice between hosts by means other than intimate contact during intercourse is very unlikely.

Crab lice are smaller than body lice and head lice (see Figure 11.9, and Figure 11.11, which follows page 254). Specimens are rarely more than 1/2-inch long. The body is broad and short, and the front legs are much smaller than the second and third pairs. The first apparent abdominal segment bears a total of 6 spiracles on its upper surface.

Control measures for this insect involve treatment of the host, and recommendations are the same as those discussed for head lice. Pest management professionals should be able to identify specimens of crab lice that might be brought to them, and then firmly recommend that affected individuals contact their physician immediately.

Supportive Measures in Louse Control

Complete control is practically impossible to accomplish without treatment of the host. However, there are certain supportive measures that may be of value in preventing the spread of head or body louse infestations among groups of people whose daily activities cause them to associate very closely.

Places such as locker rooms in schools or industrial establishments, gymnasiums and cloak rooms in schools, and homeless shelters can be treated with residual insecticide formulations such as silica aerogel or one of the pyrethroids, or a nonresidual insecticide formulation. The nonresidual materials, such as synergized pyrethrins, will provide faster contact action. Any louse that may fall or be knocked from an infested person will then hopefully come in contact with a treated surface before establishing itself on another person. Such treatments can be a particularly beneficial adjunct to control programs for body lice. Numerous body lice frequently remain on the garments of an infested person. If infested garments are then hung in a locker so that they remain in contact with treated surfaces overnight, exposure to the toxicant may be sufficient to cause significant louse mortality. It is important to understand that such treatments cannot be expected to bring about complete control of either body or head louse infestations.

Other Sucking Lice

A number of other anoplurans, particularly those that are parasites of domestic animals, may be encountered by the professional. Most of these are rather difficult to identify on the basis of structural features alone, but most are quite host specific. A parasite is said to be host specific when it is found on only one host species in nearly all cases. Tentative identification of the lice in question is often arrived at by proper identification of the host.

All of these parasites spend their entire life on the host and present no infestation threat to humans.

Chewing Lice
Order Mallophaga

The order Mallophaga is one of the smaller insect orders, including only about 2,600 species. All are parasitic on either birds or mammals. Chewing lice attach their eggs to the hair or feathers of the host, and the entire life cycle is spent on the host's body. In most cases, the insects are unable to survive for more than a few days when removed from the host. The host specificity noted for sucking lice is equally important in the chewing lice, and there are no known mallophagan parasites of humans.

Members of this order have chewing mouthparts. Identifying characteristics used to distinguish chewing lice from sucking lice include the chewing louse's head, which is always wider than its thorax, and its antennae, which are short (made up of no more than five segments—see Figure 11.12, following page 254).

With the exception of occasional situations where these parasites may survive for a few days after the death of birds or after birds leave a roosting or nesting site, the professional will seldom be concerned with chewing louse control. In such instances, aerosol, ULV, spray, or dust treatments of certain residual (e.g., silica aerogel or pyrethroids) or nonresidual (e.g., synergized pyrethrins or resmethrin) insecticides will be effective. Such situations may be encountered frequently by professionals who do a lot of bird management work.

MITES
Class Arachnida; Order Acarina

The order Acarina consists of a very large number of species, most of which are very tiny. Only relatively few species are ectoparasites on humans or other animals, such as rodents and birds (especially found around nest sites), while others are damaging pests of plants or saprophytes that feed on decaying animal or plant matter. Some mites are predators on other types of mites or insects, and many are found in soil. Mites have no antennae, and their head and thorax are fused into a single region called the cephalothorax (see Figure 11.13). There appears to be a region resembling an abdomen in some mites, but many species have the cephalothorax and abdomen combined, so that no evidence of distinct body regions can be found. Their mouthparts are grouped together at the front of the body in a sort of false head known as the capitulum.

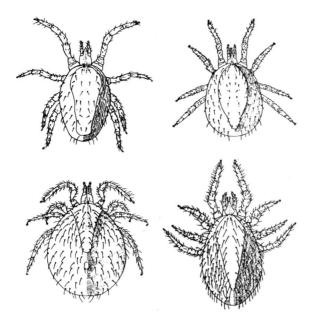

FIGURE 11.13. Ectoparasitic mites, all greatly enlarged. *Upper left:* The chicken mite is a common parasite of domestic fowl and wild birds. *Upper right:* The northern fowl mite, like the chicken mite, occurs commonly on both wild and domestic fowl. Invasions of homes by these pests often occur just after the young birds leave the nest. *Lower left:* The mouse mite is often found in great numbers associated with the house mouse. It is a proven vector of the causal agent of rickettsial pox. *Lower right:* The tropical rat mite is a common parasite of rats and may occur in great numbers immediately after a rodent control program is completed. (National Pest Management Association)

are known to bite or parasitize humans can be seen. The costly optical equipment needed to study and positively identify the various species of mites, combined with the difficult terms used by experts (who write the keys used to identify mite species) for the various body structures, deter most pest management professionals from attempting detailed mite identification. Detailed descriptions suitable for positive identification are beyond the scope of this text. Information of this sort can be found in the selected references listed at the end of the chapter, or specimens can be sent to trained specialists (called acarologists) if positive identification is absolutely necessary.

Tropical Rat Mite
Ornithonyssus bacoti (Hirst)
Family Macronyssidae

This common parasite of the Norway rat is found most often in the warmer parts of the United States, but it may be found in small numbers almost anywhere. These mites (see Figure 11.13) vary in color from bright red to black with whitish markings. As parasites, they pierce the skin of their hosts to feed on blood and other fluids that ooze from the tiny wound.

Engorged females begin laying eggs 2 days after feeding and continue laying for 2 to 3 days. Eggs are usually laid in groups within rat nest materials, but not on the rat itself. Eggs hatch in 1 to 2 days, and six-legged larvae emerge. These larvae molt within

The larval stage is the first immature stage, which hatches from the egg. Mite larvae have only three pairs of legs. When they molt to the second, or nymphal, stage of the life cycle, a fourth pair of legs appears. Adult mites also have four pairs of legs, which readily distinguishes them from tiny insects such as booklice (or psocids) or the true lice (insect orders Anoplura and Mallophaga). Some very specialized adults may have fewer than four pairs of legs, and in some mites the nymphal stage does not occur because the larvae molt directly to the adult stage. In other specialized forms, the females produce living nymphs instead of eggs that hatch into larvae.

Most mites are so small that they are barely visible to the naked eye. However, they can be seen and usually identified as mites (rather than insects) with the aid of a good hand lens, or better yet a good dissecting microscope with a strong light source back at the office (see Figure 11.14). Therefore, cases of delusory parasitosis should not be falsely attributed to mites if no actual mites that

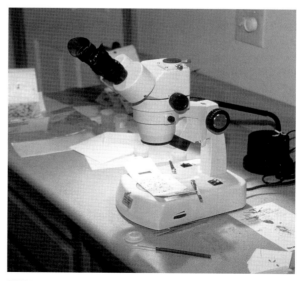

FIGURE 11.14. Pest management professionals who expect to do much work involving mites, ticks, lice, and other very small pests often invest in a good dissecting microscope, also sometimes called a stereomicroscope because there are two ocular (eye) tubes. A good light source is also highly desirable. (Myers)

about 24 hours to become protonymphs, with eight legs. Protonymphs feed and then molt in about 24 hours to become deutonymphs. These nymphs do not feed but molt in 24 to 36 hours to become adults.

This mite readily feeds on humans, even where rats are abundant. Their bites cause intense itching and skin irritation. In infested buildings they can be found on basement walls, in kitchens, bathrooms, or drawers, and near hot-water pipes.

Northern Fowl Mite

Ornithonyssus sylviarum (Canestrini and Fanzago)
Family Macronyssidae

This mite (see Figure 11.13) is a parasite of domestic fowl and many wild birds, including pigeons and starlings, throughout the temperate regions. It frequently attacks humans, causing severe itching. It normally lives only on its host, but it may leave the body of a dead bird to feed on other hosts, such as humans. It commonly migrates in great numbers from the nests of house sparrows and starlings after the nestlings depart or after bird-control programs. This migration can result in serious problems for residents indoors.

Chicken Mite

Dermanyssus gallinae (De Geer)
Family Dermanyssidae

This mite (see Figure 11.13) is also a pest of domestic fowl and many wild birds. Its appearance and life history are very similar to those of the northern fowl mite. Mild skin irritation and itching result when this mite attacks humans. Specks of blood on bed sheets are sometimes observed as a result of crushing blood-filled mites during sleep. Most infestations have been reported in rural areas, while cases in urban areas are generally associated with canaries, pigeons, and nests of other birds.

Mouse Mite

Allodermanyssus sanguineus (Hirst)
Family Dermanyssidae

This mite (see Figure 11.13), a parasite of mice, carries the causal organism of rickettsial pox, which is a mild and nonfatal disease of humans. The mouse mite is sometimes known as the Pomerantz mite because of research done on it by a pest management professional, Charles Pomerantz, of New York. It is a common household species. The mite leaves its mouse host after feeding and is frequently found on walls and in other areas, from which it can contact people.

Chiggers

Trombicula spp.
Family Trombiculidae

Chiggers are larvae of the common harvest mites, which are actually harmless to people in the adult stage. They are extremely small and are generally invisible to the naked eye unless they are fully engorged with blood (see Figure 11.15). They are found in all states and are active throughout the year in the southern United States. In northern states, their activity is confined to the late spring and summer months. Chiggers will feed on a number of hosts besides humans, including rabbits, dogs, horses, rats, mice, snakes, poultry, turtles, and toads.

Eggs are laid on the soil, and, after hatching, the larvae wander about until a suitable host is located. They usually inhabit areas where grass or weeds are overgrown, and they may swarm over a host that comes in contact with the vegetation. Larvae crawl onto people and generally move upward until reaching a place where clothing is tight against the skin (such as under socks, around the waistline or under undergarments).

Chiggers do not burrow into the skin like scabies mites do. After piercing the skin, the chigger introduces a salivary secretion into the wound. This fluid causes the surrounding tissues to harden, forming a little tube of hardened flesh. The chigger then draws body fluids from the host through this tube. Depending on the reaction of the individual host, a characteristic red welt with a hard, white central area appears on the skin after about 24 hours. This host reaction apparently results from a protein in the chigger's salivary fluid, and intense local itching generally occurs at the site of the welt. After feeding for several days, the larva drops off the host, molts, and then continues feeding and developing on insect hosts.

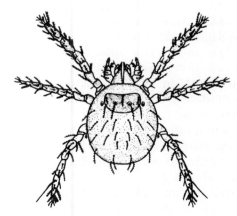

FIGURE 11.15. Larval stage of the chigger mite greatly enlarged. (National Pest Management Association)

House Dust Mites
Dermatophagoides farinae
D. Pteronyssinus
Euroglyphus maynei
Family Pyroglyphidae

House dust mites are a very widespread and commonly occurring group of mites that inhabit microhabitats associated with the nests of animals, such as mammals and birds, and including many areas of homes. They are not ectoparasitic on any of these animals, but rather they feed primarily on the scales of skin or other fallout, commonly called dander, from human and animal activity. Thus, in homes they are most numerous in areas of high human activity, such as beds, overstuffed furniture, and adjacent carpeted areas where both the scales of skin that serve as a food source and relatively high humidity levels prevail. Localized areas of elevated humidity are created where humans or other animals sleep and lounge, because all warm-blooded animals release considerable water vapor when they exhale while breathing.

While many species of mites can be found in homes and in dust samples from homes, in most areas house dust mites will be 90% or greater of the mites present in mattresses, and 70 to 95% or greater of those in furniture and carpeting. House dust mites are more likely to be present, and in higher numbers, in areas with a distinctly humid climate, or during seasons when the average humidity indoors is high. Seasonal fluctuations in average humidity within homes, often due to indoor heating, will significantly affect mite populations—with the lowest numbers found during the driest periods and in the driest regions. For example, studies in homes of warm, humid areas such as New Orleans, Memphis, Galveston (Texas), and even Cincinnati have shown that nearly 100% of homes have these mites present, and their numbers can range as high as 18,000 per gram of house dust. In much drier regions such as Denver, less than 10% of the homes had detectable levels of house dust mites, and there were generally fewer than 100 mites per gram of house dust where they were present.

Since these mites are not parasitic and are not large enough or numerous enough to be noticed, their significance as pests is due primarily to the allergens associated with their fecal material and cast skins. The presence of house dust mites, and the high levels of the allergens they produce (as a component of house dust), is generally a function of humidity and availability of food. They are generally not associated with conditions of free moisture. Long- and loose-pile carpets and some types of upholstery and bedding provide especially favorable conditions for the buildup of food material and humidity in microhabitats favored by mites. However, house dust mite populations can be significantly reduced by using short- and tight-pile carpeting, encasing upholstered furniture in plastic or vinyl slipcovers, or replacing favorable carpeting and upholstery substrates with tile, wood, or other smooth surfaces. Frequent and thorough vacuuming and other house-cleaning activities have not been shown to significantly and consistently suppress house dust mite populations. Vacuuming may also seriously exacerbate allergy problems for sensitive individuals by increasing, at least temporarily, airborne levels of respirable mite allergens.

The house dust mite life cycle consists of five stages: egg, larva, two nymphal stages (protonymph and tritonymph), and adult. Development from egg to adult requires 23 to 30 days under optimal conditions of 22 to 26°C and 75% relative humidity. Except for the desiccation-resistant protonymph stage, which can survive prolonged periods at low relative humidity and serve as a source of mites to rebuild populations when optimal conditions return, active stages of the house dust mite do not survive well at relative humidities less than about 60 percent. However, the other factors that regulate population levels and the species composition of the house dust mite population are not well understood. Since these mites are very tiny, they can be positively identified only when specially prepared and mounted on microscope slides and then examined under a compound microscope.

Management or control programs for house dust mites should be considered only in homes where the program will be a necessary adjunct to medical treatment of those who are reliably diagnosed as allergic to house dust mite allergens (as opposed to other allergens that may be components of house dust, such as molds, pollen, and cockroach allergens), and where the symptoms of patients are not adequately controlled through medical treatment. Since house dust mites will be very numerous and difficult to suppress in homes where climatic conditions are favorable, and since their distribution within the home will require treatment of surfaces that will force frequent and intimate exposure of residents to whatever pesticides might be applied, non-chemical pest management procedures should be emphasized, and only properly labeled pesticides of very low toxicity to humans should be applied. If possible and

(Continued)

House Dust Mites *(continued)*
Dermatophagoides farinae
D. Pteronyssinus
Euroglyphus maynei
Family Pyroglyphidae

practical, lowering the ambient relative humidity within the home to levels consistently below 50% (or even lower) should help suppress house dust mite populations over time. Removal or modification of surfaces that provide favorable microhabitats with regard to food buildup and relative humidity should then be undertaken (e.g., eliminate loose- and long-piled carpeting and dense upholstery with many folds and tucks).

In the United States the only pesticide currently labeled for house dust mite control is benzyl benzoate (Acarosan™), which is available in powder and foam formulations for treatment of carpeting, upholstery, and other surfaces. Treatments should be made only in accordance with label directions, and they are usually repeated only one to two times per year. In other countries, there are products labeled for house dust mite

control that contain nonresidual pyrethroids, permethrin, methoprene, and combinations of other active ingredients such as surfactants, certain plant extracts, and alcohols.

However, even after high levels of house dust mite control have been achieved, it may be many weeks before the mite allergen levels are significantly reduced to alleviate symptoms in allergic individuals. Some of the products registered for house dust mite control are designed to also reduce allergen levels, but their efficiency and effectiveness in this regard should not be assumed. Formulations of tannic acid are available and specifically designed to rapidly reduce house dust mite and other allergen loads in carpeting or other household surfaces, but caution should be exercised in their use, due to staining problems on some surfaces.

Mite Control Measures
Rodent and Bird Mites

The first general rule for ridding structures of rodent mites is to eliminate the normal host animals. This involves implementing an appropriate rodent management program (see Chapter 15). Spray or dust applications of residual miticides (or acaricides) should then be made to all rodent runs, floors, or other appropriate areas within the structure. Residual dusts labeled specifically for use indoors include formulations of silica aerogel (e.g., Dri-Die™ or Drione™ dust) and certain of the pyrethroids (e.g., cyfluthrin and deltamethrin). Contact sprays of synergized pyrethrins or pyrethroids are also available. In addition, many of the residual spray formulations labeled for tick and clover mite control, such as various pyrethroids, will effectively control most other mite species.

For bird mites, all bird nests must be removed, and the area immediately adjacent to the nests must be carefully and thoroughly sprayed or dusted with residual miticides (see Figure 11.16). More extensive treatment of walls or other surfaces may be required where substantial spread of mites from the original bird nesting areas has occurred. Mist or ULV applications of nonresidual miticides, such as synergized pyrethrins, are often used to allow especially thorough coverage and quick mite kill. In cases where the bird hosts have already left the

premises, their nests should still be located and removed. These nests can provide excellent sources for the development of infestations of some of the most destructive fabric pests, such as carpet beetles. Masks or respirators should be worn while removing nest materials, because fungal spores or other disease organisms may become airborne during this operation. Wetting the nest area and nest material before removal reduces this hazard.

Chiggers

Chiggers can be controlled in lawns and other infested areas by careful and thorough spraying with residual miticides, such as certain pyrethroids. Unfortunately, many of the acaricides previously used for mite control in non-agricultural situations, such as Kelthane® or dicofol, dioxathion, or certain carbamates, are no longer available in the United States and many other countries; and most of the effective miticides remaining for use in agriculture are not labeled for urban pest control. Similarly, organophosphates like diazinon and chlorpyrifos that were effective for chigger control are no longer available for these uses. Sanitation practices are a management technique that can be very important in prevention and control. By keeping grass and weeds cut, harborage sites are removed, and miticide applications will be more effective (see Figure 11.17). If possible, mowing and

FIGURE 11.16. Bird nests on the exterior of homes or buildings; or bird and rodent nests, and bat roosts in attics, above drop ceilings, or in wall voids; can be sources of ectoparasitic mites and insects that may move from these nest areas to affect people indoors. This is expecially likely soon after the nests are removed, or the bird or rodent hosts die or leave the nest for some reason. When nests are removed that may have been contributing to an ectoparasitic mite problem indoors, the immediate area should be treated with a residual dust or spray that is labeled for control of mites, lice, and other ectoparasitic pests. (Myers)

any other sanitation procedures should be done before the miticide treatment is applied. Sanitation will also aid by reducing populations of wild hosts, such as rodents, on which large chigger populations build up. These sanitation practices are especially important for chigger management in fields, vacant lots, and recreational areas, such as parks.

If it is necessary to go into chigger-infested areas, some degree of personal protection may be gained through treatment of clothing with a repellent (e.g., containing DEET or permethrin). DEET-based repellents may be applied directly to the skin or to clothes around the cuffs, waist, crotch, sleeves, and neck. Permethrin repellent products should not be applied directly to the skin. Applications should be thorough for maximum protection.

Other Mites That Attack, Annoy, or Are Associated With Humans

Some types of mites may migrate from human food material (some of these are discussed in Chapter 12) or other vegetable matter to attack people. Still others are true parasites of humans—they attack humans directly rather than incidentally while relying on rodents, birds, or other animals

as primary hosts. Most of these mites are referred to as itch, mange, or follicle mites. They are extremely small, difficult to find, and encountered infrequently by the pest management professional. These factors often make precise diagnosis of the pest problem a difficult task. To properly diagnose these mite problems, it is important to find and collect specimens that can be seen with a good hand lens, and then to have them identified by a qualified individual. If skin rashes or other "bites" are involved, the affected person should see a doctor. If the professional can determine the source of an infestation, providing sanitation and miticidal control services may be important. Whenever possible, destroy or otherwise correct the source of the infestation. If chemical control is required, be certain to use miticides labeled for this use and apply them strictly according to label directions.

The **grain or cheese mite**, *Acarus siro* Linnaeus, may be found infesting all types of grain, flour, cheese, and other stored foods. These mites generally occur in situations where moisture or high humidity has caused residues of these food items to become moldy. Thus, both general sanitation and removal of the moisture conditions necessary for mite development will greatly aid short- and long-term control. This mite can cause a skin rash known as vanillism in vanilla pod handlers, or grocers' itch in other cases where infested products are handled. These mites are not blood-sucking forms, so they cause only mild irritations that can be easily remedied once the source of exposure is eliminated.

Species closely related to *A. siro* that may cause similar problems include several species of *Tyrophagus*. The most common are *T. castellanii*

FIGURE 11.17. In regions where chiggers are common, their numbers will tend to build up in grassy or weedy locations such as this, due to the presence of rodents and other hosts. Keeping these areas mowed closely will greatly reduce chigger populations, or they may require acaracide treatment. (Myers)

(Hirst); *T. putrescentiae* (Schrank), the mold mite; and *T. longior* (Gervais).

The **straw itch mite**, *Pyemotes tritici* (La Greze-fossat and Montagne), is a widely distributed predaceous mite that attacks the larvae of many insects, including the Angoumois grain moth. Many outbreaks of human skin rashes have been traced to these mites. Infestation may result from sleeping on a straw mattress, laboring in grain fields at harvest time, or otherwise coming in contact with grains, hay, or other materials infested with the larvae of this mite. Their feeding produces a rash-like dermatitis that may cover large areas of skin and causes severe itching. Their attack can be so intense that vomiting, headache, sweating, and fever will also result. Recovery is usually fairly rapid if further infestation is avoided and proper medical diagnosis and treatment are received.

Glycyphagus domesticus (De Geer), the **house mite**, is often found in dried fruits and in such organic matter as skin and feathers. It causes the so-called grocers' itch when infested materials are handled. It is frequently associated with certain materials used to stuff antique furniture.

Some mites are true parasites of humans. **Itch mites**, *Sarcoptes scabiei* (De Geer), variety *hominis* (Hering), cause a skin rash or disorder called scabies, or seven-year itch, as they burrow into the skin. Intense itching is caused by toxic secretions and excretions of the mites in their burrows. Scratching may cause secondary infection and result in oozing of fluids or bleeding that favors the spread of these mites. Infestation occurs only through close personal contact with an infested individual, such as by sharing a bed. These mites cannot survive off a human host, so no pesticide treatment of indoor surfaces, such as bedding, upholstery, or carpeting, is necessary. Affected individuals should be referred to a physician or a dermatologist who specializes in the diagnosis and treatment of skin disorders.

Other mites associated with humans include the **follicle mite**, *Demodex folliculorum* (Simon). The follicle mite inhabits hair follicles and sebaceous glands, particularly around the nose and eyelids. It is considered to be of no medical importance but may, under certain conditions, produce cystic lesions or acne-like conditions. The mite is very common, as most humans harbor it. A dermatologist should be consulted when rashes occur in facial areas where these mites are typically found.

BED BUGS
Order Hemiptera; Family Cimicidae

Bed bugs and their close relatives in the insect order, Hemiptera (the true bugs), are universal pests of humans and domestic animals, as well as of bats, birds, and various other mammals. The sole food of bed bugs is the blood of warm-blooded animals. Common names used for the bed bug include mahogany flat, chinch, and red coat.

Common Bed bug
Cimex lectularius Linnaeus

An adult bed bug is about 1/5-inch long and 1/8-inch wide. Its reddish-brown to mahogany-colored body is greatly flattened and oval shaped (see Figure 11.18, and Figure 11.19, which follows page 254). After feeding, the bug's body enlarges considerably, becoming longer and much less flattened. Although the body is covered with tiny hairs, these hairs are so small that they are almost invisible to the naked eye, so the general body appearance is shiny. Bed bugs have piercing-sucking mouthparts that enable them to pierce the skin and suck blood from their hosts.

Bed bug eggs are elongated and usually attached to an available surface when laid. Eggs are not known to be placed directly on the host's body but are typically found on surfaces near where the host sleeps or nests. Each female bed bug lays about 2 eggs per day until she has laid approximately 200. At normal room temperatures these eggs will hatch in 6 to 17 days, producing small, almost colorless nymphs that have the general body appearance of the adult. The nymphs undergo a gradual metamorphosis through five instars before becoming adults.

There is considerable variation in the rate of development, even among individuals hatched on the same day and living under nearly identical conditions. As a result, individuals in all stages of development are usually present in an infestation. Nymphs must have a blood meal during each instar in order to molt. At room temperature, and with a readily available food supply, the nymphal period will last from 14 to 30 days. However, in the field, where blood meals may not be readily available, development can take much longer. Bed bugs will mate soon after becoming mature, so the time from egg hatch to egg laying will often be 4 to 9 weeks.

Bed bugs are very hardy insects. Both adults and nymphs can survive prolonged periods without food or under adverse temperature conditions. Adults can live for a year or longer without feeding and can survive over winter in an unheated building. Nymphs are not as hardy as adults, but they can survive for considerable periods under adverse conditions.

Humans are the preferred host for the common bed bug, but it will feed readily on other animals, such as poultry, mice, rats, canaries, dogs, and cats, when necessary. Normally the bugs feed at

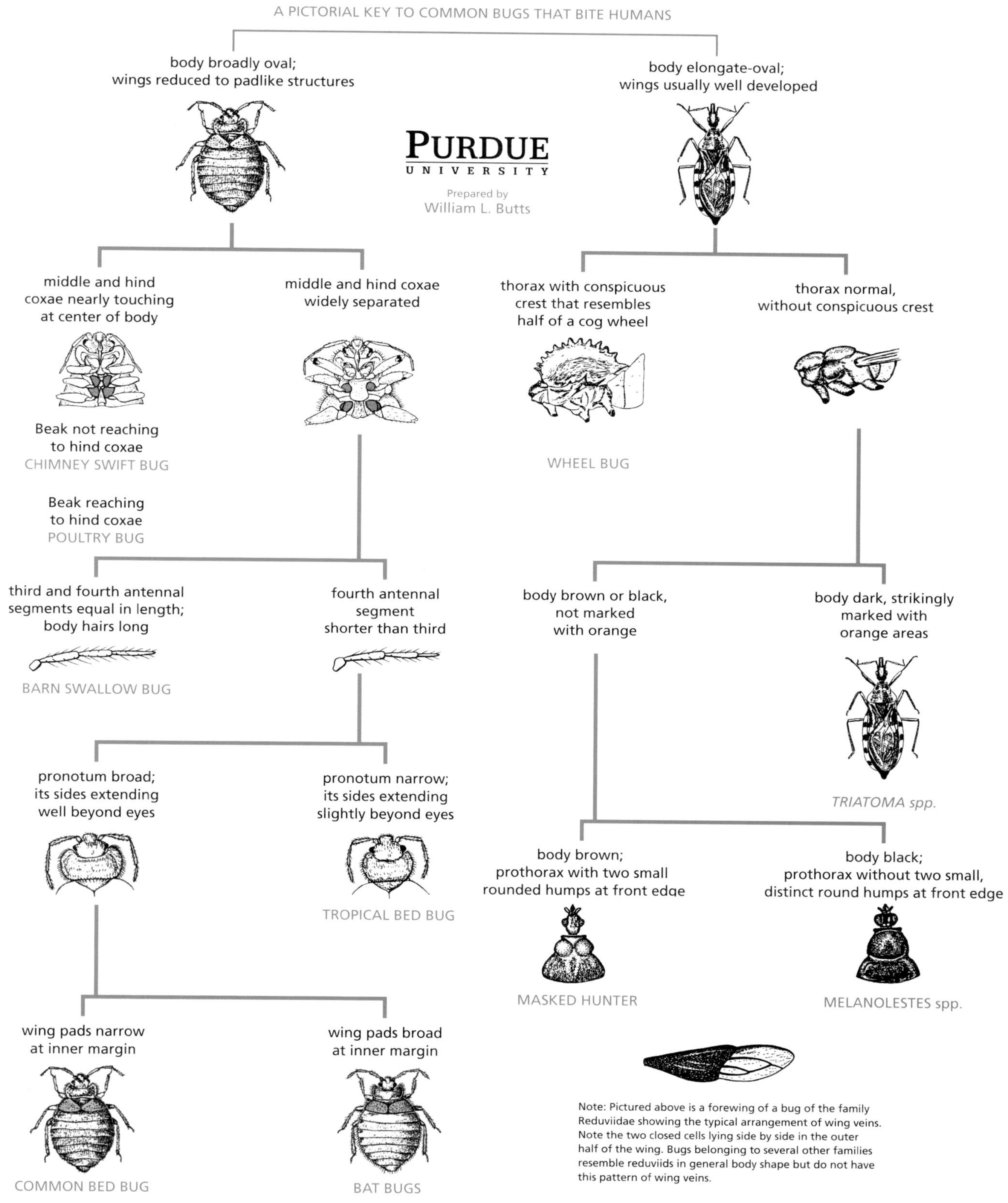

A PICTORIAL KEY TO COMMON BUGS THAT BITE HUMANS

body broadly oval;
wings reduced to padlike structures

body elongate-oval;
wings usually well developed

PURDUE
U N I V E R S I T Y
Prepared by
William L. Butts

middle and hind
coxae nearly touching
at center of body

middle and hind coxae
widely separated

thorax with conspicuous
crest that resembles
half of a cog wheel

thorax normal,
without conspicuous crest

Beak not reaching
to hind coxae
CHIMNEY SWIFT BUG

WHEEL BUG

Beak reaching
to hind coxae
POULTRY BUG

third and fourth antennal
segments equal in length;
body hairs long

fourth antennal
segment
shorter than third

body brown or black,
not marked
with orange

body dark, strikingly
marked with
orange areas

BARN SWALLOW BUG

TRIATOMA spp.

pronotum broad;
its sides extending
well beyond eyes

pronotum narrow;
its sides extending
slightly beyond eyes

body brown;
prothorax with two small
rounded humps at front edge

body black;
prothorax without two small,
distinct round humps at front edge

TROPICAL BED BUG

MASKED HUNTER

MELANOLESTES spp.

wing pads narrow
at inner margin

wing pads broad
at inner margin

Note: Pictured above is a forewing of a bug of the family
Reduviidae showing the typical arrangement of wing veins.
Note the two closed cells lying side by side in the outer
half of the wing. Bugs belonging to several other families
resemble reduviids in general body shape but do not have
this pattern of wing veins.

COMMON BED BUG

BAT BUGS

FIGURE 11.18. A pictorial key to common bugs that bite humans.

night, but they will feed during daylight hours in places such as theaters, offices, and rest rooms that are not ordinarily used at night.

In laboratory tests, bed bugs have been found to carry the causative agents for several diseases, such as anthrax, plague, tularemia, yellow fever, relapsing fever, and typhus. However, there is little evidence that they carry these disease organisms under normal conditions, so they are not considered an important factor in disease transmission.

Bed bugs generally hide in cracks and crevices during normal daylight hours. They enter such areas easily because of their extremely flattened bodies. Typical hiding places are in the folds and tufts of mattresses, coils of springs, cracks and hollow posts of bedsteads, and upholstery of chairs and sofas. However, they are not restricted to these places. In heavy infestations, bed bugs are frequently found in places such as behind loose wallpaper, behind pictures on the wall, under door and window casings, behind baseboards, and even in light fixtures or medicine cabinets. When inspecting for bed bugs, the pest management professional must look in any place that offers darkness, isolation, and protection.

Bed bugs give off a distinct odor from glands on their thorax. The experienced professional can easily recognize this odor, particularly when the infestation is heavy. Bed bug bites cause welts and irritation to some people, but other people may not react at all.

As in most pest management work, it is necessary to first make a thorough inspection to determine the extent of an infestation (see Figure 11.20). The professional must look in all of the normal hiding places and, in addition, remember that these bugs will often wander. Carefully inspect all rooms immediately adjoining any rooms where an infestation is found. The bugs may be found in seemingly unlikely places, such as in cracks in the floor under carpeting, behind electric switch plates, in folds of draperies, in unused ovens or broilers, and in motor compartments of electric refrigerators.

Frequently, even when the bed bugs themselves cannot be easily found, their hiding places can be located by looking for the spots of fecal material they often leave in easily visible places. Fecal spots and the bloody spots left on sheets and pillowcases when engorgedbugs are crushed serve as sure signs of infestation.

Bed Bug Management

Bed bugs are usually controlled using insecticide spray or dust applications, although in extreme cases the premises may be fumigated. Insecticides

FIGURE 11.20. There are many potential bed bug harborage sites available within a relatively short distance from where the host will sleep each night in this bedroom. (Myers)

labeled for use on or near beds and furniture include permethrin, resmethrin, synergized pyrethrins, malathion, silica aerogel and some combination sprays or dusts of these nonresidual insecticides. Bed linens should never be sprayed, and mattresses should be treated only at seams, folds, buttons, or tears. Treat each tuft in the mattress individually, and do the same with the folds at the edges. Be sure to treat appropriate spots on the bottom and sides of the mattress as well as on the top. Mattresses should be thoroughly dried and covered with clean linens before reuse. Large quantities of spray or dust are usually not required, and a hand pressure sprayer or duster is adequate for the job. Either a fan pattern or crack and crevice spray will be satisfactory, depending on the situation and types of surfaces to be treated.

While nonresidual formulations should be used on the bedding surfaces where direct contact with humans could occur, formulations with more extended residual action can be used away from the bedding and direct (human) contact areas. In recent years, some of the residual organophosphate and carbamate insecticides that were more effective and preferred for control of bed bugs have been removed from the marketplace, and so the professional must choose from a limited number of products containing permethrin or other residual pyrethroids. Since bed bugs have piercing-sucking mouthparts and cannot ingest particles from residues left by application of dust or wettable powder formulations, and the active ingredient from those particles may not readily dissolve and absorb into the cuticular waxes on the exoskeleton, oil-based or emulsifiable concentrate formulations should be preferred. However, some surfaces that need to be treated may be damaged by those formulations, and so use of a dust or nonwetting aerosol formulation may be necessary.

Be careful to treat all places where the bugs may be hiding. Other than the mattresses on beds, pay particular attention to hollow bed frames and springs, and including inside any small coils that may be visible. On box springs, treat all folds and overlaps on the covering fabric. On the bed frame itself, treat all cracks and hollow framework. Spray under any loose baseboards and around all window and door casings near the infested bedding areas, as a minimum treatment. In addition, treat any other bed bug hiding places that may be found, and do not overlook the possibility of hiding places in bedside tables, bureaus and other furniture in the room. A thorough application is essential to achieve adequate control.

It is usually desirable to apply insecticide for bed bugs early in the day, so that insecticide spray residues will have several hours to dry, or dusts will have time to settle, before the room will be used again for sleeping. As a safety consideration it is particularly important to dry and cover mattresses completely before they are reused.

Other Bed Bugs

There are several species of bed bugs (closely related to the common bed bug) that professionals may occasionally encounter and that are frequently mistaken for the common species. These insects also feed on blood and have body shapes very similar to the common bed bug. They usually have preferred hosts other than humans, but many will feed on humans if the opportunity arises or the preferred host becomes unavailable. The pictorial key in Figure 11.18 can be used to separate the common bed bug from some of these other species.

The **tropical bed bug**, *Cimex hemipterus* Fabricius, is a tropical species that has become established in Florida. It is a parasite of humans, with habits very similar to those of the common bed bug.

The **bat bug**, *Cimex pilosellus* Horvath, is a pest of bats and is frequently found in houses in the western United States (see Figures 11.21 and 11.22, following page 254). The bat bug of the eastern United States is Cimex adjunctus Barber. Bats are the primary host of both species, but both bugs can, and often do, feed on humans. They can be distinguished from the common bed bug by the presence of long hairs on the body (see Figure 11.21, following page 254) and by the other charac-

teristics shown in Figure 11.18, and Figures 11.19, 11.21 and 11.22, which follows page 254). The European **bat bug**, *Cimex pipistrelli* Jenyns, will also occasionally be found in homes.

The first control measure for all bat bugs is to eliminate their preferred bat hosts from the building and seal all openings so that bats cannot re-enter. Thorough insecticide treatments with any of the previously mentioned residual insecticides should then be applied.

Another group of bugs resembling the bed bugs infest birds. *Cimexopsis nyctalis* List is a small bug parasitic on chimney swifts. It occasionally becomes a pest in homes in the eastern and midwestern United States and is found as far south as North Carolina. This small, light yellow to amber-coloredbug is 1/8 inch or less in length.

The **swallow bug**, *Oeciacus vicarius* Horvath, and the European swallow bug, *Oeciacus hirundinis* (Lamarck), are found in swallow nests or in chicken houses. They frequently infest homes. These bugs are usually confined to the nests of their bird hosts and do not normally infest elsewhere in homes until late summer and fall, when the fledgling birds leave their nests.

Cimex columbarius Jenyns is a common pest of pigeons, starlings, and other fowl. The poultry bug, *Haematosiphon inodorus* (Duges), is another pest of birds. It can be distinguished from the common bed bug by the characteristics given in Figure 11.18.

To control these bird parasites, the birds and their nests must first be removed from the premises. A careful and thorough application of any of the previously mentioned residual insecticides will then give control of these insects.

CONENOSE BUGS
Order Hemiptera; Family Reduviidae

A number of true bugs of the family Reduviidae will occasionally inflict rather severe, painful bites on people. Most of these insects are predaceous on other insects, but a number are definitely adapted to blood feeding. Some of these bloodsucking species are important as vectors of the causal agents of Chagas' disease. This disease is not common in the United States but is a significant health problem in many other countries of the American tropics and subtropics.

Triatoma spp.

The genus *Triatoma* (see Figure 11.18) and a few related genera make up the subfamily Triatominae. All members of this subfamily for which feeding habits are known feed solely on the blood of vertebrates. The **bloodsucking conenose**, *Triatoma sanguisuga* (LeConte), is probably the most widely distributed species in the United States. Infestations are generally associated with loosely constructed, substandard housing. This is particularly true in situations where the area immediately surrounding the home and crawlspace beneath are open to the activities of domestic fowl or other animals. These bugs are usually brown to black in color and strikingly marked with orange or red.

Triatoma protracta (Uhler), the **western bloodsucking conenose**, is prevalent on the West Coast. Its natural habitat is pack rat nests, but it will invade new homes as they are built in the foothills of the coast or perimeters of urban areas. This species is attracted to lights at night and can be a serious pest around lighted swimming pools. They are poor flyers but can glide. The bite of this insect can for some people result in an allergic reaction that can include nausea, heart palpitation, breathlessness, and violent itching.

Masked Hunter
Reduvius personatus (Linnaeus)

Another member of this family that inflicts a severe wound when it bites is the masked hunter, sometimes called the kissing bug. This is a widely distributed species common in the eastern and midwestern United States. This insect is not a bloodsucker but is a predator on other insects. Masked hunters bite readily when handled or otherwise disturbed, apparently as a defensive mechanism. This is a grayish-brown bug without any outstanding contrasting markings (see Figure 11.18, and Figure 11.23, which follows page 254).

Other Reduviids

A number of other species of this family are known to bite on occasion. One of the most common of these is the wheel bug, *Arilus cristatus* (Linnaeus); a large grayish-brown bug with a distinctive crest on the thorax (see Figure 11.18, and Figure 11.24, which follows page 254). Two smaller species, which are black and sometimes called the black corsairs, occasionally enter homes and bite when handled. These insects belong to the genus *Melanolestes* (see Figure 11.18).

Control of Conenose Bugs

The relationship of domestic animals to the presence of the blood-feeding conenoses has been discussed previously. Excluding domestic or other animals from both the actual dwelling and the crawlspaces and similar areas is important to an effective control program. The presence of these animals represents a constant hazard to people and to the success of a conenose control program. These animals are a ready supply of blood that will be available if a reinfestation occurs. Homeowners and tenants should be strongly encouraged to make any structural alterations that will help solve such problems. A general residual application of malathion or, if no poultry or livestock are present, one of the insecticides recommended for tick control earlier in this chapter should be made.

The kissing bug and black corsair are not normally feeders on mammalian blood. These insects bite people more or less by accident. Residual insecticide applications are also effective against these bugs, but there is rarely much need for structural corrections.

DELUSORY PARASITOSIS AND INSECT PHOBIAS (IMAGINARY ITCHES)

Insects, spiders, and other arthropods frequently cause people acute annoyance and worry that may lead to nervous disorders, imagined itches, or even extreme fear of pests that do not exist. The "bugs," if any were ever present, may be innocuous or may have been eliminated, except within the mind of the affected individual. If the professional is faced with the possibility of an imaginary infestation, a very careful and thorough examination of the premises should be conducted before reporting the absence of arthropods to the customer. Professionals might then seek help from other pest management professionals, consultants, or university experts to be certain that an infestation has not been overlooked. If a true problem with a biting pest is identified—for example, with an ectoparasitic mite—then the situation should be managed appropriately (i.e., as discussed elsewhere in this chapter). However, professionals occasionally are contacted to control infestations of bugs or mites where no infestation exists.

It is important to know that many things can cause itches. Of course, one cause is the bite or invasion of certain pests known to bite humans, such as fleas, lice, certain mites (but not house dust mites), ticks, some species of thrips or psyllids (see Chapter 12 on occasional invaders), and so forth. However, other causes include allergies, airborne irritants, dermatologic conditions, reaction to medications, systemic diseases such as diabetes, chicken pox, and many others. Common irritants encountered in certain workplaces or other environments include tiny airborne particles of paper, metals, ceramics, fiberglass fibers, or other insulation materials. Exposure to other chemicals, changes in temperature or humidity (e.g., seasonal changes, like the dryness that occurs when the winter heating season begins), or simply reaction to scratching as a result some other condition may be involved.

Emotional or sensory problems such as an overwhelming fear of bugs or, if no arthropod is involved, the delusion of their presence may be the customer's true problem. When confronted with these situations, pest management professionals should not put themselves into the position of making a medical or psychiatric diagnosis or recommendation. A general knowledge of these other causes of itches can be very helpful in reporting the absence of pests to the client. Another useful approach is to give the affected client a small, stoppered vial containing some rubbing alcohol. Ask the client to put any of the biting pests into the vial, for later inspection. If no pests capable of biting are found in the vial upon close examination (e.g., under a microscope), this evidence can be very effective. Explain that no evidence of bugs could be found and that certain medical conditions, chemical irritants, or medications may cause itching. Suggest that relief from the sensation of bites might be obtained from medical attention. Do not suggest that the client see a psychiatrist, but rather a physician, who can investigate the possibility of some organic problem. The physician may then recommend psychiatric help. In industrial situations where airborne particles or severe humidity changes might be involved, an industrial hygiene group with the state department of labor or a medical department within the plant should be consulted. If a family residence situation is involved, the family physician should be consulted.

Whatever the problem, the pest management professional should not attempt a pest management treatment if no arthropod pest is involved. Remember that it is illegal to use a pesticide where no pest is present. In addition, treatment for a pest that does not exist is not the most ethical approach. Honesty is the best policy. To retain the confidence of the client, be frank in making a recommendation. Show continued interest in the problem, and offer to talk with the physician or others who might become involved, if desirable. Treat the client with dignity, consideration, and patience.

SUPPLEMENTARY READING MATERIAL

Arlian, L. G. "Biology and Ecology of the House Dust Mites, *Dermatophagoides* spp. and *Euroglyphus* spp." *Immunology and Allergy Clinics of North America* 9, no. 2 (1989): 339–56.

Colloff, M. J. "House Dust Mites—Part II: Chemical Control." *Pesticide Outlook* 1, no. 2 (1989): 3–8.

Furman, D. P., and E. P. Catts. *Manual of Medical Entomology*. 3d ed. Palo Alto, Calif.: Mayfield, 1970. 163 pp.

Habicht, G. S., G. Beck, and J. L. Benach. "Lyme Disease." *Scientific American* 257, no. 1 (1987): 78–83.

Harwood, R. F., and M. T. James. *Entomology in Human and Animal Health*. 7th Ed. New York: Macmillan, 1979. 548 pp.

Kettle, D. S. *Medical and Veterinary Entomology*. Wallingford, England: C.A.B. International, 1990. 658 pp.

Krantz, G. W. *A Manual of Acarology*. 2d ed. Corvallis, Ore.: Oregon State University Book Stores, 1978. 509 pp.

Mallis, A. *Handbook of Pest Control*. 6th ed. Cleveland: Franzak & Foster, 1982. 1,101 pp.

Orkin, M., and H. I. Maibach, Eds. *Cutaneous Infestations and Insect Bites*. New York: Marcel Dekker, 1985. 321 pp.

Rust, M. K., and M. W. Dryden. "The Biology, Ecology, and Management of the Cat Flea." *Annual Review of Entomology* 42 (1997): 451–73.

Smith, R. L. *Venomous Animals of Arizona*. University of Arizona Extension Bulletin no. 8,245. 1982. 134 pp.

Tapley, D. F., R. J. Weiss, T. Q. Morris, G. J. Subak-Sharpe, and D. M. Goetz, Eds. *The Columbia University College of Physicians and Surgeons Complete Home Medical Guide*. New York: Crown, 1985. 911 pp.

U.S. Centers for Disease Control (CDC). *Lyme Disease Home Page*. http://www.cdc.gov/nci dod/dvbid/lyme/index.htm

U.S. Centers for Disease Control (CDC). *Division of Vector-Borne Infectious Diseases (Home Page)*. http://www.cdc.gov/ncidod/dvbid/index.htm

U.S. Centers for Disease Control (CDC). *Division of Parasitic Diseases, Insects & Worms (Home Page)*. http://www.cdc.gov/ncidod/dpd/parasiticpath ways/insects.htm

U.S. Centers for Disease Control (CDC). *Delusional Parasitosis*. http://www.cdc.gov/ncidod/dpd/ parasites/delusionalparasitosis/default.html

CHAPTER 12 | Occasional Invaders

This chapter discusses many of the insects or other types of arthropod pests encountered by urban pest management professionals but not mentioned in other chapters. These pests will be divided into three general groups: occasional invaders, light-attracted pests, and miscellaneous pests.

The term **occasional invaders** includes those pests that often occur in buildings at some stage of their life cycle but that do not usually complete their entire life cycle within the building. Most of these pests live outside of buildings and come indoors only on occasion. Although they may enter in large numbers, they usually do little damage and are considered a nuisance simply because of their presence. Many of these pests enter buildings while they are flying around at night, because they are attracted to lights in or on the home or building (thus the term **light-attracted pests**).

The term **miscellaneous pests** applies to those pests that usually complete their life cycle within the confines of a building. Some of them are common in many parts of the country, while others may occur in great numbers only in certain regions. Some cause extensive damage to household goods and furnishings, while others are venomous or cause allergic reactions. Of course, miscellaneous pests can be further distinguished in any number of ways, such as autumn invaders or other seasonal pests, pests associated with firewood or Christmas trees, or attic pests, all of which will challenge pest control professionals on occasion.

While there may be some overlapping of these groups, placement of a pest in its proper group will enable the professional to understand important aspects of the pest's behavior, inform the customer about the habits of that particular pest, and help the professional in planning and conducting an effective management program. No one general management method exists for all these pests, so

the pest management professional must properly diagnose and treat each case individually.

Many of these pests are most effectively and efficiently managed by eliminating conditions that allow them to harbor and build up to great numbers near the structure. This generally involves some sort of sanitation procedure or basic change in landscaping. Alternatively, application of exclusion techniques may be necessary. Techniques such as caulking cracks and crevices around doors and windows or inserting screening into weep holes of a brick facade on the structure's exterior can be very useful for long-term relief from these pests. There may be some factor or stimulus that is causing the pests to enter the structure. This is the case for light-attracted pests, and manipulation of lighting will often give the most satisfactory long-term relief. Other factors that may stimulate pest movement into structures include environmental extremes (such as unusual dry spells), excessive rainfall (and poor drainage adjacent to the foundation), onset of winter (some pests seek to overwinter in structures), or presence of some unusual food source within the structure. Often there will be little that the professional can do or recommend to overcome the effects of such environmental extremes.

Professionals are sometimes called to deal with an apparent occasional invader problem that may not really be a problem, but only an occurrence. The presence of one or a few individuals of some species indoors may indicate only that a few individuals got lost, and it does not necessarily indicate a need to institute substantial pest management actions. Professionals must use their ability to identify the pests involved, their knowledge of pest habits, and an open-minded assessment of the factors causing the problem before deciding on a course of action.

Even though we will be discussing the use of pesticide technology as a direct control procedure for many of the pests listed in this chapter, professionals should give strong consideration to the many available nonchemical pest management procedures when dealing with occasional invaders (see Figure 12.1). For some types of pests, this can mean habitat removal, such as removal of boxelder or other trees that foster boxelder bug infestations, removal or relocation of firewood piles stored inside the home or garage, or removal of a Christmas tree or other plant that is the source of a nuisance insect infestation indoors. For pests that truly invade from outside, there are many effective exclusion techniques that should be considered after thorough inspection of available pest access routes through the building's exterior and before insecticide applications are relied on. These include caulking or sealing of cracks and voids around utility entrances to the building, use of screening over or under vents (such as in soffits or weep holes of brick facades on homes), and basic repair of and proper weather-stripping around doors and windows. In some cases sprays of residual pyrethroids can be used effectively on exterior surfaces of homes or buildings, with the objective of repelling pests that would otherwise aggregate on those surfaces and then work their way indoors, perhaps for overwintering. Careful use and timing of such repellent sprays can be effective to exclude cluster

FIGURE 12.1. Managing occasional invaders involves taking a holistic approach to the problem. Many areas on and around a building can be managed, modified, or repaired to aid in excluding or reducing pests.

flies, multicolored Asian lady beetles, overwintering paper wasp queens (*Polistes* spp.), or others.

OCCASIONAL INVADERS

Clover Mite
Bryobia praetiosa Koch
Order Acarina; Family Tetranychidae

The clover mite often becomes a serious household pest, especially in situations where new lawns have been established and where a heavy growth of succulent, well-fertilized grass exists close to foundation walls. These mites are smaller than a pinhead, usually dark red, and have pink front legs as long as the body and much longer than the other six pink-colored legs. These front legs characteristically extend forward from the body (see Figure 12.2, following page 254). Clover mites often occur in extremely large numbers, and although they do not bite people or pets or cause damage indoors, they are extremely annoying and leave red stains when crushed on light-colored walls or drapes.

Clover mites do not feed exclusively on clovers. They attack a number of grasses and other plants commonly found in yards. Migration into homes is triggered by overpopulation or by the onset of unfavorable feeding conditions, which may occur during periods of drought, or by the onset of cold weather.

Adult mites lay eggs in cracks in concrete foundations, inside exterior walls, and on the underside of bark at the base of trees. Mature mites frequently spend the winter within exterior walls of houses. They are inactive during cold weather as well as during the very hot weather of midsummer. During even brief periods of warm weather in late winter or early spring, they migrate both to the outside and inside walls of the house. These migrations are particularly noticed on the south and west sides of buildings because of the warming effect of bright sunshine on the building. The mites are usually noticed around windows, but they may overrun the entire home. Heavy migrations into houses are also common in early summer and fall.

The number of clover mites entering the structure will be reduced where a plant-free band of pea gravel or coarse sand (18- to 24-inches wide) is maintained around the foundation. This is generally not acceptable to homeowners but may be appropriate for food plants, office buildings, and similar structures. Other nonchemical pest management techniques can be used to eliminate or minimize clover mite problems that originate in the landscape near the building's foundation. Closely mowing grass, clovers, or other ground covers that support mite population build-up will greatly reduce mite numbers. Avoid excessive watering or fertilization, so that lush growth of these host plants is not encouraged. The use of bark or other mulches below shrubs will discourage mite populations around foundations. Where clover mite populations seem to build up to high numbers repeatedly, creating chronic problems, determine what types of plant material are supporting these mites. These plants should then be removed, if possible.

Satisfactory short-term chemical control of clover mites depends on thorough application of an effective miticide. A number of miticides and insecticides are quite effective for clover mite control although those labeled for use in landscapes around homes (as opposed to in agricultural settings) may be limited. Some effective materials include bifenthrin or any of several other pyrethroids that are labeled for this pest, and boric acid or silica aerogel (Tri Die™) dusts (for indoor use only). These materials are effective primarily against the active stages. Either wettable powder or emulsion sprays can be used. Sprays must be applied to a band of lawn area up to 20-feet wide around the house, and to the foundation and outside walls of the building. Very thorough treatment is required for consistent results. These materials are usually applied at the rate of 15 to 20 gallons of finished spray per 1,000 square feet of lawn area, to give the most effective control (check the label of the miticide selected). However, the professional must be careful to follow label directions and not to overdose with emulsions, since burning of the vegetation might result.

Spot treatments of formulations labeled for indoor use should be made to baseboards, around windows, to areas between the screens or storm windows and the window sash, and to any other entry points. Aerosol or ULV treatments (space sprays or directed) of synergized pyrethrins or nonresidual pyrethroids can also be used for rapid knockdown of mites crawling around indoors. Soapy water is effective on masses of mites crawling on surfaces, as it will kill exposed mites on contact.

Centipedes
Class Chilopoda

Centipedes other than the house centipede (which we will discuss under miscellaneous pests later in this chapter) usually live outdoors in damp areas, such as under leaves, stones, boards, or tree bark or in mulch around outdoor plantings. When these centipede habitats are near a home's foundation, centipedes will wander inside, where they may be found at floor level almost anywhere. If provoked, larger centipedes may bite, causing some pain and slight swelling. Actually, their "bites" are not caused

by their jaws or mouthparts, but by their front legs, which are modified to look and function like jaws and contain venom glands. Smaller species are not large enough to penetrate human skin. Centipede bites are usually not serious, but an antiseptic should be used on the wound and a physician consulted in all cases where the skin is punctured.

Centipedes are usually brownish, flattened, and elongate animals that have many body segments. One pair of legs is attached to most of these body segments. They differ from millipedes in that millipedes have two pairs of legs on most segments and bodies that are not flattened (see Figure 2.7 in Chapter 2). Centipedes range in length from 1 to 6 inches and can run very rapidly.

Centipedes do not damage food supplies or household furnishings. Since they eat insects, spiders, and other arthropods, they are beneficial; however, most people consider them a nuisance when they wander indoors and want them controlled.

Chronic problems with centipedes should be addressed by reducing the types of habitats outdoors that encourage their presence. This should include removal of trash, rocks, boards, poorly maintained compost piles, and other hiding places around the structure. Also, caulking and other exclusion techniques may be effective in preventing centipedes from entering homes or other buildings. Residual treatments of one of the residual pyrethroids, or carbaryl where still available, will give good control both indoors and outdoors when applied to cracks, crevices and other hiding places. Pyrethroid dust formulations alone, or in combination with silica aerogel, are useful for treating wall voids and crawlspaces. Synergized pyrethrins, resmethrin, or other pyrethroids will also give rapid control when used indoors as aerosol or ULV applications. When treating outdoors, it is necessary to treat thoroughly around the foundation and to treat the mulch in flower and shrub beds. Emulsion or wettable-powder sprays of the various residual insecticides just listed are effective.

Millipedes
Class Diplopoda

Millipedes normally live outdoors in damp places, such as under decaying leaves and in mulch around outdoor plantings. They feed on damp and decaying vegetable matter as well as on new roots and green leaves. In wooded areas millipedes live in piles of leaf litter. In dry weather they will migrate out of the litter piles as the leaves dry, and they may cross roads and enter buildings in large numbers. This behavior may also occur in lawns that contain thick thatch layers, or yards where large piles of leaves or compost piles are present.

Millipedes, or thousand-leggers, as they are commonly known, are elongate brownish animals that are oval in cross section and appear to have two pairs of legs attached to most body segments (see Figure 12.3, following page 254). Actually, each apparent body segment consists of two segments that are fused together and appear as one. Millipedes that commonly invade homes are 1/2- to 1-1/2 inches long and tend to coil up when resting (see Figure 2.7 in Chapter 2).

Chemical and nonchemical management techniques for millipedes are basically the same as those just discussed for centipede management. However, a more thorough outdoor treatment is often necessary for millipede control with pesticides. Residual sprays must be applied in a 5- to 20-foot-wide barrier around the structure. The treatment should be thorough and done in such a way as to ensure the insecticide gets down to the soil surface. Since millipedes feed and reproduce in decaying organic matter, it may be necessary to remove plant mulch, leaves, and so forth around the foundation to obtain acceptable suppression.

Pillbugs and Sowbugs
Class Crustacea; Order Isopoda

These pests are crustaceans, so they are more closely related to shrimp and crayfish than to insects. The dooryard sowbugs, *Porcellio laevis* Koch and *Porcellio scaber* (Latrielle), possess two tail-like appendages at the tip of the abdomen and are incapable of rolling into a tight ball. The common pillbug, *Armadillidum vulgare* (Latrielle), lacks such appendages at the tip of the abdomen and can roll itself into a ball (see Figure 12.4, and Figure 12.5, which follows page 254). This habit is the reason they are often called roly-polies in some areas.

Both pillbugs and sowbugs feed on decaying vegetable matter and are found under mulch, vegetable debris, or other objects on damp ground. They frequently invade damp basements and crawlspaces and may infest potted plants. A heavy infestation indoors generally indicates that there is a large population immediately outside the building.

FIGURE 12.4. Left: A sowbug. Right: A pillbug. (Provonsha)

The behavior and feeding habits of pillbugs and sowbugs are very similar to those of the millipedes. Therefore, the management and pesticide control methods are the same.

Slugs and Snails
Phylum Mollusca: Class Gastropoda

These animals belong to the phylum Mollusca, and are related to clams and oysters. At times, they gather in large numbers in damp basements or crawlspaces, leaving glistening mucous trails as they move about at night. They are basically plant feeders but sometimes deface buildings with their fecal material. They must have a large amount of moisture to survive, so they are most active during periods of wet weather, at night, and in moist areas.

Snails are easily recognized by their shells. Common land species are usually some shade of gray or brown and 1- to 1-1/2-inches long. The giant African snail, found in Florida, California, and Hawaii, may have a shell reaching 5 inches in length. Slugs are soft-bodied, gray or mottled, slimy creatures measuring up to 4-inches long. They do not have a shell (see Figure 12.6, and Figure 12.7, which follows page 254).

FIGURE 12.6. A slug. (USDA) (Provonsha)

Before applying chemical treatments to control slugs or snails, all rotting boards and other clutter or debris that provide hiding and breeding sites should be removed. Anything that can be done to reduce or eliminate the damp conditions these animals require will also aid greatly in long-term suppression. Pay special attention to crawlspaces or other dark, shaded areas. Overwatering of landscape beds is one practice that contributes to problems with these pests.

Chemical control is often most efficient with bait formulations of methiocarb (Mesurol®) or metaldehyde. These baits should be applied to the infested area (under shrubs, in crawlspaces, etc.) according to label directions. They work well under a variety of conditions, and a single treatment is often satisfactory. Metaldehyde is sweet and naturally attracts snails and slugs. However, its effectiveness decreases during cool or wet weather. Care should be exercised when using baits, so that they are unavailable to children and pets. Irrigation systems should be turned off for several days after a bait application.

Crickets
Order Orthoptera; Family Gryllidae

The house cricket and the field cricket commonly invade homes. Camel crickets and Jerusalem crickets are also occasional pests indoors, especially in damp and dark basements that have a partial dirt floor. When present in large numbers, crickets are a considerable annoyance and can cause damage to some fabrics, such as linens, rayon, and furs. They will attack paper, all kinds of foods, and even rubber. However, unless large numbers occur, such damage is usually minor.

Crickets are rather closely related to cockroaches, so they have a gradual metamorphosis and similar, omnivorous feeding habits. The young, or nymphs, look like adults, except that their wings and genitalia are not developed fully.

The **house cricket**, *Acheta domesticus* (Linnaeus), lives outdoors but may invade houses in great numbers. Adults are about 3/4-inch long with three dark bands on the head and long, thin antennae (see Figure 12.8, and Figure 12.9, which follows page 254). The body is light yellowish brown. This cricket is active at night, usually remaining hidden during the day. They are omnivorous, eating or drinking almost anything that is available. In households, they may chew on or damage silk, woolens, paper, fruits, and vegetables.

Field crickets, *Acheta assimilis* Fabricius, and closely related species are widely distributed over the United States (i.e., so-called "black crickets" are actually considered a species complex by entomologists). They are larger than house crickets and have wings extending beyond the wing covers. They are usually dark brown to gray or blackish. Field crickets frequently invade houses and may feed on organic matter in soil or a wide variety of materials. Smaller field crickets of the genus *Nemobius* may also invade homes in late summer. Field crickets prefer to live outdoors, where they feed on soft plant parts, but they will move inside when grasses dry up or environmental conditions outdoors become unfavorable (e.g., excess heat or rainfall). Individuals are unlikely to survive more than two weeks indoors.

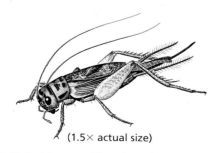

(1.5× actual size)

FIGURE 12.8. A house cricket. (Walerstein)

Field crickets are often attracted to lighted areas at night. Thus, problems with crickets can be lessened by turning off these lights during periods when crickets are numerous, or at least manipulating lights so the crickets will not be attracted directly to the building and so will be less bothersome. Otherwise, exclusion techniques should be applied to keep crickets from entering structures as much as possible.

Satisfactory control of crickets frequently involves treating both inside and outside the structure, as well as removing breeding and feeding sites outdoors and using tight-fitting screens and doors. Any opening to the building near ground level should be properly sealed. Sprays of one of the residual pyrethroids are recommended for chemical control. Wettable powder and microencapsulated formulations will give superior residual action on outdoor surfaces. Nonresidual sprays containing synergized pyrethrins or other pyrethroids can be very useful when applied as ULV applications to attics, ceiling voids, crawlspaces, or other areas when fast knockdown and kill are required. Dust formulations of a residual pyrethroid, boric acid, or silica aerogel may be preferred in some circumstances, such as for treatment of crawlspaces, wall voids, or attics.

Various granular bait formulations, such as are used for cockroach control, are available and are particularly effective when scattered around the foundation outdoors. Caution should be exercised when using such (properly labeled) baits indoors, so that the insecticide does not become exposed to people or pets within the structure. Insecticide spray or bait applications to damp areas of the basement and ground-level floors are recommended when crickets are present in those areas. Other areas may have to be treated for house crickets or seasonal swarms of field crickets, which may be found almost anywhere in a structure. Apply residual pesticides outdoors to foundations, window wells, flowerbeds, around doors and windows, into crawlspaces, under garbage cans, and into weep holes in brick facings are necessary. If heavy infestations are encountered, a 5- to 20-foot band around the structure should also be treated with either a residual spray or a bait.

Earwigs
Order Dermaptera

Earwigs are insects that are readily recognized by the pincers or forceps-like appendages at the end of the abdomen (see Figure 2.19 in Chapter 2, and Figure 12.10, following page 254). They sometimes build up to large numbers in warm weather and then may invade homes or other structures.

Earwigs are primarily scavengers on dead animal and plant material, but some species are predators. Other species may actually feed on living plants. They are active at night, and some species are attracted in large numbers to lights. During the day they usually find shelter beneath stones, boards, and debris. Only a few of the winged species are good fliers. Earwigs are often transported great distances in potted plants, nursery stock, or other plant material.

The **European earwig**, *Forficula auricularia* Linnaeus, is an introduced species that has become an important household pest in numerous local areas in the United States. It attacks a broad range of food material of both plant and animal origin but prefers green plants. Adults of this species are poor fliers; females rarely fly. All stages may enter houses in significant numbers and are easily carried from place to place by people. This earwig is about 5/8-inch long and dark reddish-brown in color.

The **ring-legged earwig**, *Euborellia annulipes* (Lucas), is another common species with habits similar to those of the European earwig. However, it is more commonly found indoors or in protected situations, such as in greenhouses. This earwig is just over 1/2-inch long, dark brown to shiny jet black in color, with yellow-brown legs that have one or two dark cross bands.

Considerable difficulty has been experienced in the southern United States with the **striped earwig**, *Labidura riparia* (Pallas). It is larger than the species just discussed, about 1-inch long, and readily attracted to lights. It produces a strong odor when disturbed or crushed. The striped earwig is lighter in color than the other earwigs, and the pronotum and front wings are usually marked with pale stripes along the edges and in the middle. This insect has the ability to develop large populations within a single season, and it can be a severe pest in new subdivisions or where land is being cleared for new buildings.

Earwig populations will often build up in areas around foundations similar to those already discussed for centipedes, millipedes, and crickets. Habitat removal procedures will greatly aid in suppressing problems with earwigs indoors. Residual sprays of pyrethroid insecticides can give effective control. Dust formulations are preferred for situations such as voids and other indoor areas where the dusts will stay dry. Various scatter baits developed for cockroach, cricket or other crawling insect control have been found effective, so their use outdoors in landscape areas adjacent to the foundation may a be necessary adjunct to control programs in some situations. Outdoor applications should be made around the foundation, in crawlspaces, and to flower beds and turf within a couple of yards of the buildings. The entire yard should be treated when infestations are heavy. Granular insecticide applications in turf can give excellent results. Indoor treatment is basically a supplement to outdoor treatment and will eliminate only earwigs already inside. Residual insecticide sprays or dusts applied to baseboards, beneath cabinets, along door and windowsills and to other hiding places at floor level are effective. As with crickets and various other occasional invaders, various nonresidual formulations (e.g., as ULV applications) of synergized pyrethrins, resmethrin, or other pyrethroids can also be used indoors.

Chinch Bugs
Blissus spp.
Order Hemiptera; Family Lygaeidae

These insects can be important as occasional invaders throughout most of the southern United States. Their populations develop outdoors, feeding on the grass in lawns, fencerows, and open fields. They often enter houses in great numbers. The most important chinch bugs commonly found in lawns are *Blissus insularis* Barber, the **southern chinch bug**; *B. leucopterus leucopterus* (Say), the **chinch bug**; *B. leucopterus hirtus* Montandon, the **hairy chinch bug**; and *Nysius raphanus* Howard, and the **false chinch bug**. These are small black-and-white bugs, with wings that extend only about half the length of the abdomen when at rest. Some species also have red markings, especially during immature stages. False chinch bugs are gray, without white markings.

Chinch bugs, in addition to being a nuisance when they invade structures, are also severe pests of certain common turf grasses. Different species are found in various parts of the country, affecting a number of grasses. Saint Augustinegrass is seriously damaged in the southern United States. Nymph and adult chinch bugs suck plant juices through their needlelike mouthparts, which are inserted at the base of the grass plants or along aboveground stems called rhizomes. Moderate to heavy infestations in lawns result in yellowish patches that rapidly turn brown and die. These injured areas are frequently noticed first along the edges of lawns, in sunny areas. The bugs can be found in the yellowing areas by pushing aside the grass plants and looking down at the soil surface. As the infestation grows, bugs can be seen crawling over sidewalks, on the sides of houses, and indoors.

Certain pyrethroid insecticides, imidacloprid, acephate, and trichlorfon (Dylox™ or Proxol™) are labeled and recommended for chinch bug control in turf. The entire lawn, or portions of the lawn, may need treatment. Spot treatments should extend at least ten feet beyond sites with evidence of damage. Use of properly labeled residual spray or dust applications, such as of one of the pyrethroids, around doors, windows, and other points of entry is also helpful in lowering the numbers that enter a home.

Boxelder Bugs

Leptocoris trivittatus (Say)
Order Hemiptera; Family Corizidae

Boxelder bugs and similar species are common pests over much of the United States. Adults are about 1/2-inch long. They are bright red or black, with narrow reddish lines on the back (see Figure 12.11).

These insects feed principally by sucking juices from the boxelder tree (*Acer negundo*), but they are sometimes found on other plants, especially other maples.

When they build up to large populations, many will be found crawling on the outside walls of homes and other buildings, and many will find their way inside. They are usually pests only by their presence, although their piercing-sucking mouthparts can sometimes puncture skin, causing slight irritation. They usually do little damage indoors, although the bugs may stain curtains and other resting sites with fecal spots and produce a foul odor when crushed. Adult boxelder bugs will also enter structures in the fall, and they will overwinter in protected areas, such as wall voids or in attics. They then emerge in the spring to seek out host trees on which to feed and lay eggs.

Control is best accomplished by treating infested trees with labeled insecticide formulations during the early summer months when the bugs are immature. Immature stages are generally much easier to control than adult stages. Pest management professionals are not usually called, however, until populations build to high levels or the adult bugs invade a home. At this time, the bugs are frequently gathering in masses along foundation walls and fence rows, at the bases of trees, and inside the house.

(2× actual size)

FIGURE 12.11. A boxelder bug. (Provonsha)

Outside, they can be controlled by thoroughly wetting the visible bugs and the surfaces over which they crawl with a spray of one of the newer residual pyrethroid insecticides, such as bifenthrin, cyfluthrin, deltamethrin or lambda-cyhalothrin. Microencapsulated and wettable-powder formulations are generally more effective than emulsions when used to treat surfaces outdoors. A more permanent solution is to remove host trees on which the bugs thrive nearby the house, if the trees have no great value and are not too expensive to have removed. However, these bugs may still be a nuisance if other boxelder trees are in the neighborhood. Boxelder trees are common in natural and other areas that may not be under control of the client. There is evidence that the bugs may fly up to one-half mile to sunlit building surfaces. Planting desirable trees to shade the south and west walls of the building can be a long-term solution.

Indoor treatment can be accomplished using the residual sprays just listed. Dust formulations of silica aerogel or some residual pyrethroids are also available and are preferred for some situations. Dusts are often preferred for treating wall voids and other appropriate areas that may serve as overwintering sites for the bugs. Space treatments of synergized pyrethrins or resmethrin can be used for quick knockdown indoors. When applying these materials, fill the entire room or attic area with the space treatment and then close the room off for several hours. A vacuum sweeper can be used to pick up the bugs for later destruction.

Hackberry Psyllids

Order Homoptera; Family Psyllidae

Hackberry gall psyllids of several species are common in the midwestern United States and other areas where hackberry trees and other host plants are grown. Nymphs infest hackberry trees in the spring and summer, and large numbers of adults frequently invade homes in the fall.

Control may be attempted against the nymphs while they are just beginning to feed on host trees in the spring, before large galls begin to form on the leaves. Properly timed insecticide applications, before the galls form, can provide relatively simple control. Once galls form, insecticides are ineffective. The professional is most frequently called, however, to control the adults invading homes later in the year. These small insects are tiny enough to enter a house through ordinary window screens, and they are attracted to lights at night. On occasion, large numbers may gain entry into a home and create a great nuisance.

Residual treatments with one of the pyrethroid

insecticides applied to screens and window or doorframes will help to prevent these psyllids from entering a house. Inside, aerosols or ULV applications of synergized pyrethrins or resmethrin will kill insects contacted directly with the insecticide. Vacuuming may be the preferred control technique for some homes.

Thrips
Order Thysanoptera

These very small, slender insects are important pests of many crops, and are common in flower gardens (see Figure 2.8, order Thysanoptera, in Chapter 2). Adults and nymphs of the onion thrips, *Thrips tabaci* Lindeman, and the grass thrips, *Anaphothrips obscurus* (Müller), will sometimes invade homes, where they may cause an itching bite or become pests simply because of their presence. Grass thrips are sometimes also called oat bugs. Control measures discussed for hackberry psyllids are appropriate when thrips control becomes necessary. Such indoor infestations are temporary, as thrips must have preferred plant hosts to survive.

Elm Leaf Beetle
Pyrrhalta luteola (Müller)
Order Coleoptera; Family Chrysomelidae

This pest of elm trees frequently occurs in great enough numbers that it becomes a problem in homes. American elm trees are no longer present in most neighborhoods throughout the United States due to Dutch elm disease. However, this insect is a particularly severe pest on Siberian elms, and found in lesser numbers on Chinese elms, both of which are very common in many areas. Adult beetles are yellow to dull green in color, with a black stripe down each side of either forewing, or elytron (see Figure 12.12). They are about 1/4-inch long.

The eggs are bright yellow and spindle shaped. They are laid in clusters of 5 to 25 on the underside of elm leaves. Young larvae are black and slug-like. Full-grown larvae are about 1/2-inch long, dull yellow, with a black head, legs, and hairs and a pair of black stripes along the back.

Adult elm leaf beetles pass the winter in protected places, such as under rough bark, in cracks and crevices of fences or outbuildings, or in houses (especially in attics). In such cases, adults may become a household nuisance in the fall when they go into hibernation, or again in the spring when they attempt to leave the house.

Shortly after emergence of new foliage in spring, overwintering beetles deposit their eggs on the underside of elm leaves. Eggs hatch in about a week, and the larvae feed on the underside of the leaves for the next two to three weeks. Only the veins and upper surface of the leaves are left after larval feeding, giving them a skeletonized appearance. Leaves on heavily infested trees turn brown, as if scorched by fire.

When full grown, the larvae crawl down the trunk or drop to the ground and pupate at the base of the tree or in crevices in the bark. The adults emerge in about 10 days (during July), feed again on the elm leaves, and lay eggs for a second generation. Adults from this second generation go into hibernation as described earlier. The number of generations per year depends on the length of the growing season, but in most parts of the country there are only two.

In addition to being a nuisance indoors, severe feeding on elm trees will weaken the trees and make them more susceptible to attack by other insects and diseases (especially Dutch elm disease for American elms). Control is best accomplished by treating host trees on which the young larvae are feeding. Applications of acephate, imidacloprid, one of the labeled pyrethroids, spinosad, carbaryl or some other labeled insecticide can be effective. Additional applications may be necessary, especially if a second generation develops.

Control measures recommended indoors are the same as those discussed for the boxelder bug.

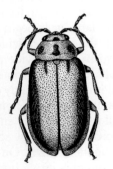

(6× actual size)

FIGURE 12.12. An elm leaf beetle. (Provonsha)

Root Weevils
Brachyrhinus spp.
Order Coleoptera; Family Curculionidae

There are several species of weevils in the genus *Brachyrhinus* whose larval, or grub, stages attack the root systems of various wild and cultivated plants (some of which are used in landscape plantings). The adult weevils enter homes in late summer and early fall, causing considerable annoyance. The snout or beak, which bears the mouthparts at its tip, is a characteristic common to all weevils, but in this genus it

Multicolored Asian Lady Beetle
Harmonia axyridis

Many different common names are used for this species, which has become a serious nuisance pest in much of the eastern and midwestern United States during recent years—including the multicolored Asian lady beetle, Japanese lady beetle, or Halloween lady beetle. This species is common in eastern Asia, where it is thought to be native. It is quite hardy, even in areas with fairly severe winters, and it has a high reproductive capacity. These characteristics made it an attractive candidate for introduction into several areas of the United States as a beneficial predator of certain orchard and field crop pests. Unfortunately, it has become a fairly common nuisance pest in the eastern and midwestern United States because of its habit of congregating in large numbers inside homes for overwintering. It is also known to be present throughout much of the United States and Canada.

Adults of this species are about 1/3-inch long and oval and convex in shape, which is very typical for lady beetles. However, many different color variations can be found, even within a single handful of overwintering adults. They can be yellow to red or reddish-brown, or any shade in between. Many beetles will have blackish spots on their wing covers (elytra), with the number per individual variable up to 19 spots, but some will have no spots. The most common and useful identifying characteristic is the presence of a very dark or black M-shaped marking on the upper surface of the thorax, just in front of the wing covers. This M-shaped marking is more readily apparent on some individuals than on others, but it is usually visible and is diagnostic for this species (see Figure 12.18, following page 254).

After feeding high in trees and in soybeans throughout most of the summer, large numbers of adult beetles are attracted to light-colored buildings in the late autumn for overwintering. They orient especially to those homes or buildings that are illuminated and warmed by sunlight, and to resting spots on the southwestern facings. From these aggregation areas they will eventually work their way into the home, building, or garage through small cracks and crevices, and then recongregate to hibernate for the winter inside wall voids, attics, or other secluded areas. They may occasionally become mobile during especially warm periods of the late winter or early spring, but they generally remain fairly inactive until it is time to disperse when the trees begin to leaf out in the spring. They often become disoriented during either the premature or normal dispersal periods and wander about inside the home or building, which causes alarm, disgust, or just nuisance for homeowners or building occupants (see Figure 12.19, following page 254). In these cases they can be considered essentially lost because they belong outdoors, feeding on leaf-dwelling insects, prior to mating in the spring.

After exclusion techniques, such as caulking and weatherstripping, have been implemented, the beetles can sometimes be adequately controlled by simple removal through vacuuming or sweeping. Vacuum cleaner bags should be destroyed, or the beetles removed and destroyed, because otherwise they may well survive and later emerge from the vacuum cleaner. Indoor light traps will catch many individuals at night. When necessary, clusters of beetles can be sprayed directly with an aerosol insecticide. If residual insecticide treatments of exterior surfaces are used in an attempt to kill beetles as they congregate and seek to enter, wettable-powder, microencapsulated, or suspension formulations of one of the pyrethroid insecticides should be chosen for their more effective and long-lasting residual action. These should be applied onto areas where the beetles are congregating and into cracks, crevices, or voids where they might enter the home. Over time, natural controls of this species may build up, so that it may not be such a common and locally numerous pest around homes, but even then sporadic outbreaks will occur.

---

is shorter than usual. These adult weevils do no actual damage indoors but are annoying to the homeowner. The **strawberry root weevil**, *Brachyrhinus ovatus* (Linnaeus), is one of the more common pests of this genus. It is a stoutly built black beetle about 1/4-inch long (see Figure 12.13, and Figure 12.14, which follows page 254).

The **black vine weevil**, *Brachyrhinus sulcatus* (Fabricius), differs in being slightly larger and in having small patches of golden hairs on the exposed wings (elytra). Black vine weevils are frequently associated with some common shrubs used around foundations, including yews (*Taxus* spp.), azaleas, rhododendrons, euonymus, and junipers. They begin emergence in late-May to early June, and continue emerging for up to several weeks. Egg laying, at the soil surface, occurs a couple of weeks after emergence. A related species, *B. rugosostriatus*, is found more commonly in the southern United States and does not have the yellow patches. None of these weevils fly, so they must gain entry into homes by crawling or by being carried in on plant materi-

(5× actual size)

FIGURE 12.13. A strawberry root weevil. (Provonsha)

als or other articles.

Any number of other weevils, many of them agricultural pests, can be occasional invaders if their source of plant food is close enough to human habitations.

All of these weevils feed on the foliage of plants as adults. They typically hide beneath debris or in the soil at the base of the plants during the day. There is usually one generation per year. They are most damaging in the larval stage, as the larvae (or grubs) feed on root systems of certain ornamental plants often used around the foundation. The larval stages of these beetles are quite difficult to control with soil insecticide treatments. Adults wander indoors seeking hibernation or feeding sites. Once indoors, they may be found crawling over the floor or hiding under rugs or in other concealing places.

Since these weevils originate outdoors, outdoor treatment is essential to prevent continued migration indoors. Even then, the beetles may get indoors before dying from the effects of insecticide, since they are difficult to kill. Applications to control larval stages (grubs) in the soil of landscape plantings can help suppress adult weevil populations emerging and entering homes. Grub control can be achieved with products labeled for this purpose in landscape settings including acephate and imidacloprid. For customers who do not wish to use chemical soil treatments, insect-attacking nematodes (*Heterorhabditis* spp.) can be effective. Residual applications of carbaryl or one of the residual pyrethroids can be used to treat aboveground plant parts and the soil surface below foundation plantings. Wettable-powder or microencapsulated formulations provide superior residual action on exterior surfaces of the home. Foundations and all points of entry, such as doorways or windows, should be treated. These residual treatments can also be used indoors. In addition, dust formulations can be used when necessary for treating wall voids

and other hiding areas. Space treatments are not practical for controlling weevils.

Ground Beetles
Order Coleoptera; Family Carabidae

Various ground beetle species (see Figure 12.15, and Figure 12.16, which follows page 254) wander into homes from time to time. These beetles vary greatly in size, shape, and color. Most of them are dark, almost blackish, shiny, and somewhat flattened, although some species are brilliantly colored. Ground beetles typically live on the ground under leaves, logs, stones, and other debris. They feed mostly at night. Only a few species fly or are attracted to lights. These pests usually gain entrance to houses by crawling through small openings around windows or doorways, or through open doorways. When they get inside, they will wander around rather aimlessly, as their preferred habitat is outdoors. Most of these beetles are predators on other insects that crawl around on the ground at night.

Where control is necessary, it should consist of eliminating outdoor hiding places or, whenever possible, manipulation of lighting that may be attracting the beetles to the structure. Relocate lights on buildings to poles placed so that the light illuminates the area around buildings, rather than the building walls. Use of caulk and weatherstripping around door and window frames, or around any other possible access points to the home, will also aid in preventing ground beetle problems indoors. Treatment of outdoor areas with insecticide may also be necessary. Firewood or other sources of harborage should be moved as far away from the house as practical. For homes in wooded areas, debris should be cleared from around the perimeter of the house.

Insecticides labeled for ground beetle control outdoors include certain of the residual pyrethroid insecticides. Ground areas around the building should be thoroughly treated for a distance of 20 to 50 feet from the building. Indoors, these same residual materials, or dust formulations of these residuals or silica aerogel, should be applied to any access points (doorsills and window moldings) and floor areas where the beetles have been seen entering and crawling about. Perimeter walls should receive special attention in ground beetle control applications.

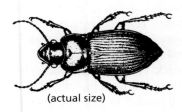

(actual size)

FIGURE 12.15. One of the many species of ground beetle.

Ladybird Beetles
Order Coleoptera; Family Coccinellidae

This large family of beetles, which are also commonly called lady beetles, includes some of the most beneficial insects. They are predators as adults and larvae on plant-feeding pests, such as aphids, scale insects, and many others that attack trees, shrubs, flowers, or vegetables in the garden. However, adult ladybird beetles (see Figure 12.17) may cause considerable annoyance when their populations occasionally build up to very large numbers during the summer and coincidentally enter homes. A few species, such as the multicolored Asian lady beetle (see Figure 12.18, following page 254), also congregate on the outside of buildings in autumn and then enter wall voids or attics to hibernate over the winter (see Figure 12.19, following page 254).

Ladybird beetles will not feed on or otherwise damage anything on the exterior surfaces of or inside buildings. They become pests in and around homes or other buildings merely because of their presence. Their success in feeding and reproducing occurs outdoors and is associated with trees, wooded areas, gardens, and so forth. After exclusion techniques have been considered and implemented, there may be a need to either remove the congregating beetles (e.g., by vacuuming or sweeping them up) or to control them with an insecticide (though then they often still need to be physically removed). Since overwintering beetles generally congregate within a quite limited area, a thorough treatment of these areas with the residual insecticides listed for root weevil control will usually give efficient lady beetle control.

Picnic Beetles
Glischrochilus spp.
Order Coleoptera; Family Nitidulidae

Picnic beetles occasionally invade buildings but are better known as those black, hard-shelled intruders that persistently swarm around picnics or barbecues. They drop lazily into both food and drink, or otherwise make themselves a great nuisance for such outdoor events at certain times of the summer. The beetles are about 3/16- to 1/4-inch long and jet black, with four pale yellow spots on their wing covers. They are difficult to control, for even if killed in large numbers, more are likely to come in from untreated areas.

Picnic beetles are outdoor scavengers that feed primarily on overripe or damaged fruits and vegetables, and to some extent on decayed portions of bulbs and roots. Anything that can be done to eliminate overripe or damaged fruits and vegetables, in the garden or at picnics and other social gatherings, is helpful in reducing this beetle's presence. They are also attracted to overripe odors, such as the vinegar or mayonnaise in salad dressings, cole slaw, and potato salad as well as beer. Keeping foods sealed before serving and promptly cleaning up debris will reduce their numbers at picnics. Apples, mulberries, and other fruits that fall to the ground and decay should be picked up and destroyed, or sprayed with carbaryl. Likewise, melon rinds and other garbage should be kept in tightly sealed containers.

Reasonably good control around outdoor eating areas can be obtained by (1) treating the area with a residual insecticide, (2) applying a space spray just before eating, and (3) using a bait (such as sliced, open melons) to attract the insects away from the area.

Residual insecticides that can be safely applied to grass and most vegetation around eating areas include various pyrethroid insecticides and carbaryl. Space or ULV treatments containing pyrethrins or a nonresidual pyrethroid can also be used just prior to putting food on the tables.

Scavenger and Fungus Beetles
Order Coleoptera; Families Lathridiidae and Cryptophagidae

Scavenger and small fungus beetles (see Figure 12.20) are very tiny (1/25- to 1/10-inch long), reddish-brown beetles that are sometimes found in large numbers inside buildings. They are nuisance pests

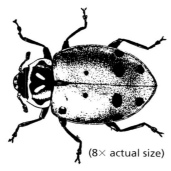

(8× actual size)

FIGURE 12.17. A lady beetle. (USDA)

(16× actual size)

FIGURE 12.20. One of the fungus beetles. (Provonsha)

that generally feed on molds. Many species have wing covers (elytra) and other body parts covered with rough surfaces, and the wing covers are often marked by rows of tiny pits visible only under strong magnification. The head and exposed part of the thorax are narrower than the abdomen. The antennae have eleven segments, and in most species the tips are enlarged into small clubs. The eyes are rather prominent, dark in color, and located behind the antennae. All of these features require a good hand lens or dissecting microscope to see. The larvae are very small, spindle shaped, and usually pale in color.

These beetles are associated with fungi, such as molds and mildew. Both larvae and adults often accumulate in large numbers around windows and lights. Since good moisture source is necessary for the growth of fungi, the beetles are often found where there are plumbing leaks, ventilation problems, or other accumulations of moisture indoors. These beetles can usually be eliminated with appropriate moisture control.

One of the most commonly encountered species with this behavior is the foreign grain beetle, *Ahasverus advena*, which is actually a species from the closely related family of flat bark beetles (family Cucujidae). Adult beetles of this species are only about 1/10- to 1/8-inch long and reddish-brown (see Figure 12.21, following page 254). They often become a serious nuisance problem in newly constructed homes and homes where exterior wall voids or other spaces contain unusually high levels of moisture, which fosters growth of surface molds and mildew within those voids.

In new construction, this mold and mildew may be caused by use of wood that was not adequately dried before construction, or had been left out in the rain before actual use in construction. Newer homes may also be inadequately heated during some cool or cold periods prior to occupancy, which can create temporary moisture problems within wall voids or basements, due to condensate formation. Tight building and insulation techniques, and overuse of humidifiers, also often contribute to excessive moisture problems in certain localized voids or other areas, for varying periods after construction. These various factors and conditions foster buildup of foreign grain beetle populations until the home's heating system and natural ventilation can dry out all the voids where moisture had built up. Thus, foreign grain beetle infestations in new home construction often fade away as the mold and mildew films that are the source of food for the larval stages of this species disappear due to adequate heat and ventilation.

However, foreign grain beetles or similar species can be chronic or perennial (seasonal) problems where the construction is too tight to allow adequate ventilation of interior space, where there are ongoing sources of moisture and condensation due to an improperly vented clothes dryer or shower stall fan, or where a poorly designed exterior wall insulation system creates a barrier to escaping water vapor (generated indoors), so that moisture and condensate build up within wall voids.

When necessary, immediate control can be obtained with the residual insecticides or with non-residual space treatments recommended for boxelder bug control. Control using insecticides will be enhanced if the moldy areas that are the source of the infestation can be found and the problem corrected.

Caterpillars
Order Lepidoptera

Any number of caterpillars will move indoors on occasion. This migration may result from the insects searching for food, moisture, pupation sites, or numerous other needs. Before pupating, some species will excavate a shallow depression in wood surfaces. Some of the more commonly encountered caterpillars include the armyworm (see Figure 12.22), tent caterpillars, Gypsy moth, woolly bears, webworms, and cutworms. These larvae are plant feeders that attack trees, shrubs, grasses, and so forth. The caterpillars often tend to wander about during certain times of the year. This is especially true of the webworms and tent caterpillars that leave their food sources in late summer in search of a suitable place to build a cocoon for pupation. After pupation, they emerge as adult moths or butterflies, depending on the species involved.

If necessary, these insects can be controlled by treating their feeding areas and other outdoor surfaces over which they crawl. Carbaryl, spinosad, *Bacillus thuringiensis* (BT), tebufenozide (Confirm™ 2F), residual pyrethroids, or other insecticides labeled for control of moth larvae (caterpillars) in landscapes, will be effective for this use outdoors. Indoor control can be accomplished using any of a variety of residual insecticides.

LIGHT-ATTRACTED PESTS

Pest management professionals are often called on to control insects attracted to lights at night. People at

(actual size)

FIGURE 12.22. An armyworm caterpillar.

Other Yard and Garden Invaders

A myriad of insects found in the yard and garden occasionally invade buildings either by flying or crawling in at times when their populations become particularly large. Some of the more frequently encountered pests include wood roaches, leaf-footed bugs, aphids (see Figure 2.18 in Chapter 2), bean leaf beetles, blister beetles, click beetles (see Figure 12.42, following page 254), rove beetles, cabbage worms, Colorado potato beetles, cucumber beetles, corn earworms, flea beetles, grasshoppers, Mexican bean beetles, spider mites, squash bugs, and conenose bugs. Any number of others can occur in numbers great enough to constitute a nuisance. They are primarily plant feeders and are usually outdoor pests that, for one reason or another, move inside. Many times, when damage is being done to flowers, shrubs, vegetables, or other yard and garden plants, control of the pest should have been attempted long before the insects became a general nuisance. Applications of carbaryl are effective for most of these insects. Treat all infested plants and around foundations, points of entry into buildings, and other surfaces on which insects are crawling outdoors. Carbaryl dust can be used on plants outdoors, but observe label directions carefully. Only formulations labeled for vegetable, fruit and other plants should be used. However, if the pests begin to migrate and move inside, then some form of insecticide treatment will be needed indoors as well. The insecticides recommended for boxelder bug control provide control of these pests.

drive-in restaurants and theaters, golf driving ranges, dairies, paper manufacturers (or other types of manufacturing facilities), and outdoor swimming pools, and people who use their patios at night, are particularly bothered. Various leafhoppers (order Homoptera), moths (order Lepidoptera), stoneflies (order Plecoptera), mayflies (order Ephemeroptera), gnats (order Diptera, family Chironomidae), and beetles (order Coleoptera), and some members or the order Neuroptera (alderflies, dobsonflies, lacewings), are the insects most frequently attracted to lights. Several of these insects are illustrated in Figure 2.8 (Chapter 2).

Because most insects found around lights can fly for a considerable distance, those killed by residual insecticide treatment of surfaces around lighting are usually quickly replaced by new arrivals. Space treatments—for example, those using synergized pyrethrins—can kill insects present in an area at any given time but must be used over and over again as new insects fly in. Where the rate of fly-in is not too great, residual insecticides, such as one of the residual pyrethroids, may give a useful degree of control if applied to available surfaces in the affected area. Wettable-powder, suspension concentrate or microencapsulated formulations will give superior residual action on most exterior surfaces.

Another important pest management technique to consider will have much greater long-term impact on these flying insect problems: reducing attraction of these insects to buildings by manipulation of lighting. Indirect lighting should be used where practical, so that the actual source of light is shielded from the areas or directions from which the insects may come (if this direction can be determined). In many cases it is possible to use spotlights mounted at a considerable distance from the building. In this way, insects attracted to the lights are attracted away from the building. This procedure is more likely to succeed in cases of buildings with dark-colored or dull-finished masonry rather than light-colored or glass and metal exterior surfaces, which strongly reflect remote light. Try to shield lights so they are not visible in the surrounding areas from which the insects may come. Light fixtures inside buildings should be placed so insects outside are unlikely to see the lamp itself. Excessive illumination should be avoided wherever possible.

There is little, if any, evidence that any light is repellent to insects, but yellow is generally the least attractive to most insects. Avoid insect-attractive lights, especially mercury-vapor lamps and black lights (BL or ultraviolet). Green fluorescent tubes are very attractive to many leafhoppers. Sodium-vapor or other lighting systems that have a pink, yellow, or orange glow will be less attractive than the bright whitish or bluish mercury-vapor or fluorescent lights. Careful observation, some experimentation, and application of common sense in manipulating lighting can often result in considerable reduction of a building's attractiveness to insects.

Depending on the circumstances, it may be possible to use light traps to intercept insects moving into an area. If the expense of installation can be justified, a series of suction or electrocuting light traps can be installed. These traps should be mounted just above the reach of humans and located between the source of the insects and the structure being protected. The best light to use may require experimentation, as different insects respond to different kinds of light. It is highly unlikely that any light or combination of lights will attract all pest insects, all the time.

Several studies have been conducted to test the effects of backyard insect electrocution traps, often called **bug zappers**, which generally use black lights to attract flying insects for the control of mosquitoes near patios outdoors. While these traps usually attract and kill many insects, and perhaps a few mosquitoes, these carefully designed studies have shown that the light traps tested are not effective in reducing mosquito or other biting fly nuisances to people. It should also be considered that they kill numerous beneficial insects.

MISCELLANEOUS PESTS

Mites of Processed Foods
Order Acarina

Two mites often found infesting processed food products are the **mushroom mite**, *Tyrophagus lintneri* (Osborn) (see Figure 12.23) and the *grain mite*, *Acarus siro* Linnaeus. The former is a serious pest of mushrooms and will also infest cheese, grain, cereal products, and, occasionally, dried meats. Grain mites will attack any grain or cereal product that has a moisture content above 12 percent.

Control of these mites in commercial food storage areas is often very difficult or impossible except by fumigation. Areas around infested packaged foods can be treated with residual sprays of various labeled pyrethroid insecticides. In some cases, dust applications of silica aerogel (Drione™ or Tri-Die™) or diatomaceous earth will be effective and practical if combined with careful sanitation procedures. While these dust treatments may not give the desired total, long-term control, they will usually contain the infestation. Treatment by direct contact applications containing synergized pyrethrins will usually give a satisfactory measure of short-term control. Most infestations by these mites can be remedied (or prevented) if proper sanitation procedures are conducted to both remove food sources and reduce the moisture content of food products to less than 12%, so surface molds will not be present.

House Dust Mites
Dermatophagoides spp.
Order Acarina

A number of species of house dust mites have been found throughout the world. The most common one in the United States is the **North American house dust mite**, *Dermatophagoides farinae*, although *D. pteronyssinus*, the **European house dust mite**, is also a problem. See Chapter 11 for further discussion of these mites and their management.

House Centipede
Scutigera coleoptera (Linnaeus)
Class Chilopoda

The house centipede is a common pest in many parts of the United States. Unlike most other centipedes, this species generally lives its entire life inside a building.

The body of this centipede is usually only 1- to 1-1/2-inches long at the most, but its fifteen pairs of very long legs make it seem much larger. The body is grayish yellow with three dark stripes extending along the full length of the back. The legs are quite long in proportion to the body, and have alternate light and dark bands running around them (see Figure 12.24, and Figure 12.25, which follows page 254).

In homes, the house centipede prefers to live in damp areas, such as cellars, closets, bathrooms, attics (during the warmer months), and unexcavated areas under the house. Eggs are laid in these same damp places, as well as behind baseboards or beneath bark on firewood. Centipedes develop by gradual metamorphosis, so immatures have a similar appearance to adults but are smaller. All life stages can be observed running rapidly across floors or accidentally trapped in bathtubs, sinks, and lavatories.

The house centipede forages at night for small insects and their larvae, and for spiders. Although this centipede can bite, its jaws are quite weak. There usually is not more than a slight swelling if a bite occurs. From an entomological point of view, they could be considered beneficial. Most homeowners, however, usually take a different point of view and insist that they be eliminated.

Control is a relatively simple operation if conducted with thoroughness. Residual applications of one of the several pyrethroid insecticides that are labeled for this pest, boric acid, silica aerogel, or

FIGURE 12.23. A mushroom mite, greatly enlarged. (Baker and NPCA) (Provonsha)

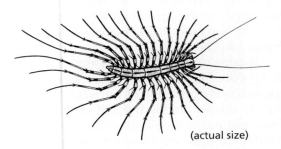

(actual size)

FIGURE 12.24. A house centipede. (Provonsha)

carbaryl should be applied to all of the usual hiding places, such as crawlspaces, dark corners in basements or attics, and behind baseboards. Dusts are particularly useful for reaching and treating hard-to-reach hiding areas. Dusts provide superior long-term residual action under most circumstances. Contact sprays (ULV or aerosol) of synergized pyrethrins or other nonresidual pyrethroids are also available for use to obtain rapid flushing and knockdown action, but without residual control.

Scorpions
Class Arachnida; Order Scorpionida

Scorpions (see Figure 12.26) are quite common in much of the southern and southwestern United States. Most species that enter houses are not very poisonous, their stings being comparable to those of bees or wasps. However, certain species in the desert Southwest can be dangerous, especially to sensitive or allergic people. Most scorpions are active at night. During the day they hide under bark, boards, and rocks or in rubbish. In houses, they are most often found in undisturbed areas, such as closets, seldom-used shoes, or folded clothing.

Typical of the scorpions is the **striped bark scorpion**, *Centruroides vittatus* (Say), which is widely distributed in the southern United States. It has two broad, dark bands extending the length of the back, on an otherwise yellowish brown body. Mature specimens are slightly less than 1-inch long. The bite of this scorpion is not considered medically important, but it can deliver a painful sting.

The most dangerous scorpion is *Centruroides exilicauda* (Wood), which may reach a maximum length of about 2-inches. It is found in southern Arizona and adjacent areas of California and New Mexico. In these areas, scorpions are generally found in homes because of the availability of water and shade in and around the house.

Scorpions feed on small spiders and soft-bodied insects. They will eat other species of scorpions and even small individuals of their own species. They have poor eyesight, so they do not stalk or chase prey but lie in waiting to grab it with their pincers. Small insects are eaten immediately, but larger prey are stung and eaten after they cease to struggle.

The first step in managing scorpions around dwellings is to remove all debris, such as loose boards, rocks, stacked wood, or any other materials under which they can hide. This will greatly reduce the numbers of scorpions in the area. If necessary, outdoor areas can then be sprayed with a residual insecticide, such as bifenthrin, cyfluthrin, or lambda-cyhalothrin. Granular formulations of these pyrethroids may also provide control, but

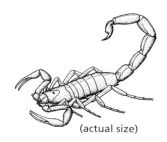

(actual size)

FIGURE 12.26. A scorpion. (Provonsha)

should be watered after application to release the active ingredient. Indoor areas, such as crevices in woodwork and closets, spaces around plumbing, doorways, or windows, and any other areas where scorpions might hide, should also be carefully treated with an appropriate spray or dust. Nonresidual or contact applications (ULV or aerosol) of synergized pyrethrins or nonresidual pyrethroids can be useful when rapid control is needed indoors.

Spiders
Class Arachnida; Order Araneae

Spiders have a characteristic appearance easily recognized by most people (see Figure 2.7 in Chapter 2). They possess eight legs, which immediately separates them from insects, which have only six. Spiders lack wings and antennae, and their bodies have only two major regions—a carapace, or cephalothorax, which includes the fused head and thorax, and an abdomen. Young spiders, or spiderlings, resemble the adults except for size and, sometimes, coloration. All spiders have a pair of jaw-like structures, called chelicerae. At the end of each is a hollow, claw-like fang. Each fang has a small opening in the end through which venom is injected into the prey. Spinnerets, located at the tip end of the abdomen, are linked to glands from which silk is spun for web making.

Many species of spiders are common household inhabitants in the United States (see Figures 12.27, 12.28, and 12.29, following page 254). Certain common household spiders spin webs over lamps, in corners, and in basements. This is unsightly but causes no real harm. Remember that every "cobweb" was made by a spider. Although all spiders use venom when they bite and kill their prey, the black widow, hobo, and brown recluse spiders (none of which create cobwebs indoors) are the North American species well documented as dangerous to humans. The agrarian sac spider, *Cheiracanthium inclusum* (see Figure 12.30, following page 254), also is documented to cause painful bites, redness, swelling and itching—and occasionally a necrotic wound similar those caused by the brown recluse. Even though there is generally little danger of complications from spider bites, pest management professionals should advise all spider bite victims to take the spider specimen with them (if possible) when consulting their physician.

Under most conditions outdoors, spiders are considered beneficial because they feed on insects. However, they are undesirable to most homeowners when indoors, and the unsightly webbing spiders use to catch insect prey usually outweighs this beneficial behavior.

Some spiders are associated with moisture and, therefore, are found in basements, crawlspaces, and other damp parts of buildings. Others live in warm, dry places so are found in sub floor air vents, in upper corners of rooms, or in attics. Most species hide in cracks, darkened areas, or other retreats that they construct of silk.

The **black widow spider**, *Latrodectus mactans* (Fabricius), is widely distributed over the warmer portions of the United States. Females are easily identified because of their globular, shiny black abdomen with two reddish or yellowish triangles on the underside. These reddish or yellowish triangles form a characteristic hourglass marking (see Figure 12.31, following page 254). The abdomen is about 1/4 inch in diameter but may be as large as 1/2 inch when the female is full of eggs. Males are much smaller and lighter colored, with light streaks on their abdomens.

The black widow's web is an irregular mass of fibers with a small central area to which the spider retreats while waiting until its prey becomes ensnared. These webs are frequently constructed underneath boards, stones, or the seats of outdoor privies. They are also found along foundation slabs, behind shrubs, and especially where brick or wood siding extends close to ground level. This spider does not usually enter residences, though it may do so occasionally.

Black widow spider venom contains toxins that are neurotoxic (toxic to the nervous system). The severity of a person's reaction to the bite depends on the area of the body where the bite occurs; the person's size and general sensitivity; the amount of venom injected; the depth of bite; the seasonal changes in venom potency; and the temperature. The bite produces a sharp pain similar to a needle puncture, which usually disappears rapidly. After a variety of other symptoms, convulsions and death may result with some victims, especially if the person is sensitive to the venom and no treatment is received. An antivenom specific for the black widow is readily available to most physicians.

The **brown recluse spider**, *Loxosceles reclusa* Gertsch & Muliak, can also inflict a dangerous bite.

The initial pain associated with the bite is not intense and is generally less troublesome than a bee sting. Within 8 to 12 hours the pain becomes quite intense, and over a period of a few days a large ulcerous sore forms. This sore heals very slowly and often leaves an ugly and disfiguring scar.

The brown recluse is a soft-bodied and secretive species found in homes and other outbuildings. The adult body varies from 1/3 to 1/2 inch in length, with the arrangement of the legs producing a larger overall size of 1 inch in diameter or greater. The body is yellow to dark brown and has a rather distinctive darker brown violin-shaped mark on the top of the cephalothorax (see Figure 12.32, following page 254), and a distinctive eye pattern (see Figure 12.33, following page 254).

The brown recluse spider has been widely reported in the southern, western, and midwestern United States, and it is a particularly serious pest in Oklahoma, Missouri, Arkansas, and surrounding states. Other venomous species of *Loxosceles* are distributed in the drier areas of the southwestern United States, including much of west and southern Texas; the southern portions of New Mexico, Arizona, and California; and the extreme southern part of Nevada. The brown recluse is usually found indoors, particularly in bathrooms, bedrooms, closets, garages, basements, and cellars. In homes with forced-air heating and air conditioning and mostly above-ceiling ductwork, brown recluse spiders are commonly found harboring in or around the ductwork or registers. They may also be present in attic areas or other locations above the ceiling. They are also commonly found in cluttered closets or basements and in outbuildings where miscellaneous items are stored. Their web is not elaborate and is best described as an off-white to gray, nondescript type of webbing. The spider is not aggressive and usually retreats to cover when disturbed. Most bites occur when a person traps or crushes the spider while putting on old clothes that have been hanging in a garage, or by rolling on the spider while asleep in bed.

In the Pacific Northwest region of the United States, including nearly all of Washington State, Oregon, and Idaho and extending into adjacent areas of Montana, Utah, and the southern half of British Columbia, three venomous species of European house spiders (*Tegenaria* spp.) commonly infest in and around homes. The most common and aggressive species, which is associated with necrotic bite incidents in this region (where *Loxosceles* does not occur), is *T. agrestis*, commonly known as the **hobo spider** or the aggressive house spider. Two other species, the smaller European house spider, *T. domestica* (Clerck) (see Figure

Cellar Spiders

Cellar spiders (Family Pholcidae) are found in cellars, basements, crawlspaces, barns, and warehouses. They have very long, spindly legs (compared to other spiders), spin irregular webs, and allow their webs to accumulate in large quantities. This spider hangs in its web with the abdomen pointed upwards, and exhibits the unusual behavior of shaking its web violently when disturbed, spinning around rapidly. Although not considered one of the more important spiders from the standpoint of affecting human health, their extensive webbing creates not only a nuisance, but will contaminate all objects and items in the infested area. Management strategies for cellar spiders are similar to those used for other structure-invading spiders.

12.34, following page 254), and the large European house spider, *T. duellica* Simon, are also commonly found in homes in this region but appear to be less aggressive in their biting behavior than *T. agrestis* and probably account for few serious bite incidents.

Spider experts also classify these species as agelenid or funnel web spiders, family Agelenidae. These three particular species have eight eyes in two rows on the front of their head and, like other spiders of this family, make a web that is a flat or curved sheet of dense silk curved up at the outer edge and slanted downward toward a corner, where it funnels into a tube-like retreat with a rear exit below. The spider is typically found in this corner. Males and females construct these webs in, under, or near homes in such areas as rock walls or gardens, along foundations, in crawlspaces, in garages, in piles of discarded lumber or stacked firewood, in or under sheds, and in corners of basements. Their webs are designed to capture prey such as cockroaches, crickets, earwigs, silverfish, other spiders, pillbugs and sowbugs, various beetles, and an occasional fly.

These spiders are fairly large at 25 to 50 millimeters (or sometimes more) in overall length, brown with grayish or darker markings, hairy, and quite fast moving. (They have been observed running up to 1/2 to 1 meter per second.) These three species of *Tegenaria* are difficult to tell apart except for size, which is variable, and various structures on either sex that require a microscope and a fair amount of expertise to distinguish (see the references cited at the end of the chapter). As adults, all species have a pair of fingerlike spinnerets extending from the rear of the abdomen and two leg-like palps projecting from the front of the body. Associated with the chelicerae are fangs

that deliver the venom used to subdue prey. *T. domestica* is the smallest species, with the body (without legs) about 7 to 11 millimeters long and an overall length (with legs) of 15 to 37 millimeters. The legs are usually banded with gray rings. The life cycle of this species is not seasonal, and adults may be seen indoors in any month. *T. agrestis* has a body length of 7 to 14 millimeters and an overall length of 27 to 45 millimeters. The abdomen usually, but not always, has a distinct pattern of dark herringbone-shaped stripes, and the legs are not banded. The life cycle of this species is strongly seasonal, with egg hatch in April or May and mature adults becoming present in late July through August. As the males mature, they leave their webs and begin to wander in search of females for mating. The males die by late October, and the females somewhat later, after leaving an egg sac or sacs. The eggs hatch the following spring, and the immature spiderlings wander somewhat in search of suitable sites to build their webs. *T. duellica* has a body length of 12 to 18 millimeters and an overall length of 35 to 60 millimeters for the females and 40 to 95 millimeters for the males. Their life cycle is distinctly seasonal, similar to that of *T. agrestis*. Where *T. duellica* is present in a building, it appears to out compete and exclude the other two species.

It is beyond the scope of this book to discuss in detail the severity and progression of symptoms suffered by the human or pet victims of bites from these spiders, but they cause similar serious necrotic lesions to those caused by brown recluse spiders. A few people have died due to severe reaction to these bites. Many bites occur when spiders are disturbed or trapped against the skin—such as when firewood or stored clothing harboring these spiders is carried—during the late summer and fall periods. At this time, males of *T. agrestis* mature and typically abandon their webs to search for females; they often become quite aggressive and will bite when apparently unprovoked. During approximately late August through October it is not uncommon for basement apartments or the basements and ground floors of homes in infested communities to experience several or more adult male hobo spiders wandering indoors each day. As winter cold approaches, females of these species may also enter homes, though they will be less conspicuous than the males of *T. agrestis*. Fortunately, these spiders are not very good climbers, so they are not often found up on walls or in the upper floors of homes, but they can crawl onto (and bite) people who are sleeping, if the bed linens hang down to touch the floor.

Control efforts for hobo spiders should first focus on removing the habitats and other conditions that favor nesting and significant population levels. Besides physical removal of some infestation sources such as firewood piles and clutter around the yard or in crawlspaces, some landscaping changes, such as elimination of grass or other ground covers against foundations, may be necessary. Then, the insecticidal techniques to be discussed for spider control should be considered. Pest control professionals working in crawlspaces and other areas with significant numbers of these venomous spiders should take care to wear protective clothing, including long sleeves tucked into gloves, a jacket or sweatshirt with a hood, and pant legs tucked into boots. Rubber bands or masking tape should be used over pant legs and sleeves, or over boots and gloves, to prevent spiders from crawling up onto the skin of arms and legs. Any clothing or other items stored in spider-infested areas should be carefully shaken out and inspected prior to use.

Control of spiders indoors may involve nothing more than vacuuming up the spiders and their webs and egg sacs. Removing clutter and taking other sanitation steps directed at conditions favoring spiders indoors, around or under the home, or in the landscape are necessary to help reduce spider problems. Thorough inspections are necessary to find all these spider harborages for later sanitation, removal, or insecticide treatment. Space treatments of synergized pyrethrins, or especially other non-residual pyrethroids, are often useful for cleanouts and for eliminating outdoor species that may be found indoors. Long-term residual control of spiders is difficult to achieve. If spiders are established indoors or if outdoor species are migrating indoors, residual applications of one of the labeled pyrethroid insecticides or silica aerogel can be used. All areas where the spiders have been found should be treated, paying particular attention to dark corners. Dusts are especially useful for treating inaccessible void areas, crawlspaces, and attics. Wettable-powder, suspension, or microencapsulated formulations will generally give somewhat better and longer residual action on most surfaces.

Outdoor treatment may be necessary to control spiders migrating inside or to eliminate spiders on or under porches, in crawlspaces, under eaves, and in other areas on the outside of the building. For some venomous species such as the European house spiders, black widow, or tarantulas (see Figure 12.35, following page 254), insecticide applications may be necessary in landscape areas such as foundation plantings or rock gardens. Spiders often become particularly numerous on exterior surfaces of homes and buildings built near lakes. They spin webs to catch and feed on the many flying insects that come out of the lake and adjacent marshy areas. Chronic spider problems result, for which there are few good management options except reducing night lights (which attract flying insects) and applying residual insecticide treatments at necessary intervals. Spider fecal droppings can disfigure fiberglass boats or latex-painted surfaces. Occasionally, area treatments may be necessary to eliminate heavy infestations. The residual insecticides just listed are also recommended for use outdoors. Consult the label to be sure that application to or around plant material can be done safely where necessary.

Silverfish and Firebrats
Order Thysanura; Family Lepismatidae

These insects of the order Thysanura all have the same characteristic shape. Their bodies are flattened, long and slender, broad at the front and tapering gradually toward the rear. The antennae are long and slender. Three long, slender appendages are found at the rear of the body. These give rise to the common name bristletails. All silverfish and firebrats (see Figure 2.9 in Chapter 2) are wingless. The young look like small adults, and their development takes place without metamorphosis.

Silverfish may be found almost anywhere in a house (see Figure 12.36, following page 254). However, they usually are found living close to their source of food. They eat a wide variety of foods containing proteins or carbohydrates. Such things as rolled oats, dried beef, flour, starch, paper, cotton, some synthetic fibers, sugar, beef extract, dead insects, glue, paste, and linen are all normal items of their diet. In damp basements or attics they can also feed on the surface molds that grow on cardboard boxes and other substrates. Silverfish can live for long periods of time without food.

Most firebrats, except for the common pest species, live outdoors under rocks, bark, or leaf molds, in the nests of birds and mammals, or in ant and termite nests. They prefer warm temperatures and are numerous outdoors, especially in the tropics. In the United States, depending on the species, they are usually found indoors in areas associated with heat, such as boiler rooms, or moisture, such as near water pipes. They are commonly found in bathtubs, where they become trapped while seeking food or moisture. Firebrats and silverfish are most active at night and can run very swiftly.

These insects are primarily a nuisance, but they do consume small amounts of human foods and contaminate it with their body scales and droppings. They can do considerable damage to some natural and synthetic fibers, books, and other paper products. Their feeding marks are irregular and often appear as a surface etching that may not even penetrate paper. They may also leave yellow stains, especially on linens.

The **silverfish**, *Lepisma saccharina* Linnaeus, is found in all parts of the United States as well as over much of the rest of the world. The adult's body is about 1/2-inch long, with a uniform silvery color over the upper surface (see Figure 12.37). This species prefers temperatures of 70 to 80°F and moist situations. Eggs are laid in protected areas, such as behind baseboards, and hatch in from 20 to 40 days, depending on temperature and humidity.

The **four-lined silverfish**, *Ctenolepisma quadriseriata* (Packard), attains a maximum body length of 5/8 inch. The back is marked with four dark lines extending the length of the body (see Figure 12.37). This species may live either inside or outside a building, and this must be taken into account when attempting control. They may live in either extremely dry or more moist situations.

Ctenolepisma longicaudata Esch., is the largest silverfish species encountered by the professional, reaching a maximum body size of 3/4 inch. It is a silvery or gunmetal color on the back. This silverfish is common in California and New England.

The **firebrat**, *Thermobia domestica* (Packard), lives under rather unusual conditions, generally in areas not frequented by silverfish (see Figure 12.37,

and Figure 2.9 in Chapter 2). It prefers temperatures in excess of 90°F and is frequently found around ovens or in bakeries, boiler rooms, or tunnels containing steam pipes. The bodies of adult firebrats are about 1/2-inch long and marked on the back with numerous dark patches that give them a mottled gray appearance.

Silverfish are unable to reproduce or even to survive in buildings where winter heating and moisture loss results in low relative humidity. Airtight houses with efficient humidifiers that keep the relative humidity above 50% year-round can develop silverfish infestations that are very difficult to control using typical insecticide applications. To achieve control under those conditions, the relative humidity will need to be reduced.

Besides cleanup of clutter and other food items that may be supporting the infestation, insecticide applications are required for silverfish and firebrat management. Again, careful and thorough inspections should be conducted to guide sanitation or insecticide treatments. Many residual and nonresidual insecticides are labeled for control of silverfish and bristletails. Residual insecticide applications of pyrethroid insecticides, boric acid, or silica aerogel are recommended. Space treatments of synergized pyrethrins or nonresidual pyrethroids, such as resmethrin, are often used to supplement residual treatments.

Insecticides should be applied thoroughly into all possible cracks, crevices, or other hiding places in basements, attics, cupboards, and clothes closets, behind baseboards, under bathroom fixtures and wooden partitions, and around steam and water pipes. In the case of the four-lined silverfish, it may also be necessary to treat plant mulch around the building's foundation. Dusts are particularly useful for treating wall voids and areas behind baseboards, under commodes, and in crawlspaces and attics. Space treatments may also be useful, especially in attics.

Springtails
Order Collembola

These insects are sometimes found in houses, although they occur most commonly outdoors. They are very small, usually less than 1/12-inch long (see Figure 2.10 in Chapter 2 and Figure 12.38, following page 254). The body may be white or gray. In most species a forked appendage is attached to the lower back of the abdomen and can be moved away from the body suddenly, causing the insect to jump. This jumping action and its unique mechanism result in the common name of springtails. Springtails have no wings.

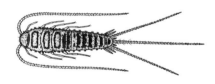

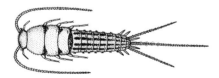

(3× actual size)

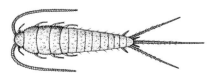

FIGURE 12.37. *Top:* The firebrat. *Center:* The four-lined silverfish. *Bottom:* The silverfish. (Provonsha)

Collembola feed on algae, fungi, and decaying vegetable matter, although a few species may feed on living plants (especially very tender seedlings) and dead animal matter. Springtails can develop in large numbers in mulched areas and thatch of lawns surrounding homes. During periods of favorable weather, such as after a rainy spell, they can become so abundant as to form floating mats or "scum" on surfaces of swimming pools, and enter homes in significant numbers.

Indoors, springtails are sometimes found in damp places such as cork insulation, kitchens, and bathrooms, around drains, in moist basements, on damp walls, in the soil of potted plants and in stored plant bulbs, and, especially, around window moldings. Springtails generally do no damage, but homeowners consider them pests because they are often encountered in large numbers.

Since collembola are generally restricted to rather humid habitats, the best means of obtaining control is to either advise or institute measures that will lower the humidity, condensate, or other moisture availability. In many cases, providing simple ventilation or airing of the room is sufficient. Use of a fan to keep the air moving through the infested area may have the necessary drying effect. Clean up any loose boards or similar materials from damp floors. In short, any procedure that eliminates moist places of concealment will likely be of value in managing springtails.

Springtails are easy to control if the dampness and organic matter that allows them to build up populations can be eliminated. Prevention of invasions from outside areas is more difficult. Residual applications of one of the pyrethroid insecticides should be applied to surfaces where Collembola occur, either indoors or outdoors. If insects are under debris, loose soil, mulch, or other protective materials, a thorough treatment should be made to penetrate into these areas. Contact applications of synergized pyrethrins or resmethrin are also useful where these insects are exposed.

Psocids
Order Psocoptera

Psocids, or booklice, are common household pests throughout the United States. Although there are more than a hundred species in the United States, only a few are common pests in homes. The two most commonly found are the **common booklouse**, *Liposcelis corrodens* Heymons, family Liposcelidae (see Figure 12.39, following page 254), and **the deathwatch**, *Trogium pulsatorium* (Linneaus), family Trogiidae. Both species are found in all states.

These insects are quite small, attaining a maximum size of only 1/25 to 1/12 inch (see Figure 12.40, and Figure 2.14 in Chapter 2). The booklouse is wingless, while the deathwatch has very small, scale-like wings. Both species have similar habits. They may be found either outdoors or indoors. Outdoors, they live in damp places, such as under bark, in grass or leaves, and on damp wood. Indoors, they find similar situations in stored grains or other foods, in crawlspaces under houses, in insect collections, and around books. Some other species may be found infesting bagged feed in warehouses. They are often found in feed concentrates that contain antibiotics of fungal origin. Their food consists of microscopic molds and fungi, so they prefer damp, warm, undisturbed situations where these molds are found. They cause no damage or destruction, so they are pests only by being present. They are frequently found in great numbers and crawl over everything in areas where they occur. Control can be obtained using the same materials and methods listed for springtail control. Moisture control, as described for the management of springtails, is also quite useful and is usually required to obtain long-term or permanent control. Infested grain should be dried to stop the mold growth that the psocids are feeding on. The grain may then require fumigation.

Dermestids
Dermestes spp.
Order Coleoptera; Family Dermestidae

Several species of the genus *Dermestes* often cause considerable difficulty in homes and in various industrial establishments.

The **larder beetle**, *Dermestes lardarius* Linnaeus, is a common pest of hides and stored foods, particularly in products with a high protein content (see Figure 2.20 in Chapter 2). The larval food source is commonly meat such as jerky, dry dog or cat food, dead mice or other mammals in wall voids, or dead birds on the fireplace damper. Adult beetles are dark brown with a pale yellow band across the front half of the wing covers. Six darker spots are found on

(20–30× actual size)

FIGURE 12.40. A psocid, also called a booklouse. (Provonsha)

this yellow band. The adult's body is 1/4- to 1/3-inch long, while larvae will grow to nearly 1/2-inch long and have two curved spines on the upper side of the last visible body segment. The larval body is irregularly covered with long, stiff hairs. Damage is caused by both the larval and adult stages.

The first step in larder beetle control is to locate and dispose of the infested materials. Migrating, mature larvae are typically found near their food source. All infested products should be removed from the immediate area, and a thorough application of one of the residual insecticides, such as one of the pyrethroids, labeled for the particular site of application should be made. Adults are attracted to lights at night; so occasional beetles found indoors may not indicate an infestation.

When the infestation occurs in a cupboard or storage closet, all food materials should be removed so that all the shelves can be treated with the residual insecticide, as recommended in Chapter 10 for control of household infestations of stored product insects. After the deposit is completely dry, the treated surfaces should be covered with shelf paper before the food is reshelved. If dead animals are being fed upon in wall voids and other inaccessible locations, it may be less expensive for the client to allow beetles to consume the animal rather than open the wall to remove it. The animal skeleton that these insects leave should not be a problem in the wall. Assist the client in eliminating access by rodents and other animals to prevent future occurrences.

The **black larder beetle**, *Dermestes ater* De Geer, infests the same type of materials as the larder beetle. The adults are black with a scattering of yellow hairs on the body. The larvae are similar to those of the larder beetle. They can be eliminated from incinerators, where they sometimes occur, by removing unburned organic materials and then applying a residual insecticide as discussed for larder beetle control.

The **hide beetle**, *Dermestes maculatus* De Geer, is similar in general appearance to the black larder beetle (see Figure 12.41, following page 254). The wing covers each taper to a fine point at the inner margin of the tip. Larvae are similar to those of the

other species of *Dermestes* and have a strong tendency to burrow into wood and other building materials. The pupal stage is passed in these tunnels, which are sometimes so numerous as to weaken the building structurally. Materials used for larder beetle control are effective against this pest. Sometimes, when infestations are found in the wooden or Styrofoam insulation of stored food or grain facilities, control by tarping and fumigation (e.g., with methyl bromide) is required.

SUPPLEMENTARY READING MATERIAL

Akre, R. D., and E. A. Myhre. "The Great Spider Whodunit." *Pest Control Technology* 22, no. 4 (1994): 44–46, 50.

Crawford, R., and D. K. Vest. "The Hobo Spider and Other European House Spiders." *Burke Museum Educational Bulletin* no. 1, 1988. 4 pp.

Davidson, R. H., and W. F. Lyon. *Insect Pests of Farm, Garden, and Orchard.* 7th ed. New York: Wiley, 1979. 596 pp.

Ebeling, W. *Urban Entomology.* Los Angeles: University of California, 1975. 695 pp.

Gertsch, W. J. *American Spiders.* 2d ed. New York: Van Nostrand Reinhold, 1979. 274 pp.

Gold, R.E. and S.C. Jones. *Handbook of Household and Structural Insect Pests.* Entomol. Soc. of America.

Headstrom, R. *Spiders of the United States.* Cranbury, N.J.: A. S. Barnes, 1973. 267 pp.

Hedges, S. A. "Millipedes, Centipedes, and Isopods." *Pest Control Technology* 23, no. 4 (1995): 80, 82–84.

Johnson, W. T., and H. H. Lyon. *Insects That Feed on Trees and Shrubs.* Ithaca, N.Y.: Cornell University Press, 1976. 464 pp.

Keegan, H. L. *Scorpions of Medical Importance.* Jackson, Miss.: University Press of Mississippi, 1980. 140 pp.

Levi, H. W., and L. R. Levi. *Spiders and Their Kin.* NewYork, NY.: Golden Press,1987. 160 pp.

Mallis, A. *Handbook of Pest Control.* 6th ed. Cleveland: Franzak & Foster, 1982. 1,101 pp.

Mitchell, R. T. and H. S. Zim. *Butterflies and Moths, A Guide to the More Common American Species.* New York, NY.: Golden Press, 1977. 160 pp.

Potter, M. F. "Ladybug, Ladybug, Fly Away from My Home." *Pest Control* 63, no. 8 (1995): 58, 62, 64, 66–67.

OLD FASHIONED
MOTH BALLS

*Kills Clothes Moths, Eggs, and Larvae
in Air-Tight Containers and Storage Closets*

CHAPTER 13 | Fabric Insects

Fabric-destroying insects cause much damage each year. In addition to large losses in commercial fabric and garment manufacturing or storage operations, the many small damages caused in households add up to a significant figure. A hole in an expensive suit usually means a new suit will be purchased, and a patch of wool carpet damaged under a sofa may require purchase of new carpeting the next time furniture is rearranged. Other materials that are readily infested include sweaters, coats, upholstery, piano felts, blankets, and any other silk or woolen products. Furs, hair, leathers and hides, feathers, horns, insect and animal collections, and such stored foods as meat, fish, meal, and dried milk products are also vulnerable to these insects. Synthetic fibers and cellulose materials are damaged only incidentally, often because they are soiled with greasy food stains, body oils, or other residues that are the primary object of the insect attack.

Just as the termites and some of the other pests discussed in Chapters 7 and 8 create problems because of their ability to attack and use cellulose, the insect pests of fabrics are troublesome because of their ability to digest and use keratin as an energy source. Although the word *keratin* may seem rather foreign to many pest management professionals, it is a very important material to people. **Keratin** is the chief constituent of such human tissues as hair, fingernails, and skin. In other mammals, keratin is the chief structural protein in horns, hoofs, and feathers. Keratin is quite stable chemically and is very resistant to most means of digestion. Few animals are able to digest keratin, and these include only a relatively small number of insects. This unusual ability to digest keratin, coupled with our widespread use of wool and other animal hair, is the basis of fabric pest problems.

There are other insects capable of damaging fabrics by chewing or shredding, but they do not have the ability to digest keratin. Silverfish, cockroaches, crickets, and earwigs fall into this category. However, they are not considered true fabric pests and will not be discussed here.

The most important fabric-destroying insects in the United States include two moths and four carpet beetles, although various other insect species may cause some damage occasionally or may be important locally. There seems to have been an increase in carpet beetle and clothes moth problems throughout much of the United States. The reasons for this resurgence are not clear. However, contributing factors probably include a trend in consumer preferences toward garments made of wool, furs, or feathers (and away from polyesters and other synthetics), and cancellation of registrations for use of long-residual chlorinated hydrocarbon insecticides, such as DDT and aldrin, that were previously used commonly to control ectoparasites on sheep and other livestock and in pest control (including for fabric pests) around homes.

CLOTHES MOTHS
Order Lepidoptera; Family Tineidae

The term *clothes moth* is properly used in connection with the **webbing clothes moth**, the **casemaking clothes moth**, and the **carpet moth (tapestry moth)**. The first two species are more common, while tapestry moths occur infrequently. These are all small moths, with wingspans of less than 1/2 inch. Their habits are different from most moths because they are rarely seen flying around lights at night, as carpet beetles will. Rather, they prefer dark closets, attics, or other areas, and they tend to live in dark corners or in folds of fabric. Newly emerged adults of both sexes fly readily, usually at dusk, or they may occasionally fly on the edges of a lighted area, so they usually remain quite inconspicuous. Once female moths have mated and develop eggs, they will fly much less and become rather sedentary. They are capable of running and making very short, hopping flights to escape disturbance. The females will seek out suitable areas for egg-laying, most commonly in quiet, out-of-the-way locations with low light, and where suitable food materials for development of the larvae are present. In some museums and other specialized facilities where clothes moth problems are common, professionals can use glue boards placed on windowsills to detect and monitor for the presence of these moths indoors. Collections at windows indicate that when clothes moths are actively flying, they can be attracted to light. Interestingly, experience has shown that clothes moths can be captured readily with glue boards that contain no pheromone or other lures, though specialized sex pheromone lures for these species are available.

Clothes moths have a complete metamorphosis. Adults are unable to feed, and it is the larval stages, which are small, cream-colored caterpillars with brown head capsules, that damage fabrics as they feed. In houses, they are most frequently pests of clothing, carpets, rugs, upholstery fabrics, piano felts, brush bristles, blankets, hair from pets, furs, lint from woolens, and any stored wool products. These products all contain the animal-derived protein keratin.

Clothes moth larvae will, at times, damage other products, such as cotton, linen, synthetic fibers, and paper. Such damage, however, is usually incidental, resulting from the larvae damaging such fibers while eating their natural food. Clothes moth larvae are particularly damaging to fabrics stained with materials such as oil from human hair, human sweat, urine, beer, tomato juice, milk, or soft drinks. These caterpillars require a certain balance of nutrients in their diet to develop properly, and they especially need vitamin B. First instar larvae cannot survive on clean wool but require the nutritional supplements found in soilage (e.g., body oils from the wearer of a garment).

Common clothes moth adults can be identified by use of the key in Figure 13.1. Larvae are difficult to identify morphologically but can be easily separated by their habits, which are discussed later in this chapter.

Webbing Clothes Moth
Tineola bisselliella (Hummel)

This is the most commonly encountered clothes moth in the United States, found in all states. The body and wings of the adult are uniformly buff colored, and its head has lightly reddish hairs on top (see Figure 13.1, and Figure 13.2, which follows page 254). The wings are silvery brown to golden tan in color, without spots, and measure less than 1/2 inch across when extended. Adult males are capable of flying as far as 100 yards, but seldom do so. Females are not good fliers, although they can fly for short distances within homes and elsewhere. Adults normally live about 15 to 30 days, although in colder weather this time may be somewhat extended.

The eggs are oval, ivory-colored, and about 1/25-inch long (see Figure 13.3). They are laid either singly or in small groups among the threads or in the cracks of a suitable food material, and they are usually attached to this food material with a gelatinous secretion. Each female lays an average of 40 to 50 eggs, but some may lay up to 200. In the summer these eggs will hatch in 4 to 10 days, but in winter it may take a month or more. Pest management professionals occasionally encounter homeowners and others who believe that clothes moth eggs can remain dormant for months, or even years, and still hatch, but this is untrue. When using a microscope to examine damaged goods, pest management professionals must be careful not to confuse eggs with the tiny, hard, and characteristically bun-shaped particles of excrement, called "frass," that are left scattered about wherever the larvae have been active. These excrement particles are frequently of the same color as the fabric the larvae are feeding on.

Larvae are shiny, creamy white in color, and not more than 1/2-inch long (see Figure 13.4, following page 254). They shun lighted areas, and usually spin feeding tunnels of silk, but may produce somewhat randomly placed patches of silken webbing as they move about on the surface of a cloth article they are attacking. Some particles of the material on which they are feeding and bits of their own excrement are often entangled in the silk. These feeding tubes and silken patches together make up the webbing that is characteristic of this moth. Webbing is generally sparse in fur, but it may be present (though not obvious) at the base of the hairs.

Each larva molts from five to ten times during its development. The time necessary to complete larval development can vary greatly and is dependent on such things as availability and quality of food, relative humidity, and temperature (and up to 45 molts have been observed under unusual conditions). This variation may be anywhere from 35 days to as long as 30 months. The larva then spins a silken pupal case and attaches bits of fiber to the outside of it. This case is usually well hidden in the fabric that has been attacked. Length of the pupal stage varies from about 8 to 40 days.

Adult webbing clothes moths may be found at

A PICTORIAL KEY TO THE ADULTS OF COMMON FABRIC INSECTS

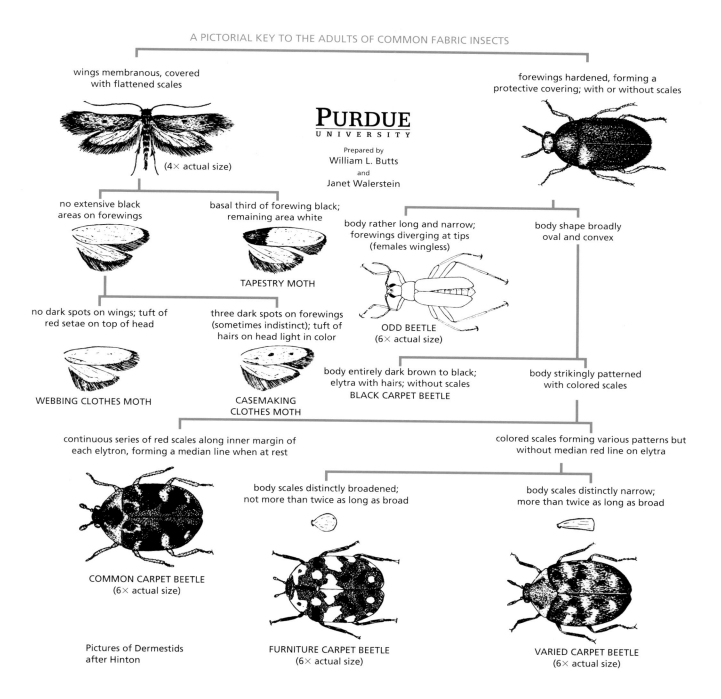

FIGURE 13.1. A pictorial key to the adults of common fabric insects.

FIGURE 13.3. Webbing clothes moth eggs. (Myers)

any time of the year but are more abundant during the warm summer months. They also develop quite well in heated buildings in the winter. The entire life cycle may vary from 55 days to 4 years, but normally will be between 65 and 90 days. This moth seldom occurs in very dry areas of the United States.

Casemaking Clothes Moth
Tinea pellionella Linnaeus

This species is not nearly as common in the United States as the webbing clothes moth. It is more frequently encountered by professionals in the southern states, although it is rather generally distributed in all states.

This moth is more brown in color than the webbing clothes moth and has three dark spots on the wings, which help to identify it (see Figure 13.1). However, this characteristic should not be relied on, since the spots are frequently quite indistinct, and many wing scales may have been worn off any particular specimen, leaving no spots. Adult casemaking clothes moths vary in size as compared to the webbing clothes moth, but typically have a somewhat smaller wingspread in the United States. The size of adult moths will vary for all clothes moth species, depending on the larval diet. No tuft of reddish hairs arising from the top of the head of adult casemaking clothes moths is usually apparent, though fresh specimens may have some pale reddish hairs present (upon close inspection).

The larva spins a small silken cell, bag, or case around itself and carries it about while it feeds (see Figure 13.5, and Figure 13.6, which follows page 254). It moves about by extending its head and legs from the front end of the case. There is rarely any silken webbing spun on the fabric or other material where the larva feeds. Larvae wander about on food material, feeding a little here and a little there, but rarely do extensive damage at any one spot or in a small area.

When ready to pupate, the larva draws itself completely within its case, seals both ends of the case with silk, and pupates in this cocoon. In the northern United States, pupae are usually the only stage found during the winter months, but all stages can be found in the South throughout the year.

This moth is a particular pest of feathers and down, although it can feed readily on almost any material listed as food for webbing clothes moths.

Carpet Moth (Tapestry Moth)
Trichophaga tapetzella (Linnaeus)

This moth is rarely found by pest management professionals but can cause considerable damage when a severe infestation occurs. It is most common in old woolens, horsehair, furs, and feathers.

The adult wingspread is somewhat greater than that of either the webbing or casemaking clothes moths. Carpet moths can be distinguished from

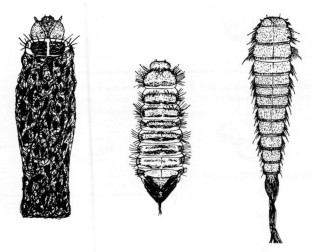

FIGURE 13.5. Some representative larvae of common fabric pests, all enlarged several times. *Left:* Dorsal view of the larva of the casemaking clothes moth. The head and the first segment of the thorax are exposed at the anterior end of the case. Note the darkened, plate-like areas on the top of the thorax. Such areas are not present on the larva of the webbing clothes moth, and it never constructs a portable case. *Center:* The larva of the varied carpet beetle. This is a typical larva of the genus *Anthrenus*. It is rather difficult to make positive identifications of larvae of this genus without examining the fine structure of the spearheaded setae, which arise from the posterior segments in dense clumps. Larvae of this genus can be separated from those of the genus *Trogoderma* (see Chapter 10) by the placement of these clumps of peculiarly shaped setae. In *Anthrenus*, these setae arise from the membrane between the segments rather than from the segment itself, as is the case in *Trogoderma*. *Right:* The larva of the black carpet beetle, the most important insect pest of fabrics in the United States. The tapering body, which bears no spearheaded setae, has a long brush of hair extending backward from its posterior end.

these other species by the fact that the front third of the forewing is black and the rest of the wing is white with a few black or gray spots (see Figure 13.1). The adult moth's head is white.

The larva of this moth makes a silk tube as it burrows through the material on which it feeds, and it feeds inside this tube. Otherwise, the life cycle of this species is similar to that of the preceding species.

CARPET BEETLES

Order Coleoptera; Family Dermestidae

Several species of dermestid beetles may damage fabrics. Four species are most commonly encountered: the **black carpet beetle, varied carpet beetle, common carpet beetle,** and **furniture carpet beetle**. Together, this group is usually considered more economically important as fabric pests than the clothes moths.

Many other common beetles resemble adult and larval carpet beetles. The hide beetles (discussed later in this chapter), museum beetles, bird nest carpet beetles, and cabinet beetles all have a somewhat similar appearance. Although both adults and larvae may be mistaken for carpet bee-

tles, close attention to the descriptions of the carpet beetles, together with an understanding of their larval habits, will usually allow proper identification.

Larvae of these beetles are the only stage that causes damage to fabrics, and all of the adults are small and inconspicuous beetles rarely seen by homeowners. Adults may be found indoors or outdoors and frequently on flowers surrounding a house, where they feed on pollen. Flowering shrubs, such as spirea and pyracantha, are particularly attractive to adult carpet beetles, but other species of flowering plants may be visited. Adult carpet beetles fly readily and actively when indoors, and are attracted to windows and lamps or light fixtures, so live or dead specimens can often be found on window ledges or in light fixtures.

Black Carpet Beetle
Attagenus unicolor (Brahm)

This is an abundant and widespread carpet beetle that is found throughout most of the United States. It is commonly found on dead animal carcasses in nature, and can cause considerable damage indoors especially to furs, stuffed animals (taxidermy), and articles such as hair-bristle brushes that also have deposits of other animal proteins and body oils. This species is less common than the other, smaller carpet beetle species described below as a pest indoors on woolen fabrics and other keratin-containing articles.

Adults are shiny black with brownish legs and 1/8- to 3/16-inch in length (see Figure 13.1). They are frequently found outdoors in flowers and are most numerous in the spring and early summer. They lay eggs either indoors or outdoors, beginning 4 to 8 days after the adult emerges. Each female lays approximately 50 eggs over a period of about 3 weeks, after which she dies. Indoors, these eggs will commonly be deposited on accumulations of lint in air ducts, along the edges of carpets or floors, underneath baseboards of walls, or in gaps between hardwood floorboards. This "lint" usually contains significant amounts of human and pet "dander," which is shed hair and skin that provides the same high quality source of keratin and other essential proteins and oils which larvae of this species develop most successfully on (i.e., such as they do when this species is so commonly found at dead animal carcasses in nature). The pest management professional should keep these habits in mind when making inspections for this species in homes or other facilities, and emphasize to the homeowner or client steps that can help minimize the availability of these resources. Eggs hatch in 6 to 11 days in warm weather.

Larvae are quite tiny when they hatch but have the same distinctive elongated carrot- or cigar-shaped bodies and long, brushy tail bristles that are so easily seen on the larger larvae. Body color varies from a light brown to almost black (see Figure 13.5, and Figure 13.7, which follows page 254). They can develop under a wide range of temperature and humidity conditions and are much less susceptible to environmental changes than are clothes moths. Larvae may grow to 1/2-inch long over a series of 5 to 11 molts. They tend to avoid exposed and lighted areas, so are found most frequently in the lower parts of clothes closets, rolled up or wrapped into woolen materials, at the edge of carpeting under baseboards, or inside upholstered furniture (see Figure 13.8). Mature larvae can wander rather widely, so they may be found anywhere in a building. It is not at all unusual to find them in a bathtub, kitchen sink, or even crawling on walls and ceilings.

Black carpet beetle larvae are general feeders, feeding on dead animal materials, hair, fur, hides, and horns, and occasionally on woolen products. They tend to be surface feeders on wool, usually eating the nap from fabric and leaving the base threads relatively unaffected. However, they are quite capable of eating large, irregular holes through any suitable food material. In fur, hairs are cut at the base, with no injury to the hide. The hair then readily drops out, leaving a bare appearance to the hide. Black carpet beetle larvae frequently burrow through containers to obtain food, leaving small openings through which other insects may enter to cause additional damage. Cast skins, which appear banded, and frass in the form of fine powder are frequently found on infested items. Their frass is often the same color as the substrate they are feeding upon.

Black carpet beetle larvae may live as short as nine months to as long as three years, depending on their diet and environmental conditions. Larvae pupate in the last larval skin, with the pupal state lasting from 6 to 24 days.

Varied Carpet Beetle
Anthrenus verbasci (Linnaeus)

The varied carpet beetle is widely distributed in the United States. Adults are much smaller than the black carpet beetle. Their body shape is more rounded when viewed from above, and they have a pattern of white, brown, and yellow scales on the upper surface of their wing covers, or elytra (see Figure 13.1).

Eggs are laid in various locations, where they hatch in 17 to 18 days. Larva molt seven or eight times over about 7 to 11 months. Mature larvae are rarely more than 1/4-inch long and bear two pairs of hair tufts on the back end of the abdomen (see Figure 13.5, and Figures 13.9 and 13.10, which follow page 254). The hairs in these tufts are technically called **haustisetae**, because they are made up of segments shaped like arrowheads. These hairs can be irritating to the skin or if breathed into the nose or lungs. The larva is rather wide in proportion to its length and has a hippy appearance, since it is usually broader at the back than at the front.

Varied carpet beetle larvae are scavengers. They are quite common in nests of birds and spiders, on dead animals, and in insect collections. They feed on a variety of animal products, such as woolens, hides, feathers, horns, bone, and insect pupae. They will feed on dead insects such as flies and have also been found in drywood termite workings after fumigation has killed the termites, or even subterranean termite galleries after soil or bait treatments have done likewise. Pupae are formed in the last larval exoskeleton and take 10 to 13 days to develop into adults. Empty cast skins are often found attached to fabrics.

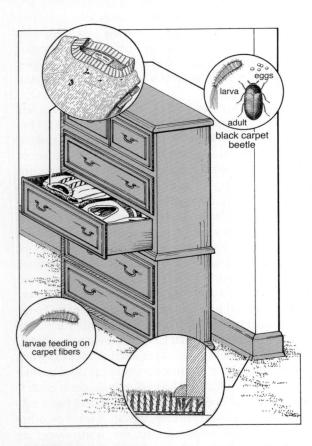

FIGURE 13.8. Larvae of the black carpet beetle and other fabric pest species can wander widely. (Shuster and Provonsha)

Common Carpet Beetle
Anthrenus scrophulariae (Linnaeus)

Adults of this carpet beetle are small, rounded, and gray to blackish in color with a varied pattern of white and orange scales on the back (see Figure 13.1). There is an orange-red band of scales down the middle of the back or dorsal surface. Adult beetles feed on nectar and pollen in flowers. Each female deposits 30 to 40 small, white eggs, which hatch in 10 to 20 days.

Larvae are rather active, frequently moving about rapidly. Their body is an elongated, oval shape and is rarely more than 1/4-inch long. They are reddish brown and covered with numerous black or brown hairs. There is an average of six molts over a period of 60 to 70 days, after which pupation occurs in the last larval skin. The pupal stage lasts for 12 to 15 days, but the beetle typically remains in the old larval skin for approximately 18 days before becoming active. Larvae of this beetle often attack carpets, but they also eat other woolens, furs, feathers, museum specimens, and similar materials.

Furniture Carpet Beetle
Anthrenus flavipes LeConte

This beetle often attacks upholstered furniture. Adults are small, rounded, and blackish, with a mottling of yellow and white scales on the back and a heavy coating of yellow scales on the femur of the legs. The color pattern varies considerably. In some specimens the yellow scales are darker and more numerous, while in others the white scales predominate (see Figure 13.1, and Figure 13.11, which follows page 254).

Females lay a total of 35 to 100 eggs in one to three batches. At room temperature these hatch in approximately 3 weeks. Larvae then develop through 6 to 12 molts over a period of three to six months. They are oval shaped, somewhat elongated, and thickly covered with brownish hairs (see Figures 13.9, 13.10, and 13.11, following page 254). *A. flavipes* larvae may often appear nearly black, and are usually much darker than *A. verbasci* larvae. The pupa is white and develops in the last larval skin. At room temperature the pupal stage will last from 14 to 19 days. The adult remains in the pupal skin for 1 to 10 weeks before becoming active.

Furniture carpet beetles are found frequently on furniture, where they feed on hair, padding, feathers, and woolen upholstering. They commonly feed on other woolens, carpets, fur, bristles, horns, silk, and other such materials. They will also feed on such fibers as linen, cotton, rayon, and jute when these are stained with animal body oils or other excreta.

Odd Beetle
Thylodrias contractus Motschulsky

This insect has been called the tissue paper bug, but this in an unfortunate misnomer. It is closely related to the carpet beetles, but the general appearance of the adult hardly suggests such a relationship. Adult males have a long, narrow body with long legs and antennae (see Figure 13.12). These characteristics contrast quite sharply with the rather oval body and shortened appendages of the typical carpet beetle. The male is yellowish brown with a moderately dense covering of hair on the body. When at rest over the body, the wing covers touch each other on the inner margin for only a short distance and then separate noticeably toward the tips. This characteristic, plus the presence of a single median ocellus between the compound eyes, should serve to identify the beetle.

Adult females do not even look like a beetle in general body form (see Figure 13.12). The body is broader and more stout than that of the male, and there are no wings. The antennae are thin and about twice as long as the head is wide. There is a median ocellus between the rather small compound eyes.

Odd beetle larvae are similar in appearance to those of the other carpet beetles, but they do not have long hairs at the tip of the abdomen nor on the upper surface of the body. However, there is a row of coarse, stout bristles across the top rear edge of each body segment, and those hairs on the rear edge of the prothorax are distinctly club shaped. The larva tends to roll up into a C-shape or ball when disturbed, another characteristic that will aid identification.

As with the black carpet beetle, this species is not normally found on woolen fabrics in homes or museums; but more commonly on taxidermy, bird mounts, in seashell collections, and other natural

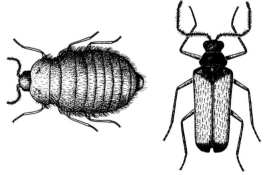

FIGURE 13.12. Adult male (right) and female odd beetles, both greatly enlarged. The female lacks wings and has the appearance of a larval form. Odd beetle larvae are similar in appearance to the carpet beetles, although they lack haustisetae. (Provonsha)

history collections (where a source of keratin is present). The odd beetle is an introduced species. Since adult females are wingless, dispersal of the species depends primarily on its being carried from place to place in moving and commerce. This insect has been found in situations that seem remote from its normal food. Control methods for the odd beetle are similar to those used for carpet beetles.

HIDE BEETLES

Dermestes spp.

There are several species of the genus *Dermestes* that are considered fabric pests since they can be found in tanneries and warehouses that process hides and skin. They can also be found in homes, attacking furs, animal skins, feathers, and meats or cheeses, but usually not sound fabrics. The three most economically important hide beetles are *Dermestes lardarius* Linnaeus, the **larder beetle** (see Figure 2.20 in Chapter 2); *D. ater* (DeGeer), the **black larder beetle**; and *D. maculatus* (DeGeer), the **hide or leather beetle** (see Figure 12.41, following page 254). These beetles were discussed in Chapter 12 as miscellaneous pests, since they occasionally invade homes and infest other products of an animal base. They are also found in bird nests, attacking dead bird or mouse carcasses in attics, in museum collections of stuffed animals, or in beehives, where dead bees and wax are eaten. Both the adults and larvae damage materials during feeding.

The female beetle must feed before laying eggs. Eggs are about 1/12 inch in length and are laid in foodstuffs such as hides and other dry animal matter. Egg laying continues for two to three months, and the total number laid varies from 200 to 800. Larvae begin to feed soon after hatching. They are active and relatively agile in dark areas, but in the light they may become immobile. There are normally five or six larval molts. The fully grown larva measures about 1/2-inch in length. The larva wanders when it matures, seeking a pupation site. It may burrow into such materials as wood or other soft substrates before pupating. The final larval skin acts as a plug, protecting the pupa from predaceous insects. If the larva is unable to bore a tunnel, the skin remains attached to the pupa.

The identification and control of hide beetles are discussed in Chapter 12.

CLOTHES MOTH AND CARPET BEETLE MANAGEMENT

Fabric pest detection requires a thorough knowledge of pest biology and behavior. Homeowners

can also be a source of useful information, as they will know where pet foods, mounted animal specimens, insect collections, skins, furs, woolens, seeds, organic fertilizers (e.g., bone meals), and other items likely to be infested are stored. They may also know if there are bird nests under eaves or in the attic, or if there are any wasp or hornet nests around. The professional can save a great deal of time on inspection, insecticide treatment, and other management steps by first asking questions.

Inspection

Pest management professionals should make a thorough inspection of infested premises to find all sources of infestation before making any attempt at control. It is important to remember that adults of these insects do not feed on woolens or on any of the other materials that may be attacked by the larvae. The presence of adults in an area does not necessarily mean that larvae are (or will be) in the same area, since the adults may have already laid their eggs in some other room and may be moving around at random or orienting toward bright sunlight shining through windows (i.e., they want to disperse to outdoor areas).

Clothes moth and carpet beetle larvae are most commonly found feeding in secluded and protected places. When searching for them, a good flashlight and a knife, nail file, or small spatula are essential tools. Larvae will usually be found in dark clothes closets or on furs, taxidermy, bristle brushes, hair padding, woolens, bits of carpeting, or other such materials in storage. They are also found in lint (especially under baseboards and around door casings), under the edges of carpeting, in and under wool-upholstered furniture, in collections of animal hair, in air ducts, and anywhere else where suitable food material containing keratin might be available. When inspecting for carpet beetle larvae, be especially careful to examine under baseboards, around the bottoms of door casings, under the edges of carpeting, and in closets. Use the knife blade or other implement to bring out bits of lint that are usually found in these areas, and examine them closely for live larvae or their cast skins. Cast skins are sometimes more numerous than live larvae, but they resemble live larvae so closely that they can be used for identification purposes.

Along the edges of carpets, such as Oriental carpets, roll the carpet back several inches if possible, and inspect the backing and the floor (or on both sides of the pad). If eggs have been laid along the edge, the larvae will hatch out and feed (damage) usually for only a few inches in from the edge, and then the larvae will migrate back to the edge

A Key for Recognition of Damage Done to Wool, Fur, and Leather
By Dr. John V. Osmun, Professor Emeritus, Purdue University

1. Usually fixed silk tubes sometimes bearing frass, this frass often showing the color of the cloth. Nap of wool eaten away in spots if lightly damaged; holes completely through the fabric if infestation is extensive. Larvae may be present in the tubes. If fur, hairs are cut at base, causing loose fur and exposing the hide, with some webbing present. Fecal pellets are bun shaped. **webbing clothes moth**

2. Cigar-shaped cases 1/16 to 3/8 inch (depending on larval stage), usually attached to the fabric at one end. Cases white or bearing slight colors of the infested fabric. Cases appear to move about if larvae are inside, or are stationary if they contain pupae or are empty. If cases are absent, damage is recognized as surface feeding in irregular furrows or, when damage is severe, by holes through the fabric. Webbing essentially absent. **casemaking clothes moth**

3. Fabric actually cut; threads pulled, broken, torn, or looped; exposed ends frayed. No loss of threads unless a section of fabric is torn out. Damage to neighboring areas not expected. In rugs, loops pulled out. **mechanical damage**
   a. Similar damage, but soiled and with hairs. **rodents**

4. In wool, irregular or round holes that might penetrate fabric. Tips of exposed threads usually curled and charred. In fur, curling of damaged hairs; leather scorched. **burns**

5. Fabric damaged, with no traces of silk-like threads. Much surface damage, with various penetrating holes. If infestation is light, damage may be limited to scattered holes, with surrounding surface damage. A few or many cast larval skins may be present. Frass in the form of fine, uniform powder, often the color of the fabric. **carpet beetles**
   a. In fur, hairs cut at base, with no injury to hide; hair drops out readily, and hide may be bare in severe infestations. Cast skins; no webbing. **black carpet beetles**
   b. In fur and brushes, principal damage to tips of hair, leaving numerous uneven areas. **varied, furniture, and common carpet beetles**

6. a. In wool, slight surface damage and occasional holes. **Species not readily identifiable unless larvae or cast skins are present (though unusual for cabinet beetle).**
   b. In fur, hide damaged at base of hairs; hairs, therefore, become loosened and usually fall out. **cabinet beetle**

7. Hide badly damaged on exposed side (not fabrication scars). If on fur, damage is on the inner surface; holes and loss of hair result from complete larval penetration of hide. **hide beetles**

8. Cotton or hemp binding of wool rug eaten, leaving the wool untouched. Hard mastic substance present. **subterranean termites**

for pupation and adult emergence. Thus, the infestation and damage often does not extend too far away from the perimeter of the carpet, or from other areas (e.g., under seldom moved furniture) where the infestation originated and is focused. Use a flashlight when examining dark closets and other such places.

In addition to the above-mentioned sources, it is very important that certain natural sources of infestation be considered. Look for articles of woolen clothing that may have been stored and neglected, and check the premises for old furniture and rugs that may be a source of continuing infestation. Other important reservoirs that should not be overlooked include sites that represent the natural habitat of these insects. Sparrow, starling, or other bird nests, inside or outside of the premises, are common points of origin (or continuation) for fabric pest infestations. Yellowjacket, mud dauber, hornet, and bumble or honey bee nests found under eaves, and in attics, wall voids or crawlspaces are also common sources of carpet beetle infestations. Moth or beetle

larvae feed on the remainders of dead insects fed to the wasp larvae, on cast wasp larval skins, and sometimes on the living wasp larvae. Paper wasp (*Polistes* spp.) nests are unlikely to contain larvae of fabric pest species, since the nest cells open downwards and typically do not provide for an accumulation of cast skins or dead insect prey.

Anthrenus and *Attagenus* larvae may also be found living on accumulations of dead cluster flies, multicolored Asian lady beetles, or certain other occasional invader pests (as discussed in Chapter 12) in attics or other areas. The presence of pets, which shed a lot of hair that may provide an important reservoir of food material for carpet beetle and clothes moth larvae, should be considered. Shed hair may accumulate in heating ducts, beneath furniture, in crevices between floorboards, or in hard-to-clean corners. These loose tangles of hair may be sufficient to sustain a small population of fabric pests for a long period of time, even in places where all wool products have been treated.

An additional aid to inspections and monitoring for certain of the clothes moths and carpet beetles are glue boards or folded sticky-card traps. As described earlier with regard to adult clothes moth flying behavior, glue boards or sticky traps can be placed near windows indoors for detection and monitoring of clothes moths. Sticky traps, similar to those used for monitoring cockroaches, or stored product pests in food warehouses (see Chapter 10), can also be baited with pheromone or food-attractant lures. Most are intended to collect adults that can fly to the traps, but there are also sticky traps with food-attractant lures for monitoring the presence and activity of carpet beetle larvae (which can be surprisingly mobile in the vicinity of a source of infestation).

Specific adult sex pheromones useful as lures are available for the webbing clothes moth and certain of the carpet beetles, and new lures are being identified, synthesized, and made available to professionals for use in pest management programs all the time. The clothes moth traps are especially useful for locating hard-to-find sources of infestation that may have been missed during the visual inspection, because the moths (which are generally weak flyers) will often respond by flying toward a nearby lure within a few minutes. There is some evidence that pheromone lures for *Tineola* moths, such as the webbing clothes moth, can also attract *Tinea* moths like the casemaking clothes moth, but not as effectively.

Besides serving as an aid to detection and pinpointing sources of infestation within homes or large and complex facilities, these moth and beetle traps are especially useful for timing the emergence and periods of presence of the egg-laying stages of key fabric pest species in the area, and for monitoring relative levels of adult abundance within or around facilities. These monitoring traps are used primarily in relation to commercial, industrial, or other specialized accounts that have particular problems with these fabric pests (e.g., clothing and textile manufacturers, museums, etc.), but they can be used at residential accounts if needed. As with the use of monitoring traps in food warehouses for stored product pest management, these fabric pest traps should be placed out in a systematic array or grid-like pattern within and around the facility. This will allow the traps to serve the functions of pinpointing incipient infestations and monitoring the broader seasonal patterns of adult presence.

Some professionals who use these traps primarily for seasonal monitoring of pest biology feel it is most useful to start with trapping for fabric pests outdoors around the facility, beginning at the time of the earliest flowering of any trees and shrubs in spring. In this way they can know what is happening with natural populations of these species in the surrounding area, as a key to knowing what will likely happen with these pests indoors (i.e., because some adults will inevitably seek to enter the home or facility for egg laying). The traps should then be checked as frequently as possible (e.g., at one to two week intervals during seasons when pest species of interest are being collected), and data recorded on the numbers of each species captured (by date, site, and specific trap location). Records should be kept over multiple seasons to establish and compare trends of emergence and relative abundance. Specialized computer database and graphics software are advertised in pest control industry magazines or are available from suppliers of the traps and lures, to facilitate storage and handling of these trap data. These software packages will allow the professional to get the most practical benefit from monitoring data over time. However, other more generic database and graphics software should be adaptable for these purposes. The arrangement of the traps should not be too rigid or unchanging. They should be moved around within or outside of the facility, and the number of trap locations used indoors at each site may be changed over time to allow better pinpointing of hidden areas of infestation that might arise. The monitoring program should also be flexible enough to respond to changes in the arrangement of susceptible items and other relevant factors in the field.

The overall goal of the seasonal monitoring is to allow a more precise and effective timing of detailed inspections, possible preventive insecticide applications, or other fabric pest management procedures. These pest management activities can be determined by observing the trends in adult presence and using your understanding of the biology and behavior of each pest species you detect in significant numbers. Remember that although adult carpet beetles can feed on woolens or other valuable items to a limited degree, the key usefulness of these monitoring data is to allow you to know when and where to act in order to protect susceptible items from the much more damaging larval stages of these pest species. After two or three seasons of such monitoring and record keeping, you should be able to fairly accurately predict the peaks of fabric pest presence in your area (though surprises will occur!), which should allow you to provide much more efficient and effective service to those clients with homes or facilities where fabric insect control is a priority.

Sanitation and Prevention

The prevention and correction of fabric pest infestations require special skills, extensive knowledge of the insects and the problems they can create, and careful workmanship. Preventive measures should be practiced whenever possible, because once a hole is made, the damage is done and may not be repairable. Preventive procedures include preventive sanitation and exclusion, usually by bagging or packaging susceptible items in other tightly sealed containers, and related chemical measures. Furs are commonly stored in specialized cold storage facilities. There are also some methods of mothproofing garments or fabrics.

Many fabric pest problems can be prevented, and even controlled without the use of insecticides, by means of household cleanliness, including the thorough and frequent cleaning of carpeting and upholstery with a vacuum cleaner and the brushing, airing, and dry cleaning of susceptible clothing or other articles. When carpets are cleaned in place, the use of a nozzle-type cleaner that includes nozzles directed at the edge of the carpet will be important for effective control, since many of the eggs and damaging larval stages will be at the edges of the carpet. Upright machines, that do not reach the edges of the carpet, may not help control many of these fabric pest life stages at the key edge locations of the carpet. Whenever possible, the infested carpet should be rolled back several inches to a foot, and the underside vacuumed or cleaned to remove or kill all eggs or larvae present.

Avoid prolonged storage of discarded garments, bedding, fur or animal pelts (e.g., unprotected taxidermy), and old wool rugs or furniture upholstered with vulnerable fabrics. Remember that a clean environment is not conducive to the activity of fabric-destroying insects. It is not absolutely necessary that the item itself support fabric insect development. Soiled articles of otherwise indigestible materials can be attacked, as can garments of wool-blend fabrics.

In all moth and carpet beetle control work, it is essential to eliminate as many potential breeding places as possible. Old pieces of woolen fabric, cutoff pieces of carpeting, old feather pillows, dried insects in collections, and other such sources of fabric insect food should be destroyed. Areas under baseboards, behind door casings, under heat radiators, and inside furnace or air-conditioning registers should be thoroughly cleaned with a vacuum cleaner to remove as much lint as possible. A vacuum cleaner with strong suction is a good piece of special equipment for the professional to use in such operations. Careful, routine attention to such sanitation procedures by the homeowners or the housekeeping staff (for other facilities) is a key to limiting fabric insect problems.

Items in storage that may be subject to attack

Mothproofing— Direct Fabric Protection

Mothproofing and clothes moth control are two different things. Mothproofing implies preventive applications of an insecticide to avoid infestation. Clothes moth or carpet beetle control is the correction of an existing infestation. Mothproofing is often accomplished by a special treatment during the manufacture of woolen fabric or other susceptible items. In some instances it is also a service of the dry-cleaning industry. Pest management professionals most often engage in mothproofing in connection with the treatment of rugs, furniture, and carpets.

Various mothproofers will give protection from moth and carpet beetle damage. These chemicals depend for their action on killing larvae after either light feeding or brief contact (before feeding occurs). Many fabrics treated with a mothproofing solution at the time of manufacture are safe from damage until the chemicals are removed, either by washing, dry cleaning, or simple degradation. Pest management professionals should never attempt to mothproof articles of clothing. When the homeowner desires to have clothing treated, it is usually best to recommend that treatment be made during dry cleaning, if such treatment is available. Such mothproofing of clothing is usually quite effective over the length of time between cleanings or for storage during the summer months.

Certain pyrethroid insecticides like permethrin, and formulations of nonresidual insecticides such as pyrethrins or other pyrethroids, are currently labeled for general mothproofing applications to other articles besides clothing (e.g., carpets, area rugs, tapestries, and drapes). These are generally applied after these items have been removed and dry cleaned (if possible), and while located in a convenient place that facilitates thorough application. Fine sprays should be carefully applied to obtain thorough coverage, but only after possible staining problems have been considered and tests done to ensure such problems will not arise.

can be protected if placed within tightly sealed, heavy-gauge plastic bags or other tight and insect-resistant containers. Adult clothes moths have no mouthparts, so can not chew through anything, and adult carpet beetles are unlikely to chew through thick plastic bags or other tight, heavy-gauge containers that have no indication of a favorable larval food source on the outside. Thus, careful bagging or other containerization of uninfested items (e.g., previously dry cleaned, or cold treated as described below) will generally be very effective and reliable.

Other preventive approaches can be used in close association with these sanitation procedures, though their limitations should be recognized and some are falling out of favor due to safety concerns. The most commonly used chemical for preventive control in storage situations has been **paradichlorobenzene** (**PDB**), which acts as a repellent and continuous fumigant (though it may not effectively control carpet beetle larvae, except at very high concentrations and if tightly contained). Stored woolens should be interspersed with crystals of this material wrapped in clean paper, as the fabrics are packed into tightly sealed trunks or boxes. Recommended rates for PDB are 1- to 1-1/4 pounds of active ingredient per 100 cubic feet, or 10 to 12 pounds per 1000 cubic feet, of storage space (see product label directions). Use of tight containers, such as large, sealed plastic bags, which are then kept in tight boxes or chests, is important toward obtaining optimum protection for the longest possible time. Remember that it is important to maintain the highest possible concentration of the PDB vapors inside the plastic bag or other space containing the susceptible items. The use of PDB appears to be falling out of favor with regulatory officials in many countries due to the large amounts of material necessary for effective protection of woolens, and health concerns over the exposure of family members, often including children, to vapors of this material for such extended periods. Naphthalene (in moth balls) is also effective, although it is less desirable to use than PDB and no longer available for pesticidal uses in the United States and some other countries. Recommended rates for naphthalene are 1- to 2-1/2 pounds of active ingredient per 100 cubic feet of storage space (see product label directions).

There are some consumer products marketed for clothes moth control that use lavandin oil or other plant-derived oils (terpenes) as their active ingredients. At high concentrations, these terpenes are generally effective for repelling clothes moths, but may not effectively repel adult carpet beetles. Their effectiveness for controlling or repelling clothes moth larvae should be suspect, and they are not considered effective for controlling carpet beetle adults or larvae of carpet beetles. Cedar closets and most cedar chests may have some repellency but are generally ineffective for killing or controlling the various life stages of these pests (especially carpet beetles), primarily because a sufficiently tight seal is rarely maintained. Garment storage in cold vaults is an effective preventive measure and is commonly used for very valuable furs or other especially susceptible garments.

Controlling Existing Infestations

For some types of infested articles and where the use of chemical insecticides is not allowed, desirable or preferred, complete control of all stages of these fabric pests can be achieved if the article can be sealed tightly in a polyethylene bag, from which as much of the air as possible has been removed (which will serve to prevent condensation within the bag after freezing, and potential water damage to the article), and placed in a deep freezer for three days at −20°F (which most chest freezers are capable of). The entire article must be chilled down to this temperature, so it may take longer than three days to complete this treatment with certain bulky articles. When large, bulky items must be stored in commercial freezers, which typically maintain −5 to 0°F, professionals usually allow at least two weeks. In other cases, vault fumigation may be the chosen method for controlling an infestation on or within specific articles (see also Chapter 20, on fumigation). Of course, neither freezing nor fumigation will leave any effective residual insecticidal protection on the article, but in some cases this can be achieved by application of an inorganic desiccating dust (e.g., Drione® or Tri-Die®) to the article.

When infestations of clothes moths or carpet beetles are encountered, a rather extensive program of insecticide applications, guided by the observations of a thorough inspection, will sometimes be necessary after appropriate sanitation and infestation source reduction have been implemented. Spray or dust applications of residual pyrethroid insecticides, and various nonresidual materials (e.g., synergized pyrethrins or other nonresidual pyrethroids) are recommended for spot treatment or more general applications, as necessary. Desiccating dusts, such as silica aerogel and diatomaceous earth, will be effective against carpet beetle larvae in wall, floor or roof voids. Residual sprays are generally applied with a compressed-air sprayer, using a fine-fan spray nozzle. Some pressurized aerosol formulations are also available.

Critical areas of infestation identified during the inspection process should receive special attention. In carpets, this will typically be around baseboard areas and under furniture. As mentioned previously, roll the carpet back several inches to a foot from its edges wherever possible, and treat the underside of infested areas. In furniture, apply insecticide around seams, buttons, cracks and crevices, and padding areas. Void areas within furniture, such as under seating or seat backs, can be dusted with a residual insecticide. Any of the just-listed insecticides can be used alone, but some are available in prepared or ready-to-use combinations (e.g., a residual material combined with an IGR or a nonresidual insecticide); alternatively, labels on individual materials may permit the professional to prepare a suitable combination spray mixture.

All insecticide sprays should be applied as a fine, wet spray directly to material being treated. Applications to upholstery fabrics should be made lightly, moving rapidly while spraying. Do not apply excessively or "soak" the fabric, because this frequently results in staining. However, when carpets must be treated from above, it is important to apply a sufficient amount of spray to get the insecticide down into the pile where the larval stages are feeding. Since the clothes moth or carpet beetle larvae typically do not feed in exposed conditions, treatment of the top of the carpet pile will be ineffective. Knowing the right application technique and amount of spray liquid to use for maximum effectiveness requires experience. Depending on the length and density of the carpet pile, professionals sometimes use specialized rakes or combs during the application to help allow the spray to penetrate down into the pile more effectively. This may even require the assistance of a second technician to do the raking, while the professional applies the insecticide.

Sprays may be applied as either water-based or oil-based formulations. Water-based sprays are preferable where foam or rubber pads or backing are present behind fabrics, because oil will distort and damage the foam or rubber. With either type of formulation, the professional may first want to apply some of the chemical to a small, inconspicuous portion of the fabric or to some scraps that have been saved by the customer. Check these test spots after two to three days to be certain that dyes in the material are not stained or otherwise affected by the formulation. Keep in mind that foot traffic or sunlight can interact with some chemical residues over a period of time to produce a staining problem that may not be apparent shortly after the initial treatment dries. Many carpet and upholstery manufacturers use dyes that are particularly sensitive to certain insecticides. Check the references cited at the end of this chapter for further details.

Before treating carpets or upholstery, note any stains that are already present and bring them to the attention of the client. When treating carpets, be careful to prevent staining or soiling. If possible, the carpet should be cleaned before insecticide treatment. Where water-based chemicals are used, the carpet can be treated immediately after cleaning, but if an oil-based spray is used, the carpet must be thoroughly dried before being treated. Be very careful not to soil the treated carpet with dirt

from shoes or other sources, and try not to walk on treated areas until after they have thoroughly dried. Use either polyethylene or flannel slip-on shoe covers on your own shoes, such as those often used by window trimmers or by workers in clean rooms of medical facilities or the electronics industry. Some professionals carry a clean pair of shoes often to be used only inside homes.

Whenever possible, it is best to remove all furniture from a room where the carpet is to be treated. This may not be possible because of the size and weight of the furniture involved or the lack of space to put it elsewhere. Furniture can be moved and the carpeting under it treated, after which it can be replaced in its original location. When placing furniture on treated carpet, be sure to place some kind of temporary pad under the casters or skids on the bottom, as well as entirely underneath any other wood or metal articles that may touch the carpet. Failure to do this may result in the formation of rust marks on the carpet from metal parts, or stain marks from the wooden portions of furniture. Both types of stain are almost impossible to remove and can result in costly damage claims. Corrugated cardboard, cut into strips or squares, makes good padding for this purpose; folded paper towels and small paper or aluminum pie plates can also be used. The pads should not be removed until the carpet is thoroughly dry, usually after two or three days. Carpets should be evaluated for the presence of susceptible fibers in the jute or backing, and for the presence of any feeding damage there. Where necessary and appropriate, such carpets should be treated on both sides before being replaced. However, be careful when handling delicate carpets or those with significant damage to the jute or backing, as such handling may result in further serious damage (and liability claims).

Regardless of the insecticide being used, be very careful to tell the homeowner to keep small children and pets away from treated furniture and carpeting until they are thoroughly dry. These chemicals may be hazardous while they are wet. Check the insecticide product label for any other caution statements that may apply to this use.

These residual chemicals will be removed to some extent by subsequent washing, vacuuming, and dry cleaning. The insecticide manufacturer's recommendations about length of control and retreatment intervals should always be observed.

If furniture is infested, it may be necessary to open cushions or to remove the covering from the bottom of sofas or chairs, so that the padding is exposed. Special attention should be given to the padding inside upholstered furniture, which may be composed of feathers or horsehair (especially in antique furniture) and is susceptible to insect damage. Low temperature can be a very effective treatment for cushions, seat covers, curtains, rolled carpets, and other readily portable items that can fit into the freezer. If large commercial deep-freezing chambers are available, whole chairs, sofas and mattresses can be treated in this way. Items that can withstand elevated temperatures (use caution) can be treated in one hour at 60°C (140°F), though again bulky items may require longer so that the insects within will be exposed to that level for at least one hour. Exposed padding can be treated with sprays that will not harm the padding, or it can be thoroughly dusted with a suitable insecticidal dust. Dust applications are generally preferred for this situation, because there will be no drying time required and dusts usually give long residual control. Dusts should not be used where subsequent contact with skin or clothing can be expected, so exposed upholstery surfaces or carpeted areas on which people or pets will sit should not be dusted.

SUPPLEMENTARY READING MATERIAL

Baker, J. E., and R. E. Bry. "Nutritional Ecology of Wool- and Fur-Feeding Insects." In *Nutritional Ecology of Insects, Mites, Spiders and Related Invertebrates*. Ed. F. Slansky Jr. and J. G. Rodriquez. New York: Wiley, 1987.

Fields, P. G. "The Control of Stored-Product Insects and Mites with Extreme Temperatures." *Journal of Stored Product Research* 28, no. 2 (1992): 89–119.

Griswold, G. A., and W. Greenwold. *Studies on the Biology of Four Common Carpet Beetles*. Cornell University Agricultural Experiment Station, memoir 240. Ithaca, N.Y.: 1941.

Kingsley, H. *Integrated Pest Management for collections*. In Proceedings of 2001—a pest odyssey. London, James and James, 2001. 150 Plateway Press.

Mallis, A. *Handbook of Pest Control*. 6th ed. Cleveland: Franzak & Foster, 1982. 1,101 pp.

McPhee, J. R. *The Mothproofing of Wool*. Watford Herts, England: Merrow,1971. 52 pp.

Osmun, J. V. "Recognition of Insect Damage: Wool, Fur, and Leather." *Pest Control* 23, no. 1 (1955): 11–15.

Pinniger, D. *Insect Pest Management in Museums, Archives, and Historic Houses*. London: Archetype,19942001. 58 pp 115 Plateway Press.

Pinto, L. "The Clothes Moth—Yesterday's Pest Resurges." *Pest Control* 62, no. 3 (1994): 14, 16.

Pinto, L. "Controlling Insects by Freezing." *Pest Control* 63, no. 5 (1995): 13.

Pinto, L. "Getting Rid of a Severe Carpet Beetle Infestation." *Pest Control* 62, no. 7 (1994): 10, 76.

Pinto, L. "Winning the Battle against Carpet Beetles." *Pest Control* 62, no. 6 (1994): 8.

Waterhouse, D. F. "Wool Digestion and Mothproofing." *Advances in Pest Control Research* 2 (1958): 207–62.

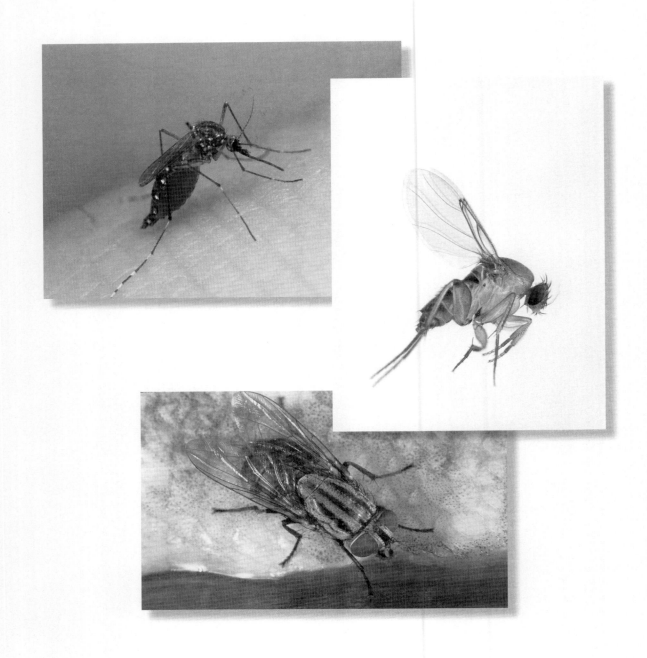

CHAPTER 14

Flies and Mosquitoes

Flies and mosquitoes belong to the order Diptera (*di* means "two," and *pteron* means "wing"). Winged members of this order have one pair of functional wings, with the hind pair being reduced to a pair of knobbed balancing organs called halteres. A few members of the order are wingless. The adult does not possess mandibles; instead, the mouthparts are modified into a proboscis for sponging, sucking, or piercing and sucking. Some larvae are legless and dirty white in color, with heads that are often reduced or indistinguishable and retracted into the thorax. Many are commonly called maggots. Others such as aquatic mosquito larvae, have distinguishable head capsules.

FLIES

Flies of many kinds have affected humans and human welfare for thousands of years. Some flies suck blood; others are scavengers. Many transmit disease organisms, some are pests of cultivated plants, some live at the expense of other insects, and others aid in the pollination of plants.

Flies of importance to urban pest managers fall into several groups. The family Muscidae includes the house fly and its relatives; the members of the family Sarcophagidae are flesh flies; the family Calliphoridae is made up of the bottle flies and blow flies. Other families of importance are Simuliidae, black flies; Psychodidae, filter flies, or moth flies; Tabanidae, horse flies and deer flies; and Drosophilidae, vinegar flies.

All flies have a complete metamorphosis, with egg, larval, pupal, and adult stages. Larvae feed differently and occupy different habitats than adults. The pupae are usually quiescent and often enclosed in a heavy pupal skin or puparium. Once the adult female has emerged and mated, she selects the larval habitat and deposits her eggs. The habitat

Medical Importance of Filth Flies

Filth (domestic) flies have evolved to live in close association with humans. They are typically found around and within structures and can become extremely annoying by their constant presence. More importantly, flies are identified with the disease-causing organisms of typhoid, paratyphoid, cholera, bacillary dysentery, infantile diarrhea, pinworm, roundworm, whipworm, hookworm, and tapeworm. These flies have filthy habits that make them efficient mechanical vectors of disease. Pathogenic organisms are picked up by flies from garbage, sewage, and other sources of filth and then transferred on their mouthparts, other body parts, vomitus, or feces, to human and animal food.

selected is species dependent and may also differ seasonally, geographically, and with regard to types of habitats available. The length of the life cycle is both species and environmentally dependent.

Exact identification of many types of flies can be quite difficult. Adults of many of the species important to the pest management professional can be identified by the use of the pictorial keys in the text (see Figures 14.1, 14.2, and 14.3). Figure 14.4 can be used to identify the larvae of some of the common flies.

Table 14.1 presents important summary information on the domestic flies.

The House Fly and Related Forms
Family Muscidae

Musca domestica Linneaus, the **common house fly**, is a worldwide pest. The adult has the fourth wing vein sharply angled and four lengthwise dark

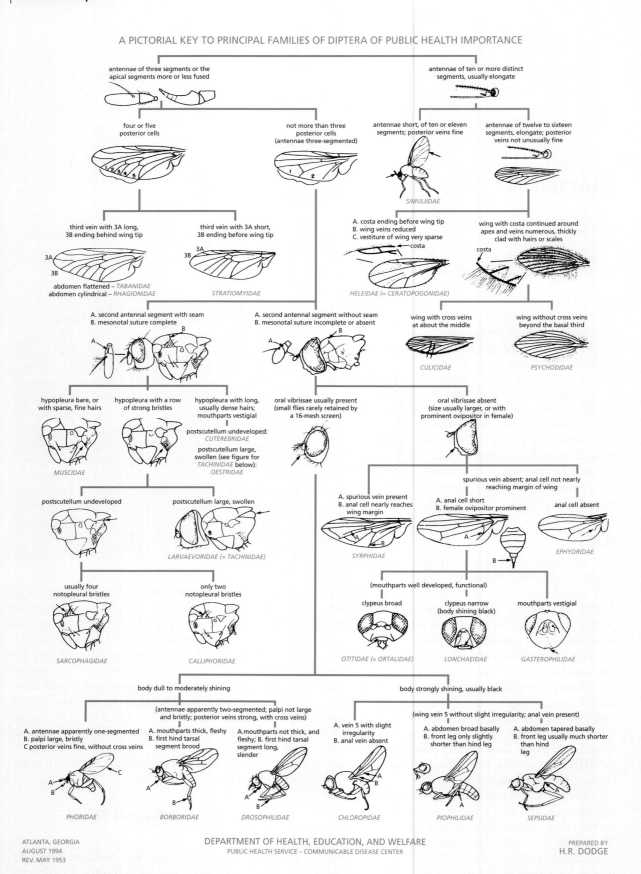

A PICTORIAL KEY TO PRINCIPAL FAMILIES OF DIPTERA OF PUBLIC HEALTH IMPORTANCE

FIGURE 14.1. A pictorial key to principal families of Diptera of public health importance.

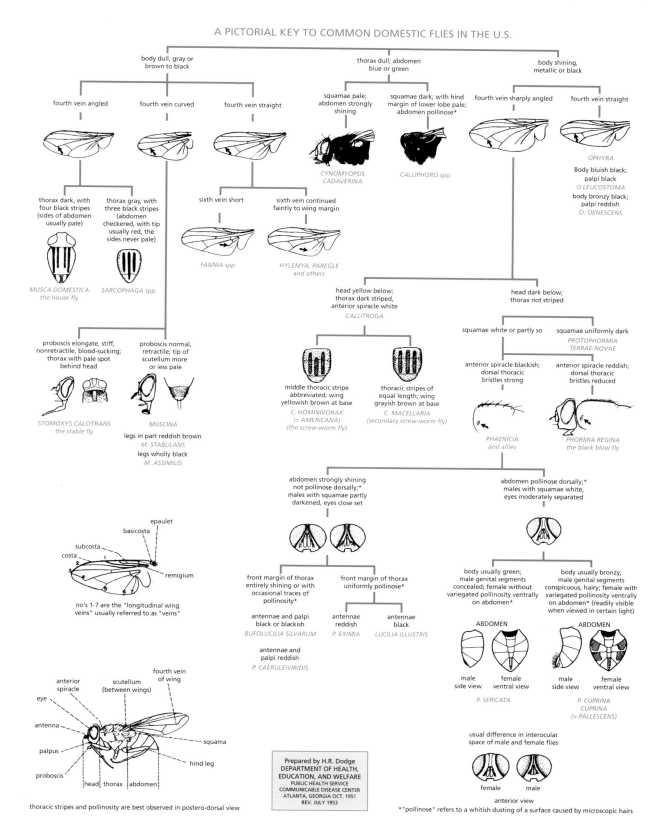

FIGURE 14.2. A pictorial key to common domestic flies in the United States.

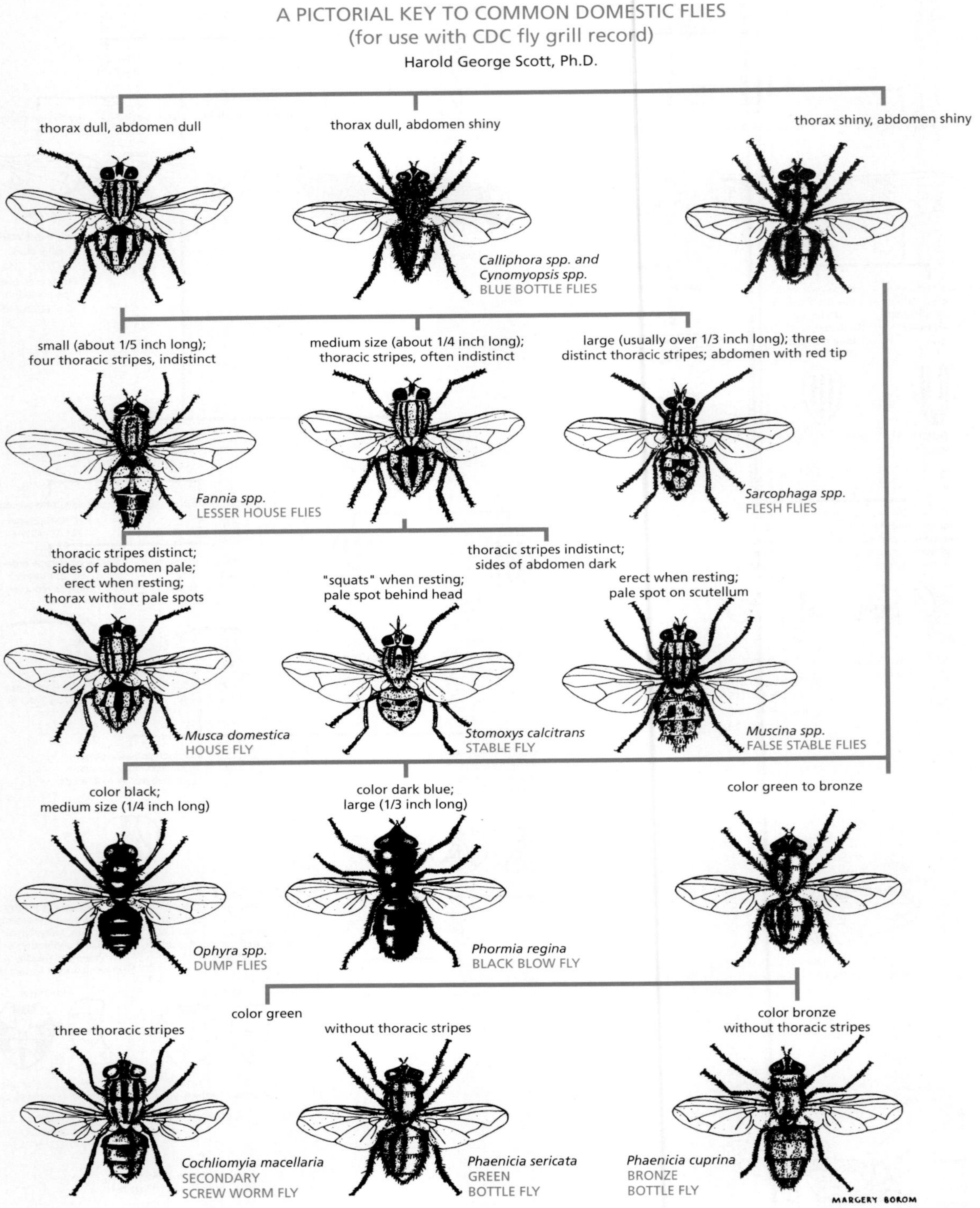

A PICTORIAL KEY TO COMMON DOMESTIC FLIES
(for use with CDC fly grill record)
Harold George Scott, Ph.D.

thorax dull, abdomen dull

thorax dull, abdomen shiny

thorax shiny, abdomen shiny

Calliphora spp. and Cynomyopsis spp.
BLUE BOTTLE FLIES

small (about 1/5 inch long); four thoracic stripes, indistinct

medium size (about 1/4 inch long); thoracic stripes, often indistinct

large (usually over 1/3 inch long); three distinct thoracic stripes; abdomen with red tip

Fannia spp.
LESSER HOUSE FLIES

Sarcophaga spp.
FLESH FLIES

thoracic stripes distinct; sides of abdomen pale; erect when resting; thorax without pale spots

"squats" when resting; pale spot behind head

thoracic stripes indistinct; sides of abdomen dark

erect when resting; pale spot on scutellum

Musca domestica
HOUSE FLY

Stomoxys calcitrans
STABLE FLY

Muscina spp.
FALSE STABLE FLIES

color black; medium size (1/4 inch long)

color dark blue; large (1/3 inch long)

color green to bronze

Ophyra spp.
DUMP FLIES

Phormia regina
BLACK BLOW FLY

color green

three thoracic stripes

without thoracic stripes

color bronze without thoracic stripes

Cochliomyia macellaria
SECONDARY SCREW WORM FLY

Phaenicia sericata
GREEN BOTTLE FLY

Phaenicia cuprina
BRONZE BOTTLE FLY

MARGERY BOROM

FIGURE 14.3. A pictorial key to common domestic flies.

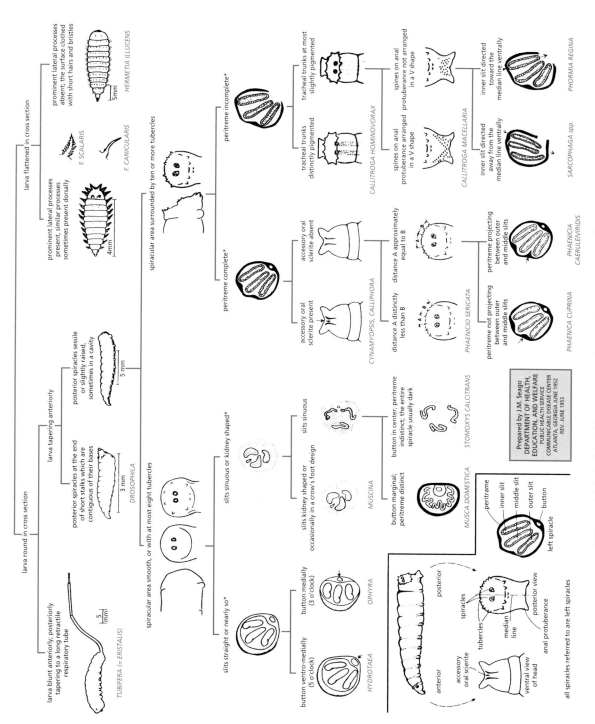

FIGURE 14.4. A pictorial key to mature larvae of some common flies.

stripes on the top of the thorax. Its face has two velvety stripes that are silver above and gold below (see Figures 14.2 and 14.3).

Each adult female (see Figure 14.5, following page 254) begins laying eggs a few days after hatching, laying a total of five to six batches of 75 to 100 small, white, oval eggs. In warm weather these hatch in 12 to 24 hours into cream-colored larvae (see Figure 14.4, and Figure 14.6, which follows page 254) that burrow into the food material on which they hatched. These larvae grow and pupate in four to seven days in warm weather.

The mature larva usually migrates away from its breeding source, seeking a dry place to pupate. It then contracts until its skin forms a case about 1/4-inch long. Inside this case, the true pupa forms. When fully formed, the adult fly breaks open the end of the pupal case and emerges. It is ready to mate within a few hours after emerging. The hardened larval skin that is left behind often exhibits most of the characteristics used in larval identification; thus, determination can in such cases be made on the basis of the skin alone.

During warm weather two or more generations may be completed in a month. Normally the population builds up and is greatest in the early fall months. The method of overwintering is not well understood, but in some areas populations develop indoors throughout the winter.

House fly eggs are laid in almost any warm, moist material that will furnish suitable food for the growing larvae. Animal manure, human excrement, garbage, decaying vegetable material, and ground contaminated with such organic matter are suitable materials.

Although they are attracted to a wide variety of food materials, house flies have mouthparts that enable them to ingest only liquid materials (see Figure 14.7, following page 254). Solid food is liquefied by means of regurgitated saliva. This lique-

TABLE 14.1. Summary of important domestic flies.

Insect	Identifying Characteristics	Preferred Host Material	Adult Occurrence	Life Cycle	Management Methods	
					Chemical	Other
house flies	1/4-inch long; dull gray with 4 stripes on thorax; 4th wing vein sharply angled	Animal waste, garbage, and other decaying organic matter	Most abundant later summer and early fall	7 to 45 days	Residual and contact sprays; baits, traps; larvicides	Sanitation, exclusion, habitat destruction
flesh flies	2 to 3 times larger than house fly; gray and black checkerboard pattern on the abdomen	Garbage, manure, and animal carcasses	Common in warm months	2 to 4 weeks	Residual and contact sprays; larvicides	Sanitation and habitat destruction
blow flies	About twice as large as house fly; metallic blue or green color	Animal carcasses, garbage, and manure	Spring and summer	2 to 4 weeks	Residual and contact sprays; larvicides	Sanitation and habitat destruction
fruit flies	1/8-inch long; yellowish brown; hover around ripe or decaying fruits	Decaying fruits and vegetables; garbage	Most abundant in late summer and early fall	1 to 2 weeks	Residual and contact sprays	Sanitation and habitat destruction
phorid flies	Superficially resemble fruit flies, but are more humpbacked	Decaying vegetation and animal matter	Most abundant in warmer months	1 to 2 weeks	Residual and contact sprays	Sanitation, habitat destruction, and moisture control
moth flies	1/8-inch long; body and wings densely covered with long hairs	Decaying organic matter, especially around drains and sewers	More common in warm months	2 to 3 weeks	Residual and contact sprays	Sanitation, habitat destruction, and moisture control
cluster flies	Superficially resemble house fly but are slightly larger and more sluggish in there movements	Parasitic on earthworms	Abundant in spring and fall	4 to 6 weeks	Residual and contact sprays	Screening and caulking around eaves, windows, etc.

From M. C. Wilson, G. W. Bennett, and A. V. Provonsha, *Practical Insect Pest Management: Insects of Man's Household and Health* (Prospect Heights, Ill.: Waveland Press, 1977).

fied food is then drawn up by the mouthparts and passed into the digestive tract.

During daylight hours house flies will rest on floors, walls, and ceilings indoors. Outdoors they will rest on plants, the ground, fence wires, garbage cans, and other similar surfaces. At night they will rest principally on ceilings, electric wires, and dangling light cords indoors. Outdoors they will rest chiefly on fences, electric wires, edges of buildings, and plants. In all situations they prefer corners and edges or thin objects, such as wires and strings. Night resting places are usually near daytime sources of food and are usually 5 to 15 feet off the ground.

Stomoxys calcitrans (L.), the **stable fly**, can easily be distinguished from the other common domestic flies by the long, pointed proboscis that extends in front of the head (see Figure 14.2, and Figure 14.8, which follows page 254). Both males and females use this proboscis to pierce the skin of a host and suck blood. The bite is painful, and outdoor human activity may be curtailed when these flies are numerous.

Refer to Table 14.2 for a summary of important biting flies that attack humans.

Eggs are laid in such places as decaying hay, straw, fermenting weeds, grass, and seaweeds. Stable flies are commonly found around stables and houses, and also along the seashore and near dog kennels. In these last two areas they are frequently called biting beach flies and dog flies.

Stable fly eggs hatch in one to three days into yellowish white maggots, or larvae (see Figure 14.4, and Figure 14.6, which follows page 254). These larvae pass through three instars and pupate in the last larval skin. In warm weather the pupal stage lasts 6 to 20 days. The average adult lives about 20 days.

TABLE 14.2. Summary of important biting flies that attack humans.

Arthropod Pest	Damaging Stages	Preferred Host(s)	Public Health Importance	Management Methods	
				Chemical	Other
biting midges	Adult midge	Warm-blooded vertebrates	Irritating bites	Residual and contact sprays; repellents	Habitat destruction
eye gnats	Adult gnat	Warm-blooded vertebrates	Irritating skin lesions (do not bite—feed on mucous and sebaceous secretions, pus, and blood)	Residual and contact sprays; repellents	Habitat destruction
horse flies	Adult fly	Domestic animals	Irritating bites	Residual and contact sprays; repellents	Habitat destruction
deer flies	Adult fly	Domestic animals	Irritating bites	Residual and contact sprays; repellents	Habitat destruction
black flies	Adult fly	Domestic animals	Irritating bites	Residual and contact sprays; repellents	Habitat destruction
stable flies	Adult fly	Domestic animals	Irritating bites	Residual and contact sprays; repellents	Habitat destruction
Aedes vexans	Mosquito adult	Warm-blooded vertebrates	Irritating bites	Residual and contact (ULV) sprays; larvicides; repellents	Source reduction
Aedes sollicitans	Mosquito adult	Warm-blooded vertebrates	Irritating bites	Residual and contact (ULV) sprays; larvicides; repellents	Source reduction
Aedes aegypti	Mosquito adult	Humans	Irritating bites; vector of yellow fever and dengue	Residual and contact (ULV) sprays; larvicides; repellents	Source reduction
Anopheles quadrimaculatus	Mosquito adult	Warm-blooded vertebrates	Irritating bites; principal vector of malaria	Residual and contact (ULV) sprays; larvicides; repellents	Source reduction
Culex pipiens complex	Mosquito adult	Warm-blooded vertebrates	Irritating bites; vector of encephalitis	Residual and contact (ULV) sprays; larvicides; repellents	Source reduction

From M. C. Wilson, G. W. Bennett, and A. V. Provonsha, *Practical Insect Pest Management: Insects of Man's Household and Health* (Prospect Heights, Ill.: Waveland Press, 1977).

The false stable flies, *Muscina* spp., and dump flies, *Ophyra* spp. (see Figures 14.2 and 14.3), may also be problems in certain areas. They are nonbiting flies.

Musca autumnalis (DeGeer), the **face fly**, is a pest that may be encountered by pest management specialists in many areas in the northeastern and central portions of the United States.

The face fly is similar in appearance to the common house fly but is somewhat larger and darker in color. Males can be separated easily by the fact that the eyes nearly touch on the top of the head, while those of the house fly do not. The females of the two species are somewhat more difficult to separate. Both male and female flies of the genus *Musca* have a narrow band of very small hairlike pile on each side of the face, so that the front appears to be bordered by two delicate, velvety stripes that run from near the top of the head to the lower margin of the face, separating the eyes from the bases of the antennae. In the face fly this velvety stripe has a silvery sheen throughout its entire length, but in the house fly, the upper half is silvery and the lower half grades into a definite yellowish-gold hue. Males commonly congregate on certain types of flowers.

Eggs are laid on fresh undistributed cow manure in pastures during the summer months. The yellowish larvae live in the manure until they are mature and then pupate either in the soil or on the surface of the soil under the manure. Adults feed on mucous and watery secretions around the eyes and nostrils of horses and cattle, causing great annoyance to the animals.

During the fall and winter months, adult face flies may hibernate in the walls of buildings, including houses, in the same manner as cluster flies. On warm days these hibernating flies become active and frequently move to the inside of the building in large numbers.

Little House Flies and Latrine Flies
Family Muscidae: *Fannia* spp.

These flies usually appear in the early spring before house flies become numerous. They are smaller than house flies and more slender in appearance. Their fourth wing veins extend directly to the edge of the wings instead of curving sharply upward, as in house flies (see Figure 14.2). Eggs are laid in animal excrement, decaying vegetation, and sometimes in vats in cheese plants.

The **little house fly**, *Fannia canicularis* (L.), is frequently seen hovering in midair or darting about in the middle of a room (see Figure 14.9, following page 254). It differs from the house fly in that it is found throughout the house and very seldom on a spread table. This species lays its eggs on decaying vegetable matter and excrement, particularly that of chickens, humans, horses, and cows. The larvae emerge in about 24 hours and may be recognized as flattened, spiny organism, about 1/4-inch long when full grown (see Figure 14.10, following page 254). The pupal period lasts about seven days under favorable conditions. The complete life cycle requires 15 to 30 days.

Fannia scalaris (F.), the **latrine fly**, is similar to the little house fly, but the latrine fly adult is slightly larger. Its biology and habits are also much the same.

Flesh Flies
Family Sarcophagidae

Flesh flies are often very numerous in populated areas but seldom enter houses or food-handling establishments in significant numbers. Females of many species lay living larvae on meat scraps or on dog excrement. Adult flies are frequently annoying outdoors near dog runs.

Flesh flies are larger than house flies (up to two or three times larger) and are grayish in color. Adult flesh flies have a familiar gray and black checkerboard pattern on their abdomen (see Figure 14.3, and Figure 14.11, which follows page 254).

Bottle Flies and Blow Flies
Family Calliphoridae

These flies are common in populated areas and are particularly abundant near such places as slaughterhouses, meat-processing plants, and garbage dumps. Flies of this family have feeding habits and mouthparts similar to those of the house fly and are mechanical carriers of disease organisms. Adults are usually large flies with a metallic blue or green color (see Figures 14.2 and 14.3). Eggs are usually laid on meat or dead animals, although they may be placed in decaying vegetable materials when meat is not available. They are frequently found in meat scraps or wastes contained in garbage. Garbage cans are the most important sources of bottle flies and blow flies in urban areas. Single cans have produced more than 30,000 flies in a week. Newly hatched larvae feed for a short time on the surface of the decaying material on which the eggs were laid and then burrow into the less decayed material underneath. When mature, the larvae leave the food materials, burrow into the ground, and pupate.

Blue bottle flies belong to the genera *Cynomyopsis* and *Calliphora* (see Figures 14.2 and 14.3). These flies require 15 or more days to develop from egg to adult. They are common in homes and other buildings in cool weather, especially if suitable breeding materials are present. They are attracted to dead animals, meat, and decaying vegetable matter.

The most common **green** and **bronze bottle flies** belong to the genera *Phaenicia*, *Lucilia*, and *Bufolucilia*, although there are several other less common genera (see Figures 14.2 and 14.3). Green bottle flies are frequently the most numerous members of the family Calliphoridae found throughout the United States. Most commonly found around humans are the bronze bottle fly, *Phaenicia sericata* (Meigen), and the green bottle flies, *Phaenicia pallescens* (Shannon), and *Phaenicia caeruleiviridis* (McQuart).

These flies have a relatively short life cycle. They develop from egg to adult in only 9 to 21 days. Eggs are laid on decomposing animal material or on mixtures of animal and vegetable debris. Larvae feed on this material for 2 to 10 days and then burrow into the ground to pupate. These flies normally overwinter in the soil as full-grown larvae.

Phormia regina (Meigen), the **black blow fly**, is common throughout the United States (see Figure 14.3). It is most abundant during the warm spring months but is frequently seen on warm days during the winter. Adults are a dark, metallic green color (see Figure 14.12, following page 254). Eggs are laid in meat or garbage or at the necrotic edges of open wounds in living animals. The life cycle requires 10 to 23 days from egg to adult.

Pollenia rudis (F.), the **cluster fly**, is common in all of the United States, except those states that border the Gulf of Mexico. It is so named because of its habit of forming compact clusters of hibernating individuals, usually in upper rooms, attics, or window frames. Adults are frequently mistaken for house flies, although they are somewhat larger and darker (see Figure 14.13, and Figure 14.14, which follows page 254).Unlike house flies, cluster flies fold one wing over the other when at rest. They are also much more sluggish in their movement and fly much more slowly. The presence of several curly, yellow hairs on the sides of the thorax separate this species from any other North American calliphorid.

Eggs are deposited at random in cracks in the ground. Newly hatched larvae enter the bodies of certain earthworms, where they develop for 11 to 14 days. When mature, they leave the body of the earthworm and pupate in the ground.

In the fall, adults congregate in the voids of houses, particularly in the walls. They can enter through any number of small openings. Therefore good screens are often of little value in excluding them. On warm days during the winter, or the beginning of spring, they leave these voids in large

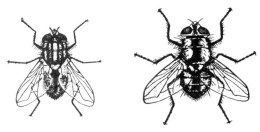

FIGURE 14.13. Comparison of the house fly (left) and the cluster fly. Note the four longitudinal stripes on the thorax of the house fly. The cluster fly is slightly larger and has golden hairs on the thorax. (Provonsha)

numbers and are frequently trapped inside the building. They will also frequently be found outside buildings on warm sunny days, particularly on the south and east walls, which have been warmed by the sun most of the day. They are of no particular harm but are a nuisance because of their great numbers. Mixed infestations of cluster flies and face flies are not uncommon.

MISCELLANEOUS FLIES
Vinegar Flies
Family Drosophilidae

These common flies are also called **fruit** and **pomace flies**. They are widely distributed over the world. The most common species the pest management professional will encounter is *Drosophila melanogaster* Meigen. These insects are of concern both as nuisance pests and as contaminators of food. Large populations can build up quickly in food service establishments. Food processing plants, such as wineries, pickle plants, and canneries, consider Drosophila to be their most important pest.

Drosophila adults of this fly are about 1/8-inch long. Their eyes are red, the thorax is tan, and the abdomen is black on top and gray underneath (see Figures 14.1 and 14.15, and Figure 14.16, which follows page 254).

Eggs are laid near the surface of fermenting materials, such as fruit, dirty garbage containers,

FIGURE 14.15. A fruit fly. (Provonsha)

rotten vegetables, or slime in drains. Minute larvae hatch from the eggs in about 30 hours and feed near the surface of the fermenting mass on which the eggs were laid (see Figure 14.4). When mature, the larvae move to a drier area and pupate.

Each adult female lays approximately 500 eggs. Because these flies require a period of only 9 to 12 days to develop from egg to adult, their reproductive potential is tremendous. Very large numbers of them may appear in a short time.

Adult flies are strong fliers. They have been known to travel as far as 6-1/2 miles within a 24-hour period. Populations tend to build during the summer, becoming very abundant at harvest time. Indoors, *Drosophila* are frequently active at all times of the year. They are readily attracted to any number of materials, including ripened fruit and vegetables, fermenting products, empty bottles and cans, drains and garbage disposal areas, and any area where moisture has collected, including mops and cleaning rags.

Phorid Flies
Family Phoridae

The phorids, also known as **humpbacked flies**, are small to minute flies that superficially resemble *Drosophila* flies (see Figures 14.1 and 14.17, and Figure 14.18, which follows page 254). The adults are fairly common in many habitats but are most abundant around decaying plant and animal matter. Those of importance in structures can be found breeding wherever moisture exists, such as around plumbing and drains in bathroom and kitchen areas, garbage containers, crawlspaces, and basements. These breeding areas are occasionally difficult to locate.

Adults can be found flying about in most areas of the house. They are active even through the winter months, although they are most abundant in the warmer months of the year.

Cheese or Ham Skipper
Piophila casei (L.)

Larvae of this fly are important pests of cheese and meat. Eggs are laid on the surface of overripe or moldy cheese or on meat that is slightly putrid. The small larvae tend to gather together and feed in one place. They can move about by peristaltic movements of the body, as do other fly larvae. They also make sudden, snapping body movements, which may cause them to jump or "skip" as much as 10 inches—thus the common name *skipper*. When mature, larvae leave the food material and seek a dark, dry place to pupate.

Adults are black with bronze tints on the thorax (see Figures 14.1 and 14.19, and Figure 14.20, which follows page 254). The eyes are reddish brown, and the slightly iridescent wings are held flat over the body when at rest. The entire body is about half the size of that of the common house fly.

Deer Flies and Horse Flies
Family Tabanidae

Horse flies and deer flies are pests of domestic and wild animals, and occasionally of humans (see Figures 14.1, and Figures 14.21 and 14.22, which follows page 254). More than 300 species occur in North America. Adults range in size from small deer flies (about 1/4 inch in length) to large horse flies (about 1-1/4 inches in length).

Eggs of most species are deposited in masses on vegetation overhanging water or moist areas. Newly hatched larvae fall to the water or mud where they feed on organic debris or prey on other aquatic life. When ready to pupate, they migrate to drier areas of the soil. The entire life cycle may take up to one to two years or more to complete, depending on the species and environmental conditions.

Only female tabanids feed on blood. They use scissorslike mouthparts to inflict painful bites. Males feed on nectar, honeydew, or other liquids. Tabanids

FIGURE 14.17. A phorid, or humpbacked fly. (Provonsha)

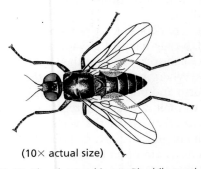

(10× actual size)

FIGURE 14.19. The cheese skipper, *Piophila casei*. (Provonsha)

are strong, robust fliers and have been implicated in mechanically transmitting tularemia. These flies may be a considerable nuisance in recreational areas.

Black Flies
Family Simuliidae

Flies of this family are also known as buffalo gnats and humpbacked flies. Adults are small insects, from 1/16- to 1/4-inch long. Most species are black, although some are gray or red. The thorax typically is somewhat humped (see Figure 14.1). Females suck blood and cause a painful inflammation where they bite.

Eggs are laid in masses on stones or on vegetation, usually in fast-running water. Larvae live in the water by attaching themselves to solid objects with tiny, suckerlike discs and by tiny hooks at the tip of the abdomen, as well as by spinning a fine thread to attach themselves. When mature, they spin a cocoon (open at one end) in which they pupate. Adults hatch under the water and emerge to feed and to mate.

Their bite is extremely painful. In areas where they are numerous, they are a severe nuisance, often making recreational areas useless in late spring and early summer.

Moth Flies
Family Psychodidae

Moth flies are also known as **drain flies**, **filter flies**, and **sewage flies**. In homes, adults are found on the walls of the bathroom, kitchen, or basement. These flies do not bite and are of little economic importance. Even those that breed in sewage apparently do not transmit human disease.

Adults are about 1/16-inch long, with a light gray or tan body and lighter-colored wings. Both the body and the wings are densely covered with long hairs that give the body a fuzzy appearance—hence the name *moth fly* (see Figures 14.1 and 14.23, and Figure 14.24, which follows page 254). When at rest, the wings are folded over the body in a characteristic rooflike manner.

Eggs are laid in irregular masses in the stones of sewage plant filters, dirty garbage containers, water traps in plumbing fixtures, built-in sinks and garbage disposal units, and almost anywhere decomposing organic materials are found. Larvae and pupae live in the decomposing film, with breathing tubes extending through the surface. Under favorable circumstances, the flies can go through one generation in as little as one week, although two or three weeks is more typical. Some activity may occur during the winter months in the southern United States.

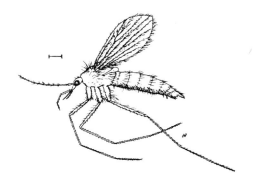

FIGURE 14.23. A moth fly, or drain fly. (Provonsha)

Adults often are found in homes. They may come from a nearby sewage disposal plant or may be breeding within the building. Usually only a few are seen at a time, because old ones die and new ones are continually emerging. They are poor fliers and are commonly seen walking or running on walls and other resting surfaces. When they do fly, their flight covers only a few feet and is in short, jerky lines characteristic of these flies. During the day, the adults rest in shaded areas, walls near plumbing fixtures, or on the sides of tubs and showers. Most of their activity occurs during the evening, when they may be seen hovering about drains and sinks.

Sand Flies, No-See-Ums, Punkies, and Black Gnats
Family Ceratopogonidae

Adults are 1/16- to 1/8-inch long, with bloodsucking mouthparts (see Figures 14.1 and 14.25). Eggs are laid in salt marshes, in mud and plant debris in fresh water, and in damp, rotten holes in trees. Larvae live in the mud or decaying plant material in which they hatch.

These insects inflict severe bites that may take several weeks to heal. In many areas, they force people to stay indoors on days when they are numerous. They constitute a serious economic problem in many summer resort areas and other recreational

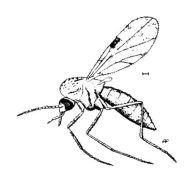

FIGURE 14.25. A biting midge. (Provonsha)

areas. Their bites are so annoying that people cannot enjoy themselves in the presence of these flies.

Hippelates Flies, Eye Gnats
Family Chloropidae

Members of the genus *Hippelates* are very small flies and are called eye gnats because they frequently come to the eyes of the victim, as well as to mucous and sebaceous secretions, pus and blood. *Hippelates* flies approach their mammalian host quietly, usually alighting some distance from the feeding site. They then crawl over the skin or resort to intermittent flying and alighting, thus adding to the annoyance of the host. They are extraordinarily persistent and if brushed away will quickly return to continue engorging themselves. They are nonbiting. However, their mouthparts possess spines capable of producing small skin lesions.

Eye gnats resemble vinegar flies and phorid flies but possess a large frontal triangle, the sclerotized plate on which the ocelli are situated (see Figures 14.1 and 14.26). The larvae develop in a wide variety of materials such as decaying vegetation and animal matter.

Eye gnats can be found infesting just about any urban or industrial area but are more likely to be found in suburban areas bordering woods or fields, especially where livestock are nearby. Eye gnats are very bothersome to livestock and are suspected vectors of diseases such as conjunctivitis, yaws, and bovine mastitis.

Midges
Family Chironomidae

This is a family of minute to moderately large flies. People are frequently alarmed by midges since they superficially resemble mosquitoes (see Figure 14.27, following page 254). However, they differ from mosquitoes in that the wings do not have scales and the mouthparts are short and not adapted for biting. Adult midges are slender, usually less than 1/4-inch long, with long, slender legs and wings.

FIGURE 14.26. An eye gnat. (Provonsha)

Fungus Gnats

The most common species of fungus gnat in and around homes comes from the families Mycetophilidae and Sciaridae. They are small (about 0.1-inch long), mosquito-like flies with threadlike antennae and long, slender legs (see Figure 14.36, following page 254). They may be black, brown, red or yellow as adults, and are found throughout the world. Larvae develop in high organic, moist environments, feed on fungi (thus the common name) and decaying plant matter, and can damage plant roots when prolonged infestation occurs.

Adult gnats are harmless to humans, although they can be a persistent nuisance. They are attracted to light and swarm around windows in homes.

Fungus gnats can be avoided indoors by not overwatering houseplants or allowing moisture to accumulate. Adult gnats can be controlled using household aerosol sprays for flying insects. Yellow sticky cards can be used to attract and trap gnats for monitoring (and control of low-level populations).

Chironomids lay their eggs on water. The larvae are usually aquatic, found in quiet water (such as lakes, ponds, reservoirs, and tanks), and are bottom feeders. Polluted water apparently favors their growth and development. In the summer, eggs will hatch in about three days, and larvae will reach adulthood in about four weeks.

During peak emergence, large numbers of midges fly into residential and industrial areas, causing annoyance and damage. They are attracted to lights at night, and thousands will rest on the outside of buildings and enter homes through the slightest crack. They fly into people's eyes, ears, and mouths and are sometimes inhaled. They contaminate everything.

FLY MANAGEMENT
House Flies, Blow Flies, and Stable Flies

Good sanitation is the basic step in all fly management. Whenever possible, food and materials on which the flies can lay their eggs must be removed, destroyed as a breeding medium, or isolated from the egg-laying adult. Killing adult flies will reduce any infestation, but elimination of breeding areas is necessary for good management. Where flies are a problem in buildings, the owner or occupants may be able to do this work; the pest management professional's job is to seek out the breeding places and advise how the work should be done.

House flies and many flesh flies, bottle flies, and blow flies breed in similar substances, such as decaying organic materials, garbage, animal excrement, or polluted ground. Removal of these from the vicinity of infested premises will frequently make other measures unnecessary. The importance of **twice-weekly garbage removal** does not seem to be a necessity for fly control when the length of the life cycle required by the immature stage is noted in a cursory manner. The important thing to remember here is that the final larval instar leaves the larval food medium and wanders for considerable distances prior to pupation; so, it is the length of time from egg laying to the molt of the last larval instar that is important and that necessitates twice-weekly pickups.

Other considerations in sanitation include regular removal of livestock or pet manures, soiled bedding, straw, and all other decaying plant and animal matter. Garbage cans and dumpsters should have tight-fitting lids and be cleaned regularly. Dry garbage and trash should be placed in plastic garbage bags. Wet garbage should first be wrapped in old newspaper and then put in plastic garbage bags. All garbage receptacles should be located as far from doors as possible.

Any sanitation program in fly management must be tailored to fit each specific situation. Basically, it should include any step that will help to eliminate or prevent the establishment of any medium in which fly larvae will develop or that will be attractive to adult flies. Don't overlook the importance of moisture in fly breeding media. Simple drainage will often aid control. Although it may not always be possible or economically feasible to practice all the sanitary measures that would contribute to fly management, simple and practical sanitation will often make the difference between satisfactory and unsatisfactory fly levels. Sometimes, significant results can be obtained through sanitation alone.

Openings to buildings should be tightly screened with screen having a mesh no larger than 12 to the inch for the larger flies and 18 to the inch for smaller insects. Eighteen-mesh screening is required to exclude mosquitoes, but this reduces the amount of light and air that can pass through. Screen doors should open outward. For extreme infestations, a double set of doors may be of value. It is usually unnecessary to screen above the third story of a building.

Doors that must open for customers, trucks, or passage of freight may permit entry of flies. Where such doors are opened constantly, an air stream (air curtain or door) may be used to prevent fly entry. An air stream must have a velocity of 1,600 feet per minute or more to be effective. Equipment must be designed for each individual installation. Many pest management companies do not get involved in such work, but professionals can help customers in the appropriate selection and use of air-moving equipment. Normally, air is released at the top of the door and moves downward. For best results, air must be released along the entire width of the door.

Fly traps or **flypaper** may also be useful in some management situations. They require a sticky surface and may contain a material attractive to flies. They may trap large numbers of flies but are most effective when used to supplement other management techniques. Their use in spots outside the limits of an area to be protected, however, may be of some value, as they undoubtedly reduce fly populations. Their use is usually limited to areas where aesthetics are not of primary importance.

Electrically charged screens and **light traps** are also available but can be used effectively only in certain areas. They should be used to supplement other management techniques. The number of light traps used in buildings (such as food-handling establishments) and their placement are critical factors in successfully using them in fly management. Thus, directions for installation, placement, and maintenance obtained from the manufacturers should be followed.

Pest management professionals are most frequently called on to control adult flies. Where breeding areas cannot be eliminated or treated, control of adults may be the only practical measure.

Residual insecticide sprays are still generally effective for fly control outdoors, but localized resistant populations may be a problem with some of these insecticides. Adulticides include permethrin and some of the related pyrethroids. These are applied most effectively as coarse, wet sprays to outdoor surfaces on which flies prefer to rest, such as porches, garbage cans, garages, doghouses or kennels, vegetation, and similar areas. Sun-exposed surfaces on outside walls should be given special attention. If picnic tables, benches, chairs, etc., are in the area, cover or remove them before spraying. Pets should be removed from the area before spraying and not allowed to return until the spray is dry.

Insecticide baits kill flies rapidly, but their effectiveness is short lived unless treatments are repeated. Baits are best used to supplement a spray program. Wet baits can be sprayed or sprinkled on fly resting surfaces outside the home. Dry baits can be scattered around garbage cans or placed in garage windows or near other fly resting surfaces. Fly baits can be purchased in ready-to-use forms containing insecticides such as imidacloprid or methomyl (Golden Malrin).

Temporary control of flies can be obtained

indoors by the use of **contact sprays**. These may contain synergized pyrethrins or synthetic pyrethroids, and they should be dispensed as very fine mists or aerosols. These materials give quick knockdown and kill of flies but have no lasting effect. They can be applied with fogging or ULV aerosol equipment. Before making such an application, food, food handling equipment, and utensils should be covered completely to avoid contamination.

Space sprays, **residual sprays**, or **ULV aerosols** may be useful outdoors. Applied over an area as a fog, mist, aerosol, or wet spray, these insecticides may be of value in reducing adult fly populations.

Fly larvae may be controlled in breeding media by the application of insecticides to the media. This method should be considered only when sanitation cannot do the job, since beneficial predators and parasites are often susceptible to common larvicides. Fly populations may increase when the insecticide has lost its residue, and natural control organisms do not return as rapidly as do the flies.

Face Flies and Cluster Flies

Both these flies frequently hibernate in the walls of buildings and emerge in the spring or on warm days during the winter. Killing the flies indoors with sprays does not give satisfactory control, because new flies constantly emerge from the wall voids. Effective treatment requires the introduction of insecticide into the wall voids. All openings through which the flies are entering the building must be located and treated. These are usually openings around window pulleys, window and door casings, under baseboards, or between the tops of wall studs.

In light infestations and where the openings are sufficiently large, aerosols of any of the space sprays listed for house fly control can be injected into the wall as contact sprays and will give effective control. On most jobs, however, openings into the wall are small and require very careful application of **dust formulations** for complete control. Hand dusters or small power dusters can be used effectively. A thorough dust application will not only kill those flies moving about inside the wall but also leave a long-lasting residual to kill flies that become active later. Where openings are few and too small even for dust applications, insecticides with good vapor toxicity can be injected into the walls.

Residual sprays of labeled insecticides can be used in attics, basements, closets, storerooms, or other areas where the flies are frequently seen. Do not apply heavy sprays in bedrooms or in papered or other well-furnished rooms.

In the fall, spraying outside the structure, especially in areas beneath the eaves and around windows, is helpful. Application of an appropriately labeled pyrethroid in August or early September has prevented cluster fly problems the following spring in some cases. The key is to have the insecticide residue on the outside surface of the building when the flies are attracted to these warm surfaces. Tall buildings may require specialized equipment, such as scaffolding, to effectively treat higher surfaces. Sealing cracks and other openings through which the flies can enter from the outside may also have merit as a preventive measure.

To kill adult flies that buzz about rooms (when the client simply does not want to wait the time it takes for a residual spray to work), use an aerosol containing synergized pyrethrins. This type of treatment provides immediate knockdown and kill but provides no residual action against flies that may emerge from hiding later. For best results, the room should be closed to reduce air circulation in the treated area.

Cheese or Ham Skipper

Openings into storage rooms for cheese or meat should be tightly screened with screen having no less than 30 mesh to the inch. Sanitation is most important in the control of this pest. All surfaces in storage areas should be thoroughly cleaned to remove all meat or cheese scraps, crumbs, or grease. Space sprays of synergized pyrethrins can be used to control adult flies, but they should be used according to label directions to avoid contamination of food products.

Moth Flies, Vinegar Flies, and Phorid Flies

Sanitation and habitat elimination are the keys to managing this group of flies. Damp organic matter in and around drains, sinks, bathing areas, mop closets, washing machines, potted plants, and so forth needs to be cleaned up, since it serves as a breeding source for these flies. In many instances, locating the source of the infestation may be difficult, since the flies can be well concealed in and around plumbing or just about any area where moisture may collect. Keep in mind that there are often numerous breeding sources in infested areas. When the source cannot be found, the use of residual sprays and space sprays (see the house fly control discussion) can be used to control the adults, but repeat applications will be necessary as long as the breeding source remains.

The management of moth flies breeding in sewage plant filters requires special attention, since the use of insecticides in these areas is not approved. The techniques include keeping weeds and grass mowed around the sewage plant so that adults will be forced to rest on surfaces such as walls, where residual sprays can be used. The flies will not be completely eliminated by these procedures, but there should be few adults present. Some larvae will still be present in the filter beds, which is desirable since they play an important role in the efficient operation of the filter. In homes, breeding sites in sinks and floor drains can often be eliminated by means of caustic drain cleaners available for home use.

For the management of vinegar and fruit flies, elimination of the attractants and breeding areas is very important. In addition, exclusion of adults with 16-mesh screens is also helpful, as are air currents in food processing and handling establishments (see the house fly management section for a discussion of the use of air currents).

Midges

Chironomid midges are rarely a problem in a well-balanced aquatic community. Pollution of water, where algae growth provides food for midge larvae to feed on, results in excessive midge populations. Certain insecticides can be applied to the water to kill midge larvae, but if the food supply that supports midge outbreaks is not removed, the source of the problem remains. Midges have been managed in small bodies of water by stocking the water with carp and goldfish at the rate of 150 to 500 pounds per acre of water surface.

When water management techniques are not practical and the treatment of larval breeding waters isn't feasible, fogging for adult flies may provide temporary relief. However, fogging provides limited results unless the entire residential area is treated. Synergized pyrethrins are an example of insecticides that have been used to control adult midges.

Midge invasions may also be abated by avoiding the use of outdoor lighting to the greatest possible extent, especially during early evening hours. For those midges that are still able to find their way indoors, the residual and space treatments described for the house fly will provide some degree of relief.

All of the methods briefly mentioned here are more fully discussed in the mosquito management section of this chapter.

MOSQUITOES
Order Diptera
Family Culicidae; Subfamily Culicinae

Mosquitoes are found from the tropics to the arctic regions. They are the only known means of transmission of the causal agents of malaria, yellow fever,

some types of encephalitis, dengue, and filariasis. All of these diseases, with the exception of filariasis, have been common in the United States in the past. Extensive control measures by public health officials have virtually eliminated all but encephalitis as a problem. Mosquitoes are also severe pests because of their annoyance to people, and many good recreational areas are not usable during certain periods of the year because of mosquitoes.

Mosquitoes can be distinguished easily from other flies by the fact that they have both a long, piercing proboscis and scales on the hind margin and veins of their wings.

Approximately 150 species of mosquitoes belonging to 12 genera are found in the United States. Only a few of these are of importance as carriers of disease organisms, but many more are important as nuisances.

Mosquitoes undergo complete metamorphosis. Eggs are laid, either singly or in bunches, on a water surface or in a place where they will become wet when flooding occurs.

Mosquito larvae and pupae live in water. Various species have become adapted to living in practically all kinds of water except fast-flowing streams and the open portions of large bodies of water, where there is considerable wave action. The choice of type of water for larvae is generally quite specific, and the discussion of individual mosquitoes in this chapter will be by type of water habitat.

Mosquito larvae live in water, but they must either surface for air or obtain it from the underwater portions of plants. Larvae have a well-defined head, thorax, and abdomen. Most species move about actively in the water and come to the surface frequently to breathe. They assume characteristic positions when at the surface of the water. Anopheline larvae lie parallel to the surface, while most other groups hang head down, with the tip of the air tube extending to the water surface.

Larvae go through four instars, usually in a period of 4 to 10 days, to form pupae. The pupa lives in water and, like the larva, is quite active (see Figure 14.28). The pupal head and thorax are greatly enlarged and enclosed in a sheath, and a pair of respiratory tubes project from the sheath's upper surface. Most species are lighter than water, so that when they are not actively swimming, they rise to the surface where the respiratory tubes contact the open air for breathing. The pupal stage lasts from a day to as long as a few weeks. When ready to hatch, the pupa rises to the surface, and the pupal skin breaks. The adult works its way out of the pupal skin and uses the skin for support until the body wall has hardened enough for the adult to be capable of flight. Males usually emerge first and wait near the

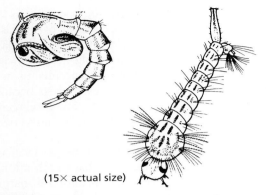

(15× actual size)

FIGURE 14.28. The pupal and larval stages of a mosquito, genus *Culex*. (Provonsha)

hatching point to mate with the females soon after they emerge. Most female mosquitoes must have a blood meal before they can lay fertile eggs. The adult female is the only stage that feeds on blood. The mouthparts of the adult male are not suitable for blood sucking. Therefore, their nourishment is normally derived from nectar and plant juices.

Identification

Reference to Figures 14.29 and 14.30 will enable the pest management professional to identify the common genera and species of mosquitoes of the United States. Because these keys are based on female mosquitoes, it is necessary to be able to distinguish males from females. This can easily be done by examining at the antennae; male antennae are bushy, while female antennae are not.

Every pest management professional who conducts mosquito control operations should obtain a copy of *Identification Keys for Common Mosquitoes of the United States*, which is listed in the selected references at the end of this chapter. Anyone interested in serious study of this group should have access to the publications of Horsfall and of Carpenter and LaCasse. Species determination of mosquitoes is rather difficult, and the professional should have all determinations checked by a qualified expert. This is true for larval identification as well, since management efforts must frequently be directed at this stage of the mosquito.

Floodwater and Rainpool Mosquitoes

Table 14.3 summarizes biological information on some of the important mosquito species found in North America.

Some mosquitoes of the genus *Aedes* (see Figure 14.31, following page 254) and all of the genus Psorophora lay their eggs on the ground or above the water line in tree holes or other natural cavities and in artificial containers. When the water rises, these eggs become wet and hatch.

Aedes vexans (Meigen) is probably the most widespread member of its genus in the United States. It is a major pest in all of the northern states and only somewhat less abundant in the South. Adults are medium sized, with narrow bands of white scales on the hind tarsi. There is a V-shaped notch at the middle of each band of white scales on the back of the abdomen. Adults may migrate long distances from their hatching site; a distance of 5 to 10 miles is common. Females are vicious biters, especially at dusk and after dark, and are attracted to light. Refer to Table 14.2 for summary information on this species and other important mosquito species that attack humans.

This species breeds in rainpools, floodwater, roadside puddles, hog wallows, or practically any temporary body of fresh water. Eggs are laid on the ground surface and hatch when flooding occurs. Depending on the temperature, the larval and pupal stages may require from 7 to 34 days.

Aedes trivittatus (Coquillet) is generally found in the northern states west of Idaho and has been found in the southern states. The upper surface of the adult thorax has two conspicuous whitish stripes. Larvae occur in flooded pools, generally in woodlands. Young larvae feed at the surface, but as they mature the larvae spend most of their time concealed in vegetation on the bottom. Adults rest on vegetation during the day and will bite if disturbed. They are most active in the evening. This species does not migrate very far from the site of larval development.

Aedes sticticus (Meigen) is a medium-sized species with pale scales on the thorax and speckles of white scales on the legs. It occurs throughout the United States but is most abundant in the northern states. Eggs are laid on the ground, particularly in the valleys of rivers and smaller streams. Eggs do not hatch until they are flooded in the spring. Thus, there is usually only one brood per year. If flooding does not occur, the eggs can lie dormant for two to three years before hatching. Adults are severe biters in the evening or when the weather is cloudy. Females are known to fly as far as 10 miles from the site of larval development.

Psorophora ciliata (Fabricius), sometimes called the gallinipper, is one of our largest mosquitoes. Adults are yellowish brown with shaggy legs. It is common in the eastern states from Mexico to Canada, often being very abundant locally in the South and Midwest. It is a vicious biter both during the day and in the evening.

Eggs are laid on the ground and can withstand drying for long periods of time. When temporary

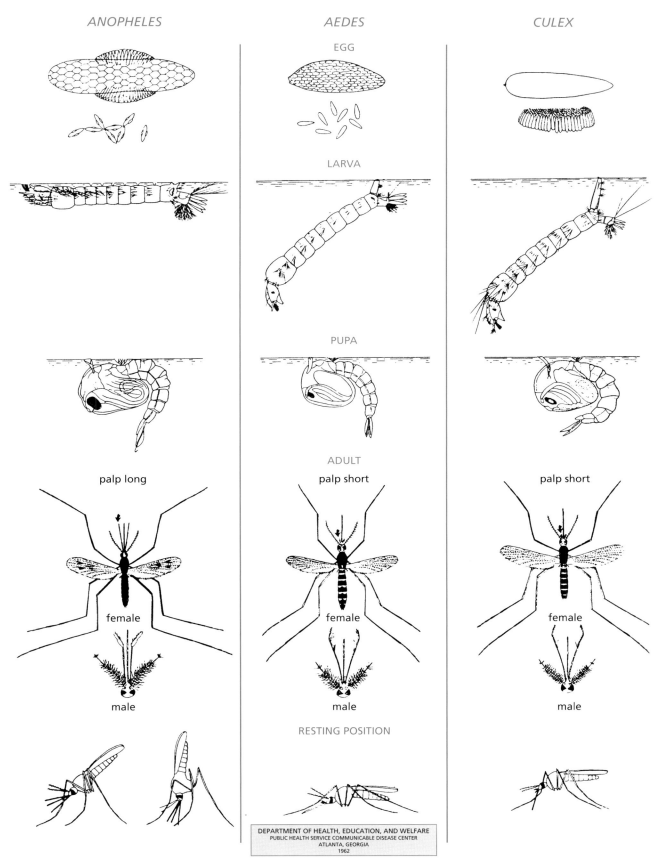

FIGURE 14.29. Characteristics of anophelines, aedes, and culicines.

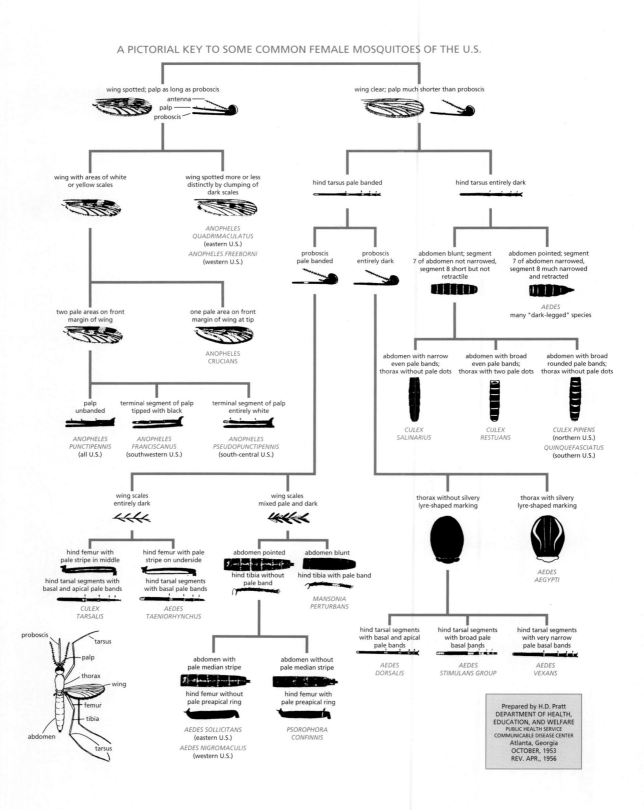

FIGURE 14.30. A pictorial key to some common female mosquitoes of the United States.

TABLE 14.3. Biological data on some important mosquitoes found in North America.

Species	Egg Deposition	Broods/ Year	Overwintering Stage	Preferred Larval Habitat	Range of Effective Flight
Anopheles quadrimaculatus	Singly on water	Many	Adult female	Clean water, partially shaded, some vegetation	1 mile
Anopheles freeborni	Singly on water	Many	Adult female	Clean water, partially shaded, some vegetation	1 to 2 miles +
Culex pipiens complex	Rafts on water	Many	Adult female	Permanent water with organic matter	1 mile +
Culex tarsalis	Rafts on water	Many	Adult female	Almost any collection of water	2 to 10 miles
Mansonia perturbans	Rafts on water	One	Larva	Permanent water with some aquatic vegetation	1 to 5 miles
Aedes aegypti	Singly on sides of containers	Many	Egg	Artificial containers	Less than 1/2 mile
Aedes triseriatus	Singly on sides of containers	Many	Egg	Tree holes, artificial containers	1/2 to 1 mile
Aedes sollicitans	Singly on ground	Many	Egg	Temporary pools, usually brackish water	5 to 20 miles
Aedes taeniorhynchus	Singly on ground	Many	Egg	Temporary pools, usually brackish water	5 to 20 miles
Aedes dorsalis	Singly on ground	Many	Egg	Temporary pools, pastures, etc.	10 to 20 miles
Aedes nigromaculis	Singly on ground	Many	Egg	Temporary pools, pastures, etc.	2 to 5 miles
Aedes vexans	Singly on ground	Many	Egg	Temporary pools	5 to 20 miles
Psorophora ciliata	Singly on ground	Many	Egg	Temporary pools, rice fields	5 miles +
Psorophora confinnis	Singly on ground	Many	Egg	Temporary pools	5 miles +
Culiseta melanura	Rafts on water	Many	Adult female and larva	Permanently shaded pools in swamps	100 to 1,000 yards

From M. C. Wilson, G. W. Bennett, and A. V. Provonsha, *Practical Insect Pest Management: Insects of Man's Household and Health* (Prospect Heights, Ill.: Waveland Press, 1977); acknowledgement is made for information in the table taken in part from H. D. Pratt, R. C. Barnes, and K. S. Littig, *Mosquitoes of Public Health Importance* (Atlanta: U.S. Department of Health, Education, and Welfare, Communicable Disease Center, 1959).

pools appear, the eggs are moistened and hatch. Growing larvae feed on the larvae of other mosquitoes that may be present in the water. They may emerge as adults in as little as five days after hatching.

Psorophora howardii (Coquillet) has habits very similar to those of *P. ciliata*. It is common in the western states.

Psorophora confinnis (Linch-Arribalzaga) is a medium- to large-sized, dark-colored mosquito with a narrow ring of white scales near the apex of the femur of the hind leg. In Florida it is called the glades mosquito, and in Arkansas and other rice-producing areas it is called the dark rice field mosquito. This is the most widespread mosquito of this genus in the United States. It is found in all of the southern states as far west as southern California

and as far north as Nebraska, New York, and Massachusetts. Adult females are fierce biters at any time of the day or night.

Eggs are laid on ground that is subject to flooding, and they hatch in four or five days when submerged. The eggs will hatch whenever they are wet and do not require a winter dormant period. Thus, this species may have several generations each year. Larval development may be completed in as little as four days. Adult flights are common as far as 10 miles from the hatching site.

Salt-Marsh Mosquitoes

Mosquitoes of this group lay their eggs on the ground, as do the floodwater and rainpool mosquitoes. The eggs are laid only in areas where they will be wetted by salt or brackish water.

Aedes sollicitans (Walker), the salt-marsh mosquito, is the most important species of this group. In areas where it is prevalent, it is one of the most important pest mosquitoes known. It is found commonly along the Gulf and Atlantic coastal plains from Maine to Texas and has been found in brackish waters in several inland areas.

The upper side of the thorax in adults is a golden color with a longitudinal whitish stripe on the abdomen. Both the proboscis and the tarsi have pale bands running around them. Adults are strong fliers, commonly found 10 miles from hatching sites and occasionally at much greater distances. Migrating flights usually begin just before dark. Adults rest on marsh grasses during the day and will readily attack anything disturbing them, even in bright sunlight. The abundance of this mosquito has severely restricted development of many coastal areas.

Eggs are laid on mud in marshes, where they lie dormant until covered by high tide. Eggs must remain dry for 24 hours before they will hatch, but after drying for one or two weeks, they will hatch in a few minutes when wet. Breeding is continuous during warm months, and thus many generations a year can be produced in the southern states.

The black salt-marsh mosquito, *Aedes taeniorhynchus* (Wiedeman), is found along the entire Atlantic coast and along the coast in California. It is a small, black-and-white mosquito, with white cross bands on the back of the abdomen and white rings on the proboscis and tarsi. It is a fierce daytime biter, and large migratory flights are well documented. It produces a number of monthly broods throughout the summer.

Permanent Water Mosquitoes

Some mosquitoes lay their eggs in permanent bodies of water, such as ponds and lakes. They lay their eggs in protected locations near the shore or in shallow water. Mosquitoes of the genera *Anopheles*, *Mansonia*, and *Culex* belong to this group.

Females of the genus *Anopheles* lay eggs singly on the surface of the water, and each egg has a float on each side. Eggs are usually laid in fresh water in which aquatic plants are growing, and egg laying is continuous during the warm portions of the year. The usual hatching time is one to three days.

Adult anophelines are usually active only at night, spending the day in protected, damp, dark resting places. They will also bite just before daylight. Adults have a limited flying range, usually being found within one mile of the hatching site.

Anopheles quadrimaculatus Say, the common

malaria mosquito, is found in the eastern and southern states west to the Dakotas, central Nebraska, Kansas, Oklahoma, and Texas. It breeds chiefly in permanent water pools and is abundant in shallow water. The larval and pupal stages may require as little as 8 to 14 days to develop under favorable conditions. Mating takes place soon after the adults emerge, and egg laying is continuous during warm months.

Anopheles freeborni Aitken, the western malaria mosquito, is similar to *A. quadrimaculatus* in appearance and habits. It is the most important malaria mosquito in the western states and is found as far east as Colorado, New Mexico, and western Texas.

Anopheles punctipennis (Say) is the most widely distributed anopheline mosquito in the United States. This species is found in almost every state. Adults have wings conspicuously marked with spots of both pale and dark scales. It is not a carrier of malaria. In addition to breeding in permanent ponds, this species also breeds in such places as rain barrels, grassy bogs, tree holes, spring pools, swamps, and along the margins of streams. This species is usually the first anopheline to appear in the spring.

Mansonia perturbans (Walker) is a large mosquito that breeds in permanent ponds containing a thick growth of water plants. This mosquito has recently been found naturally infected with the virus of eastern equine encephalitis, or sleeping sickness. Adults are speckled brown, with a pale band around the outer third of the tibia of the hind pair of legs.

Eggs are laid in rafts on the surface of the water. Upon hatching, the larvae go below the surface and insert their air tubes into the stems or roots of aquatic plants and obtain air from the plants. Both the larval and pupal stages obtain air in this manner, and the pupae do not rise to the surface until ready to emerge. Larval development requires several months, so there is usually only one generation each year. Adults emerge in late spring or early summer and may fly as far as 10 miles from the site of larval development.

Culex salinarius Coquillet is common throughout the eastern United States and is most common along the Atlantic and Gulf coasts. It breeds in both fresh and brackish water in marshes, ponds, and ditches, and along lake margins. It may fly as far as eight miles from the site of development.

Culex restuans Theobald is found in all states east of the Rocky Mountains. This species usually breeds in foul water containing decaying vegetation. Rain barrels, tin cans, woodland pools, and ditches are common breeding areas. It may be found as far as three miles from the site of development.

Culex tarsalis Coquillet, the encephalitis mosquito, is widely distributed west of the Mississippi River and is found occasionally farther east. This mosquito is a principal carrier of the viruses of both St. Louis encephalitis and western equine encephalitis. The virus is obtained when mosquitoes feed on infected birds, and it is then transmitted to other birds, horses, and humans. Adults are medium sized and dark, with a broad white band around the middle of the proboscis and white bands at each end of the tarsi.

Egg laying takes place in a wide variety of water situations, such as canals, ditches, ground pools, hoofprints, effluent from cesspools, cans, barrels, catch basins, and ornamental ponds. Eggs are deposited in rafts that hatch within two days. Larval and pupal stages develop rapidly, and breeding takes place continuously during warm weather. Adults are usually found within one mile of the hatching site.

Mosquitoes of Natural Cavities and Artificial Containers

Mosquitoes of this group lay their eggs in water entrapped in such places as tree holes, tin cans, rain barrels, roof guttering, and catch basins.

Culex pipiens pipiens Linnaeus, the northern house mosquito, is found throughout the northern United States and as far south as Georgia and Oklahoma. *Culex pipiens quinquefasciatus* Say, the southern house mosquito, occurs in all of the southern states from coast to coast and as far north as Nebraska, Iowa, Illinois, and Ohio. One or both of these subspecies is probably found in every state. These mosquitoes are found in towns, as well as in rural areas. They commonly enter houses and are severe biters. Both species can carry the virus of St. Louis encephalitis. Adults of both species are medium sized and brown, with cross bands of white scales on the abdominal segments.

Eggs are laid in clusters or rafts of 200 to 400 on the surface of water. These hatch in one to two days. The larval and pupal stages together may require as little as 8 to 10 days before hatching into adults. Breeding is continuous during warm weather. The larvae of this mosquito can also be found in open water.

Aedes triseriatus (Say) is the most common tree hole mosquito in the eastern United States and occurs as far west as Montana, Idaho, and Texas. The larvae are also found in rain barrels and other artificial containers. Adults are blue-black with silvery white scales on the side of the thorax. This mosquito is frequently troublesome in wooded areas. Adults are not usually found very far from their breeding sites. This species is a LaCrosse fever vector.

Aedes aegypti (Linnaeus), the yellow fever mosquito, is a pest mosquito in many parts of the world. This mosquito has been widely distributed among the seaports of the world, because wooden casks that were widely used on sailing vessels provided suitable sites for larval development. It is a fairly common mosquito in the Gulf Coast states. In the area in which this mosquito occurred originally, it was a typical tree hole breeder, but in areas in which the species has been introduced, it is more commonly found in small containers (particularly those with wooden walls). It has been known to overwinter in deep cisterns in some areas of the southern United States. Eggs are generally placed on the walls of the container, at the waterline. Larvae normally appear about four days after the eggs are laid, and larval development may be completed in as little as four to eight days under optimum conditions. The duration of the pupal stage ranges from one to five days, and the adult females may live as long as 50 days.

This mosquito may bite at practically any time of day, but the peak feeding activity is generally in the afternoon or early evening. It is the most important arthropod vector of the viruses of yellow fever and dengue, and it is of great medical importance in various tropical areas of the world.

Aedes albopictus is a recently introduced species from Southeast Asia known as the Asian tiger mosquito. It is an aggressive biter that has the potential to transmit numerous diseases, including dengue, yellow fever, LaCrosse encephalitis, and dog heartworm. It occurs east of the Mississippi River in almost every state from the Gulf Coast as far north as Minnesota. This mosquito can be distinguished from the yellow fever mosquito by the white band on the top of the head and down the midline of the thorax, with lighter markings on either side. Its life cycle and habits are similar to those of the yellow fever mosquito. This mosquito has become of special concern because it is readily found breeding in water in discarded tires. Huge piles of old tires are found close to most cities, and most Asian tiger mosquito occurrences have been associated with tire piles.

MOSQUITOES AS DISEASE CARRIERS

In the continental United States the most important human diseases involving arthropods are a complex of several different types of **encephalitis**. These viruses attack the central nervous system. The effects of these infections vary from a mild involvement in some people to death in others. In many instances those who recover may be left with permanently damaged nervous systems.

Causal agents (the disease-causing pathogen)

of these encephalitides are viruses. They are often called **arboviruses**, a contraction of the phrase *arthropod-borne viruses*. This term is applied to all viruses transmitted by arthropods and maintained in animal tissue. Among the common arthropods involved are mosquitoes, fleas, and ticks.

The pathogens causing arboviral encephalitides are maintained in nature in birds. Mosquitoes transmit the viruses from bird to bird. The St. Louis encephalitis virus and the eastern equine encephalitis virus have been found in 86 species of birds in North America. The origin of these viruses is unknown. We know only that a few infected migratory birds appear in the springtime at various, unpredictable places. As the birds move north, they reproduce, and nestlings appear just as mosquito populations begin to grow. As the virus is picked up and spread from one bird to another by mosquitoes, the size of the virus reservoir increases. By the end of July, if the size of the virus reservoir is large enough and if the mosquito population is high, some of the mosquitoes that have fed on infected birds may bite people and transmit the disease. Thus there is an overflow of the virus into the human population, and this causes an outbreak of encephalitis. The size of the outbreak is determined by the extent of contact between people and infect-

ed mosquitoes (see Figure 14.32).

There are several general considerations concerning these arboviral encephalitides that are valuable in understanding them better. The term equine was used in the past in conjunction with eastern and western encephalitis. This was because the horse, *Equus caballus* Linnaeus, is very susceptible to infection with these viruses. Like humans, horses are a dead-end for the virus (a mosquito cannot obtain enough of the virus from humans or horses to infest other animals). Much time and effort was expended on studies of these diseases in the horse before the relationships among virus, mosquito, and bird were understood. Outbreaks occur in horses, and they may or may not be coincident with human epidemics. Whenever cases in horses are confirmed, this should be considered a danger sign for a possible outbreak in humans, and preventive measures should be taken.

Another similarity among the arboviral encephalitides is that outbreaks occur in mid- to late summer or early autumn. This factor can be very important to the pest manager in planning vector control. By midsummer, he or she should have had time to locate sites in which mosquito larvae can develop. With this information, there is an immediate starting point for management programs.

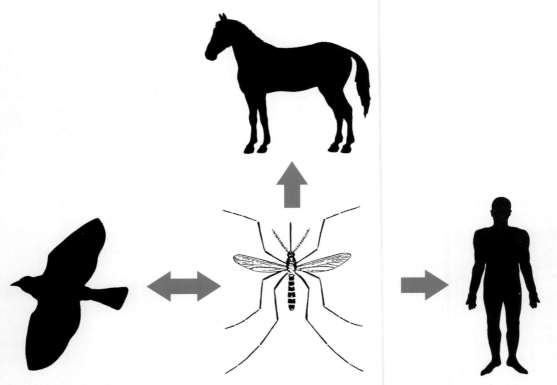

FIGURE 14.32. A generalized diagrammatic representation of the transmission of the causal agents of the arboviral encephalitides. The normal path of transmission is from bird to bird by means of mosquito vectors. Two important dead-end hosts, humans and horses, are indicated. The virus is not known to be transmitted from these hosts to other animals. (Provonsha)

West Nile Virus (WNV)

West Nile encephalitis, a mosquito-transmitted illness with symptoms that include fever, headache, muscular pain, and rash, was first documented in the United States during the summer of 1999, when an outbreak occurred in New York City. The virus, WNV, is named after the district in Uganda where it was first isolated in 1937; since that time WNV has become endemic to many areas of Africa, Asia, and Europe, but it had not been reported from the Western Hemisphere until 1999, when 62 human cases and 7 fatalities occurred in Queens, NY. Since 1999 WNV cases have been reported in most U.S. states. Horses have been seriously affected by WNV as well, although an equine vaccine is now available that will help alleviate illness and death in horses.

Exotic and native birds are the primary reservoirs of WNV, with significant mortality in some species (e.g., crows and jays) that serves as a warning that the virus may be active in an area. Other birds that are only mildly affected may, however, help to spread the virus. WNV is transmitted from infected birds to humans by mosquitoes, principally those in the *Culex pipiens* complex (the northern and southern house mosquitoes). Transmission from human to human by mosquitoes does not occur.

In some years there may be thousands of WNV cases and hundreds of deaths, but most infected humans have no symptoms (only 1 to 3% of infected people require medical attention, and less than 1% develop encephalitis). In severe cases, convulsions, paralysis, coma, and death occur. The elderly and those with immune system problems are at greatest risk.

Mosquito prevention and control, and personal protection from mosquito bites are the keys to managing this disease.

At the present time it is extremely difficult to diagnose the arboviral encephalitides accurately. These diseases have similar symptoms that are also very much like those of encephalitides caused by other pathogens not borne by arthropods. They can be diagnosed with complete accuracy only by examining the blood of a recovering patient for an increase in antibodies specific for a given virus. To make this type of diagnosis, blood samples must be taken both while symptoms are present and after the symptoms are no longer present. The concentration of antibodies that the patient has produced against the particular virus must be significantly greater in the second sample. The physician is placed in the unfortunate position of being able to give only a ten-tative diagnosis while the patient is ill. Diagnosis is still uncertain until the patient is recovering.

Because of this barrier to rapid and accurate diagnosis, an outbreak is often well underway before the nature of the problem can be defined. A vector (the mosquito carrier) control program is needed immediately when an outbreak is recognized; a day or two later may be too late for many people who are infected.

The only effective means of combating an outbreak of arboviral encephalitis is vector control. When an outbreak is recognized, there is an immediate need for persons who understand the life history, biology, and management of both the vectors and the vertebrate components of the reservoir. With few exceptions, there is seldom any group of people in a community who would be in a better position to handle such problems than the pest management professional. When such a need arises, the response time must be measured in hours and minutes, and not in days. To help the community, the pest manager must be aware of potential problems and be prepared to work to solve them.

Although several types of encephalitis are found in the United States, most cases involve one of the four following diseases.

Eastern Encephalitis (EE)

EE occurs in a rather restricted area along the Atlantic and Gulf coasts (see Figure 14.33), plus a few isolated cases in the Midwest, primarily in horses. It is probably the most dangerous arboviral encephalitis in the United States. Mortality rates may be as high as 75% of diagnosed cases, and many patients who recover have permanently damaged nervous systems. It is seen mainly in small children and has been known to cause mental retardation, convulsions, and paralysis in survivors. It is also a highly fatal disease for horses.

Several mosquito species are considered to be possible vectors, but not enough evidence is available to point to any single species as the most important. *Culiseta melanura* (Coquillett) appears to be an important vector among birds; its role in transmission to humans is probably negligible, because it rarely bites humans. *Aedes vexans* (Meigen) and *Mansonia perturbans* (Walker) are suspected vectors, and much circumstantial evidence points to *Aedes sollicitans* (Walker) in recent outbreaks. The virus has been isolated from several other species as well.

St. Louis Encephalitis (SLE)

SLE (see Figure 14.34) is a less serious disease than EE. The mortality rate in diagnosed cases is much lower, and permanent neurological damage in recovered patients occurs less frequently; however, many more cases occur each year. Most fatalities are in people 60 years or older. Species of the *Culex pipiens* complex are important vectors in urban areas. Clogged rain gutters, birdbaths, and automobile tires are principal breeding sites for the mosquito; virtually any container in which water accumulates for a period of time is a potential breeding site.

Western Encephalitis (WE)

WE is widely distributed over the western two-thirds of the United States, and numerous isolated cases have been reported elsewhere (see Figure 14.35). It is much less severe than the two preceding encephalitides discussed here. The mortality rate is low. Small children are most likely to suffer permanent damage. The mortality rate in horses may reach 30 percent. The principal vector is *Culex tarsalis*. Common domesticated fowl are important as reservoirs of the virus.

California Encephalitis (CE)

CE is the newest of the common arboviruses causing disease in humans in the United States. There are apparently a number of different strains of the virus or, as more knowledge is acquired, we may find this to actually be a group of closely related viruses. This disease is a mild form of encephalitis, with mortality rare. It is believed that many cases probably are not diagnosed; thus it may be the most prevalent type of arbovirus in the United States. Although first isolated in California, the greatest number of cases are found in the Midwest. The tree hole breeding mosquito, *Aedes triseriatus* (Say), is a proven vector.

The California group of encephalitis viruses is represented in the Midwest by the LaCrosse virus. Much more is known about the cycle of this virus than that of the other encephalitides. The reservoir of the virus is in chipmunks and squirrels. The mosquito responsible for transmission of the virus is ***Aedes triseriatus***. This mosquito is associated with woodlands and breeds in water-containing holes in trees. It is known that this virus can be passed from an infected female mosquito through her eggs (transovarial transmission). The larvae that hatch from these eggs are infected with the virus.

This is an endemic disease that remains with us constantly in localized areas. The disease affects only children. Though it is one of the less virulent of the encephalitides, the aftereffects of infection have not been sufficiently studied to determine the effect on human populations in areas where there is a high incidence of the virus.

FIGURE 14.33. The geographic distribution of the causal agent of eastern encephalitis (EE) in the United States. The shaded area on the map represents the region in which wild birds are known to harbor the virus.

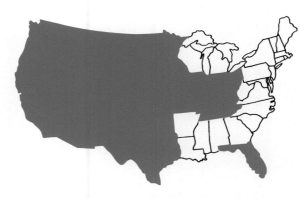

FIGURE 14.34. The geographic distribution of the causal agent of St. Louis encephalitis (SLE). The shaded area indicates the regions in which the virus is found in wild birds. This is the most widespread of the arboviral encephalitides in the United States.

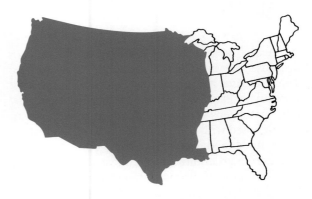

FIGURE 14.35. The geographic distribution of the causal agent of western encephalitis (WE). The shaded area represents the region in which the virus is found in wild birds.

Encephalitis—What Can the General Public Do?

The only effective method of controlling encephalitis is through mosquito management. By reducing the size of vector populations, human-mosquito contact is reduced, and the transmission cycles can be broken.

Since we know which species of mosquitoes are involved, we can selectively attack the problem by finding and eliminating their breeding sites. This can be accomplished with a *minimum* amount of insecticide use. In most cases, breeding sites can be permanently eliminated or altered to reduce the potential for breeding. This might be done through improvement of waste disposal facilities. The first step, however, as in the case of **Culex pipiens**, is to conduct thorough surveys to find these breeding sites. It is a long, hard process, but it can be done, and you can help. This should be a joint effort involving local health departments, other interested agencies, and individuals.

Cooperation of the public is absolutely essential to any good vector-control program. While a community-wide mosquito program is getting started, individuals may protect themselves and others by doing the following:

- Checking their own property for breeding sites.
  — Make sure rain gutters are not clogged.
  — Don't let water accumulate in containers such as tires, barrels, cans, wading pools, and so forth.
  — Flush out birdbaths and wading pools at least once a week.
  — Put minnows in ornamental pools—top-feeding minnows will eat the larvae (goldfish offer little, if any, control).
- Avoiding contact with mosquitoes.
- Wearing EPA-registered repellents in areas where mosquitoes are active.
- Making sure homes are well screened.
- Notifying the local health department of any breeding sites on public property. This can help tremendously with the survey, the first step in initiating a community-wide program.

MOSQUITO MANAGEMENT

Management of mosquitoes may vary from large area management of larvae and adults by organized government agencies, such as public health organizations or mosquito abatement districts, to management in limited residential or recreational areas.

Control In and Around Homes

In addition to the elimination of breeding sites, it may be necessary to control adult mosquitoes that migrate in from surrounding areas. Adult mosquitoes like to rest in vegetation. Therefore, weeds should not be allowed to grow uncontrolled near the home; weeds in nearby lots should be kept well trimmed.

For outdoor control of adult mosquitoes, residual treatments with appropriately labeled insecticides may be useful (examples are listed in Table 14.4). Apply insecticides with a hand or power sprayer, covering the lower limbs of shade trees, shrubbery, tall grass, and shaded areas around buildings where mosquitoes congregate. Nontarget insects are killed by these sprays, so sprays should be used judiciously.

In areas with heavy mosquito populations, openings in inhabited buildings should be tightly screened. Screening with 16 mesh to the inch will keep out most mosquitoes, but 18 mesh may be necessary for some small species.

TABLE 14.4. Some insecticides for mosquito control.

Insect and Application Type	Insecticide	Formulation*
Mosquito larvae:	Agnique	Monomolecular surface film
	Bacillus thuringiensis (Bt)	WP, G, briquets
	Bacillus sphaericus	G
	Golden Bear Oil	Spray
	Methoprene (Altosid)	EC, briquets, pellets
	Abate (temephos)	EC, G
Adult mosquitoes:		
Thermal fogs	Fenthion	LC, EC
Mist sprays	Synergized pyrethrins	LC
Cold aerosols (ULV)	Synergized pyrethrins	LC
Aerial sprays	Synergized pyrethrins	LC
Power sprays	Resmethrin	LC
	Permethrin	LC
	Sumethrin	LC

*WP = wettable powder, G = granule, EC = emulsifiable concentrate, and LC= liquid concentrate.

Space spraying with mist blowers, thermal fog generators, or ULV generators is the most useful technique for adult control. Pest management professionals frequently use this as their only method of

Using Mosquito Repellents

Repellents are very useful in protecting against mosquito bites and other biting Diptera, such as deer flies, horse flies, black flies, and biting midges. Available under various trade names, they include such active ingredients as diethyl toluamide (DEET), ethyl hexanediol, dimethyl phthalate, or dimethyl carbate. Use only repellents registered by the Environmental Protection Agency. Repellents provide protection for up to five hours, depending on the amount of perspiration, skin rubbing, temperature, and abundance of mosquitoes. Application should be made to clothing and to exposed skin areas but not around the eyes, nose, or lips. Follow carefully all directions on the label.

management, completely overlooking the advantage to be gained by water elimination and larviciding. Space spraying should be done during the cool hours of the night or early morning, because in high temperatures both mists and fogs are dispersed too rapidly to give good control. The application should also be timed so it coincides with the period of greatest activity of the most abundant species to be controlled. Fogging should be done only when the wind velocity is less that 5 miles per hour, but mist sprays can be applied in wind velocities up to 10 miles per hour. See Table 14.4 for examples of insecticides used for space spraying adult mosquitoes.

Mosquitoes can be prevented in the home by keeping windows and porches tightly screened. Space sprays or aerosols containing synergized pyrethrins and some pyrethroids are effective against mosquitoes found in the home.

Areawide Mosquito Management

Mosquito management on an areawide basis is a complex undertaking that should be attempted only by professionals. The administration of community programs must be flexible. This flexibility should, however, be based on the established principles of good mosquito management. A number of techniques are available, depending on the target species involved and the priorities that have been established. For example, the management of species involved as disease vectors can be quite a different problem from that of species that are strictly nuisance biters.

Health Education

All good public health programs must include education of the public for understanding and sup-

port. This is especially important with mosquitoes, because homeowners can help greatly by managing their own property to eliminate breeding sources of *Culex pipiens* and *Aedes triseriatus*, the primary vectors of West Nile Virus, St. Louis encephalitis, and LaCrosse encephalitis, respectively. In areas where extensive breeding occurs in containers on private property, the effectiveness of any community-wide effort directed at public property alone will reduce the effectiveness of the program. It is, therefore, of utmost importance to inform the citizens of the ways they can help.

Survey for Breeding Places

An effective community-wide mosquito management program cannot be planned or conducted until a survey is made to locate the major breeding sites of problem mosquitoes. This takes a great deal of time and work but is well worth the effort. Though mosquitoes usually require standing water for breeding, it is not true that mosquitoes will be produced in every body of standing water. A survey will identify those breeding sites that must be eliminated or treated. This will avoid unnecessary intrusion on areas that need not be treated, thereby saving both the environment and the taxpayers' money. Since the most efficient management programs concentrate on the control of mosquito larvae rather than adult mosquitoes, the survey is an essential prerequisite.

Any site that accumulates standing water should be examined for possible mosquito breeding. Visual inspection of sites should be made, and mosquito larvae should be sampled with "mosquito dippers" for species identification. Sites identified as actively breeding mosquitoes should be noted for follow-up control efforts.

Adult mosquito surveillance measures mosquito populations that have successfully developed and emerged from aquatic habitats. Light traps (e.g., New Jersey light trap, CDC light trap) are standard tools for adult sampling. Landing counts can also be used.

Electronic Devices

Devices that are advertised as physical attractants or repellents of mosquitoes are limited in use and should be thoroughly investigated before being purchased. Recent field tests have shown that electrocuting devices using ultraviolet light as an attractant are ineffective in reducing mosquito populations and mosquito biting activity.

When the pest management professional has determined what kinds of mosquitoes are present, where they are breeding, and how far the adults might normally be expected to fly from the breeding areas, he or she is ready to proceed to the actual control of mosquitoes.

Source Reduction and Habitat Alteration

Many mosquito problems can be permanently reduced by either eliminating breeding sites or altering the habitat in such a way as to reduce the numbers of larvae that can be supported. This might mean cleaning a shoreline of vegetation that provides natural harborage for larvae. Eliminating a source of organic pollution will alter a breeding place not only to deprive larvae of nutrients, but also to provide an environment in which mosquito predators can survive and become established. Under no circumstances should a body of water be drained or an area filled until permission has been obtained from the local drainage board and until it has definitely been established that problem species breed in the body of water in sufficient numbers to cause problems.

The following practices may be used to reduce mosquito breeding sites:

- Ditch and clean stagnant streams to ensure a continuous flow of water and to eliminate border vegetation that produces habitat for mosquito larvae to develop.
- Drain or fill backwater pools and swamps where stagnant water accumulates. Sanitary landfills can often be used in such locations, resulting in the elimination of mosquito breeding sites and improving the value of the land. Check with the state board of health, however, before establishing such landfills.
- Since all mosquitoes breed in shallow, quiet water, remove vegetation and debris from along the shores of lakes and ponds to discourage mosquito breeding. Such bodies of water should have a steep, clean shoreline with as little vegetation as possible. Weed killers may be used in some cases to eliminate or prevent emergent plant growth.
- Stock small lakes and ponds with top-feeding minnows.

Chemical Management Techniques

The use of chemicals is, at best, a temporary expedient that should be limited to only those situations for which no other alternatives exist. In general, chemical control can be divided into two major operations. The first, larviciding, is the most effi-

cient and effective and should be the backbone of any good chemical program. The second, adulticiding, is less efficient and as such should be used strictly for supplemental or emergency purposes. The detection of active transmission of mosquito-borne disease is an example of such an emergency. Some state boards of health routinely monitor levels of arborvirus transmission throughout the state and may be contacted for information on the status of disease transmission.

A number of insecticides have been registered for use in mosquito control. The relative value of chemical control varies with the mosquito species and the location conditions where control is to be applied. Because each situation differs, care must be taken to select the proper insecticide for your particular situation. Factors to consider include effectiveness against the target species (resistance problems); relative toxicity to humans and domestic animals (impact on nontarget organisms); contamination of garden or fruit; cost; availability in quantities needed; need for residual action in some situations; chemical stability; flammability; ease of preparation; corrosiveness; offensive odor, and staining.

Resistance can be a problem in mosquito control, especially when using some of the organophosphate compounds. However, before assuming that resistance is the cause of poor control, it must be established that poor control is not caused by other factors, such as improper identification of mosquitoes, poor application techniques, lack of knowledge about insect habits, or faulty source reduction procedures. Any decrease in susceptibility should be substantiated before considering a change of procedure.

Many insecticides registered for use in mosquito control are toxic to birds, fish, and other wildlife, so appropriate precautions must be taken. In addition, most of these insecticides are toxic to bees exposed to direct treatment or to residues on crops. In making applications, care should be exercised to avoid any insecticidal contact with food or feed crop areas. Instructions on the label will give precautions or restrictions on using insecticides for mosquito control.

Larval Control

Mosquito breeding sites that are undesirable or impossible to alter or eliminate may be treated with an appropriate larvicide. Table 14.4 lists some of the insecticides recommended for use as mosquito larvicides. The application of larvicides should be made only at sites where mosquito larvae of the proper target species are present. In addition, the degree of control obtained with larvicide applications often depends on the amount of pollution and the type and amount of vegetative cover present. Some of the insecticides listed in Table 14.4 thus have a range of application rates.

Where cover is heavy, granular formulations frequently provide better control than emulsions or oil sprays. Repeated treatments with some of these insecticides may be needed, especially after heavy rainfall. Generally, three or four treatments each season will be needed. For proper mixing instructions, application rates, and precautions, all label directions should be read and followed carefully. Application rates may vary depending on the extent of vegetative cover, the degree of pollution of the water to be treated, or both.

Granular larvicides can be applied from the air if the plane does not have to fly over populated areas. Granules can also be applied by crank-operated spreaders similar to those used for spreading seeds and fertilizers. Knapsack or other hand sprayers that can be carried by field workers may be used for liquid formulations. Power sprayers may be satisfactory if advantage is taken of the wind, so that the larvicide drifts into desired water areas. Larvicide treatment of fish-bearing waters should be avoided. Briquet, granular, and pellet formulations are often preferred for use in catch basins and in containers not easily disposed of.

Adult Control

Thermal fogs. Fogging provides a rapid, temporary control for adult mosquitoes but has little residual effect. Fogs are effective only where there is little or no wind in the evening or night. Table 14.4 lists some of the insecticides recommended for use as thermal fogs. With the increased use of ultra-low volume (ULV) cold aerosol application techniques, thermal fogs have become less desirable for reasons stated in the section on cold aerosols.

Mist sprays. Mist blowers are power sprayers that produce an airstream across liquid spray droplets, breaking them up and blowing them into the treatment area. In addition to the kill of active adult mosquitoes, small amounts of material are deposited on vegetation, thus providing some residual control. Table 14.4 lists some of the insecticides recommended for use as mist sprays. For proper mixing instructions, application rates, and precautions, all label directions should be read and followed carefully.

Cold aerosols (ULV). Ground equipment capable of producing ULV cold aerosols is available. These machines produce very tiny droplets of high-concentrate insecticide, which results in a greater area coverage with less dosage. This type of application is designed to kill active adult mosquitoes and provides little or no residual control. Like the thermal fog generator, the cold aerosol machine should be used during the time the adult mosquito is most active. This means from twilight until about midnight, when atmospheric conditions are usually best (because of lack of wind). ULV application is generally the preferred space treatment for adult mosquito control.

The cold aerosol method has certain advantages over thermal fog generators. Less insecticide is applied, resulting in fewer pollution problems. Smaller holding tanks and consequently smaller vehicles are needed, since small quantities of insecticide are used. There is a reduced traffic hazard compared with the near nonvisibility created by fog applications. ULV ground applications, however, are somewhat less effective than thermal fogs in heavy vegetation, because the larger ULV droplets tend to be filtered out more rapidly. Table 14.4 lists some of the insecticides recommended for use as ULV cold aerosols.

Aerial applications. Application by fixed-wing aircraft or helicopter for adult mosquito control is also a common practice. It is useful under emergency conditions or if areas to be controlled are too large or are inaccessible for economical treatment with ground power equipment. The best results are obtained in areas without dense tree cover, so that spray particles can penetrate the low shrub zone where the greatest mosquito activity occurs. To obtain uniform coverage of an area, careful observance of preplanned flight patterns, altitudes, and air speeds is essential. Applications should not be made over a food or feed crop area or over populated areas unless the insecticide is labeled for that use. Label directions regarding application over fish-bearing waters should be followed. Table 14.4 lists some of the insecticides recommended for aerial application.

Hydraulic field and hand sprayers. With these sprayers, compressed air exerts pressure on the liquid to be sprayed through a nozzle. In general, compressed-air spraying produces larger droplets than space spraying, and more liquid is applied in a given area. These sprayers are most useful for spot adult treatment and larval control. In making applications, it is of utmost importance not to exceed the recommended dosage. Table 14.4 lists some of the insecticides recommended for use with hydraulic field and hand sprayers.

SUPPLEMENTARY READING MATERIAL

Bishop, F. C. *House Fly Control.* USDA leaflet no. 182. Washington, D.C., 1946. 9 pp.

Carpenter, S. J., and W. J. LaCasse. *Mosquitoes of North America.* Los Angeles: University of California Press, 1955.

Goddard, J. *Physician's Guide to Arthropods of Medical Importance.* Boca Raton, Fla.: CRC Press, 1993. 332 pp.

Hall, D. *The Blow Flies of North America.* Columbus, Ohio: Thomas Say Foundation, 1948. 477 pp.

Horsfall, W. R. *Mosquitoes,* The Bionomics and Relation to Diseases. New York: Ronald Press, 1955.

King, W. V., G. H. Bradley, C. N. Smith, and W. C. McDuffie. *A Handbook of Mosquitoes of the Southeastern United States.* USDA agriculture handbook no. 173. Washington, D.C., 1960. 188 pp.

Mallis, A. *Handbook of Pest Control.* 8th ed. Cleveland: Franzak & Foster, 1982. 1,453 pp.

Pratt, H. D., and R. C. Barnes. *Identification Keys for Common Mosquitoes of the United States.* Atlanta: U.S. Department of Health, Education, and Welfare, Communicable Disease Center, 1959. 40 pp.

Pratt, H. D., R. C. Barnes, and K. S. Littig. *Mosquitoes of Public Health Importance.* Atlanta: U.S. Department of Health, Education, and Welfare, Communicable Disease Center, 1959. 48 pp.

Robinson, W. H. *Urban Entomology: Insect and Mite Pests in the Human Environment.* New York: Chapman & Hall, 1996. 430 pp.

Scott, H. G., et al. *Flies of Public Health Importance and Their Control.* Atlanta: U.S. Department of Health, Education, and Welfare, Center for Disease Control, 1973. 40 pp.

Service, M. W. *Medical Entomology for Students.* New York: Chapman and Hall, 1996. 278 pp.

Williams, R. E., et al., eds. *Livestock Entomology.* New York: Wiley, 1985. 335 pp.

Wilson, M. C., G. W. Bennett, and A. V. Provonsha. *Practical Insect Pest Management: Insects of Man's Household and Health.* Prospect Heights, Ill.: Waveland Press, 1977. 150 pp.

CHAPTER 15 | Rats and Mice

Order Rodentia; Family Muridae

This chapter concerns the **commensal rodents**. The word *commensal* means "sharing one's table." This is an appropriate term as rats and mice have been "sharing" people's food and shelter for many years. And the word *rodent* means "to gnaw." Like all rodents, rats, and mice possess a single pair of chisel-like incisor teeth that grow continuously throughout their lives. These incisors are kept filed and sharp primarily by the rodents grinding the incisors against one another, and secondarily by the rodents constantly gnawing on various objects.

The three species of commensal rodents pests are: (Refer to Figure 15.1):

1. The House Mouse, *Mus domesticus*; (also *Mus musculus*)
2. The Norway Rat, *Rattus norvegicus*;
3. The Roof Rat, *Rattus rattus*

Occasionally, the deer mouse, (*Peromyscus maniculatus*), and less frequently, the white-footed mouse (*Peromyscus leucopis*), harvest mice (*Rethrodontomys* spp.), and pocket mice (*Perognathus* spp.) invade buildings located near fields or wooded areas, and may be confused with the house mouse. Field mice are easily separated from house mice by certain specific characteristics. These native rodents, including meadow mice (voles), pack rats (*Neotoma* spp.) and other small mammals (e.g., shrews) that occasionally invade buildings are discussed in Chapter 17.

RODENTS AS HEALTH PESTS

Rodents have been responsible for, or implicated in, the spread of many diseases to people and domestic animals—especially in years past. Today however, because of sanitation, effective drugs, and rodent and insect control programs, the disease threat from rodents is not as significant as it once was. In fact, the spread of disease by rodents is often not the primary reason for their control. But because of the habits of rodents (traveling and dwelling in sewers, garbage, etc.), there are still cases of human and animal diseases being transmitted by rodents, and there is also the constant potential of disease outbreaks that can be intensified and accelerated by rodents in cities where rats and mice live in close proximity to people. Thus, it is the potential of disease transmission that must be kept in mind.

The following is a brief discussion and overview regarding the rodent-transmitted diseases of most concern today.

Mouse Allergens

Research in 1999 of children in inner-city areas of eight major cities demonstrated that the house mouse carries a protein within its urine that can trigger severe cases of asthma and allergic rhinitis in susceptible people. Considering that mice typically urinate in microdroplets in many, many spots as they forage about inside a room, literally thousands of micro areas on surfaces can be covered with mouse urine inside homes or schools, offices, etc., that contain significant mouse infestation. As a result of this finding, the ordinary house mouse is considered much more of a health pest than in the past.

Hanta Viruses

Viruses in the genus Bunyaviridae are the causative agents of various hanta viruses. Because of the 1993–1995 outbreaks of hantavirus pulmonary syndrome (HPS) such as the Sin Nombre hanta virus, in the southwestern United States, there is a heightened awareness regarding this strain and other hanta viruses in other areas throughout the United States. The deer mouse (*Peromyscus maniculatus*) has been

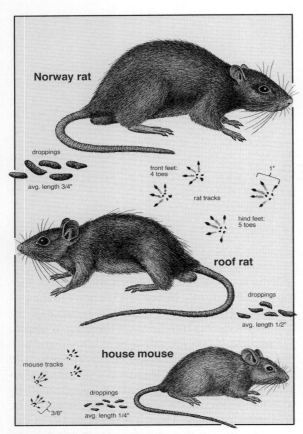

FIGURE 15.1. The commensal rodents: Nature's most adaptable mammals. (Provonsha)

identified as the primary reservoir associated with HPS, although the cotton rat (*Sigmodon hispidus*), and the white-footed mouse (*Peromyscus leucopis*), have also been implicated with certain strains of hanta virus. The commensal rodents (house mouse, Norway rat, and roof rat) have not been found to be involved as reservoirs of the more virulent HPS, but the Norway rat is associated with hanta virus strains that cause hemorrhagic fevers and renal failures. For more discussion on hanta virus refer to the discussion on deer mice in Chapter 17.

Plague is a disease caused by a bacillus (*Yersinia pestis*), that is spread from rats to people primarily by the oriental rat flea (*Xenopsylla cheopis*). Plague is the "Black Death" that killed 25,000,000 people in Europe during the 14th century, and millions of others both earlier and later in history. Although plague does not now exist in commensal rodents in the United States, it is still found in some native rodents such as ground squirrels in the western United States, as well in several other parts of the world. People coming into contact with dying wild rodents are at risk in areas where sylvatic plague exists and cases of plague in humans are recorded each year. Thus, there is still the potential of plague

outbreaks even today, and the major health concern comes when the plague infection is in the lungs in what is referred to as pneumonic plague. In this highly contagious form, it can be spread from person to person in sputum or droplets coughed up by infected individuals.

Murine typhus is a disease caused by the rickettsial organism *Rickettsia typhi* (a type of bacterium) that is transmitted from infected rats and some other rodents to people also by the oriental rat flea *Xenopsylla cheopis* and to a lesser extent, by the cat flea, *Ctenocephalides felis*. The predominant rodent reservoirs for most areas where murine typhus occurs are the Norway rat and the roof rat. The house mouse is not considered an important reservoir although it has been found infected when it occupies the same areas as infected rats. In some unique cases, the southern flying squirrel, *Glaucomys volans*, has been implicated in transmitting a unique form of typhus called sylvatic epidemic typhus when these squirrels take up residence in attics during the winter.

The rickettsial organism enters the human blood stream via the bites of fleas or when feces of infected fleas are rubbed into the skin. Chills, headache, and fever characterize typhus, with a rash appearing about the fifth day of illness, and lasting for up to two weeks frequently accompanied with respiratory symptoms. In the United States, only a few cases occur annually. Murine typhus readily responds to antibiotics and even in untreated cases, the mortality rate usually does not exceed 2%.

Rickettsial pox, also caused by a rickettsial, is transmitted by mites from infected mice. The symptoms of this disease are similar to chicken pox (a rash, fever, and headache), but the effects are usually milder. Most cases of rickettsial pox have occurred in New York City and several New England cities where large numbers of people and mice share the closely spaced urban-style housing. Several cases of this disease are still reported each year in these areas.

Salmonella bacteria are actually common in the natural environment. Thus far, it is estimated that about 2,000 different strains (serotypes) of salmonella exist. Certain types are highly pathogenic to people and other animals and can cause **salmonellosis (acute food poisoning)**. Two serotypes in particular are associated with rodents and food poisoning: *Salmonella typhimurium* and *S. enteriditis*.

Salmonella can thrive on decaying food, on poultry and meats, in sewers, livestock facilities, septic tanks, cesspools, accumulated garbage, and other similar unsanitary environments. Because rodents frequent these areas and then visit homes and food facilities, the potential for spread of the salmonella is real because the bacteria thrive in the intestinal tract of rodents, and hence are spread through food contaminated with rodent feces.

In the United States, approximately two million cases of salmonellosis occurs each year. To date, research has shown that rats and mice may do not play a major role in the direct spread of salmonellosis to humans. In livestock facilities however, such as poultry operations, the house mouse can have significant involvement in amplifying the spread of salmonella.

Rat-bite fever is caused by the bacterium *Streptobacillis moniliformis* that can live in the saliva of both rats and mice. This bacteria causes flu-like symptoms lasting for several days, but in severe cases (which are rare), it can be fatal. Rat-bite fever is uncommon in the United States, and is not of major public health significance. However, it is likely many cases go unreported, or are not properly recorded by the medical community because this fever responds quickly to antibiotics. Patients (and their physicians) may assume a case of the flu, and do not pursue further diagnosis. An accurate number of the people bitten by rats and mice each year is unknown, although conservative estimates place the numbers between 14,000 to 20,000 people each year are attacked. Most attacks occur in the larger cities, and in areas where sanitation and pest control programs are not in effect. In most cases, rodents bite sleeping babies, inquisitive children, or the bed-confined elderly.

Weils disease or **leptospirosis** is a disease caused by a spirochete bacterium of the genus *Leptospira*. It is usually transmitted by rats to dogs, cattle, or pigs. These animals in turn, may transmit the organism to people, (the rats may also directly transmit the organism to people). The leptospira organisms are spread via rat urine into the water or food of domestic animals or people. The symptoms of leptospirosis vary but may include high fevers, rashes, severe headaches, abdominal pain, and sloughing of the skin

Other Diseases

The general public (including physicians) sometimes mistakenly associate the bites of rodents with the potential of **rabies** transmission. But wild commensal rodents have not been found to transmit rabies. Thus, the U.S. Public Health Service does not recommend specific anti-rabies treatments in the event of rat and mouse bites.

Rodents have been implicated with transmitting several other diseases. **Lymphocytic choriomeningitis** (LCM) may be spread by mice, as has been identified in wild house mice in several U.S. cities over the past several years. **Trichinosis,**

caused by the trichina worm, can be harbored and shed by rats via their feces into hog feed (people acquire the disease by eating improperly cooked pork from contaminated hogs). Rats have also been shown to carry the organisms of **typhoid, dysentery**, and several other diseases.

One of the most valuable resources for the pest professional, and other personnel involved in rodent pest management operations regarding the significance of rodents and diseases can be found on the internet at the Centers for Disease Control and Prevention website (**www.cdc.gov**). This site provides updates and outstanding background on virtually all diseases of importance.

Rodents as Economic Pests

Rats and mice attack our food in the farm fields, orchards and livestock facilities, during its processing, storage and transport, and while it is in our supermarkets, restaurants, and homes. In this regard, the rodents have been referred to as *kleptoparasitic*: meaning they parasitize us via stealing our valuable resources. They also spoil tons of food by contaminating it with their urine, feces, or fur. The loss of food to rodents worldwide is staggering. Experts estimate that rats and mice destroy enough food each year to feed 200 million people.

In our buildings, rodents damage doors, floors, ceilings, and walls as a result of their burrowing and gnawing activity. They also regularly gnaw on various utility pipes and electrical wiring resulting in explosions, indoor flooding, fires, equipment malfunctions, and power shortages. And in today's high-tech production, rodents are capable of abruptly causing millions of dollars in production loss due to shutdowns of complex computer systems when they gnaw, nest, or excrete wastes inside computers and other highly sensitive equipment. In 1996, the Internet in California was shutdown because of a rat gnawing on the Net's associated wiring. One rat on board a commercial airplane recently cost an airline company nearly $1 million to eliminate the rat.

In addition to the direct economic losses (and health-associated costs) rodents are also expensive to control. In the United States alone, conservative annual estimates place the cost of rodent pest management programs to be well over **$120 million** dollars. Worldwide, the cost of rodent control is probably in the billions.

FIELD IDENTIFICATION OF DOMESTIC RODENTS

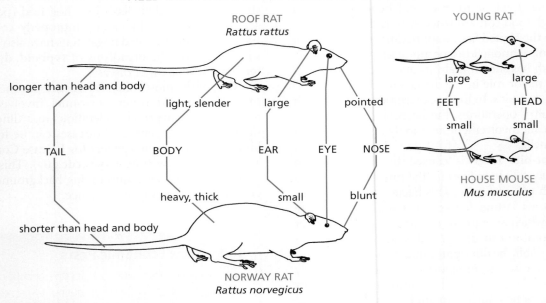

FIGURE 15.2. This key should be of value in helping to identify the most common pest rodents that the professional is likely to encounter. The relative length of the tail and body should be considered first when attempting to identify the adults. The relative size of the ears compared to the size of the body is a distinctive characteristic that can usually be observed without much difficulty. The other characteristics tend to be somewhat more subtle and should be used with caution. To distinguish between young rats and adult mice, the relative size of the feet and the rest of the body is generally a distinct and easily recognizable characteristic. (Courtesy of the U.S. Public Health Service, Atlanta, Georgia)

THE HOUSE MOUSE

Mus domesticus Rutty/*Mus musculus* Linnaeus

The house mouse originated in the grassy plains of central Asia. It was transported west on ships via early trade merchants and immigrants—probably in the 15th century. Because of its small size, adaptability and the fact that it needs extremely small amounts of food and space, the mouse is capable of survival in nearly any environment. With the exception of humans, the house mouse is the most numerous and widespread mammal on earth. The house mouse is, by far, the "number one" rodent pest.

Identification

The house mouse is identified by a small slender body weighing between 1/2 to 1 ounce (15-30 g) as an adult. The ears are large, the tail is seminaked and is as long as the head and body together. The fur is usually dark gray on the back and light gray on the belly, but many color variations are possible. Albino, black, and mixtures of black and white have been bred in the laboratory. Mice can be identified from young rats by the size of the head and the hind feet. (See Figures 15.1, 15.2, and 15.3, and Figure 15.4, which follows page 254, and Table 15.1.)

Biology

As with all pests, an understanding of the biology and behavior of rodents is essential in developing effective control programs. The potential reproductive capabilities of rodents are impressive (although often exaggerated). When living conditions for rodents are very good (plenty of food, water, and shelter) rodents can multiply rapidly. However, when living conditions are stressful, overall rodent reproduction and population growth are slowed considerably. The following discussion provides the reproductive potential of mice under average conditions.

FIGURE 15.3. The house mouse is the most common commensal rodent pest in structures.

Table 15.1. Characteristics of commensal rodents

Characteristic	Norway Rat	Roof Rat	House Mouse
General appearance	Large, robust	Sleek, graceful	Small, slender

Adult size
  weight (oz/g)
  length (nose to tip of tail)
  head and body (mm)
  tail (mm)
	7–18 oz/200–500 g
	
	7–9.5 in/18–25 cm
	6–8 in/15–21 cm
		5–9 oz/150–250 g
		
		6–8 in/16–20 cm
		7–10 in/19–25 cm
			0.4–1 oz/12–30 g
			
			2–3.5 in/6–9 cm
			3–4 in/7–10 cm

Snout	Blunt	Pointed	Pointed
Ears	Small, covered with short hairs; do not reach eyes	Large, nearly naked; can be pulled over eyes	Large, some hair
Eyes	Small	Large, prominent	Small
Tail	Dark above, pale beneath	Uniformly dark	Uniformly dark
Fur	Brown with scattered black (agouti); venter gray to yellow-white; shaggy	Agouti to gray to black; venter white, gray, or black; smooth	Light brown, light gray; smooth
Droppings	Capsule shaped, 2cm/3/4–1 in	Spindle shaped, 1 cm/0.5 in	Rod shaped, 3–6 mm/0.5 in

Senses
  sight
  smell, taste, touch, hearing
	Poor, color-blind
	Excellent
		Poor, color-blind
		Excellent
			Poor, color-blind
			Excellent

Food	Omnivorous (22–30 g/d) 0.8–1 oz	Omnivorous, especially fruits, nuts, grains, and vegetables (15–30 g/d) 0.5–1.0 oz/d	Omnivorous, prefers cereal grains (3 g/d) 0.1 oz/d
Water	15–30 ml/d	15–30 ml/d	3–9 ml/d; can subsist without free water
Feeding habits	Shy (new object reaction); steady eater	Shy (new object reaction); steady eater	Inquisitive; nibbler
Climbing	Readily climbs; limited agility	Very agile, active climber	Good climber
Nests	Usually burrows	Walls, attics, vines, trees; sometimes burrows	Within structures, stored food; burrows
Swimming	Excellent swimmer	Can swim	Can swim
Home range radius	30–50 m /98–164 ft	30–50 m /98–164 ft	3–10 m /10–33 ft
Age at mating (months)	2–3	2–3	1.5–2
Breeding season	Spring and fall peaks	Spring and fall peaks	Year long
Gestation period (days)	22	22	19
Young per litter	8–12	4–8	4–7
Litters per year	4–7	4–6	8
Young weaned/female/year	20	20	30–35
Length of life	1 year	1 year	1 year

Note: Data are averages and not representative of extremes.
Sources: Compiled from J. E. Brooks and F. P. Rowe, Commensal Rodent Control (World Health Organization, WHO/VBC/79.726, Geneva, 1979); W. E. Howard and R. E. Marsh, *The Rat: Its Biology and Control* (University of California, Division of Agricultural Sciences, leaflet no. 2,896, 1976); H. D. Pratt and R. Z. Brown, *Biological Factors in Domestic Rodent Control* (U.S. Department of Health, Education, and Welfare, Centers for Disease Control, bulletin no. 76-8144, 1976); R. E. Marsh and W. E. Howard, *The House Mouse: Its Biology and Control* (University of California, Division of Agricultural Sciences, leaflet no. 2,945, 1977);W. B. Jackson, "Norway Rats and Allies," in *Wild Mammals of North America*, ed. J. A. Chapman and G. A. Feldhamer (Baltimore: Johns Hopkins University Press, 1982).

A female produces between four and seven pups per litter following a gestation period of about 19 days. The pups are born blind and naked. Within 7 to 10 days they are covered with fur; the eyes and ears are open. By the third or fourth week the pups are weaned and begin to take short trips outside of the nest feeding on solid food and exploring and learning their surroundings. A female will typically produce about eight litters in her lifetime, although if conditions are good, she is capable of giving birth to a litter every 24 to 28 days. Young mice are sexually mature within five to eight weeks. The normal life span for a wild mouse is typically less than one year, but dominant individuals may live as long as two years. Table 15.1 provides comparative life histories of the commensal rodents.

Behavior

The behavior of rodents is dependent upon each particular situation and environment. It is difficult to describe the "typical" behavior of mice, because rodents (including rats) may react slightly or even dramatically different from one site to another. Thus, control programs must be flexible and adapted for each situation. For practical purposes however, some generalizations in behavior patterns of the commensal rodents living in and around buildings can be made.

In cities, the entire life of some mice may be spent inside buildings. In suburban and rural areas, the mouse may live in buildings, but the house mouse also commonly exists outdoors among the weeds and shrubbery or nearby building foundations, within storage sheds, garages and the crawlspaces below structures. Outdoors mice feed on weed seeds, insects, or whatever other foods may be found. When their food supply becomes scarce in the fall (especially in the colder climates), some of the mice move into occupied buildings.

Inside buildings, mice set up their nests near food sources and once established, they stay close to home, traveling short distances between the food and the nest. Good nests are important to the reproductive success and survival of mice. Nests provide warmth and protection to the mother and her pups. In buildings, nests are commonly located within walls, closets, ceiling and cabinet voids, within large appliances (e.g. the bases of refrigerators and ovens), in storage boxes, bureau drawers, desks, or within the upholstery of furniture. Outdoors, mice construct their nests among debris or in ground burrows. The nest is made from paper, insulation, furniture stuffing, or any soft material chewed into small bits to make a soft bed. When good nest sites are not available, mice quickly adapt. For example, mice have been found nesting within meat carcasses in meat storage freezers at temperatures of −10° F.

As a mouse population grows, territories are set up and controlled by the males. Each territory may be comprised of one "strong" (dominant) male, one or more females, several subordinate males, and a number of young mice from recent litters. The dominant male does not willingly share his territory with other dominant males. As a result, there is constant fighting and jockeying for social position within mouse populations. Young male mice leaving the nest must fight to take over the territory of another mouse, succumb to being a subordinate, or keep moving until an unclaimed area is located. This is how mouse infestations spread from one part of a building to another.

The size of a mouse's territory within a building varies from one situation to another. Territories depend upon the physical arrangement of the environment, the availability of food, and the number of other mice in the area. Mouse territories within buildings under "average conditions" range from 10 to 30 feet from the nest. However, the more mice and food, the less territory each has. Thus, when food is close by, and/or if there are many mice in the area. a mouse may not travel more than a few feet from its nest. In seed warehouses for example, mice may not leave the pallet of food they are nesting in! Understanding this territorial behavior of mice is vitally important when implementing mouse control programs.

Mice explore and re-explore their home territories daily and become familiar with the pathways leading to and from feeding and watering locations, burrow entrances, and spots to hide from their enemies. When changes occur, the mouse reacts by investigating the changes.

While on the job, the professional should keep in mind that territories may be three-dimensional. That is, mice may travel *within* rooms along wall areas, as well as *between* floors, such as from crawlspaces to kitchens, or from attics and suspended ceilings to rooms one or two floors below.

When mice feed, they can best be thought of as "nibblers." If food is plentiful, mice may make 20 to 30 or more short visits to various food sites within their territories each night randomly nibbling on tiny amounts of food here and there. Among their various food sites they often establish "favorite" feeding spots that they continuously revisit. These spots are usually darkened corner areas and narrow, tight spaces that provide the mice temporary protection while out of the nest. Piles of droppings and a strong mousy odor often identifies the location of these favorite feeding spots.

Feeding peaks occur during the night with heaviest activity occurring at dusk and again shortly before dawn. In buildings with continuous light, the mice may be most active during the quietest periods. Constant sightings of numerous mice during the day indicates a severe infestation, but there are exceptions to this.

An adult mouse consumes about 3 to 4 grams (about one-tenth of an ounce) of food daily. Mice are considered omnivores, but cereal grains and various seeds are preferred. Meats, peanut butter, nuts, and various types of sweet liquids and candies are also readily taken. Mice even eat each other— especially when food is scarce, or in times of stress. This is commonly seen by the professional while inspecting multiple-catch live traps. If several mice are captured in one trap at the same time, one mouse (the strongest) often kills and eats the other mice. Inside buildings infested with German cockroach, the mouse readily captures eats the roaches (probably because the cockroaches serve as a rich source of protein and moisture).

When free water is available, mice will drink between three and nine milliliters per day, and optimal health is maintained with daily access to water. But when water is scarce or in times of drought, mice can survive without free water in most urban environments because they can satisfy their water needs by extracting water from their food. Moreover, the house mouse has specialized body functions that enable it to conserve water and/or produce its own water.

THE NORWAY RAT
Rattus norvegicus (Berkenhout)

The Norway rat is also known as the house rat, brown rat, wharf rat, sewer rat, water rat, and gray rat. It was introduced into the United States by European settlers and trading ships about 1775. It is now the most widely distributed rat species in the United States, being found in all the states (in parts of some states, however, the roof rat is more prevalent, refer to Figure 15.5). The Norway rat is larger, stronger, more aggressive, and better adapted for producing young and surviving in colder climates than the roof rat and other rat species.

Identification

The adult Norway rat has a stocky body, weighing from about 12 to 16 ounces (200 to 500 grams). Rats slightly heavier than this do occur (people often claim to see—and boast of— "rats as big as alley cats") but are rare. The body fur is coarse and ranges from reddish- to grayish-brown with buff-white underparts, but many color variations exist including all black Norway rats. The nose is blunt, the ears are small, close set, and do not reach the eyes when pulled down. The tail is scaly, seminaked and shorter than the head and body combined. (A quick "field method" for separating Norway rats from roof rats is to pull the tail back over the body. The tail of the Norway rat will not reach beyond the ears. (See Figures 15.1 and 15.2, and Figures 15.6 and 15.7, which follow page 254).

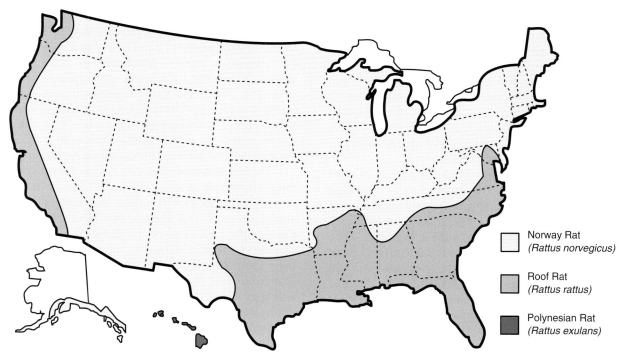

Figure 15.5. The approximate distribution of the three species of the genus *Rattus* in the United States. The Polynesian rat is limited to the Hawaiian Islands, although Norway and roof rats are also found on the islands. The roof rat is primarily confined to the coastal portion of the states of Washington, Oregon, and California, and to a much larger area in the southeast. Norway rats are found in every state; however, sizable uninhabited or sparsely inhabited areas, particularly in the western states, are free or nearly free of the introduced rat species. (Courtesy of the University of California, Davis)

Biology

Indoors, the Norway rat may breed all year long, although breeding peaks are normally in the spring and fall of the year. In outdoor colonies, breeding decreases significantly during the hot summers and cold winters. After mating and a gestation period of about 22 days, the mother rat gives birth to a litter of 8 to 12 pups. The young are naked and blind at birth. Their eyes open in about 9 to 14 days, and they are weaned 10 to 15 days later. By this time the pups begin to take short exploratory trips out of the nest, learning by imitating their mother as to their surroundings, pathways to food, hiding spots, and burrow entrances. The pups reach sexual maturity at the age of 12 weeks, although in good conditions, it may be as early as eight weeks. Females may come into heat every four or five days, and they may mate within a day or two after a litter is born. The average female rat has four to seven litters per year and may successfully wean 20 or more pups annually.

In captivity rats may live for three or more years, but the average wild rat lives for only 5 to 12 months. Many wild rats are killed by predators, other rats, people, or they die of disease or stress before they are one year old (see Table 15.1 on page 357).

Behavior

The Norway rat is a social animal and lives in colonies, often as a ground-dwelling animal in exterior earthen burrows. On farms they inhabit barns, granaries, livestock buildings, and silos. In cities, the rat nests in the ground when space is available. It may also nest and spend its entire life inside urban buildings. Rats inhabit residences, all types of food facilities, warehouses, stores, hotels, zoos, sewers, and dumps. It is also common to find rats living by ponds and lakes in parks, as well as in the wild near rivers and streams.

Adults rats consume about one ounce (25 to 30 grams) of food daily. They prefer food with a high carbohydrate and protein content although almost any type of food will be taken (food items in household garbage provide rats with a balanced diet). Cereal grains, meats, fish, livestock feed, and fresh fruits are all readily taken. Rats living outdoors will either feed outside, or they will enter buildings at night on a daily basis for food and return to their outdoor burrows after feeding. Among wild populations, rats kill and eat various small mammals, reptiles, birds, and insects. In sewers, rats capture and eat American cockroaches.

Unlike mice, the rat cannot survive for very long without free water, requiring 1/2 to 1 ounce (15 to 30 ml) of water daily when feeding on dry foods, but they need less when their food source is moist. In and around buildings, rats obtain their water directly from sinks and toilets, rain puddles, the dew off plants, or by licking the water off condensing utility pipes.

When necessary rats will climb stairways, pipes, wires, and rough walls to get into a building or to find food and water. In fact, the physical capabilities of the rat is among the most impressive of all small mammals. (Refer to section entitled **Physical Abilities and Senses of Rodents**.)

Most populations of rats are nocturnal, with peak activity periods at dusk and before dawn. But rats will adjust to other times when food is freshest, or most available. They may also be seen during the day if the colony becomes overpopulated.

Indoors, the Norway rat prefers to nest around the lower floors of buildings, but when populations are large, or the specific environment dictates, the rat will also occupy attic areas, suspended ceilings, and upper floors. Nests may be located in wall voids, underneath floors, crawlspaces, underneath and behind stationary equipment, and among stored pallets of supplies. In city apartments, rats have even been found nesting in furniture within the same rooms as the occupants. Nests are built of almost any soft material, such as paper, cloth, leaves and grass, hay, etc., that the rat chews into small bits to make a loosely matted mass.

Outdoors, the nesting places are often in burrows in the ground along side of foundation walls. Burrows of rats of new rat populations are usually short, varying between 12 and 20 inches in length. As the rats mature, begin to rear families, and the population grows, the burrows become enlarged and expanded. Eventually many burrows interconnect forming a complex network of underground tunnels. Ground burrows typically contain one main entrance, and one or two additional openings called "bolt" holes that are used for escape purposes.

The territories of most rats under average conditions range from about 50 to 150 feet from the nest. In populations where there are many rats and abundant food and shelter, the territories tend towards the lower end of the range. When necessary, rats will travel 300 feet or more daily to obtain their food and water. In urban areas, most rats remain around the buildings and yards that provide their necessities and, unless disturbed, they do not move great distances.

Several families of rats may use the same food/water sources and runways. They may share parts of large burrow systems and even nest close to one another. But as rat populations grow, competition, conflict, and fighting begin to increase. The males will fight defending territories. (Females will also fight but more so to defend the immediate area

Physical Abilities and Sense of Rodents

A thorough understanding of the physical abilities of rodents is very useful when designing a control program. For instance, rates are excellent swimmers. They can swim up to 1/2 mile in open water, travel through sewer lines against substantial currents, and tread water for up to 3 days. Climbing is also easy for them. Roof rats and house mice are excellent climbers. Norway rats, although somewhat less agile, can climb effectively. If they can't climb, they just jump. From a standing position, rats can jump vertically up to 3 feet. If necessary, rodents can drop from heights of 50 feet without injury.

If rodents can't get around an object, they go through it. Rodents are capable of gnawing through a variety of materials, including lead sheathing, cinderblock, aluminum siding, glass, and improperly cured concrete. Rodents can also squeeze through very small openings—1/2 inch for rats and 1/4 inch for mice.

All of these physical abilities have allowed rats and mice to survive hundreds of years in the human environment. The following are some of the other sensory abilities that make rodents so remarkably adaptable.

Vision

Rats and mice have poor vision beyond 3 or 4 feet, but they are very sensitive to motion up to 30 to 50 feet away. For the most part, rodents are color-blind, but very light-colored or reflective objects may stand out in their environment and cause initial avoidance among sensitive rodents.

Rodents are most active at night when light levels are low, at which time they rely less on their eyesight than they do on their other senses, particularly small, touch, and hearing.

Taste

Rodents have a highly developed sense of taste, which allows them to detect some chemicals at parts-per-million concentrations. This taste sensitivity may lead to bait rejection if the baits are contaminated with insecticide orders or other chemicals. Use of fresh, food-quality grain ingredients is the best guarantee of good bait attractability and acceptance.

Smell

Odor is one of the rodent's most important senses. Rodents mark objects and pathways with urine or glandular secretions. Rodents use their sense of smell to recognize the odors of the pathway to and from feed sources and of members of the opposite sex who are ready to mate, to differentiate between members of their own colonies and strangers, and to tell if a stranger is a strong or weak individual.

Hearing

Rodents use hearing to locate objects to within a few inches. Rats and mice have a frequency range of 50 kilohertz or more, which is much more than humans, who have a range of about 20 kilohertz. Rodents make high frequency noises in various situations, such as in mating, but the function of these sounds is poorly understood.

Touch

Rodents have a highly developed sense of touch, due to very sensitive body hairs and whiskers (vibrissae), which they use to explore their environment. A rodent in a familiar area relies heavily on the senses of touch and smell to direct it through time-tested movements learned by exploration and knowledge of its home range. Rodents prefer a stationary object on at least one side of them as they travel and thus commonly move along walls, a fact that is very useful when designing a control program. In captivity, rodents will hide quite contentedly in a clear glass jar, since it feels enclosed and secure to them.

of their nests when they have young.) A resident male will attack strange males entering his territory. As a result, the populations become divided into "social orders" made up of the stronger (dominant) rats and the weaker (subordinate) rats. The dominant rats occupy the most favorable habitat and are usually the first group to feed. The weaker individuals may be forced to occupy "fringe areas" located farther from the primary food sources. These rats will feed and be active when the dominant rats are inactive, which explains why rats are often seen during the day in heavy rat infestations. Often in rodent control programs, it is the dominant rats that are killed first.

Rats constantly explore and re-explore their surroundings, and are wary of new foods, new objects, or changes in their environment. This behavior is termed "neophobia," meaning "a fear of new." Neophobic behavior may last for several hours, days or in pronounced cases, even weeks. As a general rule, roof rats tend to exhibit more neophobic behavior than Norway rats. Even a change in position of a familiar object causes suspicion. This is why traps and bait boxes are sometimes avoided for a day or two. Rats that have become conditioned to eating a particular food, approach new food with much suspicion and taste it cautiously. If it tastes bad or makes them sick, they won't eat it again. This behavior is called "bait (or toxicant) shyness."

Occasionally, a few rats within a colony may develop an exceptionally strong sense of neophobia. These "extra-cautious" rats (sometimes called "smart rats"), are often the survivors of control programs because they avoid all baits and traps. To control neophobic rats, patience and specialized control techniques are sometimes needed. This will be discussed in the control section.

ROOF RAT
Rattus rattus Linnaeus

The roof rat is also known as the black rat, ship rat, gray-bellied rat, Alexandrine rat and white-bellied rat. This rat originated in the arboreal forests of Southeast Asia and thus it is adapted for efficient climbing on vines, narrow ledges and wires. Roof rats probably arrived in the America with the earliest explorers of Florida in the early 1500s.

Roof rats are smaller and sleeker in appearance than the Norway rat. Adults weigh from 5 to 9 ounces (150 to 250 grams). The color of the fur is usually grayish black to a solid black, the belly varies from buff-white to all gray. The snout is pointed; the ears are large and reach the eyes when pulled down. The tail is long, and reaches the snout when pulled over the body (see Figure 15.1, and Figure 15.8, which follows page 254).

The reproductive biology of the roof rat is generally similar to the Norway rat, although the roof rat is less prolific producing only four to eight pups per litter (refer to Table 15.1). Roof rats do not interbreed with Norway rats.

The roof rat is less adaptable to the cooler temperatures as the Norway rat, and thus its range is somewhat restricted to the coastal and more tropical regions of the United States. This rat occupies the coastal areas of Washington, Oregon, and California, as well as a larger area along the Gulf and Atlantic coast states from Texas to Maryland (Figure 15.3). Roof rats are the predominat rat in many coastal cities (e.g., Houston, Miami, Seattle, San Diego, etc.). In seaports, they frequently board and become troublesome on ships. As a general rule, the roof rat does not occur more than 100 miles inland, unless the population is associated with a major waterway. For example, the roof rat is well established in St. Louis Missouri. It is also occasionally transported via deliveries of all sorts. Thus, temporary and/or small populations of roof rats are reported from time to time throughout the United States.

In regions of the country where both species or rats occur, it is not uncommon to find Norway rats inhabiting the ground and lower portions of buildings, while the roof rat establishes itself in the exterior vegetation, or in the upper stories, attics, and soffits of the same building.

Behavior

Although there are specific differences in behavior between the roof and Norway rat, many of the general behavior patterns of rats relevant to the pest management professional are similar. Important differences are discussed here and in the control section.

In their natural environment, the roof rat consumes a wide variety of vegetative foods such as berries, nuts, seeds, and fruits. They also consume insects, slugs, and snails. But like the Norway rat, the roof rat is an opportunist and will eat almost anything that is nutritional and available. The roof rat tends to eat small amounts of food in several different places during its foraging activity. This has important implications for roof rat baiting strategies.

As was the case with the Norway rat, the home range of the roof rat varies according to the location and distribution of resources in its area and other factors. Within average conditions, the roof rat ranges from about 50 to 100 feet (15 to 30 m) of its nest to explore and gather resources. But this rat is also known to travel considerable distances ranging up to 300 feet (91 m) on a daily basis. In suburban neighborhoods roof rats may live in the trees or bushes of one residence but travel to feed at another residence several houses away, using various overhead utility lines or fences as their highways between their nest and "restaurants."

The roof rat, by nature is somewhat of a skittish animal and very sensitive to changes in its environment. Occasionally, when nests are disturbed during yard cleaning, flushed roof rats abandon the particular area. It also prefers to feed under cover, or will carry exposed foods back to the nest or to nearby protected areas.

Because the roof rat gravitates towards cover and is less dependent on human food than the Norway rat, roof rats tend to become especially troublesome in suburban yards and neighborhoods that contain combinations of lush landscaping, well-established dense tree cover, fruit trees, outdoor dog pens, and/or bird feeders.

The roof rat is appropriately named because by nature it is a climber and commonly lives above the ground in "roof" or aerial areas around structures. This behavior also enables this rat to remain undetected for prolonged periods.

In tropical areas of the United States, nests are often constructed in the crowns of palm trees—especially in trees where the old fronds have not been removed for some time. Roof rats will also occasionally construct globular leafy nests in much the same way tree squirrels do. Nests are also located in clinging vines, on the sides of buildings and fences, or inside buildings in attic areas, ceiling voids, or in wall voids in roofline areas. Roof rats enter buildings from the roof or by using various utility lines, much in the same manner as do the tree squirrels. In fact, they can often be seen at night running up and down trees or along utility lines and fences. However, roof rats don't restrict themselves to aerial areas only. As local populations of roof rats grow, they will expand their nesting areas to include underground burrows within residential and industrial landscaped areas, ground floor areas inside buildings, and under piles of rubbish. In some cities, such as Phoenix, Arizona, the roof rat has been found inhabiting sewers.

RODENT CONTROL

Much has already been said about the importance of the integrated pest management (IPM) approach in structural pest control operations. The IPM approach is especially important in rodent control and involves integrating the following steps:

1. Rodent inspections
2. Sanitation
3. Rodent proofing (exclusion)
4. Population reduction (rodent killing)
   a. Trapping programs
   b. Rodenticide programs

By implementing any one of steps 2, 3, or 4 alone, some degree of rodent control will be achieved. However, rodent control programs are most effective and efficient on a long-term basis when these steps are integrated.

Rodent Control Is Situational Specific

Eliminating or "controlling" rodents among the many different types of operations and facilities in urban environments varies dramatically. Eliminating a mouse or two in an orderly residential garage for example, is usually quite easy. But eliminating mice in a cluttered and messy grocery store will be difficult. Or, consider the difficulty and complexity of attempting to control rats inside zoological parks and livestock facilities with strict baiting restrictions, risks to expensive animals, and the food and harborage competition to baits and traps. Such jobs are labor intensive, sophisticated and expensive. The pest management professionals must always carefully consider each type of situation—especially when considering sales proposals. Specific management strategies for each specific urban facilities is beyond the scope of this chapter. However, a general overview of the important factors affecting rodent pest management are profiled in Table 15.2. Professionals requiring site-specific management strategies should consult the appropriate references listed at the end of this chapter.

Rodent Inspections

Good rodent control begins with good inspections. A rodent inspection should always be conducted before any actual control program is begun. A quality inspection enables a professional to implement a program that is cost-efficient while minimizing the chances for expensive and profit-eating callbacks.

To conduct a quality inspection, the professional should be alert for as many rodent signs as possible: These include: (1) fecal pellets, (2) tracks, (3) gnawing damage, (4) burrows, (5) runways, (6) grease marks, (7) urine stains, (8) live or dead rodents, (9) rodent sounds, and (10) rodent odors (especially mice).

Fecal pellets ("droppings") are the most commonly encountered signs of a rodent infestation (refer to Figure 15.1). While rodents are active they are regularly defecating. The house mouse may

Table 15.2. Characteristics of some common anticoagulant rodenticides.

Class/Common Name	% in bait	Food Bait	Liquid Bait	Tracking Powder	Comments
First-Generation Anticoagulants					
Hydrosycoumarins					Generally considered multiple-dose toxicants—must be ingested in repeated doses over 4 to 10 days for rats, sometimes longer for mice. Genetic resistance developed in some locations.
coumafuryl	0.025	X	X		
warfarin	0.025	X	X	X	
warfarin and sulfaquinoxaline	0.025	X			
sodium salt of warfarin	0.54		X		
indandiones					Chlorophacinone and diphacinone may cause death in rats occasionally after only one feeding, but two to four feedings are usually required. Genetic resistance developed to some of the indandiones in some locations. Pindone must be ingested in repeated doses over 4 to 10 days for rats—sometimes longer for mice.
chlorophacinone	0.005	X		X	
diphacinone	0.005	X	X	X	
isovaleryl				X	
pindone	0.025	X	X		
sodium salt of pindone	0.54		X		
Second-Generation Anticoagulants					
Hydroxycoumarins					Single feeding is sometimes lethal, but feeding continues death (3 to 7 days). Effective against warfarin-resistant rodents but may require more feedings.
brodifacoum	0.005	X			
bromadiolone	0.005	X			
difethialone	0.025	X			

produce 30 to 100 feces daily while rats may excrete 30 to 50 fecal pellets daily. Mouse fecal pellets measure from 1/8- to 1/4-inch (3 to 6mm) long with at least one—and sometimes both—ends pointed. The fecal pellets of the Norway rat measure 1/2- to 1-inch (13 to 25mm) in length and usually at least one end is blunt. Rodent feces are usually shiny black, but the color may vary depending on age and what the rodent has been eating. Feces that are fresh are usually soft. Mouse feces become hard and brittle in most environments in as soon as three hours. Rat feces may remain soft for up to 24 hours depending on the environment. Active infestations and the high-activity areas of the rodents can be determined by removing old fecal pellets and noting the presence and locations of any new feces.

While inspecting for rodents, the feces of rats or mice must not be confused with the feces of other animals that may also be active in the building or area such as American cockroaches, crickets, toads, bats, squirrels, etc. Cockroach fecal pellets tend to be slightly smaller and more slender than mouse droppings, and usually contain distinct ridges along the dropping. Also, American cockroach and other large insect droppings are blunt on both ends. Bat and toad droppings are made up of mostly insect fragments and disintegrate easily when pressed. In addition, toad droppings do not have any hair fragments.

Squirrel feces appear similar to rat droppings, although squirrel feces are typically about 1 inch (2.5cm) in length, and have a twist at the midpoint in the pellet, or two pellets are attached with a narrow pinch. Also, when attempting to differentiate squirrels from rats, a full inspection should be conducted analyzing animal sightings, locale, etc.

Finally, because the feces of each of these animals are most often black, color cannot be used as a distinguishing feature.

Rodent **tracks** are easily seen where there is dust or soft moist or wet soil (refer to cover page of this chapter). The commensal rodents have five toes on their hind feet and four toes on the front feet. It is usually the hind foot that leaves the most visible track. The hind foot *track* of a rat will measure about 3/4 to 1 inch (2.0 to 2.5cm) whereas the mouse's hind foot track will measure only about 3/8 inch (1.0 cm) or less. Rodents—especially rats—also leave "tail drag" marks that will appear between their foot tracks. Sometimes a tracking patch of talc (unscented baby powder) can be placed in suspected rodent areas to verify the presence of rats or mice, as well as their traveling patterns within an area.

Gnawing damage to various items or parts of buildings is often seen in rodent infestations. As mentioned earlier, rodents possess a single pair of incisor teeth that grow constantly at the rate of 0.3 to 0.4 millimeters each day (Figure 15.9). But contrary to popular belief, rodents do not have to gnaw on objects to keep these incisors in check. The rodent grinding the incisors against one another does this. Nevertheless, rodents do gnaw on all types of objects.

Mice frequently gnaw small, clean-cut holes about 1-1/2 inch (4.0 cm) in diameter. In residences, the gnawing damage of mice is often seen in kitchen cabinets where they shred paper and tear holes in the corners of food boxes and bags. In bathrooms, mice seem to enjoy gnawing on bar soap stored in the cabinets.

Gnawing damage from rats can be very significant because of their size. Gnawed holes from rats will be about 2 inches (5.0cm) or more in diameter, and often contain rough, torn edges. Rats commonly gnaw on wooden structural members such as door corners, joists of flooring and ceilings, wall studs, etc.

The burrows of rats may be found next to walls, along foundations, or beneath debris or

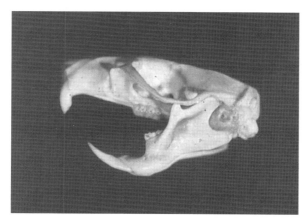

FIGURE 15.9. A rodent skull. Note the prominent incisor teeth and space behind the incisors; characteristics common to rodents.

shrubbery. Active ground burrows are usually clear of vegetation, and the burrow entrance appears compacted and smooth. In some instances fresh soil will have been recently kicked out of the burrow. To verify active burrows, wads of paper can be stuffed into the opening or the burrows can be caved in with dirt and rechecked the following day. Roof rats nests will be loosely constructed in woodpiles or in other locations off the ground in or out of structures. They also may construct globular nests within bushes, vines or trees.

Mice will also occupy burrows, but in most cases, mouse burrows occur beneath slabs inside of buildings. Entrance to these burrows is usually located at breaks in the slabs, between expansion joints, or nearby any support pillar footings. After the burrows have been used repeatedly, darkened "smudge" marks will be present around the openings to the mouse slab burrows.

Runways are usually evident in rodent infestations because rodents repeatedly and routinely use the same pathways between their nests and food sources. Runways are easier to detect with Norway rats than with mice or roof rats. Outdoors, fresh runways are smooth, well packed, and free of vegetation. Indoors, runways along floors or rafters usually show an absence of dust or dirt. In insulated attics, mouse runways are often evident beneath or through the insulation. Because runways are often well marked by rodent urine, the astute professional can identify active runways by taking a moment to smell suspected paths.

Grease marks (or rub marks) from the oil and dirt of rats and mice often appear along wall areas next to runways. Grease marks may also occur around bottoms of joists where rodents have been traveling along beams or sill plates, on stairways, or around burrow openings in walls, floors or ceilings.

Urine stains left by rodents may occur on their runways and areas that they frequent. Rodent urine will fluoresce under ultraviolet light. Thus, 12v portable blacklights can be used to detect rodent trails or urine contamination to items or food products (although a certain degree of skill is required using blacklights because other items such as food starch, and some cleaning agents will also fluoresce).

The sightings of live or dead rodents are a sure confirmation as to the presence of rodents. An inspection during the rodent's high activity period (at dusk or just after dark) often can provide information as to the severity of an infestation as well as the activity areas of the rodents.

Various **sounds** produced by rodents and their young such as high-pitched squeaks, gnawing sounds, scratching, digging, and sounds of rodents fighting can be heard if the professional is careful to listen and conducts the inspection quietly.

Rodent odors are often detectable in well-established infestations as both rats and mice produce characteristic odors from urine and various body glands. Rodent odors may be particularly pronounced in large mouse infestations, and may persist for a considerable amount of time after the mice have been eliminated from a building.

Clients often asked pest professionals to provide an estimate of the number of rodents inhabiting their building. In most cases, it is not possible to accurately estimate the numbers of rodent in any particular infestation. Generally, when rodent signs are fresh and found in abundance, you can assume there is a heavy population present. When the signs and sightings of rodents are few, the infestation may consist of only one or a few rodents. Overall, it is best to characterize rodent infestations as minor, moderate, or severe. When in doubt, it is better to overestimate the severity of a rodent infestation. Underestimating a rodent infestation often results in not placing out enough traps or baits that may then lead to a series of expensive callbacks, delayed results, and dissatisfied customers.

Sanitation

The "bottom line" to long-term rodent control is the fact that rodents must have adequate food and shelter to live and thrive. Thus, wherever there is an abundance of rats or mice, there is usually also an abundance of food and shelter available to the rodents. The removal or reduction of these factors alone via sanitation practices will have tremendous impact in reducing rodent populations, even without the use of any traps or poisons.

Good housekeeping practices are an absolute must in rodent control whether the structure be a residence, office building or food-handling establishment. By using *only* poisons on an intermittent basis to control rodents, without any attempt to eliminate their food and shelter via sanitation, rodent populations will quickly and repeatedly rebound. Moreover, without sanitation, even the highest quality rodent baits may not be able to compete with the available foods the resident rodent population is already and comfortably accustomed to feeding on.

With mice, it is often difficult to completely eliminate all food and shelter sources because of their small size and the fact that they require such small amounts of food. However, the more food and shelter *easily* available to the mice, the more quickly a severe infestation can result, and the more difficult it will be to achieve control.

Because rats require substantially more food, water, and shelter than do mice, a severe infestation of rats is usually indicative of a sanitation problem. Therefore, sanitation is the backbone of a successful rat control program, and will often mean the difference between success or failure in controlling rats.

Sanitation programs must always include both the outside and inside of affected buildings. Outside, all rubbish piles must be eliminated. Improper handling of garbage and refuse (e.g., improper selection, use, and maintenance of industrial dumpsters) may result in a prime source of food and shelter for rodents, and thus, attract them to any building. When it is necessary to accumulate food refuse, it must be kept in rodent-proof containers until it is removed from the premises. Industrial dumpsters, for example—especially those used around food-serving establishments—must be carefully selected for proper volume, pick-up schedule, cleaning, placement, and other factors so as to not attract rodents to the property.

Grass, weeds, and other undesirable vegetation adjacent to buildings should be removed. If the building is landscaped, it should be properly maintained. Overgrown landscape plantings (e.g., globular-shaped ornamental plantings) can provide rodents with both cover and food. Lumber, rock piles, rubbish, old equipment, construction materials, etc., should all be eliminated if possible. Items that must be kept should be stored at least 18 inches (46cm) off the ground and 12 inches (31cm) away from walls or fences.

Indoors, all potential rodent harborages must be identified and eliminated or modified. Such areas as obscure corners, shelves, under and in cabinets, worktables; lockers and equipment must not be overlooked or neglected as these dark, out-of-the-way areas provide rodents with ideal harborage. Where possible, rodentproofing of these areas as well as stairwells, machinery, double walls, false ceilings and floors, hollow tile partitions and boxed in pipes and conduits may be necessary.

Proper storage practices are essential in rodent IPM programs. Improper storage practices often results in creating inaccessible rodent harborages. It also prevents thorough inspections and proper baiting or trapping. Moreover, rodent damage to stored materials can be more easily detected and kept to a minimum when good storage practices are followed. In warehouses and storage areas of commercial facilities, products should be on pallets (preferably 8 to 12 inches (20 to 31 cm) off the floor), 18 to 24 inches (46 to 61cm) from adjacent walls, not stacked more than one to two pallets wide and separated by an aisle. This practice creates **inspection aisles** and is one of the most important rules of good housekeeping in commercial food accounts. Inspection aisles permit inspection and cleaning, reduce rodent (and insect) harborage areas, and allow for the installation of appropriate insect and rodent control measures.

Around residences, homeowners should be informed as to the importance of proper refuse management, storage practices, and the proper feeding of pets and wildlife to avoid attracting rodents to the yard or home. Residential garbage cans must not be overfilled and contain tight-fitting covers. Woodpiles and any other type of outdoor storage should be elevated off the ground to help eliminate potential rat or mouse harborage.

Backyard infestations of rats in urban and suburban developments are commonly associated with exterior doghouses, bird and squirrel feeders, improper garbage management, improper composting practices, and vegetable gardens and fruit trees that are not properly maintained. In each of these cases exploring rats will seize the opportunity to feed on any spilled and surplus foods associated with these situations.

A pest professional can educate their residential clients as to the importance feeding dogs and cats only what they will eat and then remove the food and any spillage. Pet and wildlife foods should be stored in areas inaccessible to rodents or in rodentproof containers. Compost piles should never contain any human food scraps (e.g., meat or fish scraps). And, fruits from trees and excess vegetables from gardens should be picked up several times each week.

Rodentproofing (Exclusion)

Ideally, the best way to control mice and rats is to make it impossible for them to gain entry into structures. It can be difficult or impractical to exclude mice completely as even adult mice can pass through openings 3/8-inch (1.0 cm) wide. Furthermore, mice commonly enter buildings through open doors or windows or are carried into buildings inside merchandise. Nevertheless, it is good pest management (for both rodents and insects) for building owners or pest professionals to rodentproof a building as much as possible.

When considering rodentproofing, every possible route of rodent access to the building must be considered. Generally, all openings greater than 1/4-inch (0.6 cm) should be sealed to exclude mice. For rats, all openings greater than 1/2-inch (1.3 cm) should be sealed.

Points where utility lines penetrate a wall are likely access sites for rodents. The openings around service conduits such as water, electricity, air conditioning, drain pipes, and vents should all be sealed.

Sheet metal, hardware cloth and mortar can be used to seal the spaces around these and other types of openings. Copper-mesh stuffing and coarse steel wool can be stuffed into gaps and holes, but should be sealed with mortar, or the appropriate durable sealant to provide for a long term closing of the holes.

Broken basement windows, warped doors and unscreened vents are all invasion routes for mice and rats. Vents should be covered with a metal grillwork, backed by rust-resistant screening

The spaces beneath doors should be checked and, if need be, reduced. A 12-inch (30 cm) sheet metal (26 gauge) kicking plate should be attached to the outside of the door with the lower edge not more than 1/4 inch (6mm) from the floor. The door casing should also be protected with sheet metal to prevent mice and rats from widening cracks by gnawing.

Rodents can be deterred from climbing pipes on the outside of buildings by fitting metal guards around the pipes. These should be made of 26-gauge sheet metal, fitted close to the wall at the rear and projecting 12 inches (35 cm) outward form the pipe. An added measure to deter climbing by Norway rats and mice is to apply a 12-inch band of hard glossy paint around the outside of brick or stone walls about 3-1/2 feet above the ground. A 12-inch band of glossy paint around a vertical pipe will also help prevent climbing. These measures however, may not be very effective against roof rats.

Roofs should be checked to see that shingles are down tight and sheathing is complete. Also, check roof ventilators, screen vents and louvered in-wall vents. Use hardware cloth (1/4-inch width screening) to prevent larger animals from entering through vents. Screen chimneys and vent pipes if they are serving as entryways.

In the normal course of commercial pest control work, it is not always possible to do extensive rodentproofing. And in some inner-city areas that contain high populations of rodents and many old decrepit buildings, permanent rodent control is nearly impossible because rodents are able to get into these buildings on a regular basis. But the professional should keep in mind that there are many cases where rodentproofing can be accomplished with a minimum of effort. Using only a few simple tools, the professional can provide a basic rodentproofing service as part of the control program. At the very least, the professional should take every opportunity to educate building owners as to the importance of building maintenance, and encourage them to seal holes and cracks in doors and windows and around pipes and wiring (refer to Figure 15.10).

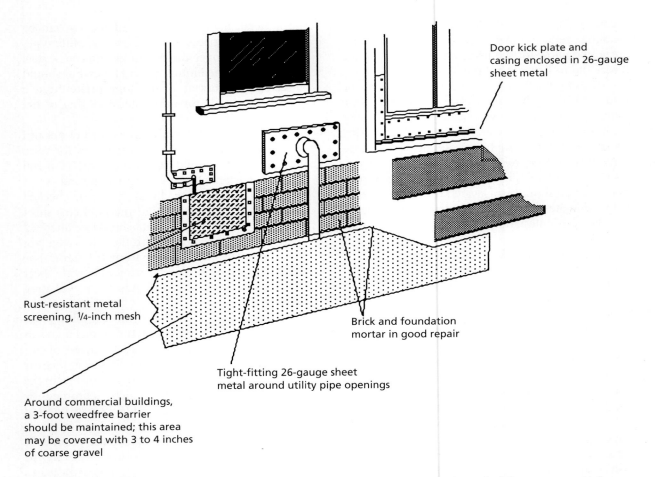

Door kick plate and casing enclosed in 26-gauge sheet metal

Rust-resistant metal screening, ¼-inch mesh

Brick and foundation mortar in good repair

Tight-fitting 26-gauge sheet metal around utility pipe openings

Around commercial buildings, a 3-foot weedfree barrier should be maintained; this area may be covered with 3 to 4 inches of coarse gravel

FIGURE 15.10. The pest management professional should take every opportunity to educate building owners as to the importance of pest exclusion principles.

Population Reduction
Nonchemical Control: Trapping

Trapping can be one of the most effective methods of controlling rodents. And trapping provides some advantages in control programs over the use of baits. For example: (1) traps provide an alternative for clients not wishing to have pesticides used at their site; (2) for small infestations, traps provide quick results; and (3) traps allow for immediate disposal of dead rodents, thereby eliminating any potential odor problems from dead rodents in inaccessible areas.

Furthermore, traps are the best rodent control tool for the following situations:

- poison baits may pose a potential hazard to children, pets, or wildlife;
- where rodenticides are not permitted or desired due to the possibility of food contamination;
- when rodents exhibit bait shyness;
- when dead rodents may create odor problems;

- to provide maintenance mouse control programs for large commercial facilities.

Trapping also has the following drawbacks: (1) in cases of severe infestations, trapping can be laborious and time consuming; (2) trapping programs are generally not as cost-efficient as baiting programs; (3) some rodents avoid traps or develop a fear of traps; (4) some traps can seriously injure people, pets, and wildlife if inadvertently encountered, and (5) some traps are not humane in the way they kill rodents. Three types of rodent traps are most commonly used in rodent pest management: (1) snap traps, (2) multiple-catch mousetraps, and (3) glue board traps.

The ordinary **wooden snap trap** is familiar to everyone. They have been used by professionals and homeowners alike for many years. However, new plastic models of rodent traps have emerged over the past several years and their shapes and designs differ dramatically (see Figure 15.11).

The key rule for using any type of rodent trap

FIGURE 15.11. Rodent traps have taken on many new shapes and sizes over the past few years, rendering many of them easier and safer for the handler to set.

is to use plenty of traps. For example, six traps is about right for one or two mice in a residential kitchen (if two traps are placed behind the stove, two behind the refrigerator, and two underneath the kitchen sink, the mice are usually caught the first night). In a storage room of a restaurant, two dozen traps might be required.

Traps are most effective when installed into the high-activity areas of the infesting rodent colony. These areas are often darkened corners, along walls, behind appliances and objects, and all areas where droppings are evident. Because mice do not travel very far, mousetraps should be spaced about 10 feet apart. In severe mouse infestations, a spacing of about six feet will provide good results. With rats, traps can be spaced 15 to 20 feet apart.

Traps should be positioned to maximize the chances of rodents passing over the traps during their natural travels along their runways. For example, traps should extend from a wall at a right angle with the trigger end nearly touching the wall. If traps are set parallel to the wall, set them in pairs with the triggers situated to intercept rodents coming from either direction. To trap roof rats, set traps on tree limbs, under vegetation on a backyard fence or trellis, or on other aboveground locations roof rats are known to frequent. Traps can also be fastened with wire to overhead rafters, beams, and pipes.

When food doesn't seem readily available to the rodents (garages or attics), baits should serve as a strong attractant. Baits that give off an aroma such as bacon, nuts, hot dog slices, or peanut butter are often effective in these situations. When solid baits are used, they are most effective if *tied* to the trigger (carrying a small packet of dental floss in the truck is a convenient method for securing baits to traps). Rodents have an uncanny ability to remove unsecured bait without setting off traps.

In situations where food is abundant (i.e., baits may not serve as a strong attractant), the use of nesting material such as dental floss, cotton, Styrofoam, or any other soft material can be tied to the trigger to lure a rodent to the trap. Also, the use of snap traps with expanded triggers ("professional models") do not need to be baited if they are strategically placed in rodent runways to trap those rodents running and stumbling onto whatever happens to be in their path (see Figure 15.12).

Improvements have been made over the years to the original rodent snap trap making them more versatile and easier and faster to set. Some newer mouse snap traps can be set quickly with one hand. Some rat traps can now be set by using one's foot to set the trap. Better-designed triggers make it much more difficult for rodents to steal the bait without setting off the trap. For large trapping jobs, where several hundred traps may be required, such traps can save valuable time and labor.

Some rats are extra-cautious (neophobic) animals and can prove difficult to catch. Other rats may be "trap shy" because of the rat narrowly escaping a previous trap encounter). Clever trapping strategies may be required for neophobic or trap-shy rats. One method is to camouflage the trap. **Unset traps** can be buried in sawdust, grain, straw or similar materials within a shallow pie pan or an empty cardboard soda carton. Place baits in several small pieces on top of the pan or box with the hidden trap below. Once these baits are taken, only the trigger bait should then be installed directly over the trigger and the trap set.

Automatic, multiple-catch traps (curiosity traps) are specifically made for catching mice. These traps provide excellent preventative mouse control in commercial accounts such as restaurants, warehouses, processing plants, etc. They are especially useful in accounts where long-term and continual protection is required. There are now several brands within each of the two basic models

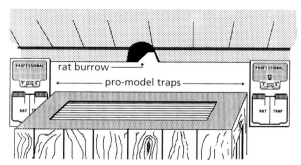

FIGURE 15.12. Rodent traps do not need to be baited if professional-model traps are used and the traps are placed in rodent runways.

of wind-up style, and low-profile style traps. With the wind-up traps, mice are flipped into a holding chamber after stepping on a spring-loaded trap platform in the trap entryway. The low-profile traps work via a trap-door principle.

If placed correctly, little difference is likely to be seen in catch effectiveness between the different style traps (see Figure 15.13). What is perhaps more important to the professional is selecting those models that allow for efficient servicing. Too, some traps are made of plastic, some of metal. Some traps contain see-thru plates, others do not.

All of the multiple-catch traps offer various options such as a plastic see-thru inspection covers and/or removable plastic trays to facilitate fast and clean inspections. The low-profile trap enables it to be placed underneath pallets and equipment, as well as in suspended ceilings. The wind-up traps can be placed either parallel or perpendicular to the wall. The low-profile trap works best if placed so that the entry hole is parallel to the wall or object, but will also work if the entry hole is positioned perpendicularly. Glue boards can be placed inside the low-profile trap to expedite inspections and mouse removal (see Figure 15.14). Inserted glue boards can eliminate the need for the inspector to carefully inspect the trap with a flashlight before opening the trap. Additionally, inserted glue boards eliminate the extra time needed to deal with live mice (via drowning or some other lethal method) caught in the trap at the time of inspection. Thus, inserted glue boards can save a significant amount of time—especially in situations where many of these traps are used, e.g., large warehouse accounts, food plants, etc.

Mice enter multiple-catch traps because they tend to investigate new "holes" in their territory. Captured mice appear to attract other mice—especially other litter mates. In heavy infestations, it is possible to capture up to 15 or more mice in one evening. Multiple-catch traps do not need to be baited, but in areas where food may be limited, smudges of peanut butter directly inside the entryways of the traps may increase their catch.

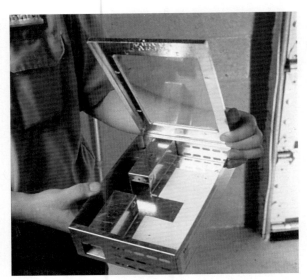

FIGURE 15.14. By inserting a glue board inside a multiple-catch trap, the trap serves as both an insect monitoring tool and as a more effective mousetrap. The glue board can be removed from the metal trap and replaced as needed.

Large numbers of these traps are often used in commercial accounts. They should be placed in areas of high or continual mouse activity, as well as in locations that may provide *potential* mouse entry such as nearby exterior doorways (see Figure 15.15), near utility openings through walls and any other openings. Particular attention should be paid to wall areas that are bordered outside by weeds, fields, accumulations of debris, or any other condition that provides harborage for mice.

For efficient use of multiple catch traps in large accounts, good records should be kept on a long-term basis. Each trap should have a slip attached to the trap recording the inspection day and number of captures. Also, it is wise to maintain a logbook listing all traps as well as a map noting the trap location and number of mice caught each month. In this way, it can be determined which are the most mouse active areas as well as those areas not requiring any traps. As mentioned, traps located along exterior walls that are adjacent to weedy fields or other types of outdoor mouse harborage often produce the most mice. In high mouse-activity areas, traps can be closely spaced and placed both indoors and outdoors to prevent serious mouse infestations from becoming established. Some pest management utilize their curiosity traps along exterior areas by installing them inside metal rat-size bait stations that protects them from the elements.

The odor of dead mice inside multiple-catch traps will not repel other mice from entering, but traps should be emptied and scraped clean as soon

FIGURE 15.13. Multiple-catch mouse-traps are now available in a wide variety of models and materials.

FIGURE 15.15. Multiple-catch traps placed directly inside of exterior commercial overhead doors helps to capture incoming mice.

as possible to prevent invasion of insects, potential food contaminants, or annoying dead animal odors. In traps such as glue boards or plastic traps that do not line the bottom of the trap, the use of nonstick food sprays can be used on the base of the traps to help prevent dead mice from sticking to the trap, and thus facilitate quick cleaning.

Glue traps can also be used to capture some rodents, although generally glue traps are less effective than snap traps or multiple-catch traps. Still, glue traps are convenient and they can provide a 2-in-1 advantage by also acting as monitoring devices for IPM programs. In areas where there is excessive dirt, dust or water, glue traps must be placed within some type of cover, as these factors will reduce their effectiveness. Hot and cold temperatures also decrease the effectiveness of some glue boards.

Glue traps are more effective for capturing mice than rats. In severe mouse infestations they can be used to help reduce the populations, although other devices will need to supplement the glue traps, since some mice are repelled by glue surfaces and learn to avoid them. When glue traps are used, they are most effective when placed in rodents' runways and high-activity areas. In areas where food is scarce, volatile foods (e.g., vanilla extract, chocolate, molasses, peanut butter, etc.) placed in the middle of the traps may help to attract rodents to the trap.

As has been observed by pest professionals for many years, it is the juvenile mice of the colonies that tend to be captured on glue traps. Moreover, many mice are capable of escaping from the more inexpensive cardboard-style glue traps. With the tray-style glue traps, mice (young and mature) that step onto the tray with all four legs rarely escape because there an ample amount of glue and thus greater holding power as compared to the cardboard-style traps.

Glue traps can also be used for rats but must be

used wisely. Rats are capable of escaping glue boards if they do not get all four feet on the trap. If a rat becomes partially captured, the rat may drag the trap around for some time and sometimes the trap becomes stuck to an object, creating somewhat of a mess. Therefore, rat glue traps should be secured to an object or to the floor, or the glue trap can be secured to the top of a piece of cardboard several inches larger than the glue board itself before being placed out on the floor. As with the other types of traps, rodents that experience a near-lethal encounter with a glue trap will learn to avoid these devices.

Glue traps should never be placed in areas where children or pets will have contact with them, nor should they be placed in high-visibility areas. In the event of a child, pet (or adult) becoming affixed to a glue trap, vegetable-cooking oil will separate the glue from the person or pet.

Chemical Control: Rodenticides

Rodenticides are pesticides that kill rodents. Every pest management professional must understand the correct use of rodenticides and always strictly adhere to each rodenticide's label directions. Safety must be the first consideration. Some rodenticides are highly toxic and can be fatal even in relatively small amounts to humans, pets, or livestock. Under no circumstances should professionally labeled

Additional Tips Using Rodent Traps

- Before starting a trapping program, eliminate as many sources of food as possible to encourage rodents to explore and forage for food and eagerly respond to bait on traps.
- Keep traps clean and in good working condition.
- Store traps in plastic bags to avoid absorption of repellent odors.
- Don't use traps with warped bases. The wobbling will frighten the rodent.
- Avoid handling dead rodents with bare hands to prevent contact with ectoparasites or disease organisms (e.g., hantavirus, LCM, etc.).
- Oil moving trap parts with an odorless, light pharmaceutical-grade mineral oil.
- Human and dead-rodent odors on traps do not cause a reduction in catch, but the odors of natural predators, such as cats or dogs, on traps may cause rodent aversion. Therefore, do not touch pets prior to handling traps.
- Glue traps can be stored in vehicles during warm weather by placing them inside Styrofoam coolers containing gelatin ice packs.

rodenticides be given to the public for application by a layperson.

Today's rodenticides are categorized into two broad categories: **anticoagulants** and **nonanticoagulants.**

Anticoagulants. These rodenticides cause death in rodents by disrupting the normal blood-clotting mechanisms, which causes rodents to die of internal bleeding. Most rodent control today is accomplished using one of the many anticoagulant baits currently available. With all anticoagulants, death is delayed and usually occurs within 3 to 10 days after feeding begins depending on the particular bait, and the amount consumed by the rodent.

Some anticoagulant baits are available to the general public as ready-to-use baits, but specific formulations are available for use by only pest management professionals. Anticoagulant baits make excellent rodenticides for several reasons.

First, rodents die slowly over a couple of days, without any pain. Thus, they do not associate their weakened condition to their feeding on the bait. Rodents return to the bait repeatedly without developing any "bait shyness." Second, anticoagulants are relatively low in hazard to people and companion animals, e.g., dogs and cats (although some anticoagulants are more hazardous to pets and livestock than others). And third, the delay in the onset of symptoms coupled with readily available antidotes (vitamin K1) provides the time and means of preventing serious consequences for accidental poisonings in humans, pets, and livestock (providing the poisoning is not too severe, and is detected early).

The commercially available anticoagulants are offered in a variety of formulations such as food baits (grain pellets, grain meals, block-style, canary-grass seeds) liquid baits, and tracking powders. The food and liquid baits have excellent acceptance by rodents and, thus, are the most widely used formulations. Tracking powders provide a versatile tool to supplement baiting programs.

Anticoagulants are classified as: (1) first-generation anticoagulants or (2) second-generation anticoagulants (see Table 15.2).

The **first-generation anticoagulants** are considered multiple-dose rodenticides. Common examples of first-generation anticoagulants include **warfarin, chlorophacinone, diphacinone, coumafuryl,** and **pindone.** However, in the pest management industry, chlorophacinone and diphacinone are the most widely used actives. For the multiple-dose anticoagulant baits to be effective, rodents must feed on the bait for several times (multiple doses) over a period of 3 to 10 days and sometimes longer for mice. Generally, the better the acceptance

(and thus intense feeding) by rodents, the better the control results. First-generation anticoagulants must be available continuously until all rodents stop feeding. This may take two to three weeks.

The **second-generation anticoagulants** were specifically designed to kill rats and mice resistant to the first-generation anticoagulants (see resistance discussion). **Brodifacoum, bromadiolone,** and **difethialone** represent the three second-generation anticoagulant active ingredients available in the United States. These anticoagulants kill rodents in the same manner as the first-generation compounds, but there are important differences.

Second-generation anticoagulants kill with very small amounts of bait (e.g., only about one-half to one or two pellets can be lethal to a mouse). Thus, a lethal dose can be ingested by the rodent in as few as one feeding ("single dose"), or at least with much fewer feedings than the first-generation anticoagulants. However, death is still delayed, usually occurring between three and five days, and sometimes longer. So, even if rodents consume a lethal dose after one feeding, they will continue to live and feed on the bait for several more days if bait is available.

Nonanticoagulants. Some of the nonanticoagulant rodenticides act as single-dose poisons, while others may need to be consumed over several days. The manner in which they produce death varies. The nonanticoagulant rodenticides include the actives **bromethalin, cholecalciferol** and **zinc phosphide** (see Table 15.3).

Acute rodenticides that were widely used in years past such as **strychnine, antu, red squill** and **sodium fluoroacetate (compound 1080)** are no longer registered for commensal rodent control in the United States.

Bromethalin was registered as a rodenticide in 1984. It kills rodents by disrupting the energy production within the cells of the body. This results in the build-up of fluid (edema), especially around the spinal column and brain, leading to a decrease in nerve impulses, paralysis, and death.

Bromethalin is a unique "acute rodenticide" because a single-dose of bait is usually lethal to rodents, but death is delayed for one to four days. Thus, bait shyness does not appear to be a significant problem. Moreover, rodents stop eating the bait after they have consumed a lethal dose (with rats, this is usually one feeding). Thus, relatively small amounts of bait need to be available. Because bromethalin's mode of action is completely different from that of the anticoagulants, it kills anticoagulant-resistant rodents.

The rodenticide **cholecalciferol**, is actually vitamin D_3, which, in small dosages, is needed for good health in most mammals. But vitamin D_3 is toxic to small mammals such as rodents in the doses they would acquire in the cholecalciferol bait. Cholecalciferol will act as a single-dose poison if a sufficient amount is consumed by a rodent in one feeding but can act as a multiple-dose poison if consumed in lesser amounts over a couple of days. With mice, this poison usually is eaten in small, multiple feedings over a period of several days.

Cholecalciferol works by releasing and mobilizing calcium from the bones into the bloodstream. This reaction produces a condition called hypercalcemia (excessive calcium in the blood) and death eventually results from heart failure. Like bromethalin, cholecalciferol kills anticoagulant-resistant rodents because its mode of action is completely different from that of the anticoagulants. An important advantage to note about cholecalciferol is that it is the only rodenticide bait that can be used for organic commodity producers (for a complete list, refer to the National Organic Program website at: **www.ams.usda.gov/nop**).

Bromethalin and cholecalciferol are considered low to moderate in hazard. Dogs however, appear to be especially sensitive to cholecalciferol, and an effective antidote to quickly and reliably reverse cholecalciferol's activity is not available. Therefore, this rodenticide should not be used when companion animals are active at the problem site.

Because of the low concentrations of the toxicants in these baits, relatively large amounts of baits would need to be ingested by people, pets, and other non-target animals to be lethal. And no secondary toxicity is reported with either compound. However, in sufficient doses, these poisons would have the same effect on people and all animals as with rodents. Thus, proper and careful use of bromethalin and cholecalciferol (as with all rodenticides) is necessary to prevent accidental poisoning.

The rodenticide **zinc phosphide** is a black powder with a distinctive garlic-like odor that is said to be attractive to rats and mice, but unattractive to people and pets. Zinc phosphide has been used successfully for many years as ready-made baits and tracking powders, as well as concentrated powders that are be mixed with food baits (e.g., dog and cat food) to obtain quick kill (24 to 48 hours) of rodents. Rats readily take to fresh food baits containing zinc phosphide especially if prebaiting is done. The safety record of zinc phosphide is good, but it is moderately toxic and requires special handling. All mixing should be done in a well-ventilated area. Potential secondary hazards are very low. Zinc phosphide's quick action and effectiveness make it one of the most useful of the acute nonanticoagulant rodenticides.

Before the advent of the newer and much more effective rodenticides, **strychnine** was used as rodenticide on poisoned seeds for mouse control. Strychnine is a highly toxic, fast-acting poison that attacks a mammal's nervous system. Only small amounts are required to kill even large animals such as dogs (death can occur as soon as 12 minutes following ingestion). Rarely is there enough time to get medical attention for pets or livestock that have accidentally consumed the bait. Dogs and other animals have died after ingesting only a couple of strychnine pellets placed in mole tunnels. Moreover, death via this nerve poison is very painful. For all these reasons, strychnine is no longer registered for commensal rodent control.

Rodenticide Selection and Use

There are three types of rodenticide materials used in the pest management industry: (1) **baits** [as food

Table 15.3. Characteristics of the nonanticoagulant rodenticides.

Class/Common Name	Precentage Active Ingredient in Food Bait	Mode of Action	Time to Death	Bait Shyness	Hazard	Rodents Controlled		
						House Mice	Norway Rats	Roof Rats
bromethalin	0.01	Central nervous system depression and paralysis	2–4 days	None reported	Low to medium	Yes	Yes	Yes
cholecalciferol	0.075	Mobilizes calcium, resulting in death from hypercalcemia	3–4 days	None reported	Low to medium	Yes	Yes	Yes
zinc phosphide	2.0	Phosphine gas enters circulatory system, causing heart paralysis, gastrointestinal and liver damage	1/2–20 hours	Moderate to high	Medium	Yes	Yes	Yes

baits and liquid baits], (2) **tracking powders**, and (3) **fumigants**.

Baits. The majority of rodent control conducted today is accomplished using rodenticide **food baits**. Most commercially prepared rodent baits are made of various mixtures of common grains, although some baits are primarily seed based (e.g., canary grass, sunflower seeds, etc.). Commercial baits are available in several forms: (1) pellets, (2) loose meal, (3) packet baits, and (4) block baits (see Figure 15.16). Some formulations are more appropriate (or required) in some situations than others.

The **pellet bait** formulation provides for a convenient, moisture-resistant bait that also offers the rodent a food particle it can readily pick up and handle. This may encourage rodents to feed. Pellet-shaped foods are also prone to being carried off and hoarded in various spots by the rodents. This can cause pesticide translocation concerns inside certain types of facilities (schools, stores, homes, and similar sensitive sites).

Loose-meal baits are less susceptible to translocation, but are more susceptible to absorbing moisture from the air. Thus, they are less suitable for use in damp or humid locations because meal baits can spoil quickly.

FIGURE 15.16. Rodenticide grain baits are available in several different formulations.

Packet-style baits are more of a application package than a bait formulation. Small amounts of meal or pellets are sealed in plastic, cellophane, or paper packets to render them ready to use. Sealed packets can add longevity to baits placed outdoors within bait boxes, and aid in rodent monitoring by visually confirming rodent activity as rodents must gnaw into the packet to feed on the bait. Ounce for ounce, packet baits are usually more expensive than the equivalent bait in bulk.

Packet baits are vulnerable to being either accidentally dropped or placed by people in areas where non-target wildlife, companion animals, and children may encounter them. Too, rodents sometimes pick up the packets (e.g., from within tamper-resistant bait stations), and translocate the bait to non-target areas. When packet baits are stuffed into rat burrows by inexperienced or lay applicators, they become prone to being pushed out of rat burrows by rats rendering them available to pets and wild animals and birds. (Thus, loose bulk pellets applied deeply into the rat burrow using a long-handled spoon provides for a less hazardous method of baiting rat burrows).

Block baits have benefited from food-processing technology and many are now made in the form of extruded blocks—similar to the method used to make dry dog food. Block baits offer versatile baiting for all types of baiting programs in both dry and damp locations. Blocks also provide attractive gnawing surfaces for rodents.

Most blocks are made to accommodate a wire or string for securing the blocks to items. Mounting blocks on rods within bait stations (see Figure 15.17) has become a standard practice for exterior rodent baiting programs around commercial facilities. This practice provides additional tamper-resistance of the rodenticide, because the bait cannot be stolen by the rodent and moved outside of the station. Moreover, blocks mounted on rods in exterior stations protects the baits from moisture and decreases attacks from insects and slugs.

Zinc phosphide (ZP) baiting programs for rats using fresh baits are done by mixing a ZP concentrate with some type of "fresh" food carrier. Whenever possible, it is important to match the baits to what the rats are already feeding on. Otherwise, prebaiting (i.e., using an unpoisoned food bait identical to the food that will be mixed with the toxicant) with a few different attractive foods will assist in the determining the most attractive bait for the target rodent pest. Generally, fish-flavored cat foods and meat-flavored dog foods are the food carriers used for Norway rat programs, while fruit and vegetable food bases are used for roof rats.

Prebaiting is typically done for several nights

FIGURE 15.17. Block baits properly secured on rods inside tamper-resistant bait stations help to prevent baits being carried out of the stations. This practice also helps to preserve the bait for longer periods.

prior to introducing the poisoned bait, and is usually a mandatory practice for fresh-baiting rat baiting programs. Prebaiting helps to overcome the rat's natural suspicion and avoidance of new foods. Once rats have eaten small amounts of new foods without any harm, they usually take the poison baits without hesitation and consume a lethal dose.

Label directions must be followed closely when preparing fresh-food baits. Using a higher concentrate than recommended is not only is it illegal, but increases the hazard of the bait to people and non-target animals. Moreover, baits containing too much concentrate may decrease the bait palatability. On the other hand, too low a concentration can result in incomplete control.

In situations where water is scarce or absent, or in dry areas (e.g., granaries, bakeries, dry-goods warehouses, etc.), **liquid (water) baits** are often preferred by rodents over dry baits. Liquid baits can also be used together with conventional grain baits resulting in better control. Some anticoagulant rodenticide concentrates are formulated to be dissolved in water to make a liquid bait. Even though mice require very little water to survive, they will eagerly drink from properly placed water baits (see Figure 15.18). When the water sources of rats can be reduced or eliminated, liquid baits can provide excellent control because rats require 1/2 to 1 ounce of water daily.

Liquid baits are typically installed for mice at dosages 4 to 16 fluid oz. (118 milliliters to 0.47 liters) per placement, while 16 to 32 fluid oz. (0.47 to 0.95 liters) are used for each placement for rats. Professional liquid baiting containers that protect the liquid bait and minimize spillage must always

be used. As with dry baits, liquid baits must be placed in rodent-active areas to be effective.

Liquids tend to evaporate quickly in hot, dry locations and are subject to freezing in very cold environments or locations. Also, the location and placement of liquid bait stations must always be carefully considered to avoid contamination of materials, food, surfaces, people or non-target animals from spillage or having the bait containers knocked over or bumped.

Bait containers. Various types of containers are used to hold placements of rodenticide baits. The simplest containers are inexpensive **bait trays** that are used to hold dry or liquid baits. Bait trays have no top, offer little or no protection to the bait or spillage of the bait, and do not protect people or animals from having access to the bait. The use of trays should be limited to situations where they will be inaccessible to children, pets, and wildlife (e.g. locked storage rooms and warehouses, underneath equipment, out-of-the-way areas in storage areas). Trays are more suitable for nonfood industrial uses and are not appropriate for most residences, schools, healthcare and food-handling facilities. Because of the threat of pesticide translocation associated with the trays, most professionals opt to avoid the use of trays and use only enclosed bait boxes.

Enclosed bait boxes (or "stations") comprise the more elaborate type of bait container. Enclosed boxes are available in **non-tamper-resistant** and **tamper-resistant models**.

Non-tamper-resistant bait boxes are designed to protect baits from spillage and the indoor elements (e.g., dust and dirt). Some rodents in a colony may also find an enclosed box to offer a protective harborage (mice, more so than rats). Non-tamper-resistant boxes are usually constructed of inexpensive thin plastics and/or cardboard. Therefore, these style bait boxes are easily broken, crushed, or torn

FIGURE 15.18. Water baits are effective in situations where free water isn't readily available to rodents.

apart by dogs, wildlife, or by the gnawing activity of the rodents themselves. Like bait trays, non-tamper-resistant bait boxes should be used in areas inaccessible to children, pets, and other non-target animals. Non-tamper-resistant stations are not acceptable for most outdoor baiting programs unless they are inserted within an outer tamper-resistant cover of some type.

Tamper-resistant (TR) bait boxes are designed to significantly decrease contact between people, most non-target animals, and the rodenticide bait, as well as provide protection and containment of the bait itself (see Figure 15.19). Tamper-resistant boxes must be used in those situations where baits may be accessible to children and/or non-target animals. Commercially manufactured tamper-resistant bait boxes are made for mice and rats and vary in their degree of resistance to tampering depending upon their design and the materials used in their construction.

Tamper-resistant boxes are usually constructed from metal or heavy, pliable plastic. Some tamper-resistant boxes provide only minimal amount of resistance to tampering. Other boxes are elaborately constructed, extremely durable and are equipped with various key/locking mechanisms, and offer a relatively high level of tamper-resistance. Regardless of how a tamper-resistant a bait box is constructed, it is important to note that the bait box is not considered "tamper-resistant" unless it is secured in place to the ground, floor, or walls. Moreover, unless baits are secured within the box, there is no preventing a rodent from carrying the bait out of the box and dropping or translocating the bait to an area where it could be encountered by people, pets, and non-target wildlife.

The selection of the bait container for a particular baiting program must be carefully considered. In some situations, bait trays may suffice. In other situations, it may be that nothing less than a tamper-resistant bait box will be required. The best guide for selecting a bait container is determined by reading any rodenticide bait label that states: **Apply bait in locations out of reach of children, pets, domestic animals, and non-target wildlife, or in tamper-resistant bait stations.**

Regardless of current label directions, most pest management professionals now default to using **only** tamper-resistant bait boxes for all their baiting efforts regardless of the situation. There are several reasons for this. TR bait boxes:

1. minimize the chances of people (e.g., children), pets, and wildlife directly contacting potentially hazardous rodenticide bait.
2. maximize the ability to keep the baits attractive to rodents by protecting the baits from dirt, dust, and moisture.
3. encourage mice to feed on the baits because the boxes provide a dark, enclosed, protected harborage.
4. facilitate the installation and maintenance of baits in those locations that would otherwise be difficult because of rain, snow, or other adverse environmental conditions.
5. decrease the chances of accidental spillage of the bait.
6. permit a professional to monitor areas of highest rodent activity via the amount of feeding from the bait boxes. This is more easily accomplished than with trays because the professional can number each box, and record on the box itself (or on a record sheet) the amount of feeding occurring at that particular box.
7. facilitate important information being located on the bait box label such as the pest control company's address, telephone numbers, contact person, etc. This information is valuable should it be needed for any pesticide contamination event.

Baiting Techniques: Mice

Proper placement of baits and the distance between placements is critically important for mouse management programs. Numerous bait placements containing small amounts of bait, rather than only a couple of bait placements containing a lot of bait is the key rule for effective mouse baiting programs.

For severe mouse infestations it is best to err on the side of having the maximum number of bait placements that the label will allow. Mice living between two bait containers placed 20 feet (6 m) apart may never visit the bait if there is abundant food, regardless of the quality of the rodenticide bait. Baits placed several inches away from a wall

FIGURE 15.19. An outdoor tamper-resistant bait box secured by a lock and staked to a heavy cement block to resist tampering.

may be bypassed consistently. In cases of persistent mouse infestations (continual callbacks), the problem is often a result of too few bait placements.

To maintain control of mice and/or to prevent invading mice from becoming established, baits can be placed near exterior openings where mice are suspected of entering, or next to all doorways within the building that remain open. In warehouses, restaurants, and similar commercial facilities, this can be done by establishing permanent bait boxes (or trap stations, if baits are prohibited or undesirable) on a year-round basis.

Additional helpful tips for baiting mice include:

- Place baits directly *between* suspected mouse harborage and the mouse's source of food. This way, the mice will encounter the bait repeatedly during their travels.
- Search out and place baits in areas that appear to be the "favorite feeding locations" of the mice (evidenced by piles of droppings, shredded paper, tracks, mousey odors, etc.) such as darkened areas, below equipment, etc.
- Corners within rooms, cabinets, and appliances are often high-activity areas of rodents because the junction of the two surfaces provides the rodent with a strong tactile feedback.
- Use mouse-size bait boxes. Encourage feeding by providing the mice with attractive artificial feeding locations. Some newer stations offer both an attractive feeding station and tamper-resistance for baiting in sensitive areas (see Figure 15.20).
- Space bait placements 8 to 12 feet apart. Use shorter distances in severe infestations.
- At each follow-up visit, move any existing unvisited bait placements five feet in another direction to intercept different mouse territories.
- Bait in a three-dimensional format. Mice commonly live above their food source (in attic spaces, suspended ceilings) or below (crawlspaces, floor voids, basements).

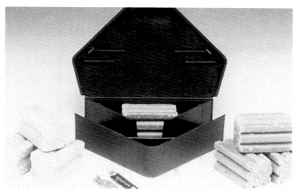

FIGURE 15.20. A tamper-resistant bait station for mice.

- Some mouse colonies develop food preferences and may ignore some foods or baits. In these cases, bait testing can be done by placing out three or four different formulations of bait and noting if there are preferences.
- Baits must be kept fresh. Rodents are not attracted to old, insect infested, or moldy baits.

Baiting Techniques: Rats

Some of the baiting concepts for mice also apply from a general aspect to rats as well. Additional tips:

- Hungry rats are easier to control than rats having multiple food options on a daily basis. To facilitate good bait acceptance by rat colonies, the rat's food sources should be eliminated as best as possible prior to installing baits.
- Baits can be spaced from 15 to 50 feet apart to reflect the foraging ranges of the rats. The closer spacings should be used in the more severe infestations.
- Every attempt should be made to place baits between the rats' harborage and their food sources.
- When baiting rat burrows, loose pellet bait or crumbled blocks (not packets or blocks), should be used. Burrows should not be caved in until about 10 days after baiting. Reopened burrows should then be rebaited and the process repeated. When baiting exterior burrows, check all labels as not all rodenticide baits are registered for exterior burrow baiting.
- Once bait boxes are in place and a rat colony begins using the feeding station, the bait boxes should not be changed or moved. Abrupt changes may prolong good control because of the neophobic reaction of some rats to the changes. Similarly, once feeding is begun, the bait type and formulation should remain the same.
- Adult rats consume up to one or more ounces of food nightly. Enough bait should be provided to permit all rats an ample opportunity to obtain a lethal dose of the bait (see Tables 15. 2 and 15.3).
- With the first generation anticoagulants, (e.g., chlorophacinone and diphacinone), rodents must feed on the baits several times over several days to be effective. Thus, these baits must be continuously available until all feeding activity ceases.
- Label directions for any particular rodenticide bait must always be closely followed regarding the amount and spacings of each bait placement.
- For baiting in sewers or in other damp locations, bait blocks that offer maximum weatherability should be used. Tie down the blocks to prevent

them from being removed or washed away.

- In dry situations or where water isn't readily available to the rats, liquid baits or a combination of liquid and dry baits can be used. Rats require 1/2 to 1 ounce of water daily.
- When conducting fresh-food baiting programs for rats using zinc phosphide concentrates, the baits should be placed out during the late afternoon to ensure the baits will be fresh when rats become active at dusk.

Baiting Techniques: Roof Rats

Roof rats can be controlled using the same baits as for Norway rats. However, because roof rats may be active at both ground and aerial areas, special care and attention must be made for roof rat baiting efforts.

Baiting tips include the following:

- The block bait formulation facilitates the baits being secured within tube bait stations. PVC pipes (2.5 to 3.0 in/6 to 8 cm diameter) that can then be used as to bait on narrow ledges and overhead areas commonly used by roof rats. Block baits can be glued or wired into the center of the stations, and the stations can be then affixed to the ledge.
- The use of PVC or other tamper-resistant stations help to minimize the chances of baits falling from aerial areas to the ground where children or dogs/wildlife may have access to them.
- Roof rats occasionally travel over long distances to reach food, such as traveling from one residence to several residences away using overhead wires or fence tops.
- Roof rats nesting in the crowns of palm trees commonly travel down to the ground to feed around garbage cans, fruit drops, or pet-food dishes. In these cases, tamper-resistant bait boxes can be situated at the bases of trees or buildings to intercept the rats before they get to these types of food sources.
- When roof rats are feeding on ripe fruits such as oranges (either fallen or directly on the tree), baiting programs are often less effective during the peak fruit season due to the food competition. Ongoing monitoring programs on a year-round basis to manage the populations on a proactive basis is essential in neighborhoods with abundant fruit trees and/or nearby fruit orchards. Still, daily removal of dropped fruits and timely harvesting of fruits off of the trees help promote the roof rats seeking out alternative food sources such as rodenticide baits or baited kill traps.
- Roof rats tend to select areas of dense cover to rest and feed, and thus, such areas are good locations for bait boxes or trapping stations.
- Roof rats tend to feed at each location in smaller amounts than does the Norway rat. Thus, a multitude of bait placements containing smaller amounts of bait is an effective baiting strategy for the roof rat.
- Some roof rats can be highly neophobic of any changes in their environment that may delay the results of control programs for several days.
- Careful consideration must be given for baiting roof rats indoors due to the possibility of the rats dying in inaccessible structural voids and creating odor problems.

Rodenticide Resistance

Occasionally, some rodents survive feeding on what would normally be a lethal dose of a rodenticide because they possess a genetic ("physiological") resistance to some poisons. These rodents may pass this genetic-linked resistance on to their offspring. Eventually, over many generations of rodents and the continued use of the same rodenticide, large portions of rodent populations may become resistant to the rodenticide.

Physiological resistance in the commensal rodents to warfarin and a few other first-generation anticoagulants (referred to as "warfarin resistance or anticoagulant resistance") is established at various levels in certain cities and locales in the United States and other parts of the world. This resistance has taken hold in those cities and areas that have been using the same anticoagulants for many years with little no use of other baits or control measures.

In locations where anticoagulant resistance is well established, control of the domestic rodents with warfarin, and possibly a few other first-generation rodenticides (e.g., chlorophacinone, diphacinone) may not be fully realized.

Resistance to the second-generation anticoagulants (brodifacoum, bromadiolone, and difethialone) has not yet been formally documented in the United States, and thus these actives are used against warfarin-resistant rodents. Resistance to the active bromadiolone has been reported in some parts of Europe, Great Britain, and Canada to some species, and there is concern as to a similar situation developing in the United States. Resistance in general is likely to be underestimated because resistance studies are lacking. Additionally, when pest management professionals encounter baiting failures, they often switch baits, and fail to attempt to document whether the baiting failure was a result of true resistance or to some other factor.

In areas where resistance has not yet developed, steps can be taken to help delay its onset and perhaps even prevent resistance from ever developing to a practical degree. For example, sanitation and rodentproofing of structures (IPM programs) should be better utilized as essential components of all rodent control programs (instead of them being optional and supplementary to baits). Remember, without food and shelter, rodents cannot survive. Thus, IPM programs can result in less frequent anticoagulant rodenticide use, which in turn, may then prolong the life and effectiveness of second-generation anticoagulant rodenticides.

Additionally, for those areas where baits are used in rodent control intensively over long periods of time, it may be a wise strategy from an industry-wide perspective for professionals to alternate between the anticoagulants and nonanticoagulants baits on an annual or even a semiannual basis. This may be especially important for personnel involved in prolonged and repeated baiting programs in large city municipalities, apartment complexes, hi-rise condominiums, and similar situations.

Tracking powders. In addition to baits, rodenticides are also formulated as **tracking powders**. The toxicant used in tracking powders may be an anticoagulant (e.g., chlorophacinone, diphacinone, pival) or a nonanticoagulant (e.g. zinc phosphide). The toxicants used in tracking powders are formulated in concentrations that are several times more concentrated than what is used in a food bait formulation.

Because of their high toxicant concentration and unique formulation, tracking powders are potentially more hazardous than other pesticide formulations and must be used with forethought and extreme care. They are generally not recommended for use in and around homes because children and non-target animals might have potential contact with the powders. Nor are they recommended in food-handling establishments and other potentially sensitive accounts (food plants, restaurants, healthcare facilities, schools, etc.).

Tracking powders can provide good control when used in situations where baits are not well accepted. They can be placed in rodent runways inside tracking containers or they can be applied into rat burrows. Rodents pick up the powder on their feet and fur and ingest the toxicant during their grooming activities. They are effective against both rats and mice—but especially against mice, as mice groom more frequently during a 24-hour period than do rats.

The following are tips for the proper and safe use of tracking powders:

• The safest method, (although not necessarily

the most convenient) of applying tracking powders is to first apply the powder within "tracking powder stations," and then install the tracking stations into areas of activity. The stations will protect the powder and reduce the potential for people and non-target animals encountering the toxicant. Enclosed bait boxes can be used for this purpose.

• By using the tracking powder stations, the powder can be monitored and recovered at the end of the program, helping to minimize the potential that persons (e.g., utility personnel, room remodelers, etc.) might inadvertently and unknowingly encounter the powder sometime in the future.

• Tracking powders can be applied using insecticide dusters, or long-handled spoons.

• When tracking powders are used for treating rat burrows, be sure the rats are not traveling to pet dishes, bird feeders, or any other areas where the translocation of pesticides could be a threat.

• Some tracking powders are labeled for indoor use only; some for exterior applications. Always check label directions for applicable restrictions.

• Tracking powders must always be applied with great care to prevent the powder from becoming airborne and being inhaled by people or non-target animals.

• Never use tracking powders in any area where there is the possibility of rodents tracking the powder on to food packages or food preparation surfaces. For example, mice nesting in a ceiling void of a restaurant's basement might easily track the powder to the upstairs kitchen area.

• Never apply tracking powder where it can blown by drafts or air currents, such as near outside doorways, utility motor fans, and the like.

• Tracking powders should only be applied at ground level (not on ledges or in suspended ceilings) unless there is no danger of the powder drifting or falling down into sensitive areas.

Fumigants. In addition to the use of poison baits and tracking powders as rodenticides, certain poisonous gases (fumigants) can be used to control rodents. Fumigants such as **aluminum phosphide, chloropicrin/ methyl bromide, carbon dioxide** and **gas cartridges** are used to obtain a quick kill of rodents (and with some fumigants, their ectoparasites) in buildings and outdoor burrows. Fumigants can be extremely dangerous to the applicator and others if not used properly. Only professionals with experience in the use of fumigants should consider their use in rodent pest management (refer to Chapter 20).

The fumigants **chloropicrin** and **methyl bromide** are occasionally used to control rodents in burrows but require specialized techniques. Label directions must be carefully read and closely adhered to in all fumigant operations. The fumigant methyl bromide is likely to be phased out of most uses in the United States by 2005.

The fumigant **aluminum phosphide** comes in a tablet form that can be dropped into a rodent borrow with a gloved hand. Unlike most of the other fumigants registered for rodent control, aluminum phosphide tablets release gas relatively slowly as they react with the ground moisture in the rodent burrow. This fumigant will also provide control of severe mouse infestations in certain types of seed and other grain warehouses when these facilities are fumigated for insect infestations.

The same gas cartridges ("smoke bombs") that are used against woodchucks can also be used against minor infestations of Norway rats. For severe infestations, gas cartridges may be too labor intensive, because many of the rat burrows are likely be interconnected which will prevent good gas distribution and containment difficult or impossible.

When planning rat burrow fumigation programs, it is most cost-effective and efficient to first conduct an activity census as to which burrows are currently active, (i.e., it is a waste of time and materials to treat inactive and old burrows. Even in simple infestations, a rat burrow system often contains multiple entrances and all openings must be sealed for a fumigation effort to be effective. A couple of days prior to the actual fumigation, all burrow openings should be caved in with either dirt or newspaper wads to identify the active systems. In general, soil fumigants are less effective in soils that are dry and/or porous.

Safety Considerations For Rodent Control Programs

Now more than ever, there is considerable concern relative to the use of pesticides, in urban environments. Pesticide safety is especially important in the use of rodenticides because rodents are mammals, as are dogs, cats, livestock, and people. As such, many of the poisons used against rodents can have similar effects on people, pets, and wildlife if the rodenticides are consumed in sufficient quantity. Simply put: Rodenticides can kill.

The following are important safety practices for rodent control programs:

- When using baits in residential areas, ensure that baits are placed within tamper-resistant bait containers. As an additional precaution, the tamper-resistant containers, if possible, should then be placed *out of reach and ideally, also out of sight* of children, pets, and non-target wildlife.
- All bait containers should always be clearly marked with *warning labels* that state: RODENT BAIT—DO NOT TOUCH and all other appropriate warnings. Bait container labels should also provide the ingredients of the bait container and the name and telephone number of the pest control company.
- All baits must be applied in a manner to prevent contamination of food or food surfaces that come into direct contact with food. Rodenticide baits must never be placed where they might be easily knocked over or bumped and contaminate the area.
- Rodenticide baits labeled for professional use must never be given or sold to the public.
- Detailed records should always be kept as to the type of bait (e.g., anticoagulant or a nonanticoagulant) a particular site contains. Some nonanticoagulant baits look similar to the anticoagulants but have completely different modes of actions. In case of accidental poisoning, the physician or the vet must know the type of bait in order to administer the proper treatment. Copies of rodenticide labels should be maintained on the service vehicle and also at the client's premises for emergency-use purposes (i.e., for physicians and veterinarians).
- Some food plants (e.g., USDA-inspected meat and poultry plants) have special regulations concerning the use of rodenticides that must be closely followed. All appropriate manuals must be checked, or permission granted from the appropriate Inspector-in-Charge (IIC) before rodenticides are applied in or around these facilities.
- Only the rodenticide cholecalciferol (vitamin D_3) is approved for use in and around organic food manufacturers and distributors. However, periodically check appropriate NOP web sites for updates.
- Some food plants closely follow the guidelines of food safety organizations (e.g., AIB, Sillika Labs, ASI, etc.), that have specific recommendations on how rodent baits and traps are to be used. Copies of these inspection companies guidelines should always be consulted for the most recent updates.
- Loose bait blocks and packets ("sachets") of rodenticide baits should not be used for insertions into rat burrows, as the rats often push these "newly appearing" objects back out of the

burrow where they can be discovered by children, pets, and wildlife.

- Bait packets should not be tossed into ceiling or wall voids, and "abandoned." This practice can lead to possible pesticide contamination in the future, or cause grain/fabric insect infestations in the building at a later time.
- Do not use poisonous tracking powders where they might contaminate food or food preparation surfaces. Nor should tracking powders be used in situations where rodents may track the powders onto food or food preparation surfaces. Always conduct a thorough inspection to ensure the tracking powder placement will not cause a problem in the future.
- Keep the telephone number of the local poison control center and/or the rodenticide manufacturer's hot line in the truck for quick reference.
- For programs involving a "one-time" baiting using fresh food baits (e.g., zinc phosphide mixed with cat food), all uneaten baits must be removed and destroyed at the end of the baiting program.
- Supplies of bait and rodenticide concentrates should be stored in a locked cabinet out of the reach of children or animals, and all appropriate warnings must be posted on the outside of the cabinet doors.
- Whenever possible, rodenticide baits should be stored separately from other chemicals to prevent absorption of chemical odors that might reduce the bait's effectiveness. If this is not possible, the baits should be stored in airtight containers.
- All rodenticide label directions must always be closely followed.
- When in doubt as to the safe and/or proper use of a rodenticide, a supervisor or the manufacturer should be contacted first.

Dead Rodents and Rodent Odors

Whenever possible, dead rodents—especially rats—should be recovered and removed following control programs. The removal of carcasses will aid in minimizing both odor problems and the chance for insect infestations to occur in the rotting carcasses. (Some insects that attack rodent carcasses can attack certain valuable fabrics and items such as expensive woolens, rugs, furs, etc.).

Dead rodents can be picked up safely with plastic gloves; a shovel; two sticks; long tongs; or by inserting a hand into a plastic bag, picking up the rodent with the same hand, inverting the bag over the rodent and tying the bag securely. All dead

Control of Rodent Ectoparasites

Both rats and mice carry ectoparasites on their bodies such as lice, fleas, ticks, and mites. Some of these ectoparasites are host-specific to the rodents (i.e., they feed only on the rodents, and when the rodents die, so, too, do the parasites). But others, such as some fleas, will also feed on people or pets. In large-scale rodent control programs, hungry fleas or other ectoparasites may seek alternate hosts after the rats or mice have been killed. Pest professionals should educate clients that if ectoparasites are numerous, an ectoparasite control program will need to be conducted in conjunction with the rodent control program. Ectoparasite control should be instigated before or in conjunction with rodent control operations, not after all the rodents have been killed.

The pesticides and techniques used for ectoparasite control as discussed in Chapter 11 can be used for these programs.

rodents should either be burned or deeply buried to avoid being dug up by pets or other carnivores. In cases of a dead mouse or two, these can be bagged and discarded with ordinary garbage.

Some rodents will inevitably die in wall voids and other inaccessible areas in buildings. And regardless of how they are killed, decaying rodent carcasses all will produce some degree of odor (no rodenticide will cause rodents to become "thirsty" and conveniently leave a premise after eating the bait to die). However, most mice do not contain enough body mass to create serious odors, and thus a mouse or two dying within a building or a home often go undetected. The exception is when a pregnant mouse dies close to where human activity is intense (e.g., within a couch, beneath the stove, beneath a bed, etc.).

Rat carcasses are another matter because a rat contains more body mass than a mouse. Dead rat odors can be annoying to building occupants and must be handled professionally. If a dead rodent cannot be retrieved, but the general location of the carcass is known, the area should be ventilated as well as possible. A **neutralizing agent** or a **masking agent** *should* be applied as close to where the carcass is located as possible. If a carcass is located in a wall void, the neutralizing or masking agent should be poured or sprayed into the area that often results in the odors being markedly reduced or even eliminated. Some of the odor-neutralizing chemicals used in slaughterhouses, mortuaries, and zoos are also effective in neutralizing dead carcass odors.

Recently, various biological control products have emerged that combine a synergistic blend of bacteria and enzymes. These products are designed to consume and eliminate the odors of organic matter such as decaying rodent odors, urine, feces, vomit, skunk odor, and others at their source. But these products are most effective if the source can be located and directly treated and this is always possible.

Several effective masking agents and deodorant compounds are also available (e.g., Epoleon®, Rohm and Haas' Styamine 1622®, Neutroleum Alpha, and Du Pont's Isobornyl Acetate). Deodorant aerosol bombs containing such materials as Metazene and Meelium will also offer temporary relief. For the most up-to-date technology and products in odor control, the professional should consult with product distributors.

If the source of the odor cannot be precisely located, a masking agent solution can be applied generally to the affected area. In severe cases, it may be necessary to use a mist or ULD machine to treat inaccessible wall spaces or even entire rooms. Repeat applications may be necessary until the carcasses dry up.

Other Methods of Rodent Control

Ultrasonic and electromagnetic machines. Ultrasonic machines generate sounds that are beyond those of human hearing (greater than 20kHz). Rats can hear within a range of up to 100kHz, and mice up to 90kHz. Because ultrasonic machines are now so readily available on store shelves and widely advertised, the pest professional is often asked as to their utility for rodent and insect pest management.

Some researchers have reported that wild rodents in lab and (a very few) field situations can be affected by ultrasonic machines causing the rodents to avoid treated areas or altering travel routes where the ultrasonic waves are present. Thus, these researchers have claimed rodents can, in some very unique situations, be channeled or repelled accordingly.

Other scientists however have not found any value of ultrasonic machines either in the lab or in the field, and do not support the use of ultrasonic devices as practical, cost-effective tools. Perhaps it is important to note that despite a history of 25+ years of availability of these machines and their use, the majority of scientists and pest professionals on a global scale have failed to embrace ultrasonic devices, even as a supplement to conventional rodent control programs.

Advertisements for pest ultrasonic devices are numerous in the public magazine markets associated with the home and garden, airplane, and specialty-gift markets. What's more, as of 2003, ultrasonic pest repeller machines are commonly sold through most of the nation's mart-style stores. Similar to "bug-zappers" hung on the back porch, fake owls placed on roof tops, spinning daisies stuck into lawns to repel moles and so on, it seems the public loves gimmicks that claim to "scare away." Considering the lack of any formal efficacy data for ultrasonic devices within everyday conditions, it is clearly a case of "buyer beware."

Electromagnetic devices are supposed to work on the principle that a magnetic field produces a barrier that has a stunning or repellent effect on rodents. Sometimes, electromagnetic devices are confused with ultrasonic devices. And some companies manufacture machines that claim to incorporate both electromagnetic and ultrasonic effects. Electromagnetic machines have been stated to have about as much effect on rodents as that of an ordinary household toaster.

Cats and dogs. Although cats, dogs, and other predators kill the occasional rodent, these "natural predators" cannot control or eliminate the typical structural rodent infestation once it is established. In fact, it is common to find rodents living in close association with dogs and cats, where they can obtain their food and water from the pet's dish or from what the pets spill. Backyard infestations of rats are often traceable to those yards with pets and pet housing. Mice coming up from a basement and foraging about inside the kitchen cabinets behind closed doors and drawers are not exactly vulnerable to the cat.

Should a cat or dog kill the occasional new rodent entering a home or building, the pet in those circumstances, can be given credit for eliminating that rodent "infestation." And if the rodent was pregnant, then perhaps the pet can even be said to have possibly prevented a more serious infestation. But whether the average house cat or dog helps to minimize the number of rodent pest occurrences to a home or any other structure is likely to be situational-specific.

SUPPLEMENTARY READING MATERIAL

Barnett, S. 1975. *The rat. A study in behavior.* University of Chicago Press, London. 287pp.

Brooks, J. E. and F. P. Rowe. 1979. *Commensal rodent control.* World Health Organization, Geneva. WHO/VBC/79.726.

Buckle, A.P. and R.H. Smith. (Eds). 1994. *Rodent Pests and Their Control.* CAB International. Wallingford, UK. 405 pp.

Calhoun, J. B. 1962. *The ecology and sociology of the Norway rat.* U.S. Dept. HEW. Pubic Health Service No. 1008. Bethseda, MD. 288pp.

Colvin, B. A. 2000. *Rodent Control at Construction Sites.* Pest Control Technology. Vol. 28 (5) 118, 120.122.124, 126.

Colvin, B. A. and W.B. Jackson, 1999. *Urban Rodent Control programs for the 21st Century.* Pages 243-257. In: *Ecologically-Based Management of Rodent Pests.* G.R. Singleton, L.A. Hinds, H. Leirs, and Z. Zhang (Eds). Australian Centre for International Agricultural Research. Canberra.

Corrigan, R.M. 2003. Rats and Mice. In: *Mallis Handbook of Pest Control.* 9th Ed. S. Hedges. (Ed.). Mallis Handbook and Technical Training Committee. Cleveland. OH. In press.

Corrigan, R.M. 2002. *Rodent Pest Management*: Pages 265-291 in: *Food Plant Sanitation.* Y.H. Hui, et. al (Eds). Marcel Dekker, Inc., New York. 745 pp.

Corrigan, R.M. 2001. *Rodent Control: A Practical Guide for Pest Management Professionals.* GIE Publishers. Cleveland. OH. 355 pp.

Corrigan, R. M., 1998. *The efficacy of glue traps against wild populations of house mice, Mus domesticus, Rutty.* Pages 268-275. In: Proceedings 18th Vertebrate Pest Conference. (R.O. Baker and A.C. Crabb Eds.) Univ. Calif., Davis, CA..

Frantz. S. C. and D. E. Davis. 1991. *Bionomics and integrated pest management of commensal rodents.* Pages 243-313. In: Ecology and management of food industry pests. J. R. Gorham (Ed.). Assoc. Offic. Anal. Chem. Arlington, VA.

Gratz, N. R. 1994. *Rodents as Carriers of Disease.* Pages 85-108 in: *Rodent Pests and Their Control.* A. Buckle, and R. Smith. (Eds). CAB International. Wallingford.UK. 405 pp.

Howard, W. E. and R. E. Marsh. 1976. *The rat: Its biology and control.* Univ. of California, Div. of Agric. Sci. Leaf. 2896.

Howard, W.E., and R.E. Marsh. 1985. *Ultrasonic and electromagnetic control of rodents.* Acta Zool. Fennica: 173:187–189.

Jackson, W.B. and A.D. Ashton, and K. Delventhal. — 1988. *Overview of anticoagulant usage and resistance.* Pages 381-388 In: Suttie, J. W. (ed.). Current Advances in Vitamin K Research. Elsevier, Amsterdam.

Jackson, W. B. 1982. *Norway rats and allies.* Pages 1077-1088 In: *Wild Mammals of Noth America. Biology, Management and Economics.* (J.A. Chapman and G.A. Feldhamer, Eds.) John Hopkins University Press, Baltimore, MD.

Jenson, A. G. 1965 *Proofing of buildings against rats and mice.* Ministry of Agriculture, Fisheries and Food, London. Tech. Bull. 12.

Kaukeinen, D.C. 1994. *Rodent Control in Practice: Householders, Pest Control Operators and Municipal Authorities.* Pages 249-272 In: *Rodent Pests and Their Control.* A. Buckle and R. Smith (Eds.). CAB International. Wallingford UK. 405 pp.

Lund, M. 1988. *Ultrasound devices.* Pages 407-409 In: *Rodent Pest Management*, Prakash (Ed.). CRC Press. Boca Raton. 480 pp

Marsh, R. E. and W. E. Howard. 1977. *The house mouse: Its biology and control.* University of California, Division of Agricultural Sciences leaflet 2945, 28 pp.

Marsh, R. E. 1986. *Vertebrate Pest Management.* Pages 253-286. In: Advances in Urban Pest Management. (G.W. Bennett and J. M. Owens Eds.) Van Nostrand Reinhold Company, New York.

Meehan, A. P. 1984. *Rats and Mice. Their Biology and Control.* Rentokil Limited. East Grinstead, Sussex, UK. 383 pp

Mullin, D. and L. Durden. 2002. *Medical and Veterinary Entomology.* Academic Press. New York. 597 pp.

Prakash, I., (Ed). 1988. Rodent Pest Management. CRC Press, Boca Raton, Fla. 480 pp.

Pratt, H. D. and R. Z. Brown. 1976. *Biological factors in domestic rodent control.* U. S. Dept. HEW. Center for Disease Control. Environmental Health Services Div., Atlanta, GA. No. (CDC) 76-8144, revised, 30 pp.

Scott, H. G., and M. R. Borom. 1967. *Rodent-borne disease control through rodent stoppage.* U.S. Dept. HEW, P.H.S., National Communicable Disease Center. Atlanta 34 pp.

World Health Organization. *Anticoagulant rodenticides.* International Programme on Chemical Safety. Environmental Health Criteria 175. 121 pp. WHO Geneva. (1995).

Zinsser, H. 1935. Rats, *Lice and History.* Bantam Science and Mathematics. 228 pp.

CHAPTER 16 | Urban Pest Birds

This chapter focuses on the biology, behavior and management of the following urban pest birds or bird groups:

1. The City Pigeon, *Columba livia*
2. The House (English) Sparrow, *Passer domesticus*
3. The European Starling, *Sturnus vulgaris*
4. Woodpeckers (Family Picidae)
5. The Canada Goose, *Branta canadensis*
6. Gulls (*Larus* spp.)
7. Crows (*Corvus* spp.)

The biology and behavior of pigeons, sparrows, and starlings are discussed in detail. The biology discussion of the woodpeckers, Canada geese, gulls, and crows are combined with their management discussion towards the end of the chapter.

BIRDS AS PESTS

Unfortunately, birds have negative aspects when they associate too closely with people. Birds can be nuisances, transmit diseases, contaminate our food, and deface our structures and many other items of importance in urban environments.

Public Health Problems

Birds can harbor disease organisms that may affect people, pets and domesticated animals. However, reports of disease outbreaks that are directly attributed to the species of urban pest birds are rare. Moreover, the actual incidence of transmission of diseases from the urban pest birds is difficult to assess. But like rodents, when flocks of birds inhabit areas and buildings in close proximity to people, the *potential* for disease transmission is very real.

The following is a brief discussion of the diseases and ectoparasites that may be associated with urban pest birds.

Histoplasmosis

Histoplasmosis is a respiratory disease caused by inhaling spores from the fungus *Histoplasma capsulatum*. Birds do not spread the disease directly. The spores are spread by the wind and the disease is contracted by inhaling them. Bird droppings however, enrich the soil and promote growth of the fungus. Inhalation of only a few spores generally produces a mild case in humans. In fact, people may be unaware that they have the disease unless it is detected through a skin reactivity test or lung X-ray. In mild cases, a person may acquire immunity without realizing it. A more severe infection may result in an acute pulmonary case with flu-like symptoms (in fact, it is sometimes misdiagnosed as flu). As with the flu, the patient generally recovers after a period of several weeks. The most serious infections, usually resulting from massive spore inhalation, may involve the fungus being dispersed through the bloodstream. Such cases may become chronic, recurring at later times.

There are also other possible sources for histoplasmosis infection, including: (1) poultry farms (chicken coops are a serious source); (2) natural fertilizers (e.g., enriched with chicken droppings and later used as fertilizer); and (3) enclosed buildings where birds or bats have roosted for several years (although indoor bird and bat roosts containing the conditions conducive for the development of histoplasmosis are rare).

Not all blackbird or starling roosts pose a histoplasmosis health threat. Although the fungus grows well in bird droppings, it cannot form spores under the acidic conditions of fresh droppings. An active, undisturbed roost may only give off a few spores

Birds as Desirable and Beneficial Animals

Unlike insect and rodents, birds are recognized by most people as friends. Many people derive great enjoyment from watching, feeding, and conversing with birds—even common city pigeons and sparrows. In inner-city areas for example, the pigeon represents one of the few naturally free forms of "wildlife" visually available to the city dweller. Some urbanites delight in watching pigeons take flight from the noisy, crowded, busy city environment. Others claim urban bird flocks add a refreshing and interesting visual variety (e.g., a "European atmosphere") to some of our city streets and parks. And there are other, more practical contributions to humankind from birds. All of the urban pest birds will, during certain times of the year, feed on considerable quantities of insects and weed seeds. Birds also provide us with food, valuable by-products such as goose down and a variety of sport such as bird watching, carrier pigeons, hunting, and raptoring. Finally, the dove (which is in the same family as the pigeon), is the symbol of peace and the bald eagle is the national symbol for the United States of America.

that may result in the normally undetected kind of case. Old or abandoned roosts however, can be a different matter. After droppings have dried out or have been leached by the rain, the right conditions develop for spore release. If the soil is stirred up under dusty conditions, as may be the case in land clearing or bulldozing, massive amounts of spores may be released. Some histoplasmosis epidemics associated with bird roosts have occurred from such conditions.

Precautions should be taken when working around an old or abandoned roost site. For pest management professionals involved with bird roost clean-up projects, the local or state board of health should be contacted for detailed instructions involving clean-up procedures. It may be also wise to test for the presence of histoplasma before beginning any work.

As a minimum however, and for conducting inspections in bird-infested buildings and areas, an approved respirator must be worn to prevent inhalation of the spores. Eye goggles, gloves, and coveralls must also be worn. For small clean-ups, all bird droppings should always be first wetted before being removed. If an area that was once a bird roost is going to be cleared or bulldozed, the work should be done when the weather is wet or cold or both.

Cleaning bird manure under the dry, dusty conditions of late summer should be avoided.

Ornithosis (Psittacosis)

Ornithosis is caused by a virus-like organism and is usually an insidious disease with primarily pneumonic involvement, but it can be a rapidly fatal infection. The pigeon is the bird species most commonly associated with the transmission of ornithosis to humans. Birds have become adapted to the disease and show no symptoms, but they act as "healthy carriers," shedding the organism in their feces that later may become airborne as dust. Because the disease has a low mortality rate (less than one percent of cases reported in the United States) and is usually mild, it is possible that many undetected or incorrectly diagnosed cases occur in humans.

Salmonellosis

The bacterial organism, *Salmonella typhimurium*, is one of several bacterial agents that can cause **salmonellosis**, a type of food poisoning that is a fairly common. Salmonella bacteria have been found in pigeons, sparrows, and starlings. All of these birds frequently habituate areas of potentially high salmonella content such as livestock feedlots, poultry farms, fertilized fields, and other areas. Thus, salmonella can be spread to people by the consumption of food contaminated with infected bird feces or by the salmonella organisms carried on the feet or body of birds. The bacteria are then spread when the birds walk across areas when people set food down (e.g., outdoor restaurant tables, park benches, etc.).

Other Diseases

Many birds can serve as reservoirs for certain pathogens. For example, birds are a major reservoir for the viruses in the Japanese Encephalitis Virus complex which include the viruses that cause **St. Louis encephalitis** and **West Nile virus** (WNV). In the recent WNV outbreaks, birds (e.g., crows, jays, and many others) have been shown to be the primary vertebrate reservoirs and amplifying hosts.

When mosquitoes feed on birds in urban areas, they can then transmit (i.e., vector) the virus when they feed on people (refer to Chapter 14 for more discussion on West Nile virus).

Pigeons, starlings, sparrows, blackbirds and other types of birds have been implicated in the transmission of various diseases of significance to humans or livestock. Starlings have been shown to be vectors of **TGE (transmissible gastroenteritis)** of swine. The virus can be carried in an infective state in the bird's intestine or on its feet for up to 30 hours. It is generally fatal to baby pigs and causes weight loss in adults. Starlings may also be involved in the transmission of hog cholera.

Cryptococcosis is a fungus causing chronic, usually fatal, meningitis and is spread by pigeons and starlings. Various species of birds may also play a part in the transmission of **encephalitis, Newcastle disease, aspergillosis, toxoplasmosis, pseudotuberculosis, avian tuberculosis,** and **coccidiosis.**

Nuisance and Damage Problems

As nuisances, birds frequently deposit their manure indiscriminately on sidewalks, people, buildings, park benches, statues, and cars. The droppings are not only objectionable to the eye and nose, but can permanently stain and cause premature rusting and corrosion of structures, statues, and expensive planes, boats, and cars. Large amounts of droppings can severely damage and/or kill valuable trees and other vegetation.

The nests of pigeons and sparrows clog gutters and rainspouts and may provide a home for several types of ectoparasites that may attack or annoy people. Insect pests that can damage people's clothing or woolen goods will also live within the nests of birds.

Of special concern to public health officials, and food sanitarians are the association of birds and bird flocks in and around food plants, food storage facilities, restaurants, and other buildings that process or handle food. In addition to the potential for disease transmission, birds can also contaminate food product with fecal matter, feathers, nesting materials, and ectoparasites. The presence of birds around livestock facilities, such as dairy farms, causes farmers to have a heavier reliance on the use of antibiotics due to contamination of feed/water with bird excrement.

Thus, even if birds are not directly existing within a food facility, they present a contamination hazard to food facilities because the Federal Food Drug and Cosmetic Act prohibits any conditions in which a food *might* become contaminated. Therefore, birds cannot be permitted to exist within or even on any exterior part of a food facility. On exterior loading docks for example, food products or food packaging materials can become contaminated with fecal matter, feathers, and dirt when they are passed beneath or stored below nesting birds.

Urban pest birds are commonly infested with various ectoparasites such as lice, mites, bedbugs, bat bugs, and louse flies, fleas, and ticks. It is not uncommon for these ectoparasites to move from birds or their nests into buildings on which birds are nesting

(especially if the birds evacuated their nests for prolonged periods or following a bird management program). Some ectoparasites are no more than a nuisance because of their presence. Others, however, may bite or irritate people. Pigeons in particular tend to harbor ectoparasites. A few of the more common ectoparasites associated with pigeons and other birds include the following:

- Pigeon nest bug, *Cimex columbarius* and other *Cimex* species
- Pigeon tick, *Argas relexus*
- Pigeon fly, *Pseudolynchia canariensis*
- European chicken flea, *Ceratophyllus gallinae*
- Flea, *Ceratophyllus columbae*
- Conenose bug, *Triatoma rubrofasciata*
- Chicken mite, *Dermanyssus gallinae*
- Northern fowl mite, *Ornithonysuss sylviarum*

Other mites may occur in birds also. A few of the genera include: *Ornithonyssus, Laminosioptes, Syringophilus, Megninia, Falculifer,* and *Pterophagus.* Genera of biting lice (Mallophaga) include: *Campanulotes, Coloceras, Colocephalum, Columbicola, Horhorstiella, Physconelloides,* and *Bonomiella.*

Finally, over the past ten years, birds have becoming increasingly more serious hazards to airports all around the United States. Human lives have been lost as a result of airplane collisions with flocks of gulls, geese, and blackbirds. Birds that suddenly rise from runways or surrounding areas to collide with aircraft taking off or landing cause the most serious hazards, since these are the most critical phases of flight.

PIGEON (ROCK DOVE)
Columba livia Gmelin
Family Columbidae

The pigeon is familiar to most everyone. It is found throughout the United States and many parts of the world. It was developed from the European rock dove and introduced into the United States as a domesticated bird. However, many of these birds escaped, and formed feral populations. Today, the pigeon is the most serious urban bird pest.

Pigeons are commonly found in both cities and rural areas. In city areas they frequent parks and sidewalks feeding on foods provided by people. They use city bridges and buildings that provide roosting, loafing, and nesting sites. In rural areas, they inhabit farmyards, livestock facilities, grain elevators, feed mills, and town courthouses.

Typically pigeons have gray bodies with a whitish rump, two black bars on the secondary

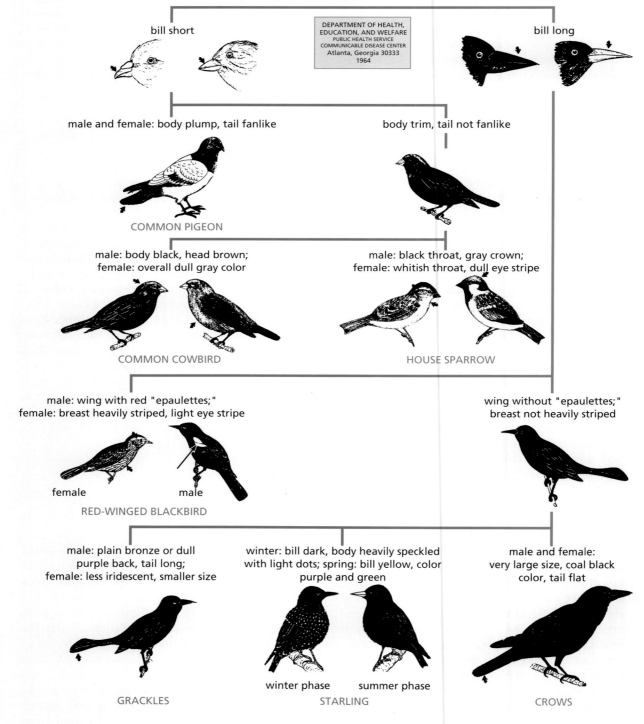

FIGURE 16.1. A pictorial key to some common pest birds of public health importance.

FIGURE 16.2. The city pigeon or rock dove. The color patterns of city pigeons vary widely. The mourning dove is similar in appearance to the pigeon, but the tail of the mourning dove is pointed, while it is fan-shaped in the pigeon. (Myers)

wing feathers, a broad black band on the tail, and red feet. However, body color can vary from gray to white, tan, and blackish. The average weight is about 10-13 oz. (0.5 kg), and the average length is 11 inches (30 cm) (see Figures 16. 1 and 16.2).

In cities, pigeons tend to move in flocks of several hundred, which frequently move about, fly, and roost together. Occasionally a smaller group will select a house or a few houses on which to roost, but in general they prefer large buildings. Pigeons inhabit roofs, ledges, drainpipes, lofts, steeples, attics, caves, and ornate architectural features of buildings where openings allow for roosting, loafing, and/or nest building. Pigeons do not construct a typical bird nest. Instead, their nests consist of sticks, twigs, and grasses merely clumped together to form a crude platform. In some cases, the accumulation of the pigeon's own feces provide the nesting platform. In addition to these marginal nests, pigeons rely on the structure itself to provide additional protection from the elements.

Pigeons subsist on garbage, various grains, and/or other food materials provided for them intentionally or unintentionally by people. In some urban areas the feeding of pigeons is practiced by many as a form of recreation, and the flocks benefiting from this activity become conditioned to depend entirely upon people for their food source and survival.

An adult pigeon consumes about a pound of food per week. The ingested food is digested with the aid of gravel or sand, which serves to grind food in the gizzard. Pigeons must have water. In fact, healthy pigeons can exist for several days without food, but they require water each day.

Pigeons are monogamous; that is, they have one mate at a time. The male cares for and guards the female and the nest. Eight to 12 days after mating, the female lays one or two eggs. Approximately 18 days later the eggs hatch. The squabs are fed a secreted substance called pigeon milk. The young leave the nest at four to six weeks of age. More eggs are usually laid before the first young are weaned. Breeding may occur during all seasons, but peak reproduction is in the spring and fall. A pigeon population usually consists equally of males and females. Wild pigeons can live for 15 years and sometimes longer. In typical urban environments, however, most pigeons do not live for more than three or four years.

Movement of pigeon flocks may be extensive and involve feeding, resting, and nesting behavior. Some flocks may travel up to five miles between feeding and nesting sites. Pigeons are mainly creatures of habit and tend to feed, nest, and roost in the same places routinely. However, if pigeons are driven from one roosting area, they select another and continue on as though they had not been disturbed. Resting, nesting, and roosting sites are frequently located in protected areas up high on structures.

HOUSE SPARROW
Passer domesticus (Linnaeus)
Family Ploceidae

Although there are many species of sparrows in the United States, the house (or English) sparrow is not a true sparrow. It actually belongs to the family called weaver finches which have their origin in North Africa. The house sparrow was introduced from Europe into the United States in 1850, and is now one of the most common and numerous of our urban pest birds.

The house sparrow is identified by its small, stocky appearance (see Figures 16.1 and 16.3). The upper parts are reddish-brown streaked with black and the underparts are gray. The female and immature birds lack any distinctive markings, but the male has a characteristic black throat, gray crown, and a chestnut-colored nape.

Flocks of house sparrows can be serious nuisances. In rural areas, they can be particularly destructive around poultry and other livestock operations because they consume and contaminate large amount of livestock feed, and are capable of destroying building insulation. In cities, they inhabit parks, city streets, and zoos. They nest in and around all types of residential and commercial buildings. Large flocks often develop around warehouses, stadiums, and airport hangars. In residential areas sparrows are pests in gardens and around yards, where they frequently displace desirable songbirds.

FIGURE 16.3. The house sparrow is one of the most common and familiar birds to nearly everyone. (Myers)

The nests of house sparrows are usually built in, on, or near buildings. The nests are typically messy, and are comprised of twigs, grass, paper, or almost anything else that the bird can carry. The numbers of places sparrows may nest are nearly unlimited. Around buildings, they often are situated in gutters, on roofs, ledges of buildings, loading docks, inside buildings on roof supports, and within commercial billboards and electronic signs, as well as in trees and shrubs using the same nesting holes and areas over and over again. Nests around power lines and in electrical substations have caused serious fire hazards.

Sparrows are prolific breeders. A "few sparrows" on the loading dock of a warehouse in April can result in a serious sparrow infestation by midsummer. Nest building and egg laying begin in March and April in the northern United States and slightly earlier in the southern states. A clutch contains between three and nine eggs. The eggs hatch in 11 to 17 days; the young are fledged at about 14 days. House sparrows can produce up to five broods per year. This high reproductive rate is offset by an annual natural mortality rate ranging between 40 and 60%, often depending on the severity of the winter. Sparrows are gregarious (i.e., group loving). They nest, roost, and feed together in flocks and usually within a small range covering only one or two miles. This is important in control operations, because where it is possible to eliminate a resident population, reinfestation by immigrant sparrows is usually slow.

The food of the house sparrow varies, but the preferred item is grain. Other vegetable matter such as the fruits and buds of some trees and bushes, as well as the green leaves of dandelion, clover, and others are regularly taken. An adult sparrow eats about six grams of food daily. During the breeding season, the nestlings are fed insects. In rural areas, sparrows thrive at cattle feedlots, dairies, and hog and poultry farms where food and shelter are plentiful. In inner-city locations, sparrows depend almost entirely upon human trash that provides foods such as bread, fat and other table scraps. As such they often become serious pests around fast food parking lots and around commercial dumpsters where food is discarded.

EUROPEAN STARLING
Sturnus vulgaris Linnaeus
Family Sturnidae

Starlings were brought into the United States from Europe. An individual, who wanted to introduce into America all of the birds mentioned in Shakespeare's works, released them in New York City in the early 1890s. Starlings are now found throughout the entire United States, including Alaska and Hawaii. The U.S. starling population is estimated at approximately 140 million birds.

Starlings are pests in both city and rural areas (see Figures 16.1 and 16.4); they travel in flocks as do pigeons and sparrows. In rural areas, they nest in tree cavities and on the ledges of farm buildings. Starlings can be serious pests around grain elevators, cornfields, orchards, and in cattle and hog feedlots. Around livestock feedlots, they may number in the hundreds of thousands and can devour enough of the food intended for the livestock to cause serious economic loss to the livestock manager.

In city and suburban areas, starlings are pests because they use buildings, parks, and residential trees for roost sites. Normally, starlings spend the warm-weather months in rural areas. When it becomes cold in the fall, thousands of birds often descend in large flocks into towns and cities at

FIGURE 16.4. The European starling. Note the speckled appearance of the feathers on the body, and the short tail. The beak is bright yellow. Immature birds have a dark beak, a longer tail, and a rather drab, unmarked coloration. (Myers)

night to seek the warmth and shelter of large buildings, or to roost in trees in residential areas and in city parks. They also use commercial structures such as lighted signs, marquees, and billboards. The vocalizations of starlings made at the roost sites and the filth they produce are extremely annoying to nearby residents and building owners. When large numbers of starlings harbor in trees, the accumulation of their feces on and around the tree will kill it unless the starlings are evicted.

The starling is a stocky, short-tailed bird about the size of the robin. From a distance it appears entirely black, but it is actually flecked with light speckles and most of its feathers show iridescent purples and greens. The bill of both sexes is yellow during breeding season (January to May), and dark for the rest of the year. Juveniles are a plain brownish-gray. Some people confuse starlings with blackbirds, but none of the blackbirds have the short tail or yellow bill (see Figure 16.1).

Starlings mate in the spring. They situate their nests in areas such as tree cavities, birdhouses, and in almost any available holes, nooks and crannies in and around buildings. Like the sparrow, the starling is annoying to the residential bird enthusiast because they often displace native hole-nesting songbirds such as bluebirds, flickers, woodpeckers, and purple martins from their residential nest sites.

Females lay four to seven eggs that hatch after 11 to 13 days of incubation. The young leave the nest when they are about 21 days old. Both parents help build the nest, incubate the eggs and feed the young. Usually two broods hatch per season. Although the starling is not as prolific a breeder as the sparrow, they are extremely hardy and able to survive difficult conditions and severe winters. This results in a lower natural mortality rate and is partly responsible for the hundreds of thousands of birds that form their flocks.

During the breeding season in the spring, starling flocks may be segregated into groups of mated birds caring for their young, and groups of young bachelor birds from the first brood. As the summer progresses, parent birds and the young from the spring broods merge increasing flock size. By fall, flocks may be extremely large. In the fall, portions of these flocks will migrate up to several hundred miles, while others remain in the same general area throughout the year.

During the winter, starlings feed and roost together in their flocks. They prefer to roost in dense vegetation such as groups of closely planted pine trees, or they utilize city buildings and parks that offer protection from wind and adverse weather.

During the daylight hours, winter urban starling flocks feed in the country at feedlots or grain eleva-

Other Pest Birds

Other birds such as ravens, swallows, magpies, Mississippi kites, scrub jays, hawks, owls, several blackbirds, sapsuckers, robins and even the bald eagle, are sometimes pests. Most of these birds, however, are pests outside the typical urban pest management situations.

Professionals needing management information on these or other birds should consult some of the references at the end of this chapter. Specific management strategies for a dozen or more bird species are also available on line at the Center for Wildlife damage Control website at **www.wildlife damage.unl.edu/**. Local wildlife authorities should also always be consulted.

tors and fly back to the protected city roost sites at night. Each day, they may fly 15 to 30 miles between roost sites and feeding sites. Starlings fly as a group from their roosts at the first sign of anything unusual such as sudden noise or flashing lights. However, they rapidly become accustomed to regular city noise and lights and are not easily disturbed in cities by heavy truck traffic or flashing neon lights.

Starlings consume a variety of foods. Insects and other invertebrates make up a large portion of their diet during the breeding season. Other diet items include fruits, seeds, and scraps of food found on the street and in garbage. During the winter months, livestock rations or food refuse from food-processing facilities make up a substantial part of their diet. In times of food scarcity, starlings will feed on almost anything to survive.

MANAGING URBAN PEST BIRDS
Bird Protection Laws and Public Relations

One of the first considerations the pest management professional must realize of bird management programs is that there are federal laws that protect birds. In fact, *all* birds are federally protected by law *except* the common pigeon, the house sparrow, and the European starling. In some locations, local ordinances or state laws may protect all birds including the three urban pest species. Moreover, some local laws may specify which methods can and cannot be used to manage a pest bird infestation.

Therefore, all state or local laws or ordinances affecting the particular pest bird must be checked prior to beginning any management programs. To do this, pest professionals should always consult with local or area fish and wildlife representatives or the state Department of Natural Resources.

The second consideration in bird management programs is **public relations**. In cases involving only a few birds, a control program may be conducted on private property away from the public view. Or, a program may involve the use of management techniques that will not harm any birds. In these cases, public relations are not a major concern.

However, in large-scale programs that involve the possible killing of many birds (e.g., pigeon control using toxic baits in a town or city), public relations can be of significant importance. Many urbanites truly enjoy the company of birds (see Figure 16.5). Local groups of bird enthusiasts, (e.g., Audubon Societies, Defenders of Wildlife, etc.), naturalists, and various other groups and organizations may be opposed to any type of animal destruction and present significant obstacles towards any lethal bird management efforts. The scope of the public relations program depends upon the complexity of a bird control program and the locale of the management program.

When public relation programs are warranted, the pest professional should inform and consult all appropriate public officials, (e.g., sanitarians, animal shelter personnel, mayor, city council members, etc.) before beginning the program. This helps to keep all concerned parties informed that only nuisance birds will be controlled.

In programs involving the killing of birds, it is important to avoid bad publicity that may result from birds that become sick or die in public view. Moreover, the death of songbirds or other desirable birds or animals (e.g., hawks, eagles, dogs, cats, etc.), can be disastrous to a pest management company's community standing. It is these types of environmental mistakes that "make the news"—sometimes on a national scale! Thus, all the efforts and costs

spent on advertising and building a positive community public relations image can be erased with one improperly managed bird problem. Such situations can also result in serious lawsuits.

Bird Management Programs

Like rodent management programs, effective bird management programs are best when they incorporate the integrated pest management (IPM) approach. In some cases, the elimination of the birds' food or water source will solve the problem. Other times, the simple repair of a broken window in a warehouse may be the solution. Often, however, when a professional is called upon to solve a bird problem, it is usually because the problem is complex and requires careful planning and integration of several approaches. Managing urban pest birds contains five broad components: (1) **survey;** (2) **sanitation;** (3) **exclusion and habitat alteration;** (4) **repellents,** and (5) **population reduction**. An overview of the various tools used in bird management work is presented in Table 16.1 on page 394.

Bird Management Surveys

The factors that may influence the outcome of a bird management program are probably more numerous than any other pest management program. Each factor must be examined and considered before any work begins. To do this, a **bird management survey** must be the first step in the overall program. The goal of the survey is to determine the following:

- which species are involved and the approximate number of birds present
- the problems or potential problems created by the birds
- whether the birds are residents or migrants
- the presence or absence of protected birds

For example, mourning doves (which are a federally protected bird) are often present around the same structures and areas as pigeons. The presence of the doves will have significant impact as to the management approach taken as compared to a situation when doves or other non-target birds are not present.

Via the survey, the professional must also determine the daily activities of the pest birds. Their nesting, feeding, watering, and roosting sites should all be identified if possible, as well as the times of the day that these sites are being used. To do this correctly, bird surveys are most informative if conducted early in the morning (just prior to dawn and shortly thereafter), again during the middle of the day, and again after dusk.

FIGURE 16.5. Many people enjoy the company or birds, and feeding pigeons in a recreational activity for people around the world.

Determining the extent of the problem. The professional must determine how many buildings, areas, and/or trees, may be involved in the overall problem. For example, pigeons may use different buildings to nest, roost, water, and feed. Their daily activity may span between several city blocks to several miles. It should be determined the likelihood of birds that are repelled off of one building simply moving to another building nearby. Or if the birds are poisoned, which areas are likely to be affected with sickened or dying birds.

Considering environmental and structural factors. To be successful in bird management programs, it is important to thoroughly understand the relationship between birds and their environment including structures, natural cover (trees, shrubs, etc.) and available food and water.

If environmental factors such as available food and water exist at the problem site that are attracting the birds, then the removal, reduction or modification of these factors will assist in correcting the problem. Therefore, management efforts should *begin* with thoughts of the bird's immediate environment. For example, before starting any type of trapping, repellents, or chemical bird management program, the professional should ask, "What can be done to change or modify this environment so it is no longer attractive to the birds?" Food is an obvious attractant to birds. Can the available food sources be reduced to discourage the birds, or to encourage a better acceptance of baits or traps? Others factors such as favorable roost sites or natural cover may also attract birds. Perhaps trees can be pruned or tree stands can be thinned out to discourage a persistent starling roost.

When conducting bird surveys two tools are necessary. **Binoculars** enable the professional to scan all affected areas such as the window sills, ledges, and roof line areas of tall buildings as well as the affected trees in the area. Birds in trees and on the faces of buildings can easily be spotted from the ground. When the birds are using the tops of tall buildings (as pigeons often do), it may be necessary to access the roof of the tallest nearby and examine not only this roof but also those of all other buildings in the vicinity (see Figure 16.6).

The second survey tool is a **survey sheet** to record all of the above collected information for future referral for customer information and for proper design of the control program itself.

Based on all the information obtained during the survey, the professional now must decide what public relations work may need to be done and what management measures are appropriate for the job. Then a cost estimate must be carefully

FIGURE 16.6. A pair of binoculars is an important tool for bird surveys. For pigeon control programs, it is helpful to have access to rooftops in the affected area, to survey the daily habits of the pigeons.

developed that will cover all costs involved. The customer should be informed as to what exactly is proposed, the method to be used, the results to expect, and the price. Any cooperation needed from the customer should be fully explained and agreed to by both parties.

Sanitation

Birds, like all living animals, must have food, water, and shelter to survive. The impact of sanitation practices in solving bird problems varies according to each situation. In some cases, sanitation efforts may significantly assist in the overall program when integrated with other tools and techniques. Other times, sanitation practices alone may solve the problem (thus, the importance of the survey). And in some cases, sanitation may have little or no impact on the problem at all.

Sanitation efforts are most effective in situations where the birds are obtaining their food and water at the problem site. For example, sparrows and pigeons often are pests around fast-food restaurants, outdoor dining areas, and various food stands. Sanitation practices at these locations will have an affect on the birds. In fact, some experts claim that the most effective means of controlling pigeon and sparrow populations is to remove their food during the winter to accelerate natural mortality rates, followed by intense sanitation activities during the spring and summer.

With pigeons, removal of either their food or water will likely have impact. Remember that pigeons must have water daily. If the pigeons' water supply (e.g., rooftop rain puddles, or clogged rain gutters) cannot be eliminated, it may be possible to treat it with an oil or detergent to render it unpalatable to the birds. If pigeons are actually feeding in,

TABLE 16.1. A comparative overview of bird management techniques.

Method	Target Pest Birds	Product Example	Mode of Action	Management Considerations	Target Site Examples
Sound/ noise deterrents	Blackbirds, geese, starlings, gulls, crows	Pyrotechnics, distress calls, sirens	Sounds frighten birds; disperse them.	Some not appropriate for residential areas; temporary results Most effective when used in combination with other methods.	Crop fields, food plants, warehouses
Taste/Gus- tatory repellents	Geese	Methyl anthranilate (ReJex-It®, Fog Force®) Anthraquinone (Flight Control®)	Taste repellency and/or intestinal discomfort in geese.	Provide fast, but usually temporary results. For turf liquid applications, certain environmental conditions must be met. Mowing and watering practices usually need to be halted temporarily. Weekly treatments may be needed for some flocks. Concentrates relatively expensive, and some application operations can be labor-intensive.	
Tactile/ adhesive repellents	Pigeons, sparrows starlings, gulls	HotFoot® Roost-No-More® Bird Barrier Gel®	Creates uncomfortable sensation on birds' feet or bodies.	For small areas of surfaces and ledges requiring only temporary results;(e.g., months). Heat, dust and cold can shorten longevity. Staining to building surfaces possible if extreme care not taken in application procedures.	Building ledges and surfaces, signs, lamp posts, etc.
Mechanical repellents	Pigeons, sparrows, starlings, other birds	Nixalite® Bird Coil® Bird Spike® Daddi-Long Legs® Bird Blox®	Sharp projections or wires prevent birds from landing. Some repellents wave and bob to frighten birds.	Installation labor varies from easy to complex and labor-intensive. Some types of prickly wires must be kept clean and maintained. Some newer, inexpensive copolymer barriers "block-out" birds from roosting and nesting on interior ledges and structural framing of garages, sheds, horse stables, barns, etc.	Building ledges and surfaces, signs, lamp posts, etc.
Visual deterrents/ repellents	Blackbirds, crows, geese	Balloons w/eyes, fake owls, flashing lights, coyote effigies, dead goose, etc.	Mimic predators; frightens	Not effective against sparrows, pigeons, starlings. Vary in effectiveness; results usually temporary unless varied, periodically moved about, etc.	Crop fields, food plants, warehouses, some building areas.
Lasers	Geese, crows, gulls, sparrows, pigeons*	Avian Dissuader® Desman®	Laser beam frightens, disorients, and disperses birds	Easy to learn and use; fast results; night time work required. Flock and situation-specific. May require several treatments. Laser equipment relatively expensive.	Bird flocks on turf, trees, buildings
Electrical bird deterrents	Pigeons, sparrows, starlings, other birds	Shock Strip® Bird B Gone®	Shocks birds alighting onto strips or charged wires	Labor-intensive installation. Regular maintenance and inspections to ensure continual effectiveness. Can provide long-term effectiveness properly installed and maintained.	Building ledges and surfaces, signs
Chase dogs	Geese	Border collies, Australian cattle dogs, others	Dogs chase/harass and frighten birds	Can be highly effective if conducted properly. May require several sessions to disperse geese for prolonged periods Trainers usually required to manage dogs during chases. Dogs and trainers not readily available in all areas.	Golf courses, parks, office parks, etc.
Netting	Pigeons, sparrows, starlings, gulls, crows	Stealth Net® Endura Net® Bird Net®	Excludes birds	Requires training, practice, and skill for correct installation. Can provide permanent protection properly installed and maintained.	Most structural environments; overhangs, signs, many uses
Baits	Pigeons, sparrows, starlings, crows, gulls	Avitrol®	Kills small percentage of flock; causes site-aversion reaction in remaining birds	Highly effective for situations where exclusion or mechanical repellents are too costly or inappropriate. Subject to negative public relations. Risk to non-target birds. Area must be monitored and re-treated as necessary.	Restricted use products; permits required in some areas. Illegal in some states

*Sucess is intermittent depending on several factors. See text for details.

on, or around the problem site, limiting or removing the food can discourage the birds from using the area or at least reduce the severity of the pest problem.

As sparrows have a high natural mortality rate, regular removal of all nests can significantly reduce the population over time. Sparrow nests and eggs should be located and destroyed at 10 to 14 day intervals. Sparrow nests can be removed using long poles with hooks attached to the ends (see Figure 16.7). The nests and all nesting materials should be discarded to force the sparrows to "start from scratch" in rebuilding the nest. Sparrows may be persistent in using the same building sites for nests for long periods, but after several nest removal/rebuilding cycles, they often vacate the area. Nest destruction is recommended around shopping malls, building signs, and other areas where it is difficult to completely eliminate the birds' food source.

If birds are using a site solely for roosting/loafing activity, as may be the case with an urban starling flock, sanitation practices are not likely to impact on the bird problem (although good sanitation should be emphasized anyway to discourage other types of pest problems).

Exclusion and Habitat Alterations

The most effective method to keep birds off and out of structures is to make it impossible for them to enter or use the structure as a nesting, roosting, or loafing site. In some cases, exclusion and habitat alterations are easily achieved; in other cases, this approach is impossible on a practical level or is not economically feasible.

Indoor nest sites of pigeons and sparrows can be eliminated by blocking off all access points.

Openings to lofts, steeples, vents, eaves, etc., should be blocked with wood, metal, glass, masonry or 3/4-inch rustproofed wire mesh or plastic nets (see Figure 16.8).

Professional-level bird netting is highly effective in excluding birds under many different conditions. Most netting products come with an assortment of assembling components to enable the netting to be used under many different situations (see Figure 16.9). Most netting is lightweight, strong and resilient (see Figure 16.10). Bird netting is an effective long-term approach for excluding birds from areas such as loading docks, church steeples, lofts, etc. Bird netting can be used to completely wall off areas such as loading dock trusses and similar areas

FIGURE 16.8. The simple closing of holes in buildings can be the solution to bird problems, but this step is often overlooked by building owners.

FIGURE 16.7. The removal of sparrow nests and the destruction of nest materials are effective for long-term population management of this species. (Myers)

FIGURE 16.9. Installing bird netting and other bird management tools requires a wide range or specialized tools.

from pest birds by enclosing the loading dock in a suspended ceiling (see Figure 16.11).

Installment of netting varies from the simple to the complex. Semi-permanent and temporary netting can be installed using Velcro strips to adhere the net, or by simply using a staple gun. For the more complex jobs, the professional must be competent in the use of the specialized tools and techniques (see Figure 16.12). Careful study and consideration of the structure is necessary to ensure an attractive, yet effective long-term exclusion program.

In general, netting programs must be conducted with a high level of professionalism and be very thorough. One of the golden rules in the use of netting is to avoid creating any gaps that the birds can take advantage of. Against sparrows for example, all gaps must be eliminated down to 0.75 inches. Sparrows are amazingly adept at locating and squeezing behind opening which appear insignificant to us standing on the ground looking up. If gaps

FIGURE 16.10. Plastic bird netting can be purchased in large rolls for commercial jobs. The rolls can then be cut and applied as needed.

FIGURE 16.11. The application of plastic netting to exclude birds from a warehouse loading dock. The rental of a cherry picker or similar platform equipment is invaluable in bird and some urban wildlife work.

larger than to 0.75 inches are available between any perimeter edge area of the netting and the support cables, sparrows will be quick to take advantage, They can then nest within the netted void, which will serve the sparrows as a protected bird haven. To ensure such gaps do not occur, the guidelines for the proper spacing of support attachments for the particular net must always be checked and rechecked (e.g., every 12 inches, etc.). The recommended spacings should never be expanded upon.

Bird netting can also be used as screen doors around shipping warehouses to prevent birds from constantly flying into the warehouse. "Net-doors" can be operated much in the same manner as drapery for patio doors or windows. Roosting can be permanently prevented by screening the underside of the rafters with bird netting or 1/4-inch wire-mesh screening in locations such as loading docks and inside tool or machinery sheds, barns, and hangars.

Some bird management product suppliers offer detailed seminars on how to use their products. Such seminars are well worth the professional's time.

Changing the ledge angle to 45° or more can discourage loafing and roosting on ledges. Sheet metal, Styrofoam blocks, wood, stone, etc., can be formed and fastened to ledges to achieve the desired angle. Ledge repellents can be used as described below. Ornamental architecture can be screened with wire or plastic net mesh to prevent roosting, loafing, and nesting. Additional tips for excluding birds from building areas include the following:

- Broken windows in upper stories of buildings should be repaired or sealed off.

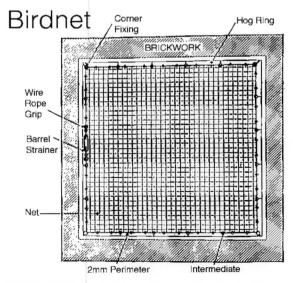

FIGURE 16.12. Plastic bird netting is affixed to buildings and various structural elements, using a variety of tools and hardware items.

- Warehouse doorways that must be used frequently during the workday (e.g., forklift truck activity) can sometimes be effectively blocked to sparrows by hanging clear plastic strips to the ground in front of the opening. These strips will not impede the warehouse workers activities, but will present an impassable barrier to the eyes of the sparrow. To be effective however, these strips *must* remain in good repair at all times. Broken strips will allow sparrows to enter beneath or between the strips.
- Plastic strips are being replaced in many commercial facilities (especially food-handling facilities) by "zip doors." Zip doors are industrial-strength vinyl doors that are rolled up and down within a second or two with the pull of cord or push of a button.
- Commercial signs should be attached flat against buildings or any spaces should be screened to prevent any sparrow roosting space.
- Spaces between window air conditioners and the building should be blocked off or screened.
- Building ventilators should be netted over using plastic netting to prevent birds from crowding their nests into ventilator slits.
- In locations where sparrows nest in palm trees, the frequent removal of the dead fronds will aid in eliminating sparrow roosting sites (as well as roof rat harborage).
- Likewise, if sparrows are using building vines, the vines can be removed from building sides or covered with inconspicuous plastic nets (in most cases, black is the most inconspicuous color choice).

Repellents/ Exclusionary Devices

Various types of repellents and exclusionary devices are available that can effectively discourage birds from using an area, or cause them to vacate buildings and tree roost/nesting sites. Repellents are designed to affect one or more of the bird's senses to either scare the birds away, or to make their roosting/loafing areas inaccessible or uncomfortable. Repellents are often used where netting may be impossible, impractical, or too costly. Often times, repellents are best employed with other devices such as netting (see Figure 16.13).

In general, there are three broad types of bird repellents: (1) tactile [touch], (2) sound, and (3) visual. Some of the newer wire repellents work as both a repellent and exclusionary devices. They are included in this section to keep the discussion simple.

For most urban and industrial bird problems, the **tactile repellents/exclusionary devices** are the most practical and effective bird repellent. There

FIGURE 16.13. Ornate buildings like this one are often birdproofed by using mechanical wire repellents in combination with netting or chemical repellents.

are two types of tactile repellents: (1) mechanical and (2) chemical.

Mechanical bird repellents and exclusionary devices include devices such as "porcupine wires," tight wire stands, coiled wire, bobbing wires, electrically charged wires, and the use of water jets. Many of these are used for the purposes of repelling or excluding birds off of various ledges. Thus, often they are referred to as ledge repellents.

Several types of **ledge repellents** (e.g., Bird B Gone™, Cat Claw™, Nixalite™) are available. Some are made of metal spikes in various arrangements with sharp points extending outward at all angles (often referred to as "porcupine wires"). Others are self-assembling devices and are made of plastic prongs (see Figure 16.14). Most of these devices are designed to be fastened to a solid base that are then installed on window sills, ledges, eaves, roof peaks, ornamental architectural features, or wherever birds are prone to roost. The sharp pointed wires inflict temporary discomfort, so birds avoid landing on these surfaces. Pigeons and sparrows are

FIGURE 16.14. The use of plastic bird spikes and netting to deny birds access to various cavities and ledges in a high bird-pressure area.

amazing in their ability to gain footholds using small spaces on buildings. Thus, the projected area of spikes for instance, should extend beyond the target surface by 0.50 inches. Ledge repellent devices must also cover the entire length of target ledges. This cannot be stressed strongly enough. Leaving only one inch of unprotected space will allow birds access because they can land on the short edge space and walk into, or nest within, certain types of spike or coil arrangements

Wire ledge repellents can be very effective, but manufacturer installation instructions must be strictly followed. If excessive ledge space remains available at the ends of the ledges, between the building and the wires, or between rows of the wires, birds, by trial and error, construct nests among the wires creating even more of a problem than if no wires were used at all. Also, the wires must be inspected periodically and cleaned of any debris such as leaves and twigs. Otherwise such debris will protect sparrows from the prickly affect of the projections, and they will continue to use the building area (especially sparrows as they can roost on ledges only 1/2-inch wide). Although wire ledge repellent and their installation can be expensive, the long-term results usually justify the cost.

Coiled wire (e.g., Bird Barrier Coil™) is another form of wire ledge repellent. This stainless steel wire coil when uninstalled appears as a large "slinky" type of wire (see Figure 16.15). The coil is easily affixed to a base mounting plate than can be attached to various ledges as one would with the other wire repellents to discourage bird activity. It is particularly important with this wire repellent that no space exists on the ledge or structure for the birds to perch at the beginning or ending areas of the coil, as they may eventually learn to enter within the coil.

Tightly strung strands of steel wire (e.g., "piano wire"), or fishing line strung slightly above the surface of some narrow ledges, support cables, conduit, or small isolated areas such as window sills and doorway areas, will prevent birds from alighting there. The metal wire should be 16- to 18-gauge steel wire. If monofilament line is used it should be at least 80-pound test for long-term durability.

To achieve the desired tautness, L-brackets are attached to turnbuckles at each end of the area to be protected, and the turnbuckles are then used to tighten the wires. The brackets should be welded or attached with a cable clamp or aircraft hose clamp (threads on standard radiator clamps become stripped under the high torque loads required for holding L-brackets supporting wire over long distances). On buildings experiencing heavy bird pressure, it may be necessary to stretch three lines at 2,

5, and 7 inches (5, 12, and 18 cm) above the surface.

New polymer **toothed repellent strips** (e.g., Bird Blox®) are now available that are highly effective in preventing birds from perching interior rafters and ledges. These repellents are very cost-effective for situations such as horse barns, hog and chicken buildings, machine sheds, and many other similar structures (see Figure 16.16).

Charged wires, similar in principal to those wires used for cattle fences, can be installed onto roosting surfaces and have been used with some success. These wires carry high voltage but low amperage that produces an unpleasant shock to birds contacting the wire. This technology can be expensive to install and must be regularly inspected to ensure the system is working. The wires must be fully insulated from the building, which can be difficult to ensure for long periods because sticks and straws dropped by the birds, as well as the bodies of dead birds can short out the wires in a brief time. Also, in areas subjected to ice and snow covers, the systems are subject to shorting out and other electrical problems. But for small areas where birds must be repelled and nets or metal projections are aesthetically unacceptable, (e.g., doorways of

FIGURE 16.15. An example of a coiled wire bird repellent.

FIGURE 16.16. Plastic surface denial/visual deterrent for birds for interior rafters and ledges of buildings.

ornate churches, museums, etc.), and the wires can be kept clean, electric wires can provide excellent long-term results providing they are kept clean and well-maintained.

Water jets are occasionally used to destroy nests and drive birds from building sites. But this must be done persistently until the birds become discouraged and move elsewhere.

Chemical tactile repellents (e.g., Hot Foot®, Tanglefoot®, 4-the-Birds™, Roost No More™, Bird-Proof™, etc.), are commonly used in the pest control industry for various types of bird roosting problems (see Figure 16.17). They are available as gels, pastes, sprays from concentrates, and as convenient aerosol-type cans for small jobs. Chemical repellents vary considerably, both in cost and in effectiveness and it is important for the professional to research the various products when considering the use of chemical repellents. Some are thick and tacky, others are jelly-like, and others are viscous enough to be sprayed. The thicker, heavier materials are most suitable for use on ledges and buildings. The spray-on repellents are designed for use on trees.

Most chemical bird repellents contain chemicals such as polyethylene or polybutylene. These substances are not toxic to the birds. Rather they produce a "warm foot" sensation to birds when they light on them, resulting in the birds moving to roost or loaf elsewhere. Sometimes however birds do become entangled in these materials and if the birds are not quickly rescued, this situation can create a public relations problem. Keep in mind however, that all potential roosting and/or loafing surfaces on a building must be treated, or the birds will move to untreated areas.

The pastes and gel formulations are usually applied with caulking guns, or from containers pressurized by an air compressor for large jobs. For

FIGURE 16.17. Chemical bird repellents come in various types of gels that can be applied by hand with a caulking gun or through power-caulking operations.

best results, all surfaces should be wiped clean of all dirt, debris, and bird droppings before any repellent is applied. Nonporous surfaces, such as metal, do not require additional preparation, but porous surfaces such as concrete, wood, brick, and stone should be sealed with a clear sealer so the liquids in the glue will not be drawn into them. Strips of impervious tape can be placed over the surface on which the bird glue is to be applied. Failure to seal the surface properly will cause the glue to dry which shortens the residual life of the repellent.

Also, certain building surfaces are susceptible to staining from chemical repellents and must be protected from the repellent dripping or running during warm temperatures. Applying the repellents on top of masking tape or waterproof duct tape can protect surfaces.

Paste and gel repellents should be applied according to each product's label directions. Generally, these repellents are applied in strips as thick as 1/2 inch to the surface of ledges, roofs, and anywhere else birds may roost or nest. This amount of material is usually necessary to ensure that the repellent remains sticky, allowing the birds to pick up some of the repellent on their feet when they land on it. The strips should be placed no more than two to three inches apart so birds will not have room enough to land between them.

Chemical repellents lose their effectiveness over time. The heavy gel formulations are effective for about one year before reapplication is necessary. In areas of excessive dust, dirt, moisture conditions, or excessive heat or cold, repellents lose their effectiveness in periods of much less than a year. The thinner spray formulations applied to trees or buildings surfaces do not last as long as the gels and pastes.

Although chemical repellents offer effective results in many situations, they have some drawbacks to consider. First, where repellents are applied to areas visible to people they may be aesthetically unpleasing. Second, for some buildings sticky repellents can interfere with professional window-cleaning operations. Third, nesting pigeons will occasionally drop sticks and straws over the repellents and continue to nest. And finally, chemical repellents are most applicable for small areas. For large commercial jobs requiring significant amounts of manpower and expensive equipment, the use of repellents may be economically shortsighted as it is costly in these situations to reapply the repellents every few years. Programs that combine exclusion techniques, habitat alteration, and judicial use of both mechanical and chemical repellents are probably the best use of the customer's money for the long run.

Chemical taste and odor repellents are available for geese and for limited use against other bird roosts and nuisance urban bird flocks. **Methyl anthranilate (or, MA)** (e.g., Rejex-It®, Fog Force®, Goose Chase®, etc.) is a taste/olfactory repellent. This repellent was originally developed to repel geese off turf and temporary stands of water. But it has also been used against gulls and other birds at landfill sites. Methyl anthranilate can be used in a "fog" formulation to repel geese, starlings, gulls and other birds where they have established loafing or roosting areas and are annoying people or causing filth with their droppings.

Methyl anthranilate occurs naturally, and is used as a food flavoring that imparts the flavor of grapes. For reasons not completely understood, MA is irritating to birds, much as ammonia or black pepper are irritants to mammals.

Another relatively new chemical repellent, **anthraquinone** (Flight Control®) works by causing an intestinal discomfort to the geese without causing any serious harm to them. Turf treated with the anthraquinone can be seen by geese in the ultraviolet spectrum of light (which people cannot see). Geese learn from their previous ill-feeling to avoid areas treated with the anthraquinone.

Both methyl anthranilate and anthraquinone are thus far intended primarily as goose repellents, with uses against other birds considered secondary.

The effectiveness of these chemical repellents varies significantly from one situation to another, depending heavily on alternative feeding or harborage areas, roost or loafing site attachments, turf and/or water management practices, and several other factors. (See the discussion on Canada geese management for additional information.)

Visual repellents vary from the valid and effective to devices that are merely "gizmos." One of the more effective visual repellents to emerge in the last five years is the use of **lasers**. The lasers designed for bird management programs have been adapted from technology used by the military. These lasers create intense red laser spots that scare birds when the spot is targeted to the areas where they are roosting and/or perching. Research on lasers has been conducted by the USDA's National Wildlife Research Center, and their results have shown that low-power, long-wave length lasers employing beams of 630 to 650 nanometers (nm) have been effective for **flock dispersal** of geese, cormorants, gulls, crows, and vultures. Depending on how the beam is directed, the laser can be used to affect the bird's vision causing it to be disoriented and frightened. When the beam is run along the ground towards a flock of geese, the geese may perceive the beam as an approaching predator (for more discussion of lasers against geese, refer to the geese management section

later in the chapter).

One laser model is handheld and powered by an ordinary small 9-volt battery, yet it projects an intense beam than can be adjusted to be effective from ranges of 25 to 500 yards. Success has been achieved using lasers to move bird flocks from park lakes, golf courses, commercial establishments, trees, and warehouse environments. Yet the beams present no hazard to the birds or to the environment.

Low-powered laser beams such as those produced by an ordinary laser pointer used by teachers and trainers at meetings have been used by pest professionals to disperse and harass sparrows inside darkened areas of buildings (grocery stores, warehouses) sometimes scaring them to leave through doors, or to fly into previously installed capture mist nets. But thus far, the success of lasers used in this manner is inconsistent. In some cases, the laser beams have no impact on sparrows and pigeons whatsoever.

The success or failure of lasers on a particular bird or bird flock is influenced by several factors, including the intensity of the laser, the diameter of the beam, the distance to the bird, the specific structural location of the bird, the species of bird, the amount of ambient and artificial light present at the time the laser beam is "shot," and perhaps others factors research will eventually reveal.

Several of the researchers involved in the development of lasers as bird deterrents predict lasers will be a highly cost-effective tool in the battle against urban bird roosts. To this point, research is continuing on their use. Thus far, the birds that have proven most vulnerable to laser harassment have not demonstrated any habituation in repeated field trials.

One of the strongest advantages of laser beams is that it reduces or completely eliminates the need for climbing ladders, chemical repellents, and expensive exclusion. But lasers also have limitations. Lasers are less effective against entrenched bird roosts that have strong fidelity to a particular roost or nesting site. In these cases, harassment with lasers may need to be repeated several times to disperse flocks and/or the lasers may have to be combined with other treatments, such as noise pyrotechnics and/or lethal shooting.

Tips and safety issues for using lasers for flock dispersal include the following:

- Lasers are more effective when used at night or in low light situations.
- Safety is important when pointing lasers, especially in public areas. Should a laser beam stray and land on an unsuspecting pedestrian's shirt, or eye, it could cause a person unnecessary consternation. Some models are considered

"eye-safe" for incidental exposure, while some of the more powerful models must be used with caution around people. For example, the normal hazard zone (NHZ) established for two models currently used in professional bird harassment campaigns range from 25 to 44 meters for 10-second exposures. Nevertheless, these lasers should not be used where their beams will land on people, roads, or aircraft. Laser dispersal of birds at airports is prohibited without prior approval of the U.S. Federal Aviation Administration. (FAA).

• Requirements for laser operations and personal protective equipment in the United States is available on the OSHA website at **www.osha.gov**.

• Information on regulatory authority and safety specifications for laser use in bird management has been compiled by the National Wildlife Research Center Library and can be accessed at NWRC's website listed in the references at the end of this chapter.

Another visual deterrent that can be highly effective when installed properly are the **spindly-wire devices** (e.g., Daddi-long legs®). These devices, typically installed on lamp-posts, rooftops, and other areas, are designed to frighten away gulls, crows and other birds attempting to roost or loaf in these areas when the spindly legs swing and "bob" about in the wind.

Other visual repellents include flashing lights, fake owls, hawks, snakes, scarecrows, shiny flags, balloons, and various other gadgets. Visual repellents have limited use in some agricultural crop situations and in woodpecker control but, in general, these types of visual repellents are ineffective against the commensal birds in urban and industrial environments. In these situations visual repellents sometimes produce an initial effect and work for short periods of time. But in most cases, urban pest birds become acclimated to the particular object and simply ignore it.

Sound repellents include sudden, loud or unusual noises such as explosions, gunfire, fireworks, loud piercing alarms, horns, and the recorded sounds of birds in distress played over amplifiers. Sound repellents have little permanent effect on either sparrows or pigeons, as these birds are well adapted to the various loud noises of the everyday activities of urban areas. Moreover, many of these noise devices are not very practical within urban and industrial environments because they are irritating to people also. Sound repellents can be effective against large tree roosts of starlings and crows in urban and residential areas when used persistently until the birds move. Some people have found that

ordinary fireworks or "canned horn" (often used by fans at football and baseball games), can be effective in scaring birds away.

To be effective, noise repellents should be administered as soon as possible after birds have established a permanent or semipermanent roost site. The longer the birds become established to a favorable roost site, the more difficult it is to drive them away. The noise should be administered early in the morning before the birds leave the roost, and again at dusk just as the birds return. The procedure may need to be repeated for several days until the birds vacate the roost sites. Also, the noise should emanate from a different spot near the roost each time it is applied. In residential tree roost problems, it is helpful if the neighbors work cooperatively together in administering the noise. Residents should also seek the help of local wildlife officials, county agents, and health officials. If the roosts persists, more drastic measures such as tree thinning procedures may be necessary.

When considering the management of residential starling, crow, and blackbird roosts, it is important to note that these birds commonly move into suburban residential neighborhoods as large flocks for one or two weeks in autumn before moving on to more permanent wintering sites. Actions should not be taken against these temporary roosts until the birds have remained for more than two or three weeks. Otherwise all efforts may be premature and needless.

Some high-frequency and ultrasonic devices have been tried against birds. But birds have a similar hearing range as humans. Thus, if the sound isn't audible to people, it is not audible to birds. Such devices are of no value in bird management programs.

Occasionally, naphthalene flakes (i.e., **"moth flakes"**) have been used in attempts to repel birds from buildings. This material must be applied in relatively large amounts (about 5 pounds per 2000 cubic feet of space) to be effective. Moreover, the strong odor produced by naphthalene can be disagreeable, irritating and/or harmful to some people. Most labels of naphthalene products caution that prolonged breathing of naphthalene vapors should be avoided. The use of naphthalene is not recommended inside occupied buildings.

Population Reduction

Three types of programs can be implemented to reduce pest bird populations: (1) toxic baits, (2) traps, and (3) shooting.

Toxic baits or other substances that poison birds are called **avicides**. Presently, the only avicides used for bird management programs are certain baits. Only properly registered avicides can be used in bird control programs and all label directions must be strictly adhered to. Additionally, in some states and in some locales, the use of toxic baits is not allowed. In other states, the use of avicides require special permits issued through the state, federal, or local agency. Because of the sensitivity and visibility associated with birds and the threat of poisoning non-target birds, extraordinary precautions must be taken whenever avicides are used to avoid accidental poisoning of non-target birds and mammals.

As of 2003, there are three toxic baits registered either for the control of pigeons, sparrows or starlings: **Avitrol®**, **DRC-1339**, and **Starlicide®**.

Avitrol is often referred to as a **bird-frightening agent**. Avitrol contains the chemical 4-aminopyridine. However, Avitrol is lethal (i.e., toxic) to birds that consume sufficient amounts of the treated bait. Dying birds display distress symptoms and erratic behavior, which frightens the rest of the flock and causes them to leave the area. Avitrol is available on several bait materials to permit maximum bait acceptance depending on the bird species and its feeding preferences. The baits are diluted with grain of the same size, form and kind. Whole corn bait is suitable for pigeons and crows while smaller grain and chopped or pelletized baits are better for sparrows and starlings.

The treated bait is diluted (blended) with clean, untreated bait to achieve the desired flock-alarming reaction. The higher the dilution, the less mortality produced. In urban areas where high mortality may cause adverse public reactions, a blend ratio of 1:29, (1 part Avitrol bait to 29 parts untreated bait) produces low mortality, but control of the problem flock may take longer. Because pigeons and sparrow flocks are not easily frightened, a high degree of mortality is usually needed to achieve reasonably quick results. A blend ratio of 1:19 or even 1:9 may be used for pigeon control and ratios of 1:5 and lower for sparrows. The lower dilution rates produce results much quicker, but there is a substantial increase in the number of dead and severely affected birds. Birds affected by Avitrol usually take several hours to succumb. Pigeons and starlings may die over a several mile radius of the baiting site. Because sparrows have a limited home range, they usually die close to their nesting areas.

Birds reacting to Avitrol suffer no pain, as the active ingredient does not affect the nervous system. Also, secondary poisoning is not likely to occur with Avitrol (i.e., a bird raptor such as a falcon consuming the carcass of a bird affected with Avitrol). However, Avitrol is toxic to any bird species directly ingesting enough of the bait. Thus, Avitrol must always be used in such a manner that minimizes the possibility of non-target birds having direct access to the bait. After initial success, Avitrol need only be applied periodically following pre-baiting to maintain control.

Poisoning birds is a complex task requiring careful attention to details. The easiest way to ensure failure of the control program is to take shortcuts, especially in pre-baiting. As a general rule of safety, toxic baits that are placed above ground level must be contained so they will not fall to a place where they might be accessible to children, pets, wildlife, or livestock.

The avicide compound **DRC-1339 (3-chloro-4-methyl benzenamine hydrochloride)** is a restricted-use product registered for the control of pigeons, crows, ravens, gulls, blackbirds, and magpies. This slow-acting avicide can only be used by USDA-APHIS-ADC employees or persons working under their direct supervision.

The toxicity of DRC-1339 to birds varies considerably. Starlings, red-winged blackbirds, crows, and pigeons are most susceptible, but house sparrows and hawks are somewhat resistant. Generally mammals are not sensitive to the toxic effects of DRC-1339. Moreover, secondary poisonings do not occur with DRC-1339. Thus, the excreta and flesh of pigeons poisoned with DRC-1339 are nontoxic to predators or scavengers. Therefore, DRC-1339 may be a toxicant that provides a higher margin of safety than other toxicants for use in cities where peregrine falcons have been introduced.

DRC-1339 causes death by causing uremic poisoning, although the bird's death is thought to be painless. DRC-1339 poisoned birds do not convulse as they do with the 4-aminopyridine. The length of time to cause mortality varies between several hours to three days. The relatively slow action of this bait does prevents bait shyness, which allows for the baiting programs to be extended until control is achieved Also because of the slow action, the majority of the dead birds are usually found at the roost site.

Baiting programs for pigeons. Before a baiting program is begun, the daily movement patterns of the pigeons between their feeding, loafing, and roosting areas must be determined in order to select baiting sites (i.e., survey). The number of sites needed depends on the size of the area being treated and the number of birds involved. If possible, several baiting sites should be used. They should be located in areas that are normally frequented by the birds, over which rigid control of human access can be maintained and that are otherwise free from disturbance.

Generally, the closer the bait site is to the normal feeding site, the more successful the baiting will be. In urban areas, flat rooftops make excellent bait sites for pigeons (see Figure 16.18). Even though pigeons do not normally feed on rooftops, they do frequent them, and access can be rigidly controlled. With persistence, pigeons can be taught to feed almost anywhere.

Once the bait sites have been selected, the pigeons must be trained to feed there by using prebaiting techniques. Prebaiting is the single most important aspect of a successful baiting program. If the prebaiting is done incorrectly, the entire program may fail.

Because pigeons are suspicious of any change in their daily routine, the prebaiting and subsequent toxic baiting should be done at the same time every day and in the same manner. Pigeons usually feed most vigorously right after leaving the roost early in the morning. Therefore, the prebait and the bait should be placed just before sun-up. The prebait (untreated corn) should be applied on firm, relatively flat surfaces or set out in wide, shallow wooden or metal trays.

The quantity of prebait placed and consumed should be recorded each day, so that the amount of poisoned bait to be used can be determined. Generally, 100 feeding pigeons will eat about seven to eight pounds (15 to 18 kg) of whole corn per day. Baits are most effective when placed in numerous small piles or heaps. For large infestations, 8 to 12 or more piles containing one pound (454 g) of grain in each pile may be necessary—smaller infestations will require less. Never place the prebait or toxic bait in one pile. The goal is to maximize the number of pigeons that can feed at one time. Prebaiting also allows a professional to gather useful information about the daily feeding patterns and bait acceptance.

Prebaiting programs are most effective when conducted for two weeks. During the prebaiting period, all bait sites must be carefully observed to ensure that no non-target birds, such as cardinals, bluejays, or doves are attracted to them. If protected birds do appear at one of the sites, prebaiting should continue to be put out because this will hold the protected birds at that site. The avicide bait can then be placed at one of the other sites not being visited by the songbirds. If only one baiting site is being used, or if protected birds begin using all the locations, modification or abandonment of the site or sites may be necessary.

Using good quality prebait is important. The best prebait for pigeons is clean, untreated whole corn for two reasons: (1) smaller resident birds, such as song sparrows, are physically incapable of swallowing it, and (2) corn is highly accepted by pigeons during the winter months when control using toxic baits is normally attempted.

The amount of toxic bait put out generally does not have to be more than half of the prebait used each day. All prebait must be picked up before the toxic bait is put out. In urban areas, toxic baiting programs are best when conducted on days and a time when visibility by the public in that particular area or around the affected building is likely to be at a minimum. For example, sickened pigeons convulsing on the ground during the lunch hour in a city area is likely to attract negative attention. In such cases, weekend baiting programs may be appropriate.

After birds have ingested the toxic baits, most will leave the bait site before the poison takes effect. Therefore a search crew should be organized before bait placement and sent out immediately afterwards to collect dead birds at likely locations, such as roosting areas and along the birds' flight lines.

A second application of bait may be necessary, but with 4-aminopyridine, some of the birds left after the initial control period will be bait shy. Therefore, wait three weeks before beginning again with prebaiting operations. The same bait sites may be used in all control efforts.

It is important for both the professional and the customer to realize that baiting programs rarely eliminate all the pest birds causing the problem. Even with the most thorough and professionally conducted baiting programs, it is realistic to expect only about 85% reduction in the flock. However, with continual monitoring of the problem, and maintenance of baiting programs, reduction can be increased over time. Total eradication of all the pest birds is rarely achieved when using baiting programs as the sole method of management. The customer must be willing to accept a few remaining birds following even the most professional program.

FIGURE 16.18. The use of Avitrol corn bait during the winter can be effective against pigeons, providing good baiting sites are selected.

Baiting programs for sparrows. Baiting techniques for sparrows are similar to those used for pigeon programs. However, bait placements for sparrow infestations must be carefully selected and placed, because sparrows are typically ground feeders and must be conditioned to feed off the ground. Sparrows frequently roost and nest inside large buildings, where they take up residence on beams and other supports under the roof. Thus, baits can be placed in pans or trays and fastened in the activity areas of the sparrows. The sides of these pans and trays should be at least two inches high so the grain will not fall down to the floor of the building, yet be large enough so birds can get into them. This technique works well under roofs over outside loading docks and other similar places.

Baiting programs for starlings. In most cases, starlings are pests in urban and industrial areas because they use buildings and trees for roosting activities only. Thus, toxic baiting programs for starlings are not applicable for most urban environments.

When baiting programs *are* conducted against large rural flocks of starlings, they are most effective when done at the starlings' feeding locations (e.g., farms, livestock feedlots, dairies, hog and poultry farms, and granaries), and by individuals who have specific experience in this area.

The toxic baits used for starling control programs are **Avitrol** and **Starlicide**. Starlicide is Compound DRC-1339 at a 97% active concentration. Starlicide is highly toxic to starlings and blackbirds, but relatively nontoxic to mammals. It is a slow-acting poison that shows very little activity as a secondary poisoning agent. Baits are made by diluting the concentrated chemical and applying it to suitable bait materials. A variety of bait materials, including poultry pellets, rolled barley, and cracked corn has been used successfully. The bait should be used so that poultry and mourning doves are not exposed, since they are highly susceptible to Starlicide.

Traps. With greater attention towards the humane treatment of birds, and the increasing restrictions on avicides, traps have become a popular alternative to lethal programs over the past ten years. Pest birds can be effectively managed by trapping them near their roosting, loafing, or feeding sites. The disadvantage of trapping is that it is labor intensive and thus costly. To offset this, some professionals charge for the initial consultation and set-up of the trapping program and let the customer conduct the daily trapping.

Bird traps vary in size and model and can be purchased or constructed (see Figure 16.19). Some traps are large enough to walk into. Others (e.g., the pigeon low-profile trap) measure only 9-inches high and 24-inches in width and length. Generally, the larger the population of birds to be trapped, the larger the traps used should be. However, even though the larger traps will hold many birds, they can be cumbersome in certain situations such as rooftop trapping programs for pigeons. In these instances, it may be more convenient to use several of the smaller, more portable traps. Bird traps are purchased through pet control suppliers or can be homemade.

Trapping pigeons. Trapping can be a very effective control approach for pigeons around certain commercial buildings (e.g., warehouses, food and pharmaceutical plants) where lethal programs are not appropriate. The best pigeon trapping locations are the pigeons' primary loafing areas. During the hot summer, traps should be placed at pigeon watering sites such as near rooftop cooling condensers of downtown buildings. Traps should be pre-baited for several days before beginning the actual trapping. This is done by placing attractive baits such as corn or milo around the outside of the traps. After three to four days, the baits are then placed inside the trap. Four or five decoy birds should be left in the trap at all times to lure in more pigeons. It must be emphasized that food, water, and shade must be maintained in the trap at all times. Stressed or dying birds inside the trap due to deprivation is both inhumane and counterproductive to attracting new birds to the traps.

Trapping sparrows. Sparrows can also be effectively trapped. The funnel trap is the most widely used and most effective sparrow trap. It is commercially available in various designs. These traps work on a funnel principle; that is, the birds fly into a compartment through the small end of the funnel and cannot find

FIGURE 16.19. A pigeon trap placed on a flat roof can be effective, but it must be maintained with food, water, and decoy birds.

Additional Tips for Bird Trapping Programs.

For all birds, it is critical to a successful trapping program that traps be well monitored, with visits at least every other day. Live healthy decoy birds must be left in traps to attract more birds. Thus, fresh food, water, and protection from the sun and rain must be provided at all times for decoy birds. Leave only a few decoy birds (one to five birds) in the traps, as large numbers of birds tend to frighten others away. If "trap-shyness" develops, traps can be left set for two to three days and then closed for four to five days. Once the trapping results begin to diminish, or the traps fail to catch any birds, the traps should be relocated.

It is also possible to trap a single bird using the common snap-type rat traps, or large sizes of rodent glue traps. This is a convenient method of bird removal when only a couple of nuisance birds in sensitive areas, such as food plants, grocery stores warehouses and restaurants, are to be eliminated. The traps can be baited by tying pieces of bread or french fries to the trap triggers or the glue surface. Tie the traps down to prevent their loss, or from falling off a ledge. Special care should be taken as to the placement of this trap, however, as it will kill any bird that should be attracted to the bait.

When using glue traps, the glue covers or cellophane should be kept on for several days with the food placed directly on top of the cover. After several feedings the cover can be removed, the food placed onto the glue surface and the bird will be trapped. The trap should be checked often to ensure dispatching the captured bird quickly.

Occasionally, racing pigeons with leg bands are found inside pigeon traps. These should be released. Most owners do not want racers back that have been captured and exposed to other foods.

Thistle Net Traps. Thistle nets (mist nets) are extremely fine nets that are placed across the flight paths of the birds in front of a dark background. Mist net traps are effective devices for dealing with wayward birds inside large commercial and/or sensitive facilities such as supermarkets, warehouses, healthcare facilities, atriums, and so forth.

Experience is required to use mist nets effectively. Thistle nets also require considerable amount of time to set up, tend, break down, and store correctly.

The nets work by entrapping birds flying about and blundering into the nets and becoming entangled. The nets are so fine that they cannot be seen by the birds. Wayward birds inside buildings can be herded into the nets using powerful halogen flashlights. Laser pointers in dark environments have also been used successfully.

Thistle nets must be installed correctly. If the net is too taut, birds will bounce off the netting; if too loose, the net and the bird will become a tangled mess.

The use of thistle nets is typically for several birds flying about inside large commercial buildings. For cases of only one or two birds, shooting the birds (where applicable) is a more cost-effective approach. (Thistle nets are also effective for capturing wayward bats that set off security alarms within large structures). Thistle nets can be purchased through pest control suppliers.

their way back out. There are two types of funnel traps: the two-compartment fish-trap-type funnel, and the center-drop modified Australian crow trap that is also used to trap starlings.

Sparrow traps are effective when placed near low shrubs, hedges, and fencerows in areas where the sparrows are active. Because sparrows are very wary of people, prebaiting the traps and trapping area correctly is critical to success. Traps should be left open for a week or more before being set. Also, in addition to the trap sites themselves, several alternative sites nearby the actual trap sites should also be pre-baited. After intensively trapping a portion of the sites for a few days, the traps can be moved to the alternate bait sites and these trapped for a like period. Prebaiting should be continued on all alternative sites throughout the trapping period. In this manner, traps can be moved to several attractive sites if any particular site becomes unproductive.

Because the sparrow is primarily a seedeater, the best baits are normally fine grains. Oats, wheat,

and a fine-cracked corn are well accepted, although many other types of baits are frequently taken. Sparrows in urban areas will readily take to the foods found in and about their activity areas such as breads, fat, and various types of table scraps as found in human refuse.

Trapping starlings. In most cases, trapping and removing starlings is impractical for urban and industrial situations, because of the wide ranging movements of starlings and the time necessary to maintain and manage the traps. Starling trapping programs can be successful however at locations where a permanent population is causing damage or where other techniques cannot be used such as in commercial fruit orchards. Detailed information on trapping starlings can be obtained from local wildlife agents, county agents, and similar personnel.

Shooting. In limited situations and where permissible, persistent shooting with a .22 caliber rifle (preferably using short-range pellets), a .410 gauge shotgun, or a high-precision air rifle with a laser scope can eliminate a small flock of persistent pigeons, starlings, or sparrows from an area. Often this method is used to eliminate the occasional nuisance bird that enters a warehouse. But, it is strongly recommended that any personnel involved in shooting programs for hire, be trained in sharpshooter/firearms use, and proof of such training should be documented and maintained. This training is available through local offices of the National Rifle Association or similar associations.

But generally, large-scale shooting programs in urban areas are not used for obvious safety reasons and because it is impossible to avoid public attention. The bad public relations that almost invariably result usually create a greater problem than the birds.

Occasionally some rural towns and cities undertake programs of shooting pigeons and starlings. This work is usually done by either the city police or by a local civic group rather than by a pest management professional. Shooting serves to kill some birds and to drive off many more. Such a program must, however, be carried out continuously if good results are to be obtained.

Because many towns and cities have ordinances prohibiting the discharge of firearms within corporate limits, local laws must be checked before using this control method.

Woodpeckers[1]

Woodpeckers belong to the Order Piciformes and Family Picidae, which also include flickers and sapsuckers. Twenty-two species inhabit the United States. They have short legs with two sharp-clawed backward-pointed toes and stiff tail feathers, that serve as a supportive prop. These physical traits enable them to cling easily to the trunks and branches of trees or to wood siding or utility poles while pecking. They have stout, sharply pointed beaks for pecking into wood and a specially developed long tongue that can be extended a considerable distance. The tongue is used effectively to dislodge larvae or ants from their burrows in wood or bark.

Woodpeckers are 7 to 15 inches in length, usually with brightly contrasting coloration. Most males have some red on the head, and black and white marks are common on many species. Identification of species by their markings is quite easy. With most species flight is usually undulating, with wings folded against the body after each burst of flaps.

Because they are dependent on trees for shelter and food, woodpeckers for the most part are found on the edge of wooded areas. Many species nest in manmade structures, and some have thus extended their habitat to include wooden fence posts, utility poles and buildings. Because of this, woodpeckers may still be found in regions where trees are scarce.

Most woodpeckers feed on tree-living or wood-boring insects; however, some feed on a variety of other insects. The majority of the food of several flickers is obtained by feeding on insects from the ground, ants included. Vegetable matter makes up a part of the diet of many species. Some feed on native berries, fruit, nuts, and certain seeds. In other areas, the diet includes cultivated fruit and nuts. The sapsuckers—as the name suggests—feed on tree sap, cambium and phloem, as well as insects.

Woodpeckers are an interesting and familiar group of birds. Their ability to peck into trees in search of food or excavating nest cavities is well known. One misconception commonly held is that they peck holes only in search of insects. While they do obtain insects by this means, as well as by other methods, many species will drill holes in sound wood such as buildings, utility poles and fence posts where no insects exist. In drilling their numerous 1/4-inch rows of holes in healthy trees, sapsuckers are primarily after sap. The acorn woodpecker (*Melanerpes formicivorus*) drills holes in wood simply to store acorns.

Woodpeckers have characteristic calls, but also have another method of making their presence known. A rhythmic pecking sequence that is referred to as "drumming" is used to establish their territories and apparently to attract or signal mates. Drumming is generally done on resonant dead tree trunks or limbs; however, buildings and utility poles, when available, are often alternatives.

The anatomy of woodpeckers, with sharp tree-grasping claws, stiff tail feathers, stout pointed beaks, and long tongues, makes them well suited for their lifestyle of drilling into trees. They nest in a cavity chiseled into a tree trunk, branch or structure, although many woodpeckers use natural or pre-existing cavities. Clutch size is generally from four to eight.

Some species are migratory. Most are not, living year-round in the same area. Most species live in small social groups.

Woodpeckers can be very persistent and are not easily driven from their territories or selected pecking sites. For this reason, visual or sound types of repellents for protecting buildings, if they are to be effective at all, should be employed as soon as the problem is identified and before territories are well established.

[1]Adapted from: Marsh, R. E. 1994. Woodpeckers. Pages E139-145 in Prevention and Control of Wildlife Damage. (Hygnstrom, S., R.M. Timm and G. E. Larson, Eds.). Great Plains Agricultural Council, Wildlife Resources Committee. Cooperative Extension Service, University of Nebraska, Lincoln

Damage

Problems with woodpeckers damaging buildings are relatively infrequent and tend to be regional and localized. Wooden houses or buildings in the suburbs or in the more rural wooded settings are most apt to suffer pecking and hole damage, for this is the type of habitat woodpeckers favor. Generally, damage to a building involves only one or two birds, but possibly up to six or eight during a season.

Woodpeckers can be particularly destructive to summer or vacation homes that are vacant during part of the year, since their attacks often go undetected until serious damage has already occurred. Barns and other wooden outbuildings also come under attack.

Damage to wooden buildings may take one of several forms. Holes may be drilled into wooden siding, eaves, or trim boards. Cedar and redwood siding seem highly preferred. If a suitable cavity results from their activities, they may use it for roosting or nesting. The acorn woodpecker found in the west and southwestern part of the country is responsible for drilling closely spaced holes just large enough for each to accommodate an acorn. Acorns may also be wedged between or beneath roof shakes, with few holes actually being drilled.

It is predicted that new damage problems will arise with woodpeckers as damage-susceptible materials such as plastic are used for rooftop solar panels. This type of building material is becoming increasingly popular in parts of the country for energy-efficient heating and hot water systems.

Nest cavities and acorn holes in utility poles can be severe. Widespread damage of this type in some regions has necessitated frequent replacement of weakened poles. Similar damage to wooden fence posts can also require costly replacements.

Drumming is the term given to the sound made by woodpeckers pecking in rapid rhythmic succession on metal or wood. This is predominantly a springtime activity, and the drumming substrates are apparently selected on the basis of the resonant qualities. These often include metal surfaces such as metal gutters, drainpipes, chimney caps, TV antennas, rooftop plumbing vents, and metal roof valleys. Drumming may occur a number of times during a single day, and the activity may go on for some days or months. Aside from any physical damage to painted metal surfaces, the noise can become quite annoying. Wood surfaces suffer much more from drumming than do metal surfaces.

Legal Status

Woodpeckers are classified as migratory, nongame birds and are protected by the Federal Migratory Bird Treaty Act. The red-cockaded woodpecker (*Picoides borealis*) and the ivory-billed woodpecker (*Campephilus principalis*) are on the Endangered Species list and are thus offered full protection. Woodpeckers other than the endangered species can be killed but only under a permit issued by the Law Enforcement Division of the U.S. Fish and Wildlife Service.

Woodpeckers are also protected under some state laws, and in those instances a state permit is also required. Methods of reducing woodpecker damage other than killing them do not infringe upon their legal protection status.

Exclusion

Two techniques for excluding woodpeckers from buildings are currently being used.

Netting. One of the most effective methods of excluding woodpeckers from damaging wood siding beneath the eaves is to net over the area with lightweight mesh nylon or plastic netting. The netting should be attached to the overhanging eaves and angled back to the siding below the damaged area and secured taut. If installed properly, the netting is barely visible from a distance and will offer a long-term solution to the damage problem.

Metal and plastic sheathing barriers. Metal and heavy-duty plastic sheathing placed over the pecked areas on building siding can provide temporary or permanent mechanical protection from continued damage depending which material is used and how it is installed. Heavy-duty plastic sheathing/drop cloths attached tightly to wooden surfaces will prevent woodpeckers from being able to grasp and cling to the side of the building, thus preventing the pecking damage of the birds as well. These materials work best if instigated as soon as damage begins. Occasionally the birds will move over to an unprotected spot and the protected area must be expanded. Aluminum flashing is easy to work with to cover damaged sites. Occasionally woodpeckers will peck through aluminum if they can secure a foothold to work at it. Metal sheathing can be disguised with paint or simulated, painted-on wood grain to match the siding.

Quarter-inch hardware cloth or welded wire has also been used to cover pecked areas and prevent further damage. The wire can be spray painted to match the color of the building. The wire can either be attached directly to the wood surface being damaged or, better yet, be raised outward from the wood siding with the use of one-inch wood spacers

Once the woodpeckers have been discouraged, frightened away or killed, the damaged area on houses should be repaired or covered to prevent other woodpeckers from being attracted to the damaged site.

Woodpeckers do not damage some of the harder compressed wood or wood-fiber siding materials. Presumably their hardness and/or smooth surface serve as deterrents. Aluminum siding can also be used as an alternative to wood siding.

It is important to note that exclusion materials should not be placed over any woodpecker wall-cavity nesting holes until it is certain the cavity does not contain any young birds.

Repellents

Several kinds of repellents can be used against woodpeckers. (see Figure 16.20). Their success varies from case to case.

Visual. Model owl and snake decoys and owl silhouettes have been, for the most part, ineffective as repellents. Toy plastic twirlers or windmills and aluminum or brightly colored plastic strips and pie pans that repel by reflections and/or movement, have all been used with some success, especially if used soon after the damage starts. These twirlers and plastic strips rely on a breeze for motion. Some woodpecker repellents are available that are comprised of various pieces of mirrors and glass fragments arranged on cords. These materials spin and

move in the wind causing flashes of bright light and frighten the woodpeckers. None of these contributes to the architectural enhancement or aesthetics of a house, however.

Sound. Loud noises such as hand clapping, toy cap pistol, and banging on a garbage can lid have been used to frighten woodpeckers from pecking on houses. Such harassment, if repeated as the bird returns, may cause it to leave for good.

Taste. Many chemicals that have objectionable tastes as well as odors have been tested for treating utility poles and fence posts to discourage woodpeckers. Most have proven ineffective or at least not cost-effective. Painted/stained surfaces are just as likely to be damaged as unpainted surfaces. Creosote and pentachlorophenol used to treat utility poles and fence posts do not resolve the woodpecker problem, **and are no longer available because the EPA has banned their use.**

Odor. Naphthalene or paradichlorobenzene (i.e., mothballs), volatile chemicals, have been suggested for woodpecker control. However, in out-of-door unconfined areas they are of doubtful merit. It is unlikely that odor-repelling concentrations of either material could be achieved to serve as a practical solution.

Tactile. Sticky or tacky bird repellents such as Tanglefoot, Bird Stop, Roost-No-More, etc., are

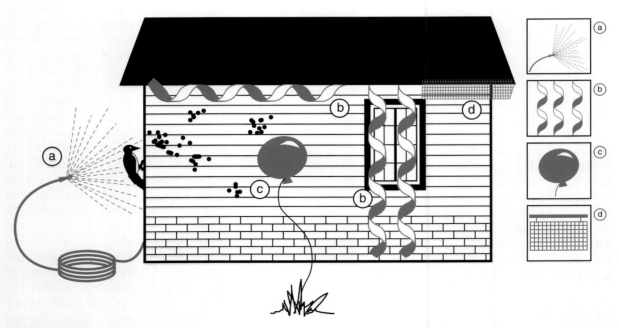

FIGURE 16.20. Woodpecker damage control methods for structures: (a) high-pressure water hose, (b) high-reflective mylar tape, (c) helium-filled mylar balloon, and (d) fine-mesh netting.

sometimes effective when applied to wood siding and other areas of structural damage. The birds are not entrapped by the sticky substances but dislike the tacky footing. A word of caution: Some of the sticky bird repellents will discolor painted, stained, or natural wood siding. Others may run in warm weather, leaving unsightly streaks. It is best to first test the material on a small out-of-sight area before an extensive application. The tacky repellents can be applied to a thin piece of pressed board that is then fastened to the area where damage is occurring.

Toxicants

Woodpecker problems can be resolved without toxicants and none are registered for such use.

Trapping

Wooden-base rat snap traps can be effective in killing the offending bird; a permit is required. The trap is nailed to the building with the trigger downward alongside the spot sustaining the damage. The trap is baited with nut meats (walnuts, almonds or pecans) or suet. If multiple areas are being damaged, then several traps can be used to make the outcome more decisive.

Shooting

Where it is necessary to remove the offending birds and the proper permits have been obtained, shooting may be one of the quickest methods of dispatching one or a few birds.

At close range, air rifles or .22-caliber rifles with dust shot or "BB" caps can be effective. Twenty-two caliber rifles or shotguns may be needed for birds that must be taken from greater distances. Considerable discretion must be used when using firearms around dwellings. Twenty-two-caliber projectiles can travel long distances if they miss their targets.

Other Methods

On occasion, two other methods are of value in woodpecker management.

Suet as an alternative attractant. Many birdwatchers in the Midwest and East put out beef suet, particularly in winter, to attract woodpeckers. Placing suet stations near damaged buildings has been suggested to entice birds away from the building or damaged area. However, some bird experts feel that such placements of suet may, in fact, attract woodpeckers or encourage transient woodpeckers to become residents of the building area.

Insecticides for indirect control. Based on the assumption that woodpeckers are after insects, some control bulletins suggest treating insect-infested siding with insecticides as a remedy for damage. While this may have some merit with insect-infested wood, woodpeckers, more often than not, attack siding, poles, and posts that do not contain any insects at all. The use of insecticides for indirect control of woodpeckers in these instances would be unfounded.

Geese, Gulls, and Crows

Over the past several years, Canada geese, gulls, and the American crow, have all increased in urban pest significance and as such, they warrant a cursory discussion because the pest management professional is often sought to help with these pests or to provide direction and information regarding corrective action for these birds. Additional information is available via the references listed at the end of the chapter, through the local county extension office, the U.S Dept. of Agriculture's Animal Damage Control (ADC). It must be stressed that all of these birds are federally protected species.

Canada Goose

The Canada goose, *Branta canadensis,* is a gray-brown bird, with a black head and neck that contrasts sharply with its light-colored breast. The most characteristic mark is the white cheek patch that runs from under the chin on to each side of the head. The eggs are laid in the spring and after a 30-day incubation period, 4 to 10 young are hatched. By mid-August, the young are capable of flight.

Compared to its relative the duck, the Canada goose is larger, heavier-bodied, and has a longer neck. In flight, geese flocks are noisy and often assemble in a line or a V-formation. Geese are more terrestrial than ducks and feed mainly on land in such areas as grassy marshes, golf courses, parks, and corn, wheat, and soybean fields.

The goose has become a serious pest of community parks, ponds, lakes, golf courses, office parks, food and pharmaceutical plants, and a wide range of residential areas (see Figure 16.21). Geese populations have increased 20-fold in the last two decades and experts predict the populations will continue to explode in many areas throughout the country. In years past, Canada geese normally migrated out of the colder northern states. Over the past 20 years, however, the geese have established residence in the northern states and no longer migrate to winter grounds.

When left undisturbed, geese flocks establish nesting territories on ponds in residential yards, golf courses, condominium complexes, city parks,

FIGURE 16.21. Canada geese have become a serious nuisance pest in many urban environments.

on farms and other areas. Most people will readily welcome a pair of geese on a pond. They can soon turn from pet to pest, however. In 5 to 7 years, a pair of geese can multiply up to 100 birds fouling ponds and surrounding yards, damaging landscapes, gardens, and golf courses. People are also attacked that come to close to the geese's nests containing goslings.

Managing Geese

Unlike any other urban pest bird problem, geese can pose complicated situations to pest professionals. Few infestations are identical; most require careful situation analysis and tailored approaches. For the majority of cases, combinations of different strategies that involve PMPs working in conjunction with federal or state officials are necessary for long-term success.

Because geese are protected, most management efforts are comprised of chemical repellents, visual deterrents, lasers, physical barriers, chase dogs, and other nonlethal methods. Some states allow qualified, experienced professionals to perform geese roundups involving the corralling, capture, and relocation of geese. In some cases, egg addling (i.e., shaking the eggs to stop the embryo development), and euthanizing of birds can be done under state and/or federal permits.

To help address the increasing need for contracted goose management efforts, specialized training academies, seminars, and publications have emerged over the past few years. Even still, for pest professionals involved in, or considering geese management efforts, the comprehensive publication by Smith, Craven and Curtis (1999) on managing geese in urban environments is an essential guidebook (see Selected References at the end of this chapter).

When geese are using ponds, cultural practices such as mowing to the edge of the pond and using herbicides to eliminate emergent aquatic vegetation in the pond helps to reduce nesting, loafing, and cover areas—all of which regularly attract geese. Additionally, the feeding of waterfowl around the affected areas should be prohibited. In cold climates, pond aerators should be shut off in the winter to allow ponds to freeze.

As mentioned previously, two chemical repellents are registered for goose control on or around turf areas: (1) anthraquinone (e.g., Flight Control®) and (2) methyl anthranilate (e.g., Rejex-It®, Goose Chase®, etc.). Although these are different chemicals, their utility, and the basic mechanisms for their applications are similar.

Anthraquinone causes intestinal discomfort to the geese without harming the birds. Turf treated with the anthraquinone can be seen by geese in the ultraviolet spectrum of light (which people cannot see). This helps the geese to learn from their previous ill-feeling experience to avoid anthraquinone-treated areas.

Anthraquinone is applied as a liquid concentrate mixed with water in power-spray rigs. In general, dosage rates per acre of turf range from 1/2 to 1 gallon of concentrate with 50 gallons of water. The higher dosages and weekly reapplications are usually required for persistent infestations or areas subject to high goose pressure.

To be effective anthraquinone repellents must be applied under certain environmental and lawn maintenance conditions. For example, it is recommended the repellent is applied when rain is not forecast and the turf is dry. Also, turf mowing should not be conducted for at least several days following application.

Additionally, anthraquinone must be applied using spray equipment that is carefully calibrated to achieve fine- to medium-size droplets. The droplet size of the anthraquinone spray mixture is essential to the product's success. If the grass blades contain too many untreated gaps on the turf due to improper droplet size, the repellent is much less effective.

Methyl anthranilate (MA) is a taste repellent labeled for repelling geese off of turf and temporary stands of water. To humans, methyl anthranilate tastes and smells of grape flavoring, but birds find the material irritating to their taste and olfactory senses.

Similar to the anthraquinone repellent, environmental conditions, proper spray methods, and turf maintenance practices must all be carefully aligned with MA's application to achieve acceptable repellency.

Goose taste/gustatory repellents such as anthraquinone and MA have greater utility for situations where immediate relief is needed to prevent geese from feeding and/or fouling an area such as for office park picnics, outdoor weddings, golf tourneys, and so forth. Moreover, feedback from professionals using these repellents under field conditions indicate these repellents are most effective when used sparingly rather than when they are broadly sprayed over an entire area (i.e., blanket spraying). If all the grass and vegetation in area smells and tastes the same, the geese will feed on even foul-tasting vegetation. Thus, it is best to prioritize those areas needing protection and perhaps sacrifice some areas to the birds. In this way, the geese will have a choice of treated and untreated areas to attack.

Considering the cost of these repellents, the amount of material and labor involved in their application, the prerequisite environmental conditions, the need for possible weekly re-treatments and the restrictions on mowing following treatments, goose turf repellents are best viewed as short-term solutions and have limited utility as a solo approach.

Visual repellents and scaring devices have also been used with varying success against geese. One visual repellent approach that seems particularly useful against geese is the use of lasers. Relative to other birds, geese seem to be particularly sensitive to laser beams. Thus, lasers have been used successfully against geese flocks attempting to linger overnight at urban sites. For more details in the use of lasers, refer to page 400.

Well-trained chase dogs such as border collies, Australian herd dogs, and others are also extremely effective, but must be used under the careful handling of a dog trainer. Both lasers and dogs usually have to be used for several times to train the geese as to the undesirability of the area.

Other visual repellents used against geese include scarecrows, plastic flags, Mylar tape and balloons, dead geese effigies, and predator birds tethered to helium balloons. Most times, these types of visual scaring devices are effective against newly arriving geese that have not developed strong attachment to the particular site. These types of visual repellents must be moved around regularly. Otherwise, geese quickly acclimate to the devices.

Gulls (Larus spp.)

Gulls belong to the avian family, Laridae of which there are 23 North American species. Many of the common gulls appear similar, being robust birds with webbed feet and slightly hooked beaks. Throughout many areas of the United States, especially the coastal regions and cities gulls are serious pests in and around airports, restaurants, landfills,

dockyards (see Figure 16.22). In particular, the ring-billed gull (*L. delawarensis*) and the herring gull (*L. argentatus*) are troublesome in cities bordering the Great Lakes, where they pose problems by nesting on rooftops. Because they are a large bird, gull droppings can be especially damaging and annoying around plane hangars, boatyards, rooftops, and restaurant buildings. Even more serious, seagulls are responsible for more aircraft collisions than any other bird.

In cities near lakes and coasts, gull populations have been increasing dramatically. In Toronto, for example, one gull colony increased from 20 pairs in 1973 to approximately 80,000 pairs by 1982. A colony of laughing gulls in the bays outside of New York City increased from 15 pairs in 1979 to 7,600 pairs by 1990. Not only are gulls quickly adapting to city environments, but large flocks of some gull species are also being noted hundreds of miles inland feeding and loafing in all types of farming fields.

Gulls have long wings that help them to achieve graceful, acrobatic, and skilled flights. Most gulls nest in colonies on sand and gravel-covered shorelines and islands. They construct their nests on the ground and usually produce three eggs per clutch. The incubation period lasts three to four weeks. Only one brood is raised per year. Most gulls are fledged in approximately one month.

Gulls feed on a wide variety of natural and human foods. On the water, they eat all types of aquatic animals and scavenge dead fish and fish refuse produced by boaters or people along the shore. The gulls' webbed feet enable them to aggressively dive and swim underwater to chase and collect aquatic foods. On land, gulls are opportunists similar to the feeding behavior of pigeons and sparrows, taking garbage, insects, small vertebrates, and even on the eggs and young birds of any nearby nesting seabirds.

FIGURE 16.22. Gulls are nuisance pests in many cities near coastal and lake areas, and they can be difficult to discourage from using buildings and rooftops for loafing and nesting.

Gull Management

Gull management is highly situational. Specific local conditions must be carefully analyzed before any program is implemented. As with all other urban bird management, gulls are managed via integrated approaches using exclusion and repelling efforts in addition to essential sanitation programs (where the gulls are drawn to the site because of food) by the client. Sanitation programs are especially important around all food-serving establishments. These programs can be supplemented with population reduction programs using toxicants or via nest-removal or egg-sterilization programs (although nest manipulation efforts must be conducted over the long term to have any appreciable effects).

Many of the same mechanical repellents/exclusionary devices such as prickly wires, spindly bobbing wires, and tight wire strands that are used against pigeons and sparrows on buildings can be modified or adapted for use against nuisance gulls. However, handiwork and ingenuity in adapting to each situation are particularly important when using these devices for gull management. The spindly bobbing wire repellents are designed specifically to keep gulls off of the tops of light poles, telephone poles and boat piers (see Figure 16.23). Parallel spaced wires have been used to exclude gulls off of garbage dumps.

For gull flocks that roost and loaf on buildings and other urban structures during the night, the use of the commercial-level lasers discussed earlier have proven useful in dispersing the flocks and reducing the amount of contamination to buildings and areas gull and annoyance to citizens.

Avitrol® concentrate is federally registered for the control of herring gulls that are feeding nesting, loafing, or roosting near or in the vicinity of sanitary landfills, airports, and structures. State and federal permits are required for Avitrol use against gulls.

Various chemical repellent gels and pastes, as are used against pigeons, are also registered against gulls to prevent them from landing on posts, beams, and ledges. The liquid repellent methyl anthranilate (MA) (see bird repellents discussion earlier in chapter) used as surface spray and as a fogging compound has been employed as a repellents for gulls around landfills.

The toxicant **DRC-1339 Gull Toxicant 98% Concentrate** (see pigeon discussion earlier) is a restricted-use pesticide registered for the control of nesting herring gulls, great black-backed gulls, and ring-billed gulls. Its use is limited to coastal areas where high gull populations are conflicting with less abundant colonial waterbirds. The toxicant is mixed with oleomargarine and spread on bread that is then

Figure 16.23. Spindly wire repellents can keep gulls off posts of all types as well as off some areas of rooftops.

placed directly on gull nests. This toxicant can only be used by U.S. Department of Agriculture personnel, or by persons under their direct supervision.

Other specialized gull management programs involving nest, egg and young removal, and egg sterilization programs that are also conducted by personnel operating under special permits. Information on these programs is available from the U.S. Department of Agriculture, APHIS Animal Damage Control personnel (available within each state). The USDA has also been investigating effective methods of gull control over the last several years, and are excellent sources for up-to-date information.

Crows (Corvus spp.)

Crows belong to the genus, *Corvus*, which translated means "harsh sound." Four species of crows inhabit the United States: the American crow, *Corvus brachyrhynchos*, the fish crow (*C. ossifragus*), the northwestern crow (*C. caurinus*), and the Mexican crow (*C. imparatus*). Ornithologists and birding enthusiasts can distinguish among the different species but it may be difficult for most pest professionals. In most areas of the country, the American crow is the most common crow pest. Thus, the American crow is also referred to as the common crow and the eastern crow.

The American crow is a relatively large bird (17 to 21 inches/43 to 53 cm). Both males and females are completely black, including their beaks. (see Figures 16.1 and 16.24) The only other bird mistaken for the crow is another Corvid and close relative, the raven. But ravens are larger and lankier than crows, have wedge-shaped tails, heavier bills, and deeper voices. Ravens also have a soaring, gliding flight pattern, whereas crows have a frequent steady wing beat with little or no gliding.

Crows are among the most intelligent of all birds, although many exaggerations are made as to their abilities. Still, crows can count up to four, have excellent memories, can solve various puzzles, and quickly learn to associate various noises and symbols with food. Crows have been recorded in parks watching people storing food inside latched coolers, waiting for the owners to walk away, and then unlatching the coolers using their beaks and toes, and stealing the food.

Crows begin nesting in February and continue through May depending on the part of the country and the particular seasonal conditions. Their nests are established in trees and various types of vertical structures (e.g., telephone poles, utility towers, etc.) as high up as 60 to 75 feet. If these harborages are scarce or occupied, crows readily adapt and build their nests among protected areas at ground level. Nests are crudely built, comprised of twigs, sticks, and various plant stems. The crow then lines the nest with grass, cloth, feathers, or any assembly of soft items scavenged from nearby.

Like other urban pest birds, crows, too, are opportunists. Crows eat virtually anything humans eat and all the foods and food scraps people discard. Road-killed carrion of all types are usually quickly located and consumed by the crows living in the area. In agricultural areas, crows feed heavily from cornfields, as well as other grains such as wheat, peanuts, pecans, sorghum, etc.

The American crow typically produces only one brood each spring, although two broods per year occur in some southern areas. Clutches contain from four to six eggs which are incubated for about 18 days. The young are fledged at about one month of age, and learn their local territory and how to forage by remaining with and mimicking the parents throughout the summer. Because of their intelligence and general wariness wild crows in city environments can avoid many predators and dangerous situations and survive for up to six years or longer. In captivity, crows have survived for more than 20 years.

During the autumn months, crows join together sometimes forming large urban flocks. Depending on the locale, the particular season and species, the crow flocks may migrate with the onset of winter. In the parts of the country where the overwintering crows gather, it can result in millions of crows loafing and roosting.

Winter flocks roost together at night and disperse over large areas to feed during the day. Their feeding range is typically within 6 to 12 miles (10 to 20 km) from the roost. These large flocks often cause people to complain to their local board of health and/or pest professionals.

Crow Management

The success in managing crows in urban environments varies considerably. In some cases, crows react quickly to even minor control efforts, and will evacuate an area or stop using a particular building or tree for roosting or loafing. But when crows locate environments that routinely provide them with their resources, and they become habituated to the people, city noises and disturbances of the area, crows often lose their wariness, and success may require fewer attempts using different techniques.

As mentioned previously, crows are intelligent birds that quickly learn which parts of town offer daily and easily accessible snacks of human food discards. This is particularly important relative to commercial dumpster areas and parking lots of supermarkets, convenience stores, gas stations, and the giant mart-style stores. These areas must be kept clean on a daily basis to prevent conditioning crows (and pigeons, sparrows) to linger on the property waiting for a "food scrap opportunity." Commercial property managers should be informed by the servicing professional that regardless of the techniques employed, it can be particularly difficult to persuade crows to evacuate an area if food is readily available each day.

Crows can be denied access to structural ledges and utility components (rooftop air-conditioning

Figure 16.24. American crow populations have increased dramatically in cities across the United States. They are annoying pests to the commercial and residential sector alike. (Myers)

units, etc,) by custom installment of any of the various types of structural repellents and/or bird netting products discussed throughout this chapter (refer to Table 16.1). For example, ledges and other areas can be protected via the use of the prickly spikes, tightly strung wires, bobbing daddi-long-leg devices, etc., to protect *specific areas* from crows.

For small flocks of crows that have not yet become entrenched, visual repellents usually provide good results in dispersing crows lingering around parking lots and building exteriors.

Visual repellents that have proven effective include metallic-looking balloons, tapes, and streamers. It seems that the more metallic-appearing the item, the better it performs against crows. Examples include ordinary metallic "birthday" balloons, Mylar tape, and the fringed streamers commonly seen strung about on various gala events. When crows are a problem in downtown commercial sectors, a variety of these objects can be used to keep the crows dispersed, while at the same time providing an attractive visual image (or message) to the public.

For example, strings of tight lines of fringed Mylar streamers, containing small American Flags spaced at intervals along the streamers can be used on the outside roof and door edge lines of mart-style stores, food storage warehouses office buildings, and so forth.

Metallic balloons tied to rooftops, and lamp and sign posts will bob in the wind and may discourage the crows from using the area. Some car dealers have had success in protecting their cars from crow damage using Mylar streamers and various-sized banners containing the car dealer's logos and names. The result is visual advertising and crow control in one clever package.

One of the keys to success in using visual repellents is to begin the repelling campaign as early as possible once crows arrive in an area. The longer the crows become established and attached to a particular site, the more difficult it is to disperse them. It is also important to move the devices regularly to minimize acclimatization by the crows.

In neighborhoods containing dense tree stands being used by the crows, the thinning of the trees and/or branches to reduce the protection offered by the trees to the crows can be effective as this opens the trees up to weather effects, and reduces the availability of perch sites. This is often unacceptable to many people whom enjoy all the benefits that mature trees provide a neighborhood.

Pyrotechnics can also be used on large, established tree roosts. Common pyrotechnics include the use of noise poppers, bird bombs, bangers, and various other noisemaking devices dispensed into nuisance bird roost areas using handheld pistols and other devices. Pyrotechnic and other bird-dispersal products/supplies are readily available on the web from companies specializing in bird management products (e.g., **www.Margosupplies.com**; **www.reedjoseph.com**, and perhaps others).

All safety and local noise ordinance issues must always be carefully considered when pyrotechnics are being considered. Practical guidelines for using pyrotechnics and other bird-dispersal methods are available online from the Internet Center for Wildlife Damage (**www. wildlifedamage.unl.edu/**).

For large nighttime tree roosts of crows, the commercial lasers discussed earlier have proven effective in dispersing the crows. Compared to the pyrotechnics, lasers offer silent, nonobtrusive interaction with the crows, safety, and ease of use. Crows seem to become frightened when they see the laser beams on nearby surfaces, or being swept through their tree roost, and usually evacuate the area immediately.

However, as has been common to all urban pest bird management, the effectiveness of the lasers can also be site-specific. For large, entrenched roosts, multiple sessions using several lasers may be necessary.

Avitrol is registered for crow control and may have some utility under certain circumstances—especially in areas away from the public. However, for crow roosts in urban and suburban areas, the use of this toxicant brings a risk of adverse public relations (as a result of dead birds). This is especially likely with the recent activities associated with people reporting dead crows, jays, and other birds in response to the West Nile virus.

SUPPLEMENTARY READING MATERIAL

ANSI Z136. 1-1999: American national standard for safe use of lasers. **www.ansi.org**

Blackwell, B., G. Bernhardt, and R. Dolbeer. 2002. Lasers as non-lethal avian repellents. J. Wildl. Mgt. 66(1): 250-258.

Booth, T.W. 1994. "Bird dispersal techniques." Pages E-19-E-23 In: *Prevention and Control of Wildlife Damage.* Vol. II. S. E. Hygnstrom, R.M.Timm, and G.E. Larson, (eds.). Coop. Ext. Div., IANR, University of Nebraska, Lincoln/USDA; APHIS; ADC/Great Plains Ag Council.

Cleary E C. 1994. Waterfowl. Pages E-129-E-139. In: *Prevention and Control of Wildlife Damage.* Vol. II. S. E. Hygnstrom, R.M.Timm, and G.E. Larson, (Eds.). Coop. Ext. Div., IANR, University of Nebraska, Lincoln/USDA; APHIS; ADC/Great Plains Ag Council.

Corrigan, R.M. 2002. *Managing Crows. Pest Control Technology.* Part I, Vol. 30 (10) 124,126 and Part II: Vol. 30 (11): 75-76.

Dolbeer, R. A., T.W. Seamans, B. F. Blackwell, and J. L. Belant. 1998. Anthraquinone formulation (Flight Control®) shows promise as avian feeding repellent. *Journal of Wildlife Management* 62: 1558-1564

Gillespie, D., J. Loven, and R. M .Corrigan. 1995. Woodpeckers. Animal Damage Control Leaflet No.17. Coop. Ext. Serv. Purdue Univ. 4 pp.

Gingrich, J.B. and T.E. Osterburg. 2003. "Pest birds: Biology and management at food processing plants." Pages 317-340. In: *Food Plant Sanitation.* Y.H. Hui, B.L. Bruinsma, J. R. Gorham, W. Nip, P.S. Tong and P. Ventresca (Eds). Marcel Dekker, Inc., New York. 745 pp.

Glahn, J. and B. Blackwell. 2001. Safety guidelines for using the Desman™ laser and Dissuader™ laser to disperse double–crested cormorants and other birds. USDA, APHIS, Wildlife Services, National Wildlife Research Center. Available from NWRC Field Stations at Starkville, MS, and Sandusky, OH

Godin, A. J. "Birds at airports." 1994. Pages E-1-E-4 in: *Prevention and Control of Wildlife Damage.* Vol. II. S. E. Hygnstrom, R.M.Timm, and G.E. Larson, (Eds.). Coop. Ext. Div., IANR, University of Nebraska, Lincoln/USDA; APHIS; ADC/Great Plains Ag Council.

Hygnstrom, S. E., R.M.Timm, and G.E. Larson, (Eds.). 1994. Pages E-1-E-4. In: *Prevention and Control of Wildlife Damage. Vol. II.* Coop. Ext. Div., IANR, University of Nebraska, Lincoln/USDA; APHIS; ADC/ Great Plains Ag Council.

Jackson, W.B. 1991. Pest bird ecology and management. Pages 229-236. In: *Ecology and Management of Food Industry Pests.* J. R. Gorham (Ed.). Assoc. Offic. Anal. Chem. Arlington, VA. 595 pp.

Johnson, R. J. 1994. "American Crows." Pages E33- E41. In: *Prevention and Control of Wildlife Damage.* Vol. II. S. E. Hygnstrom, R.M.Timm, and G.E. Larson, (Eds.). Coop. Ext. Div., IANR, University of Nebraska, Lincoln/USDA; APHIS; ADC/Great Plains Ag Council.

Johnson, R.J. and J.F. Glahn. 1994. European Starlings. Pages E109- E121. *In: Prevention and Control of Wildlife Damage. Vol. II.* S. E. Hygnstrom, R.M.Timm, and G.E. Larson, (Eds.). Coop. Ext. Div., IANR, University of Nebraska, Lincoln/USDA; APHIS; ADC/Great Plains Ag Council.

Loven, J. 2002. Pers. Comm. *Managing nuisance birds.* Indiana ADC. USDA/Aphis. West Lafayette, IN.

Martin, C., and L. Martin 1982. "Pigeon control: An inter-grated approach." Proceedings Tenth Vertebrate Pest Conference (R.E. Marsh, Ed.,) Univ. of California, Davis, Calif.

Marsh R.E. 1994. "Woodpeckers." Pages E-139- E-145 In: *Prevention and Control of Wildlife Damage, Vol. II.* S. E. Hygnstrom, R.M.Timm, and G.E. Larson, (Eds.). Coop. Ext. Div., IANR, University of Nebraska, Lincoln/USDA; APHIS; ADC/Great Plains Ag Council.

National Pest Control Association. 1983. Bird Management Manual. NPCA, Dunn Loring, VA., 118 p.

National Pest Management Association. 2003. Using lasers to disperse birds. NPMA Library Update. Jan/Feb. 4pp.

National Wildlife Research Center. 2003. Bird management publications: **www.aphis.usda.gov/ws/nwrc**

Solman, V.E.F. 1994. "Gulls." Pages E-49- E-53. In: *Prevention and Control of Wildlife Damage. Vol. II.* S. E. Hygnstrom, R.M.Timm, and G.E. Larson, (Eds.). Coop. Ext. Div., IANR, University of Nebraska, Lincoln/USDA; APHIS; ADC/Great Plains Ag Council.

Smith, A. E. , S.R. Craven and P.D. Curtis. 1999. "Managing Canada geese in urban environments." Jack Berryman Institute Publication 16 and Cornell University Cooperative Extension, Ithaca, New York.

Timm, R.M. and R. E. Marsh, 1997. "Vertebrate Pests." Pages 954-1019 In: *Mallis Handbook of Pest Control, 8th ed.* S. Hedges, (Ed.) Mallis Handbook and Technical Training Committee Cleveland, OH. 1456pp.

USDA. 2001. Compound DRC 1339 Concentrate. Label and Technical Note. USDA/APHIS/Wildlife Services. **www.aphis.usda.gov/ws/nwrc/ProductsEPA.htm**

Wegner, J. 2003. Vertebrate Pests: In: *Mallis Handbook of Pest Control, 9th ed.* S. Hedges. (Ed.). Mallis Handbook and Technical Training Committee. Cleveland. OH. In press.

Williams, D. E., and R. M. Corrigan, 1994. Pigeons. Pages E-87- E-96 In: *Prevention and Control of Wildlife Damage, Vol. II.* S. E. Hygnstrom, R.M.Timm, and G.E. Larson, (Eds.). Coop. Ext. Div., IANR, University of Nebraska, Lincoln/USDA; APHIS; ADC/Great Plains Ag Council.

CHAPTER 17 | Urban Wildlife

Technically, all of the animals that live in and around our buildings (rodents, pigeons, toads, moles, etc.) are part of our wildlife. However, most people do not think of rats and mice and the pest species of birds in that way. To most urbanites, these animals are merely pests. For our purposes we will also categorize urban wildlife as any of the wild vertebrates, other than the commensal rodents and bird pests, that interact with people in and around urban areas.

As the human population increases, we expand urban and suburban areas into undeveloped wooded areas and fields. As a result, we continue to displace the animals that previously inhabited these areas. We can thus expect people-wildlife conflicts to continue and increase. We can also expect the role of the pest management professional in solving many of these conflicts to increase accordingly. Some companies offer this service as a regular part of their business. Others provide service on a case-by-case basis only, referring the more complex jobs to companies that specialize in urban wildlife management.

Whether you perform wildlife management services full time, part time, or not at all, you can provide valuable information and expertise to your clients when they seek your help or advice regarding wildlife pests around their homes and yards.

Solving people-wildlife conflicts can present the professional with some interesting challenges. For example, in some cases, pest management professionals must not only solve the conflict, but do so without harming the animal causing the damage. In other cases, the actual destruction of the animal pest is warranted, but the program must be conducted so as not to affect any animal other than the pest itself.

As a general rule, managing urban wildlife problems requires careful analysis of each situation before implementing any type of management solution.

Rarely are any two wildlife problems alike. Therefore, the professional should always review the following questions before tackling a wildlife problem:

- What species is causing the problem?
- What is the type and amount of damage occurring?
- What additional damage, if any, is anticipated if no action is taken?
- What is the aesthetic or recreational value, if any, of the species involved?
- Are non-target animals at any risk as a result of the proposed management, and if so, how can the risk be eliminated or reduced?
- Do any federal, state, or local laws protect the animal pest, and if so, will the proposed resolution of the problem be consistent with the laws?

URBAN IPM

Similar to other pest groups (insects, rodents, birds), solving nuisance wildlife problems should employ the IPM approach.

There are four components of urban wildlife IPM programs :

1. Inspection and analysis
2. Sanitation (food and/or harborage removal)
3. Exclusion
4. Deterring, removing, or destroying the offending animal.

A general overview of the four IPM components is provided here. Each urban wildlife "pest" is then discussed separately.

It should be noted that after the inspection and analysis effort, any of the other components might be implemented in different sequences. For example, it may be that the offending animal is first removed from a house before any exclusionary efforts are made. Other times, a bird feeder is fixed to eliminate the spillage that attracted the wild animals to the premises in the first place. In still other cases, only the integration of one or more management approaches will achieve the desired long-term results.

1. Inspection and Analysis

A building or area with wildlife problems must be thoroughly inspected to determine the specific areas that are affected. Removing raccoons from a chimney for example, requires a much different level of skill and knowledge than livetrapping a woodchuck from a burrow beneath a garage.

Next, if possible it should be determined, how the animals are gaining entry or access to the structure. This is done via a thorough visual inspection of all foundation, roof, and chimney areas for possible structural defects that allow wildlife access to the building. The relationship of all nearby vegetation should also be noted at this time (e.g., tree branches, bushes, climbing ivy, etc.). Consequently, a pair of binoculars is an essential urban wildlife inspection tool to facilitate inspection outside roof and chimney areas and other aerial areas.

The clients should also be interviewed. When considering live trapping and tree squirrel removal for example, the client could point out which trees the squirrels are seen most active, or which part of the house the animals are making the most noise. The client can also alert the professional as to whether there are cats or dogs active in the area, which, will affect how live-trapping programs will be conducted.

Finally, each of the possible IPM approaches as described below should be listed and considered during the inspection and analysis phase. The list of factors that may provide long-term control, such as sanitation and building repairs, should be reviewed with the client at this time.

2. Sanitation

Wild animals will be drawn to those areas and structures that provide them with their needs for food, water, and/or shelter. The examples that could be provided here are many. For example, squirrels and raccoons quickly discover easily accessible bird seed, garbage cans, and fruit trees. Wild dogs, cats and raccoons will take advantage of human trash that is not properly managed. For example, garbage must always be placed inside heavy garbage cans with lids secured with shock cords or by a similar means to deny these animals access to the trash.

When wild animals are rewarded with food around houses and buildings, they soon begin exploring any nearby buildings in attempts to locate any openings that might provide them with a nest similar to that of a hollow tree or ground burrow.

3. Exclusion

Obviously, the best method for preventing wildlife problems inside urban structures is to prevent them from gaining access in the first place. In many cases, exclusion services provides the profit opportunity for a wildlife or pest professional. However, not all wildlife exclusion work is easily accomplished. Some animals such as bats require only 3/8 inch (1.0 cm) to gain entry. Raccoons can use their powerful front legs and elongated fingers to literally rip apart an attic louver, or tear holes directly through the shingles and roof sheathing to gain entry into an attic.

Nevertheless, most animals are opportunistic in establishing new nest locations, taking advantage of those buildings which allow easy entry and bypassing those tightly sealed structures that require excessive effort to gain entry.

In general, all areas leading into building attics must be well-sealed to deny access to squirrels, raccoons, and bats. Additionally, any conditions that allow animals, such as squirrels, to gain access to the structure should be eliminated or altered. A common example is for all tree branches to be trimmed back from buildings by at least six to eight feet to deny squirrels and other wild animals access to rooftops. Crawlspaces and areas beneath decks should be pestproofed to deny access to skunks, opossums, raccoons, and snakes. All screens and louvers must be kept in good repair.

It cannot be overemphasized that sanitation and exclusion efforts are the most important elements of any urban wildlife IPM program. Unless the conditions that attract wild animals to a building or area are not corrected, and efforts made to keep them from gaining access, future wildlife infestations will occur regardless of the removal or killing of any individual animal.

4. Deterring, removing, or destroying the offending animal

The final components of a wildlife IPM program involves either deterring, removing, and/or destroying the offending animal. These approaches can be accomplished via the use of different types of repellents, the use of live traps and, where necessary and permitted, lethal approaches.

Repellents

Sometimes, wild animals can be deterred from remaining in or around buildings via the use of different types of repellents.

Odor repellents such as naphthalene (i.e., moth flakes) are commonly sold in attempts to discourage bats, raccoons, squirrels, snakes, and other animals from harboring inside crawlspaces, deck voids, and attics (refer to the detailed discussion of odor repellents on page 423).

Taste repellents are also available for application to garbage bags and other items to reduce damage from raccoons, dogs, opossums, and other wild animals. However, many factors affect whether or not a repellent will achieve the desired affect on a animal.

Most chemical animal repellents tend to be effective for short periods of time before they have to be reapplied. They are most effective when the animals have other easily accessible alternative foods and harborages nearby. Repellents rarely deter animals that are hungry and determined.

No one should ever attempt to repel a wild animal from a building by spraying the animal with any type of caustic or irritating chemicals such as ammonia, bleach, lye, or any pesticide not labeled for such use. Not only is such practice cruel, but it is also highly unprofessional, and potentially dangerous to people and non-target animals. Moreover, such practices have many times resulted in hurt, panicked animals attacking the applicator or some other person or child they encounter after they've been sprayed.

Live trapping and removal

Live trapping and removal services are probably the most common type of service performed by wildlife damage professionals for infestations of tree squirrels, raccoons, skunks, opossums, and woodchucks. Often, in fact, a wild animal needs removal from a building before any other step of IPM can be implemented. (It is not uncommon for homeowners to call while they are literally listening to the animals scratching in the walls or running around in the attic!)

Live trapping and removal programs are discussed for each appropriate species. Additionally, on-the-job tips and important considerations regarding live trapping nuisance wildlife are provided on page 437.

LAWS AFFECTING URBAN WILDLIFE

Federal, state, and local laws usually protect at least some wild animals in urban areas. State laws are more often involved than federal laws.

In many states, wild animals may be destroyed by owners or occupants of dwellings or property, without a special permit, when these animals are damaging property or causing a nuisance. However, when building owners or occupants hire a pest management professional to solve a problem concerning a protected or game species, the professional frequently must have a permit to conduct any control program—even if the professional livetraps and removes the animal unharmed. (Permits can generally be obtained by contacting local wildlife agencies, conservation officers, or the state department of natural resources.) This may vary from city to city and state to state.

Some urban wildlife (e.g., raccoons and some tree squirrels) are protected furbearers in most states, with seasons established for hunting or trapping these animals. Other species (e.g., deer mice, moles, and pocket gophers) are considered native, nongame mammals and receive whatever protection is afforded such animals under state or local laws. It is usually permissible to control such animals without permits when necessary, but some states may protect even these mammals, or they may have special ordinances that do not allow a certain type of control method, such as the use of poisons. Thus, the professional should always check with the state wildlife agency or conservation officers before implementing any control efforts, especially those involving lethal approaches.

Always keep in mind that to most people, wildlife is a desirable and aesthetically important part of the environment. Thus, it is far better—from the standpoints of ethics, public relations, and relations with local animal shelters, humane societies, and conservation agencies—to control nuisance wildlife in an acceptable manner, which often involves nonlethal approaches.

BATS
Order Chiroptera
Families Verpertilionidae and Molossidae

Bats are among the most unique and interesting of all mammals. Unfortunately, they are also among the most misunderstood. To this day, there are many myths surrounding the lives of bats, and thus many people have acute fears of these mammals. However, these fears are unfounded because bats are, for the most part, harmless. Bats rarely attack people or get tangled in hair. In fact, most bats in the United States are biologically useful mammals, because they feed entirely on insects, many of which are pests to humans and to agriculture.

Bats are sometimes pests, however, when they take up residence within buildings, and there are good reasons for not tolerating their presence. The scratching and squeaking noises created by the bats are annoying. Their droppings and urine cause objectionable and persistent odors and may stain walls and ceilings as well as attract insects and other bat colonies, even after the original colony is broken up. Additionally, there is a slight chance of someone contacting a rabid bat, although the great majority of house-infesting bats in the United States are *not* rabid. Unfortunately, there is no way of knowing whether any bat is rabid by its appearance.

Identification

Bats belong to the order of mammals called the Chiroptera, which means "winged hand." Because they possess wings, bats are the only mammals capable of true flight. Insectivorous bats detect their prey and navigate their flights through dense tree growth and other obstructions primarily by relying on their ability to echolocate—to emit and receive ultrasonic sounds (similar to sonar). Bats are not blind. They possess functional eyes that are used for various tasks, including long-distance orientation and object identification. In fact, the visual acuity of bats is fairly good.

There are forty species of bats found in the United States. Most roost in caves, hollow trees, and other natural shelters. A few species, however, commonly roost and breed within occupied buildings during the warm-weather months. The species most frequently encountered by the pest management professional are the big brown bat, *Eptesicus fuscus*; the little brown bat, *Myotis lucifugus*; and the Mexican free-tailed bat, *Tadarida brasiliensis*.

The **big brown bat** (see Figure 17.1, following page 254) is common throughout the United States. It is relatively large, measuring about four inches in length and having a wing span between 12 and 14 inches (30 to 35 cm). The average adult weighs about 1/2 ounce (14 g). The fur and wings are usually dark brown, but the ears are blackish.

Little brown bats are common in most states except in the southeast and the Great Plains (Nebraska, Kansas, Oklahoma, and Texas). Adult little brown bats are chocolate brown and about 3-inches long, have a wing span between 9 and 10 inches (22 to 26 cm), and weigh about 1/4 ounce (7 g). Though the little brown bat is smaller than the big brown bat, the two bats can be easily confused by the layperson, even while viewing the two bats closely at the same time.

The **Mexican free-tailed bat** is identified by its free tail, which extends beyond the body. The free-tailed bat is common in many of the southern states, from California to South Carolina. Its range extends as far north as southwestern Oregon and

into the southern portions of Kansas. Adult Mexican free-tailed bats are chocolate brown, about 3- to 4-inches long, and have a wing span between 11.5 and 12.5 inches (20 to 32 cm), and weigh about 1/2 ounce (14 g).

Bats in general are difficult to identify, and even experts have trouble identifying some species. If assistance is needed in identifying bats, the professional should contact the wildlife or zoology department of a local university, a local health department, or fish and wildlife personnel.

Biology and Behavior

Bats leave their overwintering sites and enter structures during the first warm days of spring. In the North, this is frequently in April. In the South, it may be earlier. The majority of the bats entering structures at this time are females preparing to give birth. Thus, these colonies are called nursery or maternity colonies. The number of individuals in a colony may range from a couple of bats to several hundred.

Baby bats are born during June and July. Big brown bats may have one or two young per female, while the little brown and free-tailed bats produce only one young per female. Juvenile bats are breastfed until they are mature enough to fly and obtain their own food (three to seven weeks). Bats usually remain in their roosts all summer. In the fall (September to October), males increase in numbers at the nursery roost, and mating occurs. The sperm is stored in the uterus by the female during the winter, and fertilization occurs in the spring, upon departure from hibernation. As temperatures begin to drop during autumn (mid-September to mid-November), the bats leave their summer roosts and travel to their overwintering quarters.

Hibernation sites vary among different colonies of bats. Big brown bats typically do not hibernate as colonies within buildings, although in heated buildings, it is common for a few bats (e.g., one to six bats) to also use the summer roost as their overwintering site. Most of the bats, however, disperse from the summer roost and hibernate at different sites, singularly or in small groups of two or four. Such sites are usually within a 50-mile radius of the summer roost. Overwintering sites, such as hollow trees, rock crevices, drainage pipes, caves, and heated buildings, are commonly used by big brown bats. Little brown and free-tailed bats, on the other hand, tend to travel considerable distances—up to several hundred miles in some cases—and hibernate as colonies, usually selecting caves instead of buildings to pass the winter. Most bats live an average of 4 to 10 years, although some over 20 years old have been found.

Bats as Health Pests

While only a small percentage of bats are infected with rabies, any bat should be looked on as potentially dangerous and should be approached with caution. Rabies can occur in bats without the animals showing any symptoms.

A hard hat, heavy leather gloves, and coveralls should always be worn during any bat control effort, including inspections. Additionally, it may be wise for those involved on a regular basis in bat management work to obtain routine rabies prevention shots. Any bat that acts in an abnormal manner, such as fluttering around on the ground, should be avoided and handled with tongs.

If rabid bats are suspected in a building, the local health department should be contacted. If at all possible, capturing or collecting baits for rabies examination should be done in cooperation with public health personnel. If rabies has been confirmed in a bat population, control should never be attempted without supervision of the public health department. Any bat causing a bite should be captured with brain intact for examination by health authorities.

The accumulation of bat droppings in attics or soil creates an environment suitable for the growth of *Histoplasmosis capsulatum*, a fungal organism that can produce the respiratory illness **histoplasmosis** in people, dogs, cats, and other animals. In severe cases, histoplasmosis is fatal. The fungus can be present in droppings that have accumulated for extended periods. Therefore, a large, established bat roost in an attic or cave may be a potential health hazard, because fungal spores may be drawn into the lungs when people breathe in the dust in the roosting areas. Although the actual incidence of histoplasmosis in structural bat roosts is low, several cases have occurred during the past several years. Therefore, all safety precautions (e.g., the wearing of dust respirators) should be taken by all those involved in bat work.

Many types of buildings are susceptible to bat infestation, but certain factors appear to encourage maternity roosts. Bats usually select buildings that are located near water (streams, lakes, ponds, etc.) and food—that is, where insects are found in adequate numbers. No one is really sure why bats select specific buildings to roost, but bats are attracted to buildings by odors from previous infestations, coupled with high roost temperatures, which are conducive for rearing young. Obviously, a structure must also provide the bats with some type of access,

because they do not gnaw holes into structures. Actual roost sites within a building may be in exposed areas (ceiling joists, roof rafters, etc.) or in concealed areas (roof and ceiling voids, brick voids, etc.). During the daytime, the bats are restful or semirestful. They emerge from structures beginning at dusk, and most bats are out of the roost within 60 minutes from the first bat's exit. They then fly to nearby feeding and watering areas. By dawn, all the bats are back in the roost.

Management

To manage bats, it is important to first **inspect and evaluate** the infestation. The professional should determine (1) all possible exit and entry points of the bats, (2) any structural deficiencies of the building, (3) the bat roosting site inside the structure, (4) the size of the infesting colony, and (5) the species of the bat pest.

To gather this information properly, it is best to conduct two inspections: the first at dusk, when the bats emerge from the building, and the second during the day, to determine inside roosting areas, accessibility to the bats, equipment that will be needed to correct the problem, and so forth.

It is important to remember that if bats are present, they will emerge each evening unless it is rainy or unseasonably cold. For the evening inspection, it may be necessary to situate two people at opposite corners of the structure, so that each person can view two roofline areas at the same time. If a building has several wings, then more than two inspectors may be needed.

The inspection should begin approximately a half hour before dusk and continue for about an hour after the first bat emerges. This should reveal the bats' exit and entry points, and the size of the infestation. Common entry areas include attic louvers, rooflines (between the roof sheathing and the fascia boards), and any other openings resulting from building deterioration (see Figure 17.2). Openings of 3/8 inch (6 millimeters) or larger are sufficient for bat entry. In some buildings, such as barns, exit and entry points may be the actual doorways. Many times exit and entry locations can be determined by preemergence noise, droppings on the ground below the exit points, odor, or by smudge marks in the areas of entry.

When conducting evening inspections, do not flash a beam of light at suspected openings or at areas from which bat squeaks are emerging, as this light may frighten the bats enough to prevent them from emerging on time, or it may cause an incomplete roost evacuation.

The indoor inspection should be conducted

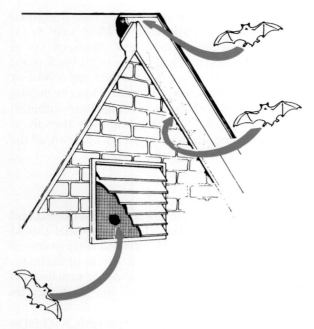

FIGURE 17.2. Common entry points for bats in a building.

during the day. The bats should all be present somewhere within the structure if they were seen during the evening inspection. Piles of droppings are frequently evident below the roosting areas. The bats usually, but not always, roost near their emergence holes, so inspect these areas first and then work your way to other areas of the structure. Indoor areas to inspect include all roof rafters where they join the ceiling, brick voids, chimney areas, and ceiling and wall voids.

Bats will also roost in the exterior portions of a structure. Always be sure to check behind shutters and gutters, behind expanded fascia boards, and within soffits.

For safety and health reasons, proper clothing and equipment are essential when conducting indoor inspections. A good drop light or field light, a bump cap, coveralls, a dust respirator, and leather gloves are the minimum.

Batproofing a structure is the most logical and biologically acceptable way to control bats, if it can be done practically and economically. Remember, the objective in controlling bats is to rid a building of the colony permanently. Exclusion is the only method that can guarantee this goal.

The best time of year to batproof a building is either in late fall, after it has been confirmed that the bats have departed for hibernation, or in late winter to early spring, before the bats return. Experienced bat management professionals can also exclude bats during certain months of the summer, but this involves specialized techniques, and these programs are beyond the capabilities and experience of most

pest management professionals. Exclusion programs should never be attempted mid-May through mid-September, because the young bats will be trapped within the structure. A summer exclusion program would not only kill many bats, but also force the trapped and panicked bats to likely encounter the building occupants, possibly resulting in bites, a rabies scare, and so forth.

All openings 3/8-inch and larger must be sealed. For permanent sealing, use materials such as 1/4-inch hardware cloth, sheet metal, plywood, or aluminum flashing. For temporary exclusion, any soft materials (rags, cheesecloth) can be used.

One of the most versatile tools for batproofing a building is **plastic bird netting**. The netting is very light and supple, yet relatively tough and resilient; it is easy to work with and relatively inexpensive. Depending on the situation, it can be draped over entire roof areas or cut and applied as needed to cover only certain sections (see Figure 16.10 in Chapter 16).

Plastic bird netting can also be used to construct bat check valves, which allow bats to exit a structure but not reenter. For example, the netting can be attached above a bat emergence hole so that it hangs in front of the hole. The bottom portion of the netting can remain unattached and weighted using fishing sinkers, or it can be attached to the side of the building directly beneath the emergence hole so that it lies flat against the building but is loose enough to provide space for the bats to emerge from their exit hole, crawl down the net cover, and escape. The attachment points should be four to six feet apart. The netting can be fastened to the structure using tape, staples, or Velcro strips.

The method of installation and use of netting check valves is very situational, as each type of structure and bat infestation is different. Thus, careful inspection of the affected premises is essential to ensure using the correct check valve design. In some cases, several check valves may need to be installed. When considering the use of plastic netting and other exclusion devices, the reader is encouraged to carefully review those references relating to bat management listed at the end of this chapter. Several of these references go into great detail and are extremely helpful.

Because of the complexity of bat management work and the associated liabilities, many pest management professionals now opt to leave bat management programs to wildlife control professionals who specialize in this service and technology.

Naphthalene (as crystals or flakes), in some cases, can serve as a **chemical repellent** to bats. However, the repelling effect of naphthalene is only temporary, and treatments must be repeated every

Odor Animal Repellents; Are They Effective?

Pest professionals and wildlife control professionals are often called upon to capture or "chase" squirrels, rodents, snakes, bats, skunks, and other urban wild animals out of buildings. For the majority of cases, this is best accomplished via live trapping and/or exclusion programs. But many homeowners also inquire as to the usefulness of simply spraying or scattering some type of chemical repellent in or around the building to repel the animals out and prevent future activity.

Many different types and brands of chemical animal repellents are available including over-the-counter products available in home stores, shopping marts, and gardening catalogs. The majority of these products are odor or odor/taste repellents. That is, their intended mode of action is to offend the olfactory senses of the animal, or cause respiratory and general discomfort and discourage animals from harboring in or around the treated building or area.

Although, there is a wide range of different chemicals employed in animal repellents (e.g, capsasin), the two chemicals most commonly employed are: naphthalene and sulfur.

Naphthalene (e.g., "moth flakes") is known to most people as an **insect** "repellent," used to protect woolen clothing against fabric pests (refer to Chapter 13). However, research has shown that naphthalene is not an effective **repellent** against fabric insects or other pests. When used in high concentrations and kept in tight containers for prolonged periods, naphthalene works as a fumigant, actually **killing** insects. How naphthalene came to be known and used as an animal repellent is not exactly clear. This fumigant and the related compound paradichlorobenzene (PDB) may have been assumed many years ago to be a general pest repellent due to their volatility and resulting disagreeable odor to people. Any mammal, including a human, within an enclosed area containing high levels of naphthalene (or any other highly volatile chemical) is likely to cause the animal to evacuate to more comfortable air.

The second common animal repellent, sulfur, is one of the oldest pesticides. Sulfur was used throughout the first half of the century for all types of "pest cleansing operations," but especially against mites and chiggers. Eventually, burning sulfur candles became commonplace for people in attempts to repel mosquitoes, gnats, and other nuisance flying insects.

Some animal repellent products are formulated with combinations of 28.0% sulfur and 7.0% naphthalene and are registered as repellents against snakes, rats, mice, and other animals.

Effective and Safe?

Under certain uses, naphthalene can be effective in dislodging some animals out of buildings. But success or failure depends on the size of the space, the amount of fresh-air flow into the area, the specific pest, the specific location the pests are using for harborage, and other factors. For example, 100% naphthalene can be used to drive bats out of exterior confined soffit voids, that are small and relatively tight. In these cases, the naphthalene vapors will penetrate the void rendering the air too concentrated with the fumigant for the bats to remain comfortably.

However the typical attics of homes, churches, schools and other buildings are too large and/or allow for too much fresh-air entry to cause repellent dosages (consider if the attics were tight, they would not permit the bats or other animals entry in the first place). Many, many cases exist of do-it-yourselfers installing literally hundreds of boxes of 100% naphthalene into attics of commercial schools and churches without any success of evicting the nuisance animals (also refer to the safety concerns discussed below).

Research on the use of sulphur/naphthalene combinations labeled for snakes failed to prove any effectiveness in driving snakes out of buildings or preventing the snakes from using an area.

Important Safety Considerations

For many people, old schools, churches, and attics containing the odor of "mothballs" is a common odor. But in a society where many chemophobes live, or where some individuals may suffer from multiple chemical sensitivities, installing odor area repellents into homes and other buildings is perhaps left to the client. Although naphthalene is often listed as "low mammalian toxicity," in various books, there are safety concerns with this mild fumigant. Some individuals are highly sensitive to naphthalene.

Naphthalene is 4.4 times heavier than air, and thus it will settle down inside a typical building. Naphthalene vapors can be hazardous to human health if they are inhaled on a continuous and prolonged basis. Descriptions on the pharmacology of naphthalene (refer to the NIOSH publication in Selected References at the end of the chapter) state "prolonged inhalation of naphthalene may cause headaches, nausea, vomiting, and sweating, followed by anemia, haematuria (i.e., blood in the urine), and optic neuritis. Some individuals may have a severe hemolytic crisis which may be delayed for several days after exposure."

These toxicity considerations are especially important for pest and wildlife professionals servicing homes and commercial buildings (offices, schools, plant sites), where many people with different chemical sensitivities may work or visit on a daily basis.

The Animal Damage Control division of USDA does not recommend administering naphthalene into occupied buildings due to these toxicity and safety concerns.

few weeks. Also, naphthalene should not be used if constant inhalation of the odors will occur. Some individuals are sensitive to naphthalene odors and should thus avoid contact with the material (refer to page 423).

Some bats may roost temporarily during the night in open structures or on outside areas of homes, such as on garages, carports, and patios, and behind shutters and building overhangs. Bats can sometimes be discouraged from using these areas by hanging a small cheesecloth bag containing about four to six ounces of naphthalene in the specific areas. Directing a breeze from a portable fan may also discourage bats from continuing to use the area.

In some cases, **bright lights** can be effective in repelling bats. Attics, carports, and similar areas can be illuminated using four or more 150-watt bulbs; direct the lights so that all darkened areas are illuminated. Although illumination can in some situations provide results, total control should not be expected. It may also be difficult and costly to adequately light some roosting locations.

Despite some claims, none of the ultrasonic sound devices have been found to be effective for repelling bats from buildings or for preventing them from entering the structure.

No pesticides are registered for bats, and pesticides should never be used as a management approach. It is illegal to do so, and poisoned bats could fall to the ground outside of their roost and come into contact with children and pets, thereby creating a great deal of attention and a possible rabies scare.

On occasion, one or two bats get into a home and fly around. Most times, it is one of the brown bats that entered accidentally through an open window, door, or unscreened fireplace. It is not wise to chase after such bats with tennis rackets or other devices with the intent of killing the bat. When this is done, the bat is often wounded but not killed. This approach is unprofessional, potentially hazardous, and inhumane.

Usually, the disoriented bat will find its way back outdoors by following fresh air movements. Therefore, leaving windows and doors open will help the bat to escape. Also, all lights should be turned off. If any are left on, the bat may seek darkened refuge behind wall hangings or drapes. If a bat refuses to leave, it can be caught with a net, coffee can, or gloved hand, taken away from the premises, and released outside. Also check with the local zoo or university as to their possible interest in the bat.

Recently, there has been interest in the use of **bat houses** as a means to either attract bats to an area or displace bats from a building to the bat house. However, simply installing a bat house on a tree or the side of a building is not likely to result in bats quickly moving into the bat house. Many factors are involved when bats select roosts and harborages, such as the location, temperature gradients, height off ground, harborage substrate, and orientation to the sun and wind.

Nevertheless, some success is being achieved with bat houses in various parts of the United States. In most cases, successful bat house programs are carefully planned, and the houses are carefully located and constructed using specialized house plans. Even with the best plans, however, there are cases of bat houses never being used by the bats active in the area. The smaller, homemade bat houses found in garden shops and bird stores are usually not properly designed and thus are not likely to attract bats.

Finally, when bat houses are being considered, they should be located away from the high-activity areas of people, to prevent children and pets from having any contact with the bats. For those readers interested in the use bat houses as part of a comprehensive bat management program, contact the Bat Conservation International Organization in Austin, Texas (**www.batcon.org**).

DEER MICE and WHITE-FOOTED MICE
Order Rodentia
Family Cricetidae

The deer mouse, *Peromyscus maniculatus*, and the white-footed mouse are among the most common semicommensal rodent species in most of the United States. Many people refer to these mice as field mice, or as white-footed mice. However, the white-footed mouse, *Peromyscus leucopus*, is a separate species than the deer mouse. The term *field mouse* can be confusing, as several mice can be categorized as field mice, including the common house mouse. Because of hantavirus, and Lyme disease both the white-footed mouse and the deer mouse have increased in their significance in urban areas.

The deer mouse is actually the most common and widely distributed mouse in the United States. But it is absent from most of the Gulf states and large sections of the eastern coastal states. The white-footed mouse is found throughout the United States east of the Rocky Mountains except in parts of the Southeast. For the specific distribution of peromyscus mice, state universities or the department of natural resources in each state should be consulted.

Both species of peromyscus mice are similar in appearance and habits. Most pest professionals cannot distingush between the two in the field. The average body length measures about six inches (155 mm), including a 2.5-inch (63 mm) tail. The body is reddish brown in color with a white chest, white feet, and a bicolored tail, brown on top and white on bottom (see Figures 17.3 and 17.4). Deer mice and white-footed mice do not usually appear in urban areas. Their natural habitat is in rural and semirural areas, where they inhabit fields, pastures, and various types of vegetation found around homes and outbuildings. Both species will frequently enter houses, garages, storage sheds, and stored campers during the colder months, where they may damage foodstuffs and furnishings. In unoccupied summer homes or cottages, damage to upholstered furniture can be extensive.

Peromyscus mice breed during the spring and fall, although under favorable conditions, litters will be produced at other times of the year as well. Most litters average about four pups, and the female produces between two and four litters per year. If not eaten by a predator, the deer mouse can live up to two years in the wild. Peromyscus mice are active all year and store food for the winter season much as the tree squirrels do. Nuts, seeds, berries, and insects are their usual food.

The nests of these mice are generally located underground in cavities about the roots of trees or shrubs, beneath a log or board, or in a tunnel built either by another animal or by the mouse itself. Aboveground nests are established in hollow trees, building voids and spaces, unused equipment, cabinet voids, log piles, unused furniture, fence posts, and old bird and squirrel nests, and along the sill plate in basements and crawlspaces.

Control

In occupied houses, peromyscus mice are easily controlled through the use of snap traps, glue boards, or any of the multiple-catch traps used for house mouse control. With snap traps, a dozen or more traps baited with oatmeal or peanut butter and placed in corners, along walls, and behind objects will capture resident mice.

Poison baits used against house mice are also effective against deer mice, although there are not any baits specifically registered against peromyscus mice. However, the baiting sites are the same as those for house mice. Baits should be placed as close to the suspected mouse activity as possible, as determined by a good inspection.

When considering rodenticide baits for peromyscus mouse control, it is important to realize that these mice tends to hoard their food. Pelletized baits may be carried off and deposited in areas accessible to pets or people. Thus, bait blocks are effective bait against peromyscus mice, but they should be secured by nails, glue, or wires (e.g., along sill plates), or preferably placed inside tamper-resistant mouse bait stations.

WOODRATS (PACKRATS)
Family Cricetidae
Genus Neotoma

The woodrat is also known as the packrat and traderat, and nine species are found in the United States. Although they are widely distributed, woodrats are absent from the New England states and several of the north central and Great Lakes states. Any of the nine species may invade human structures depending on where the building is located. Three of the more common species encountered by pest professionals around newly developed neighborhoods include the Eastern woodrat, *Neotoma floridana*; the white-throated woodrat, *N. albigula*; and the dusky-footed woodrat, *N. fuscipes*. The dusky-footed woodrat is primarily found from Portland, Oregon, south to San Diego, and in the northern third of Arizona).

The woodrat's body is about the same size as a Norway rat. To most people, the woodrat is an attractive rodent, similar in color to a large deer mouse or a "giant hamster." Woodrats have large ears, bulging, black eyes, very long, soft fine fur, hairy tails, and conspicuous facial whiskers (vibrissae). The pelage color varies with the species ranging from brown, gray, or black on the upper body. The bellies and feet tend to light in color ranging from light brown to bright white. The head and body length is about seven to eight inches (17.7 to 20.3 cm), the tail is 6.5- to 7.5-inches (16.5 to 19 cm) long.

The different species of woodrats occupy specific habitats ranging from deserts to densely wooded and cavernous areas. Some species are ground

FIGURE 17.3. A deer mouse. Note the striking white belly and feet.

Hantavirus
(for detailed discussion and case history updates, consult **www.cdc.gov**).

Since the original outbreak in the Southwest in 1993, there is a heightened awareness of hantavirus pulmonary syndrome (HPS). The Sin Nombré hantavirus in the southwestern United States was the most severe, but additional cases have also occurred throughout the United States with different, but closely related strains of hantaviruses.

As of March of 2003, 335 cases have occurred in 31 states. About 75% of these cases occur among people living in rural areas. Thirty-eight percent of all cases have been fatal. About 95% of the cases have occured west of the Mississippi River. The earliest retrospectively identified case occurred in Utah in 1959.

As the name implies, hantavirus pulmonary syndrome, attacks the lungs, as compared to other, more well-known hemorraghic hantaviruses that primarily affect the kidney systems. The most important reservoir of HPS in the United States is the deer mouse, *Peromyscus maniculatus*, which is semicommensal and often invades dwellings of all types.

Other rodents, including the white-footed mouse, *Peromyscus leucopis*, and the cotton rat, *Sigmodon hispidus*, have served as reservoirs for other hantavirus strains in the United States.

Although this virus is rare, it should be noted that the Centers for Disease Control (CDC) list pest management professionals as a high-risk group due to the nature of their work and the fact that they must perform rodent control and pest inspections in areas where deer mice are active.

Thus, it is important for professionals to note the recommendations of the Centers for Disease Control, which state, "Because of the high morbidity and mortality associated with hantavirus pulmonary syndrome and the possibility of aerosol transmission of hantaviruses, persons handling known reservoir species in the field, laboratory or classroom should take special precautions to minimize the risk of infection." This, of course, means wearing safety equipment and being careful in those areas where deer mice (and other semi-commensal species) are prevalent, or in environments that might contain, or have previously housed, infestations of these rodents. Such areas include attics, crawl-spaces, barns, sheds, and so forth.

Workers should wear a half-face air-purifying (or negative-pressure) respirator or PAPR equipped with HEPA filters when removing rodents from traps or handling rodents in the affected area. (Please note: The HEPA classification recently has been discontinued. Under the new classification system, the N-100 filter type is recommended. Read the Federal Occupational Safety and Health Administration (OSHA) directive online, **www.osha.gov**, at "OSHA Directives: CPL 2-0.120 – Inspection Procedures for the Respiratory Protection Standard."

For standard house mouse (*M. musculus, M. domesticus*) control programs (inspecting and handling multiple-catch mouse traps and exterior bait stations, conducting routine inspections, etc.) in and around buildings, the use of a respirator may not be warranted. However, whenever cleaning out traps or bait stations, it makes sense to practice personal hygiene and protection by at least wearing gloves, as there is always the possibility of contacting other pathogenic organisms or ectoparasites associated with house mouse carcasses or excrement.

The following hantavirus prevention recommendations are from the Centers for Disease Control:

- Workers in potentially high-risk settings (e.g., where there are abundant deer mouse populations) should be informed about the symptoms of the disease and given detailed guidance on prevention measures.
- Workers who develop a febrile or respiratory illness within 45 days of the last potential exposure should immediately seek medical attention and inform the attending physician of the potential occupational risk of hantavirus infection. The physician should contact local health authorities promptly if hantavirus-associated illness is suspected. A blood sample should be obtained and forwarded with the baseline serum through the state health department to the CDC for hantavirus antibody testing.
- In areas of reported cases, professionals should wear at least an HEPA-filter respirator when removing deer mice from traps or handling rodents. Respirators (including positive-pressure types) are not considered protective if facial hair interferes with the face seal, since proper fit cannot be ensured. Respirator use should be in accord with a comprehensive user program.
- Professionals should wear rubber or plastic gloves when handling rodents or traps containing rodents. Gloves should be washed and disinfected before removing them.
- Traps contaminated by rodent urine or feces or in which a rodent was captured should be disinfected with a commercial disinfectant.

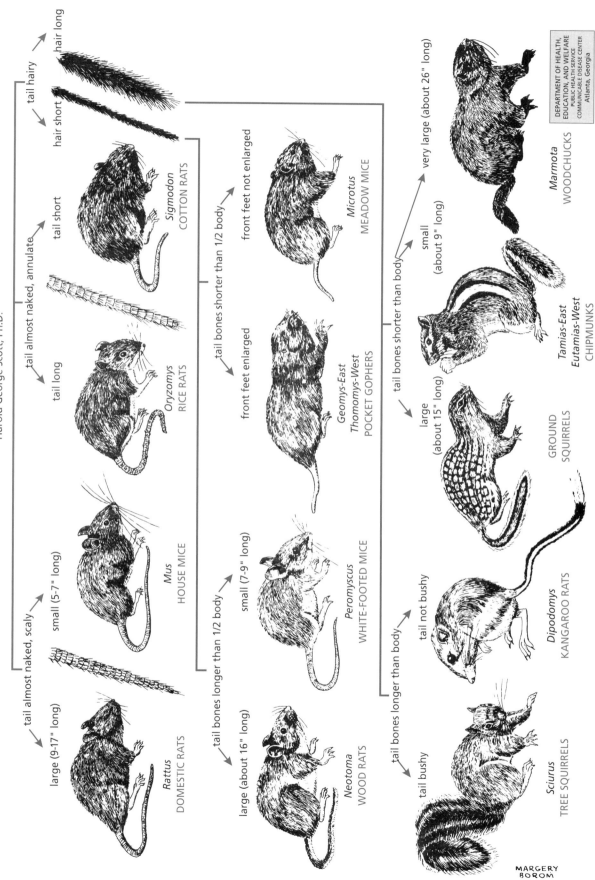

FIGURE 17.4. A pictorial key to common rodents.

dwellers some live up in trees. Some woodrat species invade summer cabins, equipment sheds, carports, garage attic voids, soffits, and various outbuildings. Over the past decade, urban sprawl in many of the western and southwestern states has displaced woodrats, causing them to adapt to human structures.

Like other rodents, woodrats have a propensity for gnawing and will readily attack wires and various conduits and lines in attics and wall voids causing shorts and fires. In unoccupied summer cabins, the woodrat can inflict serious damage to the cabin's furniture and stored materials. Chairs, couches, and beds may all be shredded as woodrats often attempt to nest in these items or drag out the furniture stuffing for their nests. Woodrats readily collect matches, cloth, and paper materials and store these materials inside their nests, creating an obvious potential for fire hazards. The woodrat has also been implicated as a potential health pest involved in the transmission of pathogenic viruses, Lyme disease, plague, and tularemia to people.

Unlike the commensal rodents, woodrat populations do not increase quickly. The spring is the peak reproductive season. Most litters contain two to four pups Gestation periods are range from 33-43 days. Most females produce one to two litters per year, but some species in good environments may produce up to five litters. Woodrats tend to be solitary animals except during mating and rearing periods. Woodrats can live for up to three years, but many are killed by predators before this.

In the wild, woodrats consume various types of vegetation, seeds, nuts, berries, insects, snails, birds, and small mammals. Around buildings woodrats will eat any pet and human foods as the opportunity becomes available. Woodrats nesting inside often continue to feed outside. Woodrats often leave distinctly visible travel paths (3- to 4-inches (8-10 cm) wide) though vegetation leading from food sources to nesting sites.

Inside buildings, these rodents will infest attics, soffits, and various hard-to-reach wall and ceiling voids. It is common for them to use overhanging tree branches and utility lines to gain access to attics or ceiling areas.

Some species construct large stick nests (called "houses") beneath porches, inside woodsheds and attics, up on carport corners, and similar structural areas. The presence of these houses is obvious indicators of woodrats. "Latrines" comprised of conspicuously large piles of feces are commonly found nearby woodrat nests. The feces typically measure 1/2-inch (1.25 cm) long and are oval in shape.

The typical home range of the woodrat is woodrats be about 200 feet from the nest to feeding locations along well-marked trails. Most woodrats are active at night, although young animals may be active at any time.

Woodrat Management

In most states woodrats are classified as non-game animals and can be controlled when they threaten or damage properties. However, a few species or subspecies of woodrats are protected in some states. Thus, the local regulations pertaining to woodrats of each state should be checked.

The tools and techniques for managing tree squirrels, roof rats, and deer mice are also applicable for managing structural infestations of woodrats. Woodrats can be excluded from homes and cabins by rodentproofing as is done for other rodents. Special attention must be given to roof and eaves, attics, and soffit louvers. Overhanging tree and vegetation limbs should be cut back from rooftops by 6 feet (1.8 m).

Because woodrat infestations usually do not involve large numbers of animals, infestations are often eliminated via the use of ordinary snap traps. Unlike adult Norway and roof rats, woodrats are actually neophilic animals (attracted to new items). As such, they readily interact with well-placed traps containing enticing food baits such as pecans, bacon, hotdog, dog food kibbles, etc. To increase capture success, baits should be tied to the trigger with dental floss or some other thin string.

Woodrats can also be live-trapped using a live traps of the same size used for chipmunks or similar sized wildlife. Enticing trails of baits with tiny pieces of the selected bait leading into the trap may expedite capture. The largest pieces of bait should be placed well behind the trigger of the traps.

Anticoagulant rodenticides when used according to label directions for roof rats and Norway rats are also effective against woodrats. In some states, specific special local needs (SLN 24c) labels exist for rodenticide baits for woodrats.

Secured block baits are the recommended rodenticide formulation against woodrats because they are the least hazardous of formulations. To secure blocks, they can be wired or nailed to structural members within the suspected travel pathways of the woodrats. Bait stations are not recommended against woodrats because the woodrat often stuffs sticks and other items into the boxes rendering them ineffective as feeding locations.

It is important to note that pellet formulations and packet-style rodenticide baits, should never be used against the woodrat (or deer mice) because of this rodent's tendency to carry off food particles (as well as entire bait packets). Cached baits may not even be consumed by the woodrats.

MEADOW VOLES (MEADOW MICE)
Order Rodentia
Family Arvicolidae

Meadow voles (*Microtus* spp.), also known as meadow mice, represent some of the most prolific, numerous, and widely distributed mammals in North America.

Meadow voles are small, chunky rodents; adults are about 7-inches (18 cm) long (see Figure 17.4, and Figure 17.5, which follows page 254). The tail is usually short, about 1-1/2 inches (3.8 cm). Their ears are furred and do not project much above the hair on the head. Mature meadow voles are chestnut brown mixed with black on the back. Their underparts are dark gray, and their feet are brown. The thinly haired tail is dark on the upper surface, shading to a lighter gray beneath. Young meadow voles are uniformly gray.

On the job, pest management professionals sometimes confuse meadow voles with moles and shrews. Moles are easily distinguished from voles because they are considerably larger and have greatly enlarged front feet with prominent digging claws. Shrews are smaller, more slender mammals, with extremely soft fur, long, pointed snouts, and needlelike front teeth. Also, the eyes or ears of the shrew are not easily seen. Meadow mice have rounded, somewhat blunt snouts and visible ear flaps, and their front teeth are chisel shaped.

Populations of meadow voles fluctuate greatly from year to year. Several hundred mice per acre may be present in years when they are abundant, and they may be extremely destructive to vegetation. Their usual foods are grasses and herbs, but during the late fall, winter, and early spring, they may gnaw (girdle) the bark of young trees and ornamental plantings (especially when snow cover is present), causing damage and even death to the plant.

Voles are prolific mammals. They can produce from five to ten litters per year, with an average of five young per litter. Gestation is about 21 days, and females may mate again the day that the young are born. Young voles grow quickly, are weaned in two or three weeks, and are sexually mature in a month or two.

In regions receiving snow, homeowners are dismayed when the snow has melted to see the ragged and chewed-up appearance of the grass where voles have been living beneath the snow during the winter. In most cases, however, the damage to the lawn is not permanent. This vole activity is sometimes blamed on moles, but moles dig their tunnels beneath the soil surface and do not construct surface runways through the grass.

Control

In cases of just a few voles in and around ornamental plantings, ordinary snap-back mouse traps are effective. A dozen or more traps should be used. If possible, vole runways should be located in the grassy borders of the gardens, and the traps set at right angles to the runways, with the trigger in the runway. Traps can be set at 10-foot intervals along the plant rows. A pinch of oatmeal sprinkled over the trigger of the trap is an effective bait. Avoid using baits such as bacon, which may be attractive to birds. Traps should be reset daily and freshly baited until no more voles are caught. Keep grassy and weedy areas well mowed to reduce the protective cover for voles.

For large infestations of meadow voles outdoors, several lethal baits are effective. In most states, some anticoagulant and zinc phosphide baits are registered for agricultural applications and may be useful in golf courses, parks, and other such areas. These baits are usually broadcasted in infested areas, but baits can also be placed within meadow mouse runways beneath pieces of plywood or shingling. Baits are also effective when placed directly into burrow openings.

Voles occasionally enter buildings, but they do not become established or reproduce indoors. They can be controlled by setting snap traps, glue boards, or live-catch traps, as would be done to control house mice.

MOLES
Order Insectivora
Family Talpidae

There are several species of moles in the United States. The **eastern mole** (*Scalopus aquaticus*) is the most numerous and widespread in the eastern United States, and it is responsible for most of the complaints concerning mole damage to lawns and gardens. The most troublesome species on the coast of Oregon and Washington is the **Townsend's mole** (*Scapanus townsendii*), and in California, the **broad-footed mole** (*Scapanus latimanus*) causes problems. Other species of moles in the United States are, for the most part, of no pest significance. Although there are some differences between the various species of moles, most moles have similar biology and behavior. Therefore, the following discussion is based on the biology, behavior, and control of the eastern mole.

Moles are not rodents; they belong to the group of mammals known as insectivores and thus are more closely related to the shrews. Eastern moles have pointed snouts, greatly enlarged, rounded front feet with stout claws, and a short, nearly naked tail. They are 5- to 8-inches (12 to 20 cm) long with short, velvety fur that is usually gray to silvery gray. The eyes and ears of moles are very small and are concealed in the fur (see Figure 17.6, following page 254).

Moles can be destructive pests in lawns, gardens, nurseries, parks, golf courses, and cemeteries. During their burrowing activities, they produce mounds and ridges that disfigure lawns and sometimes dislodge plants or injure plant roots. Their mounds also provide a medium for the germination of weed seeds.

Moles feed primarily on earthworms, beetle grubs, ants, and other arthropods and animals found in the soil. A smaller part of their diet consists of various seed and vegetable matter, but they usually do not eat bulbs or the roots of garden plants.

Moles are active day and night throughout the year, but they are most visibly active during the spring and fall on damp days or following rainshowers, when they push up more tunnels and mounds. When the ground surface becomes frozen in the winter or very dry during the summer, moles use only the deeper burrows.

Mating occurs during February and March, with a single litter of three to five young born later in the spring, following a 6-week gestation period. Young moles grow rapidly and have the appearance of, and behave like, an adult at about one month of age. Young moles may use their family's burrow system for up to six months before dispersing to establish their own burrow systems and territories nearby.

Two types of runways (tunnels) are produced by moles: subsurface runways and deep runways (see Figure 17.7). Certain tunnels of both types are used as major lanes of travel (called main runways) and may be used by several moles in the area.

Subsurface runways are feeding tunnels just below the soil surface and are commonly seen as the raised ridges running through lawn areas. The mole is capable of extending these runways at the rate of 100 feet (30.4 m) per day. Subsurface runs may be used daily, may be revisited at irregular intervals, or may be used only once for feeding and then abandoned. Often these runways are used to connect to the deep runways. Generally, few or no mounds are produced as a result of the production of subsurface tunnels.

The deep runways are located between 3 and 12 inches (7.6 to 30.4 cm) below the surface and are usually main runways, because they are used daily as the mole travels to and from the main subsurface runways or the nest. The soil excavated from the deep tunnels is deposited on the surface through short vertical tunnels in volcano-like mounds.

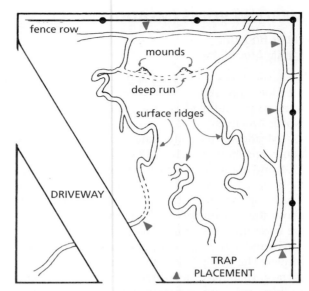

FIGURE 17.7. A network of mole runways in a yard. The arrows indicate good locations to set traps. Avoid the twisting surface ridges and do not place traps on top of mounds.

Mole mounds should not be confused with pocket gopher mounds, which are horseshoe shaped (see Figure 17.8).

The number of mounds or surface ridges seen in a yard is no indication of how many moles are present. Generally, one acre of land will support no more than two or three moles at one time. However, yards surrounded by or adjacent to large tracts of forested land or weedy fields may be subject to continual invasions by moles, because such areas may support many moles.

Control

For the pest management professional concerned with getting the best control results for the time spent on a job, trapping is the most reliable method of mole control. But trapping moles must be done carefully, with attention to details. Moles—perhaps more so than other small mammals—have an uncanny ability to detect and spring improperly set traps. If traps are placed correctly, they often produce results within a day.

When and Where to Trap

Generally, trapping is easiest and most effective during the spring and fall, when mole activity is at a peak. Once mole activity is noticed, control efforts should begin as quickly as possible to keep damage to a minimum. Also, trapping in the early spring can eliminate pregnant females, thereby reducing the

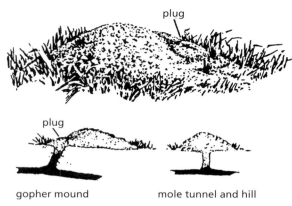

FIGURE 17.8. Mole mounds versus gopher mounds. The top mound with the plug is a typical gopher mound. Mole mounds do not contain any obvious plugs.

likelihood of having to contend with a family of moles later.

For successful trapping, it is essential to locate the main runways. To identify main runways in a yard or area, look for runways that:

- follow a more-or-less straight course for some distance;
- appear to connect two mounds or two runway systems;
- follow fencerows, concrete paths, or other human borders; or
- follow a woody perimeter of a field or yard.

Also, because nests are commonly located at protected spots along the edge of areas such as hedgerows or fencerows, border trapping at the places where runways enter the yard, field, or garden often proves highly effective (see Figure 17.7).

Unless the mole activity is extremely light, more than one trap should be used. Use between three and five traps per acre for quick results. If possible, one trap should be placed in each of the main runway areas.

How to Trap

The two most common types of mole traps are the harpoon trap and the scissor-jaw trap. For most people and inexperienced mole trappers the harpoon trap is the easiest trap to use, and it is readily available.

To properly set a harpoon trap on a surface run, carefully follow these steps:

1. Using the side of your hand, lightly press down a narrow section (approximately 1 inch in width) of an active runway, so that the runway is collapsed to one half of its original dimension.

2. Push the supporting spikes of the trap into the ground, one on either side of the runway, until the trigger pan just barely touches the depressed tunnel. Be sure the trap is centered over the runway and the supporting spikes do not cut into the tunnel below (see Figure 17.9).

3. Set the trap and leave it, taking care not to tread on or disturb any other portion of the runway system.

4. Check the trap once or twice a day. If a trap fails to produce a mole within four or five days, move the trap to another portion of the runway system or to another runway.

The scissor-jaw trap (see Figure 17.10) when used by an experienced mole trapper is a highly effective trap. This trap is inserted into the deeper tunnels of the mole, which in fact, are more often the tunnels traveled by the mole used on a daily basis than the surface tunnels. However, using the scissor-jaw requires practice. But with experience, this trap often provides the best return for the time spent. Various university extension leaflets, web sites and videos offer step-by-step approaches for using this and other mole traps. Refer to the suggested references at the end of this chapter.

Other Methods of Control

It is often suggested that if you **eliminate grubs** from lawns, you will eliminate moles. But grubs make up

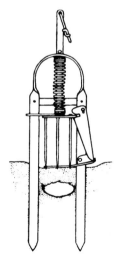

FIGURE 17.9. A harpoon trap properly set on a surface runway (ridge). A narrow portion of the runway (1 to 1-1/2 inches) is collapsed halfway down, the trap is inserted so that the support prongs straddle the runway, and the trigger rests lightly on top of it. Plastic pails can be placed over traps to prevent animals or children from tampering with them. (Modified from a Kansas State Extension Service drawing)

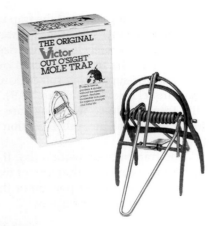

FIGURE 17.10. The scissor-jaw trap when used by an experienced mole trapper is a highly effective trap.

only a portion of the mole's diet, which also includes ants, earthworms and other soil animals. Thus, moles often are present in grub-free lawns. Consider, for example, that moles are a frequent problem on golf courses—an environment where a fair amount of insecticides are typically applied to keep turf-damaging grubs and other insects to an absolute minimum.

Theoretically, if all the earthworms, grubs, and other soil animals in a lawn are eliminated via repeated applications of various insecticides, the moles would be forced to seek other, more productive areas. However, the results may not be evident for several weeks, and damage would be likely to continue and even increase during this time. Moreover, attempting to discourage moles by eliminating their food supply is a relatively expensive and environmentally insensitive approach to discouraging moles, considering the amount of insecticides that would need to be applied to turf areas. In short, lawn spraying for grubs is not a cost-effective approach to mole control.

Two fumigants are federally registered to control moles: gas cartridges and aluminum phosphine tablets. However, **fumigating** mole tunnels has generally produced inconsistent results. Some success has been achieved when the fumigants can be inserted into the deeper tunnels. But unless repeated or large dosages are applied (which takes time and is thus expensive) or applications can be made directly to nesting areas (which are usually unknown), fumigants are rarely capable of giving good control. Like insecticide applications, fumigation is not a cost-effective approach to mole control.

Mole baits vary in their effectiveness. Some new baits have emerged in a gel formulation, which may hold promise as alternatives to trapping programs. Previous baits formulated as nut and grain pellet formulations, however, have produced only inconsistent and generally poor results. Some control has been achieved with cholorphacinone pellet baits against some moles in the western United States. But, repeated applications were necessary, and as long as four to six weeks were required to achieve the desired results.

In most cases, baits provide ineffective inconsistent results because moles feed primarily on a wide range of soil invertebrates (e.g., earthworms and insects). However, moles might be enticed to take mole bait from late fall to late winter when their natural food supplies are very low. Unfortunately, this is also the time of year when mole damage is at a minimum, and so are the complaints to pest professionals Some good results have been achieved with cholorphacinone pellet baits against some moles in the western United States. However, repeated applications were necessary, and as long as four to six weeks were required to achieve the desired results.

Moreover, several small mammals regularly forage within mole runways (voles, house mice, deer mice, and others), and these grain eaters are more likely to consume the carefully placed grain pellet bait than is the insectivorous mole.

For the time-conscious pest management professional (and the cost-conscious client), mole control is certainly a matter of dollars and cents. Considering the amount of time invested in attempting to control a mole with baits, poison gases, or insecticide applications, trapping remains the most cost-effective approach. Perhaps this will change with advances in mole baiting technology.

New formulations of soil repellents containing castor oil have shown in some cases to offer at least temporary effects in reducing the amount of burrowing activity in yards by moles. But it is important for a client to realize, repellents may only last from a few days to a maximum of about six weeks before they will need to be reapplied.

Many home-remedy approaches have been tried over the years to combat the mole. Desperate homeowners and gardeners have tried placing various irritating materials in the runways, such as broken glass, razor blades, rose branches, bleach, mothballs, lye, and even human hair. Some have hooked up their car's exhaust system to mole tunnels; others have pumped hundreds of gallons of water into them.

Frightening devices such as mole wheels (spinning daises), vibrating windmills, ultrasonic machines, and whistling bottles have also been tried. Chewing gum has even been suggested as a lethal bait for moles. Someone theorized that the gum would clog up the mole's digestive system, causing death. Overall, electronic gizmos and home-remedy inventions have no value in controlling moles.

POCKET GOPHERS

Order Rodentia
Family Geomyidae

Pocket gophers (*Thomomys* spp. and *Geomys* spp.) are burrowing rodents so named because they have fur-lined pouches outside of the mouth, one on each side of the face. These pockets, which are capable of being turned inside out, are used for carrying food. Pocket gophers are medium-sized rodents, ranging from about 5- to 14-inches (12.7 to 35.5 cm) long (head and body). Their fur is very fine and soft. Colors range from nearly black to light brown to almost white (see Figure 17.4, and Figure 17.11, which follows page 254).

Gophers are extremely well adapted and built for an underground existence. They are powerfully built in the forequarters and have a short neck; the head is small and flattened. The forepaws contain large claws. Gophers have small external ears, small eyes, and lips that close behind their large incisors.

Pocket gophers dig burrows in lawns and gardens, pushing the soil from the burrows into mounds on the surface. These mounds are characteristic in that they are built in the shape of a horseshoe around the burrow opening (moles construct volcano-shaped mounds).

Their underground burrows may be several hundred feet in length, ranging in depth from a few inches to several feet. Gophers are solitary animals except when breeding or rearing young. They are active year-round but are the most visibly active in the spring and fall, when the soil is of the ideal moisture content for digging. Cut roots are usually stored in small chambers within the burrow.

The biology of pocket gophers varies slightly according to the particular species. In the northern part of their range, pocket gophers have one litter per year. In the southern portion, they may have two litters per year. The average litter size is three to four young. In late summer and early fall, young gophers disperse from the family unit to establish their own burrows and territories.

Control

For small numbers of pocket gophers, control is best accomplished with the use of traps. Several types of gopher traps are available. Two of the most commonly used traps include the two-pronged pincer trap (e.g., the Macabee Trap™ and the Victor Easy-Set™ gopher trap) and the squeeze-type box trap. Both of these types of traps work by the gopher pushing dirt against a flat vertical pan or seizing bait attached to a trigger.

The key to effective gopher trapping is to properly locate main tunnels and then correctly place the traps within the tunnels. Traps are most effective when they are placed in pairs in opposite directions in main tunnels, as they will intercept gophers coming from either direction. In addition to the main tunnel traps, traps can also be placed in the lateral tunnels leading to mounds.

Main runways can be located by probing with a sharp stick or rod one or two feet away from a mound opposite the burrow plug. Once the tunnel is located, it should be opened with a trowel or shovel to allow for the placement of traps. The traps should be worked back and forth in the tunnel to loosen the earth. After setting the traps, it is important to exclude light and air currents by covering the opening with grass clods, cardboard, or some other material. All traps should be wired to stakes to allow for safe and easy trap and carcass recovery, as well as to prevent predators from removing the traps. Traps should be checked once or twice daily. If a trap fails to catch a gopher within three to four days, it should be moved to a new location.

Trapping can be done any time of the year (as long as the ground is soft enough to permit digging), but spring is the best time to trap, as this is when gopher activity is high and the ground is easy to work. Moreover, trapping in the early part of the year helps to maintain population levels by eliminating breeding females.

After removal of any trapped gophers, it is wise (if it does not pose any hazard to children or pets) to leave a few traps set in the burrows for a week or two, because new invading gophers often explore vacated burrows before constructing completely new burrow systems.

Poison baits can also be used to control pocket gophers. Baits containing zinc phosphide and anticoagulants, such as diphacinone, have been used. Baits can be placed directly into the burrows by using a special hand-operated bait dispenser probe or, in the case of minor infestations, the bait can be placed directly by hand by using a probe to make an opening into a main burrow and then placing the bait. Baits should be placed well into the tunnels at three or four different places. All openings into baited tunnels should be closed up with clumps of sod or soil. Baits accepted by gophers are usually eaten within a week after their placement.

Extensive infestations (e.g., agricultural infestations) of gophers require extensive baiting and specialized equipment, and they are usually not within the realm of structural pest management professionals.

Various fumigants are registered for burrowing rodents. The slow-release formulation of aluminum phosphide has shown promise for effective pocket gopher control but may be too labor intensive for large gopher infestations. In general, most other fumigants are not very effective, because the burrow system of pocket gophers is often too extensive to permit an effective level of toxic gas to be distributed. Moreover, gophers are capable of detecting poisonous gases and quickly plug off portions of the burrows to exclude the gases.

Like moles, home-remedy approaches to gopher control are not effective, nor are any type of sound- or ultrasound-producing machines. The planting of "repellent" plants (e.g., *Euphorbia lathyris*) has not proven to be of any value.

RACCOONS
Order Carnivora
Family Procyonidae

Raccoons (*Procyon lotor*), sometimes called coons for short, live near streams, lakes, or marshes. They normally use hollow trees or logs, rock crevices, and burrows for dens. Sometimes, however, they create a nuisance of themselves when they raid garbage cans, tear up lawns, or use structures—including chimneys, attics, and hollow areas beneath porches and outbuildings—for dens.

Perhaps even more important, rabies in raccoons (and other wildlife) has increased dramatically over the past 30 years. In fact, raccoons have recently been identified as the major wildlife host of rabies in the United States, primarily due to their increased prevalence in the eastern United States.

Raccoons mate in January and February, and after a 63-day gestation period, three to six young are born. At about two months of age they accompany their mother on her outings in search of food. The family group is very sociable, remaining together for about one year. Adults vary in size from 24 to 46 inches (0.6 to 1.1 m) in total length and 12 to 25 pounds (5.4 to 11.3 kg) in weight (see Figure 17.12).

In some areas, raccoons become dormant in winter. During spring and early summer, their diet consists primarily of insects, crayfish, mussels, fish, and frogs. Raccoons will frequently roll back sod in fine lawns in search of grubs and earthworms. In some cases, the damage to a lawn can be extensive. During the late summer and fall, fruits, berries, nuts, and grains are also eaten. Sweet corn is often taken from backyard gardens by raccoons. Raccoons are most active at night.

Control

Raccoons raiding garbage cans may be discouraged by storing the garbage only in metal or tough plastic containers with tight-fitting, secured lids. It frequently is necessary to wire, weight, or clamp the lids down to prevent raccoons from removing them to get at garbage. Cans should be held on a rack or tied to a support to prevent raccoons from tipping them over. Some repellents are commercially available, but they aren't particularly effective. No known home-remedy repellents are effective either.

Raccoon (as well as other urban wildlife) access to chimneys can be prevented by fastening a commercial spark arrestor cap of sheet metal and hardware cloth over the top of the chimney, or by fastening heavy screen wire securely over the opening (see Figure 17.13). Raccoon access to rooftops can sometimes be limited by removing overhanging tree branches.

When attempting to exclude or remove raccoons from buildings in the spring and summer, be aware of the possibility that the young may also be present. Do not complete exclusion procedures until

FIGURE 17.12. The raccoon is familiar to everyone. This carnivore has become one of the most serious pests of our urban environments.

FIGURE 17.13. Raccoons, tree squirrels, and other wildlife can be kept out of chimneys by using heavy-screen wire caps fitted securely to chimney tops. (Courtesy of the HYC Company)

TABLE 17.1. Generalized urban wildlife biology.

Species	Body Size/Weight	Litters/ Year	Litter size (Range)	Time of Birth	Age Young Leave Nest	Activity Period
raccoon	24–46 in, 12–25 lbs	1	3–6	Apr.–May	10–14 wks	Night
gray and fox squirrels	15–19 in, 0.8–1.3 lbs	2	1–5	Feb.–Mar., June–Aug.	10–12 wks	Day
red (pine) squirrels	10–15 in, 5–10 oz	2	3–8	Mar.–May, Aug.–Oct.	10–12 wks	Day
flying squirrels	8–10 in, 2-4 oz	2	3–8	Mar.–Apr., Aug.–Oct.	10–12 wks	Night
striped skunk	19–24 in, 2–6 lbs	1	2–10	May–June	7–9 wks	Night
spotted skunk	12–14 in, 1–2 lbs	1–2	2–6	May–June, Sept.-Oct.	7–9 wks	Night
woodchuck (groundhog)	18–27 in, 7–12 lbs	1	3–8	Mar.-Apr.	8–10 wks	Day
opossums	26–28 in, 2–12 lbs	1–2	5–13	Feb.–Oct.	12–14 wks	Night

Note: Represents the most common species encountered by pest management professionals. Other species of the same family may be more prevalent in some parts of the United States.

you are certain that all raccoons have been removed from or have left the building (see Table 17.1).

The best method to remove raccoons from around buildings is via the use of live traps. Professional live traps for raccoons are available from several manufacturers (refer to Table 17.2, and Figure 17.14).

Some raccoons readily enter live traps on first encounter, while others remain wary of the traps for several days. Wary animals can be encouraged to enter these traps by providing a natural footing of earth on the bottom of the trap. To do this, push the trap back and forth on the ground to work the bottom of the trap into the earth. Also, when the traps are located on the ground in the raccoons' travel ways, disguise the traps as best as possible using twigs, branches, and so forth.

Prebait the trap by placing baits in and around the trap and twist-tie the trap door open for two to three days. This will allow a raccoon to feed freely and become accustomed to the metal object that provides free food, thus increasing the chances of capturing wary individuals.

Peanut butter, vanilla wafers, marshmallows, twinkies, and whole raw eggs are all attractive to raccoons, but not very attractive to cats, helping to avoid wasting valuable servicing time. Tiny amounts of baits should be placed in a trail leading into the trap, with the major portion of the bait placed at the back end or closed end of the trap. Raccoons tend to be naturally attracted to shiny objects. Adding a wadded up piece of aluminum foil in the trap may help to stimulate their curiosity.

Keep in mind that raccoons have agile, elongated "fingers" that allow them to pry open lids of garbage cans as well as steal baits through the sides of cage traps. Logs, stones, or similar objects can be placed around the sides of the trap to prevent the raccoons (or other animals) from stealing the bait (although some trap models are designed to prevent this). Raccoons will also commonly tip cage traps over and shake out the bait, so all traps should be staked down to the earth or attached to some object with wire.

Traps should be placed in areas of greatest activity. When raccoons are actually inhabiting buildings, these areas include around garbage cans, near the entrances to dens located in crawlspaces (see Figure 17.15) or basements, and at the bases of trees that may serve as connection routes to the roof and chimney. For garbage-can-raiding raccoons, traps can be placed within tipped over cans.

When raccoons are merely visiting buildings from wooded areas and creating a nuisance, they tend to repeatedly follow the same trails that offer some protection, such as along fence lines and building perimeters and beneath available shrub-

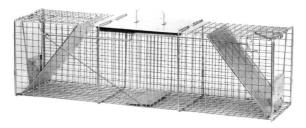

FIGURE 17.14. Cage live traps are one of the most effective tools available to the pest management professional for dealing with wildlife pests in and around buildings.

TABLE 17.2. A guide to the use of live traps for nuisance urban wildlife.

Species	Trap Models	Effective Baits
raccoons	Havahart Pro Raccoon No. 1079, 1045 or 1081, or No. 3 or 3A; Tomahawk Nos. 108 and 108.5; Kness Live Traps	Peanut butter, vanilla wafers, marshmallows, twinkies, whole raw egg in shell, jelly, and honey
gray and fox squirrels	Kness Live Traps; Tomahawk Nos. 103 and 104; Havahart No. 1078 or No. 2 or 2A	Sweet corn, nutmeats, sunflower seeds, orange slices, oatmeal, red meat, raisins
red and flying squirrels	Tomahawk Nos. 104 and 203; Kness Live Traps; Havahart No. 1025 or 0745	Nutmeats, berries, red meat, red ball (flying squirrel)
skunks	Tomahawk Nos. 104.5, 105, and 204; Havahart No. 1079; Enclosed box traps	Fish (canned or fresh), chicken parts, peanut butter or molasses on bread, bacon, hard-boiled eggs
woodchucks	Kness Live Traps; Havahart No. 1079; Tomahawk 108, 108.5, 608, and 608.5	Fresh lettuce, apple slices, carrots, sweet corn
opossums	Tomahawk Nos. 108, 108.5, and 608; Havahart No. 1079; Kness Live Traps	Fish (canned or fresh), chicken parts, red meat, vegetables, fruits

bery. Try to identify such areas and locate the traps along these trails.

Traps should be checked once or twice daily. Additionally, traps containing animals should be placed within burlap sacks or covered in some other way. By keeping the animal in darkness and handling the trap gently, the animal will remain calm. Also, it is important that only heavy-duty raccoon trap models be used. Otherwise, raccoons can easily destroy ordinary wire mesh traps within just a few hours—resulting in relatively expensive trap replacement costs.

Methods of disposing of trapped raccoons (and all other urban wildlife) vary from state to state. The professional should check with local authorities on the proper procedures for the area.

It is important for the professional to note that over the past few years, there has been an increase in the number of cases of raccoon roundworm (*Baylisascaris procyonis*), an internal parasite, in humans. This roundworm parasite, on entering its host, migrates and damages various organs, eventually traveling directly through the eye en route to the brain.

The raccoon roundworm is a relative of the dog and cat roundworms, *Toxocara* spp., which, when human infections occur, can cause damage to the liver, spleen, lungs, eyes, and nervous system, and possibly death in severe cases.

Several fatal human cases have been confirmed from raccoon roundworm, and many additional instances of larval damage to the eye have been reported. Infection occurs when the roundworm eggs are accidentally ingested after handling or contacting feces containing the eggs, such as from a contaminated raccoon live trap or from setting traps in raccoon-active areas. The incubation period is variable and may be from weeks to months. To avoid contracting this internal parasite, professionals working with raccoon programs should always wear protective gloves and clean and disinfect raccoon traps via torching.

SKUNKS
Order Carnivora
Family Mustelidae

Skunks are members of the weasel family. Two species, the striped skunk, *Mephitus mephitus*, and the spotted skunk, *Spilogale putorius*, are the most common and troublesome species in the United States. The hog-nosed and hooded skunks are found in parts of the Southwest, but are not of pest significance.

FIGURE 17.15. Live traps can be baited and placed in areas where wildlife pests enter dens or search for food. A live trap placed directly outside of a woodchuck, skunk, raccoon, or opossum den often results in a capture.

On The Job Tips For Using Wildlife Live Traps

1. **Preplanning is important.**
    Prior to any trapping program, a pest professional must already have a plan for the disposition of trapped animals, especially female with young.

2. **Skill is required.**
    Except for the most simple cases, live trapping and removing wild animals from buildings can be somewhat tricky and unpredictable. A professional must be trained, experienced, and skilled in the use of live traps before attempting to live-trap, remove transport, or dispose of wild animals.

3. **Use only quality traps.**
    Several brands and styles of live traps are available. The traps most used by professionals include: the Tomahawk™ series (Tomahawk Live Trap Co.); the Havahart™ series (Woodstream Corp.); and the Kness Live Traps (Kness company). Specialty traps for animals such as skunks are also available. Professionals should always consult with product specialists for guidance. Examples of commonly used live traps are discussed and shown in different areas of this chapter.

4. **Select the specific trap models carefully.**
    Only the trap models recommended by the manufacturer for a specific animal pest should be used. Some models are built to specifically to handle the strong and scrappy animals such as raccoons. Using a rabbit trap to trap a raccoon will usually result in the raccoon ripping the trap apart from the inside out—resulting in the loss of the animal and the trap. (refer to Table 17.2 for examples of common live-trap models).

5. **The location and placement of traps is essential to success.**
    Perhaps the most important rule for successfully live-trapping an animal is locating the trap where the target animal will readily encounter the live trap. As stressed earlier, time must be taken to *carefully inspect* and identify the high-activity areas of the pest. Ideally, the traps are most effective when located as close to den sites as possible, or at locations between the den and the feeding areas. If traps are hastily installed, they may never be discovered by the wild animal.

6. **Enough traps must be installed.**
    Although there are cases where one trap may suffice (e.g., when there is only one main entrance to the animal's den below a building), it is most cost-effective to install several traps for each job. It is not uncommon for several *families* of raccoons and squirrels to be living in one residential garage or attic. For example, when live-trapping woodchucks,

skunks or raccoons, installing a **minimum** of two to three traps is best.

For tree squirrels, up to six traps may be necessary to maximize the results of the effort. The key to a profitable live-trapping program, is to use enough traps to ensure the capture of the target animals within the first few visits to the client. If only one trap is installed, it might be set off by a roving dog or cat, wasting the professional's valuable effort and time and causing profit-eating callbacks.

7. **Effective live-trap baits.**
    Most exploring wild animals are opportunistic towards the foods they consume while foraging. That is, they tend to eat the foods they bump into during their travels. As a result, there is a wide range of baits that will attract wild animals into the traps. Nevertheless, certain baits seem to be consistently attractive to urban wild animals (refer to Table 17.2). When *small* trails containing a couple of pieces of these baits are placed leading into the trap, this trail will often entice the animal directly into the back of the trap.

8. **Precondition the animal.**
    Wild animals (e.g., feral cats, tree squirrels, raccoons) will often approach a device that has suddenly appeared in their territory with hesitation and caution. Wild animals following the trail of an attractive bait often do so in a stretched out, slow, step-by-step approach. Should the trap door come down before the animal is completely inside the trap, the door may be suspending upon the back of the animal. If the animal moves forward, the animal will be trapped. If the animal moves back however, it can escape the trap. Animals that have escaped, may then be trap shy and avoid the trap thereafter.

    This can be prevented by wedging a piece of wood or stone underneath the front portion of the bait pan, and placing the bait as far back into the trap as possible. Or, traps can be prebaited leaving the traps unset with the doors locked open until the animals become accustomed to them. Baits placed in and around the outside of the traps will attract the animals and precondition them to associated their cautious behavior.

9. **Removal and relocation.**
    Upon successful capture of the wildlife pest, the doors of the trap should be locked or tied shut to prevent the animals from escaping en route to the relocation or euthanizing sites.

    In states and regions where the relocation of trapped wildlife is permitted, the smaller animals

(continued)

On The Job Tips For Using Wildlife Live Traps *(continued)*

such as tree squirrels and chipmunks, can be relocated *at least five miles* from the trap site in areas which will not affect other property owners. Larger, more mobile mammals such as raccoons however, have been found to return to the same area after several weeks after being released up to 25 miles away.

In many states and areas, the relocation of wild animals that pose potential community health threats (rabies, roundworms, plaque, etc.) is prohibited. In these cases, all wild animals must be euthanized via the approved methods as outlined by the state's guidelines (consult local boards of health or the state's fish and game division). Certain states have specific regulations regarding the capture and relocation and/or disposal of urban wildlife. Some states allow for wild animals to be relocated or released in only specified areas. Local authorities should always be consulted before releasing or disposing of any urban wildlife.

10. **Safety considerations.**
    * Wild animals, even small ones, can inflict painful bites and scratches. And, the wild animal you trap might be carrying rabies, raccoon roundworm, or some other disease. Thus, always protect yourself by wearing gloves and long-sleeved clothing, and never place your hands or fingers where the animal can contact you. These precautions also apply for inspecting in potentially infested attics and crawlspaces. When potentially dangerous animals such as feral cats are captured, the local humane society or animal shelter for should be consulted for proper procedures.
    * Trapping on roof and chimney areas for squirrels and raccoons is not a job for the beginner. If you are not experienced in roof-area trapping, it is

best left for those more knowledgeable and skilled in this aspect of wildlife management.
    * The area intended for the placement of a live trap must be selected carefully. Generally, urban wildlife practices should be done in areas out of sight of the public. Otherwise, inquisitive children might get hurt, or vandals may steal or destroy expensive live traps.

11. **Humane treatment.**
    All pest professionals have a professional obligation to always, always, treat any wild animal captured in a live trap with utmost humaneness.

    All live traps should be checked at least once and preferably twice daily. When trapping nocturnal animals, (e.g., raccoons, skunks, flying squirrels) the traps should be checked at dawn. For diurnal animals (e.g., tree squirrels, chipmunks, and woodchucks), the traps can be checked during mid-morning and before dusk. In other words, the professional procedure is to minimize the length of time an animal remains trapped.

    Traps with successful captures should be covered with a blanket or placed within burlap sacks or covered in some other way. By keeping the animal in darkness, and handling the trap gently, the trapped animal will remain calm.

    Exclusion procedures should not be implemented until it is certain all animals have been removed from the structure. This is especially important for animals such as raccoons and tree squirrels during the spring breeding seasons. Unless the young can be accessed and removed once the parent is captured, it may be better to delay a trapping or exclusion program until the young are weaned and able to travel out of the building on their own (refer to Table 17.1).

Skunks are pests because they dig under foundations and take up residence under homes or in other buildings. They sometimes eat poultry and eggs, garden vegetables, and fruit. They can also damage beehives as they feed on adult and larval bees. Skunks commonly damage lawns when they dig in search of insect larvae, rolling back the sod much the same way that raccoons do.

Skunks are also among the more serious health pests. The striped skunk is second to the raccoon in the number of rabies cases in the United States. In some parts of the United States, the skunk is the predominant animal associated with rabies.

Of course, skunks are disliked primarily because of their ability to voluntarily discharge an obnoxious odor when provoked. Two internal glands located at

the base of the tail produce a thick, volatile, oily liquid that contains odorous sulfur compounds. This scent is released primarily in self-defense. Skunks usually stamp their front feet rapidly and loudly, growl, hiss, or walk a short distance on their front feet with their tail erect as a warning before releasing scent. When the tail is raised, a skunk can discharge one or both glands to form a stream of liquid that disperses into a fine spray. This fluid can be directed accurately for up to 10 feet, and somewhat less accurately for up to 20 feet. Skunks can discharge their scent glands several times within a short period. The fluid is painful if it gets in a person's or pet's eyes and may cause temporary blindness for 15 minutes or so.

The striped skunk is characterized by prominent, lateral white stripes that run down its back. Its fur is otherwise jet black. The striped skunk is the most abundant of the four species of skunks. The body is about the size of a large domestic cat, up to 29-inches (74 cm) long, and weighs about 8 pounds (3.6 kg).

The spotted skunk is distinguishable from the striped skunk by white spots and short, broken white stripes in a dense jet black coat. It is also considerably smaller, measuring up to 21-inches (54 cm) long and weighing about 2.2 pounds (1 kg). Spotted skunks are somewhat more active and nervous than striped skunks, and they are much better climbers. In most other respects, the two species are similar.

Skunks are usually active from early evening through most of the night. They spend their days sleeping in dens, although during the warm months they may bed in vegetation along fencerows or waterways, in hayfields, or in pastures or cropland. Dens are usually below ground but may be located in stream or pond banks, junked cars and machinery, lumber piles, and hollow tree stumps, or beneath porches or in crawlspaces of buildings.

During the cold winter months, skunks may remain inactive in their dens for periods of days or weeks. They do not actually hibernate, but they do rely on stored body fat to help sustain them through the winter. To help conserve body heat, several skunks may occupy the same den.

Mating occurs in late winter and the young are born from mid-spring until mid-summer. There are usually four to six young per litter, but under good conditions, the striped skunk may produce as many as ten young. Juvenile skunks are weaned when they are about two months old and usually leave the mother to establish their own dens by autumn. The striped skunk produces one litter per year; the spotted skunk may produce up to two (see Table 17.1).

Skunks are for the most part carnivores, preferring insects such as crickets, grasshoppers, beetles, cutworms, and various other insect larvae. They dig and root in the soil and often leave small holes in the ground where they have fed. They also eat mice, rats, shrews, moles, ground squirrels, and other small mammals. Most of their diet consists of animals often considered injurious to people. When skunks are not troublesome, they should be left alone, because they may help keep rodent populations low.

Control

Many problems with skunks around homes and farms can be prevented by **excluding** skunks from spaces beneath buildings. Use sturdy wire mesh (1/4-inch hardware cloth or similar materials) to

screen vents near ground level in houses and other structures. Tightly seal or fill in holes in foundations or under porches to prevent skunk entry (see Figure 17.16).

To identify areas around buildings where skunks may be gaining entry, **tracking patches** of a smooth layer of fine sand, dust, or flour can be placed at all suspected openings. Wait until after dark when the skunk normally leaves to seek food. Tracks will be seen at the den entrance and will indicate that the animal has left. These tracking patches also aid in determining how many skunks may be using the den site.

To temporarily exclude the skunks, a 1/2-inch hardware cloth "door" can be used. This door should be hinged at the top and left loose on the other three sides. It should be larger than the opening so that it cannot swing inward. The skunks will push it open to leave, but they cannot reenter.

When the skunks are gone, the entrance should be sealed. Extend the wire screen or other materials used to block the entrance several inches below the ground to prevent skunks from digging under it. Or, the barrier can include a wire skirt at ground level extending at least 12 inches (30.4 cm) horizontally outward from the entrance.

Young skunks may be left behind in the den any time from April through August. Be sure all animals are out before sealing up the entrance (refer to Table 17.1).

When skunks have become trapped by falling into a window well, cellar, or hole in the ground, a cleated board carefully lowered into the hole will allow them to climb out and escape.

The presence of skunks near homes and farmyards can be further discouraged by removing brush piles, stacked lumber, woodpiles, and similar sources of shelter that they may find inviting.

FIGURE 17.16. Holes beneath building foundations attract and provide excellent harborage to urban wildlife. Such holes must be permanently repaired to avoid recurring animal infestation.

Skunk Odor Control

A commercial product called Skunk-Off® provides excellent neutralizing of skunk odor. This product can be applied directly to dogs, cats, clothes, furniture, carpeting, car upholstery, and so forth. This product is virtually nontoxic and will not irritate or otherwise damage sensitive tissues of eyes, ears, or nose. The residue washes out easily.

Another product called Odor-Mute® is also available in granular form. It is to be dissolved in water and is clean, odorless and nonpoisonous and can be applied to both pets and clothes. Whenever advising the use of these chemicals, it is suggested clients test fabrics first to avoid any possible damage.

Another reportedly effective skunk odor material is made by mixing the following ingredients: 1 quart of 3.0% hydrogen peroxide, 1.0 cup.baking powder and 1.0 teaspoon of liquid detergent. Other products (e.g., neutrolium alpha) are available that, when diluted in water, can be used to bathe pets and humans or to scrub basements, garages, floors, walls, outdoor furniture, and so forth. They can also be sprayed in a room from an aerosol sprayer, or sprayed onto contaminated soil. Product distributors should be consulted on the latest developments and the availability of these products.

Tomato juice, vinegar, diluted household chlorine bleach, ammonia diluted with water, or a detergent solution can also be used to treat contaminated objects. These products are less effective than the commercially available products, but when applied liberally they will reduce some of the odor. Also, be aware that these solutions may cause color changes on certain materials. When pets need to be deodorized, a veterinarian should be consulted as to the safest and most effective procedure.

Live traps, are effective means of capturing and removing skunks. Traps can be baited with fish (canned or fresh), fish-flavored cat food, chicken parts, bacon, or peanut butter on bread (refer to Table 17.2).

Traps for skunks should be set in the trail immediately in front of the burrow's main entrance (as done in Figure 17.15). Both doors of double-door traps should be left open. Logs, twigs, or stones placed on either side of a path between the burrow opening and the trap will aid in funneling the animal toward the trap. Because skunks are nocturnal animals, all traps should be checked in the early morning hours and the early evening.

To transport a live-trapped skunk without causing it to spray, slowly approach the trapped skunk and cover the trap with an old blanket or piece of thick burlap. Or, wrap the trap in heavy cloth or burlap at the time it is set (this may also encourage the skunk to enter). When kept in the darkened trap, the skunk will be less fearful and less likely to release its scent. Carefully pick up the covered trap and place it gently in the back of a pickup truck for transporting elsewhere. Avoid sudden, jarring movements or loud noises that may frighten the skunk. It is more difficult to handle spotted skunks successfully in this manner, but striped skunks seldom release scent when these precautions are taken.

Methods of disposing of live-trapped skunks (and all other urban wildlife) varies from state to state. The professional should check with local authorities or animal shelters on the proper procedures for the areas.

Shooting is not recommended to dispose of skunks, as it often results in the release of odor. There are no toxicants currently registered for use in controlling skunks.

TREE SQUIRRELS
Order Rodentia
Family Sciuridae

Various species of tree squirrels occasionally enter buildings and cause damage. The most commonly encountered pest tree squirrels include the **gray squirrel**, *Sciurus carolinensis*, (see Figures 17.4 and 17.17); the **red squirrel**, *Tamiasciurus hudsonicus*; the **flying squirrel**, *Glaucomys* spp.; and the **fox squirrel**, *Sciurus niger*.

Tree squirrels generally inhabit wooded areas and build their nests in trees, but as people expand their settlements into these areas, the squirrels frequently establish themselves in attics and garages to store food and find shelter. Around buildings, they often gnaw on the exterior and interior walls and timbers, on cables and electric wiring, and on any items that may be in storage. They may also be very noisy in their activities, will bite if cornered, cause ectoparasite problems to occur in nesting areas, and damage trees, gardens, and ornamental plants. Squirrels also short out electric power transformers during their activities around power lines in residential areas.

Most of the tree squirrels have two litters of young each year (in early spring and late summer), although some flying squirrels may produce only one litter per year. The number of young varies between three and eight squirrels, depending on the species (see Table 17.1).

FIGURE 17.17. A gray tree squirrel, the most common structure-infesting squirrel species. (Myers)

Tree squirrels are most active in early morning and late afternoon. They feed on nuts, seeds, buds, leaves, bulbs, bark, insects, and fruit. They frequently store some of these foods in outdoor caches.

Flying squirrels are active at night, and thus their presence is often unsuspected in a neighborhood until they move into buildings. It is the flying squirrel that causes the mysterious and startling thump late in the night on the attic floor, frightening homeowners. Most times, this noise is a result of the squirrel gliding down onto the attic floor from some area above.

Control

Most squirrels are protected game animals. Thus professionals must consult with local game conservation offices to obtain any necessary permits and avoid violating any fish and game laws during control programs.

The first step in managing tree squirrels is to determine how the squirrels are entering the building and then make every effort to exclude them. Areas to pay particular attention to include utility lines, drainpipes, uncapped chimneys, ivy and other ornamental plants that cling to the house; and attic or basement vents and windows in disrepair. Tree squirrels will also occasionally gnaw straight through the exterior of some buildings, such as cedar-shingled homes, to gain entry. All existing openings should be sealed with sheet metal or 1/2-inch hardware cloth.

Squirrels frequently gain access to buildings from **overhanging tree limbs**. In these situations, all limbs should be pruned back 10 feet or more, so that squirrels cannot reach the building. Squirrels

can be kept from climbing trees by placing a two-foot-wide metal band around the tree trunk, three to four feet above ground—although this may be aesthetically unacceptable in many cases.

When screening, repelling, and removing tree limbs will not solve the problem, **live trapping/ removal** or **kill trapping** the squirrels may be necessary.

The smaller tree squirrels (red squirrels and flying squirrels) in buildings can be kill-trapped with ordinary rat-sized snap traps. Traps should be baited but unset for a couple of days to condition the squirrels to feed readily from the trap. Once this occurs, the same baits should be tied to the trigger. The trap itself should be nailed or secured with wire to prevent the squirrels from dragging it away. Any of the various nut meats, sunflower seeds, fresh orange slices, sweet corn, or oatmeal are attractive baits for tree squirrels. Snap traps should never be used outdoors unless placed under cover, as non-target animals, including birds, can be killed. Snap traps are somewhat undependable and inhumane to be used against the larger tree squirrel species.

Where squirrels cannot be killed, live trapping is usually the preferred method of control (see Table 17.2). Traps should be placed, unset (i.e., with doors wired open), until the squirrels become accustomed to them. Baits placed by the traps will attract the squirrels to them. Once they have become accustomed to the traps, a few settings will usually capture enough squirrels to eliminate the problem. Good locations to place live traps include the bases of trees (see Figure 17.18), roof areas, or immediately inside or outside the opening of the attic or area into which the squirrels are gaining entry.

All traps should be checked at least once, and preferably twice, a day to remove live-trapped animals as soon as possible after their capture. This helps to reduce the possibility of the animals injuring themselves in the trap. Additionally, by placing a blanket or similar cover over the trapped animal, the squirrel will remain relatively calm. Live-trapped squirrels may be humanely destroyed if legal, or taken at least five miles from the trap site and released in an area where they will not cause a problem for someone else. Never, never attempt to handle a live-trapped squirrel, as they are vicious biters and possess extremely sharp teeth and powerful claws.

Although there are no toxicants registered for the control of tree squirrels, some anticoagulant baits and bait blocks are occasionally eaten by tree squirrels when these baits are placed in attics and basements to control rats or mice. But like rats, squirrels sometimes nest in double-wall construction and other inaccessible areas, and any dead carcasses are difficult to recover. This may create

FIGURE 17.18. Nuisance tree squirrels can be live-trapped by placing traps at the bases of trees frequently used by the squirrels.

significant odor problems for several days until the carcasses in the walls dehydrate. Furthermore, during the warm months, various species of fleshflies may infest the rotting carcasses and regularly emerge into the structure.

GROUND SQUIRRELS

Order Rodentia
Family Sciuridae

Ground squirrels, such as the **thirteen-lined ground squirrel** (*Spermophilus tridecemilineatus*), the **California ground squirrel** (*Spermophilus beecheyi*), and others are common pests in and around building foundations, lawns, golf courses, and gardens. They can be distinguished from tree squirrels by their shorter and less bushy tails and by the fact that they live underground (see Figure 17.4, and Figure 17.19, which follows page 254).

Ground squirrels are sometimes called gophers, especially in the Midwest. They are active from late winter or early spring until mid-fall, at which time they enter their underground burrows to hibernate. After emerging from hibernation, ground squirrels mate. Depending on the species, females produce single litters ranging between four and eight young. Gestation periods range between 28 and 35 days. The young leave their home burrow system in summer to establish their own burrows and territories.

Ground squirrels are nervous, excitable animals seldom found far from their burrows. They are excellent burrowers but relatively poor climbers; thus, they do not use trees, as do the tree squirrels. Their preferred habitat is open fields or brushy areas, and they are not usually found in forests or in damp areas. These squirrels feed primarily on seeds, roots, fruits, insects, and green vegetation. They often are troublesome pests in gardens and croplands because they dig up newly planted seeds.

Control

Ground squirrel control programs vary significantly depending on the species. In some cases and with some species (e.g., the California ground squirrels), the programs can be complex and may involve several components that are beyond the scope of this book. Professionals needing detailed information on ground squirrel control are referred to the excellent references and appropriate websites listed at the end of this chapter. The following discussion is provided for those professionals seeking general control strategies for minor infestations.

Ground squirrels can be controlled with **traps** or appropriately **registered poisons**. Trapping is effective for removing small infestations. Rat snap traps (for the smaller species, such as the thirteen-lined ground squirrel), conibear traps, live traps and modified gopher traps are effective for the larger species and can be used in the same general way as described for the tree squirrels. Traps should be placed near burrow entrances. If rat snap traps are used outdoors, they should be covered with a box to prevent harming any non-target wildlife.

For large ground squirrel infestations, rodenticides provide the most cost-effective control. Registered products include zinc phosphide and, in some locations, anticoagulants such as diphacinone and chorophacinone. These grain baits are most effective in the spring, when ground squirrels are feeding on and gathering seeds. Where potential hazards to birds or other non-target wildlife may exist, anticoagulant bait may be the best choice and can be placed directly into the squirrels' burrows or into bait boxes, according to label directions.

Aluminum phosphide tablets and gas or smoke cartridges (see Figure 17.20) are available as burrow fumigants. The fumigants are placed into the burrows and then sealed with dirt. Burrow fumigation is most efficient in the early spring, when there is high soil moisture that holds the toxic gases best, or during the late summer months, when the squirrels are not readily accepting grain baits. Early spring control of the adults before the young are born is the most sound approach biologically.

CHIPMUNKS

Order Rodentia
Family Sciuridae

Although there are fifteen species of native chipmunks found in North America, the **eastern chipmunk** (*Tamias striatus*) and the **least chipmunk** (*Eutamias minimas*) are the two species of widest distribution and of most pest significance. Most people regard chipmunks as cute and amusing crit-

FIGURE 17.20. A gas cartridge (or smoke bomb) can be used to fumigate the ground burrow systems of ground squirrels and woodchucks. Such fumigants are not very effective, however, on animals with complex burrow systems, such as moles.

ters to have around the yard. But around buildings, these rodents can be among the more destructive urban wildlife. As a result of their burrowing activities, chipmunks may cause serious structural damage to slabs, foundation walls, decks, patios, and other similar structural areas. They also consume flower bulbs, seeds, seedlings, and birdseed.

Chipmunks are related to the ground squirrels. The eastern chipmunk is a small, brownish, ground-dwelling squirrel (see Figure 17.4). It is distributed across most of the eastern half of the United States, although it is absent from Florida, most areas of the Carolinas, and the southern half of Georgia. The eastern chipmunk is typically 5- to 6-inches (13 to 15 cm) long and weighs about 3 ounces (90 g). It has two tan and five blackish longitudinal stripes on its back, and two tan and two brownish stripes on each side of its face. The longitudinal stripes end at the reddish rump. The tail is 3- to 4-inches (8 to 10 cm) long and hairy, but it is not bushy.

The least chipmunk is the smallest of the chipmunks. It occurs throughout most of Canada, the U.S. Rocky Mountains, the Great Basin, and throughout parts of the upper Midwest. It is typically 3-2/3- to 4-1/2-inches (9 to 11 cm) long and weighs 1 to 2 ounces (35 to 70 g). The color varies from a faint yellowish-gray with tawny dark stripes (in the Badlands of South Dakota) to a grayish tawny-brown with black stripes (in Wisconsin and Michigan). The stripes, however, continue to the base of the tail on all least chipmunks.

Chipmunks are often confused with thirteen-lined ground squirrels (*Spermophilus tridecemlineatus*), also called striped gophers, and red squirrels (*Tamiasciurus hudsonicus*). The thirteen-lined ground squirrel is yellowish and lacks the facial stripes, and its tail is not as hairy as the chipmunk's. As this squir-

rel's name implies, it has thirteen stripes extending from the shoulder to the tail on each side and on its back.

The red squirrel is very vocal and has a high-pitched chatter. It is larger than the chipmunk, has a bushier tail, and lacks the longitudinal stripes of the chipmunk. Red squirrels spend a great deal of time in trees, while chipmunks spend most of their time on the ground.

Chipmunks are opportunistic feeders of various grains, nuts, berries, seeds, mushrooms, insects, and carrion. Although chipmunks are mostly ground-dwelling rodents, they regularly climb trees in the fall to gather nuts, fruits, and seeds. Chipmunks cache food in their burrows throughout the year.

Eastern chipmunks mate twice a year, during early spring and again during the summer or early fall. Following a 31-day gestation period, two to five young are born during April or May and again in August to October. The young are sexually mature within a year. Adults may live up to three years.

Population densities of chipmunks are typically between two and ten animals per acre. Under good conditions, such as a suburban yard with rock gardens, oak trees, abundant low-lying vegetation, and year-round bird feeders, chipmunk infestations can become severe.

The home range of a chipmunk may be up to 1/2 acre (i.e., a typical suburban yard), but the adult defends a territory only about 50 feet (15.2 m) around the burrow entrance. Although chipmunks tend to be solitary, home ranges often overlap when conditions are good.

Chipmunk burrows are often well hidden near objects or buildings (e.g., stumps, woodpiles or brush piles, basements, and garages). The burrow entrance is usually about two inches (5 cm) in diameter. There are no obvious mounds of dirt around the entrance because the chipmunk carries the dirt in its cheek pouches and scatters it away from the burrow, making the burrow entrance less conspicuous to predators. This behavior in itself makes the chipmunk a dangerous pest, because often months (or years) go by before the home-owner realizes the extent of the damage as a result of a collapsed slab or wall.

Burrow systems are typically about 20 to 30 feet (6 to 9 m) in length and normally include a nesting chamber, one or two food storage chambers, various side pockets connected to the main tunnel, and separate escape tunnels.

Chipmunks are most active during the early morning and late afternoon. With the onset of cold weather, chipmunks enter a restless hibernation and are relatively inactive from late fall through the winter months. They do not enter a deep hibernation, as do ground squirrels, but rely on the cache of food they have brought to their burrow. Some individuals become active on warm, sunny days during the winter. Most chipmunks emerge from hibernation in early March.

Control

Wherever possible, chipmunks **should be excluded** from buildings, by using approaches and materials similar to those described for rodent pests. For example, hardware cloth with 1/4-inch (0.6 cm) mesh, caulking, or other appropriate materials can be used to close chipmunk entryways.

Ground cover, trees, and shrubs should not be planted in continuous fashion connecting wooded areas with the foundations of homes, because they provide protection for chipmunks and encourage them to establish their burrows next to building foundations. It is also difficult to detect chipmunk burrows adjacent to foundations when woodpiles, debris, or plantings of ground cover provide above-ground protection.

Bird feeders should be located at least 15 to 30 feet (5 to 10 m) away from buildings, so that spilled birdseed does not attract and support chipmunks close to the building.

There are no toxic baits registered for controlling chipmunks. Baits used against rats and mice in and around homes will also kill chipmunks, although they are not labeled for such use. Some states have Special Local Needs 24(c) registrations for chipmunk control for site-specific use.

For most pest management professionals, **trapping** is the most practical method of eliminating chipmunks in residential situations, although if the infestation is severe, the client needs to be made aware that it may take several weeks of intensive trapping to eliminate the population.

Live-catch wire mesh traps or common rat snap traps can be used to catch chipmunks.. Interestingly, chipmunks also readily enter the wind-up models of curiosity mouse traps.

A variety of baits can be used to lure chipmunks into live traps, including peanut butter, nut meats, pumpkin or sunflower seeds, raisins, prune slices, or common breakfast cereal grains. Place the trap along the pathways where chipmunks have been seen frequently. The trap should be securely placed to prevent prematurely scaring the rodent away from the trap.

A helpful tip is to prebait the trap for two to three days by wiring the trap doors open. This will condition the chipmunk to associate the new metal object in its territory with the new free food source. Also work the trap into the ground to provide a familiar footing to the chipmunk and encourage quick entry.

Traps must be checked frequently. Because chipmunks are diurnal creatures, check traps at noon and just before dusk. Chipmunks are most active on warm, sunny days in the spring and relatively inactive on rainy or unseasonably cool days; this behavior offers a guide for food trapping days.

Captured chipmunks should not be handled or touched in any manner, as they inflict serious and very painful bites. Where allowed, transport and release live-trapped chipmunks several miles from the point of capture (in areas where they will not bother someone else), or euthanize them according to local regulations.

Common rat snap traps can also be used to kill chipmunks, but they must be isolated from children, pets, or wildlife. The drawback with snap traps is that some of the larger, stronger animals survive the blow of any trap that does not operate at an optimal level, and some chipmunks are captured by nonlethal areas of their bodies and will need to be quickly disposed of for humane considerations.

Snap traps can be set in the same manner as live traps. Peanut butter makes for an excellent bait. Hard baits should be tied to the trap trigger using dental floss or some other fine string. Prebait snap traps by not setting the trap until the animal has been conditioned to take the bait without disturbance for two to three days. Small amounts of extra bait may be placed around the traps to make them more attractive. Set the snap traps perpendicular to the chipmunk's pathway or in pairs along travel routes with the triggers facing away from each other. Set the trigger arm so that the trigger is sensitive and easily sprung.

To avoid killing songbirds in rat snap traps, it is advisable to place the traps under a small box with openings that allow only chipmunks access to the baited trap. The box must allow enough clearance for the trap to operate properly. Conceal snap traps that are set against structures by leaning boards over them. Small amounts of bait can be placed at the openings as an attractant.

Despite the claims of some homeowners, cats and dogs will not control chipmunk populations, nor will ultrasonic devices, clappers, or Osage oranges placed about the foundation or basement of a home.

WOODCHUCKS (GROUNDHOGS)
Order Rodentia
Family Sciuridae

The woodchuck (*Marmota monax*) is a member of the squirrel family and is found in the eastern part of the country. In many locales it is referred to as a groundhog. In the western United States, members of this genus are referred to as marmots, and they, too, become pests in some situations. However, marmots of the West are of less importance as urban pests than the woodchucks. Control methods are essentially the same.

Woodchucks are found in open pastures, woodlots, cultivated and fallow fields, and along railroad embankments, ditch banks, roadsides, fencerows, and levees. In residential areas, they often situate themselves beneath homes, patios, garages, and stored lumber, and they may cause the collapse of slabs or retaining walls as a result of their burrowing activities. One or two woodchucks are also capable of ruining a small garden almost overnight.

The woodchuck is a stocky animal weighing between 4 and 14 pounds (1.8 to 6.3 kg) with short, powerful legs, small ears, and a short, bushy tail. The body fur is long, coarse, and grizzled grayish brown in color (see Figure 17.4, and Figure 17.21, which follows page 254). There are four clawed toes on each front foot and five toes on the hind feet. Its short, stocky appearance gives the impression that the woodchuck crouches close to the ground as it moves about. Thus, the animal is often referred to as a groundhog.

The woodchuck is herbivorous (a vegetarian). Various grasses, clover, alfalfa, plantain, and other types of tender green succulents make up its diet. An adult woodchuck consumes between 1 and 1-1/2 pounds of vegetation daily.

The greater part of a woodchuck's day is spent in the burrow—presumably sleeping. Feeding periods vary according to weather conditions and the season. During the cool days of early spring, it is most active during the warmer parts of the morning and afternoon. However, during the summer, the warmest parts of the day are spent in the cool burrow, and feeding occurs during the very early morning and again at dusk. Woodchucks are least active on cool, rainy days.

Woodchucks enter hibernation beginning mid-October and emerge during February. They mate shortly after emergence, with a single litter of four to six young born about a month later (in March or April). The young leave the nest in early July to establish their own burrows and territories. Woodchucks live an average of four to six years.

The woodchuck burrow system is located about two to four feet underground and may extend horizontally 15 to 25 feet (or more). The main nest chamber is generally located at the end of the burrow system. The main entrance to the burrow is characterized by a mound of fresh earth around the opening.

Control

Woodchucks can be controlled in one of three ways: **fumigation**, **trapping**, or **shooting**. When there are several woodchucks present, the most practical method is to fumigate their dens. Around buildings, trapping is the safest method to control these animals.

Most fumigating for woodchucks is accomplished using gas cartridges (see Figure 17.20). When ignited, these cartridges release carbon monoxide into the burrow system, killing the woodchuck. Caution should be taken to avoid prolonged breathing of gas cartridge smoke. Also, since sparks may be thrown, gas cartridges should not be used near buildings or any combustible materials. Gas cartridges are available from local farm supply stores and sources of pest control supplies.

Tablet fumigants containing aluminum phosphide are also registered for woodchucks and other burrowing pests. These tablets depend on the moisture within the soil to release the toxic gas slowly. Thus they are most effective when the soil is damp (in spring and fall) and less effective during the warm, dry days of midsummer.

For best results, burrow fumigation should be done on cool, rainy days. Because vacant burrows may be reoccupied by individuals from adjoining areas, all fumigated burrows should be rechecked every couple of weeks. Any opened burrows should be re-treated. Fumigation should not be done after September, because most woodchucks will be in hibernation, and the hibernating chamber is often walled off, rendering a fumigation treatment ineffective.

It is fairly easy to live-trap woodchucks using wire-mesh live traps. The trap should be set in the trail immediately in front of the burrow's main entrance and baited with apple slices, carrots, or lettuce (refer to Figure 17.14). Both doors of the trap should be left open. Logs, twigs, or stones placed on either side of the path between the burrow opening and the trap will aid in funneling the animal toward the trap. All traps should be checked in the morning and early evening, so that captured animals may be dealt with in a humane manner.

Where legal and safe, the quickest and surest method of eliminating woodchucks is to shoot them with a varmint rifle (e.g., a scope-sighted .243-caliber rifle). A patient and good shot can significantly reduce a local woodchuck population in a few days. Shooting is most productive during periods of greatest activity and on fair-weather days.

MISCELLANEOUS WILDLIFE PESTS
Snakes

Class Reptila
Order Squamata

Most of the snakes in the United States are harmless. Be that as it may, many people possess a significant fear of all snakes and will not tolerate any type of snake around their home. Because some poisonous snakes do occasionally visit rural homes or homes located in or near to snake-infested wild areas, it is helpful to know the difference between poisonous and nonpoisonous snakes.

Poisonous snakes can be recognized by their prominent triangular head, prominent pit between eye and nostril, and elliptical pupils. Nonpoisonous snakes have narrow heads, lack a pit between eye and nostril, and have round pupils. If assistance is needed in identifying snakes, the professional should contact the wildlife or zoology department of a local college or university, or fish and wildlife personnel. In the great majority of cases involving snakes around buildings, the snake is found to be one of the nonpoisonous and very common garter snake species that readily dwell in cities and towns.

Snakes are predators and eat a variety of animal life, including frogs, toads, salamanders, insects, worms, small rodents, and birds. Their teeth are small and have a backward hook to hold food in the mouth. Poisonous snakes have sharp, hollow fangs connected to venom glands located above the jaws. These modified teeth are in the upper jaw and fold back onto the mouth when not in use. The lower jaw is hinged to allow for swallowing larger prey.

Snakes reproduce in two ways. Some species lay eggs; others give birth to their young. Young snakes develop rapidly and shed their skins to allow this growth; adults may shed several times a year.

Snakes hibernate in dens during winter, sometimes in large numbers. Otherwise, they are seldom found in large numbers.

Control

Because snakes occupy a variety of habitats, it is generally impossible (nor would it generally be desirable) to eliminate the snake population in an area. If a snake pest is removed or destroyed, it is likely others will eventually reoccupy the area, as long as it remains attractive to snakes. Thus, the most effective control measure is to **remove as much snake harborage as possible**. Areas such as woodpiles, rock piles, and other debris attract snakes and should be removed or, in the cases of woodpiles, elevated off the ground. Close mowing of grass and other surrounding vegetation also reduces snake harborage. Good rodent control will do much to reduce snake problems, as rodents make up much of the diet of many snakes, especially the poisonous ones.

Snakes occasionally enter houses or outbuildings through holes in building foundations or via broken basement or crawlspace windows (see Figure 17.22). Foundations can be repaired with mortar to seal any openings.

Snakes in a cellar may be attracted to damp pillow cases or burlap bags placed on the floor along an outside wall with the entry ends of the bags arranged in a open position (using any block of wood or rock). The bags should be checked every few hours. Captured snakes can be removed from the premises and released elsewhere.

Snakes can also be kill-trapped using **expanded-trigger rat traps**. Place traps in pairs next to walls in areas where snake entry or activity is suspected. Snakes often follow walls (as do rodents), and they will be caught when slithering over the traps. No bait is necessary. Several pairs of traps are recommended for best results.

Commercial Snake Guard™ Traps are now available that render snake trapping effective for wildlife and pest professionals. **Rat-sized glue boards** can also be used to capture snakes. Several glue boards can be firmly attached to a base plate made of a piece of large cardboard or plywood (e.g., 24 x 16 inches) by using double-sided tape or by some other means.

This glue board snake trap can then be located along wall areas, as described for rat trap placement. For quickest results, a couple of traps at different placements is recommended. Avoid placing the snake trap near pipes or any object that a snake might use for leverage to escape. The base plate should be anchored to the floor by using tape or some other means. A 1-inch hole can be cut into one of the corners of the base plate to allow for removal of the snake trap containing a live snake using a hooked stick or pole.

Captured snakes should be released back into the

FIGURE 17.22. Most snakes that enter buildings are nonpoisonous. Snakes commonly enter homes via holes or gaps in building foundations.

wild where they will not pose a problem for someone else. Snakes captured on glue boards can be freed by pouring common cooking oil over the snake. The oil will break down the glue, and the snake can be removed using a stick or pole. Glue board snake traps should only be used indoors or in protected areas around buildings (e.g., beneath porches, crawlspaces, etc.), where children, pets, or non-target wildlife will not accidentally encounter the traps.

There are no poisons or chemicals registered to repel or kill snakes. Several repellents have been used in the past, but none have worked consistently. Repellents containing mixtures of sulfur and naphthalene have not proven effective against snakes.

Rabbits
Order Lagomorpha
Family Leporidae

Rabbits are not usually a concern for the urban pest management professional. The aesthetic value of rabbits in urban and suburban areas sometimes outweighs the occasional damage they do to ornamental plants, trees, and vegetable gardens.

Rabbits are active year-round, feeding mostly in the early morning and late afternoon on various types of vegetation and on the stems, buds, and bark of woody plants. They prefer areas of heavy vegetation, brush, piles of debris, and so forth.

Control

Controlling nuisance rabbits can be accomplished via habitat removal, the use of chemical and physical repellents to protect plants, and the live-trapping and removal of problem rabbits.

Habitat removal is best accomplished via a general cleanup of all areas containing heavy vegetation, brush, piles of debris, abandoned machinery, and the like. This step in itself can have a dramatic impact on local rabbit activity, as rabbits usually do not travel great distances from cover while foraging.

Various **chemical repellents** that render plants distasteful are commercially available for reducing rabbit damage to trees and ornamental shrubs. To be effective, repellents must be applied thoroughly, and they require reapplication following heavy rains or snowfall. Chemical repellent treatment should extend two feet above the average snow depth.

Tree guards can also be effective in reducing rabbit damage to tree trunks. A guard should be strong enough to resist rabbits chewing through it. Hardware cloth (1/2 inch) placed so that it extends four inches below the surface will also protect the plant from vole damage. The guards should fit loosely to allow for several years of growth and

should extend two feet above the average snow depth.

Other protective measures include **wire fencing** for yards, gardens, and individual plants. For homes surrounded by woods or dense vegetation, a 2-foot-high fence along the yard perimeter adjacent to the obvious rabbit habitat will help to reduce rabbit activity.

Live-catch traps baited with apples, lettuce, or carrots can also be used in a manner similar to that described for live-trapping squirrels and woodchucks. For best results, several traps should be used. Locate rabbit traps so that the entrance to the trap is near tall grass, weedy areas, adjacent brush, or any other areas where regular rabbit activity has been noted. It is usually easier to live-trap rabbits during the winter than in the summer.

Opossums
Order Marsupialia
Family Didelphidae

The opossum (*Didelphis virginiana*) is a unique mammal because the female—like her relative the kangaroo—has an abdominal pouch for carrying her young.

The opossum represents the only marsupial in North America. Opossums have a repulsive, musklike odor and are occasional nuisances when they enter crawlspaces, garages, and similar areas in residential areas. Adults are long-haired, light gray, and about the size of a large cat. The tail is scaly and about 12-inches long (see Figure 17.23, following page 254). Occasionally, homeowners not familiar with this nocturnal and secretive animal will report to pest management professionals that they have seen "large, white rats with long tails" up in their trees at night.

An overview of opossum biology is seen in Table 17.1. Opossums typically produce one litter per year, containing an average of seven young, but as many as thirteen may be born. The gestation period is short, only lasting 13 days. However, the newborn young are the size of small bumble bees and are only partially developed. They continue to develop while nursing in the mother's pouch for about three months.

Opossums are sluggish animals, choosing homesites in hollow logs and abandoned woodchuck burrows, under buildings, in garages, or sometimes in squirrels' nests in trees. Where food is plentiful, travel is limited to a short distance, often only a few hundred yards.

Opossums are omnivorous, eating practically anything available: fish, birds, mammals, crustaceans, insects, mushrooms, fruits, grass, eggs, and carrion. Occasionally, they damage lawns when digging for grubs.

Control

The most effective method of controlling opossums is to deny access to structures by using exclusion techniques previously discussed for other nuisance wildlife.

Live-catch traps can be used to capture and remove problem animals (refer to Table 17.2). The traps should be set in locations the animal frequents or where it is causing damage. Fish or canned cat food or dog food are excellent opossum baits. A small trail of bait leading to the trap will readily entice the animal into the trap. Both doors of the trap should be left open.

All traps should be checked in the morning and late evening, so that captured animals may be dealt with in a humane manner. Captured animals may be humanely destroyed or released unharmed several miles from the trap site. To prevent a recurrence of the problem, all attractions for the opossum, such as food, burrows, or holes under buildings, should be removed or closed off.

Feral House Cats
Order Carnivora
Family Felidae

Feral cats are house cats that have escaped their owners or have been abandoned and have adapted to living wild. Cats are found in a commensal relationship wherever people are found. In some urban and suburban areas, the cat population size rivals that of humans.

Wild house cats may serve as potential reservoirs for human and wildlife diseases, such as plague, ringworm, toxoplasmosis, leptospirosis, distemper, and, more rarely, rabies. They may also be an important factor in introducing these diseases into susceptible wildlife populations.

Cats (and dogs) are considered personal property if ownership can be established with collars, registration tags, tattoos, brands, or legal description and proof of ownership. Cats without this protection are considered feral and are rarely protected under state law. They become the property of the landowner on whose land they exist, and the landowner can do with them as he or she wishes. State, county, and municipal laws related to cats vary, however. Before any lethal control is undertaken, consult local laws. If live capture is desired, consult the local animal control agency for instructions on the disposal of captured cats.

Feral cats produce litters ranging between two

Additional Information

Urban wildlife management is a broad topic. This chapter presents only a cursory overview. The professional seeking additional information is encouraged to contact local extension agents for information or assistance. An excellent, detailed discussion of all animal and bird pests is provided in the Hygnstrom, et al, 1994 reference *Prevention and Control of Wildlife Damage*. (**www.wildlifedamage.unl.edu**).

and ten kittens. Litters may be born any month of the year. When food and harborage are abundant, an adult female may produce three litters per year.

Feral cats are most active at night. During the day, cats use established dens or lairs to rest and hide. Dens are often located in old buildings or crawlspaces, beneath porches, around granaries, drainage pipes, and junked cars, and in similar places that afford protection. They are opportunistic predators and scavengers that feed on rodents, rabbits, birds, carrion, garbage, and leftover pet food.

Control

Problems with feral cats can be reduced by **eliminating cat habitat** or access to habitat. Exclusion by fencing, repairing broken windows and doors, and plugging holes in and around buildings will deny cats harborage. Old buildings should be sealed, and holes under foundations plugged. Brush and junk piles, bale piles, old machinery, and junked cars should be removed. Areas of vegetation in the vicinity of affected buildings should be kept closely mowed. Elimination of all obvious food sources that may be attracting or sustaining a local feral cat population (e.g., outdoor pet food dishes or garbage) must be eliminated or properly managed. For example, all garbage should be contained in tight-fitting cans, as described for raccoon management.

Commercial cat repellents are available from pet stores and garden shops and can be used around flower boxes, furniture, bushes, trees, and areas where cats are not wanted. Repellents are somewhat effective in confined areas and may also help to reduce activity around garbage cans, but large-scale use is usually expensive, time consuming, and of little value. Repellents often are irritating and repulsive to humans as well as cats.

Feral cats can be live-trapped; this is a practical approach, particularly in areas where uncontrolled pets are more of a problem than wild cats. Captured feral cats can be turned in to animal control agencies without harm, given back to the owner with proper warnings, or humanely destroyed.

The larger models of live traps are required for cats. Traps should be set in areas of cat activity, feeding locations (e.g., dumps and garbage cans), and at or nearby entry areas to suspected dens. Successful baits include fresh or canned fish, commercial cat foods, fresh liver, or chicken.

Keep in mind that cats from several generations of feral parents will completely revert to the wild in habit and temperament. To avoid being scratched, live catches should be handled extremely carefully.

No toxicants are registered for the control of feral cats.

Shrews
Order Insectivora
Family Soricidae

Shrews sometimes become a nuisance when they live in or near dwellings. They occasionally fall into window wells, attack pets, attack birds and chipmunks at feeders, and feed and contaminate stored foods with feces and urine.

Shrews are small, mouse-sized mammals with an elongated snout, a dense fur of uniform color, small eyes (often not visible), and five clawed toes on each foot. The teeth are small and sharp and may have dark tips. Shrew feces are often corkscrew shaped. Shrews are similar in appearance to house mice, except that mice have four toes on their front feet, larger eyes, and lack an elongated snout. Moles also are related to shrews but are larger and have greatly enlarged front feet (see Figure 17.24, following page 254). Both shrews and moles are in the taxonomic order Insectivora, whereas mice and rats belong to the order Rodentia.

As their order name implies, insects make up a large portion of the typical shrew diet. Shrews eat beetles, grasshoppers, butterfly and moth larvae, wasps, crickets, spiders, snails, earthworms, slugs, centipedes, and millipedes. They will also eat small birds, mice, small snakes, and even other shrews when the opportunity presents itself. Seeds, roots, and other vegetable matter round out their diet.

Shrews produce one to three litters per year with two to ten young per litter. The gestation period is approximately 21 days. They live for about one to two years.

Control

Shrews are only occasional visitors in buildings. Therefore, long-term control programs are not necessary. In most cases, a shrew in a home will either leave the home seeking its natural habitat or, failing to escape from the inside of a building, die within a day or two. In those odd times when shrew activity is recurring, **snap traps** containing small pieces of meat can be set and will capture the shrew.

No toxicants are registered to poison shrews.

SUPPLEMENTARY READING MATERIAL

Abbott, W.S., and S.C. Billings. 1935. Further work showing that paradichorobenzene, naphthalene and cedar oils are ineffective as repellents against clothes moths. J. Econ. Entomol. 28: 493-495.

Bateman, J. A. Trapping: *A Practical Guide.* Harrisburg, Penn.: Stackpole Books, 1979.

Caslick, J. W., and D. J. Decker. *Control of Wildlife Damage in Homes and Gardens.* Cornell University Natural Resources Publication no. 15, 1981. 29 pp.

Chapman, J. A., and G. A. Feldhammer, eds. *Wild Mammals of North America: Biology, Management, Economics.* Baltimore: Johns Hopkins University Press, 1982. 1,148 pp.

Corrigan, R.M. 1998. Odor Animal Repellents: Are they effective? *Pest Control Technology* Vol. 26 (10): 64, 68, 70-71,74

Corrigan, R. M. "An IPM Approach for Urban Wildlife." *Service Technician Magazine* 4 no. 5 (1996): 22–23, 26–28, 30.

Corrigan, R. M. "Field Mice." *Pest Management* 15, no. 9 (1995): 36–41.

Corrigan, R. M. "Live-Trapping Nuisance Wildlife from Buildings." *Pest Control Technology* 17, no. 4 (1989): 34–40.

Corrigan, R. M. "Mole Control: A Market for PCOs?" *Pest Control Technology* 15, no. 3 (1987): 62–67.

Courtney, A. and T.G. Barnes. 2002. The efficacy of Molexit™ for reducing damage from eastern moles (*Scalopus aquaticus*). Pages 299-302. In: Proc. 20th Vertebr. Pest Conf. (R.M. Timm and R. H. Schmidt, Eds) Univ. of Calf. Davis.

Ferraro, D. M. 1994. The efficacy of naphthalene and sulfur repellents to cause avoidance behavior in the plains garter snake. Pages 116-120. In: R. E. Masters and J. G. Huggins, eds. Twelfth Great Plains Wildl. Damage Control Workshop Proc. Published by the Noble Foundation, Ardmore, OK.

Frantz, S. C. "Batproofing Structures with Birdnetting Checkvalves." In: Proceedings Twelfth Vertebrate Pest Conference. Ed. T. P. Salmon. Davis, Calif.: University of California. 1986.

Frishman, A. M. 1999. *The Vertebrate Pest Handbook.* 2nd. Ed. Advanstar Communications. Cleveland, OH. 214 pp.

Greenhall, A. M. *House Bat Management.* U.S. Department of the Interior, Fish and Wildlife Service, Resource Publication 143, 1982. 33 pp.

Greenhall. A. M., and S. C. Frantz. "Bats." In: *Prevention and Control of Wildlife Damage.* Vol. II. Ed. S. E. Hygnstrom, R. M. Timm, and G. E. Larson. Lincoln: University of Nebraska, 1994.

Hygnstrom, S. E., R. M. Timm, and G. E. Larson, eds. *Prevention and Control of Wildlife Damage*. Vols. I and II. Lincoln: University of Nebraska, 1994.

Knight, J. E. "A Humane Method of Removing Snakes From Dwellings." *Wildlife Society Bulletin* 14 (1986): 301–6.

Loven, J. 1998-2000. Animal Damage Control Leaflets. ADC. USDA. Purdue University.W. Lafayette, IN.

Marsh, R. E. "California Ground Squirrels." In: *Prevention and Control of Wildlife Damage*. Vol. I. Ed. S. E. Hygnstrom, R. M. Timm, and G. E. Larson. Lincoln: University of Nebraska, 1994.

Marsh, R. E. "Vertebrate Pest Management." In: *Advances in Urban Pest Management*. Ed. G. W. Bennett and J. M. Owens. New York: Van Nostrand Reinhold, 1986.

Meehan, A.P. 1988. Chemical Repellents. Pages; 399-406. In: *Rodent Pest Management*. I. Prakash, Ed. CRC Press. Boca Raton. 480 pp.

Marsh, R. E., and W. E. Howard. "Vertebrate Control Manual: Pocket Gophers, Toads and Frogs." *Pest Control* 46, no. 4 (1978): 30–34.

National Pest Control Association. Snakes. Technical release ESPC043241, 1988. 8 pp.

Poché, R. 2002. Field tests of a warfarin gel bait for moles. Pages295-298 in: Proc. 20th Vertebr. Pest Conf. (R.M. Timm and R. H. Schmidt, Eds) Univ. of Calf. Davis.

Salmon, T.P., and W. P. Gorenzel. 1994. Woodrats. Pages B133-136. In: *Prevention and Control of Wildlife Damage*. Vol. I. Ed. S. E. Hygnstrom, R. M. Timm, and G. E. Larson. Lincoln: University of Nebraska.

San Julian, G. J. and D. K. Woodward. 1985. What you wanted to know about all you ever heard concerning snake repellents. Pages 243-248. In: The Proc. Second Eastern Wildlife Damage Control Conference. (P.T. Bromley, Ed). North Carolina State University. Raleigh. 281pp.

Schmidt,T. 1993. Moles make lousy pets: A video guide to trapping moles. Aztec Video Productions. Cincinnati, Oh.

Sweet, D. V. ed. 1993. Registry of toxic effects of chemical substances. January 1993. Prepared for OSHA. NIOSH Publ. No. 93-101-2.

Timm, R. M., and R. E. Marsh. 1997. "Vertebrate Pests." In: *Mallis Handbook of Pest Control*. 8th ed. Ed. S. Hedges. Mallis Handbook and Technical Training Company, Cleveland. 1455 pp.

Wegner, J. 2003. "Vertebrate Pests." In: *Mallis Handbook of Pest Control*. 9th ed. Ed. S. Hedges. Mallis Handbook and Technical Training Company, Cleveland. In press.

Williams, D. E., and R. M. Corrigan. "Chipmunks." In: *Prevention and Control of Wildlife Damage*. Vol. I. Ed. S. E. Hygnstrom, R. M. Timm, and G. E. Larson. Lincoln: University of Nebraska, 1995.

Websites for additional wildlife damage management information:

www.Wildlifedamage.unl.edu
www.entm.purdue.edu/wildlife/wild.htm

CHAPTER 18 | Sanitation and Pest Management in Food Plants

The scope of the term *sanitation* is broad, as indicated by its definition: the promotion of hygiene and prevention of disease by the maintenance of sanitary conditions.

As you might expect, sanitation is a critically important concept relative to the control of nearly all urban pests—whether they be insects, rodents, birds, or biological contaminants such as microbes, molds, or fungi. From a pest management standpoint, it is usually unsanitary conditions that provide food, water, harborage, or concealed routes of movement for pests and pathogens. Sanitary conditions influence whether pests and pathogens will be present, can become established, and can sustain themselves.

Today more than ever, consumers expect pure, wholesome food products that are prepared, stored, and served in a clean environment free of not only pests, but also pesticides and other contaminants. Good sanitation, which is but one part of good manufacturing practices (GMPs), refers to the procedures that help realize these expectations. This chapter will address the basic principles and practices of sanitation, especially as they relate to pest management in food-processing plants.

In any food plant, a sanitation program must have the full support of top-level management to be effective. Legal decisions have held ranking officials, such as the presidents of large companies, personally responsible for the company's lack of sanitation practices, even though direct supervision of the sanitation program may have been delegated to others.

Pest management professionals have for many years emphasized the role of sanitation as a regular part of pest management. When a pest management professional is properly qualified, the sale of sanitation consulting services can be profitable to the professional and worthwhile to food-processing clients. Even though a professional may not be a registered sanitarian, the use of sanitation techniques are of great value because they tie so closely with effective and long-term pest management. Increasingly, pest control companies are offering complete sanitation consulting services to food plant clients. However, this requires competently trained personnel be available.

Professionals offering these services must be familiar with, and have at least cursory training in fields such as bacteriology, chemistry, sanitary engineering, and pest management. In addition, they must have an understanding of the processes of the food plant they are inspecting. Some professionals even offer microscopic and bacteriologic examination services of the products being produced. For the majority of pest management professionals, however, this degree of sanitation work is beyond the training available in most pest control firms. As a result, firms restrict their sanitation inspections to what is generally referred to in the industry as a floor-level inspection. More-descriptive terms would be *area inspection* or *environmental inspection*, as many potential sanitary hazards occur in areas other than those at floor level. A good sanitation inspector must check everything that might potentially affect the products being produced: floors, processing machinery, raw product, doors, walls, ceilings, overhead piping, storage facilities, loading docks, and outside areas, to name only a few.

Those interested in further study of sanitation should consider enrolling in one of the several training courses offered in the United States. For example, the American Institute of Baking in Manhattan, Kansas, offers outstanding correspondence courses and annual seminars on sanitation and pest management in food plants. Purdue University also offers a correspondence course entitled *Food Plant Pest Management*. This textbook is part of the course. The interested reader should also refer to the

GMPs and Pest Management
Title 21, Code of Federal Regulations

Reading a federal code of regulations can be challenging, and not all aspects of the Title 21 code apply to pest management professionals interested in providing effective and safe pest management programs in food plants. Therefore, the following is but an overview of **Part 110—Current Good Manufacturing Practices in Manufacturing, Packing, or Holding Human Food**. The pertinent sections, as they apply most to pest management professionals working in food plants, have been excerpted or condensed here to provide a cursory overview and general understanding of the intent of the GMPs.

This overview also serves as a road map for accessing the complete code when needed. All professionals involved in food processing or food plant pest management should carefully review the following overview and also have ready access to a complete copy of the code for reference purposes. The FDA's GMP's, HACCP, and the *Food Code* are now easily available and downloadable from the Internet at **www.fda.gov**.

Or, consult the selected references at the end of the chapter.

Subpart A—General Provisions

110.3 Definitions
In this section, defined words that may be of interest to personnel performing pest management procedures in food plants include (e) *critical control point,* (f) *food,* (g) *food-contact surfaces,* (j) *pest,* (k) *plant,* (l) *quality control operation,* (p) *shall,* and (q) *should.*

110.10 Personnel
This section established requirements for preventing contamination by persons working in direct contact with food. It describes procedures for accomplishing this.

Subpart B—Building and Facilities

110.20 Plant and Grounds
This section creates guidelines for maintaining the con-

dition of the building and its grounds to ensure that these do not cause food to be contaminated. It includes requirements to exclude or exterminate pests and to eliminate harborages for pests, which includes "checking on a regular basis for pests and pest infestation" (b)(3)(iii).

Section 110.35 Sanitary Operations
This section requires that sanitary conditions be maintained to prevent food from becoming adulterated. Paragraph (c) states: "No pests shall be allowed in any areas of a food plant." Furthermore, "Effective measures shall be taken to exclude pests from the processing areas and to protect against the contamination of food on the premises by pests. The use of insecticides or rodenticides is permitted only under precautions and restrictions that will protect against the contamination of food, food-contact surfaces, and food-packaging materials."

Section 110.37 Sanitary Facilities and Controls
This section establishes a requirement for food plants to be equipped with sufficient water supply, sewage disposal, toilets, rubbish disposal, handwashing facilities, and so forth.

Subpart C—Equipment

110.40 Equipment and Utensils
This section requires that equipment and utensils be designed so that they do not accumulate food particles, dirt, and so forth and so that they can be adequately sanitized.

Subpart E—Production and Process Controls

Section 110.80 Process and Controls
This important section outlines the precautions needed to prevent raw materials and other ingredients from being contaminated or contaminating finished prod-
(continued)

---

selected references at the end of this chapter and consult with local registered sanitarians for more information.

LAWS AND REGULATIONS

Commercial food establishments must comply with the high standards of sanitation enforced by various government agencies, such as the Food and Drug Administration's (FDA's) current good manufactur-

ing practice regulations, the Occupational Safety and Health Act (OSHA) standards, the Federal Insecticide, Fungicide, and Rodenticide Act (FIFRA) guidelines, and the U.S. Department of Agriculture (USDA) sanitation requirements. Some of the more important laws and regulations are summarized here.

All food processors are subject to the Federal Food, Drug, and Cosmetic Act of 1938 (FD&C Act), its subsequent amendments, and the good manufac-

GMPs and Pest Management
Title 21, Code of Federal Regulations *(continued)*

ucts. It includes requirements for preventing food from becoming contaminated during processing, and for preventing packaging materials (e.g., containers) from contaminating clean food after processing. It necessitates quality control operations to ensure that food is suitable for human consumption.

Selected sections of 110.80 have been excerpted here to provide you with some of the more relevant information:

All operations in the receiving, inspecting, transporting, packaging, segregating, preparing, processing, and storing of food shall be conducted in accordance with adequate sanitation principles. Appropriate quality control operations shall be employed to ensure that food is suitable for human consumption and that food-packaging materials are safe and suitable. Overall sanitation of the plant shall be under the supervision of one or more competent individuals assigned responsibility for this function. All reasonable precautions shall be taken to ensure that production procedures do not contribute contamination (e.g., filth, harmful chemicals, undesirable microorganisms, or any other objectionable material) from any source.

Chemical, microbiological, or extraneous-material testing procedures shall be used where necessary to identify sanitation failures or possible food contamination. All food that has become contaminated to the extent that it is adulterated within the meaning of the act shall be rejected or if permissible, treated or processed to eliminate the contamination.

(a) Raw materials and ingredients shall be inspected and segregated or otherwise handled as necessary to ascertain that they are clean and suitable for processing into food and shall be stored under conditions that will protect against contamination and minimize deterioration. Raw materials shall be washed or cleaned as required to remove soil or other contamination.

(b)(1) Processing equipment shall be maintained in a sanitary condition through frequent cleaning and sanitizing as necessary. Insofar as necessary, equipment shall be taken apart for thorough cleaning.

(b)(2) All food manufacturing, including packaging and storage, shall be conducted under such conditions and controls as are necessary to minimize the potential for the growth of microorganisms or the contamination of food. One way to comply with this requirement is careful monitoring of such physical factors as time, temperature, humidity, pressure, flow-rate, and manufacturing operations such as freezing, dehydration, heat processing, acidification, and refrigeration to ensure that mechanical breakdowns, time delays, temperature fluctuations, and other factors do not contribute to the decomposition or contamination of food.

110.93 Warehousing and Distribution
This section requires that finished food be protected from contamination during warehousing and shipping: "Storage and transportation of finished food shall be under such conditions that will protect food against physical, chemical, and microbial contamination, as well as against the deterioration of the food and the container."

Subpart G—Defect Action Levels
110.110 Natural or Unavoidable Defects in Food for Human Use That Present No Health Hazard
This section recognizes that some defects are unavoidable and are permitted as long as the defects do not pose a hazard to humans and do not exceed levels established by the FDA.

turing practices regulations (GMPs) developed to establish criteria for determining compliance with sections of the FD&C Act that deal with pest management. It is a violation of the federal law if manufactured food products contain any objectionable extraneous matter. In this regard, Section 402(a)(3) of the FD&C Act states: "A food shall be deemed to be adulterated if it consists in whole or in part of any filthy, putrid or decomposed substance, or if it is otherwise unfit for food." Section 402(a)(4) states: "A food shall be deemed to be adulterated if it has been prepared, packed or held under conditions whereby it may have become contaminated with filth or whereby it may have been rendered injurious to health." This means that action can be brought against a food processor (and even against the pest management company servicing the operation) if insects or other potential sources of contamination are found in or near equipment, ingredients, or finished products. If the potential for contamination exists, the product may be deemed contaminated.

For the purpose of these provisions, the words *sanitary* and *sanitation* imply not only the conditions pertaining to health, but also the inclusion of anything that does not belong in a product. This definition includes, for example, microorganisms that may or may not be harmful to health, such as molds and bacteria, as well as dirt, paint chips, decomposed but not harmful foods, insect fragments, rodent hairs and excreta, and insecticides.

The legal interpretation of the word *adulteration* gives it a broad meaning. The existence of unsanitary conditions during preparation or packing or the presence of filth or other extraneous material, cooked or raw, safe or harmful, visible or invisible, is in violation of the law. Also, the law considers food products for human consumption and feed products for animals in the same manner. Regulations that apply to one also apply to the other. In other words, animal feed (e.g., dog food, rodent chow, etc.) is food.

GMPs have been developed to establish criteria for determining compliance with Section 402(a)(4) of the FD&C Act. The reader is urged to obtain a copy of Title 21, Code of Federal Regulations, for the complete and current requirements. **General**, or **umbrella**, **GMPs** emphasize the prevention of product contamination from direct and indirect sources in buildings and facilities, on equipment, and during production and processing. **Specific GMPs** are included for specific segments of the food industry, such as cacao products and confectionery.

Because most food plants are under a significant amount of pest pressure (from the exterior grounds, the many incoming supplies, the doors constantly being open for operational practices, etc.), pest problems arise even when all GMPs are followed. In fact, it is not possible, even when using pesticides, to attain zero levels of pest contamination in these environments. Thus, the FDA has established **defect action levels** for food products (as summarized under Subpart G of Title 21). These levels represent the maximum allowable levels for defects, such as the presence of insect fragments, mold, or rodent hairs. If tests show that defect action levels have been exceeded, enforcement action can be taken. The current level of defects permitted is based largely on the industry's ability to reduce the levels occurring in the raw product through good manufacturing practices. Because the defect action levels are revised periodically, the reader is advised to obtain an up-to-date list directly from the FDA.

In addition to sanitation, the use of pesticides can help ensure that defect action levels are not reached, but note that the GMPs (Section 110.35)

state, "Effective measures shall be taken to exclude pests from the processing areas and to protect against the contamination of food on the premises by pests. The use of insecticides or rodenticides is permitted only under precautions and restrictions that will protect against the contamination of food, food-contact surfaces, and food packaging materials." Thus, the pest management professional cannot allow any of the pesticides used in pest management operations to contaminate any food, surface, or packaging materials. For most pesticides, *any* level of residue in finished food constitutes an illegal residue. Only pyrethrum and some related materials, for historical rather than technical reasons, are permitted to have food residue or tolerance levels above zero. Other pesticides, including the most effective ones, must be used in ways (such as crack-and-crevice application) that ensure no residues in food or packaging materials.

Therefore, it cannot be stated enough, especially for food plants, that all pesticides must be used in strict adherence to label directions. The label will indicate the area to be treated and the method of application.

In cases of food being processed in violation of any section of the Title 21 code (including cases of pest management professionals contributing to violation of the code, such as by contaminating food with pesticide), the FDA can take the following actions:

- Prosecute individuals who violate the Food, Drug, and Cosmetic Act (resulting in fines and/or imprisonment).
- Shut down plants where insanitary conditions warrant such action.
- Seize adulterated or misbranded foods.
- Issue warnings for minor violations.

Food plants involved in meat, poultry, egg, and egg products processing and operations must operate under even more detailed and stringent **U.S. Department of Agriculture regulations**, which involve frequent inspection programs. As extensive as these regulations are, a great deal is still left up to the discretion of the **USDA inspector in charge (IIC)**. This regulatory process works as follows:

- Any pesticides used in USDA plants must be registered by the EPA for use in food-handling establishments Certain pesticides can be applied only under specific conditions and preparations. This is a case where the pesticide label does not reflect the only applicable law.
- In some cases, a USDA inspector in charge may not permit the use of a pesticide in a plant even

though it may be EPA approved for use in a food plant. As an example, an inspector may not allow any residual insecticides to be used anywhere in a processing plant. Or, an inspector may allow the use of only nonresidual pesticides, and only when the plant is in nonproduction status.

• Where pest problems are serious, the USDA may temporarily waive its restrictions on the use of certain pesticides and permit their use, but only under USDA direction.

THE SANITATION INSPECTION

The sanitation inspection, or survey, is intended to discover anything that might cause or permit contamination or adulteration. It is necessary to consider the product from the time it is a raw product until the finished product is in the hands of the consumer.

It is impossible in one chapter to include all the things to be looked for in every inspection. The inspection principles outlined here will, however, apply to most types of food handling, production, and storage. The pest management professional must be alert to each new situation encountered and apply these principles to each case. No amount of detailed instruction can substitute for good judgment.

For purposes of discussing inspection throughout the rest of this chapter, we will assume that an inspection is to be made of a food-processing plant. Methods of procedure and things to look for will be emphasized. The pest management professional can adapt any or all of these items to the specific facility involved.

OBTAINING MANAGEMENT COOPERATION

It is important for the pest management professional to communicate to the plant manager that sanitation and all pest management operations must be considered a priority item. Most plant managers understand the potential health, legal, and financial consequences of infestations. The cooperation of all senior plant managers is essential to obtain cooperation by other plant personnel. It is of utmost importance for the professional to review the entire plant layout with plant management to become completely familiar with all aspects of the plant and its operation.

Prior to the inspection, the plant management should be interviewed about past history of inspections, previous or current pest infestations, previous citations, and all plant procedures involving product receiving inspections, return product poli-

The Benefits of Sanitation Inspection

The food-processing firm and the pest management firm benefit from a thorough inspection. The food-processing firm

• is informed of actual or potential problems and how to take steps to correct them before the wholesomeness of the food being produced is compromised and before they are detected by regulatory inspection.

• receives constructive recommendations enabling it to take corrective action to prevent pest problems.

• is able to avoid regulatory action, bad publicity, and loss of customers and revenues.

• is able to achieve preventive sanitation and preventive pest management.

• is able to get the best return from its sanitation dollars.

The pest management firm

• is able to check on the quality and scope of the pest management program.

• is alerted to service deficiencies before the customer complains.

• achieves better cooperation from customers in correcting conditions that hamper the pest management service.

• increases its revenue; an inspection report will be respected by the customer and can be priced as a professional service rather than given away.

• gains a more professional image.

cy, vehicle inspections, storage and stock rotation, damaged goods storage and disposal, waste disposal, plant and grounds maintenance, and any other tasks that may affect plant sanitation and pest management. Such a review between the plant management and the professional results in both effective communication and effective pest management.

GMPs require that overall sanitation of a plant be under the supervision of an individual assigned responsibility for this function. This individual, often the plant sanitarian or the **quality assurance (QA) manager**, is usually the key contact for the pest management professional in obtaining cooperation, including agreeing on protocols and responsibilities for implementing chemical and nonchemical measures. In return for his or her cooperation, the QA manager receives from the pest management professional the benefits of another pair of trained eyes to spot problems, an expert knowledge of pests, and the resources to deal with pest problems. In many cases the recommendations of the professional help the QA manager to obtain management approval for improvements. Sanitation reports also encourage follow-up by plant personnel on actions they have agreed to carry out.

MANAGEMENT OF PESTS IN FOOD PLANTS

GMP regulations state that food plants must (through inspection, extermination, or other means) exclude pests, dirt, and other filth that may be a source of food contamination. Furthermore, no animals or birds, other than those essential as raw materials, are allowed in any area of a food plant. Effective measures must be taken to exclude pests and to protect against the contamination of foods in or on the premises by animals, birds, and vermin (including, but not limited to, rodents and insects). Clearly, the legal basis exists for substantial effort to prevent and/or eliminate pests within a food plant.

In food plants, the approach to managing pests that is most in tune with legal and consumer requirements is an integrated pest management (IPM) approach, which includes the comprehensive use of all methods and materials available to the pest management professional. Sanitation, insectproofing and rodentproofing, proper storage practices, and the use of both chemical and nonchemical tools to manage pests are all part of the IPM program.

The basic procedures for pest management in a food-processing plant are as follows:

1. Inspection of the premises
2. Nonchemical pest management measures
3. Chemical pest management measures
4. Monitoring (evaluating) the program

Inspecting the Premises

When conducting an inspection of a food plant, there is no specific rule on where to look and where not to look. The professional must observe everything that takes place in every part of the food plant (see Figure 18.1). The inspector must identify factors favoring pest entry, survival, and movement within the plant, as well as detect actual infestations. The accuracy and completeness of the initial inspection will largely determine the effectiveness of later pest management actions.

As mentioned earlier, it is essential to talk with plant personnel. Employees in each section of the plant should be asked whether they have seen pests, where they have seen them, and when they first started seeing them. Cleaning personnel are especially

---

Factors Making Pest Management Difficult

- Raw food items and packaging materials entering a plant may serve as a source of pests.
- Various food odors attract insects to food plants.
- Exterior lighting attracts insects to food plants.
- Warm buildings and warm, moist process areas favor pests.
- Machinery, wall voids, conduits, and conveyors provide ample pest harborages.
- Aging buildings and equipment are hard to maintain and clean.
- Where facilities operate 24 hours a day, it is more difficult to implement pest management measures.
- Dust, grease, high temperatures, and excessive moisture from processing can render insecticide deposits ineffective.
- Cleaning measures can quickly destroy insecticide deposits.
- Cleaning operations, forklifts, and so forth quickly destroy some insect and rodent traps.
- Federal agencies responsible for inspecting certain types of food plants may impose pesticide restrictions that contradict EPA rules.
- Management in some plants is reluctant to spend money on pest management.

---

important in this regard, as they often know where food and dirt collects, and such locations may help to identify the source and severity of pest problems.

Being properly equipped to conduct a sanitation inspection is just as important as being well equipped to conduct other aspects of pest management. (See Chapter 5 for more on equipment for conducting pest management inspections.) The following equipment is recommended:

- Tools
  — Screwdrivers (Phillips and regular)
  — Pliers
  — Adjustable wrenches
- Explosionproof, heavy-duty flashlights with powerful light potential
- Clipboard and pencil/eraser
- Flushing agent
- Metal inspection mirror on extension arm (not glass)
- Pocket knife or utility several-in-one tool
- Hand lens (10X magnification or more)
- Black light (for periodic verification of rodent urine)
- Specimen vials
- Tweezers

- Swabs and plastic vials
- Floor plan of plant
- Protective clothing that complies with plant regulations (bump caps, hairnets, and earplugs are often the minimum requirements)
- Inspection report forms, pheromone and mouse trap data forms, blank paper, and a clipboard for holding forms and small supplies
- Inspection belt for holding equipment

When inspections are to be made on a regular basis, inspection report forms can be used. These may be either general forms designed to fit many types of operations, or specific forms designed to fill the needs of an individual customer. Inspection forms are intended as a guide to make certain the inspector does not overlook certain important items that may affect sanitation and pest management. It is impossible to include all items that may occur, even when the form is specifically designed for a certain food plant. Space should always be provided on the form for listing all items that may need correction and that may not be listed on the form. The inspector must always be alert for these additional items.

One example of an inspection form that has been developed by the National Pest Control Association (from its *Sanitation and Pest Control Floor-Level Inspection Manual*) is included with minor adaptations (see Figure 18.2). Items on the form can be checked "Acceptable" or "Deficient" (this wording can be changed to fit the particular needs of the facility). The items are checked according to whether conditions meet the basic standards. Those that show deficiencies are then explained more fully on the last page, under "Remarks." Keep in mind, this form is an example, and some food plants or pest management firms may elect to use forms with more or less detail. Once an inspection has been conducted and the report completed, the inspector should review the entire report with the plant sanitarian, appropriate plant managers, or all these persons.

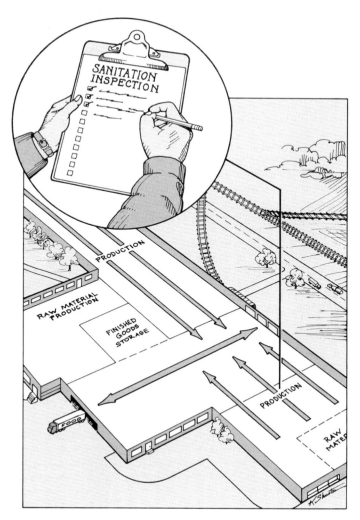

FIGURE 18.1. The sanitation professional must inspect all areas of a food plant.

CHECKLIST—REPORT OF FLOOR-LEVEL INSPECTION FOR SANITATION AND PEST CONTROL

PREPARED FOR _____ INSPECTED BY _____

LOCATION_____ DATE _____

_____ TIME _____

The items below are to be checked ACCEPTABLE or DEFICIENT to indicate if the guidelines of the *NPMA Sanitation Pest Control Floor-Level Inspection Manual* are met.

Entries in the right-hand column indicate deficiencies that should be corrected.

	ACCEPTABLE	DEFICIENT
A. EXTERIOR AREAS		
1. Absence of pest harborage	_____	_____ 1.
2. Absence of pest breeding	_____	_____ 2.
3. Garbage handling systems	_____	_____ 3.
4. Garbage storage area	_____	_____ 4.
5. Garbage containers	_____	_____ 5.
6. Garbage container cleaning	_____	_____ 6.
7. Trash disposal	_____	_____ 7.
8. Paving and drainage	_____	_____ 8.
9. Weed control	_____	_____ 9.
10. Perimeter rodent control	_____	_____ 10.
11. Perimeter insect control	_____	_____ 11.
B. BUILDING EXTERIOR		
1. Rodentproofing	_____	_____ 1.
2. Insectproofing	_____	_____ 2.
3. Birdproofing	_____	_____ 3.
4. Roofs	_____	_____ 4.
5. Other structures	_____	_____ 5.
6. Lighting	_____	_____ 6.
C. BUILDING INTERIOR		
1. Walls	_____	_____ 1.
2. Floors	_____	_____ 2.
3. Ceilings	_____	_____ 3.
4. Cleanability	_____	_____ 4.
5. Pits	_____	_____ 5.
6. Floor drains	_____	_____ 6.
7. Plumbing	_____	_____ 7.
8. Ventilation	_____	_____ 8.
9. Condensation	_____	_____ 9.
10. Lighting	_____	_____ 10.
D. FOOD STORAGE		
Packaged and Dry Food Storage		
1. Pest evidence absent	_____	_____ 1.
2. Proper storage practice	_____	_____ 2.
3. Good housekeeping	_____	_____ 3.
4. Empty container storage	_____	4.
Damaged Goods Storage		
5. Segregation	_____	_____ 5.
6. Repackaging	_____	_____ 6.
7. Proper housekeeping	_____	_____ 7.
Returned Goods		
8. Adequate handling program	_____	_____ 8.
Refrigerated Area		
9. Pest evidence absent	_____	_____ 9.
10. Condensation absent	_____	_____ 10.
11. Cleaning satisfactory	_____	_____ 11.
12. Other	_____	_____ 12.

FIGURE 18.2. An example of a sanitation and pest control inspection form.

E. FOOD PREPARATION AREAS
1. Enclosed areas easily opened _____ _____ 1.
2. Spaces under and behind equipment cleaned _____ _____ 2.
3. Counter and surface areas clean _____ _____ 3.
4. No permanent food storage in preparation area _____ _____ 4.

F. DISHWASHING AREA
1. Clean _____ _____ 1.

G. GARBAGE AND TRASH AREA (INDOOR)
1. Storage area for receptacles adequate _____ _____ 1.
2. Storage area clean _____ _____ 2.
3. Containers of proper type _____ _____ 3.
4. Garbage containers regularly covered _____ _____ 4.
5. Shows evidence of regular cleaning _____ _____ 5.

H. TOILET AND LOCKER ROOMS
  Toilet Facilities
1. Adequate for current number of employees _____ _____ 1.
2. Sanitary and in good repair _____ _____ 2.
3. Door self-closing and does not open into food area _____ _____ 3.
4. Adequate ventilation and no offensive odor _____ _____ 4.
5. Lockers regularly emptied and cleaned _____ _____ 5.
6. Area free of old clothes and trash _____ _____ 6.
  Handwashing Facilities
7. Adequate and convenient _____ _____ 7.
8. Appropriate trash receptacles _____ _____ 8.

I. LUNCH ROOM
1. Accessible for cleaning _____ _____ 1.
2. Clean _____ _____ 2.

J. VENDING MACHINES
1. Easily cleaned _____ _____ 1.
2. Pest harborage absent _____ _____ 2.

K. UTILITY AREAS
1. Clean _____ _____ 1.
2. Pest harborage absent _____ _____ 2.

L. OFFICE AREAS
1. Clean _____ _____ 1.
2. Regular trash removal _____ _____ 2.

M. PUBLIC AREAS
1. Floor areas clean _____ _____ 1.
2. Equipment and counters easily cleaned _____ _____ 2.
3. Pest harborage absent _____ _____ 3.

INFESTATION ABSENT
1. Rodents _____ _____ 1.
2. Insects _____ _____ 2.
3. Other _____ _____ 3.

EVIDENCE OF PEST ABSENT
1. Rodents _____ _____ 1.
2. Insects _____ _____ 2.
3. Other _____ _____ 3.

REPORT REVIEWED on _____ (date) by _____(inspector)
with_____
                                                    (name) for the client
       _____
                                                    (manager) for the client

REMARKS:

Nonchemical Pest Management

Sanitation is probably the most important aspect of the nonchemical pest management program in food plants. The sanitation program must be continually updated to ensure the removal of all factors conducive to pest attraction, entry, development and dispersion.

The GMPs include the following requirements: The grounds about a food plant...shall be free from conditions which may result in the contamination of food, including, but not limited to, the following:

- Improperly stored equipment, litter, waste, refuse, and uncut weeds or grass within the immediate vicinity of the plant buildings or structures that may constitute an attractant, breeding place, or harborage for rodents, insects, and other pests.
- Inadequately drained areas that may contribute contamination to food products through seepage or foodborne filth and by providing a breeding place for insects or microorganisms.

Plant buildings and structures shall be suitable in size, construction, and design to facilitate maintenance and sanitary operations for food-processing purposes. The plant shall:

- Provide sufficient space for such placement of equipment and storage of materials as is necessary for sanitary operations and production of safe food. Floors, walls, and ceilings in the plant shall be of such construction as to be adequately cleanable and shall be kept clean and in good repair. Fixtures, ducts, and pipes that drip or condensate shall not be suspended over working areas where they may contaminate foods, raw materials, or food-contact surfaces. Aisles or working spaces between equipment and between equipment and walls shall be unobstructed and of sufficient width to permit employees to perform their duties without contamination of food or food-contact surfaces with clothing or personal contact.
- Provide separation by partition, location, or other effective means for those operations which may cause contamination of food products with undesirable microorganisms, chemicals, filth, or other extraneous material.
- Provide adequate lighting to handwashing areas, dressing and locker rooms, and toilet rooms, and to all areas where food or food ingredients are examined, processed, or stored, and where equipment and utensils are cleaned.
- Provide, where necessary, effective screening or other protection against birds, animals, and

vermin (including, but not limited to, insects and rodents).

In addition to these requirements, nonchemical measures that might prove useful in most any area of a food plant include the following:

- **Doors**
  - Self-closing doors are useful, especially for employee entrance and exit doors.
  - Tight-fitting screen doors are useful where ventilation is needed.
  - Air doors or plastic curtains are helpful where flying pests can gain entry or move from one area of the plant to another (air doors are more effective on interior doors separating rooms than on exterior doors in attempting to exclude flies from entering).
- **Metal flashing, inflatable dock cushions,** or **folding dock covers** to prevent pest entry
- **Insect light traps (ILTs)**
  - Care must be taken to place these units so they do not attract outside pests. In general, these lights should not be visible from the outside looking in.
  - Insect light traps must be equipped with catch pans that can be cleaned on a weekly basis.
  - These devices, via regular monitoring and record keeping, can be used to determine the pest history and current activity around and perhaps in the plant.
- **Monitoring and pheromone traps**
  - Sticky traps can be used to locate insect pest populations.
  - Repeating traps and/or snap traps are the preferred traps for rodents.
  - Sticky traps can be placed within some repeating mousetraps to provide a two-in-one insect monitor and mousetrap. The mousetrap also protects the glue trap from dust and dirt.
  - Pheromone traps are available for detecting various stored product beetles and moths. These are limited to attracting adults only. Careful placement is critical for effectiveness.
- **Glue traps**
  - Useful in some plant areas for rodent control and insect monitoring.
  - Care must be taken that they do not contact food products.
  - These traps must be inspected daily to be sure they are clean and to remove trapped pests.

Chemical Pest Management

The pest management professional must thoroughly understand the label directions of any pesticide being considered for use in a food plant. All label recommendations for using pesticides inside food plants should address all the requirements of the GMPs, the individual agency regulations (e.g., FDA vs. USDA vs. Certified Organic), and the pesticide policies of the client.

The types of pesticides and the methods by which the pesticides can be used in food plants vary greatly between FDA-inspected plants and USDA-inspected plants. USDA plants are especially restrictive to any chemical applications. When conducting pest management operations in USDA-inspected plants, the pest management professional must be familiar with (and have ready access to) the *USDA's Meat and Poultry Inspection Manual*. The section addressing the rules and regulations of importance to the professional is Subpart 8-G on insect and rodent control.

Below are a few examples of selected rules regarding pesticide applications in USDA plants. The insecticide labels and the USDA manual must be studied prior to any pesticide applications in USDA plants. Again, it must be restated that the IIC must approve of any pesticide applications and has final say and may overrule the manual.

- In the edible product areas of these facilities, residual pesticide treatments are restricted to crack and crevice treatments in accordance with EPA label directions for the product. Production operations are not to be conducted in the area at the time of treatment. All exposed edible products must be removed, tightly covered, or stored in closed containers during treatment, and the premises must be thoroughly washed after treatment. Each product used must be approved by the USDA.
- Generally, rodent control baits cannot be placed in edible product areas until operations have ended for the day. A strict account of all bait stations must be maintained. All bait must be in stations, and station locations must be approved by the inspector in charge. All baits must be removed before operations begin the next day.
- Only anticoagulant baits can be used in edible product areas.
- Tracking powders may be used in departments having a dry cleanup, provided there are no exposed food products present. Only anticoagulant powders can be used, and they must be colored blue or green.
- Glue boards may be used in edible product

What Is HACCP?

Over the past several years, there has been great interest in the Hazard Analysis Critical Control Point (HACCP) concept—especially as it relates to pest management operations inside food manufacturing plants. The HACCP concept was first developed by NASA for astronauts, and later adopted for the food industry during the 1960s. Beginning in 1997, the FDA began mandating HACCP programs for certain food manufacturers such as meat and poultry plants, fruit juice manufacturers, and seafood-processing plants. The FDA intends to eventually use it for most of the foods manufactured in the country.

HACCP uses science and common sense to prevent biological, chemical, and/or physical hazards from occurring during food production. An essential point of HACCP is that it is a *preventative*, not a *reactive* system. It is based on the concept of identifying hazards that are likely to occur during any step in the food processing system and then determining the preventive measures for the specific hazard.

There are two prerequisites to HACCP programs that indirectly affect all pest control efforts: (1) good manufacturing practices, (GMPs), and (2) Standard Sanitation Operating Practices (SSOPs).

GMPs are the criteria as set forth by the FDA for food manufacturers to ensure that their food is free from adulteration. Specific guidelines for how a plant shall be kept clean are outlined within the SSOPs. Sanitation and pest management programs are included as two critical parts of the GMP sanitation program. Thus, HACCP, GMPs, SSOPs and IPM, are all related to one another, and together they share the same goal: to create a safe and sanitary environment that minimizes the risk of a food safety hazard occurring.

areas but cannot remain there during operating hours.

Outside food plants, pesticides should be used in strict accordance with label directions. They should be applied according to the principles and practices described in the relevant pest chapters of this book. For example, extreme care must be taken to avoid applying any exterior-applied pesticide that can be drawn into the plant via air intake points. Such areas occur at both ground and roof levels.

Inside food plants, great care must be taken when any pesticide is used, to guarantee that no contamination of food products occurs. Treatments will be confined largely to injecting cracks and crevices or voids where pests are harboring. (Refer

What Does a Pest Management Inspector Look For?

Exterior areas:
- Pest harborages under objects lying or stored directly on the ground
- Food spillage along railroad sidings and shipping and receiving docks
- Garbage handling systems (storage, containers, cleaning methods, and trash handling)
- Proper drainage
- Weed control (weeds provide both food and harborage for insects and rodents)
- Perimeter rodent control
- Perimeter insect control
- Surrounding environment (Any surrounding areas or buildings conducive to pests?)
- Rodentproofing
- Insectproofing
- Birdproofing

Interior areas:
- Wall and floor maintenance (Are cracks sealed and floors clean?)
- Ceilings (Do they leak or provide harborage areas?); suspended ceilings above processing areas are particularly suspect and must be accessed and inspected
- Elevator shafts (Is there an accumulation of debris that will provide harborage or food for insects and rodents?)
- Floor drains (Are they clean?); cover plates and catch basins must be removed
- Plumbing (Are areas where pipes come through walls rodentproof?)
- Condensation (Does it provide a breeding area for flies or other pests?)
- Lighting (Do lights attract insects into the building?)
- Railroad track areas (If spurs come into the building, is the area kept clean?)

- Doors
  — Are they in good repair?
  — Do they shut tightly?
  — Do plant personnel observe door closing policies?

Storage:
- Proper practices (Is storage kept 16 to 18 inches away from walls?)
- Proper stock rotation practices (e.g., first in, first out)
- General housekeeping (Are spilled products cleaned up so as not to accumulate and provide harborage or food sources for pests?)
- Empty containers
- Segregation of damaged goods
- Refrigeration storage

Food Preparation:
- Housekeeping around equipment
- Counters and preparation surfaces
- Storage practices

Locker and Rest Rooms:
- General sanitation
- Lockers well organized and not accumulating food trash

Vending machines:
- Machine cleanliness
- All areas beneath and behind machines

Utility areas:
- Not being used as overflow storage areas (Are utility areas cluttered?)
- Out-of-sight corners in floors and ceilings (These areas sometimes hide occasional invaders, such as beetles, ants, sowbugs, and spiders)

to the pest management section of the stored product pests chapter—Chapter 10.) Label directions for the use of each pesticide are the best guide. The pesticides to be used, the methods of application, and other relevant information should be reviewed with plant personnel before treatment.

Insecticide applications may include space treatments (fogging, ULV) with contact insecticides, crack and crevice treatments with contact and residual insecticides, and fumigations. These applications are discussed in several other chapters in this book. For their use in food-processing plants, be sure label directions are closely followed.

Ideally, when insecticides need to be applied inside a food plant, it is best that the affected area not be in operation. This allows proper preparation (including cleaning, removing or covering food, and dismantling equipment) and facilitates treating food areas and nonfood areas without disturbing employees or contaminating food or equipment. When contact insecticides are used for space treatments (fogging, ULV) in food areas, all product contact surfaces must be protected, or they must be thoroughly washed before startup. Where residual insecticides are authorized and used in food areas (through crack and crevice or spot treatments), it is recommended practice to also wash all food-contacting surfaces prior to startup to ensure no pesticide residues or dead pests remain to contaminate food.

For food plants subject to many sources of pest entry, the pest management company should arrange to be on call 24 hours a day, 7 days a week, to quickly deal with pest problems before they become serious and costly for the food plant.

Evaluating the Program

All aspects of the pest management program need to be continuously evaluated. Visual inspections, monitoring data, and feedback from plant staff will assist in this effort. Visual inspections allow the professional to note any changes in factors that might favor pest entry and development. Monitoring devices help to detect and identify pests occurring at low-infestation levels. Finally, a central log should be established for production and maintenance staff to use in recording pest occurrence and location. This log not only encourages the staff to maintain interest and involvement in reducing pest problems, but also helps the pest management professional to quickly focus on new problems. All of this evaluation information should be shared (on written service reports) with the appropriate plant managers for continued emphasis on good housekeeping, sanitation, and pest exclusion.

SUPPLEMENTARY READING MATERIAL

American Institute of Baking. *Consolidated Standards for Food Safety*. Manhattan, Kansas: AIB, 2001 48 pp.

Baur, F. J., ed. *Insect Management for Food Storage and Processing*. St. Paul, Minn.: American Association of Cereal Chemists, 1984. 384 pp.

Bennett, G. W., and J. M. Owens, eds. *Advances in Urban Pest Management*. New York: Van Nostrand Reinhold, 1986. 399 pp.

Brickey, P. M. "The Food and Drug Administration and the Regulation of Food Sanitation." In: *Ecology and Management of Food Industry Pests*. Ed. J. R. Gorham. Arlington, Va.: Association of Official Analytical Chemists, 1991. 595 pp.

Corrigan, R. M. The science behind the inspection aisle. *The Sanitarian*. Vol. 3 (1). 6, 10-11. Advanstar Communications. Cleveland, OH. 1999.

Corrigan, R. M. and J. Klotz. *Food Plant Pest Management*. Purdue Univ. Corres. Course. Purdue University. W. Lafayette, IN. 1995.

FDA. Title 21.Code of Federal Regulations. Part 110. Current Good Manufacturing Practices in Manufacturing, Processing, Packing or Holding of Human Food. Washington, D.C.: Office of the Federal Register. Gov't Printing Office . 2001.

FDA. Title 21.Code of Federal Regulations. Part 120. Hazard Analysis and Critical Control Points (HACCP) Systems. Washington, D.C.: U.S. Government Printing Office . 2001.

FDA. *Food Code*. Washington, D.C. U.S. Department of Health and Human Services. 2001.

Frishman, A. M. "Commentary on Inspection Aspects." In *Ecology and Management of Food Industry Pests*. Ed. J. R. Gorham. Arlington, Va.: Association of Official Analytical Chemists, 1991. 595 pp.

Gorham, J. R., ed. *Ecology and Management of Food Industry Pests*. Arlington, Va.: Association of Official Analytical Chemists, 1991. 595 pp.

Hohman, R. L. "Food Industry Self-Inspection." In *Ecology and Management of Food Industry Pests*. Ed. J. R. Gorham. Arlington, Va.: Association of Official Analytical Chemists, 1991. 595 pp.

Holcomb, M. Clean up your act, or the bugs may take over. *Pest Control*, Vol. 65 (11). 78, 1997.

Hui, Y.H. , B.L. Bruinsma, J. R. Gorham, W.K. Nip, P.S. Tong and P. Ventresca. 2003. *Food Plant Sanitation*. Marcel Dekker, Inc. New York. 745 pp.

Imholte, T. J. and T. Imhholte-Tauscer. *Engineering for Food Safety and Sanitation: A Guide to the Sanitary Design of Food Plants and Food Plant Equipment*. 2nd Ed. Crystal, Minn.: Technical Institute of Food Safety, 19841999. 283 382 pp.

Katsuyama, A. M., and J. P. Strachan, eds. *Principles of Food Processing Sanitation*. Washington, D.C.: Food Processors Institute, 1980. 264 pp.

Kenney, M., D. Orr, and M. J. Shannon. "Regulatory and Inspection Functions in the U.S. Department of Agriculture." In: *Ecology and Management of Food Industry Pests*. Ed. J. R. Gorham. Arlington, Va.: Association of Official Analytical Chemists, 1991. 595 pp.

Mueller, D. "Pheromones." In: *Mallis's Handbook of Pest Control*. 8th ed. Ed. S. Hedges. Cleveland: Franzak & Foster, 1997.

National Pest Management Association. *Tools and Techniques for Sanitation Inspections*. Technical release (ESPC 072137) Dunn Loring, Va., 2000. 6 pp.

Osmun, J. V. "Commentary on Regulatory Aspects." In *Ecology and Management of Food Industry Pests*. Ed. J. R. Gorham. Arlington, Va.: Association of Official Analytical Chemists, 1991. 595 pp.

Subramanyam, B. and DW Hagstrum eds. 1996. *Integrated Management of Insects in Stored Products*. Marcel Dekker. New York.

Truman, L. C., and W. L. Butts. *Scientific Guide to Pest Control Operations*. 2d ed. Cleveland: *Pest Control*; and W. Lafayette, In.: Purdue University, 1967. 187 pp.

Vetter, J. L. 1996. *Food Laws and Regulations*. American Institute of Baking. Manhattan, KS. 248 pp.

CHAPTER 19 | Pest Management in Specialized Facilities

Chapter 18 gave an overview of how to design and execute comprehensive sanitation and pest management programs for food plants. Such programs require the use of many specialized and customized pest management techniques. This chapter will discuss the application of similar techniques guided by general pest management concepts, but applied in four rather different types of accounts: **healthcare facilities, schools, supermarkets, zoos,** and **computer rooms**. Other specialized facilities that require specialized and often complex or sophisticated pest management programs include shopping malls, resort hotels and casinos, museums and commercial facilities susceptible to fabric pest infestations, research laboratories (especially where laboratory animals are used), and pet shops. However, space considerations allow us to discuss only four types of accounts in any detail. As with food plants, these situations are often specialized due to (1) the types of pest problems involved; (2) certain unusual medical or aesthetic requirements; (3) the unique structural features of the facilities; (4) the presence of favorable conditions for pests, due to the type of work or operation involved; or (5) limitations on what pest management techniques can be used. Pest management contracts in these types of facilities often require considerable record keeping and attention to program quality assurance. Properly designed and conducted pest management programs for these specialized situations must include the same basic steps as have been emphasized throughout this book—**inspection, treatment** (or application of pest management procedures), **communication**, and continuous **follow-up**.

It is particularly useful to take a **holistic approach** during the design and implementation phases of these pest management programs. The concept of a holistic approach has arisen in pest management technology and is perhaps best understood by use of a diagram such as the one in Figure 19.1. The important point is that professionals should carefully step back from the structures involved and consider all aspects of the construction, operation, and surrounding environment that can contribute to ongoing pest problems or represent difficulties toward gaining acceptable pest management results. This consideration should include the important details of interior construction, such as layout of plumbing or ventilation systems; the flow of food or other supplies into and through the facility; the possible effects of exterior lighting, landscaping, or adjacent properties; the potential for the introduction of pests, such as cockroaches, via people flow into the facility; and any other contributing factors (see Figure 19.2).

The entire situation should be evaluated and all types of pest problems addressed. Design and integrate pest management strategies in a complimentary fashion to provide a comprehensive pest management program for the specialized facility. This program should anticipate pest problems, take steps to avoid or prevent them, and include constant inspections or monitoring to detect problems in early stages. It is not acceptable to merely react to pest problems after they have grown to troublesome levels. Experience and thorough knowledge of pest biology, behavior, and ecology are essential to success in these programs.

PEST MANAGEMENT IN HOSPITALS AND OTHER HEALTHCARE FACILITIES

There are several types of healthcare facilities, including hospitals, long-term care facilities (which include nursing homes), emergency medical care centers, and physical or mental rehabilitation facilities. These facilities can be any size, from just a few beds to more than a thousand. Each will have simi-

468 | CHAPTER 19
Pest Management in Specialized Facilities

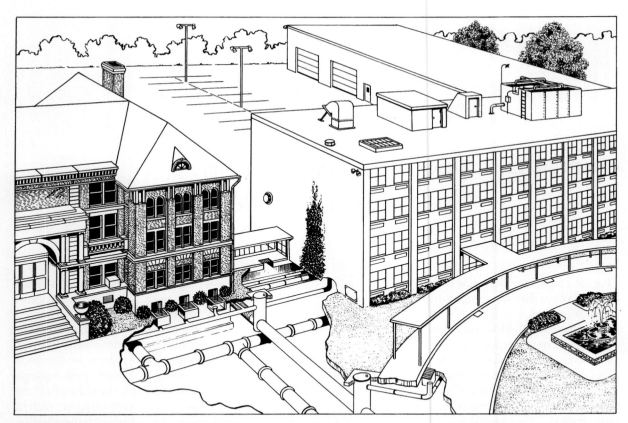

FIGURE 19.1. It is useful to view structures holistically when designing pest management programs. To do this, the professional should step back from the structure and consider the total outdoor environment of the structure in addition to the structure itself. (Whitmire/Micro-Gen)

lar pest problems and pest management requirements, though their size will affect the overall complexity of the pest management effort required. Our discussion will assume a moderate- to large-sized full-service hospital, with around 200 beds and 200,000 square feet of floor space. A suitable pest management program for such a facility should be readily adaptable to the other types and sizes of healthcare facilities.

Hospitals have a critical need to maintain an intensive pest management program. No one among the staff, patients, or visitors wants to see any pests in the hospital for aesthetic reasons, but there are important medical reasons for maintaining a pest-free environment. As places where people with serious injuries, diseases, and other illnesses come for treatment and recovery, virtually no pests can be tolerated. Several of the more common pests found in hospitals are known to carry bacteria inside or on the surface of their bodies. These bacteria can cause infections among hospital patients if these pests come in contact with patients directly (e.g., by touching skin or wounds) or indirectly (e.g., by contaminating food or medical supplies and equipment). Infections obtained while under medical

care at a healthcare facility, whether attributable to a pest-borne source or otherwise, are known as nosocomial infections. These are a major concern in the healthcare industry. Prevention of such infections is the primary responsibility of the infection control department in each hospital, and the pest management program is a key aspect of this effort.

A high level of pest management performance must be maintained. Hospitals are exceptional in their **structural and organizational complexity**. The plumbing, mechanical (i.e., heating, ventilation, and air-conditioning, or HVAC), and electrical systems are important aspects of the physical or structural complexity of a large hospital. However, many different departments and layers of administration also interact within the hospital. These include the various administrative groups, housekeeping and sanitation (including laundry care), food services, all the different medical departments, and a separate infection control group. Pest management professionals must be familiar with all these factors and must be able to communicate effectively with all hospital staff.

In addition to the demand for a high level of pest management performance, all aspects of the

MASTER KITCHEN CHART

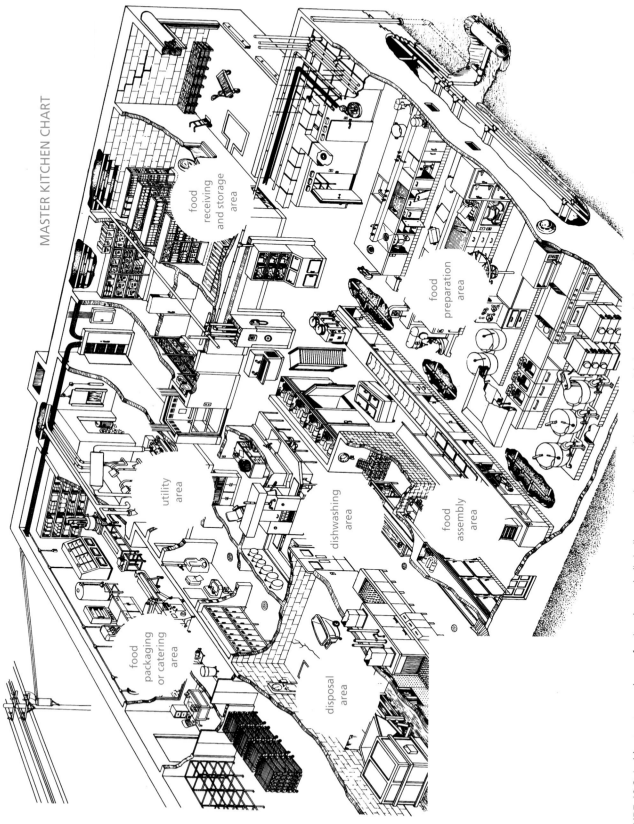

food receiving and storage area

food preparation area

utility area

dishwashing area

food assembly area

food packaging or catering area

disposal area

FIGURE 19.2. Inside structures, the professional must holistically approach pest problems by considering not only the specific room or area that may have pests, but also other indoor (and outdoor) factors that may not be immediately visible. (Whitmire/Micro-Gen)

Key Points in Pest Management for Hospitals

Key pests:
- German and brownbanded cockroaches
- Ants (especially pharaoh ants)
- Mice
- Flies (especially associated with drains and decaying materials)

Pest hot spots:
- Employee locker and break rooms
- Janitorial closets
- Laundry rooms
- Foodservice areas (kitchens, storerooms)
- Restaurants and snack bars
- Vending machine areas
- Food carts
- Bedside furniture in patient rooms
- Floor drains and sink areas
- Intensive care wards
- Surgical suites
- Kidney dialysis rooms
- Autopsy rooms
- Trash dumpsters and related facilities

During inspections:
- Work routinely with floor diagrams and checklists. Keep accurate records.
- Develop reporting sheets for nurses and other employees to use in reporting pest sightings. Educate and build relationships with these staff people to gain their assistance.
- Inspect for pest problems associated with the plumbing system (floor drains, sinks, bathrooms, scrub down areas, autopsy rooms, laundry areas, etc.).
- Do not overlook locked janitorial closets and employee lockers.

During pesticide applications:
- Always check with the head nurse or person in charge before treating in patient care or other sensitive areas.
- Patients should not be present during any pesticide applications, nor until all vapors or odors are gone. Coordinate with nursing staff to have patients moved.
- Use low-odor or odorless residual insecticide formulations, as crack and crevice or limited spot applications only.
- Do not allow sprays, mists, or dusts to become airborne.
- Use bait formulations wherever appropriate, and place bait stations carefully.
- Be careful with pesticides around sensitive electronic or medical diagnostic equipment.
- Keep detailed and accurate records of all pesticide applications.

Other points:
- Always maintain a clean, neat appearance and highly professional approach around nurses and medical staff. You will need their respect and assistance.
- Work closely with the infection control, housekeeping, maintenance, food service, and nursing staffs on sanitation and reporting of pest sightings.
- Do not discuss sanitation problems or other aspects of the pest management program in the presence of patients or visitors, or where they might overhear.

pest management program will be under constant review by the hospital administration, public health inspectors, medical personnel, and hospital accreditation boards. Often, the hospital administration will enlist the services of a consulting entomologist or sanitarian to make recommendations and otherwise oversee the pest management program. Only a carefully thought out, highly organized, and well-monitored (from a quality control standpoint) pest management program can be successful under such circumstances.

The Holistic Approach

As mentioned in the introduction to this chapter,

several interacting components of the broader situation can be recognized by stepping back from the size and complexity of this pest management task. Viewed separately, these can help professionals to choose and organize different pest management strategies to overcome the primary factors that contribute to ongoing pest problems.

Major components of the pest problems in hospitals include pests that fly or crawl into the facility from the immediate surroundings, and those that are a problem only within the structure (i.e., they have no external source in the immediate vicinity). A third major component is the movement of pests into the facility in the clothing, purses, or other items carried by the many people who enter the hospital daily. A significant inward flow of pests, especially cockroaches, ants, and various types of flies, can be associated with visitors who bring food, gifts, clothing, flowers, and other items to patients in the facility. A considerable volume of food and other supplies flows through the hospital daily. The hospital staff can also bring in pests. Education programs and other steps should be implemented to reduce the inflow of pests, especially German cockroaches, associated with the hospital staff. However, except under extreme circumstances, little can be done to limit pest inflow associated with visitors. The importance of these people-related sources of pest problems will vary depending on the proportion of staff and visitors who live in infested homes.

Steps should be taken to detect and identify the types of pests that enter the facility from adjacent landscape areas. These will generally include various rodents and birds, flies and other flying insects (some associated with the types of trees and shrubs on the hospital grounds), ants, ground beetles, or other crawling pests. Techniques of pest exclusion are discussed elsewhere in this book, especially in Chapter 12 (on occasional invaders), and they should be applied to prevent entry of pests. For example, all entry doors to hospitals and other medical facilities should be designed to reduce or inhibit entry of flying insects, and carefully maintained so they are effective (see Figure 19.3).

The complexity of the plumbing, electrical, and HVAC systems, as well as other aspects of the physical plant, make control of the indoor pest component very challenging. Focus attention on the plumbing system to find and eliminate sources of moisture (leaks, sweating pipes, clogged drains, etc.) that can encourage populations of cockroaches and various types of flies. Keep in mind that cockroaches and ants can use the plumbing system to spread throughout the facility. Caulking and other techniques can be used to limit the spread of these infestations.

The entire **food flow system** should also be given special, focused attention. Pests can come in on food deliveries, so storage areas require constant monitoring and attention. Hospitals include a number of other food-related facilities, including kitchens, snack bars, cafeterias, employee break rooms, and vending machines.

Regardless of the specialized facility or pest management situation in which you are working, it is essential to observe and analyze the interacting components of each facility or situation.

Pests and Pest Hot Spots

Pests such as cockroaches, ants, and rodents are common because they are so well adapted to the

FIGURE 19.3. If properly weather-stripped and maintained, and kept closed when not in use, this doorway should not serve as an entryway for flying or crawling pests. However, if it is near a dumpster or other sources of flies, and if there might be a consistent inward flow of air when opened (due to HVAC system imbalance), this door could be a significant entry point for filth flies. Lack of a light fixture directly near the doorway suggests that it will not attract night-flying insects. (Myers)

hospital environment. Flies such as drain flies (family Psychodidae), humpbacked flies (family Phoridae), vinegar or pomace flies (family Drosophilidae), house flies, and other filth flies are more commonly encountered in hospitals than in nearly any other type of pest management situation. In part, these fly problems are so frequent because of the complex plumbing systems typically found in hospitals. This may include literally hundreds of sinks, floor drains, lavatories, and so forth. Some of these are often clogged or contaminated with various fluids, and many are not routinely and adequately cleaned. Some that become sources for chronic fly problems will not even be known to the engineering, housekeeping, or maintenance department staff because they are not shown on any of the original architectural or construction drawings, they have been added during a subsequent remodeling or renovation, or because furnishings and equipment have been moved into the area covering or blocking access to the drains. Besides these factors, the nature of the work in many parts of the hospital is such that moisture residues are left behind, which encourages fly populations. Pest management professionals assigned to work in hospitals should be especially well trained in the identification, biology, behavior, and control of all the groups of flies just mentioned (see also Chapter 14).

In general, fly control should be a matter of searching out the source of the flies, which is usually some source of moist food where the larvae are developing. This source should be cleaned up, and steps should be taken to prevent it from recurring. The use of insecticide sprays in ongoing fly control should be avoided, and devices such as ultraviolet light traps should be used only to intercept flies or other flying insects entering exterior doors (e.g., near loading docks or other service entrances). Fly entry via doorways used by visitors is usually prevented by the use of positive, outward airflow at entryway vestibules. Absolutely no doorway should be allowed to remain propped open, even near loading docks (see Figures 19.3 and 19.4).

While hospitals will differ in the number of pest hot spots they have or in the relative intensity of pest problems in each spot, there are certain hot spots commonly found in these facilities. For example, it is often difficult to maintain German cockroach control in employee locker room areas. These areas are generally not kept as clean as they should be, and employees often store food items in their lockers. The professional may not gain easy access to all lockers for inspections or treatments. These are generally locked by the employees, who have the only keys. Large bags of crushed recyclable soda cans, usually not properly rinsed, are often

FIGURE 19.4. This loading dock area at a hospital appears to be well designed and maintained, so that it should not be a significant source of pest entry. However, the light fixtures over the doorways will attract flying insects at night, which could enter the facility in significant numbers; so moving the lights further away from the doorways should be considered. (Myers)

stashed in a corner or some other hidden area. Janitorial closets can have similar problems and generally contain damp mops, which encourage cockroach infestations. Arrangements should be made with hospital administrators to allow routine inspection and treatment (as needed) of these employee and janitorial areas. Even if access is difficult to arrange, these areas must not be overlooked.

The laundry area is usually a focal area for cockroach, ant (especially pharaoh ant), fly, rodent, and other pest problems, and control of these pests is difficult in this area. It is generally a warm and moist environment with a constant sanitation problem due to all the soiled linens processed there. These are soiled either with food crumbs and spills or with fecal material and vomitus. Unsanitary or even clogged floor drains in the laundry area are common.

All food service areas tend to be pest hot spots. This includes food storage areas, kitchens, and coffee messes throughout the facility; restaurants or coffee shops for public use; and employee break areas. Most hospitals have policies against food consumption by employees in nonapproved areas and unauthorized food consumption in patient rooms. However, enforcement of these policies is difficult and often lax. Food service in hospitals typically involves the use of many specially constructed, insulated food carts. These food carts are frequently soiled with residues from food spillage and offer many warm and moist pest harborages. Consequently, they are frequently infested with German cockroaches or other pests. Areas where these carts are stored will generally have similar sanitation and pest problems. This aspect of the food flow system within the hospital is a chronic problem for pest management professionals, requiring constant attention.

The storage of snack foods, such as candy, nuts, cookies, potato chips, and fruit, contributes to chronic pest problems in patient rooms. This food is often concealed within the patient's room, because it is brought in (contrary to hospital policy and the physician's orders) by visitors, either for their consumption or for the patient. Careful attention should be paid to bedside stands and any other furniture, lockers, closets, and window ledges. A final pest hot spot associated with food consumption in the facility is the storage of snacks, bag lunches, and stashes of recyclable beverage cans in employee locker rooms or janitorial closets. All these food-related habits create chronic sources of pest infestation in the hospital. Wards that typically have long-term patients should receive special attention in the pest management program.

Intensive care and kidney dialysis rooms will often have chronic German cockroach and ant problems. The intensive care and surgical suites are also critical for fly problems, because absolutely no flies can be tolerated in these areas (yet, some always seem to get in), and because they tend to have a lot of floor drains and sinks. Any of these drains can be a source of fly problems if not properly cleaned on a regular basis. Besides the particular pest problems of the intensive care, surgical, and other sensitive areas of patient care in the hospital, pest management is often more difficult because of the severe limitations on what pesticides or other measures can be used in these areas. In general, the use of baits and traps is permitted, along with some very discrete spray or dust applications. Finally, loading docks and garbage or trash disposal areas (dumpsters, etc.) are hot spots for fly, cockroach, rodent, and many other pest problems.

The Pest Management Program

An important consideration for any firm seeking to offer pest management services to hospitals is that the personnel assigned to actually conduct these services must be highly qualified and well trained. They must also present a clean, professional image to the various hospital professionals with whom they will interact. It is important for these pest management professionals to be alert and communicate effectively with the hospital staff, who will accept only people of high standards and qualifications. Since cooperation and support from the hospital staff are important to a successful pest management program, there must be respect among the staff for the pest management professionals involved.

Support of the hospital administration and staff, at many levels, is essential to the success of the pest management program. These people must be well informed of the necessary details of their involvement and committed to the program, from the start. Otherwise, a great deal of frustration and dissatisfaction can be expected from both sides of the relationship. This open communication between hospital administration and the pest management professional should be a continuous process, with regular meetings scheduled to review progress, issues, and modifications in the program. If the hospital has hired a consulting entomologist or sanitarian, this person can be a great asset in promoting this communication and cooperation.

The extreme sensitivity of the hospital situation, where weak, ill, stressed, and sensitive patients are present, is such that the use of pesticides in the program should be considered only after other nonchemical pest management methods are applied. Programs for hospitals should be designed as true integrated pest management programs, relying primarily on nonchemical procedures, such as sanitation, exclusion, and physical control, and only secondarily on pesticide use.

While details of a properly designed pest management program for each particular hospital cannot be described here, an outline and discussion of key steps in such a program follow. There are at least seven steps, or aspects, that should be considered in designing a complete program for a hospital: education, inspections and trapping/monitoring; exclusion and mechanical repairs; sanitation; physical control; pesticide use; and quality control, record keeping, and periodic meetings with hospital staff.

Education

It is not economically feasible for the professional to thoroughly inspect the entire hospital on each visit or even at the frequent intervals that would be desirable. Since the hospital staff members work throughout the facility at all hours of the day, they can be a great asset to the pest management program if they are educated on how to recognize and report pest presence. They should also be counseled to maintain strict sanitation in their personal areas (locker rooms, etc.), patient rooms, and elsewhere within the facility. Hospital staff members should be kept aware of the various procedures implemented in the pest management program, with an explanation of how their efforts and support will be important to its overall success. This support should be reinforced at appropriate intervals by the use of printed materials and personal communication, such as seminars and meetings.

Another aspect of this education program for the hospital staff should involve discussion of the behavior of cockroaches and other pests that can frequently hitchhike on clothing, in handbags, or on other possessions of staff and visitors. Procedures that staff members can use to control pests in their own homes can be related in newsletters or seminars. Professionals will encounter considerable interest and questioning from hospital staff about household pests and insects in general, including non-pests. Professionals who are knowledgeable about these creatures and their proper control will gain the confidence and respect of hospital staff. This relationship will be a great asset toward gaining the necessary cooperation that will make the pest management program more effective and efficient.

Inspections and Trapping/Monitoring

The initial step in the inspection process is to obtain a series of **detailed floor diagrams** of the hospital. These should include important details such as the location of plumbing facilities, food service facilities, storage areas, loading docks (see Figure 19.4), and other pest hot spots. Notes on pest sightings, pesticide applications, and other pest management procedures should be kept with reference to these diagrams. To minimize reliance on pesticides in the pest management program, frequent and thorough inspections should be conducted (at least in areas considered pest hot spots). As the pest management program proceeds, more time should be devoted to inspections and to investigating staff pest sightings than to pesticide application. These inspections and staff reports of pest sightings will guide all other aspects of the pest management program, including recommendations for sanitation, physical alterations, or pest exclusion.

Special attention should be focused on inspecting incoming food, medical, and housekeeping supplies. The hospital staff can be of great assistance in this activity, so they should be educated on how to spot pests and what to do in response. Storage areas for these supplies should also be inspected by the professional on a routine basis. Besides visual inspections using flashlights, mirrors, hand tools, and other traditional techniques, there are many types of traps that can be used to detect pest presence. These include sticky traps for cockroaches, ants, and other crawling insects; light traps or sticky traps for flies (e.g., inside of receiving areas); glue boards for rodents; and pheromone or food attractant traps for stored product insects. While trapping is generally considered a detection and monitoring technique, it can also be an important pest management procedure where populations are low and pesticide use or other options are severely restricted.

Exclusion and Mechanical Repairs

Recommendations for repairs and alterations conducted by hospital maintenance staff or outside contractors should be carefully considered and consistently monitored for compliance. Response by hospital administration and staff to these recommendations will be an indication of their overall commitment to the pest management program. Some pest problems in certain portions of the hospital will recur frequently because of deficiencies in the sanitation program or constant introduction from outside sources (see Figure 19.5). Other pest problems can be best corrected by use of caulking, installation of air doors, or more elaborate repairs. In addition to prevention of pest entrance to the hospital or movement within the facility, another benefit of exclusion techniques is that they greatly reduce the available pest harborage requiring repeated pesticide treatment. Again, these nonchemical techniques can be especially useful where pesticide use is

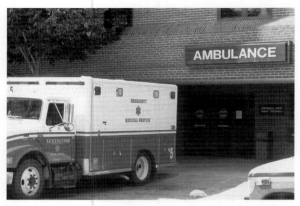

FIGURE 19.5. This ambulance entrance to the emergency room of a hospital appears designed to reduce likelihood of pest entrance. The entrance doors must be opened at any time, and may remain opened for several minutes at a time, but the exterior lighting is recessed behind the low-hanging brick facade (bearing the "Ambulance" sign), so will not directly attract flying insects at night. The pest management technician should work with the building engineers to be sure that there is positive airflow out of these entry doors when they are opened, to discourage fly entry into the emergency medical treatment area. The tree growing against the building, and overhanging the ambulance entrance (upper left of picture), is poorly placed from a pest management perspective and may warrant removal. (Myers)

greatly restricted, particularly for cockroach control. The fewer places that need routine inspection and treatment, the more efficient and effective the pest management program will become. Attention to these efforts will pay greater and greater dividends as time passes, and they should be considered an investment of sorts toward better pest management with less reliance on pesticides.

Sanitation

Sanitation is important to infection control efforts within the hospital as well as to the pest management program. These two programs are basically complementary, because any insects or other pests within the hospital represent an obvious infection risk to patients. Good sanitation can limit the food, water, and harborage (from clutter) available to pests. It can even improve the effectiveness of some pesticide applications. Most insecticides will have longer residual activity on surfaces that have no grease. Removal of competing food resources will often improve pest response to baits.

Sanitation recommendations based on the inspection phase should be shared with the infection control staff. In turn, these staff members will often seek out the pest management professional. In sanitation concerns, there should be frequent communication, consistent follow-up, and a generally close working relationship between the professional and hospital staff from housekeeping, infection control, and appropriate administrative departments.

Physical Control

Since pesticide use should generally be minimized within the hospital, other means for direct pest control should be considered. Insects such as cockroaches and stored product pests can be controlled by freezing (less than 20°F for several hours, or 0°F for 1 to 2 hours), heating (greater than 120°F for several hours, or greater than 140°F for shorter periods), or the use of modified-atmosphere techniques. Equipment such as food carts or other items can often (or routinely) be put into refrigeration rooms or specially heated areas to control insects. Alternatively, large plastic bags or tarps can be placed over TVs, radios, electrical equipment, computers, or many other items, with gases such as carbon dioxide or nitrogen used to create a modified atmosphere lethal to pests. These gases are usually more effective (i.e., give faster control) if the enclosed area can be heated somewhat to increase the metabolic rate of the insects. These methods can be very effective and leave no pesticide residue. However, professionals must be cautious when using these procedures on electronic equipment or other potentially sensitive items.

Other forms of physical control that can be useful in hospitals and other healthcare facilities are various forms of trapping and vacuuming of pests such as cockroaches.

Pesticides

Despite all the attention paid to other aspects of the pest management program, and despite the focus on minimizing reliance on pesticides, the use of some pesticides will be necessary as a routine part of the program. There are no special regulations or regulatory reviews of pesticide use in hospitals, as there are for USDA- and FDA-inspected food plants.

A general concept to keep in mind when considering the use of pesticides in hospitals is to distinguish between **patient care areas and nonpatient areas**. Pesticide use should be most careful and conservative in any patient care areas. Always check with the head nurse or some other responsible person on the medical staff before pesticides are used in patient care areas or other potentially sensitive locations. Under almost no circumstances should any insecticides be released into the air (e.g., for flying insect control or as part of a cockroach cleanout treatment) in any area where patients might be exposed. In general, patients should be removed from their rooms (or other areas) whenever pesticide applications must be made. The use of bait formulations and crack and crevice or very limited spot treatments of residual insecticide sprays (or dusts) are preferred. Be certain that any pesticide droplets, dust particles, or vapors from applications in nonpatient areas cannot be carried to patient areas by the ventilation system or other airflow patterns within the facility. Formulations that have very low or no odor are preferred for use in hospitals.

Careful records should be maintained on all pesticides used in the hospital. These records are necessary to answer any questions asked by the medical staff regarding possible interactions of pesticides with other patient care matters.

Quality Control, Record Keeping, and Communications

Careful record keeping on all pest sightings, pest management procedures applied (including pesticide applications), and other recommendations made will aid in organizing the overall pest management program and helping solve any persistent pest problems. Such record keeping is necessary whenever an ongoing program is conducted in sensitive and complex facilities, such as hospitals. Computerized record-keeping systems can make this aspect of the program more efficient.

These records will prove especially valuable during quality control reviews conducted by the pest management firm, and while reviewing progress and issues with hospital administration. Regular program reviews should be held with the appropriate hospital staff. These can be biweekly or monthly for meetings with the housekeeping and infection control departments, and at least quarterly for upper-level hospital management. If the hospital administration hires an outside consultant to oversee the pest management efforts, this person will likely expect detailed record keeping.

PEST MANAGEMENT IN SCHOOLS

Since the early- to mid-1990s there has been a trend in the United States toward adoption of IPM programs for schools, with a strong emphasis as a policy objective of substantially reducing use of pesticides in and around school buildings. Much of this policy has been driven by state legislation, and the U.S. EPA has also established an "IPM in Schools" program that involves technical representatives in each of its regions. While the mandates and regulation under state laws vary, many require that public schools establish formal IPM policies and implement IPM programs in their facilities.

Key Points in Pest Management for Schools

Key pests:
- German and other cockroaches
- Mice
- Bees, wasps, and yellowjackets
- Spiders
- Flies
- Termites
- Head lice

Pest hot spots:
- Cafeteria and break areas
- Dumpsters and other trash areas
- Vending machines
- Classrooms and lockers (where food & snacks stored)
- Perimeter foundation and exterior walls

During inspections:
- Cultivate assistance of staff to report pest sightings.
- Routinely check cafeteria and other hot spots.
- Use sticky traps routinely to monitor for crawling pests in key areas.
- Monitor sanitation problems; report them to appropriate staff and check follow-up.
- Be alert for pest entry points into the building.

During pesticide applications:
- Avoid applications when students are present if at all possible.
- Avoid any possibility of contaminating food or any food contact surfaces in cafeterias.
- Avoid contamination of surfaces that students may later contact.
- Avoid use of formulations that may leave a lingering "chemical" odor
- Prefer the use of baits, crack-and-crevice treatments, and dusting of voids.

Other points:
- Emphasize use of nonchemical techniques (sanitation, exclusion, traps, etc.).
- Work with school custodians to correct chronic problems of sanitation.
- Many schools have a policy to use pesticides only as a last resort.
- Selection of pesticides that may be used is often restricted to a list of "least toxic."
- Prior notification and posting of signs often required before pesticides can be used.
- Do not apply pesticides in classrooms, coat rooms, or lockers for lice control.

Pest management professionals considering school IPM service must realize that the key difference between these accounts and others are not the pests or environmental conditions present, but the presence of the school's students. Their habits and behavior may present some pest management challenges, but paramount in the minds of the parents and school officials will be the **health and safety of the students**. As a result, many schools and school systems have strong policies to emphasize the use of nonchemical or "least toxic" pest management methods (as prescribed by contract or regulations), while use of most conventional pesticides may be permitted as the last or least preferred option. These policies make clear that safety of students from effects of pesticide exposure, or even the potential for exposure, is a very important concern. At the same time, it is also recognized that many of the key pests in and around schools also threaten the health and safety of students, so there can be low tolerance for their presence in any significant numbers and a high standard of pest management service is necessary.

The preference for use of nonchemical pest management practices, and which pesticides are allowed and preferred (when necessary), will usually be explicit within the school's policy and the pest management contract. Pesticide applicators must usually be certified and suitably trained, and in some states only licensed commercial applicators are allowed to supervise and conduct school IPM programs. Prior notification of all pesticide applications is often required (e.g., 24 or 48 hours before treatment), and signs posted in treated areas; but exceptions will usually be allowed for emergency pesticide use, use of some bait formulations or antimicrobial cleaners. To reduce potential for pesticide exposure, applications may also be prohibited when children are present (during school hours), or if classes will resume within a prescribed time (e.g., 1 to 2 days). There may be other requirements and restrictions on what the pest management professional can do under applicable regulations or local school board policy, and often the greatest restrictions are placed on any broadcast use of pesticides, such as for insect or weed control on playgrounds or athletic fields, or residual or ULV spray treatments indoors.

All these restrictions and training, communication, and documentation requirements, along with the stated policy goal to emphasize nonchemical pest management approaches to minimize exposure of schoolchildren and staff to pesticides, mean that pest management professionals must be very knowledgeable, patient, and disciplined in their approach to school IPM service. Pest management firms must be careful to undertake such contracts only where they can afford to spend the time and other resources necessary to provide high-quality service, and remain profitable. These demands can be especially challenging where public school budgets for this service are inadequate.

Pests and Pest Hot Spots

The most common and significant insect pests in schools will vary between regions, but generally are flies and crawling pests such as cockroaches and ants, which can spread various pathogens, and allergens that cause asthma attacks; yellowjackets and other bees or wasps that can cause painful stings, for which some children may have life-threatening allergic reactions; spiders that can inflict painful bites, some of which may be life-threatening or disfiguring; mice and rats, which damage structures, contaminate food and spread pathogens and allergens; and termites. Head lice are also a common problem amongst schoolchildren, but their control is a medical concern for the school nurse or other health professionals, and parents. Pest management professionals should avoid making any insecticide treatments in schools for louse control.

Other pests include the many pathogenic bacteria, fungi and molds, or viruses that contaminate surfaces throughout the school, but are usually controlled by janitorial personnel using disinfectant cleaners; and weeds or other pests in turf or ornamental plantings surrounding the school, which may be the responsibility of the pest management professional. Discussion of pest management procedures for the pests of turf and landscape plantings is beyond the scope of this book, but it should be understood that concerns over exposure of students to herbicides used to control weeds in playgrounds and athletic fields, and insecticides applied to trees and shrubs around schools, are very important to parents, school administrators, and public policymakers who dictate school IPM policy.

The German cockroach is a common pest encountered in schools across the United States, though in warmer regions there may be problems with *Periplaneta* spp., Oriental cockroaches, or others. Occasionally, there may be brown-banded cockroaches, especially in schools that have dormitories or larger, multistory academic buildings. Cockroaches represent a significant health concern due

to the allergens they spread, which can be especially dangerous to asthmatic students, as well as various types of pathogens that can cause food poisoning or other forms of gastroenteritis. Hot spots for German cockroaches in schools will be cafeteria and food vending areas, student lounges, and localized locker areas (especially in the vicinity of certain lockers where food is kept for extended periods). Some infestations may even extend into classroom areas. Refer to Chapter 9 for details on controlling ants in and around structures, or stinging species like fire ants in schoolyards and athletic fields.

Yellowjackets, hornets and paper wasps (*Polistes* spp.) are important because their presence in classrooms will be very distracting, and because their stings can be life-threatening to a small percentage (1 to 3%) of students who are allergic to their venom. These insects generally nest outdoors, on the exterior of buildings (both paper wasps and the German yellowjacket), or in the nearby landscape (soil-nesting species, or carton nests in trees or shrubs). The late summer and fall seasons are when the most wasp problems are experienced, as yellowjacket colonies have less insect or other prey naturally available at this time, so they become more of an important pest around dumpsters and picnic areas (if students are allowed to eat lunches or take breaks outdoors). Because of their high numbers, many may also find their way into classrooms. Considerable numbers of overwintering yellowjacket and paper wasp queens may likewise find their way into schoolrooms during the fall, as they search for a suitable overwintering refuge.

The presence of spiders in classrooms will be very distracting and, of course, venomous species like the brown recluse, black widow or hobo spiders are a significant heath and safety threat. Hot spots for these latter species will be areas adjacent to exterior walls or accesses to crawlspaces, from where the spiders will enter schoolrooms; or in undisturbed harborage areas (voids) around student lockers, vending machine alcoves, or closets and storage rooms. Of course, spiders and their webs will also be a fairly constant nuisance around exterior light fixtures that are lit at night, as those lights attract night-flying insects that are a source of food for spiders. However, spiders typically found around these light fixtures, or night-lighted windows, are unlikely to be a distraction or safety concern for students, but rather just unsightly.

Mice are a very common pest in schools, and they can be rather scattered throughout since they may be entering from different locations and students may store food in lockers or desks. They can also be a common problem in, around, and above foodservice and storage areas. Mice are known to spread various pathogens and allergens that can be a significant health threat to students.

Like most other buildings, schools will be susceptible to termite infestation, especially subterranean termites. Schools will also be subject to seasonal problems with "occasional invader" pests such as crickets, sowbugs and pillbugs, millipedes, earwigs, and others (refer also to Chapter 12). In areas where fire ants are common, and especially the red imported fire ant, these ants will be a health and safety concern on playgrounds and athletic fields, and occasionally even in classrooms where they may enter to forage or nest.

The Pest Management Program

There are many sources of technical information, pest management guidelines, and other information on school IPM programs available on the Internet (see Selected References section at end of this chapter). Besides information that may be available from state lead pesticide regulatory agencies or the Extension Service, there are fairly comprehensive websites available from the US EPA and the California Dept. of Pesticide Regulation. The US EPA also provided grants to support School IPM Technical Resource Centers at the University of Florida, Purdue University and Texas A&M University, so those universities also have information available on how to design and execute school IPM programs (see Selected References section for specific URLs or use links provided at the US EPA's School IPM website). Before any school IPM program should be designed and implemented, a full understanding of federal or state regulations pertaining to such programs should be obtained, and the pest management professional must be certain of any additional local preferences or guidelines. These Internet-based resources will be a good place to gather this information.

The basic components of an IPM program for schools should be the same as for other situations discussed in this chapter—**inspection, treatment (application of pest management methods), communication** and **follow-up**. However, regulations and guidelines imposed in many states, or by local school officials and parent groups, will dictate that primary emphasis must be placed on the use of non-chemical pest management techniques, and the choices of chemical pesticides or formulations that can be used will often be limited. And when applications of chemical pesticides must be used in the overall pest management program there will likely be burdensome communication requirements for prior notification and posting of signs that must be followed to inform students and their parents (though, depending on the contract, school administrators may do much of the pretreatment notifications).

Frequent and thorough pest management inspections should be routine for school IPM programs, focusing especially on the presence of key pests including cockroaches, mice, and ants. Conditions that could allow or encourage pest entry into the school should be addressed through exclusion techniques such as sealing, screening, and use of vestibules at entry doors with positive/outward air pressure. Special attention should be paid to sanitation to reduce pest presence and infestation pressure. Pest management professionals should work to maintain communication with school staff to report all pest sightings, and custodial staff must be sufficiently thorough and effective in their routine cleaning of the facility to support the overall pest management goals (i.e., limit pest presence and reliance on pesticide use through sanitation as a key pest management technique).

Adequate sanitation is very important toward reducing and minimizing problems with cockroaches and mice. Where these pests are detected, direct control by use of traps (for mice) or pesticidal baits (for cockroaches and mice) is often necessary. As stated earlier, many state laws and regulations place relatively little restriction within school IPM programs on the use of bait formulations that result in virtually no pesticide exposure to students or staff.

Problems with bees, wasps, and yellowjackets will generally increase during the fall months, and drop off dramatically once cold nights or the first frosts occur. Leading up to these times of peak bee and wasp occurrence, inspections of the school exterior and grounds should emphasize the location of any nests or other conditions (landscape plants with honeydew-producing insect infestations, especially unsanitary dumpsters, etc.) that will attract these stinging pests to the school. Any nests found should be treated directly with an insecticide dust or spray. Accessways into the building that may be used by overwintering wasp queens should be caulked or sealed. Some usage of residual (and repellent) pyrethroid spray applications on the exterior of the school, around door or window frames, or to dumpsters and trash barrels, may be necessary and appropriate at key times to reduce the number of wasps that may enter.

Reliance on reports of sightings and thorough inspections should be the basis of pest management efforts against spiders. In warmer regions of the southern and western United States, venomous species such as the black widow or brown recluse spiders may enter from outdoor locations adjacent to the foundation, such as behind plant material or from any accumulations of scrap lumber, litter, or utilities connections. These sources of infestation should be removed, and (similarly as for food plants) a two- to three-foot-wide band around the perimeter of the building, up against the foundation, should be mulched with coarse pea gravel or stone. This will reduce the numbers of most crawling pests entering the school and creating problems, and facilitate inspections and application of exclusionary techniques around the outside of the school. Shrubs or other plant material should be planted and maintained far enough away from the exterior walls of the building so they do not touch, and the stone mulched band kept clean of debris. Vines or shrubs growing against and up the sides of the building should be removed. Use of insecticide baits or barrier treatments in these foundation areas may be necessary at times to control ants, peridomestic cockroaches, or other crawling pests (e.g., occasional invader species discussed in Chapter 12) which may present a sufficient nuisance or threat as they enter the school.

When termite infestations are detected within or around the school building, refer to Chapters 7 and 8 for control procedures.

PEST MANAGEMENT IN SUPERMARKETS

The flow of food and other materials through a large modern supermarket is enormous. Such stores can be thought of as centers of intense activity—food and supplies funnel in from many sources, and this merchandise disperses widely into the community (see Figure 19.7 and the lower part of Figure 19.8). Protecting the quality and wholesomeness of the food that flows through the market is an important responsibility that must be shared by store management and the pest management professional. In addition, supermarkets are often closely inspected by state and local public health officials and other regulatory agencies (e.g., the FDA and USDA). Any presence of pest infestation can be detrimental to the store's reputation and business.

However, despite the size and complexity of supermarkets and the large turnover of stock, these are typically large-volume/low-margin businesses that are conscious of all costs. Thus, even though the requirements for pest management services are great, there is strong pressure to provide high-quality service in a very efficient manner. Due to pest introductions on incoming shipments, the presence of several key pest hot spots, and the need for constant attention to sanitation, a highly organized program is required to achieve the desired level of pest management. An important aspect of this pest management program is frequent, direct communication with key store personnel, such as the store manager or managers of certain departments. The professional's ability to obtain a high level of pest management at a reasonable price will depend on the amount of cooperation received from store personnel. Cooperation on sanitation and various physical alterations or renovations is particularly helpful.

Pests and Pest Hot Spots

The most common and important pests encountered in supermarkets are German cockroaches, various stored product pests (such as beetles and moths), flies (such as house flies and *Drosophila*), and birds. Certain sections of the store will be key areas for pest problems, requiring constant monitoring and more frequent applications of pesticides or other pest management measures. These pest hot spots include the delicatessen area, the bakery and restaurant areas, any bottle return and storage areas, pet food aisles, natural food bins, fruit and vegetable produce sections (see Figure 19.6), employee break and locker rooms, the meat department, and trash and refuse areas (indoors and outdoors). Voids below and behind shelving and in the corners where rows or banks of shelving meet receive a lot of fallout from food spills and create an excellent environment for cockroaches, ants, and mice. These voids are difficult to clean and properly treat for the management of these pests.

The Pest Management Program

A pest management program for supermarkets should begin with a detailed floor plan of the entire facility, with all pest hot spots labeled. As with most other pest management programs, four basic steps

FIGURE 19.6. View of fruit and vegetable produce display area of a supermarket. This can be a hot spot for infestations of cockroaches, rodents, or small flies like fruit, phorid, or drain flies. (Myers)

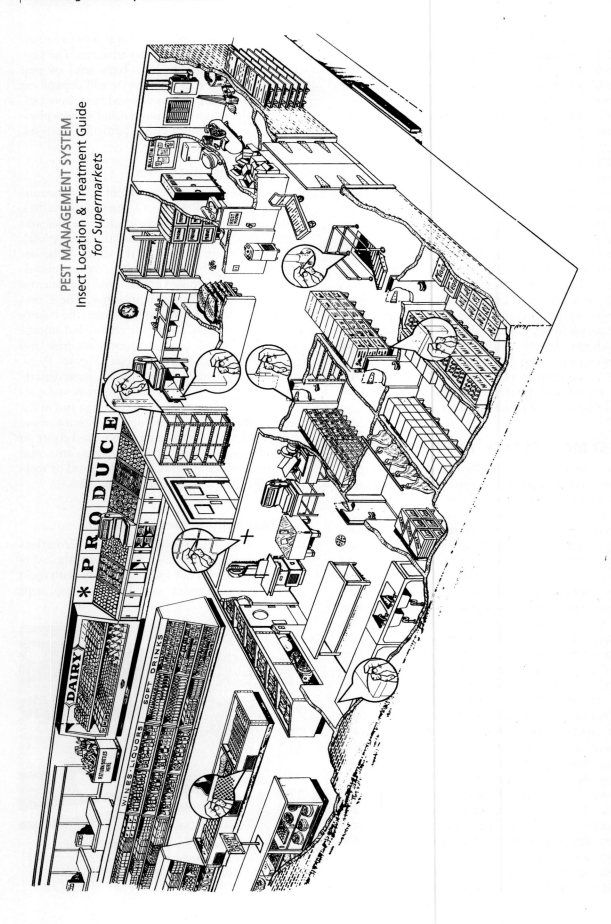

PEST MANAGEMENT SYSTEM
Insect Location & Treatment Guide
for Supermarkets

FIGURE 19.7. Large, modern supermarkets are complex structures, through which enormous amounts of food and many store customers flow each day. (Whitmire/Micro-Gen)

FOOD DISTRIBUTION CHAIN

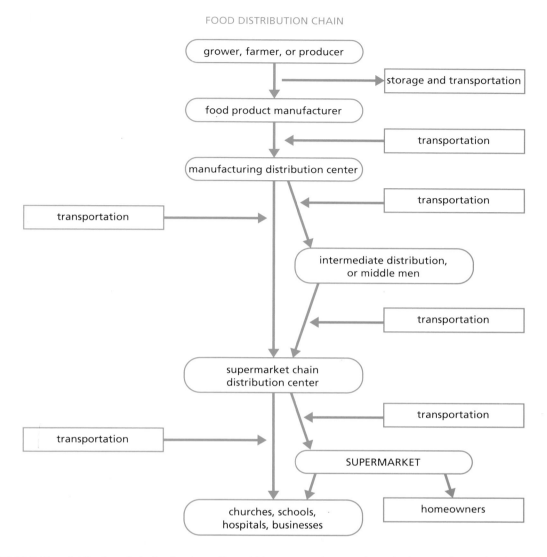

FIGURE 19.8. The distribution chain for food supplies sold in supermarkets can be quite long and complex. Several steps can occur before the supplies reach the supermarket, and many trucking or other transportation firms may be involved. Pest infestations may enter at nearly any point.

should then be followed: (1) inspection and monitoring, (2) application of pest management procedures (sanitation, non-chemical, and chemical procedures), (3) continuous follow-up, and (4) frequent and close communication with store management.

Thorough inspections should be conducted at the start of the program and at frequent intervals throughout. Recommendations for needed sanitation should be made to the store management and reinforced if no timely action is noted. Some professionals use photographs to document sanitation concerns. These can be effective aids when used in communication sessions with the store manager. Special attention should be paid to the pest hot spots. Ongoing monitoring should be conducted

using sticky traps for cockroaches and other crawling insects, glue boards or other traps for mice (see Chapter 15), and pheromone or food attractant traps for stored product pests. However, following the holistic approach, it is also important to monitor the flow of various pests into the facility on the many shipments of food or other merchandise.

A comprehensive program will not only seek to detect and eliminate infestations on incoming stock, but often requires the professional to identify sources of infestation and work with the client's suppliers to correct problems (before they enter the supermarket). Even the most thorough use of pesticides within the premises will not allow acceptable management if infestations of cockroaches, stored product pests, and mice are constantly being introduced on shipments. Most of these shipments cannot be treated directly, except by using costly fumigation. In any case, supplies infested and contaminated with pests should be discarded and not offered for sale. Therefore, surrounding areas should be treated to intercept and control escaping pests. However, in the long run, this approach of intercepting pests on incoming shipments cannot be satisfactory; better solutions should be sought. Suppliers that consistently create problems should be identified and counseled to improve their operations, or, if possible, they should be dropped. This latter step requires the strong support of store management.

When pest infestations are detected on incoming stock, it is important for the professional to understand the complexity of the food distribution chain for modern supermarkets. Figure 19.8 summarizes this distribution chain. Note that potential sources of infestation are present at two or more distribution centers and from two or three (or more) trucking firms. Only by working with store management can the professional understand relevant details of the routing for any particular type of infested stock and suggest steps to correct chronic problems of pest introduction on incoming supplies.

An important aspect of this pest management program is the **implementation of all necessary steps to eliminate pest infestations** within the facility. This includes necessary pesticide applications, physical exclusion, lighting manipulations (see Figure 19.9), and so forth. Control of German cockroaches (and other pests) must be conducted with extreme care to not contaminate any food items or food contact surfaces with insecticides. Dusts are typically used to treat void areas associated with food shelving in the retail area. Baits, residual crack-and-crevice treatments, and careful fogging (ULV) with nonresidual insecticides are also quite useful. Somewhat more extensive use of spot and crack-and-crevice treatments with residual insecticides are often needed in receiving and storage or warehousing areas. These storage areas typically have floors and walls of unpainted concrete or other porous surfaces. Wettable-powder, suspension concentrates, and microencapsulated formulations are most effective on these surfaces. Nearly all of the pest hot spots just listed are prone to German cockroach infestation.

Monitoring and control procedures for mice often involve the use of traps, glue boards, and rodenticide baits. Chapter 15 discusses in detail the inspection and control techniques for mice and rats. Indianmeal moths, sawtoothed grain beetles, flour beetles, and cigarette or drugstore beetles are commonly found in supermarkets (refer to Chapter 10). Monitoring traps are available for these and other stored product pests. These should

Key Points in Pest Management for Supermarkets

Key pests:
- German cockroaches
- Mice
- Flies (especially Drosophila sp. around produce)
- Stored product insects
- Birds (outdoors)

Pest hot spots:
- Delicatessen sections
- Bakeries
- Restaurant areas
- Meat departments
- Under and behind shelves
- Pet food aisles
- Natural food bins
- Fruit and vegetable (produce) aisles
- Bottle return and storage areas
- Employee locker rooms
- Dumpsters and other trash areas

During inspections:
- Routinely check receiving areas for incoming stock.

- Use sticky traps routinely to monitor for pests in key areas.
- Monitor sanitation problems; report them to appropriate staff and check follow-up.

During pesticide applications:
- Avoid any possibility of contaminating food or any food contact surfaces.
- Prefer the use of baits, crack and crevice treatments, and dusting of voids.

Other Points:
- Work with store management to correct chronic problems with infested incoming stock.
- Be sure that the quick and complete cleanup of all spills is routine throughout the facility.
- Check that spilled food and other clutter has not collected under or behind display shelves or in corners. Focus attention on these dead areas when inspecting and treating.
- Remember that the meat department falls under the guidelines of USDA meat and poultry regulations and is inspected by USDA inspectors.

FIGURE 19.9. View of front entrance to supermarket, showing several design and maintenance features that should reduce certain common pest problems. There appear to be no strong lights or lighted signs on the exterior of the building that can attract flying insects to, and into, the facility at night. The entryway lighting is recessed, up under the attached roofline. The parking lot lights are not on the building exterior, but on poles out in the parking lot. Finally, the trash can in the foreground appears well designed and maintained (sanitary) to discourage pests such as flies, yellowjackets, birds, and rodents. (Myers)

FIGURE 19.10. This messy, unsanitary and trash-strewn dumpster area behind a supermarket will likely serve as a key source of pest infestation within the facility. The pest management professional should prevail upon the store management to change this scene into something more like the dumpster shown in Figure 19.11. (Myers)

be used in conjunction with routine inspections of pet food aisles, natural food bins, and spice racks. When these stored product pests are discovered, infested foodstuffs are usually destroyed, and appropriate insecticide applications are made in the areas of infestation. Fogging with nonresidual insecticides and crack-and-crevice applications of residual insecticides are appropriate to contain and eliminate infestations under most circumstances. Careful sanitation should be routinely practiced by store personnel to eliminate residues of spilled grain, flour, or baked goods, which may be sources of infestation for these insects, and important food sources for mice. Storage areas for returned goods and damaged packages are particularly susceptible to infestation by stored product insects and mice. Beyond special attention during inspections and treatment, the store should have firm policies to maintain good sanitation in these areas and limit the length of time goods are stored before disposal.

Flies frequently invade supermarkets during warmer periods, typically from outdoor sources, such as trash dumpsters and loading docks (see Figure 19.10). Sources of flies should be identified and cleaned up or eliminated. Dumpsters or other trash collection facilities should be routinely cleaned (e.g., steam cleaned) (see Figure 19.11).

Applications of residual insecticides to dumpsters and nearby surfaces where flies are landing may be required. Entry of flies into the building can usually be prevented or greatly reduced by physical modification of doorways. Entryways are commonly designed to create a vestibule between the two sets of entry doors. Strong positive (outward) airflow can be created in this vestibule, which prevents most flies from entering. Alternatively, timed-release aerosol machines can be installed in the space between the entry doors to dispense non-residual insecticides, which control flying insects within the vestibule. Sometimes, the orientation of an exterior door with regard to prevailing winds, which may constantly blow flies into the building, must be corrected. Air curtain equipment can be

FIGURE 19.11. This clean and well-maintained trash dumpster at a supermarket will be much less likely than that shown in Figure 19.10 to serve as a source of pest infestation, but should still be inspected regularly by the pest management professional. (Myers)

installed in some circumstances to effectively prevent flies from entering doorways. Proper use of ultraviolet light traps can be effective for intercepting and killing flies entering some supermarkets. However, many stores are now 24-hour operations with substantial lighting that operates in much of the store, so ultraviolet light traps may be ineffective in such areas.

Birds such as sparrows, pigeons, and starlings are often a problem when they nest in light fixtures above covered walkways or in the large signs and lettering on the storefront. Occasionally, large numbers of starlings may begin roosting in nearby trees. Elimination of roosting areas is usually the most efficient means of managing these bird problems. Chapter 16 of this book discusses bird management in detail.

PEST MANAGEMENT IN ZOOS

Zoos represent perhaps the most difficult challenge for urban pest management professionals. The objective of the pest management program is to provide a pleasant, healthy, and relatively pest-free environment for the benefit of both the zoo's animal collection and visitors. Pests such as cockroaches, rodents, and flies can be responsible for spreading bacteria or other parasites that cause infections and diseases among zoo animals. At the same time, the safety of zoo visitors and the many sensitive and valuable animals must be protected by exercising care when using pesticides in pest management efforts.

While zoos vary in size, most have at least a few separate buildings that house animals for display. These buildings are complex structures that contain a very favorable environment for pest presence. Food is constantly available as a result of visitor and zoo animal behavior. Moisture, harborage, and temperature are also generally present at ideal levels for pest populations. The buildings are often connected by underground tunnels that house steam pipes and other utility connections, along with pests such as cockroaches and rodents. Many of the zoo animals are also exhibited outdoors during the warmer months, which further encourages various types of pest problems. In addition, visitors who bring in different types of food for their own consumption, or to feed to the zoo animals, contribute an added dimension to the pest management challenge.

Other factors add to this challenge. One is a general lack of funding to support adequate pest management programs. Also, the zoo's veterinarians and keepers have often become so used to relatively high populations of pests that they accept them as an unavoidable part of the situation. They are usually fearful of the possible threat to zoo animals from the pesticides that must be used. However, once the role of pests in contributing to disease problems and adding to the feeding bill for the zoo's collection is recognized, zoo personnel can become significant allies. Similar to the situation in hospitals, the confidence and support of these zoo staff members is critical to the overall success of the pest management program. This support can be obtained only if the professional develops the respect of these staff members, so only well-trained, personable, and highly motivated professionals should be assigned to work in these situations. They must understand the importance of their role and the sensitivity of the zoo animals. They must also be able to answer the many questions that zoo staff members will ask. Pest management for zoos is hard work. One or more full-time pest management people are generally required for moderate- to large-sized facilities, even where the support of zookeepers and other maintenance staff is strong.

Pests and Pest Hot Spots

Vertebrate pests, such as rats, mice, pigeons, and sparrows, are a more prominent and difficult challenge here than in most other situations. Rodents can be a problem both indoors and outdoors, while birds are generally a problem only outdoors. For most urban and suburban zoos, the surrounding areas (neighborhoods and sewer systems) are a constant source of reinfestation for these pests.

Cockroaches are also a big problem in the zoo buildings and in steam tunnels or any related sewer and drainage systems. Zoo buildings typically support, in addition to German cockroaches, large populations of American, Australian, oriental, and brownbanded cockroaches. Zoos can produce some of the most massive and persistent cockroach infestations the pest management professional will ever encounter.

Many types of flies are a problem in zoos. Manure associated with zoo animals and garbage in outdoor trash barrels attract filth flies. These are also ideal sites for fly larvae to develop, especially during warmer periods. Indoors, manure and the buildup of food residues (often of fruits and vegetables) in cages and floor drains provide ideal substrates for the development of smaller flies, such as *Drosophila* spp., humpbacked flies (family Phoridae), and moth or drain flies (family Psychodidae).

Zoos in the northern, temperate regions of the United States can also have problems with yellowjackets and paper wasps (*Polistes* spp.). These wasps forage for honeydew from the sucking insects that feed on shade trees and shrubs on the zoo grounds. They also forage at trash barrels and picnic sites for

Key Points in Pest Management for Zoos

Key pests:
- Cockroaches (several species)
- Mice
- Flies
- Birds
- Wasps and yellowjackets

Pest hot spots:
- Voids in walls, display boxes, and indoor signs
- Electric conduit, light fixtures, and switch or circuit-breaker boxes
- Trash receptacles
- Snack bars and employee locker rooms
- Animal diet preparation areas
- Floor drains
- Steam tunnels

During inspections:
- Be alert near animals.
- Pests associated with manure and outdoor display areas can move indoors.
- Spot opportunities for effective caulking and pest exclusion.

- Note correctable sanitation problems and work with zookeepers.

During pesticide applications:
- The use of bait formulations is preferred, but place them carefully.
- Do not apply into the air around sensitive animals.
- Use crack and crevice or limited spot applications with residual insecticides. Use wettable-powder, concentrated suspension, or microencapsulated formulations for longest residual action.
- Dust voids that will stay dry for pest control and as an exclusion technique.
- Be careful of possible secondary pesticide poisoning risk to zoo animals feeding on treated pests.

Other points:
- Always cultivate working relationships with zookeepers.
- Inform zookeepers about any pesticide applications made.

sugars, such as soda, melon rinds, and candy wrappers, and for meat items. This behavior makes them particularly bothersome at zoos and other public parks or recreational areas. Furthermore, a certain percentage of zoo visitors will be allergic to bee and wasp venom, so a very real health hazard may exist when these insects are plentiful on zoo grounds.

There are many pest hot spots in zoos. Some can be eliminated by the use of caulking, the application of insecticidal dusts (e.g., to voids), or other exclusion techniques. Hot spots include such areas as moldings and edges around cages, which frequently harbor cockroaches and mice. Floor drains can be a source of cockroaches, flies, and rodents. Cockroaches will use electric conduit and light fixtures as harborages, and rodents may use conduit as runways. Zoo building construction generally creates many wall voids. Hollow concrete blocks are commonly used in construction, and renovation projects often add additional layers of interior wall facings (or paneling), which have hollow spacings behind them. Many zoos use signs and display cases, often with backlighting, which will harbor cockroaches, rodents, and ants. Trash receptacles, indoors or outdoors, are attractive to a variety of insect pests. Permanently housed or built-in trash receptacles are generally very susceptible to chronic infestation.

Other pest hot spots at zoos include foodservice stands or snack bars, employee locker rooms, diet preparation areas (for zoo animals), and ponds or water holes outdoors. These locations favor pests like cockroaches and rodents in nearly any other type of account, including restaurants, healthcare facilities, or food-processing plants. These chronic pest hot spots require constant monitoring and the application of various management procedures, including pesticide applications.

The Pest Management Program
The steps of a pest management program for zoos are no different from those for other situations, but certain aspects of the program represent unique challenges for the professional.

Careful inspections and monitoring efforts (traps, etc.), guided by suitably detailed diagrams of the various buildings and grounds, are necessary to determine the extent of pest infestations. The nature of a zoo and a general tolerance among zoo visitors and staff for some low level of pest presence means that extensive use of traps or other monitoring devices to detect and pinpoint small or remote pest populations is often unnecessary. The threshold for acceptable levels of pest presence is generally not zero, so some low levels of pest presence are acceptable on an ongoing basis.

The next step in a typical pest management program is to institute, or intensify, sanitation and exclusion procedures. Certainly, whatever practical sanitation steps can be implemented should be recommended to the zookeeper and maintenance staffs. In nature, food scraps, animal excrement, and other refuse are widely scattered when animals range throughout their environment; however, the zoo situation causes these pest resources to be concentrated within the animal's cage or habitat. Furthermore, adequate sanitation is often difficult or impossible to achieve in zoo environments.

Chronic filth fly problems are best managed by placing heavy emphasis on removal of all manure or other decaying organic matter sources that support fly development. If pets, such as dogs, are allowed to enter the zoo, their excrement should also be considered. Stronger enforcement of any zoo regulations that prohibit visitors from bringing pets into the zoo should be encouraged.

Recalling that sanitation also generally stresses efforts to remove water and harborage available to pests, there will generally be few (if any) practical ways to limit pest access to water in zoos. Most zoo buildings also have nearly ideal heat and humidity conditions for pest development inside throughout the year. The zoo's animal collection generally requires these conditions, so little can be done to change them.

Zoo buildings may be quite old, because many were built by WPA programs during the Depression, prior to 1940. These buildings were not designed to limit pest problems. Due to current budget constraints for most publicly funded facilities, the typical state of maintenance and repair in zoo facilities means ample pest harborage is available. However, caulking, screening, and other physical exclusion methods to remove harborages are important contributions to efficient long-term pest management. Dusting voids or other harborages with inorganic insecticides, such as boric acid and silica aerogel, does not make them unavailable, but it will make these harborages unsuitable (and lethal) to important pests, such as cockroaches, for long periods. Either the pest management professional should do the work to reduce available pest harborages, or strong recommendations should be made to and implemented by the zoo maintenance staff.

There is often a connection between outdoor pest populations or conditions and certain pest problems inside the buildings or in outdoor animal display areas. Thus, attention should be paid to the routine trimming or removal of grass, trees, and shrubs whenever necessary. This will reduce problems with birds, rodents, and various insect pests, such as ants, wherever they might occur.

Given the limited potential for significantly reducing pest populations via sanitation and other indirect management procedures, **great reliance must be placed on the use of traps, pesticides, and other direct management procedures**. Trapping of rodents, other vertebrate pests, flies, and possibly other insects will always be a useful part of the overall pest management program. However, the careful selection and use of pesticides as the primary direct control procedure is necessary in nearly all situations. Due to the high value of many zoo animals and their extreme sensitivity to many pesticides, the use of these chemicals should be very carefully undertaken. Whenever questions arise about the relative safety of using a pesticide around certain zoo animals, either in the mind of the professional or from inquiries by zoo veterinary staff, the pesticide manufacturer should be contacted as the best source of advice. Manufacturers of pesticides generally have extensive toxicology information on their materials. This will include data on pesticide toxicity to a variety of wild and domesticated animal species. These companies also generally have professional staff members who can help pest management professionals or zoo veterinarians interpret these data and make decisions on how to use pesticides safely around zoo animals.

Pesticide formulations and applications that minimize the risk to zoo animals should be chosen. Airborne applications of insecticides in or around zoo buildings, such as by use of ULV, aerosol, mist, or dust applications, should almost never be attempted. Many zoo animals, such as birds, reptiles, fish, amphibians, insects, or other arthropods (e.g., spiders and scorpions) are very sensitive to even nonresidual insecticides such as pyrethrins or pyrethroids. Dust applications of boric acid (and similar pesticides) should be carefully confined to voids or cracks and crevices, and boric acid should not be used around exhibits of invertebrates, such as insects. Bait formulations will be particularly useful in zoos. Many insect and rodent baits can be contained in sturdy and well-concealed stations. Insect baits are not only generally safe around zoo animals, but also particularly well suited for use in the difficult physical conditions of a zoo. A variety of cockroach and ant baits are available as paste, foam, or granular forms that can be applied into cracks and crevices that are inaccessible to zoo animals. Relatively high temperatures, moist conditions, and a high proportion of surfaces that are difficult for effective residual insecticide spray applications (e.g., concrete and other masonry, steel caging, painted surfaces, and raw wood) all favor the selection of baits. Remember, too, that enhanced sanitation will limit the amount of alternative food competing with any pest bait.

Where residual spray applications are necessary, formulations such as wettable powders, suspension concentrates, and microencapsulations are preferred. They allow maximum efficacy under the difficult environmental conditions and on the surfaces typically found in zoos. However, long residual action cannot generally be achieved under zoo conditions, except where dusts are placed in remote and relatively dry voids. Microencapsulated formulations are generally much less toxic to mammals than their emulsifiable concentrate counterparts, but no such safety advantage should be assumed around other types of zoo animals. Selection of active ingredients, such as insect growth regulators, that have little or no toxicity to most nonarthropod zoo animals is sometimes necessary in zoo situations. IGR applications are especially useful for cockroach control in zoos, because of the long-term population suppression they can allow, coupled with generally good safety characteristics for use around zoo animals. Their relatively slow action in reducing insect populations is usually acceptable in zoos.

Close communication should be maintained with the zoo's veterinarians and animal keepers regarding all pesticide applications. These personnel must be aware of what materials are being used, so they can be alert and responsive if any poisoning problems arise among zoo animals. Besides avoiding spray or dust drift to non-target surfaces, consideration must be given to the possible exposure of zoo animals to pests contaminated with pesticides (and often dying). Birds, reptiles, primates (e.g., monkeys, tamarins, etc.), and other mammals often eat insects within their environment. If those insects, especially cockroaches, are carrying much insecticide, there can be a secondary poisoning hazard to the zoo animals. Such secondary poisoning hazards are also a possibility with the use of some rodenticides, if zoo animals eat poisoned mice or rats.

As with any pest management program, those conducted in zoos require continued communication, monitoring, sanitation, reliance on exclusion and physical control procedures, use of appropriate pesticide applications and other direct control procedures, record keeping, and other forms of follow-up to be successful. Pest management professionals must be alert and flexible in their thinking to adapt and alter the program as needed.

PEST MANAGEMENT IN COMPUTER FACILITIES

Computer facilities—such as large data processing centers, computer rooms in banks and scientific laboratories, and large control rooms at electric power plants, airports, or large, modern factories—are special pest management challenges. No types of pests are unique to such facilities, since no insect, rodent, or other pest feeds on the actual electronic equipment. Insects walking across computer circuitry can cause short circuits and other serious problems, however. Fecal droppings and other body secretions of pests can also damage sensitive electronic circuitry. Special difficulties arise in these facilities because **professionals are restricted in the types of pesticide applications or other direct control procedures they can use** around such sensitive and valuable equipment. We will discuss pest management for facilities such as large rooms or sections of buildings; however, professionals are often faced with these treatment restrictions when pests infest computers, cash registers, telephones, smoke detectors, or other electronic equipment in different accounts.

Pests and Pest Hot Spots

The people who work in these facilities bring in candy, snacks, soda, and other foods, some of which may be spilled on the floor or stored in desks and elsewhere (see Figure 19.12). These food items support infestations of German or brownbanded cockroaches, mice, and ants (especially pharaoh ants). Computer facilities generally have special air-handling equipment designed to provide a relatively cool and dry environment throughout the year. Occasionally, inadequate design or maintenance of the air-handling system allows various species of flies or other flying insects to become a problem within the facility.

Environmental fluctuations can also create pest problems in these facilities. During very dry sea-

FIGURE 19.12. When meals, snacks, and beverages are consumed and stored in computer facilities and office areas, problems with pests such as cockroaches, ants, and mice will be likely. (Myers)

Key Points in Pest Management for Computer Facilities

Key pests:
- German or brownbanded cockroaches
- Mice
- Ants
- Flies and gnats

Pest hot spots:
- Areas where employees consume or store food in the facility
- Break rooms or vending machines
- Coffee machines
- Inside computer equipment that offers a warm harborage to pests
- Above drop ceilings or below raised floors

During inspections:
- Keep in mind that renovations to the facility may have created hidden voids or passageways for pests.

During pesticide applications:
- Do not apply sprays or dusts into computer equipment or in such a way that droplets or particles can damage sensitive circuitry.
- Use baits and traps over sprays and dusts.
- Use a paintbrush to apply liquid residual applications safely.

Other points:
- Try to have facility management prohibit any food presence (storage or consumption) within the facility.
- Be particularly thorough with standard pest management efforts in areas of the building adjacent to the sensitive computer facility, to create a pest-free buffer zone around the facility.

sons, problems with itches due to dry skin and airborne irritants commonly occur in these facilities. These itches may be falsely blamed on pests, such as mites (see also Chapter 11). Keep in mind that these facilities often have high-speed line printers or laser printers and paper shredders, which produce a lot of very fine paper shreds. Other types of airborne irritants might also be present. If relatively high humidity (50 to 70% or greater) exists for extended periods, because of inadequate or poorly maintained air-handling equipment, molds or mildew may form on stored computer paper and cardboard boxes. This mold will support infestations of booklice or other insect and mite pests. Silverfish and firebrats are also frequently associated with such storage conditions, although some species do not require the moist conditions and mold or mildew growth to flourish.

Hot spots for cockroaches are any desks or other areas where food and beverages are consumed, stored, or disposed. Vending machines, restrooms, or locker rooms that might be in a large computer facility (or near a small facility in a larger building) are also hot spots for cockroaches and ants. In an otherwise cool and dry environment, the actual computers and other related equipment, such as printers and terminals, are sources of warmth attractive to cockroaches and other pests for harborage. The ductwork and air handlers of the air-handling system, including heating and chilling coils, may also be pest hot spots. Improper drainage of condensate from chiller coils can create favorable conditions for fly development. Cockroaches, silverfish, or spiders

may also be present in this ductwork or just behind the registers that cover ducts entering walls, ceilings, or floors.

Mice, cockroaches, and other pest infestations can originate above drop ceilings, which are common in computer facilities. These facilities are also somewhat unique because they commonly have a system of raised floor panels that create a void below the floor surface, where many wires connect all equipment. Besides harborage, this subfloor void also tends to collect crumbs and other residues from food or beverage spills.

The Pest Management Program

Focus cockroach inspections on areas where any food items are brought into the facility and consumed. The warm conditions inside nearby computer equipment are also attractive to cockroaches. Pest management professionals should not attempt to open valuable computer equipment for inspection or treatment. Obtain the assistance of a computer technician from the client's staff.

Pests such as cockroaches, ants, and mice will often rely on fallout from food consumption by the facility's staff. A critical factor in the long-term success of the pest management program for these key pests is to eliminate all food presence within the facility. Work with the facility management to ensure that soda and other vending machines, break rooms, and cafeterias are away from the sensitive computer facilities. Employees must not be allowed to store candy, gum, pretzels, nuts, potato chips, and other snack foods inside the computer facility. Coffeepots and coffee drinking should not be allowed inside the facility, if at all possible. Of course, these policies are difficult for management to establish and enforce, but they are an important step in aiding the pest management program.

Do not apply insecticide sprays or dusts into computer equipment. These applications can cause short circuits and other serious problems (see Figure 19.13). Rather, use insecticide or rodenticide baits placed near pest harborage areas, or apply residual insecticides by carefully using a paint-brush. Do not treat surfaces near circuitry or other sensitive areas of the equipment. The pests are not feeding on any internal components of the equipment; they are only harboring there. They must come out of the equipment to feed, so properly applied insecticides will allow control of cockroaches, ants, silverfish, and other pests that harbor in, but must leave, computer equipment. When external panels are removed to open the equipment for inspection, cockroaches can be vacuumed up directly. The use of sticky traps, glue boards, or mechanical traps can also be effective. Some types of equipment can be enclosed in plastic bags and the air inside the bag replaced with carbon dioxide

FIGURE 19.13. Control of pests such as cockroaches, ants, spiders and mice in and around computer equipment can be a significant challenge, which may require ingenuity and persistence by the professional. (Myers)

or nitrogen so the pests will be deprived of oxygen (for 2 to 3 days) and asphyxiated. Work with the computer technician to ensure the safety of these procedures for any particular piece of equipment.

Baits and careful crack and crevice or spot applications (sprayed or painted on) of liquid residual insecticides can be made in appropriate areas within the room, but away from the actual computer equipment. The use of dusts or any fine sprays, such as ULV or aerosol applications, should be avoided within the computer facility, or even in nearby areas.

Many computer rooms or multiroom departments are housed in areas originally designed for other purposes. Thus, renovation of the rooms and the various electric, plumbing, air-conditioning, or other utilities serving the computer facilities may have created possibilities for pests (or unwanted pesticide dusts, aerosols, or vapors) to move into the facility from adjacent areas. Professionals should be alert to these possibilities and use caulking or other pest exclusion techniques whenever possible.

As part of the long-term pest management strategy for computer facilities, it is often advisable to intensify the standard pest management effort in all areas adjacent to the sensitive computer facility. These adjacent areas often include such pest-prone areas as restrooms and break rooms with vending machines. Pest infestations should not be allowed to build up in these areas, as some pests will constantly find their way into the more sensitive facility, where adequate pest management is much more difficult to achieve.

Pest management for the other types of pests mentioned can be approached using standard techniques discussed elsewhere in this book, except that necessary precautions should be observed when making pesticide applications around sensitive computer equipment. When attempting mouse management, remember that voids exist above drop ceilings and below raised floors. Additional mouse passageways or harborage may have been created during any renovation done to create the computer facility.

For booklice, mites, or other pests that require moist conditions and molds or mildew to support infestations, successful long-term pest management requires correction of the moisture problem. Either the air-handling system will have to be redesigned and upgraded, or some other moisture source, such as a leak or chronic condensation problem, will have to be corrected. Perhaps merely increasing the airflow or air turnover rates through the facility will help. Some pesticide applications may be helpful, but the type of dust or ULV applications generally preferred to control scattered booklice and mite infestations will not be possible in a computer room.

Fly problems in computer facilities should be managed without relying on airborne spray applications. Try to determine the source or sources of the flies and either eliminate them or intercept the flies before they can enter the facility. Screens may have to be installed within the air-handling system to prevent flies or gnats from entering by this route. If flies are entering the doorways to the facility as employees come and go, the air-handling system can usually be adjusted to create a positive air pressure within the facility. This causes a rush of air to exit the facility whenever a door is opened, preventing fly entry. Acceptable results may require two or three periods of adjustment, and perhaps some adjustment of air-handling zones in areas adjacent to the computer facility.

SUPPLEMENTARY READING MATERIAL

Animal Research Laboratories, Zoos and Pet Stores. Nor-Am Chemical Company, Nor-Am Technical Protocol no. 9. Wilmington, Del., 1987.

Bennett, G. W., and J. M. Owens, eds. *Advances in Urban Pest Management.* New York: Van Nostrand and Reinhold, 1986. 399 pp.

Brady, J. "A Sanitarian's View of Pest Control in Supermarkets." *Pest Control Technology* 11, no. 8 (1983): 64–66.

California Dept. of Pesticide Regulation. *California School IPM Program website.* (**http://www.cdpr. ca.gov/cfdocs/apps/schoolipm/main.cfm**)

Fotos, V. "Pest Control in Shopping Malls." *Pest Control Technology* 13, no. 2 (1985): 39–43.

Fotos, V. "Pest Control in Zoos and Parks." *Pest Control Technology* 13, no. 5 (1985): 56–60.

Granovsky, T. A. "Health Care Facilities—Solving the Puzzle." *Pest Management* 6 (1987): 14–18.

Hospitals and Nursing Homes. Nor-Am Chemical Company, Nor-Am Technical Protocol no. 4. Wilmington, Del., 1987.

Moreland, D. "Pest Control in Supermarkets." *Pest Control Technology* 11, no. 8 (1983): 59–62, 79.

Moreland, D. "Sanitation: How Important Is It?" *Pest Control Technology* 13, no. 8 (1985): 50–52, 67.

National Pest Control Association. *Marketing Pest Control Services to Health-Care Facilities.* NPCA Management Guidelines Series. Dunn Loring, Va., 1986. 53 pp.

"Non-Chemical Pest Control." *Pest Control Technology* 13, no. 5 (1985): 52–54.

Purdue Univ. *Midwest Technical Resource Center for IPM in Schools and Daycares website.* (**http://www.entm. purdue.edu/entomology/outreach/schoolipm/**)

Robinson, W. H. *Urban Entomology: Insect and Mite Pests in the Human Environment.* London: Chapman and Hall, 1996. 430 pp.

Story, K. O. "Pest Control in High-Tech Areas." *Pest Control Technology* 13, no. 7 (1985): 42–47.

Tucker, J. B. "A Guide to Pest Control in Animal Laboratory Facilities." *Pest Control Technology* 12, no. 2 (1984): 46–53.

Texas A&M Univ. *IPM in Schools website.* (**http:// schoolipm.tamu.edu/**)

U.S. EPA. *Integrated Pest Management (IPM) in Schools website* (**http://www.epa.gov/pesticides/ipm/index. htm**).

Univ. of Florida. *School IPM website.* (**http://school ipm.ifas.ufl.edu/**)

Vega, R. "PCOs Ring-Up Profits with Supermarket Accounts." *Pest Control Technology* 15, no. 7 (1987): 62–69.

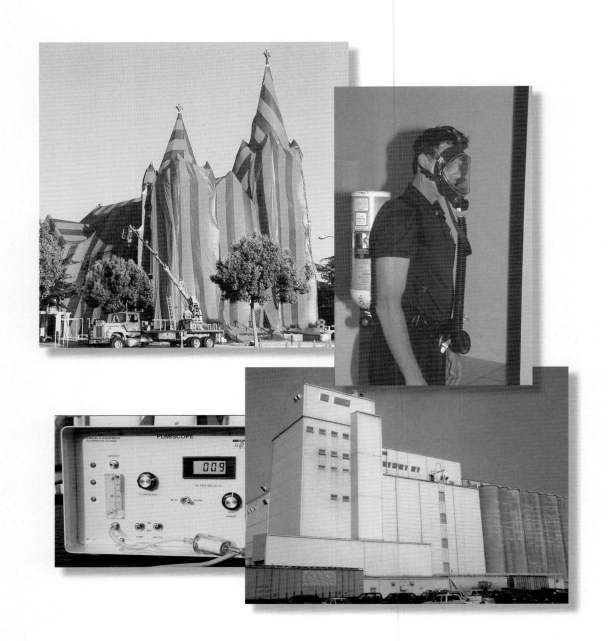

CHAPTER 20 | Fumigation

Written by Brian M. Schneider, Ph.D.*

The art and science of fumigation is highly specialized and technical in nature. Fumigation requires a great deal of knowledge, experience, and commitment to achieve effective pest control while ensuring safety for workers and bystanders. Only those individuals properly trained in the use and handling of fumigants, and dedicated to proper fumigant stewardship, should direct or participate in fumigation operations.

This chapter is designed to provide an introduction to the various types of fumigants and fumigation use patterns. It also presents information on fumigation equipment, application procedures and safety precautions. To become a licensed fumigator, in-depth classroom and field training, passing a state examination, and usually an apprenticeship period working with a knowledgeable fumigator are required.

WHY FUMIGATE?

Fumigation may be defined as the act of introducing a toxic chemical in an enclosed space in such a manner that it quickly disperses in the gas phase to reach the target organism. Liquids, granules, and dusts are more commonly used for combating pests, but they are limited in their ability to reach the target sites or pest harborages.

Aerosols, smokes, mists, and fogs, which are suspensions of particulate matter in air, also have their place in pest control strategies, but they are not fumigants because they are not gases. These formulations tend to relatively quickly fall from the air. Fumigants however, tend to remain in the air, primarily entering insect pests through their spiracles, or the lungs of vertebrate pests such as rodents, as these animals respire (breathe).

Some chemicals, such as DDVP, can exert a so-called fumigant or vapor-phase action due to their

moderately high vapor pressure by yielding small amounts of toxicant to the pest in the vapor phase. Another example is naphthalene (found in moth balls), which evaporates slowly at room temperature and performs its insecticidal function in the vapor state.

Due to their physical characteristics, fumigants disperse from the source of introduction to occupy all air spaces within an enclosed area. Fumigants penetrate cracks, crevices, pores in wood, and the commodity being treated. Their ability to penetrate and fill all voids makes them ideally suited in many situations for the control of structural and commodity pests that other types of chemicals cannot reach.

The fumigants used today are broad-spectrum pesticides, meaning they can kill a wide range of pests, and other living things in the treated area. They are widely used in the pest control industry for the control of wood-destroying insects, such as drywood termites and powderpost beetles, as well as food-infesting pests in storage, milling or food-processing facilities, and a wide range of quarantine insects and fungi.

No protective residues are left behind after a fumigation, unlike liquid and solid pesticide formulations. Without residual deposits, post-fumigation application of residual chemicals or other preventive measures may be required as part of an overall pest management program. On the other hand, minimal residues following fumigation is a positive attribute.

Key Point: So, why fumigate? Because fumigation is a practical method for providing rapid pest management. Fumigation delivers the pesticide to the target pest located in areas or materials not accessible through application of other pesticide formulations (e.g. solids, liquids). For this reason, fumigants are well suited for controlling insect pests

*Dr. Schneider is a fumigation specialist with Dow AgroSciences.

in commodity storage, milling machinery, structural wood, and a variety of quarantine products.

TYPES OF FUMIGATION

Urban pest management fumigations can be categorized in four different ways, by the:

1. object to be treated—grain, fresh fruit, processed food, log furnishings, structural timbers, artifacts, and so on;
2. place to be fumigated—residence, warehouse, food-processing plant, railcar, barge, ship, grain bin, and so forth;
3. pest to be treated—wood-destroying insect, rodent, stored product insect, and so on;
4. method of confinement—chamber, tarp, or tape-seal.

Some of these categories are self-explanatory (e.g. grain bin), while the definition of others (e.g., structural) may vary by user. The categories are not strictly defined and the names have been established by convention.

In the broadest terms, urban fumigations can be classified as "postharvest," and "structural." **Postharvest** fumigations are conducted to protect a food commodity once it has been harvested. These can include fumigations as the product (e.g., walnuts) enters a processing site, fumigation of the milling site with commodity present, and then fumigation of the finished packaged goods in a warehouse or supermarket distribution center. **Structural** fumigation does not involve targeted fumigation of any commodity at all, but rather fumigation of structural units such as houses, commercial buildings, or artifacts.

Postharvest fumigations can be subdivided into "space" or "commodity" fumigations. In postharvest **space** fumigations, a large portion of the fumigation space is air, and the target pest is not located in bulk or packaged product, such as mill or processing plant fumigations.

For postharvest **commodity** fumigations, the pests are located in the commodity. In addition, the commodity normally occupies a substantial portion of the fumigated volume. Examples include stored grain in a silo, nuts in a warehouse, or a stack of logs under a tarp.

Fumigations can also be categorized by the physical design and structure of the fumigated space, including chambers, bulk commodity, mills/processing plants, residential/commercial structures, or transportation vehicles. These fumigation categories can be further divided. Bulk commodity for example, could include silos, flat storage, or tarped stacks of commodity. Each of these sites has its own specific challenges for conducting a safe, effective, and efficient fumigation.

Characterizing fumigations by the target pest provides some insight into the type of commodity being fumigated, yet often does not provide much clarity in how or where the fumigation will be conducted. A stored product insect pest fumigation targeting the red flour beetle (*Tribolium castaneum*) can be very different if conducted in a grain silo, railcar, flour mill, or warehouse. As well, a wood-infesting beetle fumigation is very different procedure if performed on a house, a tarped pile of logs, or wood artifacts in a chamber.

Fumigators commonly categorize fumigations by the sealing process. Chambers, especially vacuum chambers, achieve the best seal. Tarping can provide a good seal, while the so called tape-seal method usually achieves the poorest gas confinement. Sealing methods are defined in more detail later in this chapter.

Key Points: There are many types of fumigation, each requiring specific knowledge and skill. Only conduct those fumigations you are trained and licensed to perform and for which you possess the proper equipment. Pick the fumigant that best fits the situation. Check that product labeling permits the planned application. Ensure all legal and safety requirements are met. Confine the fumigant well to minimize risk of exposure.

THE FUMIGATION PROCESS

Each fumigation job is unique. Environmental, structural, pest, and commercial factors will vary across fumigations. For fumigation success, the fumigator must have a thorough knowledge of the properties and qualities of the fumigant. The characteristics of the structure and commodities to be fumigated, as well as the customer's expectations, need to be understood and then incorporated into the fumigation plan.

The fumigation crew must know how to seal the structure, as well as apply, monitor, and aerate the fumigant. Safety is priority #1, and so safety procedures should be practiced until they are second nature. Nothing should be taken for granted or left to chance.

The fumigation process can be organized into seven major activities:

1. Planning and preparing
2. Sealing, securing and posting the structure
3. Fumigant introduction
4. Monitoring and adjusting for safety and success
5. Aeration

The Fumigation Process

Prefumigation planning is essential to a successful and safe fumigation. Having a written fumigation plan significantly increases the probability of success in controlling the target pest and ensuring worker and bystander safety. The following checklist presents the general considerations for all types of fumigation; however, keep in mind that additional steps for specific fumigants and specific fumigation jobs may be necessary.

Planning and Preparation:
1. Identify the pest problem.
2. Prepare scale diagram of site, include volume and connected structures.
3. Select fumigant—registered and appropriate for conditions and purpose.
4. Choose a "command center" site, where safety equipment, radio base station, first aid, emergency response information, and fumigant monitoring will take place. This must be in a "safe haven," where fumigant exposure during the application, exposure period, and aeration will never surpass the PEL.
5. Plan sealing of structure: materials, locations, workforce, and timing.
6. Ensure connected structures are sealed off or evacuated (see Figure 20.1).
7. Plan fumigant introduction and circulation—introduction sites and fan location. This is critically important when fumigant is released from within structure by fumigators.
8. Plan fumigation monitoring inside fumigated space and surrounding areas.
9. Plan fumigant aeration—exhaust location and necessary equipment.
10. Confirm with site owners/occupants the written fumigation plan, timing, and their responsibilities.
11. Assemble necessary materials and equipment. Confirm they are properly functioning, especially safety equipment and monitoring devices.

Structure Sealing, Securing, and Posting
1. Notify authorities required by state and local regulations, including: police, fire, doctor, guard service, plant personnel, etc. Include in notice: the fumigant, structure, timing, safety procedures and equipment, and fumigator contact information.
2. Review fumigation process and emergency response plan with fumigation team (fumigators always work in teams of at least two).
3. Check safety equipment (e.g., sufficient air for SCBAs).
4. Post structure with fumigation warning signs on all sides and at all entry points.
5. Restrict entry to only those involved in fumigation. Secure structure so that there is only one entrance.
6. Make certain fumigation area is vacated and all persons are accounted for by conducting a walk-through of the structure just prior to sealing the last entrance.
7. Secure the last remaining entrance. A separate locking system should be used, with the only keys available to the fumigator.
8. Post guards (if used).

Fumigant Introduction
1. Put on or have personal safety equipment and fumigant monitoring equipment at the ready.
2. Certified Applicator releases fumigant as planned. Be especially careful if introducing fumigant from inside fumigated space.
3. Check perimeter of structure for leaks; seal these while ensuring safety of fumigators and bystanders.

Monitoring and Adjusting for Safety and Success
1. Monitor inside fumigated space to make certain sufficient fumigant concentration is maintained to reach target dosage.
2. Calculate HLT and projected dosage for each monitored location.
3. Introduce additional fumigant and/or extend exposure if necessary to reach target dosage.
4. Record, by monitoring point, fumigant concentrations, half-loss time, and CT achieved for review and planning improvements in future jobs.
5. Periodically check perimeter of structure for leaks; if practical, seal these while ensuring safety of fumigators and bystanders.

Aeration
1. Initiate aeration plan. Key to success is preplanning process and locating circulation and exhaust equipment for easy and safe operation.
2. Confirm, with gas detection devices of sufficient sensitivity, that permissible exposure limits are not exceeded in surrounding areas.

Clearance
1. Confirm, with gas detection device of sufficient sensitivity, that all breathing areas within fumigated space are at or below reentry levels.
2. Notify authorities (police, fire department, plant personnel) that fumigation is over and that structure is safe for reentry.
3. Remove warning signs.

Clean-up and Follow-up
1. Remove sealing materials and fumigation equipment.
2. Dispose of, or prepare for return shipment, fumigant containers and/or residues.
3. Check on efficacy (e.g., bug checks).
4. Through discussions with customer and fellow workers, update site fumigation plan for improved safety and efficiency of future fumigations.

FIGURE 20.1. Diagram of connected structures. Structures connected to fumigated structure by pipes, tunnels, walls etc.

6. Clearance for re-entry
7. Cleanup and follow-up

See The Fumigation Process summary list in this chapter for critical activities at each stage. Successful fumigators prepare a fumigation plan, communicate it to those that need to know, execute it with dedication to quality and safety, and continuously improve it based on experience.

FUMIGANT DOSAGE = CONCENTRATION × TIME

Both insect and vertebrate pests have a **respiratory system** for ventilation of carbon dioxide out of their bodies and intake of oxygen. See Chapter 1 for a detailed description of the insect respiratory system. The primary route of fumigant exposure for the larval, pupal, and adult life stages of insect pests is through penetration of the respiratory system. For the egg stage, however, fumigants penetrate through the egg shell. For vertebrate pests such as rodents and snakes, fumigant inhalation into the lungs is the primary route of exposure.

Exposure time, or how long the pest is breathing the fumigant, is a critical factor in determining the dosage received by the pest. The other critical factor in the dosage formula is the concentration of fumigant in the air.

Fumigant dosages are calculated as the product of $C \times T = CT$. The C stands for Concentration and the T for Exposure Time. This formula is commonly called Haber's rule.

Concentration, in English units, is presented as ounce/1000 cubic feet (abbreviated here as oz/1000 ft^3). Dosage in English units of ounces-hours/1000 cubic feet (oz-h/1000 ft^3) directly converts to metric units of gram-hours/cubic meter (g-h/m^3) or milligram-hours/liter (mg-h/l). For convenience in this chapter, fumigant dosage will be reported in the shorthand form of CT units (e.g., 500 CT) and concentration in units of oz/1000 ft^3 (e.g., 20 oz/1000 ft^3).

The dosage formula C^nT = dosage, most accurately represents how insects are affected by fumigants. This formula takes into account that either exposure time (T) or concentration (C) may be more important in determining the lethal dosage of a fumigant. One dramatic example is phosphine gas (PH_3), which generally requires long exposures, regardless of concentration, to be effective. In the C^nT formula, n will be > 1 if concentration is more important in achieving the lethal dosage, while $n <$ 1 if time is more important.

The goal of any fumigation is to confine a sufficient amount of fumigant for a long enough exposure time to kill the target pest. The **lethal dosage** is the CT necessary to kill a specified percent of a pest population. For example, a lethal dosage 95%, or LD_{95}, is the CT that will achieve 95% control of the fumigated pest population. The **achieved dosage**, is the CT accumulated by multiplying the concentration level in the fumigated space by the exposure duration. When the achieved dosage is greater than the targeted lethal dosage, the fumigation should be successful.

LIFE STAGE EFFECT ON DOSAGE

The fumigant dosage required to kill a target insect pest varies by species, life stage (egg, larvae, pupae, and adult), temperature, and in some cases exposure period. For phosphine and sulfuryl fluoride, the egg stage is the most difficult life stage to kill due to limited penetration of these fumigants through the egg shell. Pupae are generally more tolerant than other life stages to methyl bromide because this fumigant binds onto the pupal case, limiting methyl bromide penetration to the pupae inside. Diapausing life stages also show greater tolerance to fumigants than active larvae and adults because of their slowed metabolic rate.

Some fumigants, such as sulfuryl fluoride, can demonstrate a delayed killing effect, called "latent mortality," whereby the percent of the pest population killed continues to increase for several days after exposure. For example, one day after the fumigation, percent control may be 85%, while four

Fumigation and Pest Management

Fumigation should be only a part of a pest management strategy, especially where stored products are involved. The ultimate goal in the management of pests in stored products should be to improve the methods of handling, storing, and processing commodities, so that the need for pesticides will decrease. Fumigants should never be used as a substitute for the following management procedures.

- Use sound structures for storage of commodities.
- Maintain clean conditions around storage facilities.
- Exclude pests—for example, randomly sample for insect pests in incoming grain, reject or treat infested shipments.
- Remove grain residues or debris from storage facility.
- Spray storage area with approved residual insecticide after removal of food or feed residues.
- Store commodity in conditions unsuitable for insect development.
  — store grain at low moisture levels.
- Aerate to cool grain and maintain uniform temperature.
- Treat grain with appropriate insecticide protectant while transferring to storage.
- Inspect regularly (e.g., pheromone traps) to determine:
  — evidence of insect activity
  — accumulation of moisture
  — changes in temperature.

Fumigations can be part of a stored product pest management plan, but should not be the cornerstone.

days after exposure 100% of the insects may be dead. When latent mortality is considered, the dosage that is ultimately effective may be substantially lower than the dosage required to kill quickly.

TEMPERATURE EFFECT ON DOSAGE

Insects are cold blooded, meaning their metabolic and respiratory rates increase as temperature increases. Thus more fumigant enters an insect's system under warm conditions. Secondarily, gases are more active at higher temperatures, commodity sorption is less, and gases are able to penetrate and reach the target pest more rapidly. Under warm con-

ditions less fumigant is required to achieve control than at cooler temperatures because of increased insect activity and better penetration.

Rodents, on the other hand, are warm blooded and maintain more constant respiratory and metabolic rates. This makes them equally susceptible to fumigant action at normal fumigation temperatures.

Carbon dioxide (CO_2) is sometimes used in conjunction with fumigants to accelerate the rate of respiration and, therefore, fumigant uptake. However, too much CO_2 can anesthetize insects, decreasing fumigant uptake, and subsequent control. An example of this treatment strategy is the use of CO_2, heat, and phosphine in combination to control stored product pests in mills.

CALCULATING ACHIEVED CT (DOSAGE)

A completely closed and leakproof system, such as a sealed laboratory flask or fumigation chamber, is the most straightforward means of calculating the achieved CT. There is no gas loss, so the rate of fumigant concentration decline over time does not complicate the calculation of dosage achieved.

For example, if 8 oz/1,000 ft^3 was introduced and after 24 hours, 8 oz/1,000 ft^3 remained in the chamber, 192 CT (8 x 24 = 192) would have been accumulated. The target pest was exposed to all of the fumigant introduced throughout the exposure period (see Figure 20.2). Following the CT concept, 192 CT is achieved whether the exposure is:

- 24 oz/1,000 ft^3 for 8 hours (24 x 8), or
- 48 oz/1,000 ft^3 for 4 hours (48 x 4), or
- 16 oz/1,000 ft^3 for 12 hours (16 x 12).

Unfortunately, most fumigated structures are not leakproof and, therefore, calculating achieved CT is not this simple. As fumigant escapes, there is a continuously decreasing amount of gas working in the confined area against the target pest.

The rate at which the gas escapes the confined area or "chamber" is referred to as the **half-loss time (HLT)** and is defined as the time required to lose half the fumigant concentration during the fumigation. Any gas that escapes is no longer available to act on the insect. Therefore, to compensate for lost fumigant, a greater initial concentration, a longer period of exposure, and possibly reintroduction of fumigant may be required to attain the lethal dosage for the target pest.

For example, assume 8 oz/1,000 ft^3 of a fumigant is introduced into a tented structure, as was used in the first example above. Half of the gas escapes in 24 hours, so that at the end of the exposure period there is only 4 oz/1,000 ft^3. Only about

VAULT (CHAMBER)	DOSAGE ACCUMULATION
• Excellent confinement • No gas loss	8 oz./1000 ft³ <u>24 hours</u> 192 ounce-hours

TARP	
• Good confinement • Variable gas loss • Long exposures	8 oz./1000 ft³ <u>24 hours with 24 HLT</u> 142 ounce-hours

TARP AND SEAL	
• Poor confinement • Variable gas loss • Short exposures	8 oz./1000 ft³ <u>24 hours with 6 HLT</u> 66 ounce-hours

FIGURE 20.2. Dosage accumulation (concentration x time), as influenced by type of confinement and half-loss time (HLT).

142 CT would have been achieved, not 192 CT (see Figure 20.2). If the HLT was 6 hours, so that at the end there was only 0.5 oz/1,000 ft³, only about 66 CT would have been accumulated (see Figure 20.2).

If the target pest required 125 CT for 100% mortality, this level of control would have been achieved in the first case, but not in second fumigation scenario. In the second case a "top-up" (adding more fumigant) would be necessary to accumulate the lethal dosage.

The structural fumigant, Vikane™ Gas Fumigant (sulfuryl fluoride) (Dow AgroSciences, LLC, Indianapolis, Ind.) is used with dosage slide rules (Fumiguide™ B and Y) or an electronic calculator (Fumiguide™ calculator) for Vikane gas fumigant. The Fumiguides can be used to estimate the rate of gas loss based on variable environmental and structural conditions. Most importantly, the Fumiguides allow the fumigator to accurately adjust the initial concentration to achieve the target CT over a range of HLTs and exposure periods.

Monitoring gas concentrations during any fumigation also helps a fumigator confirm the rate of gas loss. Any additional fumigant or time required to achieve the desired CT can then be calculated. These monitoring records and HLT calculations can also be used when planning the next fumigation of this, or similar, structures.

FUMIGANT CONFINEMENT

Fumigants must be confined long enough for the pest to receive a lethal exposure. Remember, fumigant dosages are measured as Concentration ×

Time = CT. If the fumigant is not held long enough at a sufficient concentration the lethal dosage will not be achieved.

Following the principle of gas diffusion, fumigants diffuse from areas of high concentration (i.e., the fumigation space) to areas of lesser concentration (i.e., the outside air) unless confined by a gas-impermeable barrier, such as a tarpaulin or fumigation chamber walls. Think of how exhaust fumes from an operating car can build up in a closed garage. However, in the open air, the toxic exhaust fumes readily dissipate to safe levels since there is no barrier to confine them.

The diffusion and penetration qualities of fumigants are a benefit in reaching the target pest, but a drawback when causing fumigant to escape into the surrounding air. Fumigants, for example, readily penetrate porous wood to kill termites, but also escape through wooden roofs of flour mills. If air can pass through a material, assume fumigants will also.

Many types of structures can hold fumigants effectively if sealed properly: Fumigation chambers, buildings (homes, mills, food-processing facilities, warehouses, etc.), tarpaulin-covered commodities (grains, fruits, other food products, logs, etc.), silos, ships, railcars, and the like. Each requires specialized techniques and skill to properly seal them to ensure that sufficient fumigant concentrations are maintained for long enough periods of time to kill the target pest.

There are a variety of materials, tools, and techniques available to obtain good gas confinement, which is why this aspect of fumigation can be considered more of an art than a science. The better the seal, the less gas and/or time required to achieve the target CT.

A key to good gas confinement is experience gained from monitoring gas concentrations during fumigations. Simply stated: If you don't know where the leaks are how can you seal them? Monitoring records will identify key leak areas and previously successful sealing techniques. When this knowledge is applied to enhanced sealing, the benefits, both in fumigant cost reduction and enhanced safety, can be substantial.

In many cases, sealing, as well as the rest of the fumigation process, can be carried out without disturbing the infested materials in any way. Durable nylon-coated tarps and lightweight plastic sheeting are available to envelop spaces, materials, or both, thereby creating a fumigation "chamber." These materials have increased the use of fumigants while helping to make fumigant confinement easier, more standard, and adaptable to varying fumigation situations.

Surface Area to Volume of Structure

As the size of a structure increases, the volume of the structure grows much faster than the surface area of the tarps.

Example	Dimensions	Volume of Structure (cubic feet)	Tarp Area (square feet)	Ratio of Tarp Surface Area Compared to Volume of the Structure
1	10 x 10 x 10	1,000	500	1:2
2	20 x 20 x 20	8,000	2,000	1:4
3	40 x 40 x 40	64,000	8,000	1:8

The ratio of tarp surface area compared to volume of the structure is fairly high for the small structure but is dramatically less for the large structure. In large structures, there is a relatively greater volume of fumigant to escape from a relatively small surface area. Thus, always try to use your best tarps for the small jobs to reduce the rate of gas loss and contain the fumigant for the time it takes to eradicate the target pest.

Three general methods are used to confine fumigants at the site of the pest:

• **Chamber method.** This method involves using vaults or small rooms specifically constructed to confine the fumigant. Most are designed for reuse and have features that facilitate the entire fumigation process. They are fitted with ports for monitoring the gas concentrations, special doors and ramps for easy loading and unloading, simple sealing systems, and exhaust systems for speedy aeration.

Since chambers generally hold the gas very well, they require less fumigant investment than other confinement methods. Specially constructed vacuum chambers can reduce exposure time and lethal dosage by aiding in penetration of fumigant to the target pest, but are expensive to construct. The quantity of commodity that can be fumigated is limited by the size of the chamber. Portable chambers constructed with special tarpaulin material and seals are available. One variation of the portable chamber employs vacuum technology for low oxygen treatments.

• **Tarp method.** This method involves air chambers created by using tarpaulins or plastic sheeting to contain the fumigant. Large vinyl-coated nylon tarps or polyethylene sheeting are draped over the structure or infested items and sealed at ground level (see Figure 20.3). Homes, churches, historic buildings, and other structures that have many openings for gas to escape are generally tarped to maintain a high enough gas concentration over the exposure period to kill the target pest. Commodities such as logs, stored dried fruits, and tree nuts in storage bins, and even shipping containers and railcars can be efficiently sealed with tarps.

Five major factors affect confinement and, therefore, the HLT when using tarps. These are the tarp condition, the seal condition (tarp-to-ground seal and seams), the wind speed, the volume of the tented area, and the type of underseal (e.g., concrete, clay, loam, or sand).

• **Tape and seal method.** Polyethylene, tape, or both are applied to doors, windows, vents, and other obvious openings, while caulk, spray foam, or tape can be used for smaller openings, joints, and cracks. Very large or structurally complex buildings are normally sealed this way since tarping is not usually practical. Food-processing plants are a typical example.

Generally tape and seal achieves the poorest gas confinement of the three methods. Estimating HLT is usually imprecise due to the wide range of sealing challenges. Experience and gas retention records from past tape and seal jobs is the key to more accurate HLT estimation.

FIGURE 20.3. A tarped residential structure and fumigation trucks. (Myers)

FUMIGANT CHARACTERISTICS

Each fumigant has advantages and disadvantages. The physical, toxicological, and insecticidal performance characteristics of each fumigant must be weighed to determine the best choice for a given situation. Every fumigation, must be viewed as unique, and each job planned thoroughly to ensure safety and pest control success.

All fumigants used today are very toxic. Those commonly used are currently classified by the EPA as restricted-use pesticides. Their toxicity, combined with poor warning properties (colorless and/or odorless), require that a great deal of respect and care be used when handling these products.

Fumigants vary in their pest control performance. Some kill rapidly, others much more slowly. In some cases, mortality may not be fully expressed by the pest population for several days following a lethal concentration. Sublethal dosages may have a paralyzing effect, with subsequent recovery.

Some fumigants have detrimental effects on certain commodities, even at low concentrations, while others have none. The amount of sorption by exposed items and the ability to penetrate to the target pest varies from fumigant to fumigant, as does the effort required to aerate the product after treatment.

Table 20.1 compares various key characteristics of four common fumigants and thus suggests why these fumigants behave differently. These properties are briefly described here:

- **Boiling point.** The temperature at which the fumigant changes from a liquid to a gas.
- **Vapor pressure.** The pressure exerted by a gas that is in equilibrium with its solid or liquid state. Vapor pressure increases as temperature increases and determines the pressure inside fumigant cylinders. A high vapor pressure aids in pushing fumigant through long introduction lines and up to high elevations, such as the upper floors of structures.
- **Specific gravity of gas.** The ratio of the weight of any volume of a gas to the weight of the same volume of air. Air has a specific gravity of 1. A fumigant, in the gaseous state, with a specific gravity of 3.0, is 3.0× heavier than air.
- **Physical nature.** Organic molecules are those that contain carbon. Since like attracts like, organic fumigants will tend to sorb more readily than inorganic fumigants onto/into other organic molecules, such as foods and wood.

The few fumigants registered today possess many desirable fumigant characteristics. All have been in wide use for many years, with fumigators identifying the viable use patterns for each. For example, phosphine is the dominant fumigant for grain fumigation, but due to the potential for metal corrosion, it is less commonly used around sensitive electronic and mechanical equipment. Fumigators should understand each product's particular advantages and disadvantages, (e.g., labeled uses, corrosiveness, reactivity, cost, condensation potential, ovicidal activity, rate flexibility, and aeration qualities) and select the most appropriate fumigant for each pest situation.

BEHAVIOR OF FUMIGANTS

To understand how fumigants work and how they can be used effectively, several concepts related to fumigant behavior must be studied.

Diffusion and Penetration

Diffusion is the spontaneous process whereby a fumigant moves from an area of high concentration toward an area of low concentration. Through diffusion, a fumigant will expand and mix until a gas-impermeable barrier confines it. Eventually the fumigant will reach equilibrium, which is when the fumigant concentration is the same throughout the confined space.

Diffusion, or self-mixing, is dependent on the fumigant's characteristics (molecular weight, specific gravity, and sorption) as well as environmental conditions, such as temperature and air movement. Achieving equilibrium may take 30 minutes to several hours, even days for some fumigants without forced air circulation.

The rate of fumigant diffusion and penetration is faster at higher temperatures. Some fumigant products (liquid fumigants in cylinders) lower the temperature of air near the introduction points, creating a layer of fumigant laden cold air surrounded by warmer air. Colder air is heavier than warm air (remember the winters when it seemed all the heated air was at the ceiling?), which further complicates or slows down the self-mixing.

Some fumigants used today are heavier than air. The specific gravity of air is 1. So in Table 20.1, sulfuryl fluoride as a gas is 3.52× heavier than air. If a gas heavier than air is introduced into a confined airspace and it is not mixed by fans or some other means, it will initially sink to the bottom, resulting in higher concentrations of fumigant at lower levels of the room or chamber.

The objective of a fumigation is to achieve the target CT throughout the fumigated space, not just near the introduction point. Thus, rapid fumigant mixing is necessary and achieved with the use of fans or blowers, closed circulation systems with

TABLE 20.1. Characteristics of commonly used fumigants.

Fumigant	Boiling Point		@ 25°C	Vapor Pressure Gravity (Gas)**	Specific Physical Nature
chloropicrin	112.0°C	233.6°F	23.8	5.67	Organic Cl_3CNO_2
methyl bromide	3.7°C	38.6°F	1,610	3.27	Organic CH_3Br
phosphine	−87.7°C	−125.9°F	39,000*	1.17	Inorganic PH_3
sulfuryl fluoride	−55.0°C	−67.0°F	13,442	3.52	Inorganic SO_2F_2

* Approximate value based on 40 mm Hg @ −129.4°C.
**at 0°C

ducts or pipes, and multiple fumigant introduction points. In addition to the fans providing immediate fumigant mixing, they also help to maintain equilibrium throughout the exposure period in structures with leakage rates varying across floors and sections. Also, using multiple introduction sites, particularly for big structures, can help distribute fumigant fast and efficiently.

Fans serve another valuable function. Liquid fumigants introduced into the fumigated space chill the air as they change state from a liquid to a gas. To avoid condensation of water from the humid air, a fan at the point of introduction helps to mix warm air from the entire enclosed space with the cooler fumigant-laden air near the introduction site. The fan is in essence the heat exchanger, mixing warm air from the fumigated space with the air cooled by the fumigant changing from a liquid to a gas.

Heat exchangers, in addition to fans, are used with some fumigants in certain situations to warm the fumigant (e.g., methyl bromide) as it is being introduced to ensure immediate and thorough volatilization and hasten the rate of diffusion. Once fumigants are in equilibrium with the chamber air, the two will not separate or stratify.

Sorption

An important factor affecting the action of fumigants is the phenomenon known as **sorption**. Sorption involves two processes, **adsorption** and **absorption**. Adsorption is the adherence (binding) of a fumigant on the surface of a material. Absorption is the penetration of the fumigant into the inner structure of a material. Through sorption, fumigant is removed from the air and is not available for respiratory uptake by the pest.

The loss of fumigant from the airspace (sorption) is more rapid in the early part of the exposure period, and may continue throughout the fumigation, but at a slower rate. Eventually the rate of sorption equals the rate of desorption, or loss of fumigant from the material, achieving a state of fumigant concentration equilibrium between the air and the materials in the fumigated space.

The degree of sorption will vary by the fumigant, the materials fumigated, temperature, and the fumigant dosage. More porous materials or ones with greater surface area will sorb more fumigant through both adsorption and absorption. Wheat flour, for example, is more sorptive than wheat kernels because of its greater surface area. Like materials tend to attract each other, so organic fumigants, such as methyl bromide will sorb more readily to organic material such as foods and wood. Finally, the higher the dosage, the more fumigant that will be absorbed.

Sorption must also be considered (for some fumigants) when determining the required dosage for a space occupied by large amounts of sorptive material, such as fumigation of a silo filled with grain. The amount of fumigant introduced must be sufficient to satisfy the loss due to sorption during treatment, thereby leaving enough free gas to reach and kill the pests.

As the fumigant is ventilated from the structure, **desorption**, the release of fumigant from the fumigated objects, takes place. Desorption is similar to sorption in that initially it occurs at a rapid rate in response to the dramatically lower concentration of fumigant in the airspace around the material. Then it slows as the fumigant concentration in the airspace and the materials equilibrates.

In cold materials and bulk commodity products, desorption takes place more slowly, and can be hastened by warming the space and its contents, and/or by employing fans or blowers to force fresh air around and through the material. Desorption can take hours to days depending on the fumigant, commodity fumigated, and environmental conditions.

Residues

Fumigant residues can consist of the fumigant, breakdown products, or chemicals formed by the reaction of the fumigant with materials in the fumigated space. Residues remaining after aeration do not provide any continuing control of the target pests. However, the potential risk to human health posed by fumigant residues must be considered.

The EPA strictly limits the amount of fumigant, and its potentially toxic breakdown products permitted in foods and feed after fumigation. The tolerance limit is based on the toxicity of the residue as well as the normal amount of this food in our diet. Tolerances (U.S. residue limits on food) are listed in the *Code of Federal Regulations*, 40 CFR Part 180 and are sometimes printed on the product label or manual.

Not all fumigants are registered for direct exposure to food, and the foods that can be fumigated vary by the product used. Fumigators should be careful not to exceed tolerances especially if the commodity will be fumigated multiple times. Consult the fumigant label and manual for instructions on how to limit residues below established tolerances.

Other chemical residues found following a fumigation may be reaction products formed by a combination of fumigant and components of the commodity. Also, end products of the fumigant formulation, such as an ash-like residue of aluminum hydroxide and undecomposed aluminum phosphide may remain after the formation of phosphine.

Fumigant or breakdown-product residues may also result in foul or unpleasant odors in commodities, furnishings, or other materials stored on the treated premises. Certain products may be spoiled. Some surfaces may be stained, tarnished, or corroded. It is best to check the label and available product literature or contact the manufacturer when deciding what items and conditions are suitable for fumigation.

COMMON FUMIGANTS

As with other types of pesticides, fumigants differ in their physical and chemical properties, as well as in their registered uses, offering advantages and disadvantages depending on the situation. The suitability of a fumigant for a job will vary by the physical and environmental conditions, as well as purpose and time constraints of the fumigation.

Virtually all fumigants are classified by EPA as **restricted-use pesticides** because of the combination of their toxicity, gaseous state, and lack of obvious warning properties. This means that only persons who have been trained and certified in their proper use should apply them.

Selecting a Fumigant

No single fumigant is ideally suited to control all target pests under all the various conditions encountered by fumigators. To choose the proper fumigant for a particular job, one must know which fumigants are currently available, and the advantages and disadvantages of each. Four fumigants used in urban pest management are discussed here.

Methyl Bromide

Methyl bromide has been a widely used fumigant in urban pest management for decades. The degree and range of its future use is dependent on the outcome of the Montreal Protocol, a global treaty with the purpose of limiting the production and use of ozone-depleting chemicals. In the United States, it is scheduled to be phased out by January 1, 2005, except for quarantine and preshipment uses, as well as for uses in which it is granted critical-use exemptions. However, the phase-out schedule could change.

Methyl bromide is widely used as a fumigant because it is effective against a wide range of pests and is economical. It is colorless, odorless, and tasteless. For structural uses it is mixed with no more than 2% chloropicrin as a warning agent. Formulations intended for commodity fumigation are 100% methyl bromide. Methyl bromide is also registered for use in combinations with CO_2 for structural fumigation.

Several manufacturers provide methyl bromide packaged as a liquid under pressure in steel cylinders. Several cylinder sizes are available for ease of transportation and placement in fumigated sites. Application can be made from outside structures through plastic tubing, or the cylinders can be placed inside and opened in a procedure known as an internal release. Heat exchangers are sometimes used to convert the liquid into gas during introduction.

Methyl bromide provides quick kill of insects and rodents. Labeled rates for pests are provided as ranges; generally, for structural insects this is 1 to 3 lbs/1,000 ft^3 for 24-hour exposure. There is also a very wide range of quarantine treatment schedules established in the *USDA-APHIS Plant Protection and Quarantine Treatment Manual*, as well as quarantine manuals for other countries.

Methyl bromide is the predominant fumigant for fresh fruit and vegetable treatment because of its short effective exposure period. Treatment conditions should be carefully managed to prevent phytotoxicity.

Methyl bromide is nonflammable, but it will break down to hydrobromic acid, a very corrosive compound, in the presence of an open flame, glowing heating element, or other intense heat source. For this reason, all pilot lights and heating mechanisms should be turned off prior to fumigating.

Being a reactive, organic molecule, methyl bromide is not suited for all fumigations. It reacts chemically with certain materials and foods (e.g., sulfur-containing products, foam rubber, furs) and may cause physical damage, foul odors, or both. Consult the label and manual of the methyl bromide product being used for a complete list of affected products.

Methyl bromide may be absorbed by certain materials in structural and commodity fumigations, which can limit penetration and make aeration difficult and lengthy. Preplanning the aeration process and using exhaust fans will help ventilate methyl bromide and reduce the waiting period before reentry is permitted.

A self-contained breathing apparatus (SCBA) or a supplied-air respirator is required when concentrations of methyl bromide in the treated area exceed the permissable exposure limit or are unknown. Because there are several suppliers of methyl bromide, always consult the methyl bromide label specific to the product you are using for safety precautions and safety equipment requirements.

The time required to aerate bulk commodities may be prolonged due to the potential for methyl bromide to absorb into organic materials and its low vapor pressure. A variety of methyl bromide clearance devices are available. Always check the label for current reentry levels, specific aeration procedures, and approved clearance devices. There may be additional state or local regulations that are more restrictive than the label directions.

Sulfuryl Fluoride

Sulfuryl fluoride, the active ingredient of Vikane™ Gas Fumigant (Dow AgroSciences; Indianapolis, Ind.), was originally developed for structural fumigation, primarily for drywood termites and wood-boring beetles. However, sulfuryl fluoride is also used for quarantine fumigation of nonfood items and is being developed for the quarantine timber market. A registration submission is being reviewed by EPA for the use of sulfuryl fluoride to fumigate dried fruits and tree nuts and cereal grains in storage and milling situations. The tradename for this future product is ProFume™ gas fumigant.

Sulfuryl fluoride in the gaseous state will not react with any items or compounds in the structure. Because it has a low sorption potential and has a high vapor pressure, it penetrates well to the target pest and readily aerates from structures and chambers.

Sulfuryl fluoride is nonflammable, but in the presence of an extreme heat source, such as a pilot light or electric element, it will decompose to form hydrofluoric acid. This acid is very corrosive and may etch glass or tile or tarnish and pit metal in the structure. Heat sources must be turned off prior to gas introduction.

Vikane is introduced from cylinders through introduction lines from outside the space to be fumigated (see Figure 20.4). The Vikane introduction rate is controlled by the inside diameter and length of the

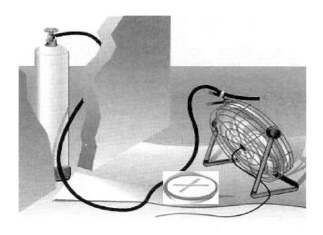

FIGURE 20.4. Vikane and chloropicrin (warning agent) introduction setup.

introduction line. The fumigator can increase the length and/or narrow the inside diameter of the introduction line to slow the rate of introduction.

Due to the extremely low boiling point, no heat exchanger is necessary to convert sulfuryl fluoride to the gaseous phase. However, as the liquid sulfuryl fluoride converts to a gas at the release site, the surrounding temperature drops as heat is pulled from the air. A fan is used at the point of introduction to mix this colder air/fumigant mixture with the warmer air of the structure and help disperse it, thereby preventing water condensation ("fog-out"). Consult the product label and manual for specific fan capacity requirements.

Because sulfuryl fluoride is colorless and odorless, a warning agent is required for nearly all Vikane use patterns. Since varying rates of Vikane are used depending on the pest and temperature involved, chloropicrin is not added to Vikane cylinders. The amount of chloropicrin to be used is based only on the size of the structure, and it is introduced separately. About 5 to 10 minutes prior to the introduction of the fumigant, chloropicrin at the rate of 1 oz/10,000–15,000 ft^3 is poured over cotton in a shallow container positioned in the airstream of the shooting fan.

Vikane use concentrations and exposure times vary depending on the practical considerations of the customer and the CT requirement for the target pest at a given temperature. Vikane Fumiguide (Dow AgroSciences, Indianapolis, Ind.) slide rules and electronic calculator are used to determine the CT requirements and the corresponding fumigant concentration needed based on the target pest, temperature, HLT, and hours of exposure.

Typically, exposure periods for structural fumigations are 20 to 24 hours, but they can be as long as 72 hours. Sulfuryl fluoride can also be used for exposures as short as two hours. By using the Fumiguides, the fumigator has the flexibility to adjust the fumigant concentration and exposure time to manage fumigant and labor costs, as well as the potential time constraints of the customer.

Vikane aerates rapidly when the seals are broken and the tarps removed. A SCBA unit is required when levels are unknown or exceed the permissible exposure limit. Reoccupancy is not permitted until label aeration requirements have been satisfied. Always refer to the label for current aeration procedures, directions, acceptable reentry levels and clearance devices.

Phosphine

Phosphine, or **hydrogen phosphide**, is an effective and widely used fumigant, primarily for stored commodity fumigation. It is approved for application on raw agricultural commodities, processed foods, animal feed and feed ingredients, tobacco and other nonfood items. It is registered for use on a wide range of food and feed commodities. Phosphine residues in commodities after fumigation are very low when properly aerated.

Phosphine possesses several positive characteristics for stored commodity fumigation. It readily diffuses in fumigated spaces, such as large grain storages, because sorption onto organic materials is low and it is only $1.17\times$ heavier than air. Recirculation is recommended however in grain masses to ensure that phosphine concentration equilibrium is rapidly achieved and maintained.

Because it reacts adversely with copper, brass, gold, and other metals, phosphine is not well suited for structural fumigations that contain these items. Fumigations are conducted in mills, however, by carefully controlling phosphine concentrations in order to minimize the potential for corrosion.

The CT concept is not entirely valid for phosphine since exposure time is more important than phosphine concentration. Minimum effective exposure periods are considerably longer for phosphine than for the other fumigants discussed. Higher phosphine concentrations should not be used to compensate for shortened exposure periods. The shortest exposure is three days, and exposure may be many days, depending on the type of pest, the product being fumigated, and the temperature.

Historically, phosphine products have been formulated as solid tablets or pellets of aluminum phosphide and magnesium phosphide for controlled release of phosphine gas over the exposure period. These formulations also minimize the potential for explosion, which can occur at high phosphine concentrations. For controlled release and easy removal of spent product, magnesium phosphide is formulated by Degesch America (Weyers Cave, Virg.) in solid plates (Fumi-Cel™), prepackaged strips (Fumi-Strip™), and porous blister packs (Magtoxin™ Prepac Spot Fumigant).

Phosphine is released from the solid formulations when exposed to moisture in the air. These metal phosphides release hydrogen phosphide + CO_2 + heat (along with aluminum or magnesium oxide hydrate depending on the formulation). Warm, moist air speeds the reaction, while cool, dry air has the opposite effect. The rate of release is also influenced by the formulation and packaging.

The faster the reaction or release, the more heat is liberated, and the greater the possibility of spontaneous combustion, because phosphine is explosive at 17,900 ppm (1.79% v/v). Magnesium phosphide formulations release phosphine gas more rapidly than aluminum phosphide. To reduce the fire hazard, tablets and pellets are coated with paraffin, which slows the penetration of moisture and helps control the release rate of phosphine. In the event of a fire, do not use water, which causes the release of additional hydrogen phosphide along with phosphoric acid. Rather, suffocate the flames with sand, carbon dioxide, or dry extinguishing chemicals, or dilute the gas concentration.

A closed-system phosphine generator (Degesch Phosphine Generator) has been developed to convert Degesch Magtoxin™ Granules to gaseous phosphine prior to introduction into the chamber or structure. With this system, the dose of phosphine introduced can be managed for greater gas efficiency. This phosphine generator can only be used by certified fumigators specially trained to use this device because substantial heat is generated and solid residues must be properly disposed of following use.

Phosphine is a colorless and odorless gas. However, the aluminum phosphide formulations include ammonium carbamate, which emits an ammonia odor like decaying fish or garlic, upon application. This additive has two purposes. The first is as a bursting agent to cause fissuring in the paraffin coating, exposing the aluminum phosphide to air. The second is to limit the potential fire hazard. A carbide odor may be detected due to impurities in the formulation. These odors will dissipate during the fumigation process and their absence should not be considered as an indication that the fumigant is absent.

Proper respiratory equipment should be close at hand during application of solid formulations of phosphine and, once the tablets begin decomposing, its use is required when in the fumigated area.

Consult the phosphine product label for specific respiratory protection requirements that are based on the phosphine concentration in the breathing zone.

Phosphine has food tolerances and is commonly used to fumigate foods. It is permissible to probe or otherwise distribute metal phosphide pellets or tablets directly into certain bulk commodities. Following the fumigation, a small amount of a fine, gray-white powder remains, consisting mostly of the metal oxide hydrate, metal oxide, and trace amounts of unreacted metal phosphide, and/or physically absorbed phosphine. When the residue is collected after the fumigation, it should be disposed of following label instructions to avoid explosion and/or human exposure.

Even though solid formulations of phosphine are easy to transport and apply, they have several drawbacks which have stimulated the development of cylinderized phosphine products. As stated earlier, the rate of phosphine release from solid formulations is difficult to control, thus there could be a significant delay in reaching the target concentration and challenges in efficiently maintaining toxic levels. Also, the degree of metal corrosion is concentration related, and very difficult to manage using the metal phosphide formulations.

Cylinderized Phosphine Formulations

Cylinderized (liquid under pressure) phosphine is a new development in phosphine formulations offering application and dosing flexibility. Cylinderized phosphine formulations offer the benefits of leaving no solid formulation residues in food and the ability to rapidly introduce precise doses. The target phosphine concentration can be achieved much more rapidly than with solid formulations which must react with moisture before phosphine gas is released. Low doses can be efficiently maintained in leaky silos for long periods through controlled introductions and recirculation systems.

Eco_2Fume^{TM} (98% CO_2 + 2% PH_3) (Cytec Industries; West Paterson, N.J.) is nonflammable and is the only cylinderized formulation presently registered in the United States. Eco_2Fume, in combination with heat and large quantities of CO_2 to increase the rate of insect respiration, is used for mill fumigations. The fumigator must consider the cost and practicality of the large quantities of CO_2 required to achieve the target concentration of 5 to 10% CO_2. Low concentrations of PH_3 are employed to limit potential for metal corrosion.

Registration of Vaporph$_3$os (99.3% phosphine) in the United States was granted in 2003. At such a high concentration of phosphine, Vaporph$_3$os requires fewer cylinders than Eco_2Fume. However, special application equipment is necessary for mixing with an inert gas such as CO_2 or air as it is released from the cylinder to prevent reaching explosive concentrations.

The Horn Diluphos System, (Fosfoquim USA, Inc.; Harrisonburg, Virg.) dilutes Vaporph$_3$os with air to below explosive concentrations prior to introduction into the space to be fumigated. Also, nitrogen is used to purge the system prior to mixing. The manufacturer, Fosfoquim SA (Santiago, Chile), requires application training prior to use.

Chloropicrin

Chloropicrin is commonly used as a warning agent for other odorless fumigants in the structural market. For this use, chloropicrin is formulated with MeBr in cylinders. It is also packaged separately as a liquid in plastic containers with special overpacking to be introduced during Vikane or MeBr fumigations.

Chloropicrin is not used for postharvest fumigation of food or feed commodities because it does not have food tolerances. There is at least one registered product, however, that can be used in warehouses, vaults, or other structures for insect control, but the space cannot contain raw agricultural commodities. Check the product label for permitted uses and restrictions.

Chloropicrin is an organic, yellowish liquid at room temperature. It is nonflammable, but decomposes violently at 233°F (112°C) especially when in contact with metal. This warning agent/fumigant has a high boiling point and vaporizes slowly. Chloropicrin sorbs readily on organic matter and desorbs slowly.

Chloropicrin is a severe lachrymator (i.e., it causes tears) at as low as 0.3 ppm, and humans cannot tolerate concentrations that are acutely injurious. It is also highly toxic to insects and humans, as described in Table 20.2.

There are specific instructions on the Vikane

TABLE 20.2. Human response to chloropicrin.

Response	ppm	Minutes of Exposure
Lachrymation threshold (tears)	0.3	Continuous
Eye closure	0.3–3.7	Continuous
Incapacitated	4.0	Continuous
Intolerable	7.5	10
Injury to respiratory system	15.0	1
Lethal to humans	119.0	30

label for chloropicrin use as a warning agent. It is recommended that chloropicrin be introduced at least on each floor of a multistory structure and at each fumigant introduction site. Establish at least one chloropicrin introduction site for each 45,000 ft³ of space to be fumigated. Take the following steps at each chloropicrin introduction site:

1. Place a handful of wicking material into a shallow container with wire mesh.
2. Place the shallow container in the air stream of a fan.
3. Pour measured amount of chloropicrin over absorbent material to achieve 1 oz/10,000–15,000 ft³ (30 ml/283 to 425 m³) (see Figure 20.4).
4. If protective respiratory equipment is not being used, leave the area immediately. When more than one introduction site is present, adequate respiratory protection should be used.
5. Start the fan.
6. Wait 5 to 10 minutes before introducing fumigant.

The other major use of chloropicrin is for soil fumigation in the agricultural market. In soil fumigation, it usually is used alone or in combination with other soil fumigants to increase the spectrum of pest control, especially diseases.

FUMIGANT REGULATIONS

All pesticides, including fumigants must be registered by the Environmental Protection Agency (EPA) under the Federal Insecticide Fungicide and Rodenticide Act (FIFRA). Pesticides may be further regulated under state and possibly local laws. The individual states enforce pesticide and pest control service regulations. The Legislation, Liability & Litigation chapter in *Handbook of Pest Control* (Mallis, 8th edition) is an excellent resource on the topic of pesticide regulation.

All commonly used fumigants are classified as restricted use pesticides, whereas most other pesticides are considered as "general use." Restricted use pesticides can only be applied by certified applicators, persons trained in the proper use of fumigants who have passed a certification test. Generally an apprenticeship period is required for hands-on experience prior to becoming certified. Check the regulations in the state that you plan to work in for certification requirements.

Fumigant suppliers may also require special training above that required by law in order to purchase the fumigant they supply. Two examples are:

Dow AgroSciences' training requirements for the use of Vikane gas fumigant (sulfuryl fluoride) and Cytec's for Eco₂Fume (phosphine). This type of training is quite important since fumigant delivery systems, detection equipment, safety precautions, etc., vary by fumigant and there may have been new label instructions and safety changes since the last training session.

If a fumigant is to be used to fumigate a food commodity, tolerances must have been established during the registration process. Tolerances are defined as the maximum permitted residues of the pesticide or its breakdown products permitted in the fumigated food or feed after treatment. The EPA establishes these tolerances (listed in the *Code of Federal Regulations*, 40 CFR) based on safety risk assessments and they may be printed on the product label. Commodities exceeding the established tolerances cannot be released for consumption.

Fumigators should read product labels carefully since an active ingredient may have distinctly different labels under which it is registered for use. An example is the Meth-O-Gas™ Q (Great Lakes Chemical Co., West Lafayette, Ind.) with the words "For Quarantine/Regulatory Use Only" printed on the label. This label requires fumigations using the product to be conducted under supervision of a state or federal agency. Other methyl bromide products do not have this restriction. Use of any fumigant product for a use pattern not on its label is strictly prohibited.

Fumigants are often used to satisfy **quarantine treatment** regulations. Quarantine fumigations are required for shipment of certain commodities from one country to another or from one region to another. The goal of a quarantine treatment is to prevent transfer of quarantine pests from regions where they are endemic, to regions where they could significantly harm the native plants and animals.

A good example of an import (into the USA) quarantine treatment is fumigation of wooden packaging from China and other Asian nations to prevent entry of the Asian Long Horn Beetle, *Anoplophora glabripennis*. A good example of an export (from the USA) quarantine treatment is oak log fumigation to prevent spread of oak wilt fungus, *Ceratocystus faegocerum*, to Europe. Quarantine fumigations are conducted under strict government treatment schedules, such as the *USDA-APHIS Plant Protection and Quarantine Manual* and the Australian Quarantine Inspection Service (AQIS) manual in which the dosage and treatment condition requirements are specified.

Key points: The label is the law, and there are significant differences among fumigant product label instructions and restrictions. Labels dictate where and how a fumigant can be used, on what, when, and by whom. Dosage requirements (application rates and exposure periods), target pests, and appropriate safety practices and first-aid techniques also vary by product and are listed in the label or application manual. Label requirements and directions can change frequently and are not the same for all fumigants, so applicators should read and fully understand the label before each fumigation. In addition to the requirements of the federal label, fumigators must also make certain they are in compliance with other applicable federal (e.g., Occupational Safety and Health Administration), state, and local regulations.

FIELD DETERMINATION OF FUMIGANT CONCENTRATIONS

It is important to be able to measure fumigant concentrations in the air during the various phases of a fumigation. Without monitoring, the fumigator is never sure of the fumigant concentration. Knowing the concentration of fumigant helps the fumigator make the appropriate dosing and safety decisions. Fumigation work should never be guesswork.

During the exposure period, the gas concentrations within the fumigated space should be monitored to determine the rate of loss due to sorption or leakage and decide if more exposure time or fumigant is necessary to achieve the target dosage. Monitoring is the only way to confirm that the target dosage was achieved.

During the fumigation, it is critical to confirm that workers and bystanders are not exposed to gas concentrations exceeding allowable limits. Using gas detection devices, leaks can be tracked down and sealed. At the end of the aeration process, the fumigator must confirm that the gas concentration is low enough for reentry and reoccupancy.

There is no single device that can economically and efficiently measure all fumigants over the range of concentrations experienced during fumigations. A variety of devices are used, depending on the gas being measured and the concentration being sampled. **Dosage monitoring devices** measure at high concentrations, for example in oz/1,000 ft³ during a methyl bromide or sulfuryl fluoride fumigation. **Leak detectors** are designed to function at high part-per-million levels, but do not provide specific concentration readings. **Clearance devices** are sensitive in the very low parts-per-million range for compliance with exposure, reentry, and reoccupancy exposure limits.

The following summary of gas detectors is an introduction rather than a complete review. Contact the manufacturer or distributor for fumigant detec-

tor functionality and specifications. Confirm with the manufacturer and fumigant supplier that the device is approved for the fumigant and purpose for which you intend to use it.

Dosage Monitoring Devices

Monitoring devices for measuring fumigant concentration during the exposure period are a critical tool for conducting efficient fumigations. Knowing the fumigant concentration within the fumigated space allows the fumigator to make informed decisions on how much fumigant to add at specific locations, when the target dosage will be achieved, and provides guidance on how to improve the next fumigation of that site.

Thermal Conductivity Analyzers

Thermal conductivity analyzers, such as the **Fumiscope** (Key Chemical Co., Clearwater, Fla.) (see Figure 20.5), are used to monitor sulfuryl fluoride and methyl bromide fumigations while they are in progress. This instrument operates on the principle that when a constant electric current is passed through a wire, the gas surrounding it affects the equilibrium temperature of the wire. Using two chambers, a constant standard of air is drawn into one and compared with the air-gas mixture drawn into the other. An electric current is run through the wires in the two chambers, and any differences are measured on a galvanometer. The units provide a direct reading in oz/1,000 ft³. The fumigator can use a gas sample of known concentration to calibrate these units, and should regularly.

Infrared Analyzers

Infrared gas measuring technology is explained below in the Clearance Devices section. Infrared

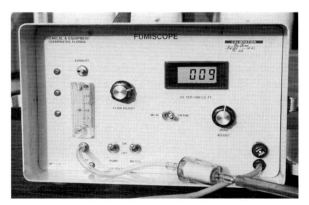

FIGURE 20.5. A Fumiscope, used to monitor the concentration of methyl bromide and sulfuryl fluoride during fumigations. (Myers)

detectors (IR) have not commonly been used for monitoring during the exposure period because of their historically high cost relative to other gas monitoring technology. However, Spectros Instruments (Walpole, Mass.) is applying recent advances in infrared sensor technology and solid-state electronics to provide a range of IR detectors for the fumigation industry. Units for measuring sulfuryl fluoride and methyl bromide may be available in the future.

The Fosfoquim Phosphine Monitor (Fosfoquim USA, Inc., Harrisonburg, Virg.) is presently available for measuring phosphine using IR technology. It is a real-time, multi-area measuring unit. Data is automatically archived and the end user can access a detailed (multi-area) dose report for any time during the exposure period. Monitoring is fumigant specific and potentially interfering gases are removed prior to analysis of air samples. This monitoring device can be linked to a manifold system with solenoid valves to provide automatic fumigant top-up introductions.

Electrochemical Sensors

The Porta Sens™ II, offered by Analytical Technology Inc. (Oaks, Pa.) and the Pac III™ from Draeger Safety Inc. (Pittsburgh, Pa.) can be used to measure high concentrations of phosphine during the exposure period. **Electrochemical sensors** operate on the principle of electrical resistance varying in the presence of the fumigant. The gas diffuses through a semipermeable membrane into a liquid electrolyte containing electrodes. The gas is oxidized or reduced at the working electrode. This process results in an electrical current. The resultant current provides a signal that is related to the concentration of gas.

Interchangeable sensors for measuring different fumigant concentration ranges make these highly portable hand held units practical for both monitoring during the exposure period, as well as for leak detection and clearance. These sensors exhibit some degree of cross-sensitivity (false positive readings) to other gases including common atmospheric gases such as carbon dioxide (CO_2), water (H_2O), ammonia (NH_3), and carbon monoxide (CO). Consult the sensor manufacturer for a list of interfering chemicals.

Leak Detectors
Halogen Leak Detectors

Halogen leak detectors are used in several industries to detect gases containing halogens, which include bromine and fluorine. In the fumigation industry halogen leak detectors provide an indication of the presence of methyl bromide or sulfuryl fluoride (SF is not detected by the open flame type) and the relative concentration of these gases in an area. Halogen leak detectors are not sensitive enough to be used as clearance devices, but are valuable in detecting fumigant leaks. Confirm with the manufacturer the detection limits of your unit.

The old open flame halogen detector operates using the principle of photometry. The color of a flame varies with the concentration of halogen gases in the air. This type of leak detector can can be used to detect methyl bromide, but should not be used for sulfuryl fluoride or phosphine.

The modern halogen leak detector units from TIF Instruments Inc. (Miami, Fla.) function by measuring the difference in electrical potential across electrolytic cells and employ microprocessor control and digital signal processing. They can be used to detect both methyl bromide and sulfuryl fluoride, but not phosphine.

The TIF units indicate the presence of the gas by an audible beeping sound and/or indicator lights (see Figure 20.6). The sound and/or number of indicator lights glowing increases as the concentration of gas increases and so can be used to find gas leaks. The latest TIF model, the XP-1, has a reported lower limit of detection of approximately 50 ppm sulfuryl fluoride.

The TIF brand halogen leak detectors have several positive features: low cost (approximately $250), lightweight, can be operated with one hand, are powered by "C" batteries, and are durable. These are well designed for tracking down leaks with the progressive visual and audible gas intensity indicator. However, the presence of other halogen gases will yield false positives.

Clearance Devices

Due to the chemical differences among the fumigants, there is a wide range of clearance detectors

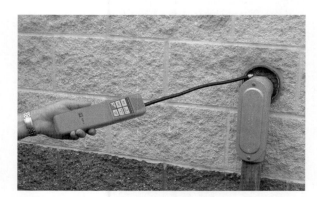

FIGURE 20.6. A TIF leak detector for detecting methyl bromide and sulfuryl fluoride leaks.

available, and no single device can measure all of the fumigants at the low clearance concentrations. In selecting a clearance device there are many factors to be considered. Can the device detect the fumigant at the legal limit of exposure? Does it provide continuous concentration readings or a point-in-time measurement? What is its response time? Consider the practicality of the approved units, weighing the pros and cons of size, weight, need for electrical power, battery life, chemical and electrical interferences, detection range, accuracy and, of course, cost. Contact your fumigant supplier and the manufacturer for model specifications.

Colorimetric Tubes for Clearance

A wide range of glass colorimetric detector tubes and associated pumps are available for measuring methyl bromide, phosphine, and chloropicrin to determine if a fumigated structure or site is suitable for reentry and reoccupancy without an SCBA. Suppliers include Draeger Safety Inc. (Pittsburgh, Pa.), Matheson Gas Products (Rutherford, N.J.), and Sensidyne, Inc. (Clearwater Fla.).

Gas concentration readings depend on reagents in the tube changing color when a given quantity of air-gas mixture is drawn through the tube with a pump (see Figure 20.7). The graduated scale on the side of the tube generally is in parts per million units. Simply read the concentration at the limit of the color change. Measurement accuracy varies by the model of tube and the proper use of the pump.

Follow directions provided by manufacturer carefully. Colorimetric tubes are both fumigant and pump specific. Also, they have a specified shelf life and should be stored at room temperature. Both low and high range tubes are available—be careful not to confuse them. Some tubes function with one stroke of the pump, others with multiple strokes for increased sensitivity.

Colorimetric tubes provide point-in-time measurements, that is, each tube provides only one measurement at one time and place. Each additional reading requires a new tube. With each tube costing approximately $5 to 9 each, the tubes are the most significant cost in using this gas measuring system. However, fumigators value the fact that colorimetric tubes do not need calibration or an electrical power supply to function and there is no warm up time.

Draeger Safety Inc. has incorporated colorimetric reagent technology into their Chip Measurement System™ (CMS) providing the flexibility to quickly take 10 spot-measurements. This hand-held lightweight detector incorporates an optical color analyzing system with a pump to provide improved

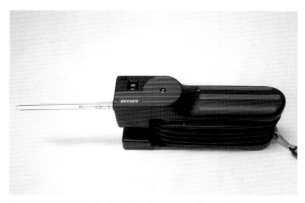

FIGURE 20.7. Colorimetric detector tube with Draeger accuro™ pump.

reproducibility and ease of use compared to the standard pump-tube system.

Electrochemical Sensors

A variety of multifunctional hand-held microprocessors employing **electrochemical sensors** are offered to fumigators for measuring down to clearance concentrations of phosphine. The electrochemical sensor specific for phosphine is placed into the microprocessor prior to use. Consult product literature for calibration instructions.

Analyzer models include: ToxiRae™ (Rae Systems, Sunnyvale, Calif.), Pac III (Draeger Safety Inc., Pittsburgh, Pa.), PortaSens II (Analytical Technology, Inc., Oaks, Pa.), and UniMax II™ (Lumidor Safety Products, Miramar, Fla.) have electrochemical sensors for phosphine. These lightweight and hand-size analyzers provide continuous readings, digital readouts, alarms, and long battery life, and quick warm-up. Prices range from approximately $500 to 1,500.

Interscan Gas Analyzer

The Interscan Gas Analyzer (Interscan Corp., Chatsworth, Calif.) (see Figure 20.8) is a clearance device designed for confirming that the sulfuryl fluoride concentration is low enough for reentry into the treated area. This portable analyzer provides rapid and continuous readings of gas concentrations from 1 to 50 ppm, while operating on AC power or a rechargeable battery pack.

During operation, the air-gas mixture is continuously drawn into the unit by an electric pump through a pyrolyzer, a furnace capable of heating up to 1,000°C. At this high temperature, sulfuryl fluoride is converted to sulfur dioxide (SO_2), which then passes through a SO_2 sensor. The sensor output is calibrated to register on a digital display as parts per million of sulfuryl fluoride concentration.

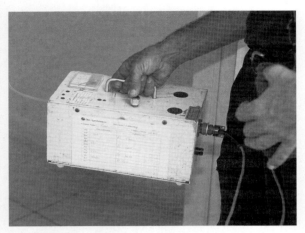

FIGURE 20.8. An Interscan gas analyzer (Model GF1900) for measuring low concentrations of sulfuryl fluoride.

Photoionization Sensors

Photoionization sensors (PIDs) (RAE Systems, Sunnyvale, Calif.) are available for measuring low concentrations of methyl bromide. A PID uses ultraviolet (UV) light of a selected energy level to ionize (displace an electron in) the fumigant. The ions give rise to an electrical current in an electrically charged field. The amount of electrical current is proportional to the concentration of fumigant. The signal from the electrometer is converted by a microprocessor to the gas concentration (ppm). PID units are generally hand-size and lightweight. Confirm with the device manufacturer and fumigant supplier that the device is approved for the fumigant and purpose for which you intend to use it.

Infrared Analyzers

Infrared analyzers (IR), a generally reliable and accurate gas detection technology, are widely used in a number of different industries, for the monitoring and detection of various gases in manufacturing and field situations. Portable units such as the Miran SapphIRe DL (Thermo Environmental Instruments, Franklin, Mass.) are available to fumigators.

Gas molecules absorb infrared radiation at specific, characteristic wavelengths. An infrared light source is created in the IR analyzer, and a certain amount is absorbed by the incoming gas sample. A detector sensitive to infrared light responds to the amount of infrared energy striking it and displays the signal on the analyzer meter in parts-per-million concentration of the fumigant. The higher the fumigant concentration in the path of the infrared beam, the more infrared light of appropriate wavelength is absorbed, measured, and converted to parts per million on the output meter.

IR detectors have the benefit of rapid response,

continuous readings, a high degree of accuracy, and a relatively wide concentration measurement range. The Miran SapphIRe DL is expensive however, costing approximately $15,000, and so is not commonly used by fumigators. In addition, it is heavy (24 lbs) and bulky to handle (21.8" wide x 14.4" high x 7.6" deep).

Spectros Instruments (Walpole, Mass.) is developing another IR clearance device for fumigators which may expand the use of IR detectors in the fumigation industry. This unit is expected to be substantially lighter and smaller in size than the Miran SapphIRe DL and substantially less expensive. As with the Miran SapphIRe DL it will also have print out functionality, and can operate on AC or rechargeable batteries.

Color Indicator Badges.

Draeger Safety, Inc. (Pittsburgh, Pa.) has a colorimetric badge available to determine TWA measurements of a worker's exposure to phosphine. The equipment is comprised of two parts, the plastic badge holder, and the indicator badge. No pump is required with the badge. The phosphine molecules automatically move onto the badge by diffusion. The sampling media is a strip of paper treated with a substrate to react with phosphine. The phosphine diffuses onto the badge and the intensity of color change is compared to a set of color standards to determine the TWA concentration. The sampling time varies from one to eight hours.

SAFETY PRECAUTIONS

Depending on the dosage, fumigants can be toxic to all forms of life—plants, animals, fungi, and in some cases even bacteria, and other pathogenic organisms. Humans, of course, are no exception.

Like the target pest, human poisoning by fumigants is related to the accumulated dosage or CT. Exposures to low concentrations for long periods, as well as short exposures to high fumigant concentrations can both be toxic to humans. Humans, however, are quite different than insects morphologically and physiologically, and the toxic effects of fumigants on humans are not completely understood.

Not surprisingly, little controlled experimentation on human response to fumigants has been conducted. Permissible exposure levels are extrapolations from laboratory animal studies including substantial safety margins for variation among humans and the fact humans were not tested. Therefore, fumigators should strive to develop and practice fumigation plans designed to minimize exposure to fumigants, and take no chances.

Similar to insects, inhalation is also the primary route of exposure for humans. Thus, proper respiratory protection per label instructions is critical to prevent injury from exposure to toxic levels of fumigants.

Fumigants in the liquid form may also be harmful through skin contact. Liquid sulfuryl fluoride can freeze skin, and liquid methyl bromide can cause chemical burns.

Fire hazard is another factor that calls for the utmost care in the handling and use of fumigants. Phosphine is explosive at 17,900 ppm (1.79% v/v). Methyl bromide and sulfuryl fluoride are not flammable but will break down in the presence of flames into acids which can damage materials. Chloropicrin is also not flammable, but heated material decomposes violently at 233°F (112°C), emitting toxic and irritating gases.

Exposure Limits

The EPA establishes **exposure limits** for fumigants in part based on exposure guidelines established by the American Conference of Governmental Industrial Hygienists (ACGIH) and the Occupational Safety and Health Administration (OSHA). Exposure limits are generally based on animal toxicological studies and are usually expressed in terms of parts per million (ppm) by volume of air. Consult the fumigant product label for permissible exposure limits and required respiratory equipment.

Fumigators should be aware that they must abide by the lowest exposure limits established by authorities governing the use of the fumigant at their location. For example, state-approved exposure limits may be more restrictive than the EPA limits. In addition, allowable exposure limits may be different for fumigant workers and the general public. As well, reentry levels, the maximum fumigant concentration permitted for occupant reentry, may differ from exposure levels allowed for fumigators.

Regardless of the established exposure limits, fumigators should take all precautions to minimize exposure to fumigants because of the wide variation in individual susceptibility. Check the pertinent state label to determine the allowable exposure for each exposure group and fumigation situation.

Respiratory Protection

Respiratory devices are designed to protect the user against inhalation of toxic or harmful substances. Proper use and care of respiratory equipment is imperative to achieve the maximum intended protection and utility these devices afford. Fumigant labels should be carefully followed for proper selection and required use of respirators.

The general term **respirator** is used to describe a device that is used by the fumigator to limit or prevent their inhalation of a fumigant. The mouth and nose, or entire face are enclosed so that the user breathes either fresh air or purified air, depending on the type of respirator.

Air-purifying respirators (canisters) cover the nose and mouth so the wearer breathes purified air from the surrounding atmosphere. These were once commonly used, but now are not approved, except during certain restricted conditions with phosphine. Check the phosphine fumigant label for restrictions.

Air-supplying respirators enclose the entire face, providing fresh air rather than removing specific contaminants from the air the fumigator breathes. **Self-contained breathing apparatuses (SCBAs)** are air-supplying respirators that provide a clean supply of air from a self-contained tank carried on the wearer's back (see Figure 20.9). SCBAs are approved for above-water uses, and should not be confused with SCUBA gear that is approved for underwater use and is not approved for use as protection from exposure to fumigants.

SCBA units consist of a face piece and breathing tube, regulator, high-pressure hose assembly, audible warning device, harness and carrier, and a pressurized air cylinder. The pressurized air cylinders generally supply 30 or 60 minutes of air.

SCBAs are positive-pressure units, meaning that the SCBA maintains a slightly positive pressure of air inside the face piece at all times. This helps prevent contaminants from seeping in around the face piece, even if there are small leaks in the face seal. As a result, a positive-pressure SCBA may be used in extremely toxic atmospheres and should be the device of choice.

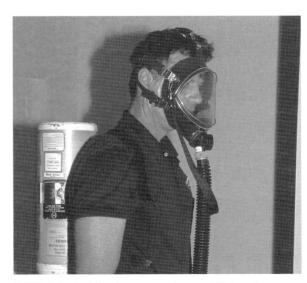

FIGURE 20.9. A fumigator wearing an SCBA unit.

Tips for Cylinder Safety

- Read and understand precautions specific to the fumigant you are using.
- Store and transport cylinders in a secure, upright position.
- Keep the safety cap and bonnet on cylinders, except when introducing the fumigant.
- Make sure fittings are tight before introducing the fumigant; noncorrosive metal fittings are recommended.
- Wear safety goggles (check label) or face shield while releasing fumigant.
- Do not stand directly in front of the cylinder valve.
- Have operable respiratory equipment (positive-pressure SCBA) readily available.
- Never suspend or lift a cylinder by the valve—suspend it with a modified bonnet.
- Be sure scale is accurate, for correct reading of the amount of gas in the cylinder.
- Use a proper-fitting wrench when releasing the fumigant, for good leverage and a tight seal.
- Close the valve tightly after use.
- Do not drop cylinders.
- Do not strike or heat the valve.

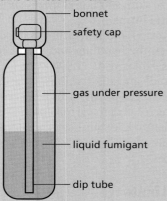

Consult the label of the fumigant product being used for specific respiratory protection requirements. Before using any respirator, learn how to use it properly.

Warning Signs

Before the fumigant is introduced, warning signs must be posted on all sides and all entrances of the fumigation site. In the United States, The information on the warning sign must include the following, and in some states the print size and color are mandated:

- DANGER/PELIGRO, and the skull and crossbones symbol
- Area under fumigation, DO NOT ENTER/NO ENTRE
- The date of the fumigation
- The name of the fumigant used
- The name, address, and telephone number (day and night) of the fumigator

Warning signs must remain on the structure or treated site until aeration has been completed. In some states, warning signs are required on tarpaulins covering a building as well as the building during fumigation. In all states, signs must be on the structure after the tarpaulins are down, while the building is being aerated to the required concentration for clearance and re-entry.

Securing the Structure

During the fumigation structures must be secured from entry by unauthorized individuals. Structure securing requirements vary by state, but in all cases entranceways must be locked. Some states and product labels require the use of secondary locks, locking devices designed to limit entry into the fumigation site to only the licensed fumigator. Secondary locks include "clam shell" locks designed to cover door handles, deadbolts on the inside of doors, and chains/lock combinations with the licensed fumigator having the only keys.

Guards are required in some states or localities for round-the-clock surveillance. Alarm systems may also provide additional security, but have the drawback of false alarms which can be costly and disruptive.

FUMIGATION PROCESS ENHANCEMENTS

The planned phase-out of methyl bromide, as well as interest in using nonchemical pest control methods has led to investigation of several potential enhancements of, and options to, fumigation. Enhancements to fumigation include, raising the temperature of the fumigated space, complementary fumigant combinations, improved sealing, and the already discussed cylinderized phosphine formulations.

The most appropriate fumigation process enhancement is improved **sealing**. First, seal the structure or enclosure thoroughly, remembering that if air can escape so will the fumigant. During exposure, monitor for leaks around the perimeter and take all practical and safe efforts to seal identified openings. Apply your experience to future jobs. When the HLT has been improved, then extending the exposure period can magnify fumigant cost savings.

Commonwealth Scientific and Industrial Research Organisation (CSIRO) in Australia has developed two **application/circulation** systems to enhance the effectiveness of fumigating bulk stored commodities. SIROFLO™ is a slow-release system for fumigation of "leaky" storage with the objective of maintaining the desired fumigant concentration over long exposure periods. The SIROCIRC™ system is designed for use in well-sealed storage and recirculates air from the headspace above the commodity to the inlet side of the recirculation fan. Both systems are beneficial in maintaining fumigant equilibrium throughout the bulk commodity and thereby enhance insect control.

Warming the fumigated space increases insect metabolism, thus reducing the lethal dosage for insect pests. Structures normally can be warmed to temperatures that significantly reduce lethal fumigant dosages (i.e., 85 to 100°F) by employing existing heating systems, running machinery, or employing temporary heaters. These methods are often practical and cost-effective. If heaters are used during fumigation, caution is necessary to prevent exposure of fumigants to open flames and hot electric heating coils which could lead to fumigant breakdown into acids that could damage materials.

Timing fumigations is also an effective strategy for optimizing fumigation efficiency. For example, fumigating when no wood-infesting beetle eggs are present in a house can substantially reduce the sulfuryl fluoride dosage necessary for kill. Fumigating mills during the warm months, when insect respiration is high, can also increase fumigation efficiency.

OPTIONS TO FUMIGATION
Heating

One option to fumigation, **heating structures** to temperatures lethal to insect pests, is used for insect control in food processing and flour milling facilities, and rarely in houses for drywood termite control. Heating food/feed commodities is not commonly practiced because of the potential for damage at high temperatures and difficulty of raising the temperature of large masses of material to levels lethal to insects.

A generally recognized temperature-time target for heat treatments to control stored product pests in flour mills and similar structures is 120 to 140°F for 24 to 36 hrs. In addition to the achieved temperature and exposure time, pest species and

life stage, as well as relative humidity will influence mortality achieved during a heat treatment. Most insects would be killed from much shorter exposures to these temperatures, but time is required to heat the microenvironments (e.g., food in machinery, cracks in floors, and wood members) where the pests are located.

The goal of a heat treatment is to maintain lethal temperatures in places where the target pest is located for at least the minimum time required to kill the pest. This is a challenging goal when the stored product pest is located in food residues in machinery or cracks in concrete floors. Structural wood is also difficult to heat to lethal temperatures when trying to control termites or beetles in houses.

High temperature heating equipment can be permanent or temporary, being incorporated into the existing heating system of mills for example or more commonly brought in for heat treatments. Some mills and food-processing facilities were designed and built for heat treatments, while others have been adapted for heat treatments after they were built.

Portable heating systems can be operated by professional heating companies or operated by the food facility employees. Electricity, propane, or fuel oils can power such heating units. Some portable heating units can be placed indoors (e.g., electrical), while the others operate outside (e.g., propane and fuel oil) using ducting to introduce the hot air into the fumigated space.

Regardless of the heating system, a hot air circulation system using strong fans is necessary to distribute the heat throughout the structure. Careful design of the heating system is required to minimize the potential for hot spots—localized high temperatures, which could damage equipment or the structure. Temperature monitors should also be placed throughout the heated area to indicate where temperatures are exceeding safe levels or are not reaching lethal levels. Heaters and fans should be redistributed to achieve target temperatures while not overheating sensitive equipment.

The advantages of high heat treatments include: sections of the facility can be isolated and heated, sealing requirements are less than for fumigants, workers can enter the heated area during treatment—being careful to prevent overheating—and heating systems can be designed to meet a wide variety of situations. Disadvantages of high heat treatments include potentially high initial equipment costs and fuel costs, substantial energy system requirements, need for high temperature sprinkler heads, and potential for physical damage to the structure and equipment. Some companies offering portable heaters and heat treatments include:

Important Reminders

- Read and understand the label, stewardship policies, and literature. Demand the information from your supplier.
- Supply your local doctor or hospital emergency room with information before use of the fumigant.
- Preplan the entire job.
- Consider outside (remote) application of the fumigant.
- Don't shortcut.
- Use the buddy system. Never fumigate alone.
- Have proper safety equipment available and checked out ahead of time.
- Preplan for any emergency that might arise.
- Properly label all containers. Never use food or beverage containers for fumigants.
- Do not wear rubber gloves, rubber boots, rings, watches, adhesive bandages, or contact lenses. Liquid phase of fumigants can collect in and under these surfaces and damage skin.
- Don't get complacent.
- Make at least one, preferably two, dry runs.
- Treat each job like a new challenge.
- Don't be the fastest fumigator, be the oldest.

Aggreko (New Iberia, La.), Rupp Industries (Burnsville, Minn.), and Ruffneck Heaters (Calgary, Canada).

Modified Atmospheres

An age-old method of insect control in stored grain is the process of modifying the atmospheric composition of the interstitial (between the kernels) air space in the stored grain bulk so that the atmosphere is lethal to the target insects. Present-day practitioners of modified atmospheres (MAs) use modern sealing materials and methods of gas generation and monitoring systems.

The process involves either decreasing the oxygen (O_2) concentration (to create a low-O_2 atmosphere) or increasing the carbon dioxide (CO_2) concentration (to create a high-CO_2 atmosphere) to such levels, that the target insects are killed. The exposure period is generally several days to a week or more, depending on the temperature and the humidity of the commodity.

The **low-O_2 process** involves displacement of oxygen (O_2) in the atmosphere of the grain bulk with high concentrations of nitrogen (N_2). Low-O_2 atmospheres require longer exposure periods than high CO_2 atmospheres. The required O_2 concentration is 1% or less (normal concentration of O_2 in air being 20.95% by volume), with the balance being primarily N_2.

The **high-CO_2 treatment** has a target composition in air of >60% CO_2 (normal concentration of CO_2 in air being 0.03% by volume). This treatment causes reduction in O_2 concentration, and the remaining gas is primarily N_2.

The effectiveness of MA treatments is enhanced at high temperature and low relative humidity conditions. However, alterations in the temperature of large grain bulks are seldom carried out to enhance the effectiveness of MA treatments. Also, the humidity of the interstitial space is dictated by the moisture content of the grain, and is difficult to modify.

The MA application process involves the use of large volumes of CO_2 or N_2 to replace the existing atmosphere in the grain bulk. Liquefied CO_2 or N_2 is vaporized as it passes through a heat exchanger and then the gases are introduced through pipes into the confined space. This process is quite similar to introducing MB from outside a structure while employing a heat exchanger.

Pressure testing the structure prior to treatment is recommended to estimate the degree of gas tightness of the structure to be treated. This test requires experienced operators and special preparations. To avoid structural damage due to daily temperature fluctuations, particularly in the headspace of metal structures, appropriate pressure relief valves must be installed.

Even in the best sealed structures a reduction in CO_2 concentration or increase in O_2 concentration is experienced over time due to gas loss through the pressure relief valves or leaks in the structure. In addition, during the high-CO_2 treatment, sorption of CO_2 causes significant reductions in the gas concentration. These changes must be considered when deciding on the required exposure time. Accordingly, except in very tightly sealed small metal chambers, additional gas introductions are likely to be required.

The substantial quantities of CO_2 or N_2 gas needed for grain storage facilities may be provided by tanker trucks or generated on site by specially designed equipment. Smaller chamber treatments may be accomplished using individual gas cylinders.

Another type of MA that can be applied for the protection of grain is **hermetic storage**. It is also called "sealed storage," "air-tight storage," or "sacrificial sealed storage." This method takes advantage of sufficiently sealed structures that enable insects and other aerobic organisms in the grain mass to generate the MA. These organisms reduce the O_2 and increase the CO_2 concentrations through respiratory metabolism to below levels permitting insect development.

The exposure time needed to control insect populations and to protect grain using hermetic storage depends on the infestation level and the activity of other aerobic organisms. For the implementation of this method, above ground structures have been developed using flexible plastic liners under the name of GrainPro Cocoon™ or Volcani Cube™ (GrainPro, Inc., Concord, Mass.).

The MAs described above are conducted under normal atmospheric pressure. There are however two additional MA application techniques; use of low pressures (vacuum) and CO_2 at high pressures.

For the application of the **vacuum technology**, fairly low pressures are required to obtain insect kill within reasonable time periods (typically 3 days at room temperature and 50 mm Hg). In a low pressure environment there is a close correlation between the partial pressure of the remaining O_2 and the rate of kill. An absolute pressure of less than 100 mm Hg (preferably about 50 mm Hg) is required to produce complete kill.

Until recently vacuum treatment could only be carried out in specially constructed rigid and expensive vacuum chambers. GrainPro, Inc., has invented a process called the vacuum hermetic fumigation (V-HF) that uses flexible liners to achieve the low pressures in transportable structures. These structures include the standard GrainPro Cocoon or Volcani Cube in which sufficiently low pressures (25-50 mm Hg) can be obtained (using a commercial vacuum pump) and maintained for indefinite periods of time.

Exposure times for CO_2 treatments can be shortened to hours rather than days using **increased pressure** (10-37 bar) applied in specially designed high-pressure metal chambers. Because of the high initial capital investment, these high-pressure chamber treatments are practical only for high value products such as spices, nuts, medicinal herbs and other special commodities.

The benefits of modified atmospheres are: elimination of pesticide residues, reduced safety risk compared to fumigants, environmental safety and potentially extended commodity shelf-life due to the confined space and the reduced O_2 concentration. Modified atmospheres also can be practical and effective for chamber fumigation of sensitive materials. Special portable chambers made of flexible tarp-like sheeting provide the benefit of treatment in any location where sufficient quantities of CO_2 or N_2 are available and allow low-cost treatment in nonrigid low-permeability envelopes.

Challenges and drawbacks of modified atmosphere treatments include: the need for long exposures to achieve high levels of insect control (except the high-pressure CO_2 treatment), the difficulty in sufficiently sealing the structures to maintain low O_2 or high CO_2 concentrations, and the potentially high gas costs when treating large structures. MA treatments are not practical for treatment of mills, processing plants, or any other structure that cannot be tightly sealed or for treatments that must be completed within a few days.

GOOD FUMIGATION STEWARDSHIP

Fumigants are highly toxic to both target pests and humans. Only trained personnel employing the appropriate equipment in good working order should use fumigants. Fumigation crew members should be well informed of the fumigant-specific risks, and trained in the proper use of the fumigant-specific safety equipment.

Prepare fumigation plans and ensure they are understood by the fumigation crew and the facility managers or property owners. Inform the site or commodity owners of their responsibilities in ensuring a safe and effective fumigation. Provide local authorities the information they need to rapidly and appropriately respond to an emergency.

The ethics of good fumigation stewardship begin with management providing the necessary training and equipment, but most importantly, the time for the crew to do their job properly. Ultimately though, good fumigation stewardship depends on conscientious crew members dedicated to safety for themselves, their crew members, site employees, and neighbors.

SUPPLEMENTARY READING MATERIAL

Banks, Jonathan and Paul Fields. 1995. Physical Methods for Insect Control in Stored-Grain Ecosystems. In: *Stored Grain Ecosystems.* Editors: D. S. Jayas, N. D. G. White, and W. E. Muir. 353-409 pp.

Bond, E. J. 1984. *Manual of Fumigation for Insect Control.* FAO paper no. 54, Rome. 432 pp.

Cytec Industries Inc. 2000. *Eco₂Fume Fumigant Gas Application Manual.* West Paterson, NJ. 41pp.

DowAgroSciences. 2002. *Vikane Gas Fumigant— Structural Fumigation Manual 2003.* Indianapolis, IN.

Mallis, A. 1997. *Handbook of Pest Control.* 8th ed. Mallis Handbook and Technical Training Company. 1,453 pp.

Oklahoma Cooperative Extension Service. *Stored Product Management.* Circular Number E-912. Editors: Krischik, V., G. Cuperus, and D. Galliart. Oklahoma State University, 1995. 242 pp.

APPENDIX A

How to Collect, Preserve, and Identify Insects (Excerpted)

Extension Circular 509

D. P. Sanders,* G. E. Lehker,* and D. L. Matthew
Department of Entomology
Purdue University

Insects, in spite of their small size, are among the most interesting and fascinating creatures known to man. To the insect collector there is no end to the number of treasures in the fields, the woods, along the shores of lakes and streams and in many other places. In fact, insects are so universally present that we can find them any time of the year almost anywhere we care to search.

It is hoped this discussion will serve as a guide to those who, for the first time, wish to delve into the world of insects and collect and study the marvelous creatures that inhabit it.

INSECT COLLECTING EQUIPMENT

Large insect collections may be made using a small amount of inexpensive equipment. Nets and killing jars are the most essential. Biological supply companies that carry collecting equipment are listed toward the end of this appendix.

The Net

A net serves two purposes. One is to *beat* or *sweep* foliage. This means that the net is swung back and forth so that it scrapes the tops of plants and collects insects that are feeding or resting there. The other use

for the net is to collect bees, wasps, butterflies, dragonflies and other flying or wary insects. A suitable net is one that is sturdy enough to sweep plants, yet light and porous enough to be swung through the air. Such a net can either be purchased or made at home.

The Killing Jars

After insects have been collected, they must be killed quickly without breaking or otherwise damaging them. A killing jar is used for this purpose. Every collector should have at least two such jars—one large enough for butterflies and moths and another for beetles and small insects.

Jars that use ethyl acetate as the killing agent can be made at home. This chemical can usually be purchased at drug stores. Select a jar of heavy glass having a large mouth and a screw cap. Do not use plastic jars.

Pour about 1 inch of wet plaster of paris (more for large jars) into the bottom of the jar. Let it harden, and then dry thoroughly in the oven. After removing from the oven, saturate the dry plaster of paris with the killing agent; pour off any excess liquid that does not soak in. The jar is now ready for use; however, keep it tightly capped when not in use. When the jar loses its killing strength, dry it out again and recharge it.

Always keep a piece of clean, crumpled paper in each jar to absorb moisture and keep the specimens from becoming rubbed or broken. Mount and label all specimens within a few hours after

Note: A complete copy of this publication can be obtained by writing Extension Entomology, Department of Entomology, Purdue University, West Lafayette, IN 47907.

*Former staff member.

they are caught. Insects left in the killing jar for a day or two will become soft and ruined, whereas those taken out but not pinned will become too brittle to handle.

WHERE TO COLLECT INSECTS

In summer, insects are the most plentiful on the flowers and foliage of growing plants, in and around pools and streams, beneath decaying logs or the bark of dead trees, around bright lights in the evening, along the borders of woods, and on the ground among grasses and weeds. Some insects come out only at night, while others are found only on or near the plants upon which they feed.

In winter, most insects seek shelter and are found in clumps of grass, beneath the loose bark of trees, under stones and logs, or beneath leaves and soil debris. Many burrow into the ground to pass the winter. Although insects are more difficult to find during the winter, searching for them is nonetheless interesting.

HOW TO PIN INSECTS

Insect pins may be obtained from any dealer in entomological supplies. Do not use common pins, since they will rust and soon ruin what may be valuable specimens. Pins come in several sizes, but No. 2's and No. 3's will be found the most useful.

Any insect that is large enough to support a pin without breaking or otherwise being distorted may be pinned directly through the body. The following rules have been set up for pinning different types of insects so that the pin may be placed firmly through the heavier parts of the body without destroying important identifying characteristics.

1. Bees, wasps, flies, etc.: Pin through the thorax between bases of forewings and just to right of middle line.
2. True bugs: Pin through the scutellum, which is the triangular area between the bases of the wings.
3. Grasshoppers, crickets, etc.: Pin through the prothorax or "saddle" just to the right of the center line.
4. Beetles: Pin through the forepart of the right wing cover near the center line.
5. Butterflies, moths, dragonflies, etc.: Pin through center of thorax between the bases of forewings.

About 1/4 to 1/3 of the pin should project above the insect to facilitate handling the specimen. As each specimen is pinned, straighten the legs,

antenna, or wings so they will dry in the desired position. Soft-bodied insects, such as crickets or walkingsticks, can be held in position by blocking them up with pieces of light cardboard placed on the pin. These temporary supports should not be removed until the specimen has become thoroughly dry.

The triangle card point method is used to mount very small insects. Cut all points to a uniform size, 3/8- to 1/2-inch long and about 1/8-inch wide at the base. They are easily cut from a strip of filing card paper as wide as the points are to be long. The insect pin is pushed through the base of the triangle and the specimen glued to the point.

HOW TO LABEL SPECIMENS

Every specimen must be accompanied by information, including the date and locality of its capture and the name or initials of the collector. These data are printed on a small label that is placed on the pin beneath the specimen. The size of these pin labels should not be over 7/8-inch long and 5/16-inch wide. This is about the smallest size upon which you can write or print with ease.

Homemade labels should be cut from stiff paper, such as filing card stock. All labels should be the same size.

DISPLAY BOXES

Pinned insects cannot be kept in good condition unless placed in boxes to protect them from dust and damage. A standard display box is 18 inches x 24 inches x 2-3/4 inches outside measurements and has a glass top.

Precaution Against Pests

Several types of small dermestid beetles as well as other incidental pests readily feed upon dry insect specimens. Naphthalene is a good repellent. If collections are infested, paradichlorobenzene flakes (PDB) can be used as a fumigant. These are the chemicals used in moth balls and moth crystals. Simply scatter a liberal amount of the flakes on the floor of each box, and close the lid.

HOW TO ARRANGE INSECTS IN BOXES

Insects are always displayed in boxes under appropriate *order* labels. These labels can be printed by hand or ordered from supply houses. The labels should be about 2-inches long and 5/16-inch wide. They are pinned directly to the floor of the box, and all specimens representing that order are arranged in neat rows in a rectangular area below the label. *Family* labels, if used, should be smaller or of a different color, and also pinned to the floor. Additional labels showing common or scientific names are placed on the floor of the box and held in place by the pin on which the specimen is mounted.

WHERE TO GET SUPPLIES

Insect pins, killing jars, nets, and other supplies needed for collecting and reserving insects can be obtained from any one of several concerns. Below are the names and addresses of a few such companies.

Indiana Farm Bureau Cooperative, Inc.
120 East Market Street
Indianapolis, IN 46204

Carolina Biological Supply Co.
Burlington, NC 27215

Entomological Supplies
P.O. Box 4748
Baltimore, MD 21211

General Biological Supply House
8200 South Hoyne Avenue
Chicago, IL 60620

Ward's Natural Science Establishment, Inc.
3000 Ridge Road East
Rochester, NY 14622

SUPPLEMENTARY READING MATERIAL

Borror, D. J., and R. E. White. *A Field Guide to the Insects of America North of Mexico*. Boston: Houghton Mifflin, 1971. 404 pp.

Borror, D. J., and D. M. DeLong. *An Introduction to the Study of Insects*. New York: Rinehart and Company, 1971. 1,030 pp.

Fichter G. S., and H. S. Zim. *Insect Pests*. New York: Golden Press, 1970. 160 pp.

Jacques, H. E. *How to Know Insects*. Dubuque, Iowa: William C. Brown, 1969. 205 pp.

Mitchell, R. T., and H. S. Zim. *Butterflies and Moths*. New York: Golden Press, 1972. 160 pp.

Zim, H. S., and C. Cottam. *Insects*. New York: Golden Press, 1972. 160 pp.

APPENDIX B | List of Pesticides

The following list includes those pesticides used most often by the pest management professional. They are listed in alphabetical order. Pesticides similar to any material listed can be found in Table 3.2.

The name used in the listing is an approved common chemical name or the most commonly used trade name for any specific chemical. This may be somewhat confusing because the approved common chemical name may not sound familiar. Thus, propoxur is the common chemical name of the active ingredient sold under the trade name Baygon; chlorpyrifos is sold as Dursban; and cyfluthrin is sold as Tempo. The trade name is always capitalized, while the common chemical name is not.

The precise chemical names of the pesticides have generally not been included with these descriptions. These names are generally quite long and used mostly by trained chemists. The EPA requires the listing of the common chemical name of the active ingredients in the ingredient statements on pesticide product labels, so there is less need for professionals to learn the more complex technical names. The longer chemical name is still listed on many labels, so it may occasionally be necessary to look up the corresponding common chemical or trade name in order to interpret the label.

The availability of each type of pesticide formulation may vary from time to time, so presently available formulations have not been listed. If an alternative pesticide formulation is desired, check with the supplier for its availability.

Abamectin (Avert, Affirm, Advance, Ascend) is a structurally large and complex chemical produced by certain soilborne fungi. In its technical form it is quite toxic to mammals by oral exposure, but it is active as an insecticide, and it has been formulated at such low levels in baits for cockroach and ant control that it has a very favorable safety profile. In agriculture it is used as spray formulations for insect and mite control, and it is also marketed as a helminthicide drug for medical and veterinary uses. As an insecticide it inhibits gamma aminobutyric acid (GABA), which is an alternative to acetylehollne as a neurotransmitter. (Acetylcholine is affected by organophosphates and carbamates.) It has slow killing action and appears to have very low or no repellency when used in baits.

Abate (temephos) is an organophosphate insecticide that has a low toxicity to mammals, birds, and fish. It is an effective larvicide for mosquitoes and certain other flies.

Acephate (Orthene) is an organophosphate insecticide of moderate toxicity to mammals. It is labeled for indoor use against certain crawling insects (including cockroaches). It is also widely used for outdoor control of ornamentals and shade tree pests. It is generally effective against German cockroaches that may be resistant to other organophosphates, such as diazinon and chlorpyrifos.

Allethrin is a synthetically produced material, the structure of which is very closely related to one of the six toxic agents of pyrethrum. The properties of this pyrethroid are similar to those of the pyrethrins, although in direct comparison it can be more toxic than pyrethrins to some insects, and less toxic to others. Its principal use is as a knockdown agent. Check the label for appropriate target pests.

aminopropionic acid, 3-[N-butyl-N-acetyl] ethyl ester (Insect Repellent 3535) is an insect repellent that is structurally related to ß-alanine, a naturally occurring amino acid. It is formulated into consumer products, like **Avon Skin-So-Soft Bug Guard Plus**, for application to skin for protection against bites of mosquitoes, deer ticks, body lice and certain other biting flies.

Anthraquinone (Flight Control) is an avian taste/olfactory repellent that works by causing an intestinal discomfort to geese without causing any serious harm to the birds. Anthraquinone is applied as a liquid concentrate mixed with water in power spray rigs. In general, dosage rates per acre of turf range from 1/2 to 1 gallon of concentrate with 50 gallons of water. The higher dosages and weekly reapplications are usually required for persistent infestations or areas subject to high goose pressure. To be effective anthraquinone repellents must be applied under certain environmental and lawn maintenance conditions

Arosurf MSF is a formulation of isosteryl alcohol with ethylene oxide. When properly applied, it will spread across a body of water and prevent mosquito larvae from puncturing the water's surface with their breathing apparatuses. Thus, it is an effective mosquito larvicide under many situations and is nontoxic to plans and nearly all other aquatic organisms.

Avitrol (4-aminopyridine) is used on treated grain for control of pigeons, starlings, sparrows, and other birds on structures and in roosting and feeding areas. Used properly, it results in distress symptoms in some birds in a flock, causing the others to be repelled from the area.

***Bacillus thuringiensis* (BT, Dipel, Thuricide,** and others) is a preparation of inactive bacteria that are insecticidal to the larval (or caterpillar) stages of certain types of moths. It is used primarily to protect stored grains from Indianmeal moths and other moth species, but some varieties are also effective against some beetles. BT is not toxic to mammals and is not persistent when exposed to sunlight or high temperatures.

***Bacillus thuringiensis* var. *israeliensis* (Bti, Teknar, Vectobac)** is a preparation of inactive bacterial cells that contain a toxin lethal to the larvae of certain flies, including mosquitoes and black flies. It is commonly used as a mosquito larvicide in formulations that are sprayed or granules that are scattered across bodies of water. It is nontoxic to mammals, fish, and most other aquatic organisms.

Base oils are common solvents or diluents used in oil-based insecticides. They are usually referred to as highly refined kerosenes. The best base oils are chemically refined, colorless, and odorless and they will dry leaving no oil film. Base oils have some slight insecticidal properties of their own; however, these characteristics are usually not a significant factor in figuring the toxicity to insects of an oil-based insecticide product.

Bendiocarb (Ficam Plus) is a carbamate insecticide characterized by having no odor and good residual action when applied as a wettable powder spray or a dust. It has been withdrawn from the pest control market in the United States. It is very active against many crawling insects, such as American cockroaches, ants, centipedes, spiders, termites (not as a soil treatment), ticks, fleas, carpet beetles, pantry pests, earwigs, scorpions, millipedes, sowbugs, pillbugs, and various beetles. As a dust, it gives quick kill when applied into bee, wasp, and hornet nests. It has relatively low toxicity to mammals.

Boric acid and **Borax (sodium tetraborate, Niban, MRF, Terro, Drax, Attrax)** are usually used as a finely divided dust or in formulations for cockroach, ant, and silverfish control. It is a slow-acting stomach poison that is more readily picked up on the insect's body when it remains as a dry residue. It has relatively low toxicity to mammals but is used as a high-percentage active-ingredient powder (often as technical material). However, there is no effective antidote for its poisoning action. Caution should be used when applying boric acid.

Brodifacoum (Talon, Final, Mouse-Pruf II, Enforcer) is a single-dose anticoagulant rodenticide effective against all species of rats and mice. It is formulated into various types of food baits and is used in and around homes and industrial or commercial sites.

Bromadiolone (Maki, Hawk, Contrac) is a single-dose anticoagulant rodenticide effective against all species of rats and mice. It is formulated into various food baits and is used in and around homes and industrial or commercial sites.

Bromethaline (Vengeance, FastTrac, Top Gun) is a single-dose rodenticide formulated into baits that are effective against all species of rats and mice. It has no odor and a very slight taste. Death occurs within 2 to 4 days, from central nervous system depression and paralysis.

Carbaryl (Sevin) is a carbamate insecticide with a relatively low mammalian toxicity and broad-spectrum insecticidal activity. Many of its urban pest control uses have been withdrawn in the United States. It is one of our most commonly used turf, ornamental plant, and garden insecticides. It is highly toxic to honey bees and wasps. It is used mainly in the public health sector against the oriental rat flea in murine typhus control programs and wild rat fleas in rural plague control.

Chlorfenapyr (Phantom) is an insecticide from the *pyrrole* class, which acts by interfering with energy metabolism within insect cells. It is available as an emulsifiable concentrate for use against termites (soil treatments) and residual applications to control various crawling insect pests like cockroaches and ants. It appears to have low to no repellency, and can be used for indoor residual applications to control various crawling insect pests like cockroaches and ants.

Chlorophacinone is a multiple-dose anticoagulant that is oil-soluble and thus suitable for use in oily baits. It is available in various bait forms and as a tracking powder. It is effective against Norway rats and house mice. It is a cumulative poison, usually requiring repeated feedings over a period of several days for best results. Rats and mice do not develop bait shyness on repeated feedings of this material. Technical chlorophacinone can be absorbed through the unbroken skin, so it should be handled with rubber gloves.

Chloropicrin (Picfume, Chlor-O-Pic) is a fumigant used to control pests in some stored grain or other stored product situations. It is the active ingredient in tear gas, which is used by law enforcement personnel. It is also added in small amounts to some other fumigants, such as methyl bromide, as a warning or signal gas to help prevent accidental exposures and poisonings.

Chlorpyrifos (Dursban, Affront, Cyren) is a moderately toxic organophosphate widely used in urban pest management for control of cockroaches, fleas, termites, and many other insects. It has been withdrawn from the pest control market in the United States, except for use as a soil termiticide. It has relatively good residual action compared to other organophosphates. If fast knockdown and flushing action are desired, pyrethrins should be added to the solution. Dursban has a longer residual life on nonporous surfaces, such as stainless steel and glazed tile, than most other organophosphate or carbamate insecticides, and it has particularly long persistence when applied to bare wood (e.g., for powderpost beetle control). It is a registered termiticide that can provide good initial control and may last for several years, depending on thoroughness of application and environmental conditions.

Chlorpyrifos-methyl (Reldan) is an organophosphate insecticide that is very similar to chlorpyrifos (Dursban). It is somewhat less persistent than Dursban under many circumstances and less toxic to mammals. It is most commonly used in treating grain that is being placed in storage, for protection against most species of stored product insects.

Cholecalciferol (Quintox, Rampage) is a rodenticide that causes death to affected rodents in three to four days. It acts by causing mobilization of calcium within the rodent's body, resulting in death from hypercalcemia. It has a very slight odor and no known taste, and it is formulated into baits.

Cyfluthrin (Tempo, Cy-Kick, Intruder) is a pyrethroid insecticide that has fair flushing action, good cockroach knockdown, and effective residual action. It has a particularly broad label.

Cypermethrin (Demon, Cynoff, Prevail, Air-Devil) is a pyrethroid insecticide that has fair flushing action, fair cockroach knockdown, and effective residual action on many surfaces, especially in wettable-powder formulations. It has a particularly broad label.

Cyphenothrin (Gokilaht) is a pyrethroid insecticide that has very good flushing action and exceptional knockdown against cockroaches, but only modest (or short) residual persistence compared to other residual pyrethroids. It is also very effective for housefly knockdown.

Deltamethrin (Suspend, Decis, K-Othrin, DeltaGard G, DeltaDust, D-Force) is a pyrethroid insecticide that has some flushing and knockdown action against cockroaches but is outstanding for its long residual action and extreme toxicity to cockroaches. Among the newer generation of pyrethroids, it has the greatest toxicity to cockroaches and the greatest persistence overall. It is moderately toxic to mammals but is used at a relatively high dilution (low-percent active ingredient in the finished spray or dust), so that it is safe under normal use indoors.

Diatomaceous earth (Diatect) is a fine-powder formulation applied as a dust to control cockroaches and other crawling insects. It must stay dry to be effective. The powder is composed of the dried calcified bodies of tiny single-celled plants, called diatoms, which exist in the oceans in huge numbers. As they die, their bodies fall to the ocean bottom as sediment. These deposits can be mined and processed for many uses, such as filtration material for swimming pools, insecticide dust, abrasive dust, and so forth. Diatomaceous earth kills insects by disrupting the waxy layers of the cuticle, causing excessive water loss and dehydration. It is nontoxic to mammals.

Diazinon (Dzn, Knox Out) is a broad-spectrum organophosphate insecticide. Diazinon emulsions have considerably shorter residual action on nonabsorptive surfaces, such as stainless steel and ceramic tile, than on absorptive surfaces. Diazinon is available in a microencapsulated formulation (Knox Out), which has good residual action against many crawling insects on a variety of porous and nonporous surfaces. Diazinon is also widely used in control of turf and ornamentals pests.

Dichlorvos/DDVP (Vapona, Vapocide) is a rather toxic (to mammals) organophosphate insecticide that is useful in situations where its exceptional vapor toxicity can be an advantage. Most pest control uses have been withdrawn in the United States. It has a short residual life (hours), but the vapor toxicity can be maintained over long periods of time by the use of specially impregnated resin formulations, called strips. These provide a slow release of the insecticidal vapors, which is especially useful against flying insects in confined spaces.

Dicofol (Kelthane) is a chlorinated hydrocarbon miticide that is generally effective against many mites that are resistant to organophosphates. It is commonly used in turf and ornamentals pest control, as well as for mite control indoors.

Difethialone (Generation) is a single-dose anti-coagulant rodenticide introduced into the market in 1995. It is active at 25 parts per million, effective against both rats and mice, and is formulated into pellets and blocks. It is registered for use in and around urban, suburban, and agricultural buildings.

Diflubenzuron (Labyrinth, Outpost) is a chitin synthesis inhibitor in the benzoyl urea family. In the United States, it is used in termite baits.

Dimethoate (Cygon) is an organophosphate insecticide with longer residual life than most organophosphates. It has been withdrawn from most pest control uses in the United States. It is used principally as a residual spray for control of adult flies and as a fly larvicide. Dimethoate is systemic in action when applied to plants.

Dioxathion (Deltic, Delnav) is used occasionally by pest management professionals and public health workers to control ticks and fleas outdoors. It is relatively toxic to mammals and has relatively long residual action outdoors.

Diphacinone is a multiple-dose anticoagulant rodenticide that is effective against all species of rats and house mice. It is a cumulative poison that usually requires several feedings over a period of several days for best results. Bait shyness does not develop. Diphacinone is formulated into several bait forms as well as into a tracking powder and a liquid bait.

Disulfoton (Di-Syston) is an organophosphate insecticide that acts as a systemic insecticide on insects that feed on plants treated by foliage spraying or by root treatment. It is highly toxic to mammals, and many of its nonagricultural uses have been withdrawn in the United States.

Dry diluents are a group of powdered materials used in formulating insecticidal dusts or wettable powders. Most of them are inert, although some have insecticidal properties of their own. Some common examples of dry diluents are talc, pyrophyllite, attaclay, bentonite, and gypsum.

Fenthion (Baytex, Rid-A-Bird) is an organophosphate pesticide with quick killing action and a long residual life. It is designed principally for outdoor use. Fenthion is used primarily for adult mosquito control. as an insecticide and in poison perches for control of pigeons, starlings, and English sparrows inside buildings. Many of its urban pest control uses have been withdrawn in the United States.

Fipronil (Regent, Termidor, MaxForce, Combat, Frontline) is a slow-acting insecticide that disrupts a different neurotransmitter system than organophosphates or carbamates. It is effective for cockroach, ant and flea control, as well as in soil treatments for subterranean termites and a variety of cockroach, ant and termite bait formulations.

Fluvalinate (Mavrik) is a pyrethroid insecticide used for control of a wide variety of urban and industrial pests. It has strong residual properties.

Heptylbutyrate is a chemical that is very attractive to certain species of yellowjacket wasps (*Vespula* spp., but not *V. germanica*). It has been used as an attractant in bait formations that also incorporate a toxicant in efforts to control these pests in urban, suburban, and recreational areas.

Hydramethylnon (Siege, MaxForce, Combat, Amndro, Subterfuge, Eclipse) is a slow-acting insecticide that acts by disrupting energy-metabolism within insect cells. It is used in bait formulations, where it has no apparent repelling or bait shyness, and its slow or delayed action allows it to be effective for colony kill of ants and termites. It is also effective against cockroaches.

Hydroprene (Gentrol) is an insect growth regulator that mimics the insect's own juvenile hormone. Cockroaches exposed to hydroprene in their late nymphal instar stages will be sterile as adults. It does not kill cockroaches but acts to reduce their numbers indirectly by stopping reproduction within the population for a period of time. It is essentially nontoxic to mammals.

Imidacloprid (Premise, Advantage, Pre-Empt, MaxForce) is an insecticide originally developed as a systemic material for use against sucking plant pests, such as aphids, scale insects, whiteflies, and others in agriculture and horticulture. It is a member of the chemical class, chloronicotinyl. Its mode of action is different than other insecticides because it affects the insect's nervous system by binding to the nicotinergic receptor sites in the postsynaptic region of the insect nerve. This prevents acetylcholine from binding and transmitting electrical impulses between nerve cells, eventually resulting in death.

Imioprothrin (Prallethrin) is a nonresidual pyrethroid insecticide that has exceptionally fast knockdown properties versus many crawling and flying insect pests. It is available in a variety of professional pest management products, and is also incorporated into some consumer aerosol insecticides (**Raid Ant & Roach Killer**).

Lambda-cyhalothrin (Demand, Karate) is a pyrethroid insecticide used for control of a wide variety of urban and industrial pests. It has strong residual properties.

Lindane is a chlorinated hydrocarbon insecticide that possesses a useful vapor action. Most of its pest control uses have been suspended by the EPA, but it may still be available in some prescription lice shampoos.

Malathion (Cythion) is one of the least-toxic organophosphates to humans. It is effective against a wide variety of insects and some mites. Malathion has moderate residual life; however, it is subject to breakdown by alkalis, so it gives poor residual activity on such surfaces as concrete and concrete block. It is used primarily in adult mosquito abatement and turf and ornamentals pest management. Many of its other former uses in urban pest control have been withdrawn in the United States.

***p*-Menthane-3,8-diol (*Off!* Botanical)** is an insect repellent compound that occurs naturally in the lemon eucalyptous plant. This compound is structurally similar to menthol. A synthesized version is used in the *Off!* product, while an extract from eucalyptus leaves and twigs is used in other brands (e.g., Repel). Personal repellent products using this compound are marketed primarily for protection against mosquito bites, and certain other biting flies.

Methoprene (Precor, Altosid, Dianex, Diacon, Pharorid, Extinguish) is an insect growth regulator that mimics the natural juvenile hormone in the insect's body to disrupt normal molting and development. Unlike hydroprene (Gentrol), methoprene has poor activity versus insects with incomplete metamorphosis (e.g., cockroaches). However, it is very active against many species that have complete metamorphosis (e.g., fleas), as it generally stops the life cycle in the late larval or pupal stages. It is used to control fleas (Precor), mosquito larvae (Altosid), and stored product pests (Diacon, Dianex). It is basically nontoxic to mammals and other organisms beside insects.

Methyl anthranilate (e.g., Rejex-It, Fog Force, Goose Chase, etc.) is a avian taste/olfactory repellent. Methyl anthranilate occurs naturally, and is used as a food flavoring to impart the flavor of grapes. For reasons not completely understood, MA is irritating to birds, much as ammonia or black pepper are irritants to mammals. This repellent was originally developed to repel geese off of turf and temporary stands of water. But it has also been used against gulls and other birds at landfill sites. Methyl anthranilate can be used in a "fog" formulation to repel geese, starlings, gulls, and other birds where they have established loafing or roosting areas and are annoying people or causing filth with their droppings.

Methyl bromide (Brom-O-Gas) is available as a liquid under pressure in cans and cylinders. It is released through tubing into the space that is to be fumigated; the liquid turns into a gas almost instantly when the temperature is above 37°F. Methyl bromide has excellent penetrating characteristics. It is nonflammable and approximately 3.3 times heavier than air. It has no odor, so chloropicrin is sometimes added to it as a warning signal. Its availability and use for pest control will likely become severely limited after 2005 because it is recognized as a depletor of the earth's stratospheric ozone layer.

Muscalure (Muscamone) is a long-chain hydrocarbon material used in house fly baits (e.g., Flytek, Stimukil, Golden Malrin, MaxForce Granular Fly Bait) to attract adult house flies. It is also produced naturally by house flies as a cuticular hydrocarbon or grease that is found on the abdomens of adult flies. It acts as a sex pheromone and is attractive to both sexes of adult flies.

Naled (Dibrom) is a moderately toxic organophosphate insecticide primarily used for outdoor spraying for mosquito and flying insect control. It deteriorates rapidly in the environment.

Naphthalene is a white crystalline solid material that gives off vapors slowly, over long periods of time. It has been withdrawn from the consumer and pest control markets in the United States. In tightly enclosed spaces, these fumes are effective for repelling female clothes moths and carpet beetles seeking places to lay their eggs. Naphthalene has been used for many years as mothballs and moth crystals, but has been largely replaced in this use by paradichlorobenzene (PDB). The odor of naphthalene is persistent in clothing.

Paradichlorobenzene (PDCB) is a white crystalline solid that gives off vapors slowly. It is the active ingredient in most deodorant blocks commonly used in urinals and in moth cakes, flakes, and nuggets. The odor of PDB is not as persistent as that of naphthalene, so it is more suitable for use in stored clothing. This compound has come under increasing scrutiny by environmental and pesticide regulatory officials in many countries, and its pest control uses may become severely limited or even eliminated (check with your lead pesticide regulatory officials).

Permethrin (Dragnet, Flee, Permanone, Astro, Prelude) is a pyrethroid insecticide and tick repellent (Permanone) with moderate residual, flushing, and repellent activity. It is used in a wide variety of ready-to-use or concentrated formulations for control of many urban and industrial pests, and as a pediculicide drug (Rid). Pest control operators use it primarily for flea (Flee) and termite control (Dragnet). It has low mammalian toxicity and is generally nonirritating.

Phosphine (Phostoxin, Mag-Tox, Detia) is a

toxic gas used as a commercial fumigant principally in stored grain and dry-food processing plants. It is applied as aluminum or magnesium phosphide tablets distributed through the grain mass or placed as small piles in structures. Phosphine gas is released by spontaneous reaction of the tablets with moisture in the air. A harmless residue of powdered ash is left behind when properly used. It is also packaged so the gas can be released without the tablets and pellets coming in contact with the commodity.

Picaridin (Bayrepel) is an insect repellent which is the active ingredient for various consumer repellent products (Autan brand outside of the United States) that are applied to the skin for repelling mosquitos and other blood-feeding flies and ticks.

Propoxur (Baygon, Larva Lur) is a carbamate insecticide used in spray and bait formulations against cockroaches and for control of many other insects. It has been withdrawn from the pest control market in the United States and some other countries. It has fair flushing action against cockroaches, fast knockdown, and moderate residual action on many surfaces. Resistance among German cockroaches in the United States to this material appears to have become fairly widespread.

Pyrethrins or **pyrethrum** is the active ingredient of one of the chrysanthemum flowers, most commonly grown in Kenya. As an extract, it is a dark syrupy liquid that must be purified and standardized for insecticidal use. It is available in a variety of concentrations and formulations, including oil solutions, emulsions, aerosols, microencapsulations, and dusts. It is actually a mixture of toxic chemicals, referred to as pyrethrins on the insecticide label. They are very unstable chemically, which accounts for their short residual effectiveness. Pyrethrum is quick acting and irritating; thus, it is an excellent flushing and knockdown material. However, it does not always kill all of the insects it knocks down. Pyrethrum is frequently combined with synergists such as piperonyl butoxide (PBO) or MGK 264 to increase its killing power. Because of its irritating characteristics, it (e.g., Whitmire-Microgen's Inspector aerosol) is frequently used by the pest control specialist to flush out insects hidden in cracks and crevices. Pyrethrins have very low toxicity to mammals but are toxic to fish and reptiles.

Pyriproxyfen (Archer, Nylar, Distance) is a juvenoid IGR that is very active against cockroaches, fleas, mosquitoes, and other urban, industrial, and medical pests. As compared to other juvenoids, this material has moderate persistance when used outdoors.

Resmethrin (SBP-1382) is a pyrethroid insecticide with slower knockdown and less flushing action than pyrethrins, but good killing power (no synergist needed). In dark areas such as cracks and crevices, it has some residual action. However, it is generally not used indoors due to its characteristic unpleasant odor.

Silica aerogel (Dri-Die, Drione) is a very finely ground dust composed of precipitated silicic acid. This material kills insects by inducing excessive water loss (desiccation) through physical disruption of the waxy layer of the epicuticle. Regular silica gels are very light and fluffy and are very difficult to keep confined to the treatment area. For this reason, commercial formulations are usually impregnated with another insecticide, such as pyrethrins (e.g., Drione), to increase the weight of the powder and reduce its drifting potential. Silica gels are not poisonous to humans and will not cause scarring of the lungs, called silicosis. However, they are extremely fine dusts and should not be breathed into the lungs.

Sodium fluoride is a heavy white powder (as a technical material) that is required by law to be tinted blue or green to prevent it from being mistaken for such things as powdered sugar or flour. It is generally used as a dust, either alone or in combination with pyrethrum, for the control of cockroaches. Its residues must stay dry to be effective. It acts as a stomach poison and, to a lesser degree, as a contact poison against crawling insects. It is quite toxic to mammals; great care should be exercised in its storage and use.

Spinosad (Spinosad, Conserve) is a biological insecticide that is a product of *Saccharopolyspora spinosa* fermentation which has been found active against some caterpillars and as a bait toxicant for fire ants.

Strychnine is an acute toxicant that must be used only in protected situations. It is rarely used today due to high toxicity and potential hazards. It is used in treated seed baits for pocket gopher control. Secondary poisoning of cats and dogs and many other animals is possible if strychnine-poisoned animals are consumed. Strychnine has a bitter taste, so bait shyness is common.

Sulfluramid (ProControlAdvance, FluorgGuard, FirstLine) is a fluorinated sulfonamide insecticide that acts by blocking energy metabolism within insect cells. Thus, it is slow acting and is used in bait formulations for cockroach, ant and termite control. There have been reports of significant resistance to this material among some German cockroach populations in the United States, but not among ants or other target insect pests. This compound has come under regulatory scrutiny because it is a member of a chemical family with certain unfavorable environmental toxicology properties. However, when used in carefully applied insecticide baits the potential for exposure to non-target animals is very limited, so its pest control uses may be retained.

Sulfuryl fluoride (Vikane, ProFume) is a non-flammable and odorless fumigant gas. It is toxic to a wide variety of insects, including stored product pests, drywood termites and other wood-destroying insects. It has been used primarily in the fumigation of buildings and penetrates most items or products very well, but is but is now being developed for many food industry uses in light of in light of anticipated restrictions on production and use of methyl bromide.

Tralomethrin (Saga) is a pyrethroid insecticide that, after application, transforms chemically within the target insects to deltamethrin, one of the most insecticidally active of all pyrethroids. In urban and industrial pest control, it is used for control of a wide variety of crawling insect pests. It has strong residual properties.

Warfarin is a moderately toxic multiple-dose anticoagulant rodenticide that requires several feedings over a period of as many days to be effective. It is effective against all kinds of rats and mice, unless these pest populations have become resistant. Warfarin is used as a dry powder with solid baits but is also available for use in liquid baits.

Zinc phosphide is a fast-acting acute rodenticide that is very toxic to all animals. Its unattractive dark gray color and strong odor serve as safety factors in its use, but rats and mice do not seem to avoid this material. Zinc phosphide deteriorates in exposed baits in about two weeks. There is no secondary poisoning hazard to other animals. It is used in food baits or as a tracking powder.

APPENDIX C | Pesticides Used in Urban Pest Management

Common Name	Trade Names	Oral LD50 (mg/kg)	Dermal LD50 (mg/kg)	Signal Words
INSECT ATTRACTANTS				
heptyl butyrate				
muscalure	muscamone (Flytek)	>23,070	>2,025	Caution
BOTANICALS AND PYRETHROID INSECTICIDES				
allethrin	Pynamin	680–1,000	>11,200	Caution
azadirachtin	Neem, Azatin	>5,000	>2,000	Caution
bifenthrin	Talstar, Biflex	54.5	>2,000	Warning
bioresmethrin	Pynamin forte	450–680		Caution
cyfluthrin	Tempo	500–800	>5,000	Caution
cypermethrin	Demon, Cynoff, Prevail	247		Warning
cyphenothrin	Gokilaht, S-2703	310–419		Warning/Caution
d-limonene	Demize			Warning/Caution
d-trans allethrin	Bioallethrin	425–860		Caution
deltamethrin	Suspend, K-Othrin, Decis	129–139	>2,000	Warning
empenthrin	Vaporthrin	1,680–2,280		
esfenvalerate	Asana, Sumi-Alpha	74–458	>5,000	Warning
fenfluthrin		85–120	1,535–2,500	
fenothrin	Sumithrin	>10,000	>5,000	Caution
fenvalerate	Pydrin, Pyrid, Tribute	451	>2,500	Caution
fluvalinate	Mavrik	>3,000	>2,000	Warning
imioprothrin	Prallethrin	1800	>2,000	Warning
lambda-cyhalothrin	Demand, Karate	19–79	1,293–1,507	Warning
linalool	Demize			Caution
permethrin	Dragnet, Flee	2,000–>4,000	>4,000	Warning
phenothrin	Sumithrin	>5,000	>2,000	Caution
pyrethrins, pyrethrum	Pyrenone, Pyrocide	200–2,600	>1,800	Caution
resmethrin	SBP-1382	1,500–4,240	2,500–>3,040	Caution
rotenone (derris)	ChemFish	60–1,500	>1,000–3,000	Caution
tetramethrin	Neopynamin	>4,640	>15,000	Caution
tralomethrin	Saga	99–3,000	>2,000	Warning/Caution
CARBAMATE INSECTICIDES				
bendiocarb	Ficam	46–156	566–800	Warning/Caution
carbaryl	Sevin	307–986	>500–>4,000	Caution
propoxur	Baygon	83–104	>1,000–>2,400	Warning/Caution

Common Name	Trade Names	Oral LD50 (mg/kg)	Dermal LD50 (mg/kg)	Signal Words
CHLORINATED HYDROCARBON INSECTICIDES				
dicofol	Kelthane	575–1,331	1,000–1,230	Caution
INSECT GROWTH REGULATORS				
Chitin inhibitors				
diflubenzuron	Exterra, Dimilin	4,640–>10,000	>4,640	Caution
hexaflumuron	Sentricon	>5,000	>5,000	Caution
lufenuron	Program	>2,000	>2,000	Caution
noviaflumuron	Sentricon			
Juvenoids				
hydroprene	Gentrol	>5,100	>5,100	Caution
methoprene	Precor, Diacon, Dianex	>34,600	3,038–>3,500	Caution
pyriproxyfen	Archer, Nylar	>5,000	>2,000	Caution
FUMIGANTS (AVT = acute vapor toxicity)				
chloropicrin	Chlor-O-Pic	250		Danger
methyl bromide	Meth-O-Gas	AVT = 200 ppm		Danger
napthalene		2,200		Caution
paradichlorobenzene	PDB	500–5,000	>2,000	Warning
phosphine	Phostoxin, MagTox	AVT = 200 ppm		Danger
sulfuryl fluoride	Vikane, ProFume			Danger
INORGANIC INSECTICIDES				
borax, boric acid		2,660–5,190		Caution
diatomaceous earth	Diatect, Diatomite			Caution
precipitated silica	Silica, Aerogel, DriDie, Drione			Caution
sodium fluoride		75–150 (to humans)		Danger
MICROBIAL INSECTICIDES				
Bacillus thuringiensis var. *israelensis*	Dipel, Thuricide			Caution
Saccharopolyspora spinosa fermentation product	Spinosad, Conserve			Caution
ENERGY METABOLISM DISRUPTORS				
chlorfenapyr	Phantom	626	>2000	Warning/Caution
hydramethylnon	MaxForce, Siege	1,131	>5,000	Caution
sulfluramid	ProControl, FluorGuard	543		Caution
OTHER NEUROTRANSMITTER DISRUPTERS				
abamectin	Avert, Affirm	13.6	>2,000	Caution
imidacloprid	Premise, Advantage, Pre-Empt	1,858–2,591	>2,000	Caution
fipronil	Regent, Termidor MaxForce, Combat	100	>2,000	Warning/Caution
ORGANOPHOSPHATE INSECTICIDES				
acephate	Orthene	866–945	>2,000	Caution
chlorpyrifos	Dursban	82–245	202–2,000	Warning
chlorpyrifos-methyl	Reldan	941–3,733	>2,000	Warning
cythioate	Proban	160	>2,500	Warning
diazinon	DZN, Spectracide	300–400	3,600	Warning/Caution
dichlorvos, DDVP	Vapona	56–80	75–107	Danger
dimethoate	Cygon	28–500	>150–1,150	Warning
dioxathion	Delnav, Deltic	19–176	53–350	Danger/Warning
disulfoton	DiSyston	2–12	6–25	Danger

Common Name	Trade Names	Oral LD50 (mg/kg)	Dermal LD50 (mg/kg)	Signal Words
fenitrothion	Sumithion	250–740	200->3,000	Warning
fenthion	Baytex, Rid-A-Bird	255–740	1,680–2,830	Warning
malathion	Cythion	885–2,800	4,000->4,444	Caution
methomyl	Flytek bait	17–24		Caution
naled	Dibrom	250–430	800–1,100	Danger
pirimiphos-methyl	Actellic	2,050	>2,000->4,000	Caution
propetamphos	Catalyst	119	2,825	Warning/Caution
ronnel	Korlan	1,740	1,000–2,000	Caution
temephos	Abate	1,000–13,000	>4,000	Caution
INSECT REPELLENTS				
deet	Off!, Muskol, Cutter's	1,950–2,000	10,000	Caution
dibutyl phthalate	Repel	12,000->20,000		Caution
dimethyl phthalate		6,900–8,200	>4,000	Warning
IR3535	Avon Skin-So-Soft	>5,000	>3,000	Caution
p-Menthane-3,8-diol	Off! Botanicals, Repel	>5,000	>5,000	Caution
permethrin	Permanone	430–4,000	>4,000	Warning/Caution
picaridin	Bayrepel, Autan	4743	>5,000	Caution
SOLVENTS (considered as active ingredients)				
petroleum distillates				
INSECTICIDE SYNERGISTS				
piperonyl butoxide	Butocide	6,150->7,500	>7,950	Caution
MGK 264	MGK 264	2,800	>9,000	Caution
AVICIDES				
4-aminopyridine	Avitrol	20		Caution/Danger
RODENTICIDES				
Anticoagulants				
brodifacoum	Talon, d-Con, others	0.27	50	Caution
bromadiolone	Maki, Contrac	1.13		Caution
chlorophacinone	Rozol	20.5		Caution
difethialone	Generation	0.51–0.56		Caution
diphacinone	Ramik, Promar	1.86–2.88		Caution
warfarin	d-Con, others	1–186		Caution
Nonanticoagulants				
bromethalin	Assault, Top Gun, FastTrac	2.0–5.0		Caution
cholecalciferol	Quintox	40–50		Caution
strychnine		1–30		Danger
zinc phosphide		45		Danger/Caution

Sources: *Commercial and Experimental Organic Insecticides* (College Park, Md.: Entomological Society of America, 1985), 105; *Farm Chemicals Handbook* (Willoughby, Ohio: Meister Publishing, 1996); *The Pesticide Manual*, 10th ed. (Surrey, England: British Crop Protection Council, 1994); and *Pesticide Factsheets* available at the .U.S. EPA Office of Pesticide Programs website (**www.epa.gov/pesticides/factsheets/**).

NOTE: Materials are listed by common chemical name, with examples of commonly used trade names; basic toxicity data (against laboratory animals) and signal words generally listed on their product labels.

APPENDIX D | Weights and Measurements

Weights and measurements for insecticide formulations and dosages are expressed in both the metric and United States systems. Most scientific work is done in the metric system, or in a combination of the two systems, while most pest management professionals are more accustomed to the United States system. For this reason, it is sometimes necessary to be able to convert the information found in the literature from one system to the other. Where temperatures are involved, they may be expressed in either the Fahrenheit (°F) or centigrade (°C) scale.

TEMPERATURE

On the centigrade thermometer, the freezing point of water is 0°C and the boiling point is 100°C, in contrast to the Fahrenheit thermometer, where the freezing point is 32°F and the boiling point is 212°F. Temperatures can be converted from one scale to the other by using the following formulas.

To Convert from Centigrade to Fahrenheit
°F = (°C 9/5) + 32
Example: Convert 10°C to °F
°F = (10 × 9/5) + 32
°F = 18 + 32
°F = 50
50°F

To Convert from Fahrenheit to Centigrade
°C = (°F−32)
Example: Convert 38°F to °C
°C = (38−32) × 5/9
°C = 6 × 5/9
°C = 3.33
3.3°C

WEIGHTS

Avoirdupois	Metric
1 ounce (oz)	= 28.35 grams (gm)
1 pound (lb)	= 453.59 grams (gm)

Metric	Avoirdupois
1 milligram (mg.)	= 0.01543 grains (gr)
1 gram (gm)	= 0.03527 ounces (oz)
1 kilogram (kg)	= 2.205 pounds (lb)

When it is necessary to convert ounces to grams, multiply the number of ounces by 28.35. To convert grams to ounces, multiply the number of grams by 0.03527.

LINEAR MEASURE

U.S. Units	Metric
1 inch (in)	= 2.54 centimeters (cm)
1 foot (ft)	= 30.48 centimeters (cm)
1 foot (ft)	= 0.3048 meters (m)
1 yard (yd)	= 0.91 meters (m)
1 mile (mi)	= 1.61 kilometers (km)
1 mile (mi)	= 1,610 meters (m)

Metric	U.S. Units
1 millimeter (mm)	= 0.03937 inches (in)
1 centimeter (cm)	= 0.3937 inches (in)
1 meter (m)	= 39.37 inches (in)
1 meter (m)	= 3.281 feet (ft)
1 kilometer (km)	= 3,281 feet (ft)
1 kilometer (km)	= 0.6214 miles (mi)

To convert inches to centimeters, multiply the number of inches by 2.54; centimeters to inches, multiply the number of centimeters by 0.3937.

CUBIC MEASURE

U.S. Units	Metric
1 cubic inch (cu in)	= 16.39 cubic centimeters (cc)
1 cubic foot (cu ft)	= 28,320 cubic centimeters (cc)
1 cubic yard (cu yd)	= 0.7646 cubic meters (cm)
1 cubic yard (cu yd)	= 202.0 gallons (gal)

Metric	U.S. Units
1 cubic centimeter	= 0.061 cubic inches (cu in) (cu cm)
1 cubic meter (cu m)	= 35.31 cubic feet (cu ft)
1 cubic meter (cu m)	= 1.308 cubic yards (cu yd)
1 cubic meter (cu m)	= 264.2 gallons (gal)

AREA MEASURE

U.S. Units	Metric
1 square inch (sq in)	= 6.45 square centimeters (sq cm)
1 square foot (sq ft)	= 929 square centimeters (sq cm)
1 acre (a)	= 4,047 square meters (sq m)
1 square mile (sq mi)	= 2.59 square kilometers (sq km)

Metric	U.S. Units
1 square centimeter	= 0.155 square inches (sq in) (sq cm)
1 square meter (sq m)	= 10.76 square feet (sq ft)
1 square meter	= 1.196 square yards (sq yd)
1 hectare (ha)	= 2.471 acres (a)
1 square kilometer	= 0.3861 square miles (sq mi) (sq km)

U.S. Units	U.S. Units
1 square foot (sq ft)	= 144 square inches (sq in)
1 square yard (sq yd)	= 9 square feet (sq ft)
1 acre (a)	= 43,560 square feet (sq ft)
1 square mile (sq mi)	= 640 acres (a)

LIQUID MEASURE

U.S. Units	Metric
1 fluid ounce (oz)	= 29.57 milliliters (ml)
1 pint (pt)[a]	= 0.47 liter (l)
1 quart (qt)[b]	= 0.95 liter (l)
1 gallon (gal)[c]	= 3.78 liters (l)

Metric	U.S. Units
1 milliliter (ml)	= 0.0338 ounces (oz)
1 liter (l)	= 2.113 pints (pt)
1 liter (l)	= 1.057 quarts (qt)
1 liter (l)	= 0.2642 gallons (gal)

NOTE: In common usage, the terms *cubic centimeters* and *milliliters* are the same.
[a]1 pint = 16 ounces
[b]1 quart = 32 ounces
[c]1 gallon = 128 ounces

APPENDIX E — Laws and Regulations Affecting Pesticides and Their Use

Without pesticides, we would not have the food, fiber, and landscape plants we need. But because pesticides can be harmful or dangerous, Congress has passed laws affecting pesticide use. These laws try to balance the need for pesticides against the need to protect people and the environment from their misuse.

FEDERAL INSECTICIDE, FUNGICIDE, AND RODENTICIDE ACT (FIFRA), AS AMENDED

A law passed by Congress in 1972 (substantially amended in 1974 and 1978, and less substantially since then) regulates the registration, manufacture, transportation, and use of pesticides. The law affects the pest management professional in many ways. Most importantly, it provides that:

- all pesticides must be used only as directed on the label
- all pesticide uses must be classified as restricted or general
- persons who buy or use restricted-use pesticides must be certified as competent pesticide applicators or must be directly supervised by a certified applicator
- persons who do not obey the law will be subject to penalties (fines and jail terms)

Use Inconsistent with the Label

A pesticide applicator may not use any pesticide in a manner inconsistent with directions stated on the label. You must use the pesticide only on the sites specified in the directions for use. You may not use higher dosages, higher concentrations, or more frequent applications. You must follow directions for use, safety, mixing, diluting, storage, and disposal as well as restrictions on reentry.

Classification of Pesticide Uses

Every use of every pesticide will be classified by the U.S. Environmental Protection Agency as either general or restricted. Many times, either all the uses of a particular formulation are classified as restricted or all of them are classified as general. Sometimes, however, certain uses of a formulation are restricted, and other uses of the same product are not. In these cases the directions for use for the two classifications must be clearly separate from one another. Entirely different packaging and labeling often are used.

A pesticide (or some of its uses) will be classified as general-use if it is not likely to harm humans or the environment when used as directed on the label.

A pesticide (or some of its uses) will be classified as restricted-use if it could cause human injury or environmental damage unless it is applied by competent persons (certified applicators) who have shown their ability to use these pesticides safely and effectively.

Classification of pesticides and pesticide uses may be based on

- the potential for poisoning of humans
- the type of formulation
- the way the pesticide is used
- the place in which the pesticide is used
- the potential for harm in the environment (especially wildlife and groundwater)

When a pesticide is restricted, the label will say "Restricted-Use Pesticide" in a box on a prominent part of the front panel. When a pesticide is classified for general use, the words "General Classification" may appear immediately below the heading "Directions for Use," or this designation may be absent.

Certification of Applicators

Persons who are not certified pesticide applicators may not purchase or use restricted-use pesticides unless they are directly supervised by a certified applicator.

Certification requires training or testing for competency in the safe and effective handling and use of these pesticides.

Your state agency will conduct the training and/or tests for certification. Your state may impose stricter standards than those required by FIFRA. The U.S. Environmental Protection Agency requires each state to maintain a program to ensure that certified applicators have current certification. Check with your state to determine the requirements you need to meet.

Many adjoining states have developed agreements to allow certification in one state to be accepted in the nearby states or throughout a region. If you will be operating in more than one state, you should check with the proper authorities to determine whether separate training and/or testing for certification is necessary for each state.

Commercial Applicators

Under federal regulations, commercial applicators are persons who use restricted-use pesticides for hire on property other than their own, and government workers (public operators) who apply pesticides in their jobs. Many states further define commercial applicators as any applicator using pesticides for hire. Commercial applicators are trained and tested in the general areas of safe use and handling of pesticides and then receive further training in one or more specific categories of application, including:

- agricultural pest control (plant or animal)
- forest pest control
- ornamentals and turf pest control
- seed treatment
- aquatic pest control
- right-of-way pest control
- industrial, institutional, structural, and health-related pest control
- public-health pest control
- regulatory pest control
- demonstration and research pest control

Several states have different or additional categories for commercial applicators. These include, for example, aerial application, wood preservation, and use of antimicrobials. Most pest control professionals are certified in the institutional, industrial, structural, and health-related categories, while some also are certified in ornamentals and turf and right-of-way pest control.

You must determine which categories best fit your business needs. It is illegal to apply a restricted-use pesticide in a category in which you are not certified.

Certification Standards for Commercial Applicators

All commercial applicators in all categories must be certified as to their competency in the use and handling of pesticides. Competence will be determined on the basis of written examinations. Some standards of testing will apply to all categories, and others will apply only to the particular category in which the applicator wishes to become certified.

Those standards that apply to all categories of certified commercial applicators are as follows: All commercial applicators must demonstrate practical knowledge of the principles and practices of pest control and the safe use of pesticides. Testing should be based on examples of problems and situations appropriate to the particular category or subcategory of the applicator's certification and the following areas of competency:

I. Label and Labeling Comprehension
   A. The general format and terminology of pesticide labels and labeling
   B. The understanding of instructions, warnings, terms, symbols, and the other information commonly appearing on pesticide labels
   C. The classification of the product, general or restricted use
   D. The necessity for use consistent with the label

II. Safety Factors
   A. Pesticide toxicity and hazard to humans and common exposure routes
   B. Common types and causes of pesticide accidents
   C. Precautions necessary to guard against injury to applicators and other individuals in or near treated areas
   D. Need for and use of protective clothing and equipment
   E. Symptoms of pesticide poisoning
   F. First-aid and other procedures to be followed in case of a pesticide accident
   G. Proper identification, storage, transport, handling, mixing procedures, and disposal methods for pesticides and used pesticide containers, including precautions to be taken to prevent children from having access to pesticides and pesticide containers

III.   Environment—the potential environmental consequences of the use and misuse of pesticides
   A. Weather and other climatic conditions
   B. Types of terrain, soil, or other substrate
   C. Presence of fish, wildlife, and other non-target organisms
   D. Drainage patterns

IV.   Pests
   A. Common features of pest organisms and characteristics of damage needed for pest recognition
   B. Recognition of relevant pests
   C. Pest development and biology as it may be relevant to problem identification and control

V.   Pesticides
   A. Types of pesticides
   B. Types of formulations
   C. Compatibility, synergism, persistence, and animal and plant toxicity of the formulations
   D. Hazards and residues associated with use
   E. Factors that influence effectiveness or lead to such problems as resistance to pesticides
   F. Dilution procedures

VI.   Equipment
   A. Types of equipment and advantages of each type
   B. Uses, maintenance, and calibration

VII.   Application Techniques
   A. Methods or procedures used to apply various formulations of pesticides, solutions, and gases, together with a knowledge of which techniques of application to use in a given situation
   B. Relationship of discharge and placement of pesticides to proper use, unnecessary use, and misuse
   C. Prevention of drift and pesticide loss into the environment

VIII.   Laws and Regulations—applicable state and federal laws and regulations

In addition to these general standards that apply to all categories of commercial applicators, there are specific additional factors that apply to each category. The category-specific requirements for industrial, institutional, structural, and health related pest control are as follows:

Applicators must demonstrate a practical knowledge of a wide variety of pests, including their life cycles, types of formulations appropriate for their control, and methods of application that avoid contamination of food, damage and contamination of habitat, and exposure of people and pets. Since human exposure, including to babies, children, pregnant women, and elderly people is frequently a potential problem, applicators must demonstrate practical knowledge of the specific factors which may lead to a hazardous condition, including continuous exposure in the various situations encountered in this category.

Because health-related pest control may involve outdoor applications, applicators must also demonstrate practical knowledge of environmental conditions particularly related to this activity.

States may vary in their requirements regarding certification and business operations. However, if there are restricted-use pesticides involved, then the use of such materials must be in the hands of a certified applicator or someone acting under his or her direct supervision.

Registration

Every pesticide bought, sold, or used in the United States must, by law, be registered by the U.S. Environmental Protection Agency and in each of the states. EPA approves not only the product itself, but also each separate use for which it is intended, and the product label. You are responsible for applying only those pesticides that are registered.

OTHER REGULATIONS
Transportation

Shipment of pesticides and other dangerous substances across state lines is regulated by the federal Department of Transportation (DOT). The DOT issues the rules for hauling these materials in the Code of Federal Regulations. DOT standards tell you which pesticides are dangerous to humans and create a health hazard during transportation.

If you ever haul pesticides between states, you should know the following:

• They must be in their original packages. Each package must meet DOT standards.
• The vehicle must have a correct sign. Manufacturers must put the correct warning signs on each package.

- The pesticides may not be hauled in the same vehicle with food products.
- You must contact the DOT immediately after each accident in which (1) someone is killed; (2) someone is injured badly enough to go to the hospital; or (3) damage is more than $50,000.
- You must tell the DOT about all spills during shipment.

State and local laws may require you to take additional precautions and obtain permits or provide notification for transporting pesticide products. There may also be detailed record-keeping requirements for all pesticide applications, or at least for applications of restricted-use pesticides (consult your state officials).

Worker Safety

The Occupational Safety and Health Act of 1970 is administered by the Occupational Safety and Health Administration (OSHA) in the Department of Labor. It requires anyone with 11 or more workers to keep records and make reports. The records must include all work-related deaths, injuries, and illnesses. Minor injuries needing only first-aid treatment need not be recorded. A record must be made if the injury involves

- medical treatment
- loss of consciousness
- restriction of work or motion
- transfer to another job

Federal and state regulations under this law require investigation of employee complaints that may be related to pesticide use, reentry, or accidents and to the training of employees in certain job-related health and safety areas pursuant to the Hazard Communication Standard. Firms must also provide employees certain right-to-know information, such as material safety data sheets (MSDSs) on all pesticides or other chemicals used. These regulations are enforced by federal and state officials.

APPENDIX F | Troubleshooting the Handheld Compressed-Air Sprayer

Problem	Cause	Solution
1. Tank not holding pressure	• Cap not tight	• Tighten cap
	• Tank gasket inside threaded cap on assembly worn	• Replace gasket
2. Tank not getting pressure	• Plunger cup inside pump assembly worn	• Replace cup, or rejuvenate cup with Neats Foot oil if cup is leather
3. Plunger rises or pushes back during pumping, or pump cylinder fills with liquid	• Check valve worn	• Replace valve
	• Dirt under check valve	• Clean
	• Chemical buildup under check valve	• Clean
4. Tank holds pressure but will not spray	• Nozzle tip clogged	• Remove and clean with soft brush
	• Strainer clogged	• Clean with water and brush
5. Nozzle drips after trigger valve is released (off)	• Seat gasket in control valve is worn or dirty	• Replace seat gasket
	• Return spring is worn	• Replace spring
6. Nozzle tip leaks	• Tip not seated properly	• Check and reseat tip
	• Tip gasket (O-ring) worn	• Replace gasket[1]
	• Dirt in tip gasket	• Clean gasket area
	• Broken valve spring	• Replace spring
7. Valve body leaks	• Packing nut loose	• Tighten nut[2]
8. Hose leaks	• Hose worn	• Replace hose
9. New hose installed, but liquid will not flow through hose	• Hose has been screwed down hose coupling washer into siphon tube, blocking the siphon tube	• Remove hose from coupling washer and replace with new washer
10. Hose leaks near tank	• Teflon washer worn or missing	• Replace
11. Hose clogged	• Swollen shut from liquid left in tank for prolonged periods with pressure on	• Release pressure when not in use (empty and rinse sprayer daily)

NOTE: Based on the B&G handheld compressed-air sprayer; excerpted in part from *How to Care for Your B&G Sprayer* by William Brehm and Les Krzak, *Pest Control Technology* (July 1983).

[1]This gasket requires replacement most often. Spare tip gaskets should be carried on the vehicle.

[2]Tighten until valve trigger will not move freely, then loosen packing nut until the valve trigger releases. If leak persists, valve packings must be replaced.

APPENDIX G | Weekly Cleaning and Maintenance of the One-Gallon Handheld Sprayer

Many insecticides are acidic in chemical makeup. If insecticide residues are allowed to accumulate in a sprayer (and all its components), these acids will erode the soft goods and produce pinholes in the base of the stainless steel tank. Therefore, regular cleaning of the sprayer is important for proper insecticide applications, safety, and economy.

Sprayers used only occasionally should be cleaned and properly stored after each use. Those sprayers used for a variety of chemicals should be cleaned every time they are used with a different chemical.

If a sprayer is used daily, it should be thoroughly cleaned at least once a week as follows:

1. Rinse and clean the tank.
- Rinse the tank thoroughly with clean water. (Be sure all wastewater containing any pesticide residue goes into an approved reservoir.)
- Fill the tank 1/3 full with warm water, add 1/4 sudsy ammonia, and scrub the inside of the tank with a stiff brush to remove any chemical residue.
- Rinse the tank with clean water.
- Scrub the outside of the tank with steel wool and detergent solution.

2. Flush the hose and valve assembly.
- Fill the sprayer to 10% full with clean water and pressurize the sprayer.
- Flush the hose by squeezing the trigger until the water comes out clean.
- Unscrew the collar and release the pressure from the sprayer. Hold the hose higher than the spray tank and backflush the hose and valve assembly by squeezing the trigger.

3. Check and clean the pump unit.
- Examine the check valve on the bottom of the pump. If the check valve is sitting tightly against the pump unit and the valve is in good condition, there is no need to remove it.
- Pay special attention to the area under the check valve. If chemical residues build up in this area, it will prevent the pump unit from operating properly. Remove the check valve and scrub away any debris or chemical residue on the bottom of the unit and the entire cylinder using a copper scrub pad and warm water/sudsy ammonia.
- Rinse the cylinder with clear water.
- Break the pump assembly down and inspect the plunger inside the pump.
- If the plunger is leather, apply a light coating of Neats Foot oil on the leather cup. If the plunger is plastic, check condition and replace if worn.
- Examine the gasket and the collar of the pump assembly for signs of wear, and replace if necessary.

4. Examine the hose.
- Gently bend the hose all along its length and inspect for cracking and soft or swollen areas. Replace the hose if any of these conditions exist. Do not wait for a worn or damaged hose to burst while you're on the job. A broken hose can result in pesticide being sprayed on the skin, clothing, or into the eyes of the operator or another person. It also can cause pesticides to be sprayed on carpets, drapes, or furniture, resulting in stains that could prove costly to repair.
- Examine the hose carefully at the points where the hose fastened to any couplings, and repair or replace the hose if breaks are found. Hose should never be carried or stored with sharp kinks in it. This practice can cause breaks in both the outer covering and in the inner liner as well.
- When replacing the hose, do not overtighten

the fittings, as this can result in a clogged hose. Hand-tighten the fitting, then with a wrench turn the fitting 1/4 to 1/2 turn.

5. Inspect and clean the strainer.
- Remove the strainer and clean by backflushing with water.
- If backflushing does not clear the strainer, use a small brush. In some cases, the strainer may need to be soaked in a solvent to dissolve any chemical residue.
- If the strainer has been damaged, or if it is impossible to clean thoroughly, discard it and replace it with a new one.

6. Inspect and clean the nozzle tip and assembly.
- Take the nozzle apart and clean all around the tip area with a bristle brush.
- Examine the seat gasket (O-ring) and replace if worn.

7. Test-check the sprayer.
- Reassemble all parts of the sprayer.
- Fill the sprayer 1/2 full with clean water and pressurize the sprayer to about 20 psi.
- Check the spray pattern on all nozzle openings to ensure that each opening is delivering the proper spray pattern.
- If there are any problems with the sprayer to which the solutions are not obvious, refer to "Troubleshooting the Handheld Compressed-Air Sprayer" (Appendix F).

When storing sprayers for extended periods, place the spray tank upside down with the hose fully extended. Place the pump unit and any accessories in a sealed plastic bag. The storage area should be free of dirt and dust.

TRUMAN'S SCIENTIFIC GUIDE TO **539**
Pest Management Operations

APPENDIX H | Building Terms of Importance to Pest Management Professionals

baseboard. A board placed against the wall around a room next to the floor to finish properly between floor and plaster.

base plate. Another name for sole, or sole plate.

beam. A structural member transversely supporting a load; for example, a beam under the floor of a house.

bearing wall. A wall that supports any vertical load in addition to its own weight.

box sill. A foundation sill in which the sole plate rests on the floor joists rather than on the sill proper. Wood structural member on outer end of floor joist.

brick veneer. A facing of brick laid against and fastened to sheathing of a frame wall or tile wall construction.

bridging. Small wood or metal members inserted in a diagonal position between the floor joists at midspan to act both as tension and compression members for the purpose of bracing the joists and spreading the action of loads.

crawlspace. A shallow space below the living quarters of at least a partially basementless house, normally enclosed by the foundation wall.

cripple, or **cripple stud.** Short stud used above and/or below windows and doorways.

decay. Disintegration of wood or other substance through the action of fungi.

ducts. In a house, usually round or rectangular metal pipes for distributing warm air from the heating plant to rooms, or cold air from a conditioning device, or as cold-air returns. May be embedded in or placed beneath concrete slabs. Ducts are also made of asbestos and composition material.

fascia. A flat board often used vertically to finish off the edge of a roof.

flashing. (1) Strips of aluminum, lead, tin, or copper that are let into the joints of a wall so as to lap over gutters or other pieces; (2) pieces worked in the slates or shingles around dormers, chimneys, and other rising parts, to prevent leaking.

footing. A masonry section, usually concrete, in a rectangular form wider than the bottom of the foundation wall or pier it supports.

foundation. The supporting portion of a structure below the first-floor construction, or below grade, down to and including the footings.

girder. A large or principal beam of wood or steel used to support concentrated loads at isolated points along its length.

grade. The slope or pitch of the ground. As distinct from the natural grade, the established grade is the level of the street curb as fixed by the municipality.

grade stake. Wood stake driven into ground to establish levels. These stakes are sometimes left in concrete floors and serve as a passage for termites.

grout. Mortar made of such consistency (by adding water) that it will just flow into the joints and cavities of the masonry work and fill them solid.

header. (1) A beam placed perpendicular to joists and to which joists are nailed in framing for basement, chimney, stairway, or other opening; (2) a wood lintel.

jamb. The side post or lining of a doorway or other opening. The jambs of a window outside the frame are called reveals.

joist. One of a series of parallel beams, usually 2 inches in thickness, used to support floor and ceiling loads, and supported in turn by larger beams, girders, bearing walls, or foundation.

laths. Thin strips of wood 4 feet long, nailed to studding as supports for plaster. Also, wire mesh or composition plasterboard.

lintel. A horizontal structural member that supports the load over an opening, such as a door or window. *See* **header.**

pier. A column of masonry or sometimes wood, usually rectangular in horizontal cross-section, used to support other structural members.

plate. *Sill plate:* a horizontal member anchored on top of a masonry wall. *Sole, or bottom, plate:* the bottom horizontal member of a frame wall. *Top plate:* the top horizontal member of a frame wall supporting ceiling joists, rafters, or other members.

rafter. One of a series of structural members of a roof, designed to support roof loads. The rafters of a flat roof are sometimes called roof joists.

riser. The vertical board under the tread in stairs; it forms the front of the stair step.

sheathing. The structural covering, usually wood boards or plywood, used over studs or rafters of a structure. Structural building board is normally used only as a wall sheathing.

shim. A strip of material used to fill a small space.

shoe mold, or **base shoe.** A strip of quarter-round that is nailed across the joint between the floor and the baseboard.

shore. A piece of timber placed in an oblique direction to support a building or wall temporarily while it is being repaired or altered.

siding, bevel (lap siding). Wedge-shaped boards used as horizontal siding in a lapped pattern. This siding varies in butt thickness from 1/2 to 3/4 inch and in widths up to 12 inches. Normally used over some type of sheathing.

sill. The lowest member of the frame of a structure, resting on the foundation and supporting the floor joists or the uprights of the wall. The member forming the lower side of an opening, as a doorsill, windowsill, and so forth. *See* **plate:** sill plate.

sleeper. Usually, a wood member embedded in concrete, as in a floor, that serves to support and to fasten subfloor or flooring.

soil pipe. A cast-iron pipe used for the house sewer line.

sole, or **sole plate.** A horizontal member, usually a 2×4, on which wall and partition studs rest.

stair carriage. Supporting member for stair treads, usually made from 2-inch-thick planks. Usually rests on basement slab but may improperly extend through concrete to dirt below, thus providing a passage for termites.

stucco. Most commonly refers to an outside plaster made with Portland cement as its base.

stud. One of a series of slender wood or metal vertical structural members placed as supporting elements in walls and partitions. (Plural: *studs* or *studding.*)

subfloor. Boards or plywood laid on joists, over which a finish floor is laid.

sump. A pit, well, or the like in which water or other liquid is collected.

termite shield. A shield, usually of noncorrodible metal, placed in or on a foundation wall, other mass of masonry, or around pipes to prevent the passage of termites.

trim. (1) The finish materials in a building, such as moldings applied around openings (window trim, door trim) or at the floor and ceiling of rooms (baseboard, cornice, picture molding). These are almost always made of wood; (2) of a door, sometimes used to denote the locks, knobs, and hinges.

vapor barrier. Material used to retard the movement of water vapor into walls or slabs and to prevent condensation in them. Also, a covering used over dirt in crawlspaces. Common materials: polyethylene film, asphalt paper.

wainscoting. Wooden lining of the lower portion of an interior wall, generally in panel form.

weep holes. Openings in mortar between bricks in lower courses to provide drainage for moisture that accumulates between bricks and sheathing.

STRUCTURAL AND HOUSING TERMS
Diagrams Identifying Structural Members

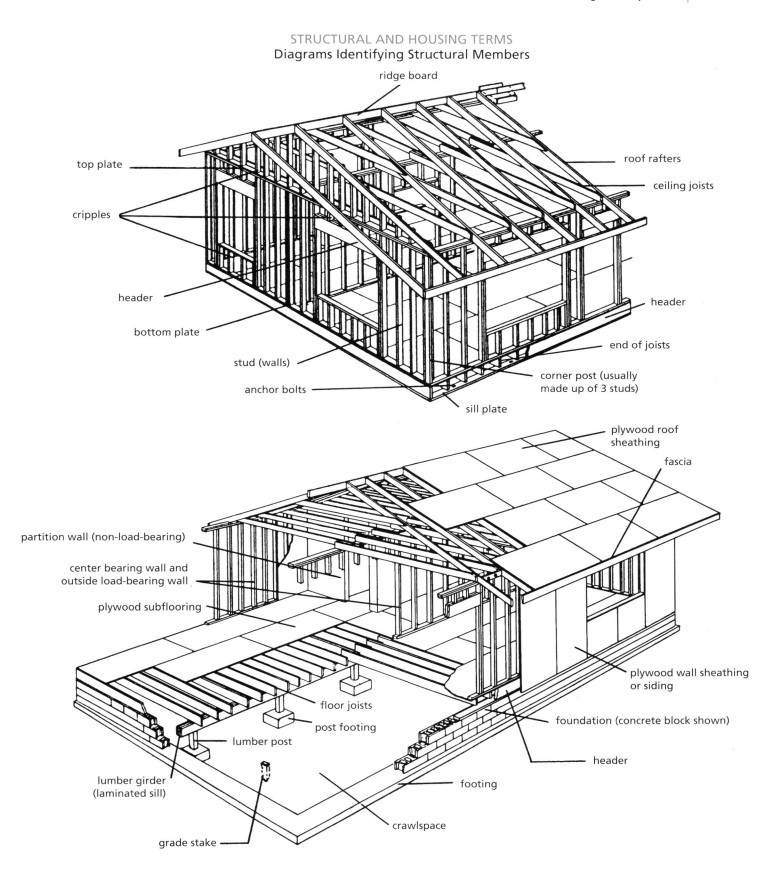

APPENDIX I | The Use of Graphs in Termite Control

The use of graphs in termite control is a practice that has been well established for many years. There are a number of reasons why the graph is an important part of good control procedures.

The graph performs many functions and is involved in every step of termite control service:

1. **Recording.** The inspector *records* findings in the form of a graph. The graph shows the size, shape, and construction of a building. It helps to locate and identify damage, hazards, and problems.
2. **Specifying.** The inspector can analyze the structure, develop a set of *specifications* for doing the work, and determine how much labor as well as the amount of termiticide and other materials that will be required.
3. **Pricing.** A fair *price* can be determined once the labor and materials needed are known.
4. **Selling.** The inspector uses the graph to help *sell* the job. The graph makes it easier to communicate with the customer—in showing how the building was constructed, what the problems are, and the control methods that should be used.
5. **Supervising.** After the job is sold and scheduled, the graph enables a manager or supervisor to determine how to get the work done efficiently, how many technicians to put on the job, how long it will take, and what tools and materials will be needed.
6. **Performing the service.** Out on the job, the graph is the guide for carrying out the necessary termite control procedures. And it often serves in helping a termite control technician to figure out how to solve unanticipated problems.
7. **Completing the record.** A vital function of the graph is to accurately record, for both the pest control company and the customer, the exact condition of the structure when the company took charge. It shows the location of existing visible damage, the location of probable hidden damage, areas of infestation or swarming, the location of possible hazards, and areas excluded from guarantee coverage, if any (modifications).
8. **Reinspecting.** Each year after the initial treatment, the structure is reinspected. The graph continues to be an important record and reference as the reinspections are made. It serves an important function in keeping a watch for further termite activity, and in performing any additional service that may be needed. If the original treatment did not work in some area, the graph enables the technician to review what has been done, and in determining an alternative solution.

This record is used again and again during all the time the contract is kept in force. It is not unusual to find graphs that are still being referred to that have continued protection services for 20, 30, and even 40 years.

Nearly everyone is familiar with graph paper. This is paper with printed lines or squares and is sometimes called cross-section paper. The predrawn lines enable a person to make sketches or drawings that are in proportion or drawn to scale.

By taking the measurements of a building's perimeter and using a ratio of one graph space for one foot of length, a person can make an accurate scale drawing of a building. This information will then show the *shape* and *size* of the building in correct proportions.

Termite control procedures are usually performed at or around ground level. If the graph drawing is to be useful, it must show where foundations and piers are located and any other structural information that may be involved in termite control.

Basically this means a scale drawing is needed of the *foundation plan* of the building. (This should not be confused with a *floor plan*, which is *not* needed.) The foundation drawing should show any construction features that allow termites to enter the building.

Next, the building areas or parts need to be identified. What type of basic construction and what kinds of building materials have been used? Sometimes a *key word* that identifies the *type* of areas or the *use* of the areas is added directly on the graph, such as *garage, porch, fireplace, brick planter,* and so forth. Any other special information is also added that will help a person understand the drawing.

Once the construction features are drawn and identified, the information about termites is added. This includes such things as the fact that live termites have been found, the location and extent of damage, and description of special hazards.

The graph is now finished. It can be used in all the activities that take place relative to the structure in performing termite control work. The graph now goes to work as a pricing guide, a sales aid, for servicing instructions, and so on.

The graph is the primary communication tool that helps everyone involved to understand what is needed and how to get the job done. Because it is a vital part of quality control, its importance should never be underestimated.

If you still aren't convinced of the importance and usefulness of the termite control graph, try *writing* a word description of a structure using no sketches or drawings. Then, describe the termite activity, damage, and hazards. Finally, describe the control procedures to be used together with the locations where they should be performed. By the time you have written three or four pages—and still aren't finished—you will appreciate the value of the graph. While it is not a photograph, it's still a picture that is worth a thousand words.

The two graphs shown here are of the same building. Graph A shows the size and shape of the building, but stops there. No one can look at Graph A and understand how the building is built, where the foundations or piers are located, where the problems are, or what needs to be done to protect the structure against termites.

Graph B required only a little more effort, but these few added lines clearly show the difference between foundations and concrete slabs.

It's easy to see where concrete block voids need to be drilled and treated. The areas where concrete slabs attach to the crawlspace area are shown. The

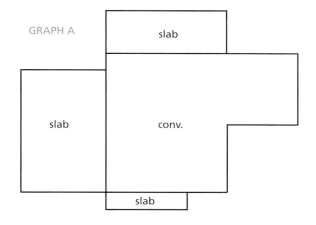

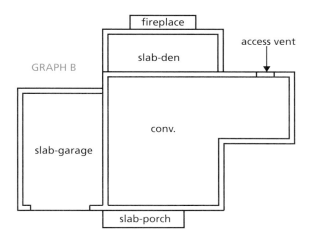

places that must be drilled, rodded, and treated can be clearly understood by any person who is familiar with termite control techniques.

The point is that Graph B provides enough information to form the basis for a professional termite control treatment, and drawing it did not require much extra work.

Graph A, on the other hand, does not show what is needed, and only goes through the motions of providing information for termite control. This graph leaves a number of unanswered questions. It may cause misunderstandings with the property owner or with the technician trying to perform the service. In short, it is a poor communication tool.

Some standard key symbols are listed on each graph so that everyone using it will be speaking the same language. Other information should be added when it is needed. Sometimes it is important to call attention to special problems or treatments.

Very often, a graph can be made more understandable by using two colors: black ink for the structure diagrams, and red ink for the key symbols, treating methods, and so forth.

KEY SYMBOLS

- Evidence of infestation = XXXXX
  Infestation may be in debris on the ground as well as in structural members.
- Repairs recommended = x x x x
  Repairs are usually recommended when members are structurally insecure. Just the fact that damage is present or that termites have penetrated a member doesn't always mean that it needs to be replaced. It *does* need to be identified, however.
- Existing damage = d
  Show the location. Describe the location when further identification is needed.
- Possible hidden damage = HD
  Areas of known termite hazard and areas near live termite activity should be identified as areas of possible damage whenever this appears likely.
- Powderpost beetles = P.P.B.
  Often these beetles have infested specific locations, and these locations should be clearly identified.
- Access opening = ACC
  This usually means an opening large enough for a person to pass through to enter a crawlspace or (in the case of plumbing, for example) an opening large enough to perform an inspection and necessary treatment.

- Wood partition = WP
  Particularly useful in identifying potential or actual problems in basements.
- Wood-ground contact = W.G.
- Vertically Drill and Treat = •••••• (red dots)
  These are treatment methods performed usually along the edge of a slab to place chemical under the expansion joint. They may also be used around plumbing or other openings in the slab.
- Short rod and treat = ↓↓↓
  A number of short (red) arrows are drawn through the foundation to show horizontal drilling and rodding under the inside perimeter of a slab.
- Long rod and treat = ——>
  A long (red) arrow drawn along the inside perimeter of a slab. This technique is used to treat areas that may be difficult to reach by any other method.
- Solid rod and treat = ⇉
  A number of (red) arrows, used to show that an area under a slab is being completely (solid) treated.
- Direction building is facing = (N/S)
  With many buildings, especially plain square or rectangular structures, the graph may not show this clearly. It is important that this information is indicated. Draw graph so that building *front* is at bottom.

APPENDIX J | Vertical Drilling

Termite treatments of existing slab or basement structures often require vertical drilling from the interior. Horizontal drilling from the outside is not always the best method, such as when the target area is more than 5 to 6 feet from the exterior foundation. At this distance, you cannot be sure of where the rod and chemical will go. In other cases, exterior slabs or high grades prevent horizontal drilling from the outside.

The following are some typical areas that could become termite entry points and therefore often require interior, vertical drilling:

- Expansion joints
  — between foundation wall and enclosed slabs
  — between slabs and enclosed dirt fills
  — between two slabs
  — in the interior perimeter of floating slabs
- Cracks in slabs
- Plumbing penetrations in slabs
- Wood columns or partition walls resting on concrete slabs
- Grade stakes in slabs
- Conduit penetrations in slabs (particularly bad if two or more conduits penetrate at the same point)

The discussion of interior vertical drilling must be restricted to generalities since it is virtually impossible to discuss each situation that may be encountered. In the field, each drilling situation (more specifically, each drill spot) must be visualized as a unique problem and handled as such. The foremost consideration is *where* the drilling should be done to ensure the best possible protection for the target area. The closer the drilling spot is to the potential termite entry point, the better.

The second consideration is the type or types of floor coverings that occur within the drilling area. Most floor coverings will be one of the following:

- Finished concrete (bare or painted)
- Carpet (tacked or glued down)
- Linoleum or vinyl (padded or conventional)
- Asphalt tile
- Rubber tile
- Vinyl tile
- Terrazzo
- Brick
- Wood
- Slate
- Stone
- Ceramic tile

Each type of floor covering has certain characteristics that must be considered before attempting to drill. Careful preparations must be made to gain access through the floor covering to the concrete below, so that on completion the area will show the least possible evidence of having been drilled. The different characteristics and methods of handling flooring types will be discussed individually in this appendix. If for some reason you are unsure of the condition in which the flooring will appear after patching, then explain this to the property owner and obtain written permission to proceed.

The proper equipment must be available to perform each task involved with interior drilling. Each termite technician should have access to, and a thorough working knowledge of, the following pieces of equipment:

- Rotohammer with sharp, straight bits
- Bit-stop device
- Variable-speed electric hand drill with masonry bits
- Tile plug cutter

- Electric iron, heat gun, or torch
- Sharp utility knife
- Small wooden roller
- Knee kicker (if carpets are to be lifted)
- Vacuum cleaner (optional)
- Electric sander (optional)

Patching the drill hole in such a way as to reduce or eliminate the visible evidence that drilling has occurred is a skill involving technique and a variety of patching materials. Each technician should be supplied with the following items to patch properly:

- Tile glue (adhesive)
- Cement
- Steel wool
- Sandpaper
- Brass plugs (specially prepared)
- Rubber corks (stoppers)
- Dowel rod or hardwood plugs
- Stains, waxes, and dyes

The following paragraphs pertain to each type of floor covering and give examples of acceptable methods of preparation and patching.

Finished concrete: This type of floor may be drilled directly and patched with cement and sand or with cement and some of the drilling dust mixed in to aid in matching the existing floor. Before patching, insert a crumpled piece of paper into the hole, about 2 inches from the surface. This will hold the patching mixture in place as it sets. If high water tables may cause seepage around the patch, a rubber stopper can be forced into the drill hole instead of the paper wad. If the finished floor is painted, the patched holes should be given time to dry, then painted to match.

Carpet: Carpet held in place with a tack strip can be lifted with an ice pick or a pair of needle-nose pliers. (Care should be taken to avoid physical damage to the carpet during the lifting process.) When replacing the carpet on the tack strip, it may be necessary to use a knee kicker to stretch the carpet and make it smooth and wrinkle free. If large areas of carpet must be lifted, or if lifting and replacing appear to be difficult, then it is advisable to contact a professional carpet layer to handle the job.

Carpet that is glued down may be cut in one of the following ways:

- Cut about a 4-inch-long line through the carpet at the spot to be drilled. Open this slit and insert a small match box or suitable item to hold the carpet back as you drill.
- Use the cookie-cutter technique to plug indoor-outdoor carpet for drilling. The cookie-cutter is a special cutting tool available from carpet deal-

ers; it cuts a perfect circular plug by rotating on its center pin.

It is important to protect the carpet from dust staining caused by the powdered concrete from the drill hole. The simplest method of preventing this is to use a vacuum cleaner with the nozzle placed as close as possible to the drilling site to pick up the dust as it comes to the surface. Homemade devices can be constructed using a coffee can or plumber's friend (with the handle removed) and an attached vacuum cleaner hose. After treating, the hole should be patched as described for concrete. The cut carpet or plug can be glued in place with a waterproof adhesive.

Linoleum or vinyl: These floor coverings require cutting a plug to expose the floor below. A special tile plug cutter obtained from floor covering specialists should be employed for this purpose to ensure uniformity and a neat patch. A leather plug cutter is also suitable and operates by striking the tool with a hammer to punch out the plug. Warming the surface facilitates plugging. This can be done using a clothes iron (placed on a cloth to prevent scorching), a heat gun, or a small torch. A clothes iron is recommended, since the heat intensity is more easily controlled and there is less hazard of fire or heat damage.

Once the plug has been cut, it can be lifted using the point of a knife. Keep the plug near the hole it came from so that when patching is complete, the floor pattern will match. A small amount of adhesive on the bottom of the plug will hold it in place (apply the adhesive after the cement patch has set).

If the linoleum or vinyl floor is padded, check with a professional linoleum layer before you begin, to learn how to prevent damage to the floor.

Asphalt tile: This type of floor can be recognized by colors that are usually dull and dark, and a surface that cannot be indented with a thumbnail. This type of tile is not commonly used now. Asphalt tiles are relatively hard and often become brittle with age. This characteristic makes it imperative to warm them prior to cutting, to prevent cracking or chipping. A plug cutter may be used as just described, or a corner of a tile may be cut using a sharp utility knife. When cutting, it is helpful to bevel the cut to aid in hiding the cut line after patching.

Vinyl tile: Vinyl tile is relatively soft and normally retains its flexibility. (It is still advisable to warm vinyl tile before working with it.) Plugging or corner cutting are easy methods with vinyl. Another method involves lifting the entire tile square by first heating the tile (to soften the adhesive) and then inserting a putty knife or spatula beneath one edge to lift. This method leaves no cut lines or plug marks; however, it does require some practice.

Rubber tile: This flooring can be recognized by its bright colors; it is not waxy or translucent. It can be indented with a thumbnail. Rubber tile (like vinyl) is relatively soft but should not be heated, due to damage by melting. This type of tile can be plugged or notched at the corner. Rubber tile is not commonly used today but was popular years ago.

Terrazzo: Terrazzo consists of white or colored grout with ornamental stones divided into sections with brass strips and ground to a smooth finish. This type of floor is common in commercial and institutional buildings; when found in a home, it is usually the pride and joy of the homeowner. The property owner must have a thorough understanding as to the necessity of drilling the terrazzo, and of the various methods of repairing the drill holes.

A sharp bit and steady pressure are required when drilling terrazzo, to prevent chipping around the edge of the drill hole. One method is to apply light pressure on the drill while quickly hitting and releasing the trigger. This prevents the bit from jumping about and damaging the surface of the floor.

The artistic method of patching terrazzo requires saving the drilling dust so that a portion of the dust can be mixed with a quality cement. With experience, this mixture can be made to closely match the original floor. This method also adds a professional touch to your work.

A special brass plug has been designed for plugging hard-to-patch drill holes. It consists of a bevel-edged brass washer with a countersunk brass screw on which is fitted a small portion of rubber tubing and a nut. As the screw is tightened, the nut compresses the rubber tubing, causing it to expand against the walls of the drill hole. When properly installed, the brass plug will not allow water to seep up from below the slab, is easy to remove should additional chemical be necessary, and does not mar the appearance of the terrazzo floor.

If the above-mentioned methods of repair are not acceptable to the property owner, then a professional terrazzo floor company can be contacted to patch the drill holes. This should be established before any drilling is started, so that the cost factor can be included in the job price.

Brick: Fired brick or Mexican brick can present problems when drilling is required. The best method is to drill in the mortar joint at a point where four bricks meet. Even if the mortar joint is not wide enough to completely contain a small-diameter bit, it is still advisable to drill at that point. Use a sharp bit under steady pressure to prevent chipping the fired surface of the brick. Should a chip occur, save the piece and glue it back in place after patching the hole. Drilling through the center of a brick is not recommended, due to the risk of cracking and the difficulty in matching the patch. By drilling in the mortar joint, it is easier to match the patch, and the visual effect of the pattern created by the four bricks will aid in hiding the drill spot.

Termiticide has been known to stain brick flooring; the stain is usually the result of the emulsification of the floor wax. In such cases a thorough cleaning is necessary, followed by the application of special, dyed waxes available from tile flooring companies. Avoid staining situations by working carefully (with low pressure) and by immediately wiping up any spills or drips.

Wood: Drilling wood floors can be done with professional results by following these basic guides:

- Always drill through the wood floor with a wood drill bit; never use a rotohammer drill. The wood bit is designed to drill a neat hole with smooth edges. The hammer drill will splinter the wood and create an irregular, jagged hole.
- Use the proper-diameter drill bit to match the diameter of the wood plug and ensure a snug fit.
- For best results, use a special plug-cutting tool that attaches to a drill press. With this tool, you can make wood plugs that match the existing flooring. Wood plugs can also be made by cutting sections of dowelling; however, the quality of the match may be poor.
- The finished plug should be tight enough to require tapping in place with a hammer. An Elmer's-type glue should be applied before insertion.
- The surface of the plug should be sanded smooth and *must* be level with the existing floor.
- Staining, varnishing, or waxing completes the job.

It is extremely important to remember that the water in the termiticide emulsion can cause serious damage to the appearance of the floor. The most common form of damage is warping or buckling of the floor as a result of chemical flow onto the surface of the slab, or splashback directly on the underside of the flooring. A warped or buckled floor is a very expensive damage claim (especially in a gymnasium or bowling alley), and it can be avoided by following these guides:

- Use a large-diameter wood bit (about 1 inch) to drill through the flooring. This will permit a slab injector to be used during treating.
- Use a suitable slab injector when treating to keep the termiticide from flowing onto the surface of the slab.

- Use low pressure for treating, to minimize the possibility of splashback or overflow from adjacent drill holes or other openings in the slab.
- Pause a few moments before removing the slab injector to allow the pressure to equalize under the slab.

Slate: Most slate floors have mortar joints wide enough to permit easy drilling. The slate itself can be cracked or chipped and may be damaged by direct drilling or by vibrations from the hammer drill. For this reason it is advisable to use an electric hand drill with a masonry bit to gain access through the mortar to the concrete below. A hammer drill may then be used to finish the drill hole. If the vibrations from the drilling cause any cracking or breaking or appear to be loosening the slate, you should finish the hole with the hand drill and masonry bit. Mixing some of the drilling dust with the patching material will help hide the drill spot.

Stone: Stone floors can be handled in the same manner as slate floors, without the danger of cracking.

Ceramic tile: A variable-speed electric hand drill combined with a sharp masonry bit will prove invaluable when drilling ceramic tile. The masonry bit is used to drill through the center of the tile to the concrete below. A hammer drill can then be used to complete the drilling. The brass plug (discussed under terrazzo) is the most attractive method of patching the drill hole.

If the customer objects to the brass plug, then an alternative is to drill in the mortar joint where four tiles meet. When patching the hole, it is necessary to partially fill the hole with cement, leaving room for finishing with matching grout.

Should you crack a tile during the drilling process, you should try to find a replacement tile to match. If a matching tile can be found, carefully chip out the damaged tile with a hammer and a sharp chisel. When installing the new piece, it is important to have a smooth, level base, so that the replacement tile will be even with the original floor and won't crack under pressure.

Treating: Before termiticide treatment is started, it is important to completely and thoroughly clean up any drilling dust that may have accumulated. On smooth surfaces, a small brush and dustpan will suffice. Any dust remaining can be wiped up with a damp cloth. Where carpet is involved, it is necessary to use a vacuum cleaner to remove the dust from the carpet pile. If the drilling dust is left around the treating hole, there is a chance it will get wet from the termiticide and result in a messy, difficult-to-clean situation or a permanent stain.

The actual termite treating should be done using a subslab injector with the insecticide under low pressure. The seal created by the expanding rubber ring on the slab injector prevents the upward flow of insecticide (and fill material) during treatment. Low pressure aids in the even distribution of chemical in the area around the treatment site. There are various methods of forming seals around standard treating tips and rods; however, the subslab injector is by far the most reliable. When treating screeded floors, the subslab injector is a must for preventing termiticide backflow onto the surface of the slab or the underside of the wood flooring. Before removing the subslab injector from the treatment hole, pause a few moments to allow the pressure under the slab to equalize, thus preventing backflow.

Costly insurance claims can result from backflow, even from drill holes many feet from the actual treating site. Termiticide seepage can also occur from expansion joints and cracks in the slab as well as from around plumbing pipes and other slab penetrations. Generally, the greater the treating pressure, the greater the risk of backflow.

For added safety, always use a bit-stop device when drilling.

APPENDIX K | Termite Control in
Slab Floor Construction

Refer to Figure 7.16 for diagrams of the three basic slab types:

- **Monolithic slab:** The foundation footing and the slab floor are formed as one continuous unit. Concrete is the material used in this type of slab foundation.
- **Floating slab:** The foundation wall and footing are separated from the slab floor by an expansion joint. The slab floor is concrete, while the foundation wall can be a variety of materials, such as solid block, hollow block, or concrete.
- **Supported slab:** The slab floor and the foundation wall are separate units, with the slab floor extending over the top of the foundation wall. The slab floor is concrete, while the material used for the foundation wall may vary.

The following general treating specifications apply to all slab types:

- **Treat perimeter soil:** The soil around the exterior of the foundation wall must be treated *to the footer*. This can be accomplished by trenching or rodding.
- **Drill and treat attached slabs:** Holes should be drilled 3 to 6 inches from the building foundation and spaced *no farther* than 18 inches apart. To be effective, the chemical application must reach to the footer of the foundation wall. This is best achieved by rodding in conjunction with subslab injection.
- **Provide access to bath traps:** All bath traps in a slab structure are critical areas for termite access. An access panel should be installed to permit periodic inspection and adequate treatment. A careful inspection of the premises will determine where the access should be located (even through exterior walls, if necessary). Termiticide

is applied directly into the soil around the drain pipe by rodding.
- **Drill and treat plumbing penetrations:** All major drain penetrations (other than bath traps) should be drilled and treated. Drill as close as possible to the site of penetration; a bit-stop device is recommended during this operation.

Follow these additional treating specifications for floating and supported slabs:

- **Drill and treat foundation voids:** Voids in foundation walls must be drilled and treated. It may be necessary to drill every void in hollow block foundation walls when *less* than 60 blocks form the foundation wall.
- **Drill and treat inside perimeter of slab:** This can be accomplished by rodding from the exterior (if grade level permits), or by vertical drilling and rodding from inside. Vertical drilling and rodding is the preferred method, since termiticide can be applied to the footer more easily. In either case, application sites should not exceed 18-inch centers.

The following common difficulties are encountered with slab foundations:

- **Cracks in slab floors:** Hairline cracks in slab floors may develop for a variety of reasons, such as improper curing of the concrete, ground water pressure, soil expansion due to freezing, and weight stress on the slab from the building structure or its contents.

  Determining the exact location of these cracks is very difficult because they are often hidden from view by floor coverings (carpet, tile, hardwood flooring, etc.). If the floor covering can be removed, the visible cracks should be treated along their entire length. Where severe cracking is encountered, treatment may require drilling the entire surface of the slab on 18-inch centers, and using a subslab injector. This procedure is known as checkerboarding.

- **Grade stakes embedded in slabs:** Prior to pouring the concrete slab floor, contractors may drive grade stakes into the compacted fill to serve as an aid in creating a level (or properly sloped) finished floor. Locating the position of these stakes for treating is nearly impossible, but the termites will have no difficulty entering the structure through this route.

- **Wooden structural components embedded in the slab:** Door frames, wood siding, screeds, support columns, and various form boards may extend into or through the slab. This is most likely encountered in older structures where a new slab or basement floor has been poured without regard to existing wooden components. Newer homes with step-down living rooms, conversation pits, or multiple slab levels may have wooden forms still in place (and possibly used to tack down carpeting).

The preferred treatment is to remove the portion of wood embedded in the concrete, treat the void with termiticide, and then fill the void with cement.

Where it is impossible to remove the wood, drill and treat the slab adjacent to the site of penetration.

- **Radiant heat systems:** Radiant heat piping does not in itself create a termite hazard. Problems do result when attempting to use the conventional drill-and-treat methods. Blind drilling will usually result in puncturing the radiant heat pipes.

One method of mapping the radiant heat pipes (in areas to be vertically drilled) is to lay damp newspaper on the floor, then turn on the heat. The warmth from the pipes below will dry the newspaper directly above the pipes and make it possible to trace their pattern.

- **Air-conditioning and heat ducts in slabs:** Any type of ductwork in or below a slab presents numerous hazards in respect to termite entry and treating.

APPENDIX L | Termite Re-treatments

Termite re-treatments are one of the most difficult and challenging problems the termite technician will encounter. Re-treatments are a result of the original treatment being incomplete. Incomplete treatment may be caused either by technician error or by unusual construction that prevented proper treatment. In either case, the termites gained access to the house, and the specialist must determine the source of infestation and do the treating needed.

Generally, the technician can determine if an area was improperly treated. If this is the case, the remedy is simply to treat the property correctly. The difficult re-treatment is when the infested area was properly treated but still has an active infestation. In this situation, the technician needs to carefully inspect the infested area to determine the treatment needed. The answer to these reinfestations is generally not found in a book; however, the technician can solve the problem by applying the knowledge he or she has gained through studying termite habits, knowing construction methods in the area, and carefully checking for unusual conditions.

When a customer calls concerning a reinfestation, one of the following conditions may be found:

- No active infestation is found, and no treatment is needed.
- No active infestation found, but due to the construction or some other factor, it is difficult to determine exactly if an infestation exists. In this case, a preventive treatment in the area is recommended.
- Active infestation is found.

When an active infestation is found, the technician must determine the point of entry into the structure before beginning treatment. To determine all entry points, a thorough inspection of the entire structure is needed. There may be more than one area of reinfestation; consequently, all areas must be found at this time to avoid further retreatment. The areas of original infestation should be carefully inspected, as studies have shown that most reinfestations are in the same areas. This is because the termites have established these areas as their routes into the structure and will seek out the slightest break in the chemical barrier for reentry.

Determine the reason for the reinfestation. Do not simply open the old drill holes and re-treat; if it didn't work before, it probably won't work this time. When looking for entry points, the following areas should be checked:

- Expansion joints—particularly under interior walls
- Multiple foundation walls
- Base plates buried in concrete
- Concealed bath accesses
- Dirt-fill porches
- Foundation voids drilled too far apart or below grade level
- Cracked slabs
- Room additions
- Grade stakes
- Basement steps next to a foundation wall
- Removal of treated soil next to the foundation, due to planting of new shrubbery

The following situations can cause frequent re-treatments:

- Expansion joints along interior walls where there is a footing for the interior wall are often sites of reentry. When this occurs, both sides of the wall need treatment to prevent infestation. This type of construction can be determined by inspection and by knowing local construction practices.

- In many slab homes, an interior expansion joint is hidden by building an interior wall over the joint. This type of construction provides easy access of termites directly into the wall. This can be determined by looking for any unevenness of the floor at doorways.
- Improper rodding of slabs causes many re-treatments. When doing this operation, make sure the tip of the rod penetrates to all critical areas under the slab and sufficient termiticide is used to provide even coverage.
- If reinfestation occurs at the corner of a block wall, it may be because the end void in the corner block was missed during the original treatment. This can easily occur when voids are drilled from the inside.
- If an infestation occurs on the outside wall of a building with a slab floor, the technician should check to see where the original holes were drilled. If they were drilled several inches below the slab or at a downward angle, the termites may be gaining entry by going over the chemical barrier.
- Dirt-fill porches are one of the most common points of reinfestation. A careful inspection is needed to find the reentry point. Dirt-fill porches may have debris in the fill, veneer below grade, wood below grade, or brick added over the concrete. All of these situations provide easy access for termites.

The following procedures should be followed when a re-treatment is necessary:

1. Determine where the termites are active (joists, sills, window frames, interior walls, etc.).
2. Determine how they are gaining entry.
3. Determine why the area is used as an entry point (faulty construction or improper treatment).
4. Determine the best method for treatment.
5. Remember to inspect adjoining areas for infestation.

Index

Page references in **Bold** indicate figures; *t* indicates a *Table*.